GEOLOGY AND ECONOMIC MINERALS OF CANADA

Available by mail from

Printing and Publishing
Supply and Services Canada
Ottawa, Canada K1A 0S9

or through your bookseller

Catalogue No. M43-1/1976-8-13 Price: Canada: $8.00
ISBN 0-660-00552-2 Other countries: $9.60

Price subject to change without notice.

D. W. Friesen & Sons Ltd.,
Altona, Manitoba, Canada
Contract No. OKX6-0236

GEOLOGICAL SURVEY
OF CANADA

ECONOMIC GEOLOGY
REPORT No. 1

GEOLOGY AND ECONOMIC MINERALS OF CANADA

Part B (Chapters VIII - XIII and Index)

R. J. W. Douglas,
Scientific Editor

DEPARTMENT OF
ENERGY, MINES AND RESOURCES
CANADA

For the convenience of readers, this work is published in three volumes. Part A comprises Chapter I to VII; Part B, chapters VIII to XIII; and Part C, a folio of charts and a map related to both Part A and Part B.

COVER Malak
ENDLEAVES
Inco's reduction works at
Copper Cliff, Ontario (George Hunter)

CONTENTS

VIII. Geology of Western Canada

INTRODUCTION

Western Canada is the part of Canada that lies west of the Precambrian rocks of the Canadian Shield. It includes the geological regions known as the Interior Platform, the Cordilleran Orogen, and parts of the Pacific and Arctic Continental Shelves and Coastal Plains (Fig. VIII-1).

The Interior Platform, underlain by Phanerozoic sedimentary rocks, is the northwestern part of the North American craton, the stable interior region of the continent. The nearly horizontal bedrock is covered by a thick mantle of glacial drift to form the plains and plateaux of the Interior Plains physiographical province. It is a region of grassland, forest, and tundra, 775,000 square miles in extent, that embraces parts of the prairie provinces of Manitoba, Saskatchewan, and Alberta, the northeast corner of British Columbia, and much of western District of Mackenzie, Northwest Territories. The southern part is composed of a relatively thick blanket of Mesozoic and Tertiary clastic rocks that overlie carbonates and evaporites of Paleozoic age, with most systems represented. They rest on a basement of Precambrian crystalline rocks. The region has been extensively drilled and the geology is well known. The northern part, however, is less well known and partly unknown; few wells penetrate the entire Phanerozoic succession. Devonian and older clastics, carbonates, and evaporites lie on Precambrian sedimentary and crystalline rocks and are covered by a thin veneer of late Lower Cretaceous rocks. Other systems are either unrepresented or are present only near Cordilleran Geosyncline and Arctic Continental Shelf. Interior Platform is linked to the St. Lawrence Platform of Southeastern Canada through the central United States of America and merges with Arctic Platform in the north, beyond the mainland.

The mainland part of Arctic Coastal Plain comprises the Cretaceous and Cenozoic rocks of Mackenzie Delta and a narrow belt that truncates the Richardson Mountains or borders the British Mountains of Eastern Cordilleran Orogen. The geology of the bordering part of Arctic Continental Shelf, 100 miles wide, is but little known.

The Cordilleran Orogen forms part of the circum-Pacific orogenic belt. It is a region, some 500 miles wide, of mountains and plateaux, trenches, valleys, and fiords. Parts are heavily forested dry grassland or tundra. Numerous peaks project above timberline or grassline and many bear glaciers. The eastern part of the orogen embraces the parts of Cordilleran Geosyncline that generally received miogeosynclinal and exogeosynclinal sediments and that underwent surficial or *décollement* deformation with little or no metamorphism, volcanism, or plutonism

[1] The accounts of the geology of the northern and southern parts of the Western Cordilleran Orogen have been prepared by H. Gabrielse and J. O. Wheeler, respectively. The stratigraphy of the Paleozoic rocks of the southern Interior Platform has been prepared by H. R. Belyea. The Mesozoic stratigraphy of the Interior Platform and Eastern Cordilleran Orogen has been written by D. F. Stott. R. J. W. Douglas is responsible for general coordination and the geology of the remaining parts of the Interior Platform and Eastern Cordilleran Orogen. When acknowledging, reference should be made to individual author and page number.

VIII
Geology of Western Canada

R.J.W. Douglas, H. Gabrielse, J.O. Wheeler, D.F. Stott, and H.R. Belyea[1]

Valhalla Range, southern Selkirk Mountains, British Columbia. Looking south to Mount Gladsheim (left) and serrated ridge carved from veined gneiss of the Shuswap Metamorphic Complex in the core of Valhalla Dome.

during the orogenic phases. The region is divisible into three main sectors. The southernmost sector, the Rocky Mountain Thrust Belt, was produced by the Columbian and Laramide Orogenies during the Cretaceous and early Tertiary. The dominant structures are subparallel, west-dipping thrusts that produce a series of narrow, linear mountain ranges formed of resistant Paleozoic carbonates. The mountains are bordered, on the east, by the Foothills belt of deformed Mesozoic and Tertiary clastic sediments. In the more southerly parts, very closely spaced thrust faults are characteristic, whereas in the central and northern Foothills they are less prominent and open and tight folds are more typical. The central sector comprises the arcuate Mackenzie Fold Belt that embraces Liard Plateau, Mackenzie, Franklin, and Wernecke Mountains, and the Taiga Ranges of Porcupine Plateau. The fold belt, characterized by Paleozoic carbonate and clastic rocks thrown into broad simple folds with intervening zones of complex folds and faults, was also produced during the Columbian and Laramide Orogenies. However, in some culminations the effects of the Hadrynian Racklan Orogeny on Helikian rocks are also evident. The northernmost sector, the Northern Yukon Fold Complex, includes Richardson and British Mountains, Porcupine Plateau, and Old Crow Range. A great variety of structures and trends has been produced as a result of several orogenies, mainly the Upper Devonian Ellesmerian Orogeny, the Columbian Orogeny, and the early and late phases of the Laramide Orogeny.

The western part of Cordilleran Orogen embodies the parts of the Cordilleran Geosyncline that received eugeosynclinal and epieugeosynclinal assemblages. The eugeosynclinal belt was at times dominated by northwesterly elongate troughs separated by geanticlines; the latter were repeatedly the site of regional metamorphism, granitic emplacement, and intense deformation. The deformation of the rocks in the troughs was controlled largely by their lithology; where volcanic rocks are predominant, broad folds, warps, and numerous steep faults developed, whereas the sedimentary rocks were deformed principally by folding and locally by thrusting. Ultramafic rocks are spatially restricted to the eugeosynclinal belt and temporally associated with basaltic volcanic rocks. They occur along thrusts or near the faults bounding major structural units. The younger epieugeosynclinal basins, which are separated by arches and geanticlines, are partly successor basins and partly synorogenic basins. While the adjoining geanticlines were being deformed, they received thick assemblages of rapidly deposited, marine and non-marine, clastic sediments and minor volcanic rocks. They were subsequently folded and faulted. Post-orogenic, slightly deformed, continental, clastic and volcanic rocks were deposited locally in fault troughs and are commonly associated with extensional zones of normal faults. Late Tertiary and Pleistocene clastic sediments occur along Pacific Continental Shelf and parts of the Coastal Plain.

The two belts of crystalline rocks, the Coast Plutonic Complex and the Omineca Crystalline Belt have been generally positive geanticlines since mid-Paleozoic time. They merge northwestward to form the Yukon Platform.

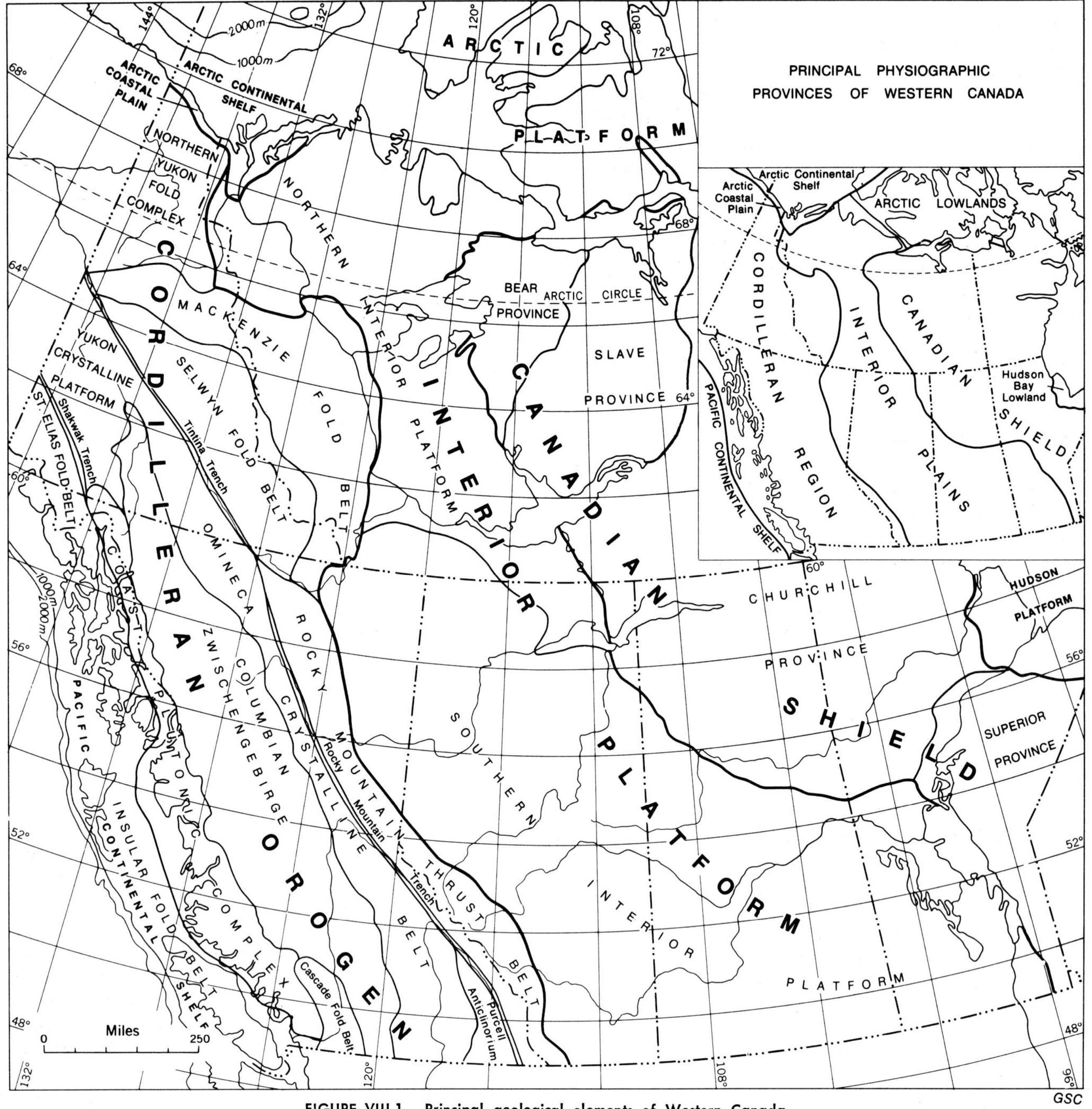

FIGURE VIII-1. Principal geological elements of Western Canada.

The western or Coast Plutonic Complex is composed predominantly of granitic rocks. It and the Cascade Fold Belt have gneiss–migmatite cores. Both belts were affected by a mid-Paleozoic orogeny, the late Jurassic to Cretaceous Columbian Orogeny, and by a late phase of the Laramide Orogeny. The northern part of Coast Plutonic Complex was also affected by the Middle Triassic Tahltanian Orogeny. The eastern or Omineca Crystalline Belt includes extensive areas of metamorphic rocks that form the core zone of an alpine-type orogen, the marginal zone of which is the Eastern Cordilleran Orogen. Metamorphic complexes occur as anvil-shaped culminations. Part of the belt was deformed during the Hadrynian East Kootenay Orogeny and the Upper Devonian to Mississippian Caribooan Orogeny. Most was redeformed during the Tahltanian and Columbian Orogenies. In the south, the eastern and western parts of the Cordilleran Orogen are separated by Rocky Mountain Trench, a linear erosional zone partly controlled by normal faults.

Columbian Zwischengebirge between the Omineca Crystalline Belt and the Coast Plutonic Complex is structurally heterogeneous, but dominated by an elongate northwest-trending geanticlinal belt of disconnected horsts and by two broad transverse arches. Thick eugeosynclinal sedimentary and volcanic rocks were deposited during the late Paleozoic and early Mesozoic, partly synchronously with orogeny in the bordering crystalline belts. Deposition was locally interrupted by the Triassic Tahltanian Orogeny and the Jurassic Inklinian and Nassian Orogenies. As a result of the last orogeny, the region was segmented into three epieugeosynclinal basins, the sediments of which, partly non-marine, were folded and block faulted during the late phase of the Columbian Orogeny. In the Tertiary, the Zwischengebirge was subjected to transcurrent and normal faulting and extensive sheets of basic volcanic rocks were extruded. The early Tertiary volcanism was coeval with emplacement of small high-level granitic plutons.

Bordering the Pacific Ocean are the St. Elias Fold Belt in southwestern Yukon Territory, the Insular Fold Belt embracing Vancouver and Queen Charlotte Islands, and the Pacific Coastal Plain and Continental Shelf. The St. Elias Fold Belt, bounding the Gulf of Alaska, contains rocks of Devonian to Pliocene age. It is composed of a core of crystalline rocks flanked by outwardly directed thrusts. The orogen was produced by late Paleozoic deformation, by the Columbian Orogeny, and by Tertiary deformation as young as late Pliocene. It is bounded on the northeast by the Shakwak transcurrent fault, part of the Denali system of Alaska. The Insular Fold Belt contains late Paleozoic to Tertiary rocks and is characterized by thick sequences of Mesozoic volcanic rocks that are only slightly warped and faulted. Deformation was not synchronous; on Vancouver Island it took place during the Middle Jurassic Nassian Orogeny whereas on Queen Charlotte Islands it occurred during the early Columbian Orogeny. Following the development in latest Cretaceous time of the epieugeosynclinal Georgia and Hecate Basins between the Coast and Insular Geanticlines, the region underwent local folding, faulting, and volcanism. The Pacific Continental Shelf is narrow, terminating a few miles west of Vancouver and Queen Charlotte Islands. Small parts of the islands underlain by flat clastic Tertiary sediments form the Pacific Coastal Plain. The Queen Charlotte fault, a transform fault related to the San Andreas–Denali linkage is steeply east-dipping with recent right-lateral movement. It lies near the foot of the steep Continental Slope and truncates the north to northeast magnetic trends of the ocean floor.

The Cordilleran Orogen of Canada is one of great geological variety and complexity that developed during the evolution of the Cordilleran Geosyncline from mid-Proterozoic to Recent. At present the region is tectonically quiet, relative to other parts of the circum-Pacific orogenic belt.

PRECAMBRIAN

Beneath the Phanerozoic strata of the Interior Platform are Precambrian sedimentary and crystalline rocks (Fig. VIII-2), the latter forming the basement of the western part of the North American craton. Potassium–argon age determinations (Burwash, *et al.,* 1962) on material obtained in the drilling of wells indicate that the structural provinces established on the Canadian Shield by Stockwell (Map 1251A) extend beneath Interior Platform. A small part in the southeast is an extension of Superior Province, formed of Archean rocks deformed by the Kenoran Orogeny, the major structural trends of which strike predominantly east-west. The greatest part however, represents a westward extension of the Churchill and Bear Provinces, composed of rocks of Archean and Aphebian ages deformed by the Hudsonian Orogeny. The major gneissic and structural trends, although predominantly northeast-southwest, vary to easterly, northerly, and northwesterly, and form complex arcs or bend around the borders of Slave and Superior Provinces. Major post-orogenic faults, on which displacements are transcurrent and normal, fall into three distinct sets: northeast, north, and northwest. On some, minor displacements occurred in the Phanerozoic.

Unmetamorphosed, slightly deformed Helikian and Hadrynian sedimentary rocks of Coppermine Subprovince of the Shield lie unconformably on the crystalline rocks of Bear and Slave Provinces and probably extend beneath the Paleozoic of the northern part of the Interior Platform. The thickness of these sediments is not known, nor whether they occur in geosynclinal development or only as cratonic cover. The depth and configuration of the crystallines accordingly are unknown and the position of the margin of the craton is uncertain. Helikian and Hadrynian sediments are common in the more easterly parts of the Cordilleran Geosyncline but have yet to be recognized in the more westerly parts. Known stratigraphic successions measure several tens of thousands of feet but are not known to be floored by basement. Some pre-Devonian and pre-Lower Cambrian crystalline basement occurs in the southern Cordillera but the time of its formation and the age of the constituent rocks have not been established. The little that is known about isopach and facies trends in the sedimentary rocks suggests that the loci of much of the margin of Cordilleran Geosyncline, and possibly also some of the major elements in the north, were established in the Helikian. Some prominent faults occurring within or bounding areas of Proterozoic rocks were in existence at the close of Precambrian time. They were active during the Phanerozoic and served to separate areas of strong depression from areas that were less depressed or uplifted.

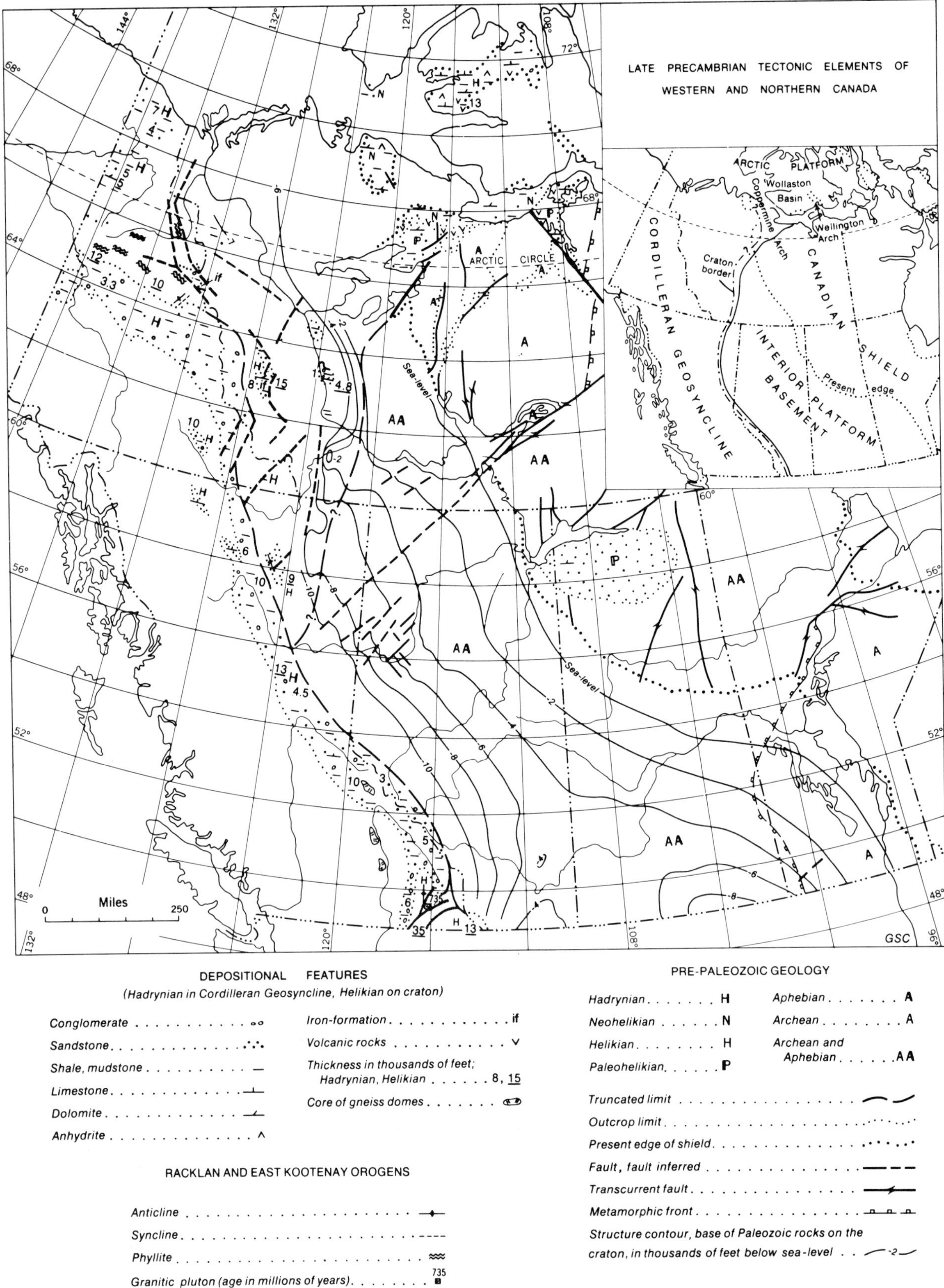

FIGURE VIII-2. Pre-Paleozoic paleogeology of Western Canada, geology of adjacent parts of the Canadian Shield, and some features of Helikian and Hadrynian sedimentation and tectonism.

Their trends are comparable to those cutting Archean and Aphebian crystalline rocks of the craton and the faults accordingly may also involve crystalline crust, as those in the geosyncline bordering the continent are more active and impart greater mobility to the crust than those in the interior.

The Proterozoic successions of the southeastern Cordillera are customarily referred to the Purcell and Windermere Systems. They are separated by a widespread unconformity and an interval of folding, metamorphism, and intrusion of granite stocks, these effects being considered to be the result of the East Kootenay Orogeny. The granites (Leech, 1962a) have yielded K–Ar dates of 675 to 745 million years which suggest that the orogeny occurred within the Hadrynian era, being somewhat younger than the Grenvillian Orogeny of the Canadian Shield. The Purcell is probably therefore mainly Helikian in age although part may be as young as early Hadrynian and, by virtue of its allochthonous position with respect to Hudsonian metamorphosed basement, part of the Purcell may be late Aphebian. The Windermere falls entirely within the Hadrynian and, as it is locally conformable with Lower Cambrian sediments, probably represents all or most of the late Hadrynian. Elsewhere, most Proterozoic sequences bear some lithological similarity to either the Purcell or Windermere, or may be metamorphosed by Phanerozoic orogenies. In the northern Cordillera, the sedimentary successions are likewise separated by a profound angular unconformity which resulted from the Racklan Orogeny that produced easterly and north-northeasterly trending folds and phyllitization, and subsequent taphrogenic activity, tilting, and volcanism. The Racklan Orogeny is presumed to be temporally equivalent to the East Kootenay Orogeny. The Moyie and other gabbro sills in Purcell Mountains have been dated at about 1,100 m.y., and the lead minerals of Sullivan orebody in the Aldridge Formation of the Purcell have yielded isotopic ages at about 1,340 m.y. (Sinclair, 1966). In adjacent northern parts of the Shield faulting and intrusion of diabase sills occurred very late in the Proterozoic and an interval of strong faulting, volcanism, and ultramafic extrusion, the Muskox disturbance, occurred at about 1,100 m.y or about mid-Helikian time.

Helikian (Middle Proterozoic)

Tectonic Summary

Helikian sedimentary strata, the oldest known in the Cordillera, comprise a thick sequence of fine-grained clastic and carbonate rocks predominantly of shallow-water marine origin (Fig. VIII-2). Andesitic flows and gabbro dykes and sills occur sporadically. Facies changes in the lower part of the succession from fine deep-water clastics to conglomeratic red-bed and shallow-water sediments and a general eastward convergence suggest that the sequence was deposited on a shelf or in a miogeosyncline bordering the western margin of the craton. Farther north, lateral changes in facies of Helikian rocks have not been recognized although, in general, the strata resemble the eastern facies of the south. Orange-weathering and varicoloured rocks and carbonates containing abundant stromatolites are particularly characteristic. It seems probable that the easternmost and northeasternmost exposures of these rocks fairly closely approximate the western and southwestern margin of the North American craton during Helikian time. The nature and extent of depositional troughs to the west is unknown.

Cordilleran Geosyncline

The succession and correlation of the Purcell rocks in the Clark, Galton, and Hughes Ranges of the *southern Rocky Mountains* and in the *Purcell Mountains* has become well established (Price, 1964a). The Purcell is divisible into two main parts by an hiatus, partly represented by the Purcell lava, a very extensive basalt flow several hundred feet thick (Fig. VIII-3). In Galton Range the lava is absent through erosion. In southern Purcell Mountains, the hiatus may be represented by 2,000 feet of strata with several thin flows. The lower part of the Purcell is divisible into three main units. The lowest includes the thin, varicoloured, laminated, and stromatolitic carbonates and the conglomerates with pebbles of quartzite and dolomite that comprise the near-shore Waterton and Altyn Formations in Clark Range, and which grade westward into various facies including that of the very thick Aldridge Formation. The Aldridge comprises rusty-weathering, fine-grained, laminated, argillaceous quartzite and dark argillite with graded bedding and scour and fill structures, indicating deposition in deep water. The middle unit contains red and green argillite and quartzite that comprise the Appekunny and Grinnell Formations in the east. These rocks contain such tidal flat and shallow-water features as channel fillings, torrential ripple-marks, mudcracks, and salt hopper and raindrop markings, features that are generally lacking in the equivalent but thicker Creston Formation of the west. The upper unit of the lower Purcell, represented by the Siyeh Formation in the east, contains much clean carbonate typically with "molar tooth" and stromatolitic and oölitic structures, interbedded with shale and siltstone in the lower and upper parts. The latter unit constitutes the Siyeh of the Purcell Mountains and the underlying rocks, argillaceous and silty dolomites, form the Kitchener Formation. The upper part of the Purcell, the Sheppard, and lower Gateway Formations contain much argillaceous and silty dolomite whereas the conformable higher units of alternating argillite and quartzite vary from green and grey to purple and red and exhibit shallow-water sedimentary structures. The Purcell is intruded by the Moyie gabbro sills and is unconformably overlain by the Hadrynian Windermere System in western and northern Purcell Mountains and by various Paleozoic formations in the eastern Purcell and southern Rocky Mountains.

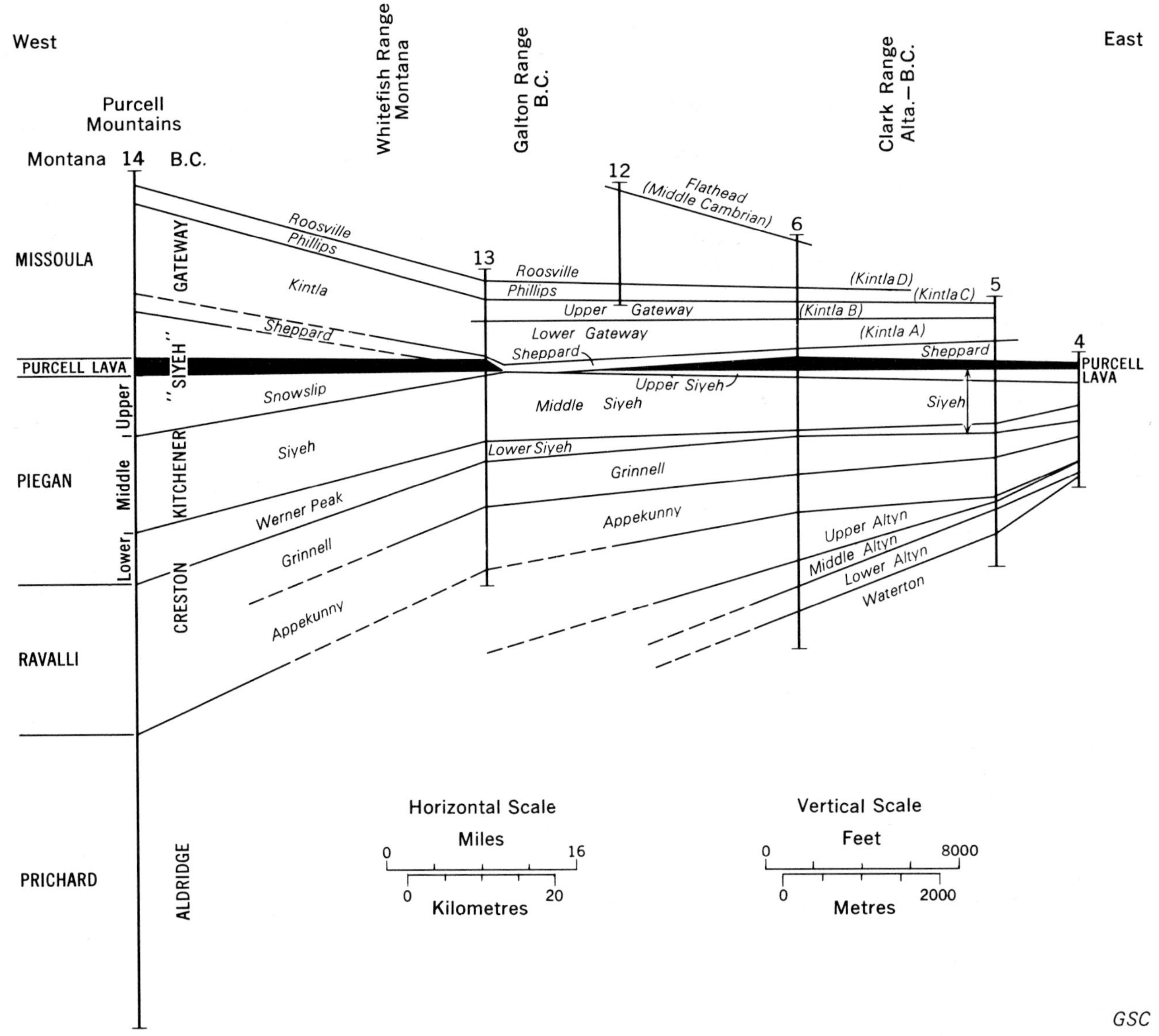

FIGURE VIII-3. Correlation of the Helikian (Purcell) rocks of southern Rocky Mountains and eastern Purcell Mountains, Alberta and British Columbia (Price, 1964a).

In *northern Rocky Mountains* rocks of probable Helikian age are divisible into a lower carbonate and quartzite part, 1,000 feet thick, and an upper pelitic part, 8,000 feet thick (Bell, 1968). The lowest unit in the core of an anticline, the Chischa Formation, is composed of pale grey, pastel-hued, aphanitic dolomite with stromatolites, desiccation cracks, ripple-marks, and "molar tooth" structures, interbedded with quartzite near the base and top. It is unconformably overlain by the Tetsa Formation, of dark siltstones and shales 1,065 feet thick. The grey carbonates of the George Formation are similar to those of the Siyeh Formation of the Purcell. It thins southwestward from 1,750 feet to 1,200 feet and is transitionally overlain by the Henry Creek Formation that thickens from 700 to 1,500 feet in the same direction. The Henry Creek consists of grey calcareous mudstone, siltstone, and conglomerate with pebbles of carbonate similar to the George Formation. The Tuchodi Formation is 5,000 feet of resistant brown-weathering feldspathic quartzite, dolomitic siltstone, and argillaceous dolomite with minor varicoloured shale. The uppermost formations, the Aida and Gataga are mudstone and siltstone with a general flysch aspect. The former is buff to grey weathering and the latter is dark olive-grey with a few poorly sorted and graded sandstones. The succession is intruded by gabbro dykes and overlain with angular unconformity by Lower Cambrian to Silurian formations. The Hadrynian and Helikian of the region are exposed in separate structures.

In *Omineca Mountains* (Roots, 1954) the Helikian may be included in regionally metamorphosed strata of the Tenakihi Group and the Wolverine Complex. The quartz–mica schists and quartzites include minor conglomerate with boulders as much as 8 inches in diameter of quartz, plagioclase, and potash feldspar, presumably derived from a granitic or metamorphic source. Part of the Shuswap Metamorphic Complex of Monashee Mountains may also be Helikian.

Helikian rocks near the headwaters of South Redstone River in *Mackenzie Mountains* comprise an apparently conformable succession more than 15,000 feet thick (Gabrielse, *et al.,* 1965). The basal unit, underlain by a thrust fault, is about 4,000 feet of recessive, dark grey and green shale interbedded with fine- to medium-grained quartzite and minor orange- and buff-weathering sandy dolomite. It is overlain by 4,300 feet of pink, white, and purple quartzites containing minor slate and orange-weathering dolomite, succeeded by stromatolitic and oölitic limestones and dolomites and orange-weathering sandy dolomites as much as 6,500 feet thick. A basalt flow or sill up to 100 feet or more thick occurs within the carbonates. In places, the carbonate strata are overlain by, and may be in part stratigraphically equivalent to, pink-weathering gypsiferous siltstones, locally 1,100 feet thick, that contain disseminated copper minerals. East of Keele River beds of gypsum more than 100 feet thick are conspicuous. Locally the siltstones are overlain by 675 feet of limestone, siltstone, slate, and limestone conglomerate. The Helikian strata in Mackenzie Mountains are overlain with angular unconformity by the Hadrynian Rapitan Group or the lower Paleozoic.

In *Franklin Mountains* (Douglas and Norris, 1963) the Helikian is probably represented by 4,800 feet of fine-grained, grey, quartzose sandstone and siltstone interbedded with dusty red and olive-green shale in the upper 3,100 feet and with cryptocrystalline green and brown dolomite in the basal 1,700 feet. The sequence is underlain by a thrust and overlain with moderate angular unconformity by the Lone Land Formation considered to be Hadrynian.

The oldest rocks exposed in *Ogilvie, northern Selwyn, and northern Mackenzie Mountains* are dark weathering slate, argillite, and phyllite, probably more than 5,000 feet thick (Green and Roddick, 1962). In most places the rocks are folded and sheared, mainly as a result of the Hadrynian Racklan Orogeny. The overlying, deformed, but not metamorphosed carbonate succession is variable. The most complete sequence, in southern Ogilvie Mountains, contains a basal unit, about 1,000 feet thick, of dark grey, thinly laminated dolomite, a middle unit of thin-bedded, orange-weathering dolomite, black shale, quartzite, limestone, and argillite, apparently more than 4,000 feet thick, and an upper unit of massive cherty and quartzose grey dolomite about 2,000 feet thick. To the east, in northwestern Selwyn Mountains, basal Helikian strata are slates and argillites overlain mainly by brilliant orange-weathering, thin-bedded dolomites. Still farther east, in northern Mackenzie Mountains, quartzites are dominant.

Helikian strata are present in the lower part of the Tindir Group of *southwestern Porcupine Plateau.* Dolomite, limestone, quartzite, shale, and slate, possibly 5,000 feet thick, are locally intruded by diabase dykes and sills. Succeeding strata of the group are referred to the Hadrynian. The Neruokpuk Formation of *British Mountains* consists of red and green argillite, feldspathic quartzite, shales, and phyllite. It possibly includes Helikian and Hadrynian rocks and also the lower Paleozoic as Silurian graptolites were obtained from Barn Mountains and the formation is overlain with angular unconformity by the Mississippian.

East Kootenay and Racklan Orogenies

Helikian sedimentation was brought to a close in southern Cordilleran Geosyncline by the East Kootenay Orogeny (White, 1959; Leech, 1962a). It is manifested by uplift, gentle folding, tilting, faulting, granitic intrusion, and regional metamorphism to greenschist facies and locally to sillimanite grade. In the southeastern Cordillera Hadrynian Windermere sediments and the Lower or Middle Cambrian rocks rest unconformably on Purcell strata. Fold trends related to the East Kootenay Orogeny are subparallel with those of younger orogenies. Muscovites from three coarse-grained to pegmatitic leucocratic granodiorite stocks in Purcell Mountains have given K–Ar ages of 675, 705, and 745 m.y. Micas from metamorphic rocks have given ages of 710 and 790 m.y. Whether these effects are only part of a much more intense orogeny farther west is unknown.

The Racklan Orogeny brought to a close the distinctive miogeosynclinal phase of Proterozoic sedimentation in the eastern part of the northern Cordilleran Geosyncline. Folding, block faulting, tilting, and uplift of the Helikian rocks resulted in one of the most spectacular unconformities in the northern Cordillera (Pl. VIII-1). In northern Selwyn Mountains Helikian strata form tight north-northeasterly trending folds and are overlain unconformably by the Rapitan Group. In the Taiga Ranges of southern Porcupine Plateau they form tight east-west folds and are unconformably overlain by Cambrian strata. Low-grade regional metamorphism of argillaceous rocks in northern Wernecke, Ogilvie, and Richardson Mountains possibly also took place at this time. In Mackenzie Mountains uplift, tilting, and block faulting followed deposition of Helikian rocks. The base of the Hadrynian Rapitan Group is marked by an angular unconformity, beneath which the degree of truncation varies greatly from one fault block to another. It is probable that the faulting was accompanied by the widespread emplacement of mafic dykes and flows that constitute a large proportion of the boulders in the Rapitan conglomerates.

Hadrynian (Late Proterozoic)

Tectonic Summary

A thick sequence of Hadrynian rocks, dominantly clastic and sedimentary, extends as an almost continuous

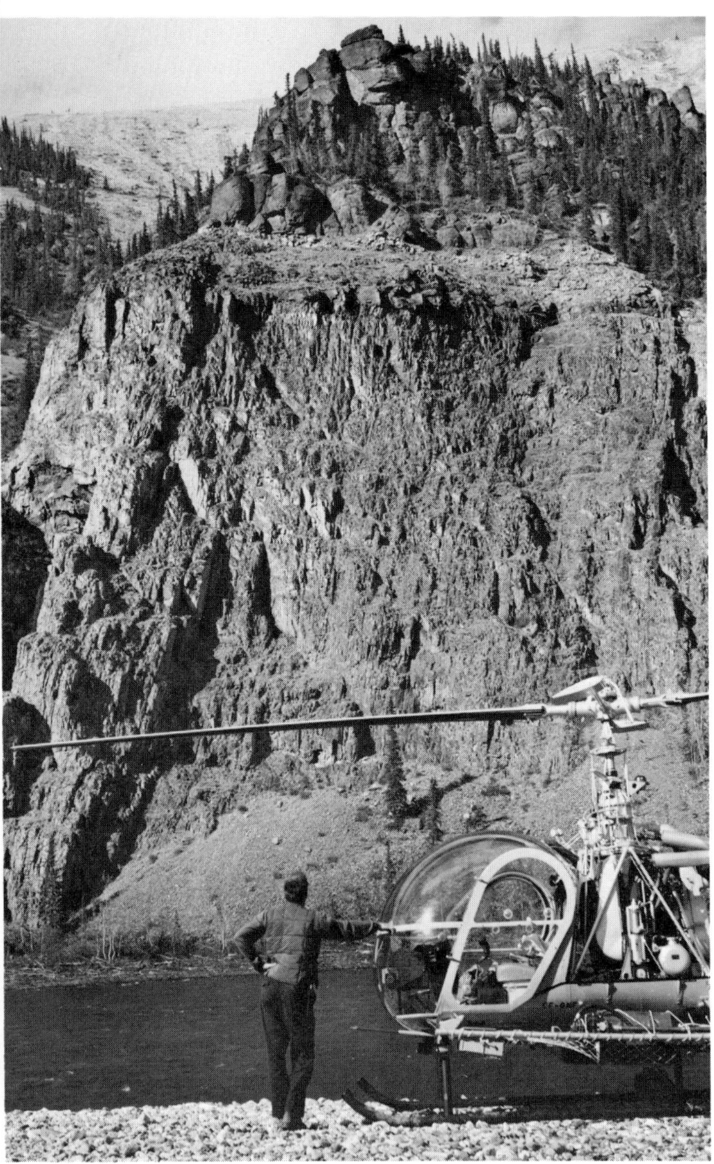

PLATE VIII-1. Angular unconformity on northwestern Mackenzie Arch between flat-lying Upper Cambrian dolomites and steeply dipping, easterly trending Helikian phyllite on Hart River, northern Yukon Territory.

belt through the eastern part of the Cordilleran Geosyncline (Fig. VIII-2). The sediments are of marine and shallow-water origin and probably partly miogeosynclinal, flanking a cratonic mass of Hudsonian crystallines with remnants of Helikian sedimentary cover. The source in the south is from uplift of the southern Purcell Geanticline following the East Kootenay Orogeny, and partly from the east as suggested by sedimentary features of the Miette Group which indicate westward transport. Part is locally derived from fault scarps, particularly the conglomerates of the Rapitan Group in the northern Wernecke and Mackenzie Mountains. The grits and pebble-conglomerates so extensive in the northern Cordilleran Geosyncline contain abundant potash feldspar and point to source areas containing granitic or metamorphic rocks. It remains for future work to determine whether the source was mainly the craton to the east, or a crystalline area to the west that was uplifted following the Racklan and East Kootenay Orogenies.

Cordilleran Geosyncline

Several thousand feet of amygdaloidal basalt, shale, tuff, conglomerate, iron-formation, dolomite, and limestone of probable Hadrynian age form the upper part of the Tindir Group in *southwestern Porcupine Plateau*. Possibly correlative rocks in *Ogilvie Mountains* consist of coarse conglomerate, 300 to 2,000 feet thick, overlain by dark shale and platy sandstone about 1,300 feet thick.

The Rapitan Group in *Mackenzie Mountains* (Gabrielse, *et al.*, 1965) consists typically of as much as 5,000 feet of dark weathering, fine-grained, feldspathic clastic rocks. Bedded chert–hematite iron-formation and poorly sorted conglomerate and conglomeratic mudstone form the lower part. Tuffaceous sediments are common and volcanic flows are present at several localities. Near the headwaters of Redstone River two unconformities, the lower one strongly angular in places, divide the Rapitan into three units: a lower unit, 0 to 1,285 feet thick, of reddish brown, maroon, and green mudstone, conglomeratic mudstone, and iron-formations; a middle unit, 1,215 to 2,705 feet thick, of grey-green to dark grey conglomeratic mudstone; and an upper unit, 1,870 to 3,845 feet thick, of dark shales, siltstones, and fine-grained sandstones. The Rapitan is overlain unconformably by orange-weathering dolomitic sandstones and sandy dolomites having a maximum thickness of 2,500 feet. The uppermost member of this unnamed formation is a widespread buff-weathering dolomite less than 100 feet thick, and locally, a basalt flow, 70 feet thick, occurs just below the top. The uppermost formation is a distinctive sequence of recessive dark weathering shale, siltstone, and sandstone, 2,000 to 3,000 feet thick.

In *Franklin Mountains* the Lone Land Formation, 965 feet thick, consists of grey shale with a basal ferruginous quartzose conglomeratic sandstone 200 feet thick that rests with angular unconformity on the Helikian and is overlain also with angular unconformity by the Lower Cambrian.

Large areas in *Selwyn Mountains* and northern *Rocky Mountains* (Bell, 1968) are underlain by a great thickness of impure clastic sediments consisting mainly of argillite, phyllite, slate, and siltstone but characterized by beds of gritty, feldspathic sandstone or feldspathic pebble-conglomerate, and by the presence of maroon, red, and green slates with minor limestone in the upper part. These rocks, informally termed the 'grit unit' are similar to Kaza, Miette, and Windermere strata of the southern Cordillera. The base of the sequence has not been observed and in most places no definite break with Lower Cambrian strata has been recognized.

The oldest exposed rocks in *Cassiar Mountains* (Gabrielse, 1963) are the Good Hope Group which consists of typical 'grit unit' rocks overlain by several thousand feet of well-bedded limestones, locally pisolitic and oölitic and commonly containing particles of ferrodolomite. The uppermost strata include crossbedded, sandy limestones, calcareous sandstones, and red and green shales and slates, overlain apparently conformably by Lower Cambrian.

In *Cariboo Mountains,* the Kaza Group of quartzose and feldspathic sandstone, grit, and phyllite is overlain by the argillaceous Isaac Formation, in turn succeeded by the Cunningham Limestone (Sutherland Brown, 1957). Limestones mapped as the Cunningham form three belts, the western two of which merge along a fault. Only the central limestone contains fossils and where stratigraphic relations appear unequivocal the fossiliferous limestone lies more than 4,500 feet above the unfossiliferous limestone. Thus, the eastern and western belts of limestone may be either unfossiliferous Lower Cambrian or equivalent to the carbonate member at the top of the Hadrynian Miette Group in the Rocky Mountains (Campbell, 1967).

In *Purcell and westernmost Rocky Mountains,* the Toby Formation forms the base of the Windermere. It is extremely variable in thickness, up to 2,000 feet, and also in lithology, being either a breccia or a conglomerate with a great range in ratio of matrix to clasts. Near the Rocky Mountain Trench, gneissic granite boulders as much as 2 feet in diameter are at the top. Reesor (1957) concluded that the material must have had a source nearby, probably Archean rocks, now buried beneath Paleozoic cover in the Rocky Mountains. The formation has been considered a fanglomerate by J. F. Walker but H. M. A. Rice thinks that it was deposited along the shoreline of a sea that spread rapidly over a subsiding landmass reworking loose surficial deposits. The Toby is conformably succeeded by the Horsethief Creek Group. The basal unit, 3,000 feet thick, is principally of quartzose and feldspathic grit, sandstone, and some varicoloured quartz-pebble conglomerate. It is overlain by a grey, green, and purple slate more than 1,000 feet thick, and succeeded by a limestone 650 feet thick. A unit of slate and quartzite at the top varies in thickness from zero to 1,000 feet. The group thickens westward and becomes generally finer grained and more abundant in carbonate in Selkirk Mountains and in the northern Purcell Mountains and Dogtooth Range (Reesor, 1957). Southwest of Kootenay Lake, the Irene Formation overlies the Toby Formation conformably. The Irene is a fine-grained, sheared, andesitic greenstone with interbeds of conglomerate and limestone. Considerable thicknesses of breccia and minor calcareous tuff may be present locally.

In *southern Rocky Mountains* the Miette Group is composed of a basal unit, 3,000 feet thick, of argillite and argillaceous sandstone, succeeded by 2,000 feet of sandstone, grit, conglomerate, and argillite, which is overlain by 3,000 feet of argillite and, locally at the top, by a carbonate 0 to 1,000 feet thick (Mountjoy, 1962). The Hector and Corral Creek Formations farther south are lithologically similar to the Miette and Horsethief Creek Groups.

Hadrynian rocks are possibly present in the regionally metamorphosed Yukon and Horseranch Groups and the Wolverine and Shuswap Complexes.

PALEOZOIC

Cambrian

Tectonic Summary

The Lower Cambrian (Fig. VIII-4) is restricted to the Cordilleran Geosyncline, and is generally thickest in linear troughs marginal to the craton. It is of miogeosynclinal facies. Thick extensive sheets of orthoquartzite and conglomerate overlain by limestone, commonly archeocyathid-bearing, grade westward into thinner calcareous shales and argillaceous limestones. The orthoquartzites of Alberta Trough are locally feldspathic and were derived from the Hudsonian crystallines of the craton or possibly its former Helikian cover. Their maturity relative to the underlying Windermere clastics, with which they may be locally conformable, suggests reduction of relief and a general tectonic stability of the craton by the beginning of and during the Early Cambrian. Northeast-trending Eager Trough, possibly bordered on the southeast by the Moyie fault, separates Purcell Arch from an emergent block to the south (Montania). Quartzose sandstone and conglomerate derived from adjacent uplifts transgress the arch and lie unconformably on Purcell and Windermere strata. Within Lardeau Trough the Lower Cambrian reaches a thickness of 9,000 feet and contains intercalated basic flows and pyroclastics.

Several tectonic elements of the northern Cordilleran Geosyncline, more evident in some later periods, appear to be established in the Early Cambrian. Polymictic conglomerates on the west flank of the MacDonald Platform were derived from a west-dipping homocline of Helikian sediments, the uplift bounded, in part at least, by faults active during deposition. Shallow-water orthoquartzite and limestone on the Cassiar Platform contrast with thick, deeper water, dominantly pelitic sediments in eastern Selwyn Basin, the latter grading easterly to shallow-water sandstone and carbonates of the western flank of Mackenzie Arch. On the arch they are absent through convergence and post-Lower Cambrian truncation. *Olenellus-*

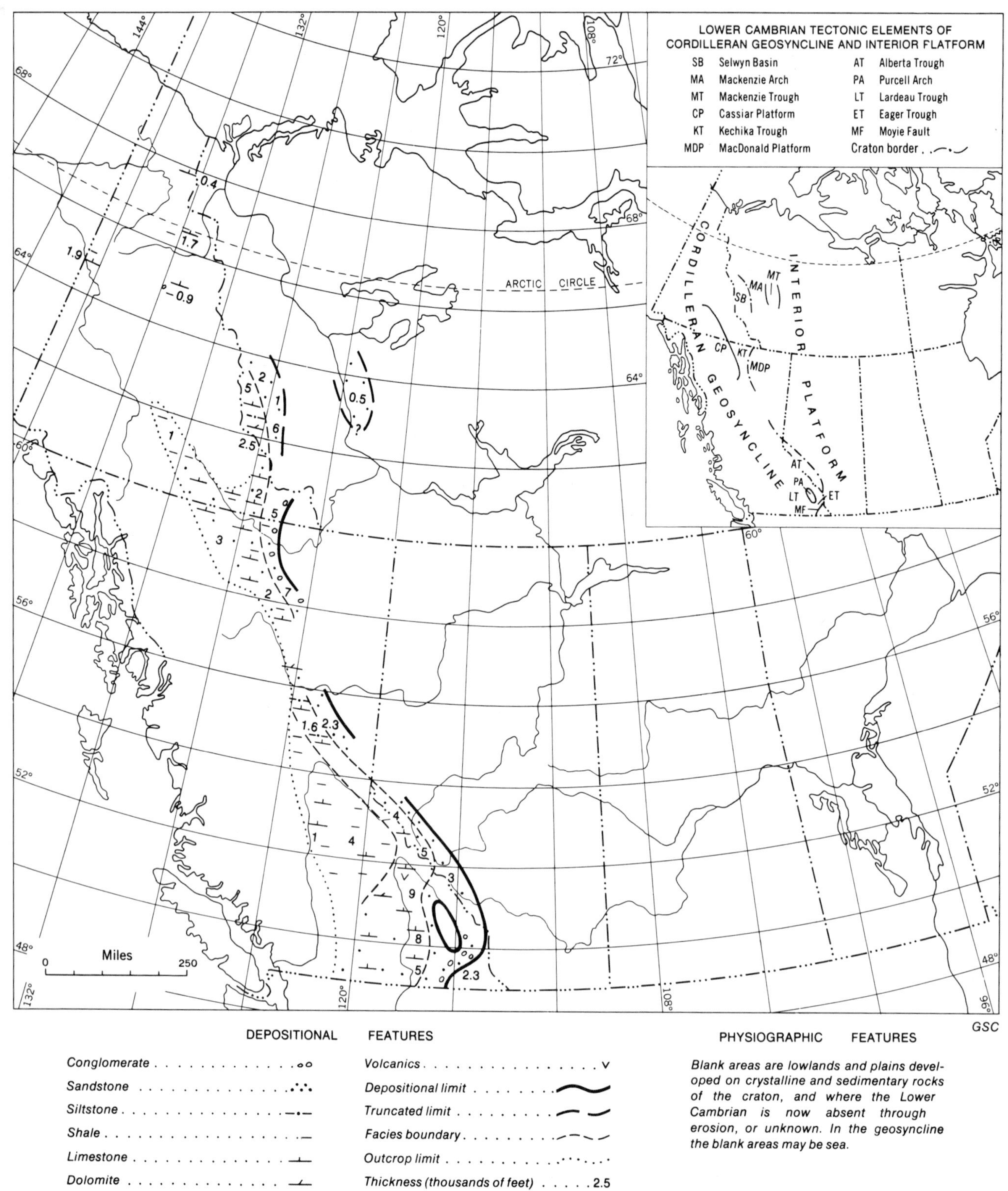

LOWER CAMBRIAN TECTONIC ELEMENTS OF CORDILLERAN GEOSYNCLINE AND INTERIOR PLATFORM
SB Selwyn Basin
MA Mackenzie Arch
MT Mackenzie Trough
CP Cassiar Platform
KT Kechika Trough
MDP MacDonald Platform
AT Alberta Trough
PA Purcell Arch
LT Lardeau Trough
ET Eager Trough
MF Moyie Fault
Craton border
CORDILLERAN GEOSYNCLINE
INTERIOR PLATFORM
ARCTIC CIRCLE
Miles
0
250
GSC
DEPOSITIONAL FEATURES
Conglomerate
Sandstone
Siltstone
Shale
Limestone
Dolomite
Volcanics
Depositional limit
Truncated limit
Facies boundary
Outcrop limit
Thickness (thousands of feet) 2.5
PHYSIOGRAPHIC FEATURES
Blank areas are lowlands and plains developed on crystalline and sedimentary rocks of the craton, and where the Lower Cambrian is now absent through erosion, or unknown. In the geosyncline the blank areas may be sea.

FIGURE VIII-4. Lower Cambrian sedimentation and tectonism in Western Canada.

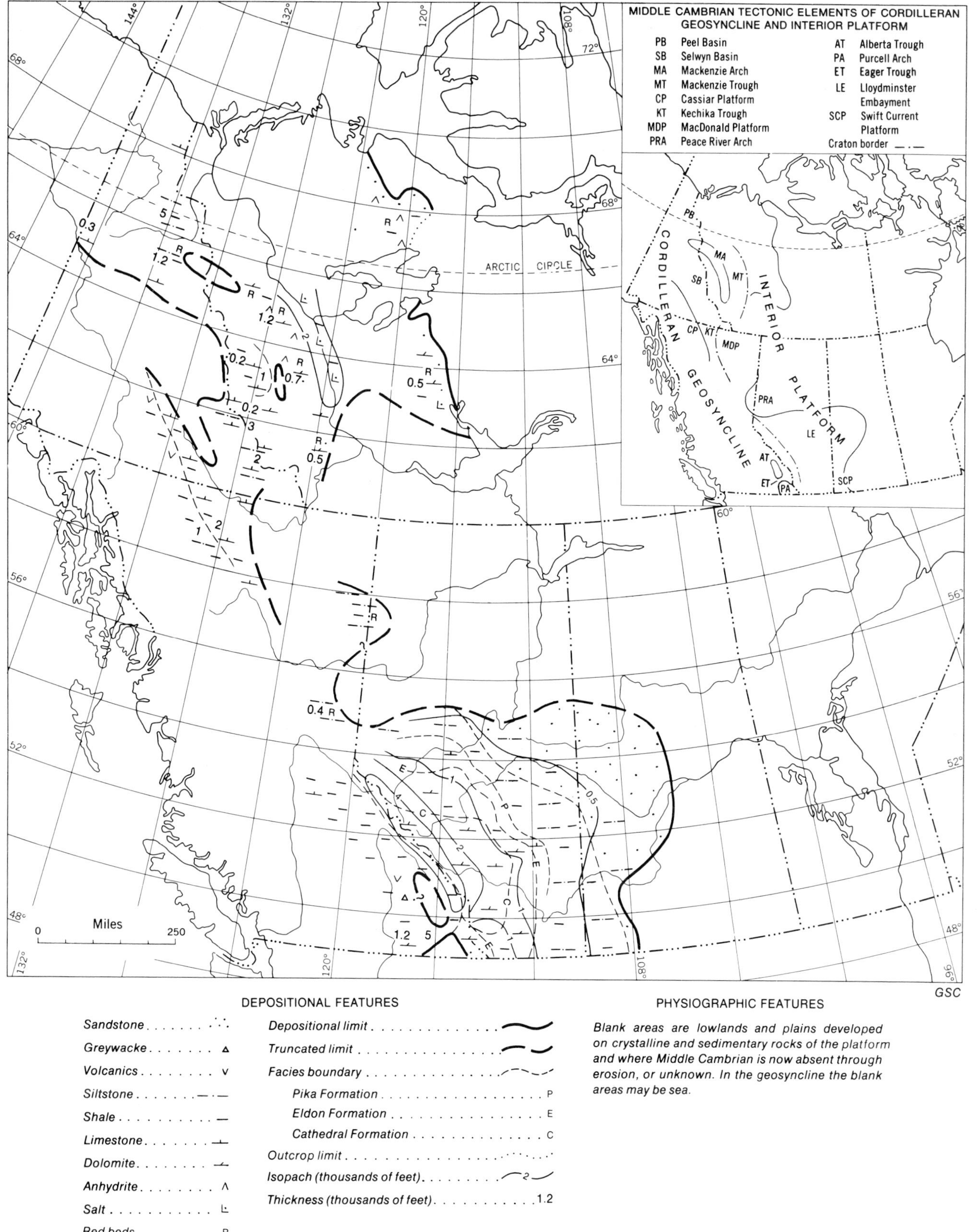

MIDDLE CAMBRIAN TECTONIC ELEMENTS OF CORDILLERAN GEOSYNCLINE AND INTERIOR PLATFORM
PB Peel Basin
SB Selwyn Basin
MA Mackenzie Arch
MT Mackenzie Trough
CP Cassiar Platform
KT Kechika Trough
MDP MacDonald Platform
PRA Peace River Arch
AT Alberta Trough
PA Purcell Arch
ET Eager Trough
LE Lloydminster Embayment
SCP Swift Current Platform
Craton border
CORDILLERAN GEOSYNCLINE
INTERIOR PLATFORM
ARCTIC CIRCLE
Miles
0
250
GSC
DEPOSITIONAL FEATURES
Sandstone
Greywacke
Volcanics
Siltstone
Shale
Limestone
Dolomite
Anhydrite
Salt
Red beds
Depositional limit
Truncated limit
Facies boundary
Pika Formation P
Eldon Formation E
Cathedral Formation C
Outcrop limit
Isopach (thousands of feet)
Thickness (thousands of feet) 1.2
PHYSIOGRAPHIC FEATURES
Blank areas are lowlands and plains developed on crystalline and sedimentary rocks of the platform and where Middle Cambrian is now absent through erosion, or unknown. In the geosyncline the blank areas may be sea.

FIGURE VIII-5. Middle Cambrian sedimentation and tectonism in Western Canada.

bearing limestone occurs in Peel Basin and orthoquartzites with overlying green shale in Mackenzie Trough; these strata lie unconformably on the Proterozoic.

Middle Cambrian sediments (Fig. VIII-5) in the southern Cordilleran Geosyncline conformably overlie the Lower Cambrian in the deeply depressed Lardeau and Alberta Troughs and overlap parts of Purcell Arch and the depressed margin of the craton. Lardeau Trough received shale, thin beds of limestone and quartzite, with intercalated basic pillow lavas and pyroclastics. In Alberta Trough several thousand feet of massive carbonate grade westward into thick shale and argillaceous limestone which in turn grade into westerly thinning carbonates that lie unconformably on the Proterozoic along the eastern edge of Purcell Arch. Shale was probably deposited in Eager Trough, the land to the south covered in part by thin sandstone, shale, and dolomite overlapping from the east, and fringed on the west by thin carbonates. East of the strong hingeline bounding the craton (Fig. VIII-7) Middle Cambrian rocks occupy Lloydminster Embayment, a broad northeast-trending depression within which the carbonates progressively grade eastward to shale and siltstone and basal overlapping sandstone and conglomerate. The depression is subparallel with the grain of the Hudsonian crystalline basement and is flanked on the southeast by Swift Current Platform and on the northwest by Peace River Arch. Thin Upper Cambrian (Fig. VIII-6) shaly siltstones and sandstones overlap the Middle Cambrian and Precambrian crystallines of Swift Current Platform. They extend to truncated margins and are deeply eroded by post-Lower Ordovician uplift along the margin of the craton that later developed as Alberta Arch. Thick, bedded carbonates occur in Alberta Trough, the upper part intertonguing westward with shale and the lower part, more persistent westward, merges with the late Middle Cambrian carbonates along the east flank of Purcell Arch.

In the central part of the craton, Middle and Upper Cambrian rocks are absent probably mainly through non-deposition. Thin undated shales occur west and north of Peace River Arch, but it is not known whether a depositional trough existed between the craton and MacDonald Platform, where Middle and Upper Cambrian rocks are missing, joining Alberta and Mackenzie Troughs. In southern Kechika Trough thick calcareous phyllite and argillaceous limestones grade westerly into calcareous phyllite and dark shale on Cassiar Platform. Thick carbonates extend along the southern and western flanks of Mackenzie Arch. Along the crest of the arch the Upper Cambrian is absent and the Middle Cambrian locally absent, mainly through pre-Upper Ordovician truncation. The Middle Cambrian on the arch consists of a thin red-bed facies of shale, sandy dolomite, and gypsum with sandstone and conglomerate in the west, where unconformably overlain by Upper Cambrian limestones that thicken northward into argillaceous limestone and shale in Peel Basin. In Mackenzie Trough the Middle Cambrian is mainly salt and the Upper Cambrian is dolomite. An undated red-bed facies borders the Canadian Shield but is absent on Coppermine Arch; it is Middle Cambrian east of the arch.

Lower Cambrian

In *Richardson Mountains* R. M. Proctor reports well-bedded grey limestones, 1,200 feet thick, with *Olenellus*. They are overlain, apparently conformably, by rocks of probable Middle Cambrian age, but their base is not exposed (Brabb, 1967). Less than 1,000 feet of limestone and limestone-conglomerate outcrops along the Alaskan boundary north of Yukon River. These rocks are overlain by 900 feet of argillite, siltstone, and minor quartzite and sandy limestone, in part of Early Cambrian age. In northern *Wernecke Mountains* about 900 feet of pelletoid limestone with interbedded reddish weathering sandstone and conglomerate lie unconformably on the Helikian. In *Franklin Mountains* 500 feet of fine-grained, white quartzose sandstone of the Mount Clark Formation lies with angular unconformity on Proterozoic strata, and is conformably overlain by 200 feet of grey, green, and red shales of the Mount Cap Formation.

The Lower Cambrian is as thick as 6,000 feet in eastern *Selwyn Mountains* and western *Mackenzie Mountains* (Gabrielse, *et al.*, 1965) but decreases eastward to zero as the result of depositional thinning on Mackenzie Arch and truncation beneath the regional unconformity at the base of Middle Cambrian rocks. In western Mackenzie Mountains the Lower Cambrian is mainly sandstone but includes minor pebble-conglomerate, siltstone, and shale. The base is probably a regional unconformity with little angular discordance. In northeastern Selwyn Mountains, limestones, dolomites, sandy dolomites, sandstones, and argillites, characteristically buff, mauve, cream, and brown weathering, range in thickness from 1,600 to 3,200 feet. In southeastern Selwyn Mountains the Lower Cambrian sequence consists of: calcareous siltstone and impure limestone, 200 feet; limestone, 200 feet; sandstone, sandy and silty dolomite, 2,000 feet; orange-weathering silty and sandy dolomite, 1,000 feet (Blusson, 1968). Basic volcanic flows and breccias, locally 200 feet thick occur in the upper part of the member below the orange-weathering beds.

In *Pelly Mountains* and *Cassiar Mountains* the Lower Cambrian Atan Group is represented by a basal sandstone or quartzite 1,000 to more than 2,000 feet thick, a middle shale about 150 feet thick, and an upper limestone unit as much as 1,500 feet thick (Gabrielse, 1963). Typically the limestones are massive, relatively pure, partly pelletoid, and yield abundant well-preserved archeocyathids. Strata of the Atan Group are structurally conformable with the underlying Proterozoic rocks and the overlying Middle or Upper Cambrian sequence.

In *northern Rocky Mountains* is a highly variable sequence of clastic and carbonate rocks, according to G. C. Taylor, more than 5,000 feet thick locally. In the east, the base rests, with marked angular unconformity (Pl.

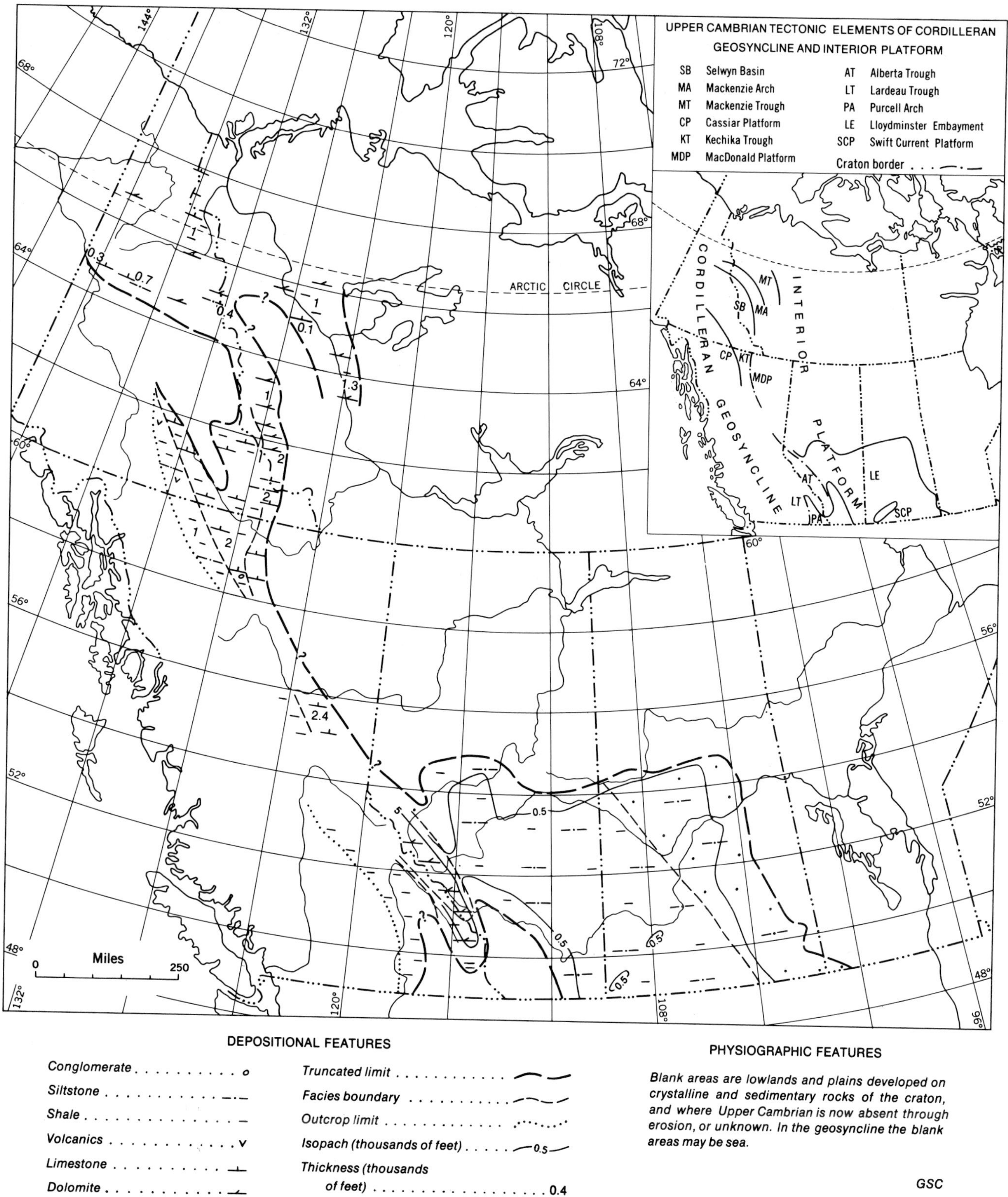

FIGURE VIII-6. Upper Cambrian sedimentation and tectonism in Western Canada.

PLATE VIII-2. Angular unconformity on MacDonald Platform between the Ordovician and Helikian, Yedhe Mountain near Alaska Highway, northern Rocky Mountains, British Columbia. Looking northwest along axis of anticline produced in Racklan Orogeny. Sn—Silurian Nonda Formation; Ok—Lower Ordovician Kechika Group; Ht—Helikian Tuchodi Formation.

VIII-2), low in the Helikian succession, whereas a few miles to the west no apparent break separates the Cambrian and Hadrynian strata. Thick, coarse, red-weathering conglomerates with pebbles of quartzite, dolomite, and greenstone are interbedded with and grade westward into sandstone, shale, and argillaceous limestone. The conglomerate occurs adjacent to northeast- and northwest-trending faults bordering the west flank of MacDonald Platform and demonstrates Lower Cambrian faulting. In Terminal Range to the west, a widespread conglomerate, 50 feet thick, containing slabs of archeocyathid limestone occurs within a shale and calcareous sandstone sequence. Relatively minor, coarse, polymictic conglomerates also occur locally within limestones and dolomites immediately east of Rocky Mountain Trench. The limestones are underlain by sandstone and in general aspect the sequence is much like that of Cassiar Mountains except for the presence of well-bedded oölitic and sandy dolomites. In southern Rocky Mountains, in Alberta Trough, as much as 7,000 feet of quartzite, conglomerate shale, and limestone comprise the Gog Group (Aitken, 1968). A limestone, the Mural Formation, occurs near the top and thins to the south and east.

Lower Cambrian strata occur in isolated remnants and fault blocks as part of thick lower Paleozoic sections northwest of Moyie fault in *Purcell Mountains* and north of Dibble Creek fault in Hughes Range east of Rocky Mountain Trench. The basal Cranbrook Formation, a quartzite and quartzitic conglomerate, lies unconformably upon various units of the Purcell System. Northwest of Moyie fault it contains coarse fragments of the Creston Formation. About 20,000 feet of strata was eroded from Purcell Arch prior to overlap by the Cranbrook westward from Alberta Trough and northward from Eager Trough (Reesor, 1957). The Cranbrook locally includes a middle unit of magnesite. The succeeding Eager Formation contains late Lower Cambrian fossils in the lower part. It is probably more than 6,000 feet thick near Cranbrook and indicates that considerable subsidence occurred in Eager Trough during the Cambrian. However, south of Moyie and Dibble Creek faults, the Lower Cambrian is absent and the Upper Devonian lies unconformably on the Purcell although locally south of Dibble Creek fault some Middle Cambrian beds intervene. The rapid northwesterly truncation of Purcell strata beneath the sub-Cambrian unconformity (Norris and Price, 1966) and the presence of coarse debris in the Lower Cambrian near Moyie fault indicate that Eager Trough was probably bounded by an uplifted block (Montania) during Early Cambrian time.

In *Selkirk* and *western Purcell Mountains* the Hamill Group generally lies gradationally and conformably upon the Horsethief Creek Group. Fossils have been found in the Hamill Group at only one locality, in Dogtooth Range, where mid-Lower Cambrian *Callavia* occurs in the uppermost 20 feet. The delineation of the base of the Cambrian in this region and adjacent metamorphic terrane is therefore a problem. The base of the Hamill Group is used rather than, alternatively, the first unconformity below Cambrian fossils, which here would be the base of the Hadrynian Windermere System. In Dogtooth Range the Hamill Group consists of two quartzite formations separated by an argillaceous unit. It thins southeastward towards Purcell Arch from 4,000 feet to 1,500 feet and overlies the Horsethief Creek Group with erosional unconformity. The Hamill Group is overlain conformably by the Donald Formation, 1,500 feet of sandstone, slate, limestone, and at least one flow of basalt. The Donald contains archeocyathids, *Olenellus,* and *Bonnia.* Near Kootenay Lake, the lower two-thirds of the Hamill Group, the Quartzite Range, and Mount Gainer Formations are composed mainly of thick-bedded, commonly crossbedded orthoquartzite locally containing sodic plagioclase and potash feldspar. In northern Selkirk Mountains the group contains abundant greenstone flows, breccia, and tuff, and rare stretched quartzitic conglomerate. The upper third of the group, the Reno and Marsh Adams Formations, is thinly bedded and contains much argillaceous sediment. The Hamill Group is overlain conformably by phyllite and limestone of the Mohican Formation (Fyles and Eastwood, 1962) and then by archeocyathid-bearing limestone of the Badshot Formation. The equivalent archeocyathid-bearing beds of the Laib Formation in Salmo area are also limestone (Little, 1960). The group thickens westward from about 4,000 feet in northern Dogtooth Range to about 8,000 feet in the Selkirks but thins westward from 4,500 at Kootenay Lake to 2,000 feet 30 miles southwest near the International Boundary.

The presence and thickness of the Hamill Group in the Shuswap Metamorphic Complex is uncertain but it is probably represented by a highly deformed, relatively pure quartzite (Wheeler, 1965). The quartzite thins northwestward and is apparently represented in the *Cariboo Mountains* by the Yanks Peak Quartzite, 600 feet in the southeast and 1,600 feet in the northwest. The Yanks Peak Quartzite is overlain by 500 feet of shales of the Midas Formation succeeded by archeocyathid-bearing limestone similar to the Mural Formation of the Gog Group of Rocky Mountains. The Yanks Peak, which therefore must be a tongue of quartzite of the Gog Group, is underlain by 2,500 feet of shales of the Yankee Belle Formation, which in turn overlies the Cunningham Limestone (Campbell, 1967).

In *Omineca Mountains* archeocyathid-bearing limestone has been included in the Ingenika Group together with orthoquartzite of possible Early Cambrian age (Roots, 1954). The remaining lower part of the group, consisting of grit, quartzite, phyllite, and schist, is like the Horsethief Creek Group and presumed Hadrynian.

Middle and Upper Cambrian

In *southern Richardson Mountains* about 5,000 feet of platy and nodular limestone, siltstone, and shale, probably mainly Middle Cambrian, are overlain by more than 1,200 feet of platy limestone and argillite with an Upper Cambrian, Dresbachian fauna in its lower part. Along the Alaskan Boundary north of Yukon River the Middle Cambrian is represented by the upper part of a sequence 900 feet thick of argillite, siltstone, and minor quartzite and sandy limestone overlain by 400 feet of limestones and limestone-conglomerates partly of Upper Cambrian age. In *Taiga Ranges* and *Wernecke Mountains* well-bedded, commonly buff-weathering limestones and dolomites of Middle and Late Cambrian age are generally 1,000 to 2,000 feet thick and overlie Proterozoic rocks with regional unconformity.

In the *Franklin Mountains* the Middle Cambrian is probably represented by salt and green, red, and grey shales of the Saline River Formation. A thickness of 2,783 feet was penetrated by the Imperial Vermillion Ridge No. 1 well. H. G. Bassett considers the Franklin Mountain Formation to be of Late Cambrian age. It consists of 1,300 feet of light brown weathering, fine-grained, dull dolomite with minor variegated shale. The McDougall Group in *northern Mackenzie Mountains* is about 1,000 feet thick and consists of green, brown, and maroon shales and sandstones with gypsum and grey limestone in the upper part. The formation has yielded a single fossil of Middle or Late Cambrian age and rests with regional unconformity on quartzites of the Helikian Katherine Group (Hume, 1954).

Throughout much of *western Mackenzie Mountains* Middle Cambrian strata overlie older rocks with regional unconformity. Their distribution and thickness are also strongly influenced by major regional unconformity at the base of the Upper Cambrian. Near the headwaters of Redstone River the Middle Cambrian sequence comprises recessive, thin-bedded, argillaceous limestones, siltstones, and shales as much as 1,500 feet thick structurally conformable with underlying Lower Cambrian sandstones. Southeast of Sekwi Mountain the Middle Cambrian succession is reduced to only a few hundred feet. Franconian fossils have been collected from basal beds above the unconformity at several localities. A conspicuous silver-grey-weathering sandstone or dolomitic sandstone locally more than 300 feet thick occurs at or near the base of the Upper Cambrian sequence and is overlain by several hundred feet of buff- and orange-weathering limestone and dolomite conformable with overlying Lower Ordovician strata. The Upper Cambrian rocks are truncated on Mackenzie Arch to the east beneath the regional unconformity at the base of the Upper Ordovician.

In *southwestern Mackenzie Mountains* northeast of South Nahanni River, buff-weathering Middle and Upper (?) Cambrian rocks including dolomitic siltstones, silty dolomites, and stromatolitic dolomites and limestones are at least 1,500 feet thick and are overlain by massive limestones and dolomites of Late Cambrian age at least 600 feet thick (Gabrielse, *et al.,* 1965).

About 2,000 feet of well-bedded silty limestone of Middle Cambrian age in *eastern Selwyn Mountains* near the big bend in South Nahanni River is bevelled southerly to zero beneath Upper Cambrian (Franconian) strata. The basal Upper Cambrian rocks are maroon weathering sandstones 200 feet thick and are overlain by grey weathering carbonates also of Late Cambrian age that grade upward into Lower Ordovician carbonates. Near the Canada Tungsten mine and to the south Middle and Upper (?) Cambrian to Lower Ordovician silty limestones are more than 4,000 feet thick. They are commonly argillaceous in the upper part. The base of the sequence is marked by a regional unconformity, or, locally by an angular unconformity.

In *Pelly Mountains* thin-bedded and recessive glossy calcareous shales and argillaceous limestones are dated only by their stratigraphic position between the Lower Cambrian and Lower Ordovician (Green, *et al.*, 1960a, 1960b). Locally minor green volcanic breccia and tuff are intercalated. Middle (?) and Upper Cambrian rocks in *Cassiar Mountains* are dominantly calcareous in the east and argillaceous in the west. In *Kechika Ranges* several thousand feet of thin-bedded argillaceous limestones and calcareous phyllites locally including intrusive bodies of diabase and minor bodies of green volcanic breccia appears to lie conformably between Lower Cambrian and Lower Ordovician rocks (Gabrielse, 1962b). Farther west rocks in the same stratigraphic interval are in part of the Upper Cambrian (Trempeleau). They are dominantly dark weathering, thin-bedded shales and phyllites, variably calcareous and about 1,000 feet thick (Gabrielse, 1963).

In Terminal Range of *northern Rocky Mountains* as much as 1,000 feet of well-bedded calcareous sandstone overlies archeocyathid-bearing conglomerate and is in turn overlain by a thick assemblage of thin-bedded, nodular, argillaceous limestone mainly of early Ordovician age. The latter assemblage may include strata of Cambrian age, particularly in westernmost exposures.

The Middle and Upper Cambrian rocks of *Purcell Mountains* were deposited on the eastern flank of Purcell Arch which probably remained emergent until some time in latest Early or Middle Cambrian time. They occur at intervals within Rocky Mountain Trench, and along its west side, consisting of the unfossiliferous dolomite of the Jubilee Formation and the lower part of the overlying thin-bedded limestone and shale of the McKay Group (Reesor, 1957). West of the trench the two formations total no more than 300 feet whereas to the east they thicken to nearly 5,000 feet and fossiliferous mid-Upper Cambrian strata overlie the Jubilee. On both sides of the trench, near Columbia Lakes, the Jubilee lies disconformably on the Horsethief Creek Group, but to the northwest and southeast it lies on late Lower Cambrian strata.

In southernmost *Selkirk Mountains* fossiliferous Middle and Upper Cambrian strata in Lardeau Trough are the limestone, dolomite, and calcareous shales of the Nelway Formation (Little, 1960) and its equivalent in Washington, the Metaline Formation (Park and Cannon, 1943). These rocks accumulated as carbonate banks fringing the southern part of Purcell Arch and the uplifted

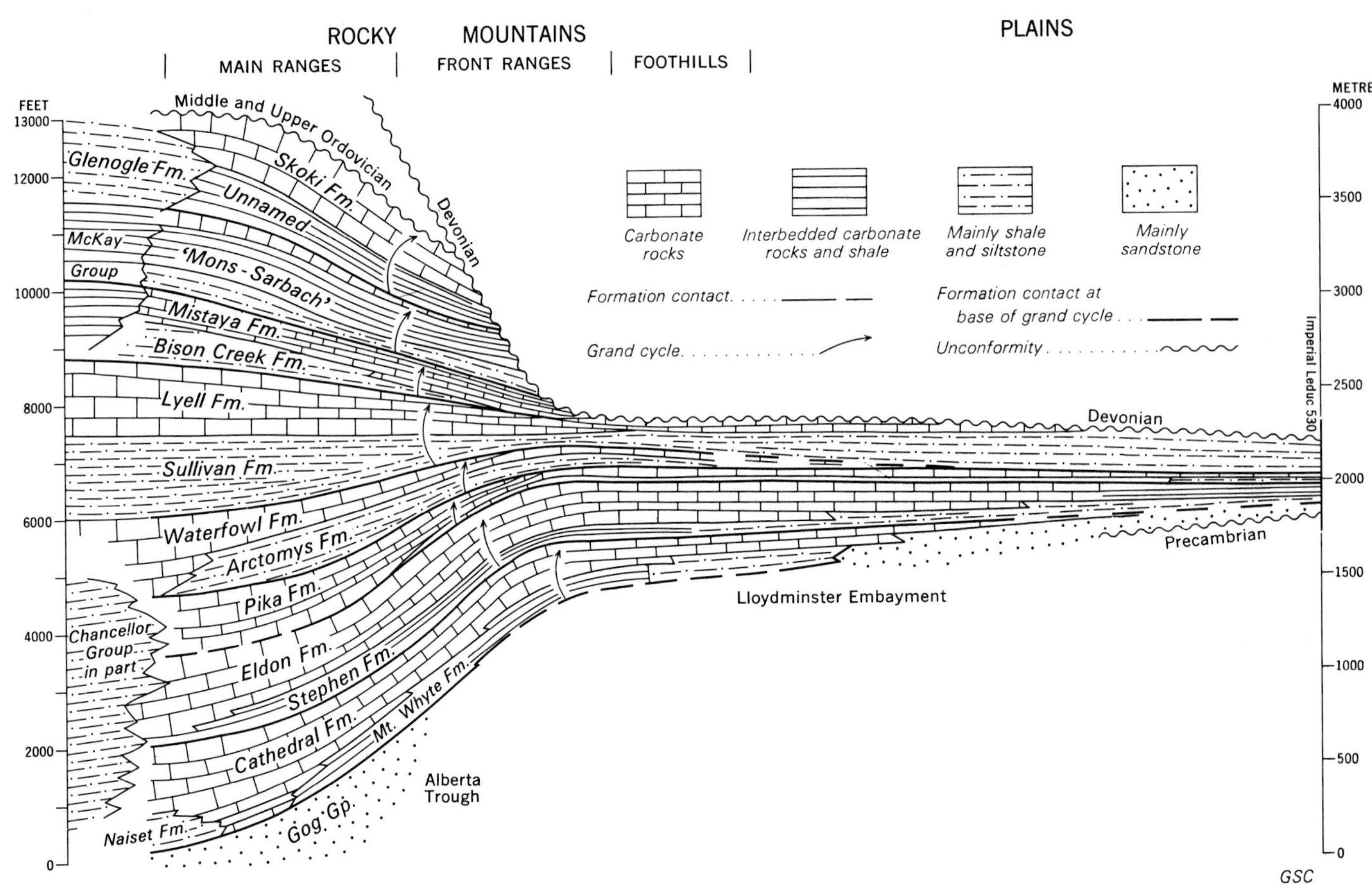

FIGURE VIII-7. Schematic restored stratigraphic section of Cambrian and Ordovician rocks, southern Rocky Mountains and Interior Plains of Alberta and British Columbia (Aitken, 1966).

block south of Eager Trough. The Nelway Formation lies gradationally and conformably upon the Laib Formation and is overlain with structural conformity by the Active Formation. The Nelway Formation contains no diagnostic fossils but the Metaline has yielded two Middle Cambrian faunas, the higher of which resembles the one in the Stephen Formation. Elsewhere in Lardeau Trough the fossiliferous Lower Cambrian limestone is conformably succeeded by the unfossiliferous, predominantly argillaceous Index Formation (Fyles and Eastwood, 1962) that also contains thin beds of limestone, quartzite, and amygdaloidal and pillowed greenstone flows and breccia.

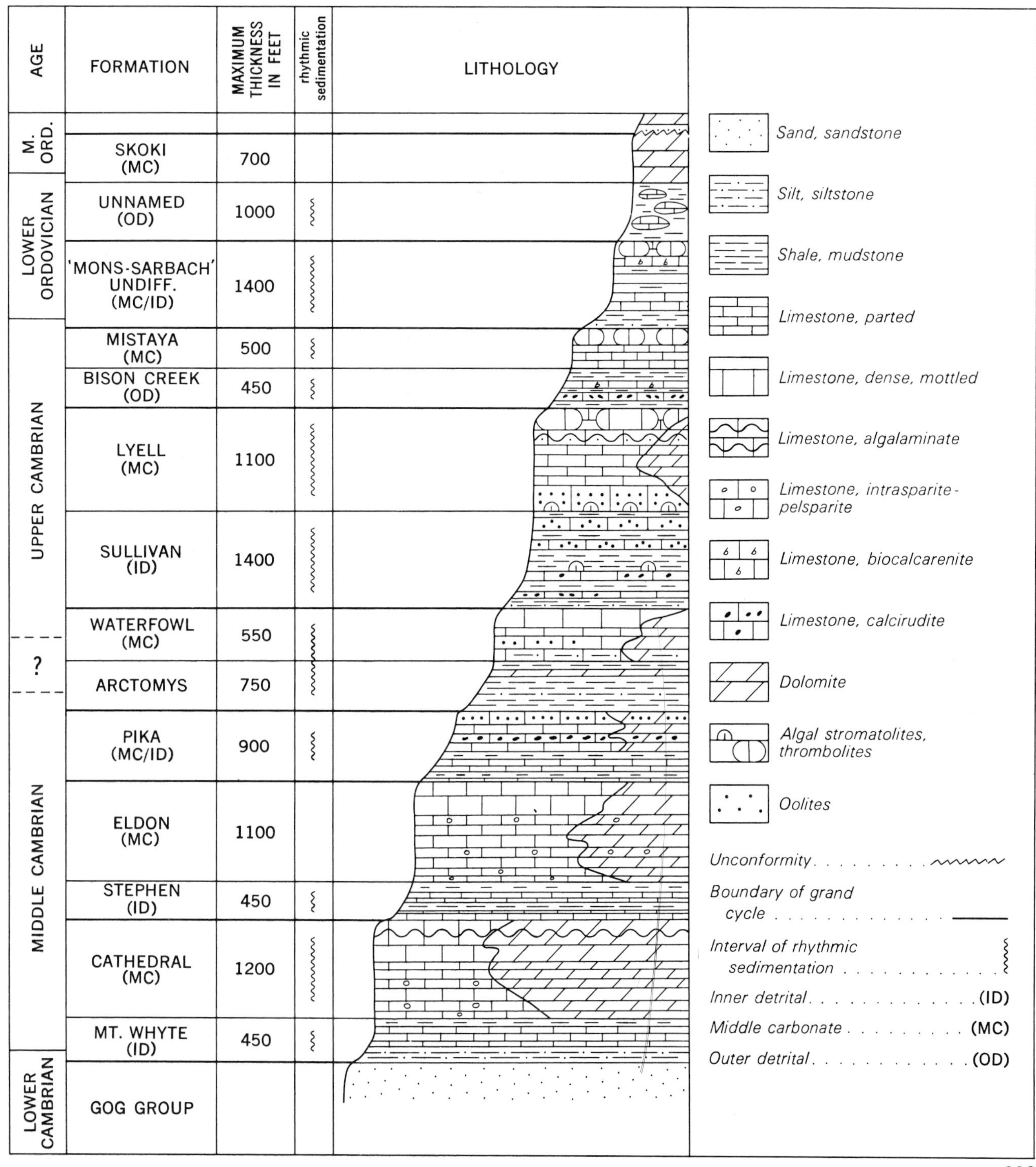

FIGURE VIII-8. Composite stratigraphic column of Middle Cambrian to Middle Ordovician rocks of southern Rocky Mountains (Aitken, 1966).

Cambrian Lithofacies of Alberta Trough and Lloydminster Embayment

The Cambrian rocks of Alberta Trough and Lloydminster Embayment (Aitken, 1966) record continuous marine conditions of deposition that began in the early Cambrian or before and continued into the Ordovician. During this interval, as the margin of the craton was depressed to form Lloydminster Embayment, the seas gradually trangressed eastward. No major unconformities are known to interrupt the deposits produced during this prolonged transgression, but a series of lesser regressions and transgressions also occur so that the second order and even higher order movements are evident as cycles or alternations of facies (Fig. VIII-7). Typically, in the carbonate succession for example, each cycle begins with the abrupt appearance of shale and siltstone lying with sharp contact upon carbonates, continues as interbedded clastic and carbonate, and ends with a sequence of uninterrupted carbonates. The clastic strata that were derived from the craton to the east and north generally reflect conditions of rapid regression and shallowing of the sea whereas the building of the carbonate banks reflects a gradual transgression. Many formation boundaries coincide with the beginning and mid-points of the cycles, eight of which are recognized in the Middle and Upper Cambrian (Fig. VIII-8).

Three major facies belts arose during the major transgression, each of which is also characteristic of a general tectonic environment; an inner detrital belt of thin sandstone and siltstone that occupies most of Lloydminster Embayment; a middle carbonate belt of thick carbonate and shale mainly in Alberta Trough but extending also into the embayment; and an outer detrital belt occupying the axis of Alberta Trough and extending westward to the flank of Purcell Arch. However, as a result of the second order cycles, the dominant facies of each belt also occurs in the other belts.

The inner detrital belt of Lloydminster Embayment is characterized by shallow-water and near-shore clastic facies. Those of Middle Cambrian age are unnamed and those of the Late Cambrian comprise the lower part of the Deadwood Formation which is lithologically inseparable from the upper part of Early Ordovician age. The Deadwood reaches a maximum thickness of 1,100 feet, some 500 to 700 feet of which are assigned to the Upper Cambrian. The basal or near-shore facies of Middle Cambrian age are glauconitic quartzose sandstone and fine conglomerate with minor shale, grading into offshore facies of fissile, dark green and maroon shale and thin-bedded glauconitic siltstone with subordinate high glauconitic fine sandstone and green sands. Mudcracks are prevalent. The sandstones and siltstones are commonly intensively reworked by burrowing animals and are ripple-marked and crossbedded. The Upper Cambrian shales, sandstones, and siltstones are similar to those of the Middle Cambrian. The Middle Cambrian rests directly on Precambrian crystalline rocks and is overlapped by the Upper

PLATE VIII-3. Bedding surface with algal mounds in Upper Cambrian Mistaya Formation, Chaba Creek, southern Rocky Mountains, Alberta.

Cambrian on the south and north sides of the embayment. Numerous knobs on the Precambrian surface, particularly on Swift Current Platform, cause local thinning and irregular isopach trends. On part of the north side of the embayment the Upper Cambrian is less extensive than the Middle Cambrian, but the relationship of facies trends to truncated edges suggests that the original depositional margin was subparallel with the present margin and that Peace River Arch probably existed during the Cambrian, forming the northern flank of Lloydminster Embayment. Subsequently uplift and erosion also took place.

In western Lloydminster Embayment clastic facies alternate with carbonate tongues, the sequence reaching a maximum thickness of 1,500 feet. The carbonates represent the easternmost extremities of the Cathedral, Eldon, Pika, and Lynx Formations and are predominantly the dense limestone facies. The clastic units are composed mainly of fissile shale and greenish grey to brown, predominantly calcareous mudstone, interbedded with thin siltstone beds, particularly near the base, and with coarsely particulate and glauconitic limestones, pelmatozoan–trilobite calcarenite, oölite, and conglomerate near the top.

The middle carbonate belt of Alberta Trough in the Middle Cambrian is dominated by dense limestones, largely the micrite, pelsparite, and intrasparite types (Pl. VIII-2). Where thinly bedded, the limestones are characterized by partings, and where not bedded by mottlings of tan-weathering, argillaceous, very fine crystalline dolomite. Pale birdseye limestones, oölite, and algal pisolites also occur predominantly near the base of the carbonate parts of a cyclic unit. In the Upper Cambrian the rocks are more varied and display a greater abundance of features indicative of very shallow water and emergence. Stromatolites and stromatolitic limestones are prominent (Pl. VIII-3), silty and sandy carbonates with minor beds of non-glauconitic siltstone and sandstone are common, and many thin beds of oölite and limestone–pebble conglomerate occur. Mottled and dense limestones are relatively unimportant. Biocalcarenites are minor and non-glauconitic.

The western margin of the middle carbonate belt has many of the attributes of a reef. Possible reef-builders are blue-green algae (for whose activities there is abundant evidence), *Stromatactis*-like structures, and an encrusting organism suggestive of a stromatoporoid or encrusting calcareous algae that forms reefal masses at Mount Assiniboine. Also found near the margin are large, reef-like masses of megacrystalline white dolomite, which appear to have shed coarse debris that was incorporated into adjoining beds at the same stratigraphic level. No trace of the organism that formed these masses has been found, if indeed they do represent organic accumulations.

Dolomitized equivalents of all limestone lithofacies in the middle carbonate belt are recognized; the bulk is considered secondary but several lithofacies are known only as dolomites. The dolomites thought to be of early diagenetic origin are common in the Waterfowl, Lyell, and Mistaya Formations. They occur as laterally persistent beds, fine to microcrystalline, argillaceous, laminated with silt or sand, and are associated with indicators of very shallow water and emergence such as mudcracks, ripple-marks, breccia, and pebble-conglomerates. A widespread zone of dolomite at the top of the Pika Formation is attributed to dolomitization during deposition of the overlying evaporitic Arctomys Formation. Great masses of secondary dolomite, probably of post-diagenetic origin, are characteristic of the Cathedral, Eldon, and Pika Formations, and are found also in the Upper Cambrian. They are medium to coarsely crystalline and commonly vuggy, and in many instances the lateral contacts are steep and cut across the bedding so that the masses have a greater height than width.

The outer detrital belt is characterized by thin-bedded and laminated, green to dark grey, calcareous and silty shales and by thin-bedded argillaceous limestone. The rocks are poorly fossiliferous and generally strongly deformed or metamorphosed to phyllite. Indicators of shallow water are few, and evidence of slumping and sliding of the sediments on depositional slopes can be seen at several places. Glauconite is absent. The facies is represented by the Chancellor and Canyon Creek Formations and the lower parts of the Goodsir and McKay Groups. Tongues occur in the middle carbonate belt as the Naiset Formation at Mount Assiniboine and as a thin shale in the Eldon Formation at Vermilion Pass and Field. The facies changes to most formations of the middle carbonate belt occur approximately along the same line and form a fairly abrupt front. That of the Cathedral Formation is readily seen near Field and Mount Assiniboine. The early Upper Cambrian carbonates, the Ottertail or Jubilee Formation, extend much farther west across Alberta Trough, and the latter overlaps the older rocks of Purcell Arch.

Ordovician and Silurian

Tectonic Summary

Throughout the eastern Cordilleran Geosyncline, Lower and Middle Ordovician rocks form a conformable sequence, conformably succeeding the Cambrian. The Upper Ordovician unconformably overlies all older systems and is conformably succeeded by the Silurian. In the more northerly and internal parts of the geosyncline deposition locally appears to have been continuous from the late Cambrian into the Devonian. Remnants of Lower and Middle Ordovician carbonates border the craton (Fig. VIII-9). They are truncated along their eastern limit beneath the Upper Ordovician and Devonian, but thicken rapidly westward into the geosyncline and grade abruptly either into relatively thinner graptolitic shales or into an intervening calcareous shale and argillaceous limestone facies. In Peel Basin shales are interbedded with limestone turbidites and are interpreted as a deep-water facies lying between the thick carbonates covering Porcupine Platform to the west and Mackenzie Arch to the south. The shales are oldest in the north and possibly represent the southwestern continuation of a similar facies in the Franklinian Geosyncline of the Arctic Archipelago. In Selwyn Basin bedded cherts and shale accumulated. Basic flows are intercalated in the northwest and are also present in Middle Ordovician carbonates near southern Mackenzie Arch. Black shales occupy the axis of Alberta Trough and occur in Lardeau Trough. Calcareous shale and limestone overlie at least part of Purcell Arch suggesting deposition in shallow water and relatively less depression of the arch. Tongues of orthoquartzite, possibly derived from uplift of Peace River and Alberta Arches, are intercalated in the Middle Ordovician carbonates of eastern Alberta Trough and west of Peace River Arch, indicating some uplift of the arches. In eastern Lloydminster Embayment thin, shallow-water Lower Ordovician shales and siltstones are preserved. During retreat of the sea gentle uplift of bordering arches initiated development of the weakly negative Williston Basin, centring in Montana.

In the Late Ordovician the craton was generally uniformly depressed, the seas transgressing the truncated margins of earlier Paleozoic rocks and the Precambrian of the Shield (Fig. VIII-10). Although now absent, Upper Ordovician carbonates probably covered parts of the central-western part of the craton, Severn Arch, and the northern Shield, as the Upper Ordovician is faunally similar throughout western and northern Canada, and also Hudson Platform. Facies relationships in the northern Cordilleran Geosyncline are similar to those of the Lower and Middle Ordovician rocks with which, in Peel and western Selwyn Basins, Upper Ordovician and Silurian carbonates, shales, and minor pyroclastics form a conformable sequence. Differences are mainly in the greater extent of the graptolitic shale facies, particularly in southern Mackenzie Trough which was deeply depressed. MacDonald Platform was possibly not covered by the Upper Ordovician; Middle Silurian dolomites lie with

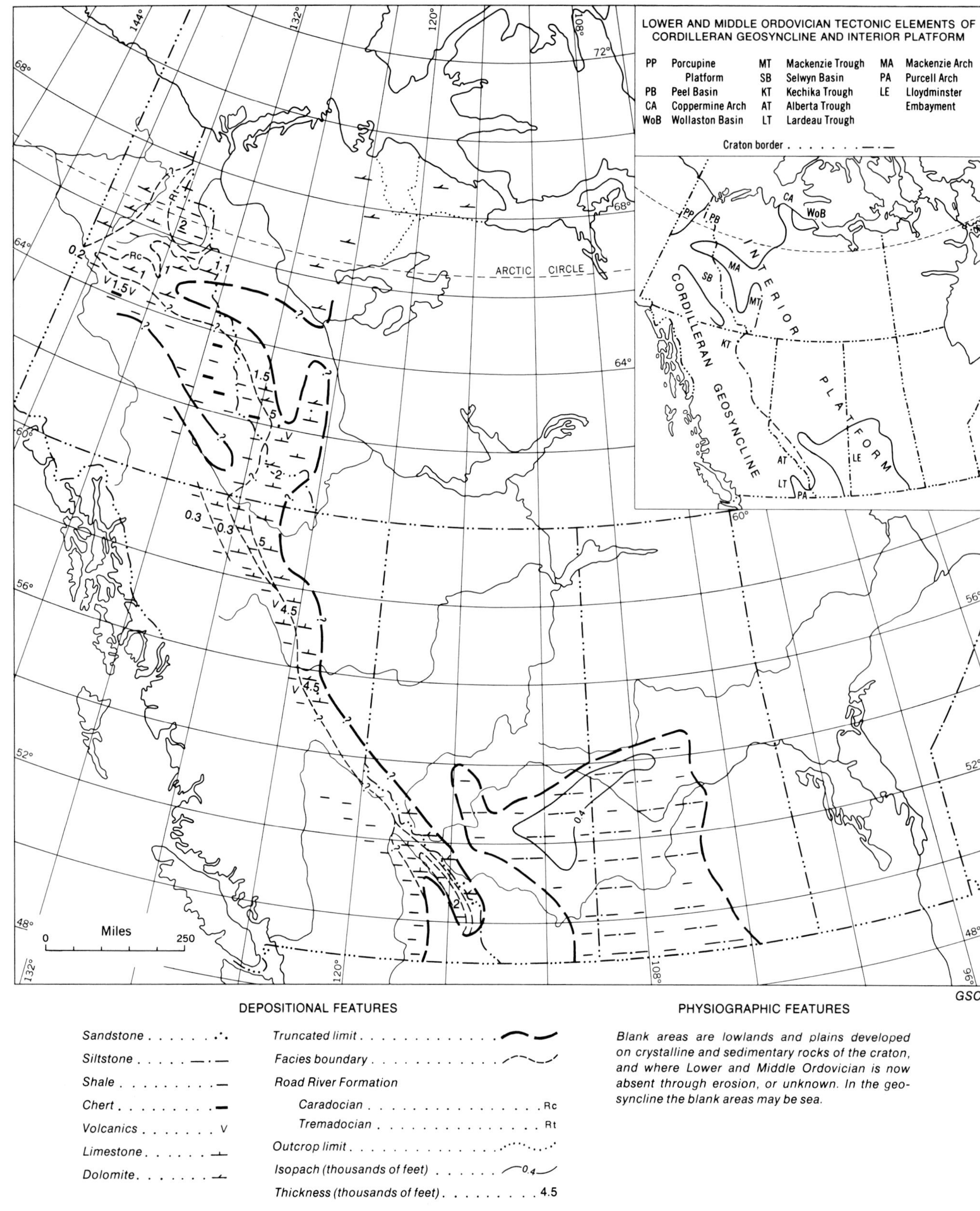

LOWER AND MIDDLE ORDOVICIAN TECTONIC ELEMENTS OF CORDILLERAN GEOSYNCLINE AND INTERIOR PLATFORM
PP Porcupine Platform
PB Peel Basin
CA Coppermine Arch
WoB Wollaston Basin
MT Mackenzie Trough
SB Selwyn Basin
KT Kechika Trough
AT Alberta Trough
LT Lardeau Trough
MA Mackenzie Arch
PA Purcell Arch
LE Lloydminster Embayment
Craton border
CORDILLERAN GEOSYNCLINE
INTERIOR PLATFORM
ARCTIC CIRCLE
Miles
0
250
GSC
DEPOSITIONAL FEATURES
Sandstone
Siltstone
Shale
Chert
Volcanics
Limestone
Dolomite
Truncated limit
Facies boundary
Road River Formation
Caradocian . . . Rc
Tremadocian . . . Rt
Outcrop limit
Isopach (thousands of feet) . . . 0.4
Thickness (thousands of feet) . . . 4.5
PHYSIOGRAPHIC FEATURES
Blank areas are lowlands and plains developed on crystalline and sedimentary rocks of the craton, and where Lower and Middle Ordovician is now absent through erosion, or unknown. In the geosyncline the blank areas may be sea.

FIGURE VIII-9. Lower and Middle Ordovician sedimentation and tectonism in Western Canada.

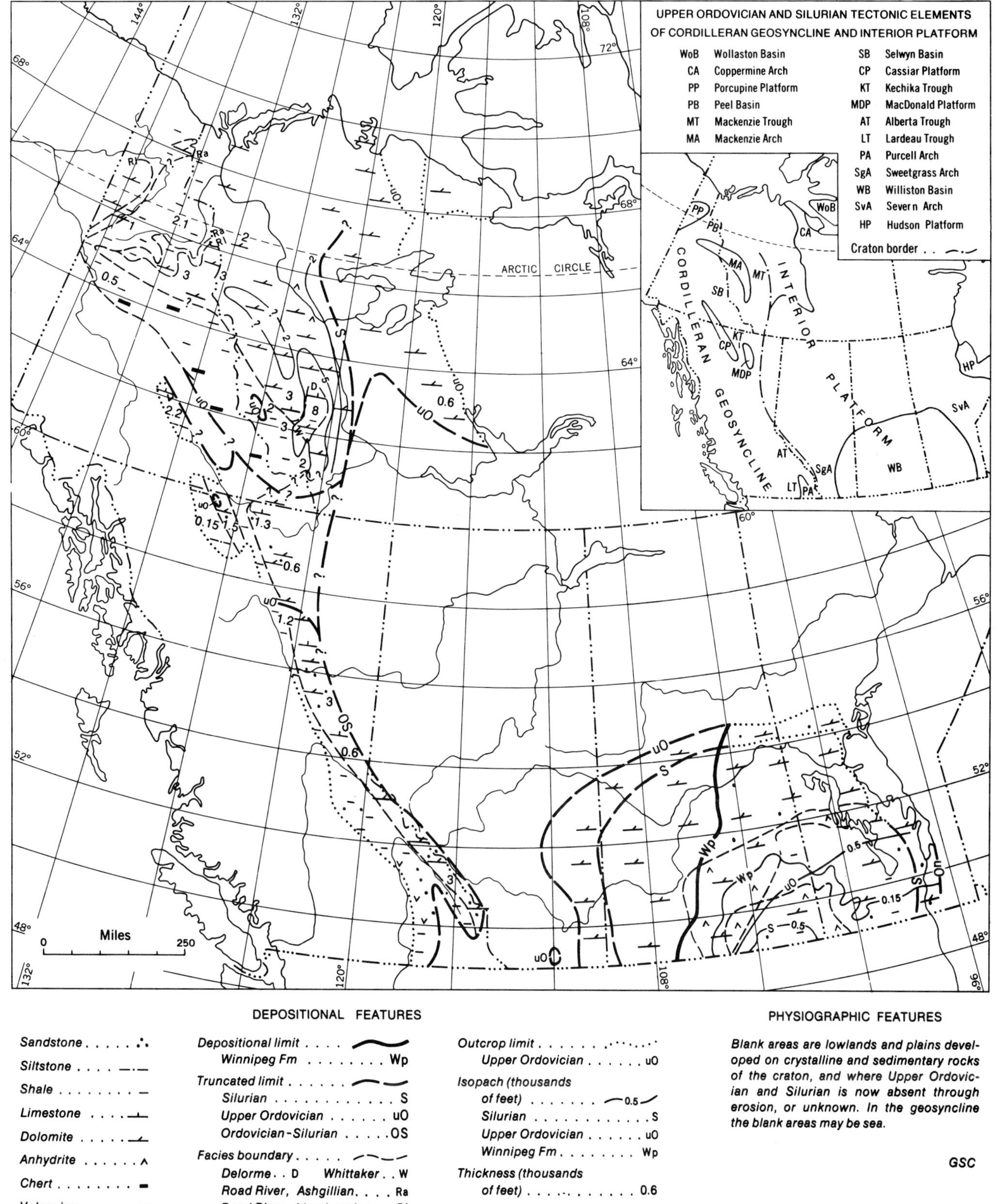
UPPER ORDOVICIAN AND SILURIAN TECTONIC ELEMENTS OF CORDILLERAN GEOSYNCLINE AND INTERIOR PLATFORM
WoB Wollaston Basin
CA Coppermine Arch
PP Porcupine Platform
PB Peel Basin
MT Mackenzie Trough
MA Mackenzie Arch
SB Selwyn Basin
CP Cassiar Platform
KT Kechika Trough
MDP MacDonald Platform
AT Alberta Trough
LT Lardeau Trough
PA Purcell Arch
SgA Sweetgrass Arch
WB Williston Basin
SvA Severn Arch
HP Hudson Platform
Craton border
CORDILLERAN GEOSYNCLINE
INTERIOR PLATFORM
ARCTIC CIRCLE
Miles
0
250
DEPOSITIONAL FEATURES
Sandstone
Siltstone
Shale
Limestone
Dolomite
Anhydrite
Chert
Volcanics
Depositional limit
Winnipeg Fm . . . . Wp
Truncated limit
Silurian . . . . S
Upper Ordovician . . . . . . uO
Ordovician-Silurian . . . . . OS
Facies boundary
Delorme . . D Whittaker . . W
Road River, Ashgillian. . . . Ra
Road River, Llandoverian . . . Rl
Outcrop limit
Upper Ordovician . . . . . . uO
Isopach (thousands of feet) 0.5
Silurian . . . . S
Upper Ordovician . . . . . . uO
Winnipeg Fm . . . . Wp
Thickness (thousands of feet) 0.6
PHYSIOGRAPHIC FEATURES
Blank areas are lowlands and plains developed on crystalline and sedimentary rocks of the craton, and where Upper Ordovician and Silurian is now absent through erosion, or unknown. In the geosyncline the blank areas may be sea.
GSC

FIGURE VIII-10. Upper Ordovician and Silurian sedimentation and tectonism in Western Canada.

angular unconformity on the Proterozoic. Purcell and Alberta Arches, earlier sources of quartz sand, were possibly covered by Upper Ordovician carbonate. In Alberta Trough, the latter was succeeded by Lower Silurian graptolitic shale and siltstone and in Lardeau Trough by black shale, basic flows, and pyroclastics. The seas transgressed from the southeast into the newly formed, weakly autogeosynclinal Williston Basin, on the northern flank of which thin evaporites were deposited.

Northern Cordilleran Geosyncline and Interior Platform

In the *Richardson Mountains* and *Porcupine Plateau* most of the Ordovician and Silurian is represented by the Road River Formation, a thick sequence of thinly bedded graptolitic shale, argillaceous limestone, limestone turbidite, and chert, the lower part being Upper Cambrian and the upper part being Lower Devonian (Norford, 1964). It is overlain, generally conformably, by Lower Devonian shales or unconformably by the Middle Devonian. Graptolites are rather common, ranging from Lower Arenigian to Lower Devonian, one of the most continuous successions known (Jackson and Lenz, 1962). Those representing the Wenlockian are absent, suggesting a possible hiatus, although there is no stratigraphic evidence. The turbidites, thick graded-bedded limestone breccias and calcarenites, are thought to have been derived from banks of carbonate bordering Peel Basin on the south and west. The carbonates of northern Wernecke Mountains and western Porcupine Plateau are thin to massive-bedded, grey weathering, fine-grained dolomites and some pelletoid and bioclastic limestones, and are generally unfossiliferous. The facies change from shale to carbonate is abrupt, the shales in general being less extensive in the Ordovician than in the late Silurian, when carbonates were deposited only in Keele and Iltyd Ranges (Figs. VIII-9 and -10). The carbonates are thickest adjacent to the shale facies and thinner on Mackenzie Arch and probably also Porcupine Platform.

A sequence, uniquely condensed but apparently complete, of Ordovician and Silurian shale and chert only 400 to 900 feet thick occurs in *western Ogilvie Mountains* near the Alaskan border just north of Yukon River (Churkin and Brabb, 1965). It is overlain disconformably by Midde Devonian chert and shale. In *central Ogilvie* and *Wernecke Mountains,* Lower Ordovician to Upper Silurian strata are dominantly carbonate with minor interbedded shale. Basal Lower Ordovician or Upper Cambrian (?) carbonates unconformably overlie rocks as old as Helikian. In southern Wernecke Mountains the Ordovician is represented by as much as 1,900 feet of dolomite, argillaceous limestone, tuffaceous argillite, limestone, shale, and very minor sandstone and chert-pebble conglomerate. Brown tuffaceous argillites and thin beds of limestone ranging from 580 to possibly 1,000 feet thick grade south and southeast into massive volcanic rocks, in part vesicular (Green and Roddick, 1962).

In *southern Ogilvie* and *Selwyn Mountains* graptolitic shales, siltstones, and cherts are widespread throughout Selwyn Basin. The facies change to carbonate rocks of the western flank of Mackenzie Arch is fairly abrupt and coincides roughly with the boundary between Mackenzie and Selwyn Mountains (Fig. VIII-11a). In the few places where thicknesses can be measured the graptolitic sequence seems to be considerably thinner than the correlative carbonate sequence. Great thicknesses of graptolitic shales, cherts, and siltstones outcrop in the MacMillan Plateau region (Roddick and Green, 1961a). Locally, the oldest strata of this assemblage may be Silurian but in most places Ordovician strata are included. The rocks appear to overlie unconformably clastic rocks of Proterozoic and possibly Cambrian age and may grade upward conformably into the Devono-Mississippian shales and chert-pebble conglomerates.

Throughout northern and central Mackenzie Mountains, Franklin Mountains, and the northern Interior Plains the Upper Ordovician overlaps the Lower and Middle Ordovician and rests unconformably on rocks as old as the Helikian. Beneath the *northern Interior Plains* the Ronning Group, according to E. J. Tassonyi, is divisible into a lower part comprising about 300 feet of microcrystalline, partly silty, and anhydritic dolomite, a middle part of 635 to 1,500 feet of pale grey, fine to coarse, porous dolomite with milky chert, and an upper part of as much as 1,400 feet of light grey and buff, finely crystalline dolomite. The Mount Kindle Formation of *Franklin Mountains* is formed from thickly bedded, grey, porous dolomite of Late Ordovician age and succeeding, finely bedded, silty dolomites of possible Silurian age. The Chedabucto Lake Formation between Great Bear and Great Slave Lakes is similar but only 580 feet thick compared with the 900 feet for the Mount Kindle.

In *southwest Mackenzie Mountains* thick sequences of Ordovician and Silurian carbonates and shales are included in Sunblood, Whittaker, and Delorme Formations (Gabrielse, *et al.,* 1965; Douglas and Norris, 1961). In Backbone Ranges the Sunblood Formation is entirely Middle Ordovician in age and comprises about 4,000 feet of distinctively banded, grey, cream, dark grey, and wine-coloured dolomite and limestone with minor orange-brown-weathering sandstone. Locally, the formation includes one or two andesite or basalt flows as thick as 150 feet. To the north and east the Sunblood appears to be arenaceous and is commonly absent beneath the unconformity at the base of the Upper Ordovician Whittaker Formation. To the southwest, the Sunblood is underlain by more than 1,000 feet of Upper Cambrian and Lower Ordovician limestones and dolomites. The Whittaker Formation consists of banded light and dark grey weathering, massive, dark grey coarsely crystalline dolomite, thinly bedded argillaceous limestone, and grey graptolitic shale. The dolomites comprise the middle part of the formation and carry the coralline Upper Ordovician fauna; the upper part has yielded graptolites as young as Ludlovian. The

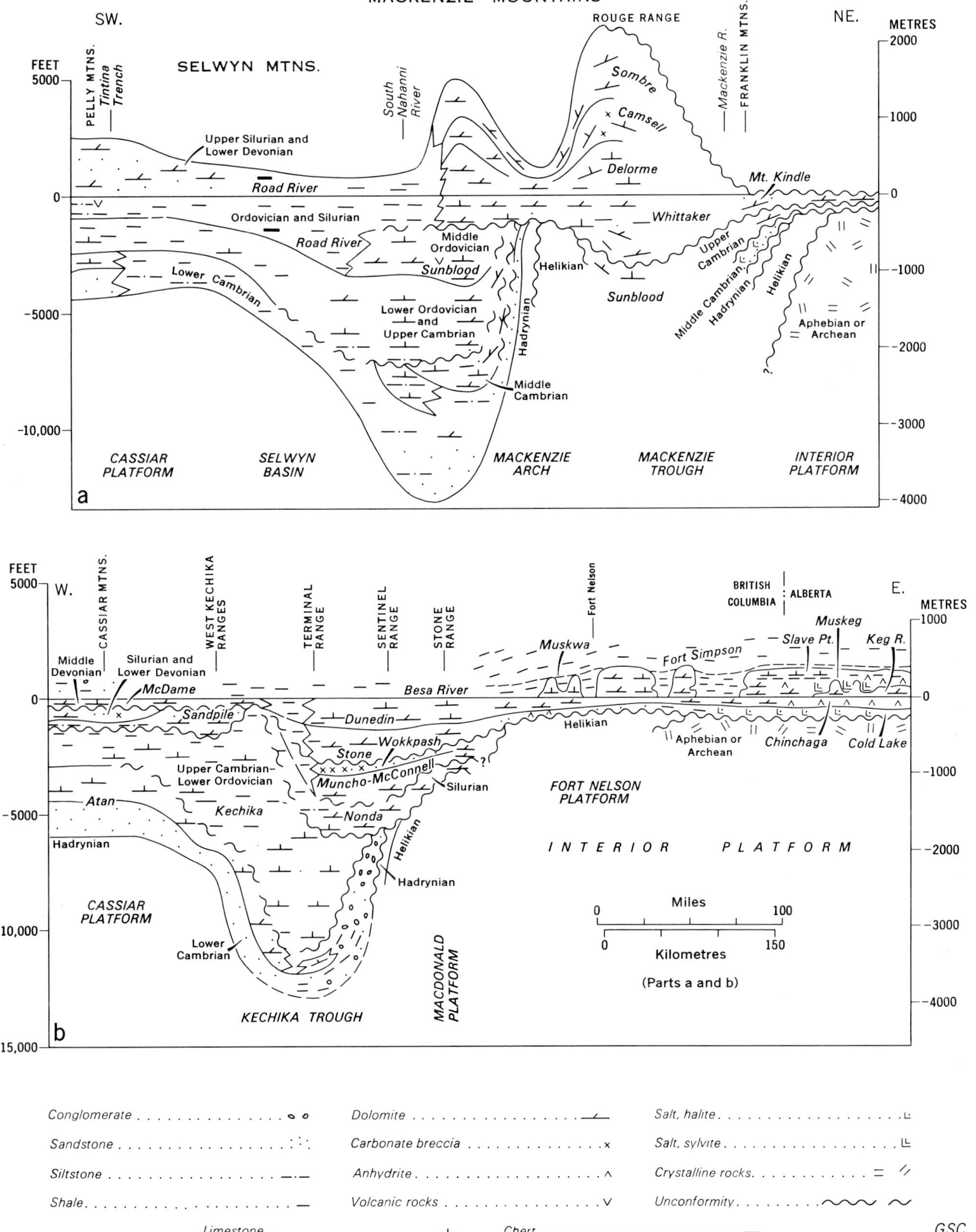

FIGURE VIII-11. Diagrammatic restored sections of lower Paleozoic rocks between Cassiar Platform, Cordilleran Geosyncline, and northwestern Canadian Shield: (a) Pelly Mountains, Yukon Territory, to southern Franklin Mountains, District of Mackenzie (by R. J. W. Douglas and H. Gabrielse); (b) Cassiar Mountains to Fort Nelson, British Columbia (by H. Gabrielse and H. R. Belyea).

conformably overlying Delorme Formation may include Lower Devonian in its uppermost part. It is typically banded buff and brown weathering, thinly bedded shale, limestone, and dolomite that grade southeastward into silty dolomite. The succession as a whole attains a thickness of about 10,000 feet in the axial part of southern Mackenzie Trough (Pl. VIII-4) thinning westward to less than 1,000 feet on southern Mackenzie Arch, partly through convergence in the Whittaker and Delorme Formations, and partly by removal of the Whittaker strata. To the east, the succession, together with the thick conformably overlying beds referred to the Lower Devonian, is rapidly bevelled beneath the Middle Devonian. To the southwest the Ordovician and Silurian change facies to graptolitic shales, siltstones, cherts, and argillaceous limestones in Selwyn Mountains.

Southwest of Tintina Trench graptolitic shales of

PLATE VIII-4. Whittaker and Iverson Ranges, southern Mackenzie Mountains, Northwest Territories. Looking north at easternmost structure of Mackenzie Fold Belt and conformable succession from Middle Ordovician to Upper Devonian more than 15,000 feet thick. Width of Whittaker anticline is 10 miles.

Ordovician age, ranging from a few hundred feet to a maximum of about 750 feet in thickness, outcrop in *Pelly* and *Cassiar Mountains*. They appear to be conformable with underlying Cambrian rocks and are overlain unconformably by latest Ordovician or Silurian rocks. In Cassiar Mountains the upper part of the Kechika Group of Cambro-Ordovician age includes dominantly argillaceous strata in the west that change to a much thicker, dominantly calcareous facies in the east (Gabrielse, 1963). Highly altered greenstones are common and may be in part extrusive. Upper Ordovician (Richmond) cherty dolomites are present locally beneath the Silurian Sandpile Group. Near Rocky Mountain Trench Lower Silurian graptolites occur in the siltstones of a thick, recessive assemblage that includes strata of the Cambro-Ordovician Kechika Group and is unconformably overlain by Mississippian carbonates. Cherty and sandy dolomites of the Sandpile Group, about 1,500 feet thick, disconformably overlie Lower and Middle Ordovician graptolitic shales in Cassiar Mountains. The westernmost exposures are 100 to 200 feet of graptolitic siltstone disconformably overlying Lower Ordovician shales and overlain by laminated dolomites and dolomitic sandstones possibly in part of Late Silurian age. In Pelly Mountains, andesitic tuff and breccia as much as 300 feet thick are interbedded with Silurian graptolitic siltstones overlain by sandy and silty dolomites of Middle and Late Silurian age (Green, *et al.*, 1960a, 1960b).

Southern Cordilleran Geosyncline

In *northern Rocky Mountains* the upper part of the Kechika Group includes two facies: the upper Cloudmaker Formation as much as 1,255 feet of calcareous shale, siltstone, and cherty carbonate mainly of Middle and Late Ordovician age, and the lower Mount April Formation, more than 4,500 feet of argillaceous limestone mainly of Early Ordovician age (Jackson, *et al.*, 1965). The contact is diachronous, the lower or carbonate facies rising stratigraphically eastward and the whole bevelled beneath the late Lower Silurian Nonda Formation (Norford, *et al.*, 1966). The Nonda is mainly a thin dark grey dolomite with basal and upper quartz sandstones. It lies with angular unconformity on the Helikian on the crest of MacDonald Platform (Pl. VIII-2), and unconformably on the Ordovician as far south as Peace River Arch. It grades westward into thicker limestone and thence into black graptolitic shales in Kechika Trough.

In *central* and *southern Rocky Mountains* the Lower and Middle Ordovician are represented by the Chushina, Survey Peak, and Outram Formations of shale, argillaceous limestone, and silty dolomite (Aitken and Norford, 1967). The succeeding Monkman and Tipperary Formations are easterly derived, fine quartz sandstone or equivalent brown shales and nodular limestones. Overlying beds are the finely crystalline silty dolomites of the Skoki Formation and the locally present Owen Creek dolomite. These rocks grade westward into the upper part of the Cambro-Ordovician McKay Group and the black graptolitic shales of the Glenogle in the axial region of Alberta Trough. The Upper Ordovician lies unconformably on the older rocks, which are basal pure quartz sandstones, easterly derived, and termed the Mount Wilson or Wonah quartzites, the latter possibly also derived from Purcell Arch to the west. Succeeding strata are massive grey Beaverfoot dolomites as thick as 3,000 feet with a shelly fauna, and the thin, early Silurian Tegart dolomites and graptolitic shales. In eastern and northern *Purcell Mountains* and in the Rocky Mountain Trench, the McKay Group, possibly entirely Upper Cambrian, is disconformably overlain by thin unfossiliferous dolomite typical of the Beaverfoot Formation.

The predominantly argillaceous Active Formation of southern *Selkirk Mountains* contains Lower Ordovician graptolites (Little, 1960). The Active lies with structural conformity on the calcareous shales of the Nelway Formation and probably extends through the Ordovician and into the Silurian or even Middle Devonian, as the lithologically similar Ledbetter slate, just south in Washington, contains Lower and Middle Ordovician graptolites and an overlying formation includes Silurian graptolites and Middle Devonian fossils. Elsewhere in Lardeau Trough, formations lithologically similar to the Active, but unfossiliferous, are in the middle part of the Lardeau Group, particularly the sooty black argillaceous Triune and Sharon Creek Formations that are separated by the Ajax Quartzite (Fyles and Eastwood, 1962). The Ajax and Triune may be equivalent to the lithologically similar Ordovician Wonah and Glenogle Formations of the Rocky Mountains.

Northern Flank of Williston Basin

The Lower Ordovician of Williston Basin (Fig. VIII-12) is represented by the upper part of the Deadwood Formation, described previously, as it is partly of Late Cambrian age. The Middle Ordovician is missing. The Upper Ordovician and Silurian (Porter and Fuller, 1964) form a conformable succession. The basal unit is the unfossiliferous Winnipeg Formation, which may be of Middle Ordovician age. It has a maximum thickness of 350 feet in North Dakota but thins northward and lies with regional unconformity on Lower Ordovician and Cambrian strata and the Precambrian crystalline rocks of the Canadian Shield. It consists of basal light grey to white, fine- to medium-grained, well-sorted, porous quartzose sandstone with calcareous or ferruginous cement, overlain by green to greenish grey, non-calcareous, locally waxy, pyritic shales, siltstones, and sandstones. Hematitic or limonitic oölites, phosphatic and siliceous pellets, and pyrite are found at some horizons. The northwest termination is abrupt possibly due to regression and erosion before deposition of the succeeding Red River Formation. Its present limit, however, may mark a shoreline against an underlying linear topographical feature.

The overlying strata show a general upward progression from fossiliferous limestones through rhythmic alternations of carbonates and evaporites into cryptocrys-

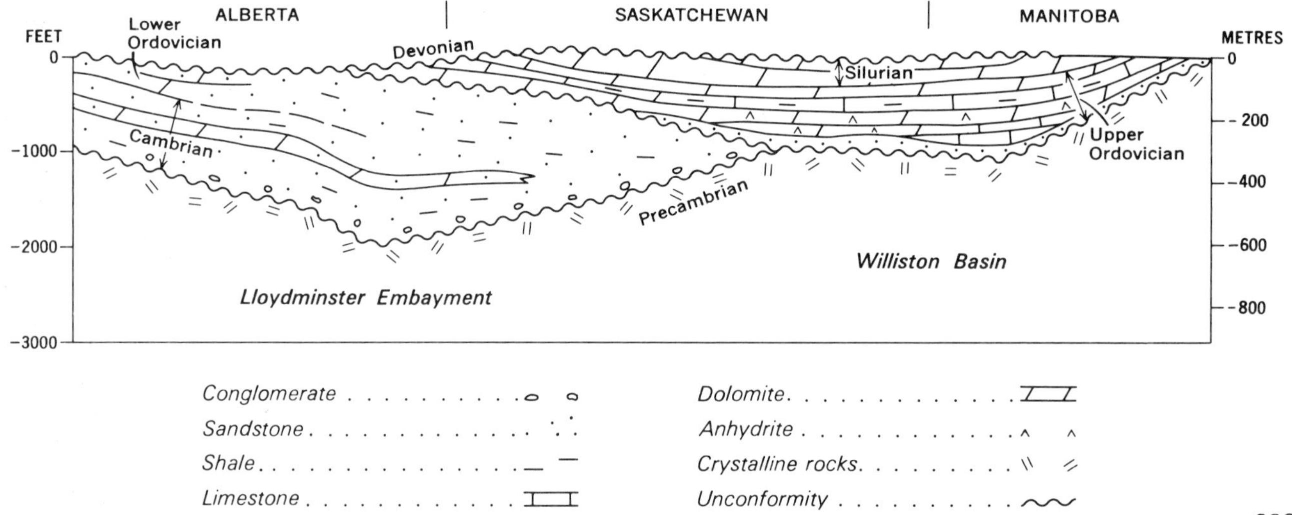

FIGURE VIII-12. Stratigraphic section of Cambrian, Ordovician, and Silurian rocks of Lloydminster Embayment and Williston Basin, Alberta, Saskatchewan, and Manitoba (by H. R. Belyea).

talline dolomites with sandy layers. A gradual shallowing of the basin and upwarp of adjacent land areas is indicated. Also, each formational unit shows a progressive change shoreward from fossiliferous limestones, interpreted as marine shoals, through a rhythmical carbonate–evaporite facies into cryptocrystalline dolomites interpreted as littoral to sub-littoral deposits. These facies relationships are less pronounced in the predominantly shallow, evaporitic Silurian rocks.

The basal unit of the Red River Formation, the Yeoman Member, is 350 feet thick in southern Saskatchewan and thins to 100 feet before truncation by post-Silurian erosion. It consists predominantly of mottled tan and brown dolomitic limestone carrying bryozoa, brachiopod, echinoderm, and coral fragments and grades north and west to cryptocrystalline and finely crystalline varicoloured dolomite, locally cherty. The overlying Herald Member consists of a rhythmical sequence of dolomitic fossiliferous limestone, dolomite, and anhydrite grading southeast offshore to a predominantly dolomitic, fossiliferous limestone shoal and shoreward to cryptocrystalline and finely crystalline evaporitic dolomite.

The Red River is sharply overlain, probably disconformably, by fossiliferous shaly limestone and shales of the Stoughton Member of the Stony Mountain Formation which is thin and grades to limestone indistinguishable from the Gunton. The Gunton, 55 feet thick, is mottled fossiliferous dolomitic limestone, dolomite, anhydrite rhythmically alternating like the Herald, overlain by a basin-wide grey to red-brown silty dolomite that completes the cycle. The succeeding Stonewall, 100 feet thick across the basin, comprises carbonate–evaporite rhythms interrupted by thin basin-wide beds of argillaceous dolomite and shale that contain lenses of coarse, rounded, frosted quartz sand, and fragments of the immediately underlying dolomite and shale. The top of the Ordovician in the subsurface is taken by Porter and Fuller (1964) as the uppermost grey and red arenaceous shale and is placed by Brindle on paleontological evidence at the "t marker", an argillaceous zone with floating quartz sand grains.

The Silurian Interlake Group (Stearn, 1956) consists of a sequence of dolomitized fossiliferous limestone, stromatolitic and oölitic dolomite, porous vuggy dolomite, and fossiliferous biostromal dolomite at the top. These units are not readily recognizable in the subsurface. Across Saskatchewan (Porter and Fuller, 1964) the lower Interlake consists of cryptocrystalline and finely crystalline dolomite with shaly, silty anhydritic layers, some with salt casts. The middle Interlake, preserved only in the south, consists of pale, cryptocrystalline, and very fine grained dolomite interbedded with fossiliferous dolomitic limestone and sandy layers, crossbedded and mudcracked. Dolomitized pelletoid limestone with nodules, possibly algal, and clotted dolomitic mudstones complete the Saskatchewan section although still younger light coloured, cryptocrystalline, anhydritic, and halitic pelletoid dolomite and vuggy fossiliferous dolomite are present in North Dakota.

Devonian

Tectonic Summary

Lower Devonian rocks, poorly fossiliferous, are restricted to the Cordilleran Geosyncline (Fig. VIII-13). Thin dark shales conformably overlie Silurian shales in Peel Basin and eastern Selwyn Basin. The latter grade eastward into thick carbonates and breccia bordering Mackenzie Arch, thin over the southern part of the arch through convergence and pre-Middle Devonian erosion, and thicken eastward into Mackenzie Trough (Fig. VIII-11a). There, the Lower Devonian is represented by massive dolomite and limestone breccia that grade southeast to sandy dolomite. Thin sand zones on MacDonald Platform grade westerly into carbonate breccia and thence

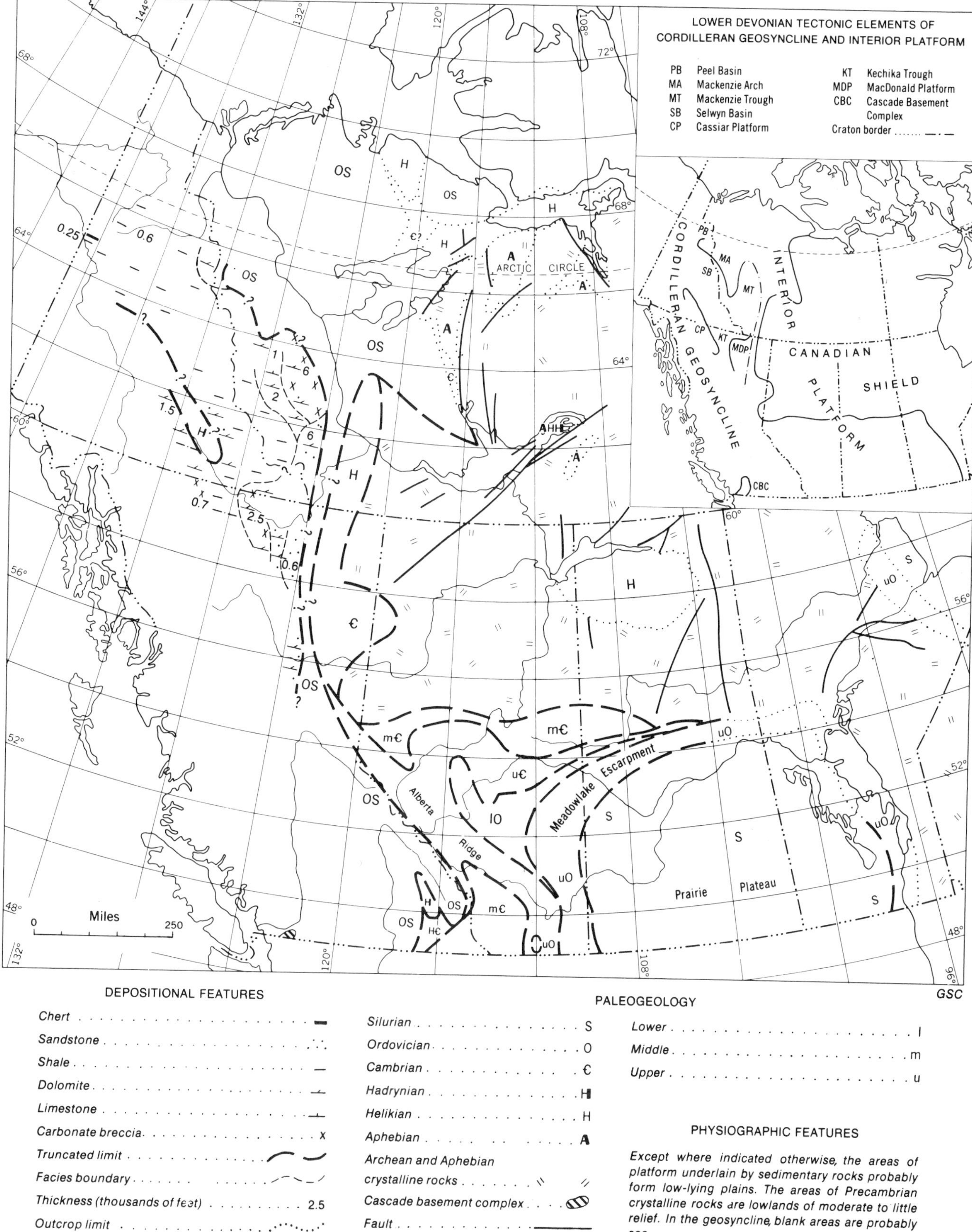

FIGURE VIII-13. Lower Devonian sedimentation and tectonism in Western Canada, and some features of the pre-Devonian geology and physiography.

to carbonate and shale of Kechika Trough. Widespread but relatively thin sandstones, carbonates, and carbonate breccia occur on Cassiar Platform, the quartz presumably derived from an emergent western part. The craton was generally high during the Early Devonian and under active erosion. The sedimentary cover was stripped back from Precambrian crystalline lowlands and a topography of considerable relief established. Prominent features were broad valleys such as the one surrounding the Tathlina Upland and gentle cuestas carved in Paleozoic sediments such as Meadowlake Escarpment and Alberta Ridge. Possibly at this time the Ice River alkaline complex was emplaced into Cambro-Ordovician rocks on southern Alberta Arch.

Various products of erosion of Middle Devonian or late Early Devonian age, part non-marine, fill stream channels and low areas on the erosion surface (Fig. VIII-14). The streams on the west flank of Alberta Ridge drained into Burnais Basin where anhydrite, gypsum, and sandy dolomite were being deposited on the site of the axis of the former Alberta Trough. Burnais Basin was flanked on the west by the Purcell Arch that was partly overlapped by shale and carbonate and bounded on the south by an escarpment along Moyie fault from which conglomerate and breccias were derived. In Elk Point Basin during the early Middle Devonian, and possibly also in the late Early Devonian, clastics, salt, and anhydrite were deposited in land-locked lakes or tongues of the sea. The sea may have initially penetrated the continental interior via valleys in the northwest or crossed the Shield from the northeast and withdrawn at the close of the early Middle Devonian. The evaporites and clastics grade northwestward into thick carbonate, breccia, and anhydrite that flank islands and peninsulas along the margin of the craton and cover weakly positive elements in the northern Cordilleran Geosyncline—Mackenzie Arch and the MacDonald, Cassiar, and Porcupine Platforms. The carbonates grade into shale in adjacent weakly negative troughs and basins. In the present Cascade Mountains Middle Devonian carbonate and clastics were deposited unconformably on a metamorphic complex intruded by diorite.

In the late Middle Devonian (Fig. VIII-15), extensive limestone sheets blanketed the northern craton and adjacent geosyncline, grading northward and westward into thin shale. A continuous bank was formed north of Peace River landmass over and between the slightly depressed Fort Nelson, Liard, and Tathlina Arches, and probably extended along the west flank of Alberta Arch. Limestone at the front grades northwestward to shale and southeastward to dolomite and evaporites. The front is irregular and flanked by stromatoporoid reefs. The limestones near faults in the basement are recrystallized to coarse vuggy dolomite, locally containing galena and sphalerite. Within the barrier reef complex, and to the southeast within the evaporites, are areas of prolific small reefs and atoll-like bodies separated by salt, anhydrite, and dense dolomite. The anhydritic facies passes southward into halite and sylvite bordered by reefy carbonate on the northeast which suggests that formerly the basin extended beyond the present truncated limit and that influx of sea water in that direction was less restricted. Regression occurred at the close of the Givetian, producing an extensive unconformity.

The Ellesmerian Orogeny of the Arctic Archipelago is represented in northern Yukon Territory by granites dated at 355 and 370 m.y. (Fig. VIII-16). They intrude low-grade, southeast-trending metamorphic rocks of Proterozoic and possibly early Paleozoic age that are overlain with angular unconformity by the Lower Mississippian. The products of erosion of this orogenic belt, a thick clastic sequence, are coarsest and non-marine in the north, lie with minor unconformity on the Givetian, and interfinger southward with dark marine shales and siltstones. The bulk of the sediments accumulated in Peel Basin where the miogeosynclinal elements of the Franklinian and Cordilleran Geosynclines merge, and also in Mackenzie Trough which was strongly depressed. Possibly Mackenzie Arch was high, preventing most of the clastics from reaching Selwyn Basin. Thick black shale and ribbon chert accumulated in Selwyn Basin, intercalated with chert-pebble conglomerate derived from an adjacent uplift to the west. Andesite, basalt, shale, and limestone occur farther west. The sedimentary record of the southern Cordilleran Geosyncline may be contained in the extensive metamorphic complexes. Poorly sorted, feldspathic, quartzose clastics of uncertain age and locally having intercalated basic flows and pyroclastics may have been deposited in Lardeau Trough during the Devonian and, if of that age, must have been derived from uplifts farther west.

Early Late Devonian seas transgressed on the craton from the north, enveloping the landmass formed by the gradually subsiding Peace River Arch, and overlapped westward, covering Alberta Arch. Depression of the craton in the Frasnian was uniform over broad areas and greatest adjacent to the present truncated margin, suggesting a broad embayment. Early Frasnian shales of the north grade to carbonate banks and reefs. Shoreline clastics and evaporites flank the landmasses, the latter extending across the southern part of the embayment as a broad evaporite basin bounded on the south by Continental Arch and Central Montana Uplift in the United States. During the mid-Frasnian, carbonate deposition and reef growth kept pace with subsidence and coincided with earlier shoal areas or lines of lesser basement depression. The banks and reefs accumulated on shallow water shelves fringing Peace River Arch, over Alberta Arch, and across southern Alberta and Saskatchewan on shelves fronting land areas in Montana and North Dakota. Chains of reefs and banks extend into the basin where thin black shales and thick greenish grey shale accumulated. Behind the front the carbonates grade into anhydrite. In the late Frasnian, subsidence of the craton decreased and, with cyclical regression, the site of evaporite deposition shifted northwestward and thin sheets of carbonate, mainly clastic,

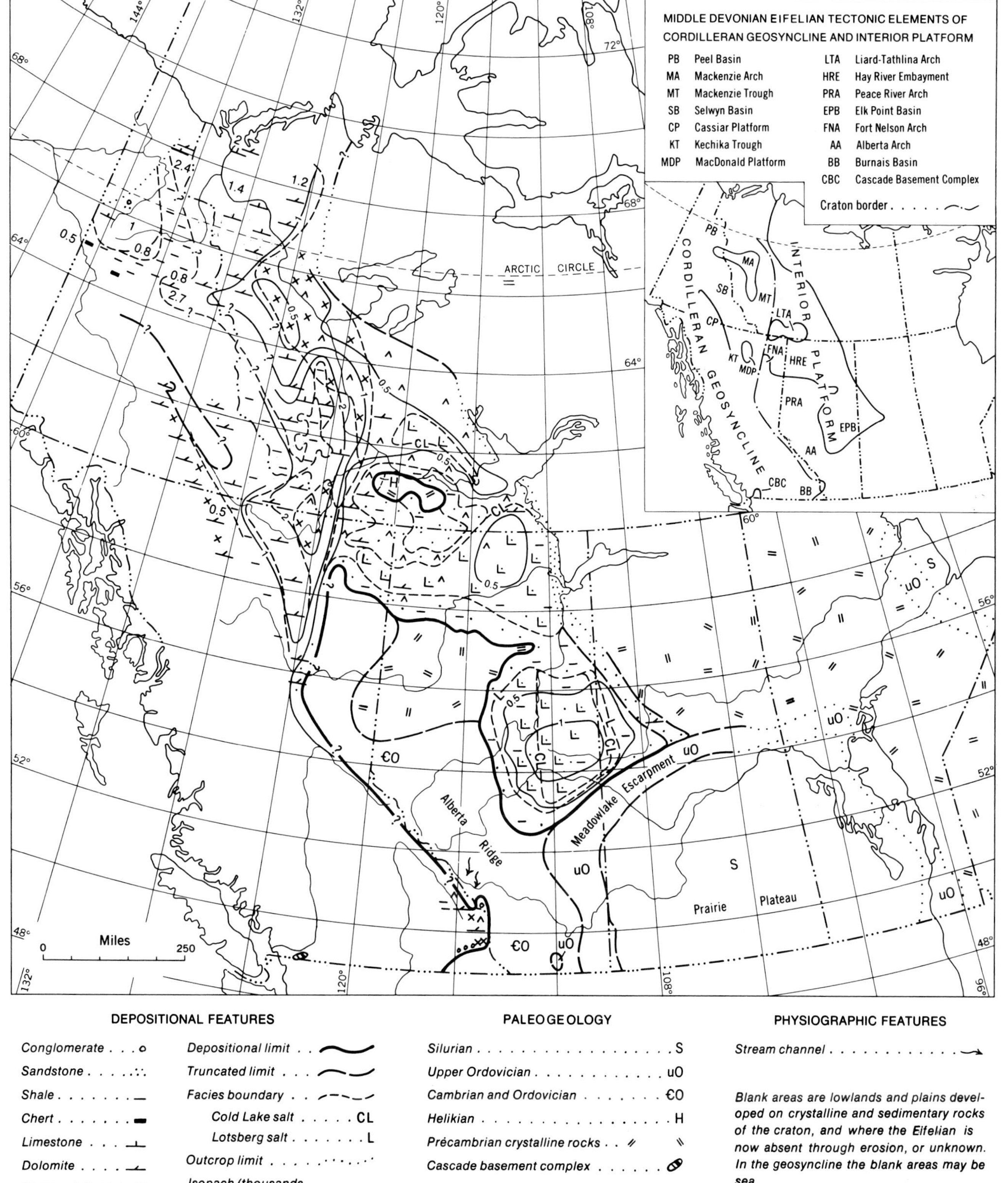

FIGURE VIII-14. Middle Devonian, Eifelian, sedimentation and tectonism in Western Canada, and some features of the pre-Eifelian geology and physiography.

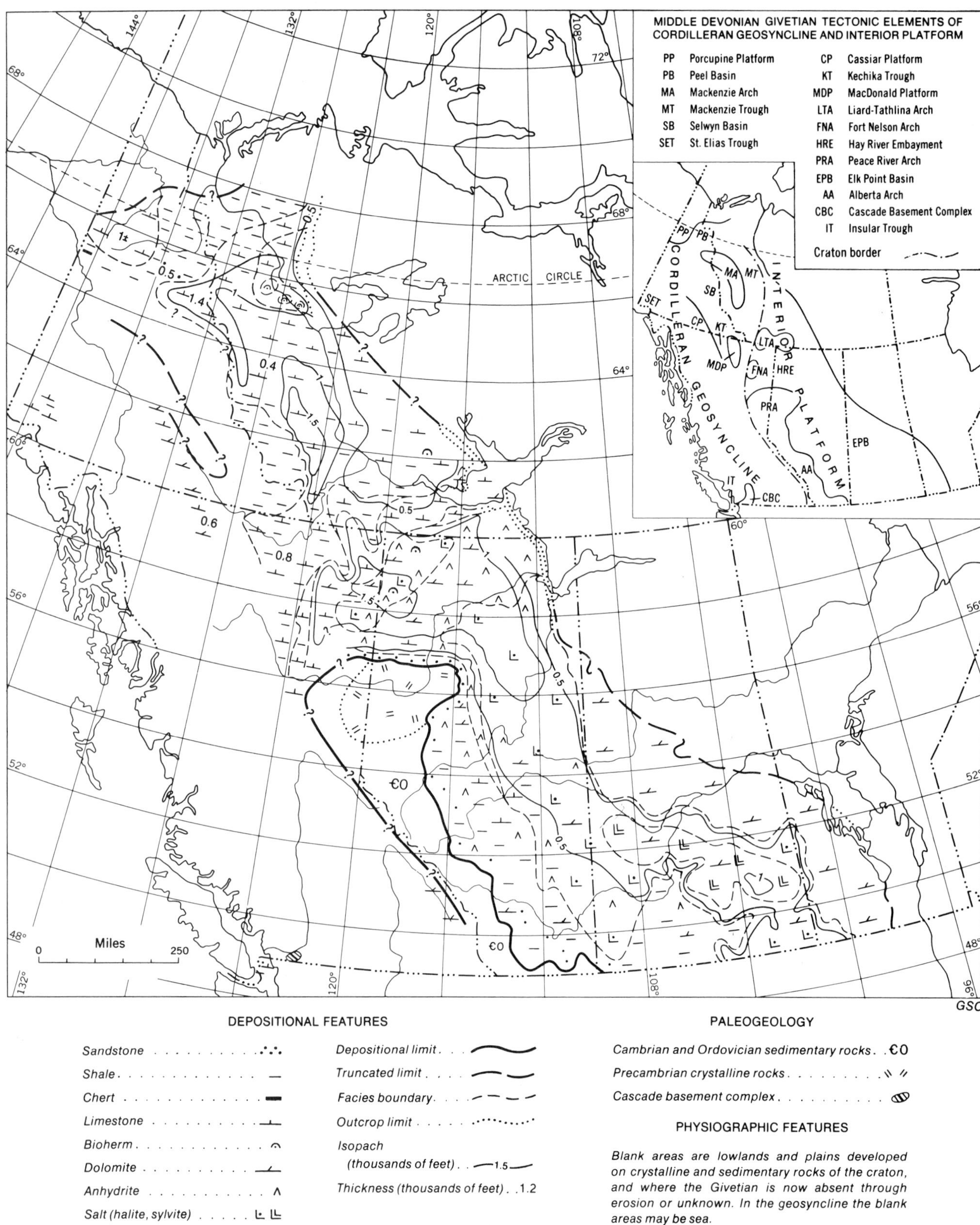

FIGURE VIII-15. Middle Devonian, Givetian, sedimentation and tectonism in Western Canada, and some features of the pre-Givetian geology.

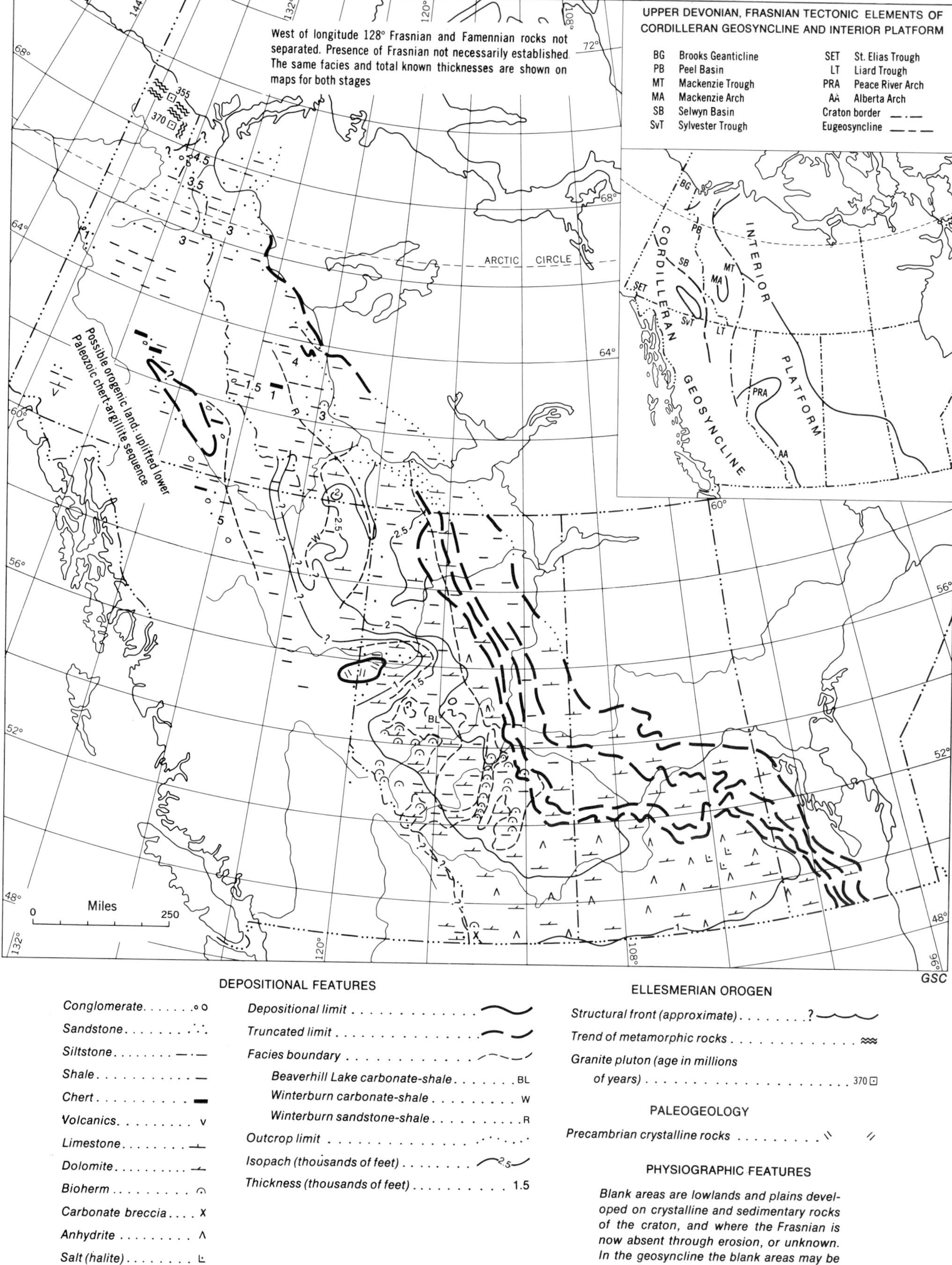

West of longitude 128° Frasnian and Famennian rocks not separated. Presence of Frasnian not necessarily established. The same facies and total known thicknesses are shown on maps for both stages
UPPER DEVONIAN, FRASNIAN TECTONIC ELEMENTS OF CORDILLERAN GEOSYNCLINE AND INTERIOR PLATFORM
BG Brooks Geanticline
PB Peel Basin
MT Mackenzie Trough
MA Mackenzie Arch
SB Selwyn Basin
SvT Sylvester Trough
SET St. Elias Trough
LT Liard Trough
PRA Peace River Arch
AA Alberta Arch
Craton border
Eugeosyncline
CORDILLERAN GEOSYNCLINE
INTERIOR PLATFORM
ARCTIC CIRCLE
Possible orogenic land: uplifted lower Paleozoic chert-argillite sequence
Miles
0
250
GSC
DEPOSITIONAL FEATURES
Conglomerate
Sandstone
Siltstone
Shale
Chert
Volcanics
Limestone
Dolomite
Bioherm
Carbonate breccia
Anhydrite
Salt (halite)
Depositional limit
Truncated limit
Facies boundary
Beaverhill Lake carbonate-shale BL
Winterburn carbonate-shale W
Winterburn sandstone-shale R
Outcrop limit
Isopach (thousands of feet)
Thickness (thousands of feet) 1.5
ELLESMERIAN OROGEN
Structural front (approximate)
Trend of metamorphic rocks
Granite pluton (age in millions of years) 370
PALEOGEOLOGY
Precambrian crystalline rocks
PHYSIOGRAPHIC FEATURES
Blank areas are lowlands and plains developed on crystalline and sedimentary rocks of the craton, and where the Frasnian is now absent through erosion, or unknown. In the geosyncline the blank areas may be sea.

FIGURE VIII-16. Upper Devonian, Frasnian, sedimentation and tectonism in Western Canada, and some features of the Ellesmerian Orogeny.

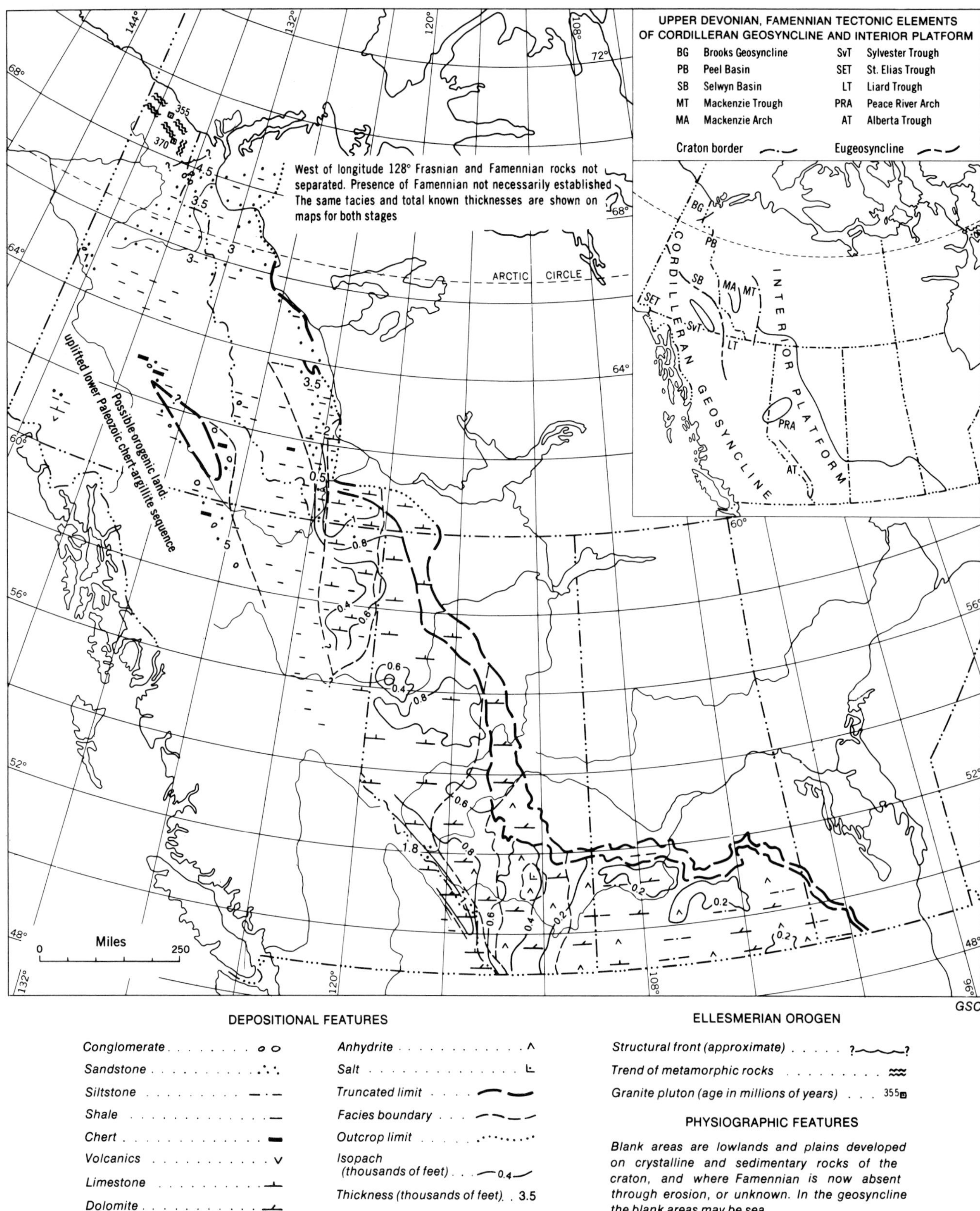

FIGURE VIII-17. Upper Devonian, Famennian, sedimentation and tectonism in Western Canada, and some features of the Ellesmerian Orogeny.

blanketed extensive areas, intertonguing westward with shale. An hiatus separates the Frasnian and Famennian stages, marked by a profound faunal change, slight erosion, and channelling.

Famennian seas transgressed on the craton from the west and north, dark shales grading eastward into dense bahamite-type limestones partly mottled with dolomite in Alberta Trough and covering the weakly negative central part of the craton (Fig. VIII-17). Alberta Trough was re-established as a strongly negative linear element. Peace River Arch persisted, an island existing until it was submerged near the close of the Famennian. MacDonald Platform was possibly static, as in Frasnian times, and was covered by extremely thin black shales. The limestone grades eastward to dolomite and thence to thin rhythmic repetitions of dolomite, anhydrite, shale, and siltstone. The latter, partly red, increases in abundance to the south and east. The latest Famennian is known only in southern Mackenzie Trough; non-deposition or regression occurs on the craton where the Famennian is succeeded by a thin transgressive black shale that may straddle the Devono-Mississippian boundary.

Lower Devonian of Cordilleran Geosyncline

In *Richardson, Ogilvie,* and *Wernecke Mountains* the Lower Devonian is represented by some black shales that form the upper part of the mainly Silurian and Ordovician Road River Formation and by the partly Middle Devonian Michelle and Gossage Formations (Norris, A.W., 1967). The Michelle, 200 to 600 feet thick, is black calcareous shale and aphanitic silty limestone with rich fauna. The trilobites from the lower third and the goniatites represent the Emsian, and the corals are possibly Eifelian. The Gossage Formation, the lower part of which is thin-bedded limestone and dolomite, is of Early Devonian age and has yielded fish remains, considered Gedinnian, from near the base.

The Lower Devonian in southern *Mackenzie Mountains* is represented by the upper Delorme, Camsell, and Sombre Formations (Douglas and Norris, 1961). These units have an aggregate thickness ranging from less than 1,000 feet in northern and central Mackenzie Mountains to more than 6,000 feet in the southeast, and are generally unconformably overlain by the Middle Devonian (Fig. VIII-11a). On southern Mackenzie Arch the Delorme and Camsell Formations comprise a single distinctive buff-weathering, well-bedded, cryptograined dolomite unit in places only a few hundred feet thick. In southern Mackenzie Trough, the uppermost beds of the Delorme Formation, recessive, creamy or reddish weathering, buff argillaceous limestone and shale, are possibly of Early Devonian age. The conformably overlying Camsell Formation consists of grey limestone breccia that grades west and south into bedded cryptograined limestone and dolomite, about 1,500 feet thick, and southeast on Nahanni Plateau, into thick-bedded laminated and crossbedded sandy dolomite. The overlying Sombre Formation comprises well-bedded, resistant, banded, light and dark grey dolomites, 4,000 feet thick in the axial part of the trough but thinning to about 1,500 feet on the flanks. It may be locally absent through pre-Middle Devonian erosion. In southwestern Mackenzie Mountains the Lower Devonian strata change facies to siltstones and shales, generally less calcareous than those of the underlying Ordovician and Silurian strata.

According to G. C. Taylor the McConnell Formation, in *northern Rocky Mountains,* comprises laminated and banded dolomites and minor buff-weathering dolomitic siltstone, ranges in thickness from 300 feet in the east to 2,000 feet in the west, and disconformably overlies the Middle Silurian Nonda Formation (Fig. VIII-11b). In Sentinel Range the overlying Lower Devonian Wokkpash Formation comprises 200 feet of sandstone formed of frosted sand grains. It grades westerly into 500 feet of limestone and dolomite breccia. The westernmost facies, in Terminal Range, are well-bedded, silty dolomites containing fish fragments (Gabrielse, 1962c).

In *Cassiar Mountains,* Upper Silurian and Lower Devonian rocks consist essentially of very pure sandstone or dolomitic sandstone with an average thickness of 500 feet overlain by a similar thickness of laminated dolomite. Locally, dolomitic breccias are abundant. In *Pelly Mountains,* these rocks are included in the Askin Group, the sandstones of which are characterized by extreme purity and exceptionally well developed crossbedding. To the northeast, across Tintina Trench, are sandstones, dolomitic sandstones, and dolomites containing Eifelian fossils near the top.

Ellesmerian Orogeny

In northern Yukon orogenic movements occurred that are herein related to the late Devonian and early Mississippian Ellesmerian Orogeny of Arctic Islands (Chap. X). Three main effects of the orogeny are evident on the mainland: 1) low-grade metamorphism of the Neruokpuk Formation which is probably mainly Proterozoic and lower Paleozoic. Southeast-trending folds were also probably produced, but these have not yet been distinguished from those of later orogenies. The early Mississippian Kyak Formation unconformably overlies the Neruokpuk; 2) the intrusion into the Neruokpuk of small stocks of coarse porphyritic granite at Mount Fitton in Barn Mountains and Mount Sedgewick in British Mountains. Biotite from the former was dated at 370 m.y. and hornblende from the latter at 355 m.y. by K–Ar methods. These dates represent the Givetian and Frasnian, respectively. Biotite from the light grey porphyritic granites of Old Crow Range has yielded ages of 265 m.y. and 220 m.y., possibly indicating younger orogenies; 3) indications of the presence of uplift in the British Mountains or land beneath the present Arctic Ocean as reflected in the northerly source of Upper Devonian clastic rocks constituting the Imperial Formation of the mainland and its temporal facies equivalents of Arctic Islands, the Melville Island Group.

Pre-Devonian Crystalline Rocks of Cascade Mountains

A complex of metamorphic rocks known as the Vedder "greenstone" comprises schists and gneisses of almandine amphibolite facies intruded by saussuritized diorite. It occurs as a fault wedge (W. J. McMillan) upthrust to the northwest into an unfossiliferous assemblage of volcanic arenite, argillaceous rocks, ribbon chert, limestone, and conglomerate locally carrying granitic clasts. This assemblage is on strike with similar beds in Washington with lenses of limestone containing Frasnian fossils. Misch (1966) considers that the lithology of the complex resembles that of the Yellow Aster Complex of Washington which he regards as a correlative of similar rocks unconformably underlying Middle Devonian clastic sediments, limestone, chert, and spilitic volcanics on San Juan Islands.

Ice River Complex

Intrusive into the shales and limestones of the Cambro-Ordovician Goodsir Formation and the underlying Ottertail limestone are two small laccoliths of alkaline rocks of the Ice River Complex (Allan, 1954). Skarn and marble occur at the upper and lower contacts. Petrologically, the complex comprises an intergrading series of nepheline- and sodalite-syenite, urtite, ijolite, and jacupirangite. K–Ar dates range from 327 to 392 m.y.

Middle and Upper Devonian of Cordilleran Geosyncline

The Middle Devonian of *Northern Yukon* (Fig. VIII-18) is represented by three main facies; the Gossage dolomites, the overlying Ogilvie limestones, and the equivalent Prong's Creek shales (Norris, A. W., 1967). The Gossage, partly of Early Devonian age, is generally 1,500 to 2,000 feet thick and consists of banded, grey to dark grey, fine-grained dolomite and dolomitic limestone. At Mount Burgess, it includes thin chert-pebble conglomerate and red shale that may represent a shoreline facies. The lower contact of the Ogilvie is sharp and probably disconformable. The formation consists of brown to grey fine-grained, partly bioclastic and reefal limestones, locally cherty or dolomitized. The thickness varies considerably being least on Mackenzie Arch and thickest where it represents all Givetian as well as upper Eifelian time, as on Porcupine Platform. The Prong's Creek Formation consists of 2,500 feet of black shale with argillaceous limestone and chert. Black, non-calcareous, rusty-weathering shales of the Canol Formation disconformably or unconformably overlie the Middle Devonian and grade upwards into the shales, siltstone, sandstones, and pebble-conglomerates of the Upper Devonian Imperial Formation. The latter attains a maximum thickness of more than 6,000 feet, and is in part non-marine and coarser in the northwest indicating a source in the Brooks Geanticline in the British Mountains or beneath the Arctic Ocean. Commonly the Imperial Formation has a distinctive mauve colour and the coarse beds contain abundant angular to subangular fragments of black chert and siltstone. Macrofossils are Frasnian in age, but spores in the upper part are possibly of Famennian age.

In *western Ogilvie Mountains* just north of Yukon River, in northwestern Selwyn Basin, the Middle and

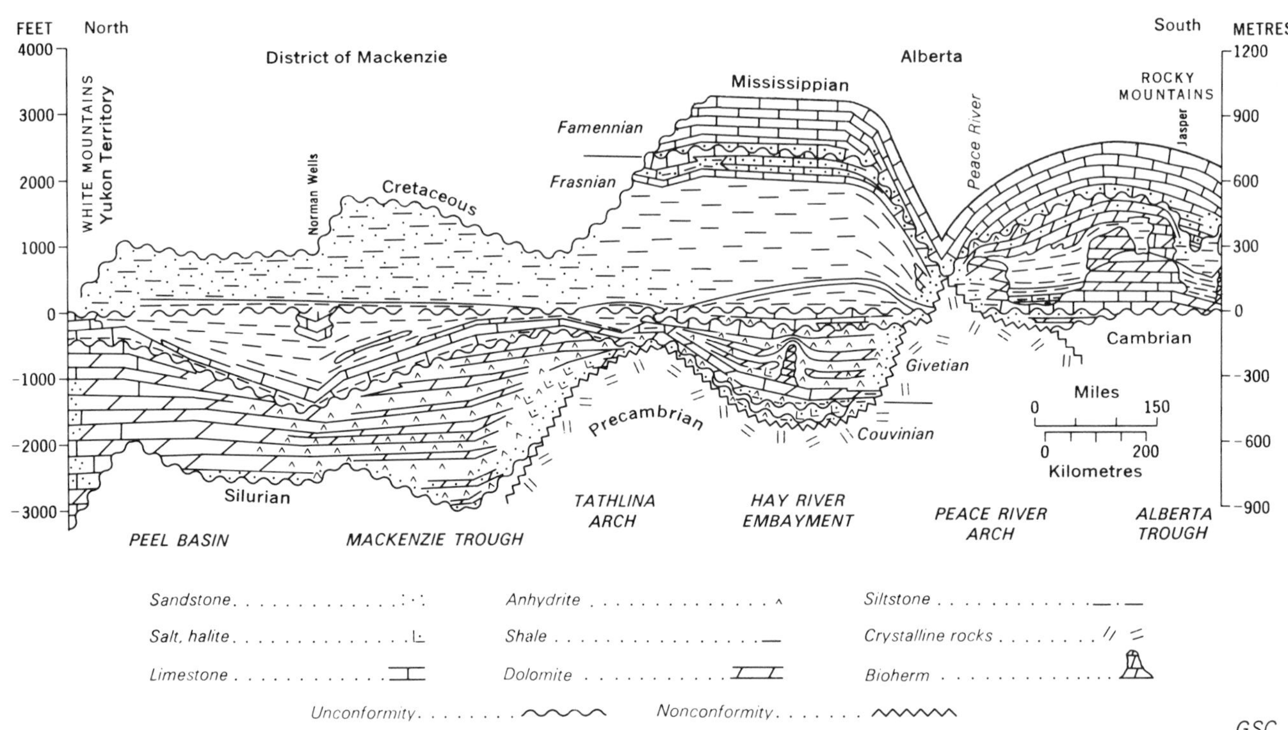

FIGURE VIII-18. Stratigraphic section of Devonian rocks between White Mountains, Yukon Territory, and southern Rocky Mountains, Alberta (by H. R. Belyea).

Upper Devonian McCann Hill chert and shale ranging from 200 to 800 feet in thickness are overlain by more than 3,000 feet of Upper Devonian mudstone, sandstone, gritstone, and conglomerate of the Nation River Formation (Churkin and Brabb, 1965). The latter contains plant fragments and spores and may be partly or mainly non-marine. A succeeding unit of shale and chert, about 3,000 feet thick, is partly Lower Mississippian.

In the subsurface of eastern Peel Basin, according to J. Tassonyi, the Gossage Formation comprises a lower 170 feet of buff aphanitic limestone with waxy green shale, a middle finely crystalline, finely porous dolomite 670 feet thick, and an upper pelletoid aphanitic limestone as much as 250 feet thick. It grades eastward and southward into the Bear Rock Formation of brecciated dolomite and anhydrite, which is orange weathering and hoodoo-forming where it outcrops in *Franklin* and *northeastern Mackenzie Mountains*. The disconformably overlying Hume Formation contains 145 feet of bioclastic and argillaceous silty limestones at the base overlain by 150 feet of grey and greenish grey shale succeeded by coral- and stromatoporoid-bearing bedded limestones as thick as 200 feet. The Hare Indian Formation comprises as much as 700 feet of light, greenish grey calcareous shale grading upwards into the basal, brown, bedded limestones of the Ramparts Formation that form a widespread platform upon which local reefs of the Kee Scarp Member have grown. These are composed of massive bedded, light buff and grey, coral and stromatoporoidal limestones as thick as 400 feet. Disconformably overlying are dark brown bituminous shales of the Canol Formation, which are thickest between the reefs. The Canol grades upwards into greenish grey marine shale, siltstone, and sandstone of the Imperial Formation which is unconformably overlain by Lower Cretaceous or Tertiary strata.

In *southern Mackenzie Mountains* (Douglas and Norris, 1961), banded dark grey dolomites of the Arnica Formation overlie Lower Devonian strata disconformably or unconformably. They range in thickness from less than 500 feet on Mackenzie Arch to about 2,000 feet in Mackenzie Trough (Pl. VIII-4) and eastern Selwyn Basin. The upper part exhibits several facies changes, grading laterally into the calcareous shales and argillaceous limestones of the Funeral Formation, the coarse-grained porous dolomites of the Manetoe Formation, the cryptocrystalline limestones of the Landry Formation, or the breccias and anhydrites of the Bear Rock Formation. To the southwest the Arnica banded dolomites grade through

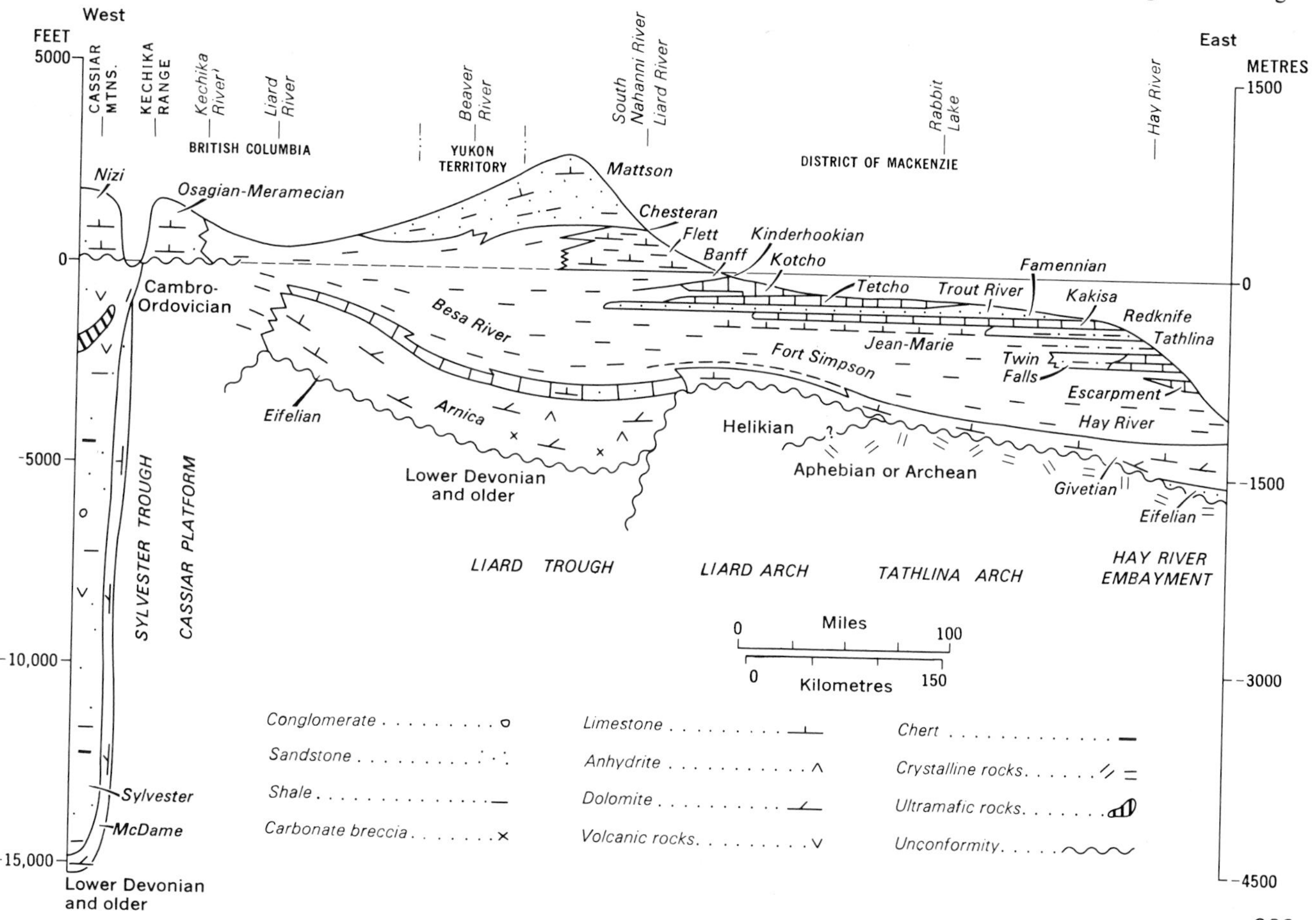

FIGURE VIII-19. Diagrammatic restored section of Devonian and Mississippian rocks between Cassiar Mountains, British Columbia, and Hay River, District of Mackenzie (by R. J. W. Douglas and H. Gabrielse).

diachronous facies of coarse dolomite, crinoidal limestone, and argillaceous limestone into a dominantly shale sequence (Fig. VIII-19). The Headless Formation disconformably overlies the Manetoe, Landry, and Funeral Formations. It consists of recessive argillaceous limestones and shales that grade upwards into the Nahanni Formation and also laterally eastwards into it. The Nahanni is a resistant, well-bedded, dense and bioclastic limestone, remarkably uniform in thickness at about 700 feet, but it may thicken to 1,500 feet near the line of facies change to the Headless shales. Upper Devonian rocks are commonly the youngest Paleozoic exposed. They may be extensively developed in Selwyn Basin also but have been rarely separated from underlying rocks of similar lithology. In Mackenzie Trough, 600 feet of hard black shales of the Horn River Formation is overlain by several thousand feet of grey shale of the Fort Simpson Formation and units of maroon and green siltstone, grey shale, and minor limestone. The latter beds grade eastward to thinly bedded, laminated, fine-grained, green, calcareous siltstone and sandstone with thin beds and isolated masses of reefy limestone.

In *Pelly Mountains* the upper part of the Askin Group includes about 1,000 feet of partly fetid, dark grey dolomite of Middle Devonian age containing *Stringocephalus*, overlain unconformably by early Upper Devonian chert arenite, quartz arenite, siltstones, shales, and pebble-conglomerates (Green, *et al.*, 1960a, 1960b). In the clastic rocks, fossil plant fragments have been found at several widely separated localities. Northeast of Tintina Trench on *MacMillan Plateau* (Roddick and Green, 1961b), a dominantly sombre weathering clastic sequence comprises quartz arenite, chert arenite, chert, quartzite, slate, limestone, and chert-pebble conglomerate. It contains sparse Famennian and early Mississippian faunas. The base of the sequence appears to be a regional unconformity. An assemblage of sandstone, dolomite, and argillaceous limestone, locally more than 1,000 feet thick and containing Eifelian fossils near the top, forms scattered outcrops in southwesternmost Selwyn Basin.

In *Cassiar Mountains* (Gabrielse, 1963) Middle Devonian carbonates comprise a lower member of dark grey, fetid, locally bituminous and vuggy dolomite, characterized by abundant *Amphipora*, 300 to 550 feet thick, and an upper platy limestone member containing *Stringocephalus*, about 200 feet thick. The lower member lies with angular unconformity on Silurian and Ordovician rocks of Kechika Ranges and locally includes a basal chert-pebble and chert-cobble conglomerate. Farther west in Cassiar Mountains the Middle Devonian strata are structurally conformable with underlying, possibly Lower Devonian rocks and are overlain by bedded chert, chert and quartz arenite (Pl. VIII-5), shale, siltstone and pebble-conglomerate forming the lower part of the Sylvester Group. The upper part of the group, which may be as much as 10,000 feet thick, consists of mafic saussuritized and uralitized volcanic rocks, serpentinized ultramafic

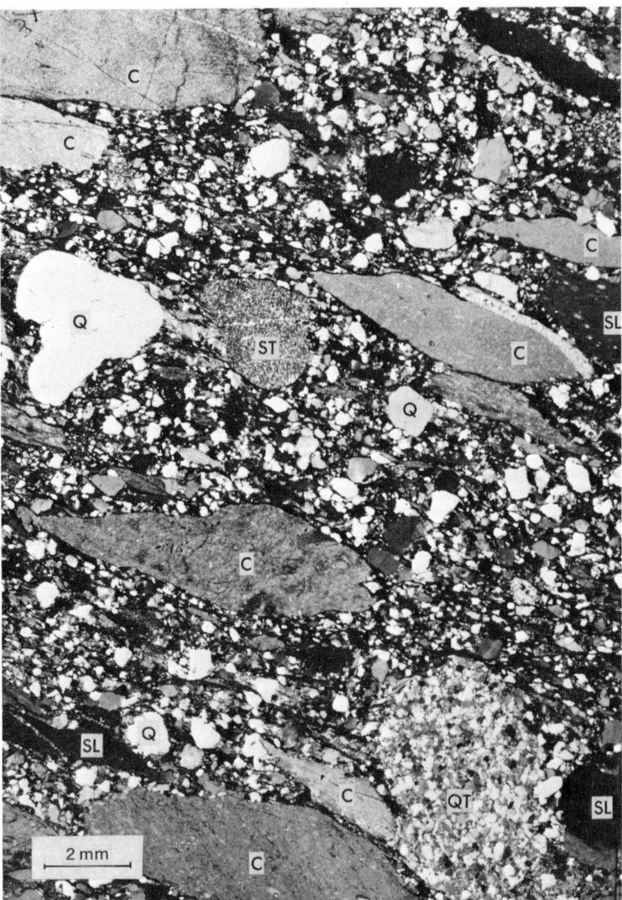

PLATE VIII-5. Photomicrograph of fine pebble-conglomerate of subgreywacke composition from the Devono-Mississippian Sylvester Group, northern Cassiar Mountains, Yukon Territory. Q—quartz; C—chert; SL—slate; ST—siltstone; QT—quartzite.

rocks, greywacke, and limestone possibly entirely of Mississippian age. Similarly, in Pelly Mountains, the clastic Upper Devonian rocks are overlain by mafic volcanic rocks that are in turn overlain by felsic and mafic volcanic breccias. Locally associated are shattered syenites that may be possibly of Mississippian age. These great thicknesses of Devonian and early Mississippian strata in Cassiar and Pelly Mountains were deposited in the western part of the Sylvester Trough which lies on the site of the former Cassiar Platform, stable until the end of Middle Devonian time.

The Kaskawulsh Group in *St. Elias Mountains* consists of about 2,500 feet of Middle Devonian limestone, dolomite, limestone breccia, slate, and argillite overlying 2,000 feet of argillite, slate, and quartzite that may be older than Middle Devonian (Wheeler, 1963). An overlying assemblage including volcanic rocks and chlorite schist is partly of Late Devonian age.

In *northern Rocky Mountains* banded dark grey and grey, Middle Devonian dolomites and brecciated dolomites, locally barite-bearing, are probably correlative with the

Arnica Formation (Fig. VIII-11b). They increase in thickness westerly from about 1,000 feet in Stone Range to more than 1,500 feet in Terminal Range (Hughes, 1963) and thin southward, becoming sandy. They are overlain conformably by about 1,000 feet of limestone correlative in the north with the Nahanni Formation and become progressively younger at the top as the Peace River Arch is approached including equivalents as young as the Slave Point Formation near Halfway River. The limestone varies from brown calcilutite to coarse-grained bioclastic calcarenite, partly dolomitized. The Middle Devonian, if present farther west, is part of an undivided chert, shale, and siltstone sequence in the Kechika Trough. The Middle Devonian is also represented by the Besa River Formation that includes Upper Devonian and Carboniferous equivalents (Kidd, 1963). It is characteristically thin, about 1,000 feet thick, and composed of black, pyritic, non-calcareous shales and siliceous mudstones. Between Gataga and Kechika Rivers sandstone, shale, and conglomerate, locally with well-developed crossbedding, are more than 1,000 feet thick and lie unconformably on Cambro-Ordovician strata. The age of this assemblage is uncertain but it is believed to be correlative with the widespread Upper Devonian clastic rocks of Cassiar Mountains. The Besa River Formation extends south of Pine Pass where part grades into the carbonates of the Famennian Palliser Formation or the Mississippian Kindle Group. The shale facies extends still farther south, to Athabasca and Bow Rivers grading into the carbonate reefs of the Frasnian Fairholme Group. The basal Fairholme overlaps the Middle Devonian along Alberta Arch resting unconformably or disconformably on Ordovician or Cambrian strata.

The Upper Devonian in the *southern Rocky Mountains* is represented by the Frasnian Fairholme Group and the unconformably overlying Famennian Sassenach and Palliser Formations (McLaren, 1955). The Fairholme embraces two megafacies, the carbonate and clastic facies, which grade laterally into each other either abruptly or by intertonguing (Fig. VIII-20). The basal formation of the clastic facies, the Flume, is 100 feet of grey argillaceous limestone and dolomite, cherty and stromatoporoidal in the upper part. It is succeeded by 50 feet of argillaceous thinly bedded limestone, the Maligne Formation, which grades upwards into the black, nodular, and calcareous shales of the Perdrix. The contact with the overlying lower Mount Hawk Formation is transitional, the shales becoming interbedded with argillaceous limestone; the two formations commonly total about 1,000 feet. The Cairn Formation is the basal unit of the carbonate sequence, the lowermost beds being similar to the Flume and the upper part comprising as much as 600 feet of dark grey, thick-bedded, fine-grained, dolomitic limestone and dark brown, coarse, biostromal dolomite, stratigraphically equivalent to the Maligne and Lower Perdrix Formations (Fig. VIII-21). The succeeding Southesk Formation is divisible into three members, the Peechee and Arcs consisting mainly of light grey, bedded, aphanitic to finely crystalline limestone or dolomite separated by the Grotto Member of dark brown, finely crystalline, dolomite with abundant corals, stromatoporids, and *Amphipora*. The Southesk, and particularly the Peechee Member, is less extensive than the Cairn, locally forming pinnacle reefs (Pl. VIII-6), reflecting general, rapid, upward reef growth. It is partly organic, but mainly consists of lime sand. The Arcs is somewhat more extensive, the reef detritus and the laminated silty carbonates of the overlying Ronde Member overlapping the basinal lime muds of the Mount Hawk and reflecting a regression that locally left the carbonates emergent and subject to erosion at the end of the Frasnian.

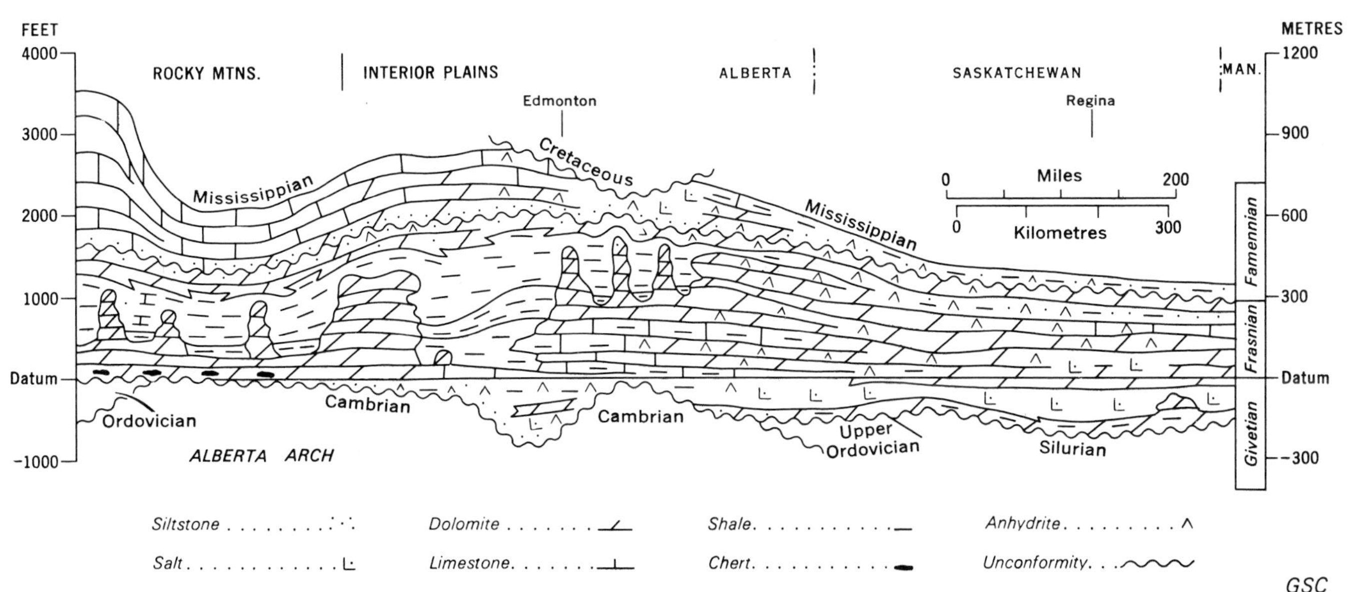

FIGURE VIII-20. Stratigraphic section of Devonian rocks between the southern Rocky Mountains and Manitoba (by H. R. Belyea).

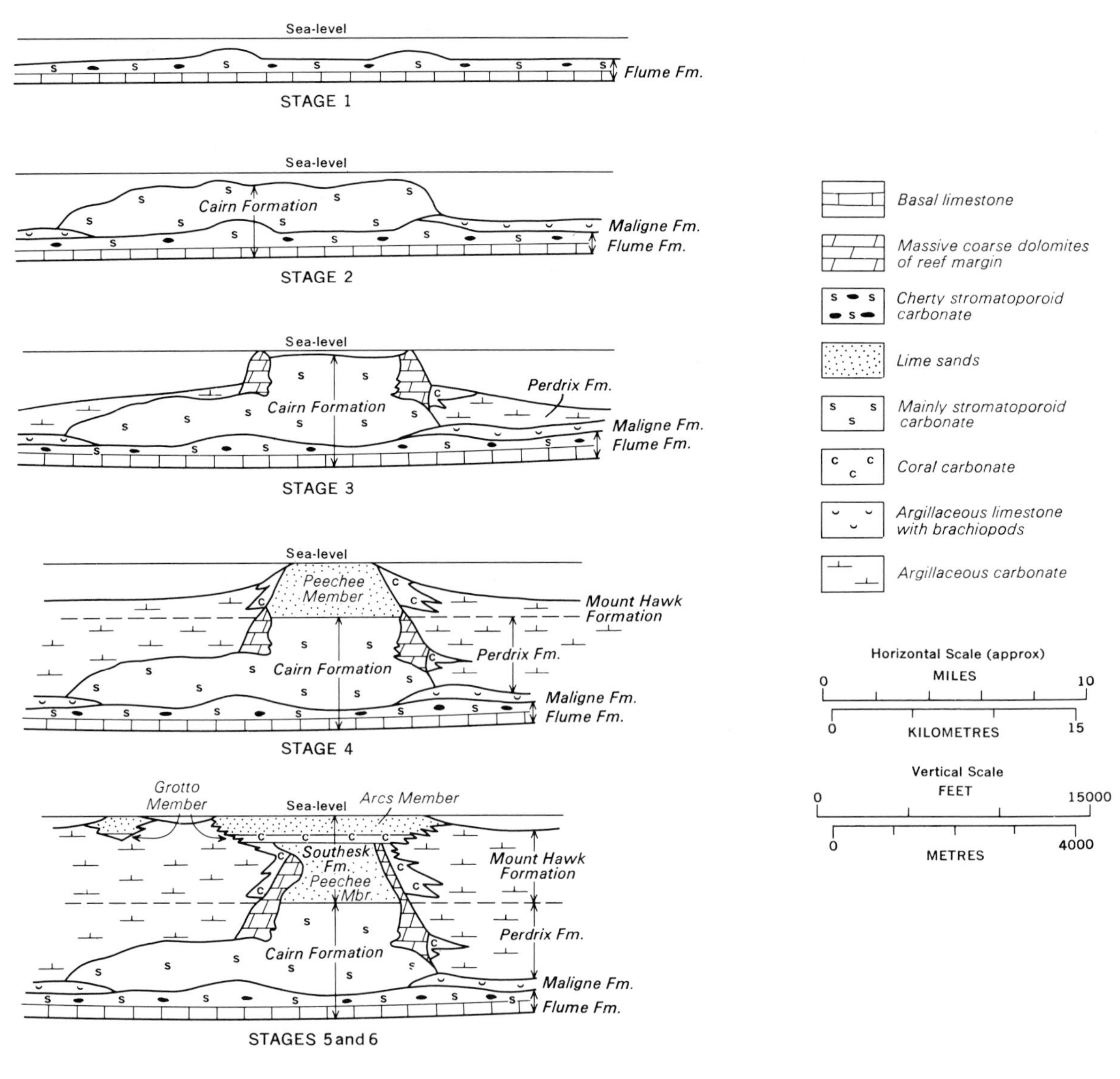

TRANSGRESSIVE PHASES *(progressively increasing water depth in basin)*
Stage 1: Main transgression and development of stromatoporoid carbonate platform (Flume Formation)
Stage 2: Growth of stromatoporoid biostromes (lower half of upper Cairn Formation)
Stage 3: Growth of marginal bioherms (upper half of upper Cairn Formation)

STABLE PHASES *(filling of basins surrounding reef complex)*
Stage 4: Development of lime sand bank (Peechee Member, Southesk Formation)
Stage 5: Growth of coral and Amphipora biostrome (Grotto Member of Southesk Formation)
Stage 6: Extensive development of lime sand bank (Arcs Member of Southesk Formation)

REGRESSIVE PHASE *(not illustrated)*
Stage 7: Influx of quartz silts and spreading of carbonate bank (Ronde Member of Southesk Formation)
After an interval of non-deposition the Famennian transgression occurred

GSC

FIGURE VIII-21. Main depositional stages in the formation of the Upper Devonian, Frasnian, Miette reef complex (Mountjoy, 1965).

The Famennian Sassenach Formation is variable in thickness, the thicker sandstones and silty dolomites, as thick as 600 feet, filling irregularities in the erosion surface. The Morro Member of the overlying Palliser Formation is a massive, cliff-forming, grey aphanitic limestone mottled with buff dolomite, which in the central Foothills grades to fine-grained brown dolomite. The uppermost 100 feet are the Costigan Member, an argillaceous limestone that is abruptly overlain by the Exshaw shale of probable Mississippian age.

Strata representing the early Frasnian, the Beaverhill Lake Group of the subsurface, are only locally present in the southern Rocky Mountains as the thin basal beds of the Flume and Cairn Formations, or as the Hollebeke

PLATE VIII-6. Upper Devonian succession and remnants of protuberances along Peechee reef front, Flathead Range, southern Rocky Mountains, Alberta and British Columbia. Looking west. P—Palliser Formation; s—Sassenach Formation; Sa—Arcs Member, Southesk Formation; Sg—Grotto Member; Sp—Peechee Member; M—Mount Hawk Formation; B—Borsato Formation; H—Hollebeke Formation; E—Cambrian Elko Formation.

Formation of Flathead Range. The latter consists of 500 feet of dark grey, very finely crystalline limestone and laminated argillaceous and silty dolomite with beds of carbonate breccia near the base. It overlies the Cambrian Elko Formation either disconformably or with indications of channelling. The succeeding Borsato Formation of the Flathead region is lithologically similar to the upper Cairn Formation.

In *southwestern Rocky Mountains,* in Stanford and Hughes Ranges, the Middle Devonian Cedared Formation unconformably overlies the Silurian and grades laterally into the Burnais gypsum (Belyea and Norford, 1967). It consists of as much as 700 feet of light grey and brown, sandy aphanitic dolomite, agrillaceous dolomite, breccia, sandstone, and red shale. The conformably overlying Harrogate Formation consists of as much as 300 feet of dark brown limestone, shale, and dolomite with a fauna similar to that of the Pine Point Formation near Great Slave Lake. In Lussier syncline east of Hughes Range, these beds are overlain by shaly limestones equivalent to the basal Fairholme Group, which are succeeded by dark grey shale and siltstone, presumably of Upper Devonian age, as they are overlain by cherty limestones of the Mississippian Banff Formation.

On the west flank and floor of *Rocky Mountain Trench* south of Moyie fault, the Devonian sequence consists of a basal fanglomerate, with slabs of Purcell strata, that rests unconformably on the Purcell lava and the Gateway Formation (Leech, 1962b). It is succeeded by a sandstone containing fish remains and thence by thick gypsum, dolomite, and solution breccia. The overlying beds are fossiliferous limestones equivalent to the Maligne Formation of the Fairholme Group and strata similar to the other formations of the group. Similar, but unfossiliferous fanglomerates occur along the trace of Moyie fault. In northern Purcell Mountains thin, incomplete sequences suggest that the east side of Purcell Arch was periodically emergent during the Devonian. Unfossiliferous red and green shale of the Mount Forster Formation probably represents a marginal facies of the Burnais gypsum. The Mount Forster disconformably overlies the Beaverfoot Formation and is disconformably overlain by 200 feet of limestone and gypsum of the early Upper Devonian Starbird Formation (Reesor, 1957).

The age of the Broadview and Jowett Formations at the top of the Lardeau Groups in *Selkirk Mountains* and of the Snowshoe Formation in *Cariboo Mountains* is not known. The Broadview and Snowshoe Formations are characterized by poorly sorted, quartz-rich, slightly feldspathic arenites and represent a profound change from the preceding argillaceous régime. If these units are Upper Devonian or even early Paleozoic then it is difficult to contemplate an eastern source. As such clastics are lacking in eastern Purcell Mountains and the Snowshoe Formation is fine grained and more calcareous in the east (Sutherland Brown, 1957), the source for these formations must have been west of Lardeau Trough. An alternative is that the Broadview Formation is equivalent to the Horsethief Creek Group. The arenites from the two units are remarkably similar and the greenstone in the former would then be correlative with the Irene Formation. Structural relations lend support, particularly in the western part of Kootenay Arc where the Broadview is separated from the underlying Index Formation by a slide (P. B. Read). Broadview rocks were deformed prior to the deposition of the Mississippian Milford Group (Wheeler, 1966b). It is possible, therefore, that the Broadview Formation is part of the Horsethief Creek Group thrust over the lower formations of the Lardeau Group during the Caribooan Orogeny prior to the deposition of the Milford Group. In Cariboo Mountains, Sutherland Brown (1963) has commented on the similarities of arenites in the Snowshoe Formation and Kaza Group but maintains that they are separate stratigraphic units.

Middle Devonian of Interior Platform

Eifelian (Fig. VIII-14). The formations exposed in Franklin and southern Mackenzie Mountains are present in the Interior Platform in southwestern District of Mackenzie and northeastern British Columbia, but are much thinner. Dolomites, apparently coeval with the Arnica Formation, are grey and light brown, banded and mottled, cryptocrystalline to finely crystalline, and locally brecciated. Floating sand grains are common; some form sandstone beds near the base. The dolomites grade eastward into the Cold Lake salt and associated red beds and carbonates that border Tathlina Upland on the south and into about 1,200 feet of anhydrite, halite, and dolomite to the north. The latter thin eastward to 300 feet of breccia and shaly anhydritic dolomites unconformably overlying the Upper Ordovician northwest of Great Slave Lake. The overlying Manetoe dolomite, southwest of Tathlina Arch, consists of medium to coarsely crystalline, vuggy dolomite that grades upwards and laterally to light brown, fine-grained, pelletoid limestone. It is missing or grades eastward in northern Alberta, into argillaceous, anhydritic dolomites and anhydrite and southward into sandy anhydrite and shales of the lower Chinchaga. The upper part and top of this unit commonly contains green or blue-grey, waxy, pyritic, non-calcareous shales as irregular layers enclosing blebs or pebbles of limestone and as fracture fillings. A sandstone occurs at this horizon on the flank of Tathlina Upland. The shale suggests an hiatus in deposition accompanied by fracturing, leaching, and soil formation. It is considered to mark the Eifelian–Givetian boundary in the subsurface but no faunal control is available.

In Elk Point Basin, the Eifelian is probably represented by the lower part of the Elk Point Group. The lowest formation, the Lotsberg, occurs in central Alberta and may be represented in basal sandstones and red beds north of Peace River Arch. It may be Eifelian or older. It consists of a maximum of 500 feet of sandstones overlain by orange-red, sandy, silty dolomitic and anhydritic claystones with anhydrite and one, or locally two, halite beds as thick as 400 feet in central Alberta. The halite grades laterally westward through interbedded anhydritic dolomite and mudstone, to the sandstones of the basin margin. It is succeeded by a red claystone with high gamma radiation, followed by the light grey to light brown, very fine grained, slightly argillaceous, thin-bedded limestones of the Ernestina Lake Formation. This formation, although not present over Peace River Arch, is present between the arch and Tathlina Upland as a finely crystalline, locally porous dolomite with intergranular porosity carrying the same fauna as the limestones south of the arch. These beds are transitional upward to light coloured, massive anhydrite succeeded by red claystones and the Cold Lake salt. The salt occurs in two basins, one flanking Tathlina Upland to the south, east, and north and the other between Meadowlake Escarpment and Peace River Arch (Fig. VIII-14). Red beds were deposited over the eastern part of the Peace River Arch. The Cold Lake salt is thought to have been deposited in lagoons, as much as 1,000 miles long, or in lakes of a playa type into which streams drained from the bordering ridges. The Cold Lake salt seems to fill Elk Point Basin to the level of the Upper Ordovician beds forming Meadowlake Escarpment; the Givetian upper part of the Elk Point Group overlaps it.

Givetian (Fig VIII-15). On the craton the thick carbonates of the Nahanni and Hume Formations converge southwards and eastwards. In the subsurface, coeval beds consist of fine-grained and pelletoid limestones, locally fossiliferous, that grade eastward to cryptocrystalline, light brown, brittle limestones, and thence into anhydrite and dolomite of the upper part of the Chinchaga Formation. Equivalent beds farther southeast are argillaceous dolomites with shale laminae of the Contact Rapids Formation. This formation is probably equivalent to Members 1 and 2 of the Methy Formation of eastern Alberta. In Saskatchewan the Contact Rapids grades into 50 feet of red and green siltstone, shale, and grey argillaceous carbonate of the Ashern Formation which unconformably overlies the Silurian and Ordovician (Fig. VIII-20).

South and east of the carbonate front, the base of the carbonate facies rises progressively higher stratigraphically and forms a platform carbonate that covers Tathlina Arch and Elk Point Basin as far south as the Manitoba outcrop. This carbonate, the lower member of the Keg River Formation, consists of 100 to 170 feet of brown, fine-grained, argillaceous dolomite and limestone, with brown, argillaceous limestone and bituminous shale in the upper part. It thins southeast to less than 50 feet where it overlaps the Meadowlake Escarpment in Saskatchewan. Above the platform carbonate the sediments are differentiated into laterally contiguous shale, carbonate, and evaporitic facies. The shale facies, the Horn River Formation, consists of about 100 to 300 feet of brownish grey bituminous shales, interbedded with dark brown, fine-grained limestones and greenish grey calcareous shales. It thickens into northeastern British Columbia where it consists of 50 to 100 feet of basal, dark brown to black, bituminous shale and brown, bituminous, fine-grained limestone, the Evie Member, overlain by about 550 feet of grey, calcareous shales of the Otter Park Member succeeded by 20 to 150 feet of black, bituminous, locally pyritic and siliceous shales of the Muskwa Member. The base of the Upper Devonian lies within the Horn River Formation, possibly at the base of the Muskwa Member.

The contact between the shale and carbonate facies is abrupt and follows a sinuous pattern that outlines platform and basin areas. Margins of platform areas are characterized by what appears to be a persistent carbonate barrier, composed in part at least of reef and reef detritus and constituting the Pine Point and Sulphur Point Formations. Small carbonate banks or "island reefs" occur on the basin side of the barrier. Locally, along the front, the limestones are replaced by as much as 1,200 feet of white, coarsely crystalline, vuggy dolomite that completely destroys the original textures and may preclude recognition of the stratigraphical equivalence of adjacent formations within it. Behind the barrier, the equivalent beds comprise the Keg River carbonates and overlying Muskeg evaporite–carbonate sequence. The upper member of the Keg River Formation is divided into the Rainbow (reef) Member, as thick as 800 feet, which may in part be continuous with the Muskeg Formation, and a nonreefal, fine-grained, brown limestone, locally crinoidal, about 150 feet thick. In the Rainbow Member the wide variety of carbonates includes organic reefs and reef detritus on the flanks of atolls or banks and back-reef to lagoonal non-skeletal calcarenites and calcilutites. Locally, they are altered to dolomite. The upper part, locally stromatoporoidal, is predominantly laminated dolomite, possibly of shallow-water algal origin. Eastward in Saskatchewan the Keg River Formation is termed the Winnipegosis Formation, which includes a lower unit of fine-grained, argillaceous dolomite unit less than 30 feet thick and, equivalent to the upper Keg River, light yellow-brown, cryptocrystalline to finely crystalline dolomite. The Winnipegosis locally contains stromatoporoids, bryozoans, and corals, but it generally is barren and exhibits relict pelletoid, oölitic, and pisolitic structures. Tight beds are interspersed with beds characterized by intercrystalline or vuggy porosity. On outcrop in Manitoba the stromatoporoid reefs are draped with bedded dolomites. They presumably also occur in the subsurface where thicknesses vary from 50 to at least 345 feet. The reefs have been interpreted as atolls by Edie (1959), as patch reefs on a fringing carbonate bank by Grayston, Sherwin, and Allan (1964), and as banks partly supported by an organic framework by Jones (1965). The Winnipegosis grades southward to light grey, finely crystalline dolomite with a thin, greyish red, silty dolomite at the base, before reaching the depositional edge in Montana.

Throughout Elk Point Basin, between the topographically high reefs and atolls, salt was deposited. In the northwest, the Black Creek salt at the base of the Muskeg Formation does not cover Tathlina Arch indicating that it either was not deposited there or was eroded later. Southeastward, the Muskeg grades into the Prairie Formation, 250 to 600 feet thick in Saskatchewan and a maximum of 1,000 feet in northeastern Alberta. In part, this variation is caused by infilling of the irregular surface of the Keg River and the Winnipegosis carbonates but it may also be due to subsidence or faulting during deposition. Sylvite and carnellite, economically important, occur in the upper 100 to 200 feet south of Saskatoon. Along the eroded northeast margin the Prairie evaporites have been dissolved and lie back of the Winnipegosis reefs and bedded dolomites. Towards the south and west margins of Elk Point Basin, extensive channelling, brecciation, and slumping have been caused by solution of halite. Both the Winnipegosis and Prairie Formations grade through a thin sequence of brown argillaceous limestone, dolomite, and shale, to red shale and sandstones near the shoreline. Marine conditions must have extended farther northeast than the present subcrop.

Overlying the Pine Point, Muskeg, and Prairie Formations is a thin green shale in the northwest that grades to red claystones in the southeast; these beds represent a depositional break or disconformity. The overlying Sulphur Point Formation to the north and west contains limestones interpreted as having been deposited in reefs, lagoons, or intermittently exposed shallows. Stromatoporoids and corals occur in situ or as detritus in a fine- to coarse-grained, largely skeletal, light grey to buff matrix. The formation is 300 feet thick in the barrier and fringing reefs, but thins on the crest of Tathlina Arch to 25 feet of brecciated limestone and green and blue-grey, non-calcareous pyritic shale suggesting subaerial exposure. Where altered to coarsely crystalline dolomite the equivalent beds are termed the Presqu'ile Formation. The Sulphur Point grades southward to aphanitic limestone, evaporitic dolomite, and anhydrite thinning to the southeast. It is represented by the Gilwood sandstones in the vicinity of Peace River Arch. It thins to about 10 feet of anhydrite in east-central Alberta, possibly the equivalent of the Dawson Bay Formation of Saskatchewan as both contain *Stringocephalus*. The Dawson Bay Formation in Saskatchewan comprises a basal unit 30 feet thick of mottled red and green dolomitic claystone, that gradationally overlies the Prairie evaporite and is interpreted as a soil. It grades upwards into shaly limestone and dolomite with a coral–brachiopod fauna, and overlying, buff and brown, fine- to coarse-grained skeletal limestones containing stromatoporoids and corals. The latter are, in part, altered to euhedral, porous dolomite largely filled with halite. Succeeding, buff, brown, bituminous, cryptocrystalline and pelletoid limestones are interbedded with anhydrite or halite. The Dawson Bay Formation is overlain by a thin red and green shale apparently coeval with the green shale of the Watt Mountain overlying the Sulphur Point. It is thickest, as much as 230 feet, in southeastern Saskatchewan, oversteps the Winnipegosis depositional edge in North Dakota, and thins to about 10 feet of dolomite and anhydrite in southwestern Saskatchewan.

The Slave Point Formation thins southeastward from a maximum of 500 feet at the carbonate front to zero against the Peace River Arch and to less than 50 feet in east-central Alberta. It has not been identified in Saskatchewan. Near the front it contains globular stromatoporoids set in a coarse skeletal calcarenite matrix or present as fragments in calcilutites and pelletoid limestones recrystallized locally to coarse, white, vuggy dolomite. Southeast of the front the stromatoporoid-rich beds decrease in abundance, the rock becomes bedded, largely cryptograined to fine grained, and contains chert nodules and scattered ostracods and brachiopods. Evaporitic dolomite and anhydrite constitute the Fort Vermilion Member at the base which increases in thickness eastward; the Slave Point Formation is represented by 60 feet of anhydrite and a few feet of overlying limestone in the vicinity of Fort McMurray.

Upper Devonian of the Interior Platform

Frasnian (Fig. VIII-16). The Frasnian rock sequence is the result of oscillatory but essentially continuous deposition. The basal beds are still undated locally but are included herein with the Frasnian. They consist predominantly of black, pyritic, locally siliceous shales of the Muskwa Formation, which fill irregularities resulting from post-Givetian warping, faulting, and erosion and may represent westward convergence of the lower part of the overlying Fort Simpson Formation or may include one or more disconformities that cut down westward. In Great Slave Lake area, where Frasnian carbonates occur at a lower stratigraphic horizon than they do to the west, the tongue of shale is named the Hay River Formation. It is about 1,200 feet thick, and like the Fort Simpson, which ranges from 2,000 to 2,500 feet in thickness, consists of greenish grey to greyish green shales with thin siltstone and silty carbonate layers and locally, dark grey and black shales. Both formations are transitional into the overlying carbonates by interbedding of shales with skeletal calcarenites and coral- and stromatoporoid-rich lenses. The Hay River is overlain by the Twin Falls Formation, about 500 feet of algal–stromatoporoid–coral limestone bioherms, biostromes, and associated calcarenites, pelletoid and cryptograined, clotted lagoonal limestones which grade south to the Grosmont dolomite and upper part of Leduc Formation. The Twin Falls is overlain by 450 feet of silty limestones, calcareous siltstones, and shales of the Tathlina Formation and the Redknife limestones and siltstones that thicken westward and include a basal, coral-bearing, bioclastic to reefoid limestone, 50 feet thick, the Jean Marie Member. The Jean Marie thickens southwestward at the expense of the Fort Simpson shales before disappearing as a separate carbonate rock unit. The uppermost Frasnian, Kakisa Formation, 200 feet thick, contains coral–stromatoporoid reefs and skeletal calcarenites as well as pelletoid and cryptograined limestones, and grades west to greenish grey shales. It was subjected to erosion before deposition of the Famennian Trout River Formation. The Redknife and Kakisa converge southward and change to dolomite over Peace River Arch; more southerly equivalents are the uppermost Woodbend and Winterburn Groups.

The Beaverhill Lake Formation and the almost equivalent Waterways Formation of east-central Alberta are 500 to 700 feet thick. The basal, skeletal, calcarenitic limestone of the Beaverhill Lake, which is not included in the Waterways, is abruptly overlain by the Firebag Member which consists of dark brown calcareous and greenish grey shales that are succeeded by light yellow, brown, and buff, very fine to medium grained limestones of the Calumet Member. Greenish grey shales of the Christina Member grade up to the complex of limestone facies of the Moberly Member, which includes stromatoporoid-rich biostromes, skeletal calcarenites, clotted limestone, bedded anhydrite, and greenish grey shale. The Moberly is overlain by interbedded shale and fine-grained limestone of the Mildred Member.

The interbedded shale and limestone facies of the Beaverhill Lake changes along an irregular front to a shelf or platform carbonate facies. The carbonates flank and overlap the Peace River and Alberta Arches and the broad shelves in Montana, North Dakota, and southern Manitoba. The platform front at that time lay mostly in the subsurface of west-central Alberta. A widespread, dark brown, bedded, fine-grained limestone carrying dispersed stromatoporoids, corals, and *Amphipora* with a basal brachiopod–crinoid layer forms a widespread platform on which developed isolated reef-fringed banks as much as 500 feet thick. These are predominantly limestone, although grading southwest to dolomite and possibly forming a continuous but irregular, vuggy, reefoid, dolomite barrier from north of Athabasca River in Jasper National Park to eastern Saskatchewan. The reef-fringed banks, the Swan Hills Member, contain a great variety of carbonate rock types (Murray, 1965). A framework of massive and tabular stromatoporoids, solenaporid algae, and some corals forms a wave-resistant barrier that became progressively restricted to mound-shaped structures. Skeletal debris flanks the reefs as talus both seaward and lagoonward of the reefs, and forms bedded deposits that may separate reefs low in the sequence from those above. The back-reef calcarenites grade to a variety of lagoonal deposits, mostly calcilutites and non-skeletal calcarenites carrying *Amphipora* and dendroid stromatoporoids. Green, waxy, pyritic shale breaks occur locally.

The reef and bank and vuggy dolomite facies in Alberta grade eastward into Saskatchewan to bedded dolomites and evaporites of the Souris River Formation, which encompasses approximately the same stratigraphic interval as the Beaverhill Lake. The Souris River Formation, about 400 to 600 feet thick in central Saskatchewan, comprises (Lane, 1965) from the base up: A unit—red and green claystone, locally brecciated (First Red Beds of the Elk Point Group); B unit—cryptograined, argillaceous or dolomite limestone; C unit—brown, dolomitic, fine- to medium-grained, skeletal and pelletoid limestone, containing stromatoporoids and corals overlain by and laterally equivalent to D unit (the Davidson halite) and forms the barrier that permitted the latter to be precipitated. The Davidson halite grades upwards and westwards to anhydrite. The upper part of the Souris River consists of cyclical alternations of grey, green, and red shale, fine-grained, fossiliferous limestone and anhydrite, and locally, halite, succeeded by fine-grained, argillaceous limestone, and grey shales.

The succeeding, middle Upper Frasnian rock sequence is represented by the greater part of the Fort Simpson shale facies north of the Peace River Arch, by the platform carbonate and reef-fringed bank facies of the Woodbend and Lower Winterburn Groups in central Alberta, and by the evaporite facies of the Duperow and Birdbear Formations, Saskatchewan. The shale facies covers the Beaverhill Lake Platform of western Alberta and embays the platform facies in west-central Alberta (Fig. VIII-16). The basal platform carbonate, the Cooking Lake Formation, consists of interbedded fine-grained limestone with varying amounts of skeletal debris, fine- to coarse-grained skeletal calcarenites, locally with abundant stromatoporoids, *Amphipora*-rich beds, and pelletoid beds. Stromatoporoids increase in abundance towards the front and form biostromes and patch reefs over broad areas. Away from the front, pelletoid and very fine grained limestones become more numerous, and are interbedded with anhydrite, as the latter increases southward. A prominent brachiopod–crinoid shaly limestone and shale zone in the middle of Cooking Lake extends across Saskatchewan. A similar zone occurs at the top of this formation. The shale equivalent to the Cooking Lake Formation, the Majeau Lake Formation, is present between the Windfall platform and Rimbey–Meadowbrook reef chain. It consists of a black shale that grades up to greenish grey shales that filled the basin and spread over the Cooking Lake Platform. Subsequently carbonate deposition was restricted to areas controlled by organically bound banks and reefs that could present a rigid framework to the seas. These post-Cooking Lake carbonates, the Upper Cairn Formation and upper part of the Wymark Member of the Duperow Formation, form a continuous, though irregularly arcuate front from the Rocky Mountains to southeastern Saskatchewan and, as the lower part of the Leduc Formation, form the base on which the grey dolomites of the reef chains accumulated. These strata consist predominantly of brown stromatoporoid biostromes, reefs, and bars that are interbedded with *Amphipora*-rich beds, skeletal calcarenites, and fine-grained laminated limestones. They are commonly altered to fine- to coarse-crystalline brown dolomites. The stromatoporoid beds grade away from the front to bahamites or pelletoid limestones and fine-grained limestones, commonly dolomitized. South and east of the Drumheller front these facies intertongue with cyclically alternating dolomites and evaporites chiefly anhydrite but locally salt. Tongues of black and dark grey shales penetrate the carbonate front at the top of the Cairn Formation. The Cairn and its equivalents extended farther south than any other part of the Frasnian and probably represent the maximum Upper Devonian transgression. In northeastern Alberta and southwest of Great Slave Lake, stromatoporoid–coral lenses, reefs, and calcarenites of the Escarpment Member and lower part of the Twin Falls Formation intertongue with shales, the base of the carbonate facies rising stratigraphically westward as the carbonate tongues grade to shale. Carbonate deposition on the southeast flank of the Peace River Arch also began at this time.

Distribution of the overlying carbonates is largely related to these carbonates. They similarly form an almost continuous front from the Rocky Mountains across southern Alberta (Peechee Member of Southesk Formation) into Saskatchewan (Seward Member of Duperow Formation) and form the Upper Leduc of the reef chains, the fringing reef of the Peace River Arch, and the Grosmont dolomite of northeastern Alberta which grades northward into the Twin Falls limestone of the Great Slave Lake area. Contact with the adjacent shale facies may be abrupt or may interdigitate. These strata most commonly consist of 200 to 500 feet of light grey, medium to coarsely crystalline, vuggy dolomite in which original structures have been almost completely destroyed. Where preserved as limestone, reefs, organic debris, non-skeletal and pelletoidal calcarenites, and laminated and clotted lime mudstones have been recognized. A typical, isolated carbonate mass (Klovan, 1964) is made up of discontinuous organic reef facies on the flanks of the structure, but about 20 to 40 feet below the surface. The reefs are built of massive stromatoporoids, and are separated and flanked seaward by coarse reef detritus with tabular stromatoporoids, and lagoonward by skeletal calcarenites including reef detritus with massive stromatoporoids. In the protected back reef, or lagoon, non-skeletal calcarenites, locally bored, algal-laminated limestones, and *Amphipora*-rich beds are the most common facies and discontinuous green waxy shales occur as laminae or are disseminated through the rock.

The massive-bedded, locally crossbedded, dolomites forming the front of platform areas also include reefs. They grade south and east of the front in southern Alberta and Saskatchewan to cyclically alternating shaly limestone and shale carrying a brachiopod–coral–crinoid fauna, dolomite, and anhydrite. The shaly fossiliferous beds are absent over the Swift Current Platform and in Montana and North Dakota. The uppermost cycle changes to red shale across southern Saskatchewan. The equivalent Grosmont of northeastern Alberta similarly acts as a barrier behind which the Hondo evaporites and siltstones accumulated.

The shale facies of the Woodbend Group east of the Rimbey–Meadowbrook chain rests on the Cooking Lake Platform carbonate. At the base, the Duvernay Formation, 180 feet thick, consists of dark brown limestone, black, pyritic, in part silty shale, thin sandstone laminae with corrosion surfaces commonly overlain by pyrite and fragments of underlying rock. Northward it is interbedded with greenish grey, calcareous shale and grey limestones that pass northward to become part of the greenish grey shales of the Hay River Formation. South and west of the Rimbey–Meadowbrook chain it and the Majeau Lake Formation condense to about 50 feet of black shale that possibly includes a disconformity. The Duvernay grades up to the greenish grey, poorly fossiliferous shales of the lower part of the Ireton Formation, 500–900 feet thick. The upper part of the clastic sequence represented by the Ireton, Mount Hawk, and Fort Simpson Formations shows the influence of stabilization of the basin and gradual marine regression. Tongues of carbonate extend from the banks that almost surround the basin into the clastics of the upper Woodbend and lower Winterburn Groups, and the Mount Hawk Formation of Rocky Mountains. The lower, more restricted tongue, the Camrose of the subsurface and Grotto Member of the Southesk Formation, contains abundant corals and stromatoporoids, locally forming reefs, in a dark agrillaceous bituminous matrix. The succeeding Nisku Formation of the Winterburn Group of Alberta and the essentially coeval Birdbear Formation of Saskatchewan and the Arcs Member of the Southesk Formation consist of light grey to light brown, crystalline dolomites that cover the shelf carbonates and extend over the Ireton shales of eastern Alberta. These carbonates grade to anhydrite and siltstone in eastern Alberta and Saskatchewan.

In the western Alberta Ireton basin and north of the Peace River Arch the upper Woodbend, lower Winterburn unit thickens as it grades to silty dolomites, calcareous siltstones, and shales, as much as 450 feet thick, known as the Tathlina Formation west of Great Slave Lake and northeastern Alberta. It condenses to a carbonate siltstone unit of 0 to 300 feet thick over the Peace River Arch and thickens westward in the southern District of Mackenzie and northern Alberta to comprise the Redknife and Kakisa Formations. The Redknife greenish grey shales contain at the base the Jean Marie Member, a stromatoporoid–coral bioclastic limestone, locally reefy, 50 to 200 feet thick. The uppermost Frasnian Kakisa Formation, a maximum of 200 feet thick, contains coral–stromatoporoid reefs and skeletal calcarenites as well as pelletoid and cryptograined limestones and grades west to greenish grey shales. It was subjected to erosion before deposition of the Famennian Trout River Formation. Equivalents of the silty units of the north are probably to be found in the Calmar siltstone and shale and the Graminia siltstone, dolomite, and anhydrite of central Alberta.

Famennian (Fig. VIII-17). The Famennian part of the Fort Simpson and Besa River shales of southern District of Mackenzie and northeastern British Columbia grades eastward into carbonates of the Wabamun Group. An intermediate sequence of intertonguing carbonates and clastics contains, at the base, the Trout River sandstones, siltstones, silty limestones and shale, as thick as 200 feet, that thin eastward to less than 20 feet and rest disconformably on the underlying Winterburn Group. The gradationally overlying Tetcho Formation is limestone and the succeeding Kotcho Formation comprises dark grey and black shales. The carbonate facies, the Wabamun Group of Alberta, consists, in northern and western Alberta, of 700 feet of brown, fine-grained and pelletoid limestones including bahamites and sparse oölites locally dolomitized. Locally it contains mounds of vuggy dolomite. It extends over the whole of Alberta, the uppermost part overlapping the Precambrian of the Peace River Arch. Dolomitization increases around the Peace River Arch and into south-central Alberta where interbedded dolomite and anhydrite with local halite form the 500-foot-thick Stettler Member. This member thins towards Saskatchewan as it grades to the cyclically alternating variegated shale, dolomite, and anhydrite of the Torquay Formation which is 60 to 130 feet thick. The Torquay changes towards Manitoba to the red sandy facies of the Lyleton Formation. The Big Valley Formation overlies the Stettler and Torquay Formations but is not readily separable from the Wabamun limestone facies to the northwest. It consists of greyish green shale and argillaceous limestone carrying a crinoid–brachiopod fauna. The Wabamun is overlain by the black shale of the Exshaw Formation in Alberta, and in Saskatchewan by the basal black shale of the Bakken Formation of Devonian and/or Mississippian age.

Carboniferous and Permian

Tectonic Summary

Mississippian. The early Mississippian and earlier Caribooan Orogeny (Fig. VIII-22) is represented in the Omineca Geanticline by pre-Osagian metamorphism and deformation of lower Paleozoic and Proterozoic rocks, by the presence of boulders of low-grade metamorphic rocks and felsite in basal conglomerates of the unconformably overlying Osagian and later successions, and by a generally lower degree of metamorphism in the younger rocks. Boulders of granitic and high-grade metamorphic rocks in conglomerate associated with Mississippian rocks in northern Omineca Geanticline indicate that the orogeny may have been accompanied by plutonism. Deposition of black clastic and mafic volcanic rocks in Sylvester Trough probably continued into the early Mississippian, the clastic rocks being derived from uplifted regions to the west, first manifest in the Upper Devonian. In northern Omineca Geanticline, quartzose sediments in an otherwise predominantly volcanic assemblage, probably Mississippian in the Pelly and Omineca Mountains, were derived from the erosion of Lower Cambrian and earlier quartzose sediments and possibly also metamorphic rocks of the eastern part of the geanticline. In Cariboo Mountains the basal clastics were derived from uplifts within the western part of the geanticline. Folding occurred prior to the deposition of Osagian carbonates which are locally associated with clastic and mafic volcanic rocks and lie with strong regional unconformity on strata as old as the Cambro-Ordovician of Kechika Trough to the east. Limestone, fine-grained clastics, and volcanic rocks were deposited in the subsequent site of Stikine Arch east of the northern Coast Geanticline. In British Mountains, Meramecian shales overlap the peneplaned, low-grade, metamorphic rocks of the Ellesmerian Orogen (Fig. VIII-23). Mississippian rocks of the Interior Platform succeed Upper Devonian strata with slight disconformity and, in the more easterly elements of the Cordilleran Geosyncline, may be conformable, particularly where the two systems are represented by very thin black shales that were deposited under starved basin or leptogeosynclinal conditions of deposition. Easterly and northerly derived sands and silts occur low in the successions in Williston, Liard, and Peel Basins and recur at several higher levels, one aspect of the regionally progressive but cyclically interrupted, westward regression of the sea from the craton that occurred during the Carboniferous. A great variety of facies occurs in several types of cyclical alternations. In Liard and Alberta Troughs and adjacent parts of Interior Platform the dominant facies are extremely widespread sheets of crinoidal limestone that grade westward into cherty limestone and shale. Linking of Liard and Alberta Troughs and the establishment of a continuous belt of depression along the margin of the craton east of MacDonald Platform is evident for the first time, the latter element persisting as an arch. In weakly autogeosynclinal Williston Basin the environments of deposition and facies gradually changed from those of euxenic black shale through normal marine shales and limestones with nearshore oölites, into those of a restricted evaporite–red bed basin.

Pennsylvanian. The presence of Pennsylvanian rocks in the southern Cordilleran Geosyncline is established at only a few places but may be represented by greenstone, limestone, and clastic rocks in the upper part of the Mississippian sequences or in the lower part of other sequences established as Permian. In places on northern Coast Geanticline, Pennsylvanian strata are definitely absent, whereas in Fraser Trough, Lower and Upper Pennsylvanian rocks are known and may be fairly abundant to the southeast, in the region between Coast and Omenica Geanticlines. A generally positive behaviour of the geanticlinal belts is indicated during or immediately after Pennsylvanian deposition. Volcanic activity in the southern Coast Geanticline formed islands, probably surrounded by aprons of clastic volcanic material. In northern Yukon the granites of Old Crow batholith have yielded a K–Ar date of 265 m.y. suggestive of an orogenic event perhaps equivalent to the Melvillian Disturbance of the Arctic Islands in latest Pennsylvanian time (Fig. VIII-23). It is not known, however, whether some pre-Permian, northeasterly trending structures of that region are attributable to this disturbance or to the earlier Ellesmerian Orogeny. In northern Liard Trough thick easterly and northerly derived clastics, in part non-marine, reflect uplift of the northern part of the craton and in the south, on the site of the former Peace River Arch, following or during the deposition of red beds and evaporites, warping took place that produced northeast-trending Peace River Embayment. The warping was accompanied by displacement along northwest- and northeast-trending faults which produced horsts and graben, and by peneplanation prior to the deposition of the Middle Permian.

Permian. In the eastern Cordilleran Geosyncline the Permian (Fig. VIII-24) everywhere lies disconformably or unconformably on Carboniferous to Ordovician strata, locally with angular unconformity, as a result of the Ellesmerian and Caribooan Orogenies. In several places in western Cordilleran Geosyncline the Permian lies unconformably or disconformably on Mississippian or Pennsylvanian strata but nowhere are the relationships clearly demonstrable. In general, quiescent conditions prevailed in the southern part of the geosyncline, deposition of carbonate, chert and fine clastic sediments being common. Coarse clastic and pyroclastic rocks are lacking except in the southern Insular and St. Elias Troughs. In the north-central part of the geosyncline the Permian is represented by carbonates and volcanics lying between assemblages of chert, greenstone, volcanic clastic, ultramafic, and fine-grained clastic rocks. Volcanic rocks were extruded mainly as flows and were accompanied by the emplace-

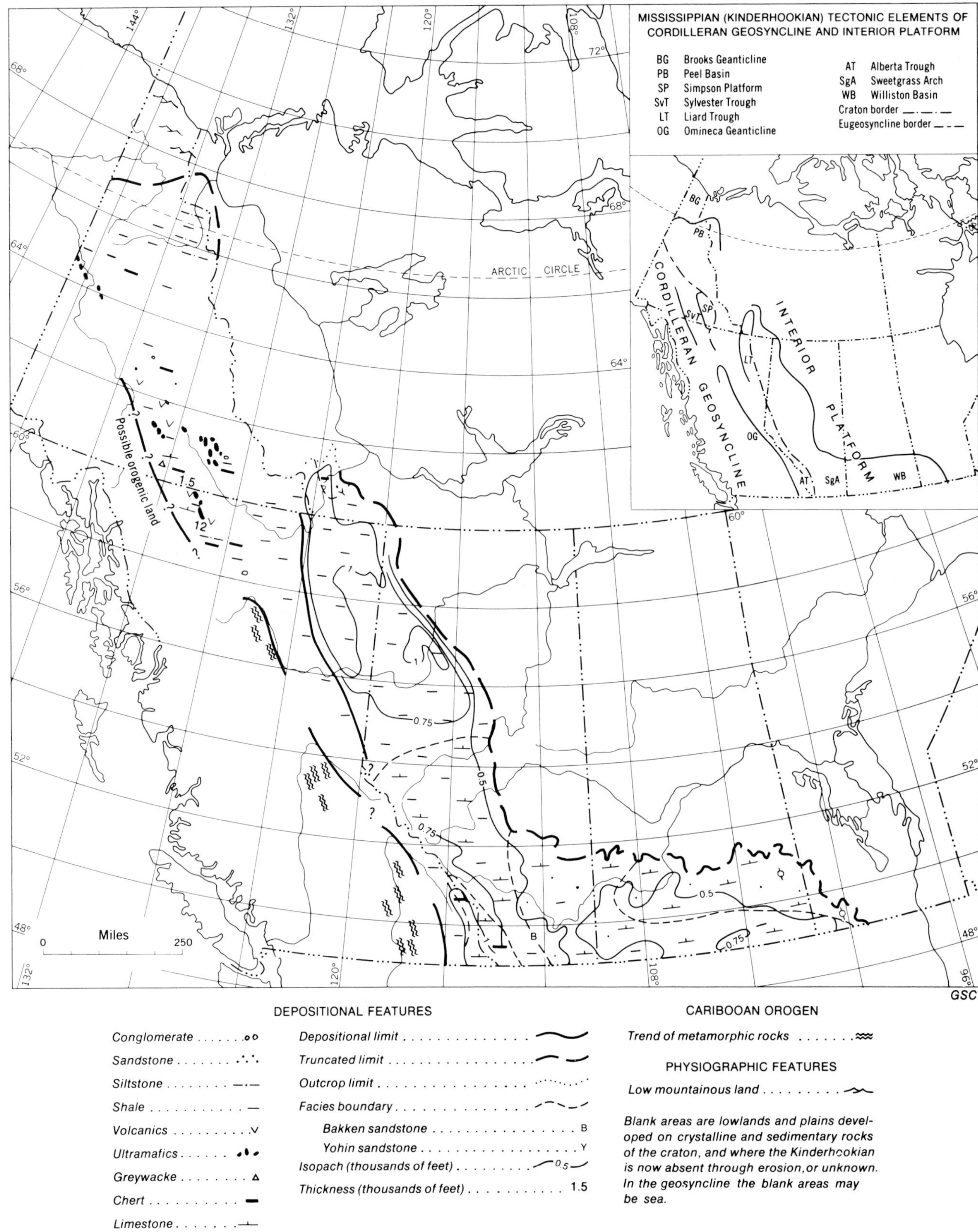

DEPOSITIONAL FEATURES

Conglomerate
Sandstone
Siltstone
Shale
Volcanics
Ultramafics
Greywacke
Chert
Limestone
Oolite

Depositional limit
Truncated limit
Outcrop limit
Facies boundary
Bakken sandstone . . . B
Yohin sandstone . . . Y
Isopach (thousands of feet)
Thickness (thousands of feet) . . . 1.5

CARIBOOAN OROGEN

Trend of metamorphic rocks

PHYSIOGRAPHIC FEATURES

Low mountainous land

Blank areas are lowlands and plains developed on crystalline and sedimentary rocks of the craton, and where the Kinderhookian is now absent through erosion, or unknown. In the geosyncline the blank areas may be sea.

FIGURE VIII-22. Early Mississippian (Kinderhookian) sedimentation and tectonism in Western Canada, and some features of the Ellesmerian and Cariboan Orogens.

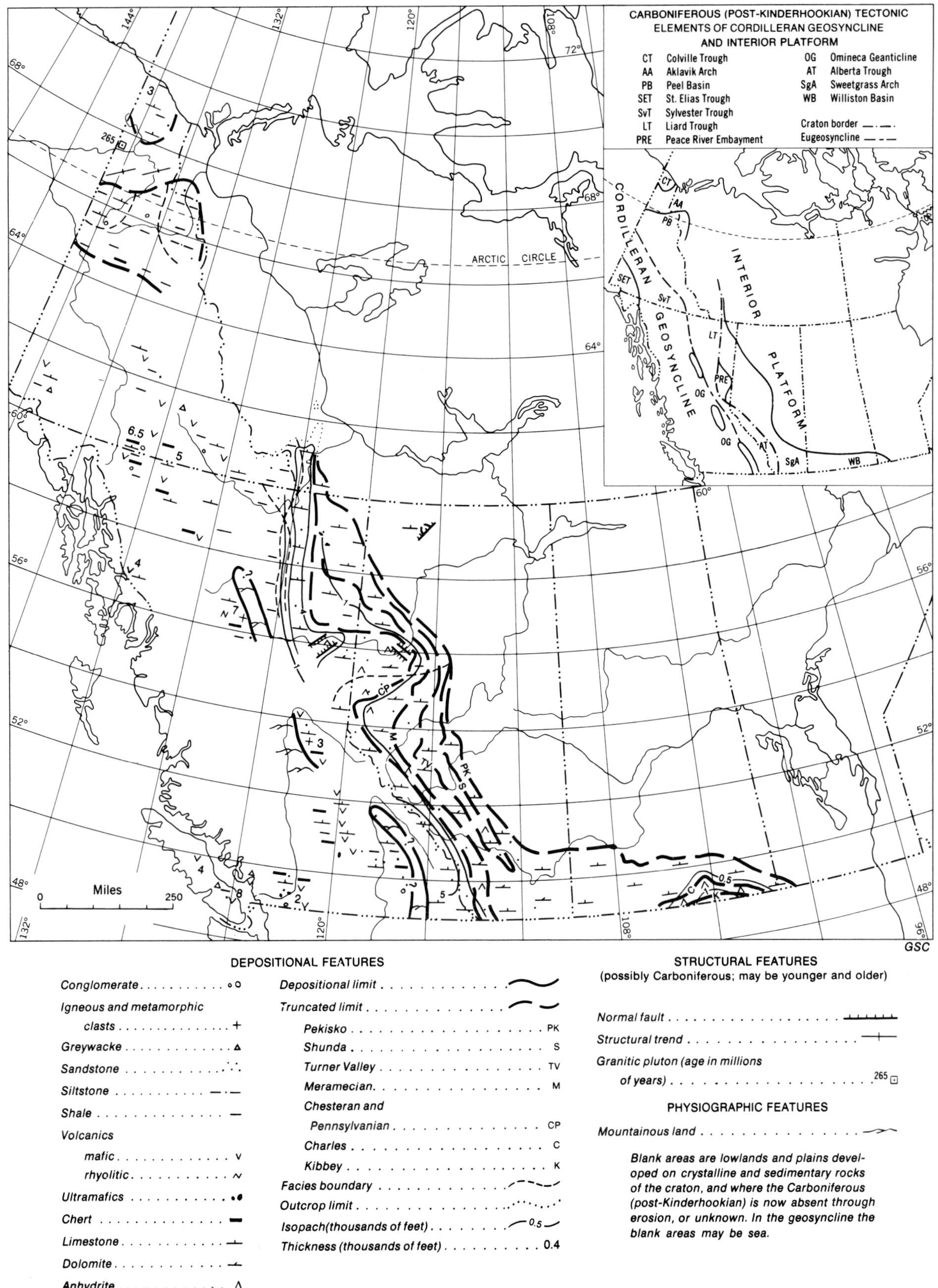
CARBONIFEROUS (POST-KINDERHOOKIAN) TECTONIC ELEMENTS OF CORDILLERAN GEOSYNCLINE AND INTERIOR PLATFORM
CT Colville Trough
AA Aklavik Arch
PB Peel Basin
SET St. Elias Trough
SvT Sylvester Trough
LT Liard Trough
PRE Peace River Embayment
OG Omineca Geanticline
AT Alberta Trough
SgA Sweetgrass Arch
WB Williston Basin
Craton border
Eugeosyncline
CORDILLERAN GEOSYNCLINE
INTERIOR PLATFORM
ARCTIC CIRCLE
Miles
0
250
GSC
DEPOSITIONAL FEATURES
Conglomerate
Igneous and metamorphic clasts
Greywacke
Sandstone
Siltstone
Shale
Volcanics
mafic
rhyolitic
Ultramafics
Chert
Limestone
Dolomite
Anhydrite
Depositional limit
Truncated limit
Pekisko PK
Shunda S
Turner Valley TV
Meramecian M
Chesteran and Pennsylvanian CP
Charles C
Kibbey K
Facies boundary
Outcrop limit
Isopach (thousands of feet) 0.5
Thickness (thousands of feet) 0.4
STRUCTURAL FEATURES
(possibly Carboniferous; may be younger and older)
Normal fault
Structural trend
Granitic pluton (age in millions of years) 265
PHYSIOGRAPHIC FEATURES
Mountainous land
Blank areas are lowlands and plains developed on crystalline and sedimentary rocks of the craton, and where the Carboniferous (post-Kinderhookian) is now absent through erosion, or unknown. In the geosyncline the blank areas may be sea.

FIGURE VIII-23. Carboniferous (post-Kinderhookian) sedimentation and tectonism in Western Canada.

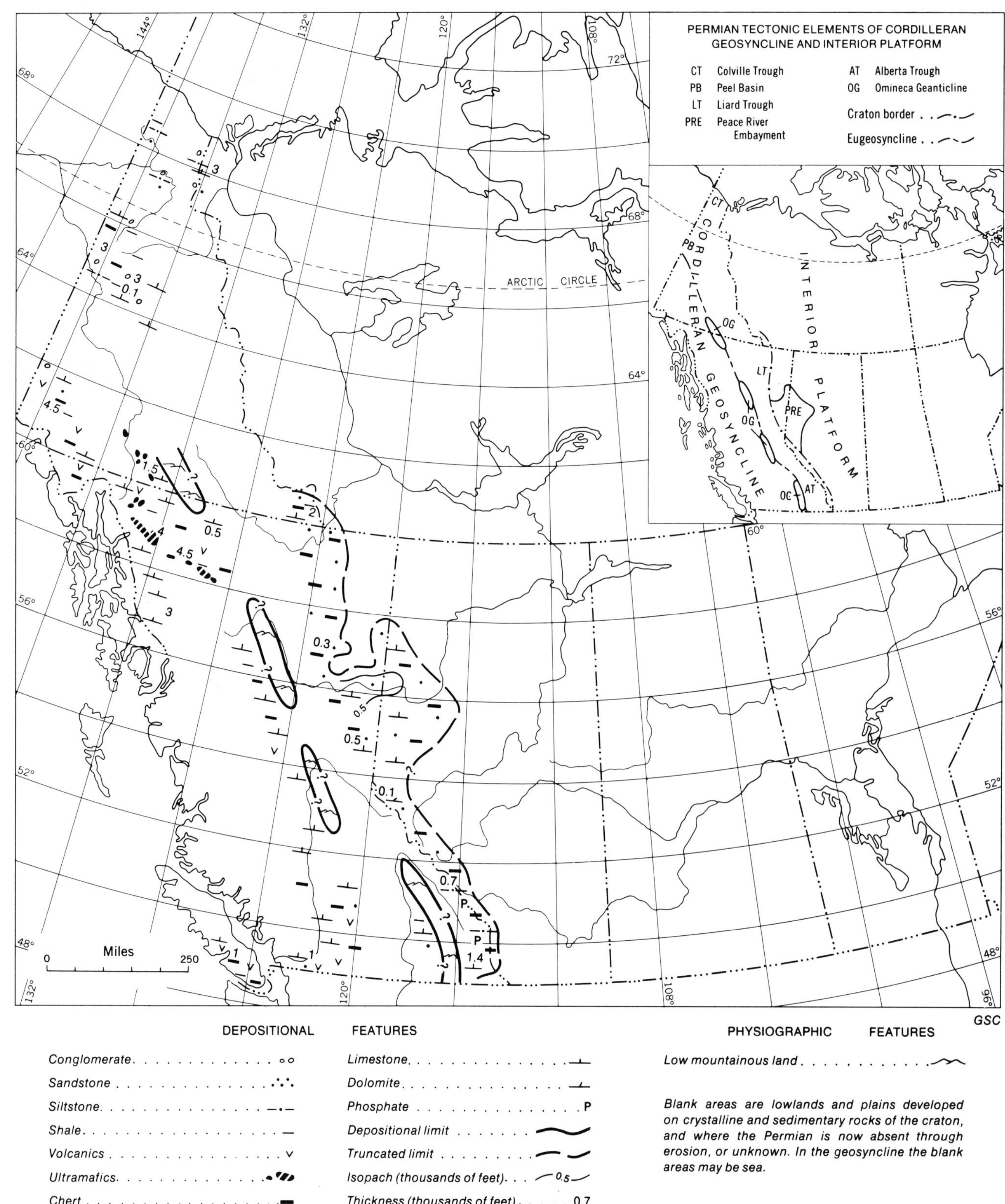

FIGURE VIII-24. Permian sedimentation and tectonism in Western Canada.

ment of ultramafic rocks near major fracture zones. Volcanoes, built up above wave base, were eroded and local thick sequences of volcanic arenite, mud, carbonate, and chert were formed.

Cariboan Orogeny

In early Mississippian time, the region of Omineca Geanticline was deformed and uplifted. The orogeny is not closely dated except in the Cassiar region where the Osagian and younger Nizi Formation overlies with angular unconformity strata as young as Upper Devonian (Gabrielse, 1963). In Cariboo Mountains the Slide Mountain Group, which overlies the Lower Paleozoic Cariboo Group, is dated as Mississippian, possibly Osagian on the basis of the provisional identification of *Spirifer minnewankensis* Shimer (Sutherland Brown, 1963). Coarse conglomerates of the basal Guyet Formation contain clasts of quartz, quartzite, and chert with subordinate phyllite, argillite, limestone, felsite, and volcanic rocks. The conglomerate was evidently derived from the west, from a terrain comprising rocks of the Cariboo Group previously subjected to low-grade regional metamorphism and intrusion of the Proserpine felsite dykes.

Less certain evidence for the Cariboan Orogeny comes from Aiken Lake map-area (Roots, 1954). A predominantly volcanic unit has yielded poorly preserved fossils thought to be of Mississippian age, but some may be Permian. The upper part contains conglomerate and sandstone derived from a siliceous metamorphic terrain that probably lay to the east. Roots has also included in the unit a bed of coarse conglomerate with clasts of massive and foliated granite he regarded as identical with rocks of the Wolverine Complex. As this complex contains Lower Cambrian rocks it must have been metamorphosed later, most likely during the Cariboan Orogeny. However, the conglomerate containing the granitic clasts lies along a fault, and according to Souther and Armstrong (1966) it may represent a sliver of Mesozoic rocks and be the product of a later orogeny.

Further evidence for the Cariboan Orogeny comes from southern Selkirk Mountains where the Upper Mississippian and younger Milford Group contains a basal conglomerate with clasts of quartz, chert, argillite, and phyllitic grit. One lens contains clasts as large as 12 inches of phyllitic grit and greenstone of the Broadview Formation (Wheeler, 1966b). The foliation within the clasts is randomly oriented in contrast to the regional foliation which is restricted to the matrix of the conglomerate. Thus, the Broadview Formation must have been deformed, metamorphosed to low greenschist facies, and, as previously mentioned, possibly thrust over Lower Paleozoic rocks prior to the deposition of Milford sediments.

Granitic plutons may have been emplaced locally into the Omineca Geanticline as post-tectonic plutons following the Cariboan Orogeny. The Adamant batholith in northern Selkirk Mountains and the Toby stock in Purcell Mountains, both hypersthene monzonite plutons, have yielded K–Ar dates only as old as 281 m.y. and 232 m.y., respectively, but these plutons may have been modified during periods of Mesozoic regional metamorphism.

It is probable that in early Mississippian time orogeny and some uplift took place in the region of the Omineca Geanticline. Uplift apparently was greatest in the north as a large amount of clastic rock occurs in the Upper Devonian to Lower Mississippian sequences. Uplift was probably less in the south, as there are no indications of coarse clastics derived from the west having been deposited in adjacent Liard and Alberta Troughs.

Mississippian of Western Cordilleran Geosyncline

Along the Omineca Geanticline where evidence of Cariboan Orogeny is best, formations containing sparse Mississippian fossils overlie older units. These are: the Milford Group near Kootenay Lake, the Slide Mountain Group in Cariboo Mountains, and an unnamed group in Omineca Mountains. All are characterized by clastic sediments, commonly carrying recognizable detritus of older formations.

In *southern Selkirk Mountains,* the Milford Group is either unconformable on or faulted against the Broadview Formation of unknown age. The lower part of the Milford Group contains late Meramecian and early Chesteran corals whereas the upper part contains poorly preserved Pennsylvanian or Permian fossils.

The Slide Mountain Group in *Cariboo Mountains* is relatively unmetamorphosed and overlies the characteristically low-grade metamorphic rocks of the Cariboo Group with great unconformity. The basal Guyet Formation is not in contact with the Snowshoe Formation, the youngest of the Cariboo Group, but successively overlies other formations from the Cunningham to Midas. The conglomerate contains clasts of quartz, quartzite, and chert and, subordinately, of phyllite, argillite, and limestone derived from the Cariboo Group and of felsite from the Proserpine dykes. The conglomerate was apparently derived from a nearby westerly source (Sutherland Brown, 1963) where the Cariboo Group had been deformed during the Cariboan Orogeny and subsequently intruded by the Proserpine dykes. The Greenberry limestone at the top of the Guyet Formation yielded poorly preserved fossils of probable Osagian age. It is overlain by pillow basalts, chert, and argillite of the Antler Formation into which are intruded Mount Murray diabase sills. The Slide Mountain Group is deformed into broad north-trending folds in contrast to the tightly folded and cleaved Cariboo rocks beneath.

In *Omineca Mountains* possible equivalents of the Slide Mountain Group include pillowed greenstone, ribbon chert, slate, and limestone yielding Permian or Carboniferous fossils mapped with the Cache Creek Group southwest of Wolverine Complex (Armstrong, 1949) and volcanic and sedimentary rocks that are separated from older and younger formations by faults (Roots, 1954).

The latter unit has yielded poorly preserved fossils ranging in age from Mississippian to Permian. It is composed principally of green bedded tuff and andesite and basalt flows with subordinate limestone, argillite, greywacke, chert, sandstone, and conglomerate. Although occurring within a predominantly volcanic succession, the sandstone is unusual as it contains no volcanic material but is composed mainly of quartz, quartzite, and mica. This detritus is the product of erosion of quartzose metamorphic rocks, presumably the Lower Cambrian and older formations lying to the northeast. Conglomerate is rare and most beds contain clasts of chert, quartz, quartzite, sandstone, andesite, tuff, jasper, and cherty argillite set in a limonitic gritty matrix. One bed included in the sequence by Roots occurs along a red-weathering fault zone. The boulders, as much as 14 inches across, are foliated granitic rocks like those in the Wolverine Complex enclosed by a hematitic gritty matrix. Roots considered the conglomerate to be part of the late Paleozoic sequence and consequently inferred that an episode of plutonism and deformation took place which produced the Wolverine Complex subsequent to the Lower Cambrian and prior to the late Paleozoic. The conglomerate resembles that of the fault-bounded Aptian Uslika Formation and if it is indeed part of the Uslika then the plutonic episode represented by the clasts may be dated only as pre-late Lower Cretaceous.

In eastern *Cassiar Mountains* Osagian and younger strata comprising about 1,200 feet of cherty limestone with basal siltstone, sandstone, and shale, unconformably overlie strata as old as Cambrian (Gabrielse, 1963). Farther west, the Chesteran Nizi Formation, comprising 1,600 feet of limestone with basal greywacke and conglomerate, overlies the Sylvester Group unconformably. In northern Cassiar Mountains an assemblage of andesitic and basaltic volcanic rocks, chert, slate, quartzite, argillite, limestone, and conglomerate probably correlative with the Sylvester Group is more than 8,000 feet thick and probably includes Mississippian rocks. The overlying sedimentary assemblage of chert, slate, quartzite, argillite, limestone, and conglomerate, more than 10,000 feet thick, probably includes rocks younger than Mississippian. East of Teslin Lake the Englishmans Group contains a lower unit of limestone, as much as 1,500 feet thick, and an upper unit dominantly of slate, quartzite, chert, and conglomerate (Mulligan, 1955). Mississippian rocks may also be included in the underlying or partly correlative Big Salmon Complex, an assemblage of schist, gneiss, greenstone, amphibolite, and limestone that probably also includes equivalents of the Sylvester Group to the east.

On *MacMillan Plateau,* chert-pebble conglomerate of the Crystal Peak Formation is at least 4,000 feet thick and may be entirely Osagian as the unit appears to be underlain and overlain by fossiliferous limestone of that age (Campbell, 1967). Shattered syenite stocks in Pelly Mountains and numerous ultramafic bodies in Cassiar and Pelly Mountains are considered to be of Mississippian age. In Simpson Range northeast of Tintina Trench are thick eugeosynclinal rocks of Mississippian or later age. Similar rocks are believed to form part of the metamorphic terrain of the Yukon Group southwest of Tintina Trench.

Between Stikine and Iskut Rivers in *Stikine Plateau* a limestone, 250 to 300 feet thick with Mississippian fossils, is separated from another limestone unit more than 1,800 feet thick by 2,000 feet of volcaniclastic rocks (J. K. Rigby). The strata structurally overlie phyllitic and volcanic rocks of unknown age and are either overlapped by Triassic rocks or faulted against them.

No Mississippian rocks have been positively identified in *St. Elias Mountains* but may be present in a complex of volcanic rocks, chlorite schist, greywacke, slate, phyllite, conglomerate, and a limestone that contains Upper Devonian fossils (Wheeler, 1963; Muller, 1967).

Pennsylvanian and Permian of Western Cordilleran Geosyncline

The Cache Creek Group of Pennsylvanian and Permian age is exposed in *eastern Interior Plateau* along a northwesterly trending belt, the Pinchi Geanticline, and in a belt *en echelon* to the southeast that extends southeastward into the Shuswap Metamorphic Complex. The group consists of a variable assemblage of limestone, ribbon chert, slate, and volcanic rocks and relatively minor arenite and conglomerate. The volcanic rocks are mainly massive greenstone, originally andesitic and basaltic lavas, pyroclastics, and volcanic arenite, within which ultramafic rocks occur locally. The stratigraphy of the group is not yet understood because of the intense deformation of the rocks, the poor exposure, and the lack of distinctive marker beds which can be recognized from place to place. Fossils occur most commonly in the limestones, the fusulinids being the most diagnostic types and representative of the Early and Late Pennsylvanian and all stages of the Permian (Danner, 1964). Shelly fauna range in age from Late Pennsylvanian to Early Permian although some northeast of Kamloops have been referred to the late Mississippian (Cockfield, 1948). Estimates have been made that as much as 20,000 feet of strata are present but wherever detailed work has been done repetition has been recognized and thicknesses vastly reduced. The Lower Permian and earlier Asitka Group at the northernmost end of the Pinchi Geanticline is unusual in that it contains abundant rhyolite that is locally spherulitic (Lord, 1948), although it contains andesitic lavas and associated pyroclastics also. The Cache Creek Group is overlain with erosional unconformity by the Upper Triassic or Lower Jurassic on the flanks of the Pinchi Geanticline (Armstrong, 1949; Tipper, 1959), separated along the east side by the Pinchi and related faults.

Near Vernon in the *Monashee Mountains,* unfossiliferous rocks correlated with the Cache Creek Group appear to lie with angular unconformity on the Monashee Group of the Shuswap Metamorphic Complex (Jones, 1959), but the contacts may be faults according to V. A. Preto. Other unfossiliferous rocks west of Vernon similar to the Cache Creek Group lie with angular unconformity on the Chapperon Group and the Old Dave ultramafic dykes that intrude it. In the Vernon area the rocks beneath the unconformities, and also the Mount Ida Group, are isoclinally folded whereas the rocks above are not. It is uncertain, however, when this deformation took place because of the uncertainty of the ages of the beds above and below the unconformities. Jones considered the rocks beneath to be Precambrian but recent work (Hyndman, 1968) suggests that the Monashee Group contains rocks as young as late Paleozoic and perhaps early Mesozoic as well. Furthermore, fossils presumed to be of Carboniferous or Permian age occur in a northwest extension of the Mount Ida Group (Campbell, 1963). The Chapperon Group contains rocks similar to the fossiliferous strata and on this tenuous basis may be considered partly Permian or Carboniferous. Accordingly, if the overlying strata are Cache Creek Group, which are late Pennsylvanian to early Permian nearby, then the Chapperon Group must be Carboniferous and the deformation and unconformity intra-Carboniferous. Furthermore if the Mount Ida and Chapperon Groups are Permian then the unconformably overlying strata may be Lower or Middle Triassic, and the deformation would be earliest Mesozoic, possibly the Tahltanian Orogeny which is also evident near Greenwood.

On *Stikine Plateau* the upper part of the Cache Creek Group includes a lower limestone member, locally about 300 feet thick of Middle Permian age (Monger, 1968). The succeeding middle member comprises jasper-bearing, maroon to green, basic to intermediate volcanic flows, locally pillowed, and foliated lithic tuff and agglomerate, with a maximum apparent thickness of about 2,000 feet. The upper member of Upper Permian limestone is possibly as much as 2,000 feet thick. This succession overlies a thick assemblage of silica-rich phyllites and slates, thin-bedded cherts, and minor limestone, rhyolite, and volcanic greywacke of the lower part of the group that may be Lower Permian and Pennsylvanian in age. A single mass of limestone north of Atlin Lake contains fossils ranging in age from Middle Pennsylvanian to Upper Permian. In the Coast Mountains near Stikine River limestone sequences, as much as 2,000 feet thick, represent all stages of the Permian except the Ochoan. Drift covers the contact between Permian and Mississippian beds and although the beds are structurally discordant, their stratigraphic relations are not known.

About 150 feet of sandy tuffaceous limestone in northern *Cassiar Mountains* may be correlative with the upper limestone member of the Cache Creek group. The limestones overlie the Sylvester Group with marked discordance but whether the contact is a fault or unconformity is not known. In northwestern *Cassiar Mountains* about 1,500 feet of early Pennsylvanian limestone is overlain by about 5,000 feet of chert, argillite, and limestone, with a basal conglomerate of well-rounded cobbles and boulders of chert and quartzite. On *MacMillan Plateau* and to the southeast, the Pennsylvanian may be represented by a belt of volcanic rocks, limestone, chert, and fine-grained clastic rocks that extend along the northeast side of Tintina Trench (Tempelman-Kluit, 1968).

Permian rocks in *St. Elias Mountains* are as much as 3,000 feet thick and include a lower unit of volcanic breccia and conglomerate and an upper unit of greywacke, sandstone, argillite, and limestone (Muller, 1967). They apparently unconformably overlie Devono-Mississippian metamorphic rocks and are overlain by Middle Triassic strata.

Limestone containing Lower Permian fusulinids and shelly fauna is associated with argillite and greenstone in the eastern *Coast Mountains* near Skeena River (Duffell and Souther, 1964). Permian limestone also occurs farther southeast, west of Whitesail Lake (P. B. Read) and much of the metasediments and metavolcanics in roof pendants within the Coast Plutonic Complex may be of the same age. Generally unfossiliferous groups such as the Fergusson in southeastern Coast Mountains and the Hozameen consist of assemblages of greenstone, ribbon chert, argillite, and minor limestone that strongly resemble parts of the Cache Creek Group.

The Chilliwack Group, in western *Cascade Mountains,* contains much volcanic arenite and tuff in contrast with effusive greenstones and non-clastic sediments characteristic of the Cache Creek Group. Furthermore, the Chilliwack Group includes a conglomerate with volcanic clasts that lies not far above Lower Pennsylvanian (Morrowan) limestone. The conglomerate is associated with beds containing fossil plants of Pennsylvanian age. Overlying volcanic arenite and tuff are succeeded, apparently conformably, by andesitic lavas. Equivalent limestone beds and lenses contain Lower Permian (Leonardian) fusulinids (according to J. W. H. Monger).

On *Vancouver Island,* near Buttle Lake, the Sicker Group consists of altered basalt flows and pyroclastics underlying Lower Permian limestone (Yole, 1963). In the southeast, however, greywacke and chert more commonly underlie the limestone. Although younger Permian strata are not recognized on Vancouver Island, late Permian ribbon chert, argillite, greywacke, and volcanic rocks containing lenses of limestone are present on nearby San Juan Island (Danner, 1964).

Melvillian Disturbance

During the late Pennsylvanian and early Permian, tectonic disturbances, possibly orogenic, took place (Fig. VIII-23). In northern Yukon the structures have not been differentiated from earlier ones. Evidence of plutonic activity are the K–Ar dates of 225 and 265 m.y. from the granites of Old Crow Range. General instability is indicated by the widespread pre-Permian unconformity and by the presence of much chert-pebble conglomerate in the Permian and some in the Pennsylvanian. Post-Mississippian displacement occurred on the southwest extension of the McDonald fault system of the Precambrian basement.

As a result of late Pennsylvanian to early Permian movements, probably normal, on the faults bordering Peace River Arch, this tectonic element ceased to exist as a positive feature and subsequently the region was generally relatively more negative than adjacent regions (Figs. VIII-23, -25). It is possible that some structures in northern Yukon Territory also reflect normal or transcurrent fault movements. The anomalous north trends of Barn Mountains, relative to the southeast trends of British Mountains and the northeast trends of Keele Range may indicate the presence of a northeast-trending dextral transcurrent fault system passing south of Barn Mountains. North-trending pre-Albian, post-Middle Devonian faults in Colville Hills west of Great Bear Lake may have had displacement at this time.

In the White River region of southern Rocky Mountains, diorite sills and dykes are intrusive into the Cambro-Ordovician McKay Group (Leech, 1964). Associated diatreme-like breccias with fragments of diorite and the host and other formations cut strata as young as the Rocky Mountain Group.

Carboniferous and Permian of Eastern Cordilleran Geosyncline and Interior Platform

In *British Mountains* the Mississippian lies with regional angular unconformity on low-grade metamorphic rocks of the Neruokpuk Formation, the deformation of which has been treated as part of the Late Devonian Ellesmerian Orogeny. According to E. W. Bamber, the basal 600 feet of calcareous black shale and limestone carry Meramecian fossils near the top, and is provisionally termed the Kyak Formation. In the Barn Mountains it is represented by 300 feet of non-marine sandstone and shale with basal conglomerate. The Kyak is conformably overlain by 2,000 feet of finely crystalline limestone and coarsely crystalline dolomite of the Lisburn Formation which is Chesteran and Pennsylvanian in age. Disconformably overlying it is at least 600 feet of light grey shale, siltstone, and sandstone constituting the Permian Echooka Member of the Saddlerochit Formation, the upper member of which is Triassic. In southern *Porcupine Plateau* the Mississippian probably conformably succeeds the Upper Devonian, the boundary between the systems lying within thin black shales. The oldest known Mississippian is thin Meramecian limestone on upper Peel River, and shales and siltstones of possible Kinderhookian age east of Richardson Mountains, conformably overlying the Imperial Formation. The Pennsylvanian is incompletely represented by a sequence of massive-bedded bioclastic limestone alternating with black silty shale that grades eastward and southward into shale, siltstone, and chert-pebble conglomerate. The Permian Tahkandit Formation contains grey shales, grits, fossiliferous limestones, and grey chert as much as 1,000 feet thick. In northern Yukon, the Permian generally lies disconformably or unconformably on older beds. In *Keele Range,* where crossed by Porcupine River, the conglomerates lie with angular unconformity on the Silurian and Devonian Road River shales, and on the Devonian Imperial Formation in northern *Richardson Mountains.* Along the Alaska Boundary near Yukon River in *Ogilvie Mountains* all or part of the Mississippian may be represented in a post-Middle Devonian to pre-Permian sequence of black shale, siltstone, and argillaceous limestone generally about 2,000 feet thick.

No Mississippian rocks have been identified in Selwyn and Mackenzie Mountains although they may be present locally in the fine clastic sequences generally referred to the Upper Devonian. In *Liard Plateau* and southernmost *Franklin Mountains,* nearly 6,000 feet of Carboniferous and Permian strata conformably succeed Upper Devonian black shale in the axial part of Liard Trough. Brown, fine-grained sandstones of the Yohin Formation, 600 feet thick, are considered Mississippian, and are conformably succeeded by 550 feet of non-calcareous, black shale of the Kinderhookian and Osagian Clausen Formation (Harker, 1963). Thin-bedded, dark, argillaceous calcarenite and shale of the Flett Formation, nearly 2,000 feet thick, contain intercalations of sandstone in northern Liard Range and grade westward, together with the Yohin, into dark grey, non-calcareous shale and siltstone of the Etanda Formation. The latter shales are 2,300 feet thick and are inseparable from the Besa River Formation. The Mattson Formation is a thick, northeasterly derived sequence of sandstone, siltstone, and shale, mainly Lower Pennsylvanian with late Mississippian coal seams in the lower part. It is overlain with regional unconformity by sandstone and bedded grey chert of the Permian Fantasque Formation. Most of the Mattson probably grades southwestward to shale of the Besa River Formation and the Fantasque to siltstone and shale of the upper Kindle Formation (E. W. Bamber). South of Liard River, and in the subsurface to the east, massive dark cherty limestones of the Prophet Formation representing the Osagian and Meramecian grade westward into the Besa River shale. The vestigial remnant of the Prophet is in many places a persistent thin bed of black chert and limestone. The Prophet grades eastward into the Shunda, Pekisko, and Debolt Formations, about 1,000 feet of interbedded carbonates, shales, and minor anhydrite. Conformably succeeding the Prophet and Debolt Formations is the Stoddart Group, best known in the subsurface of the Peace River Basin. The basal Golata Formation is composed of dark grey to greenish grey shale transitionally overlain by the Kiskatinaw Formation of grey and black shale, siltstone, light grey sandstone, and sandy cherty limestones and dolomites. The Kiskatinaw grades eastward into more sandy beds and upwards into a predominantly carbonate sequence, possibly partly Pennsylvanian in age, forming the Taylor Flat Formation. It consists of dark grey and brown, cherty, silty and sandy dolomites, siltstones, and sandstones. Uplift and movements along faults trending northeast and northwest, in part possibly contemporaneous with deposition of the Stoddart (Fig. VIII-25), were followed by extensive erosion prior to the deposition of the Lower

Permian Belloy Formation. The latter consists of thin glauconitic sandstone, white, silty limestone, and chert with minor conglomerate.

Throughout most of Alberta Trough in the southern Rocky Mountains and beneath the southern Interior Platform the Mississippian has been truncated by pre-Mesozoic erosion, and its present distribution is only the southwesterly remnant of its original extent. The boundary between the Devonian and Mississippian systems is generally considered to be marked by the Exshaw Formation, although its assignment to either system is still unsettled. The Exshaw is a thin, black, bituminous shale, spore-bearing in the subsurface, and with cherty layers in outcrop. It is missing locally in the mountains near Athabasca River. The Exshaw seems to be continuous with the basal black shale of the Bakken Formation of Williston Basin which is overlain by the Coleville sandstone, a light grey to brown, very fine grained, calcareous sandstone about 60 feet thick (Fuller, 1956). The upper Bakken is black shale, about 25 feet thick, fissile, and slightly calcareous. The base of the Kinderhookian Banff Formation is commonly marked by a thin dolomitic siltstone. Succeeding beds are alternating dark grey fissile shales and bands of argillaceous limestone, locally cherty, that grade upwards into dark grey, calcareous or dolomitic shale and limestone in Bow Valley and to the north, or into dark grey, massive, finely crystalline, cherty limestone and dolomite in the south. Near the transitional upper contact with the Rundle Group is a thin persistent siltstone which may be the eastern part of some 400 feet of sandstone, siltstone, and silty limestone near Connor Lake and which apparently has a western source.

On Sweetgrass Arch of southern Alberta, the Banff Formation, 500 feet thick, grades into green shales and shaly limestone, and thence to cream, buff, or pink, cryptograined, cherty limestone, with echinoid and bryozoa debris, interbedded with thin silty argillaceous layers and at the top of variably persistent, red and green, glauconitic shale and siltstone (Penner, 1959). The essentially coeval Souris Valley Formation of the Williston Basin in eastern Saskatchewan and Manitoba consists of a lower shaly unit 20 feet thick, lying with sharp contact on the Bakken and overlain by 400 feet of grey and dark grey, argillaceous, fine-grained, cherty limestone, and an upper argillaceous limestone about 100 feet thick. Along the eastern margin of the basin the middle carbonate thins and becomes lighter and more granular, and interfingers with a complex of calcareous shales and thin beds of coarse oölitic and crinoidal limestone of considerable purity (Stanton, 1958).

The Rundle Group in southern Alberta Trough is Osagian to Chesteran in age. It is dominated by extensive sheets of crinoidal debris, intercalated with beds of dark grey argillaceous limestone and cherty limestone, presumably tongues of a more westerly facies, or with anhydrite and dolomite with shale and sandstone derived from the east. The Rundle Group embraces three formations, the Livingstone, Mount Head, and Etherington (Douglas, 1959). The thick, massive-bedded, crinoidal limestones and dolomites of the Livingstone transitionally overlie the Banff Formation in southern Alberta Trough and thin eastward on southern Sweetgrass Arch. The formation thins and changes facies northward and eastward, with rock units of member status (the Pekisko, Shunda, and

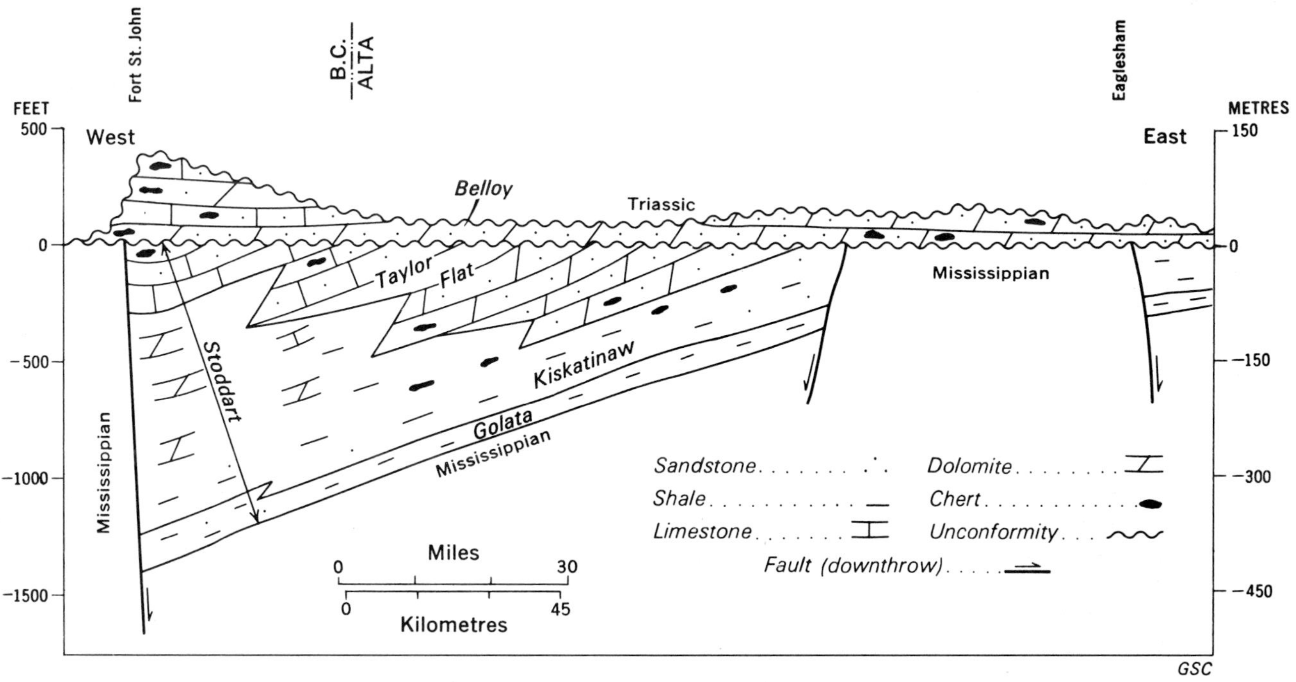

FIGURE VIII-25. Cross-section of Carboniferous and Permian rocks of Peace River Embayment, British Columbia and Alberta, showing pre-Permian (Belloy Formation) normal faults (by H. R. Belyea).

Turner Valley) attaining formation status. The lowest unit, the Pekisko Formation, consists of medium to coarsely crystalline crinoidal limestone in beds as much as 50 feet thick interbedded with finely crystalline, dark grey to brownish grey, argillaceous dolomitic limestone with dark green chert nodules. It grades eastward to about 200 feet of light yellowish brown, coarse-grained, bioclastic chalky limestone, with dark shale and siltstone, and northward into dark grey shales. The overlying Shunda Formation is a very finely crystalline limestone and limestone breccia that grades northward into shale. To the east it consists of argillaceous silty dolomite, breccia, and anhydrite. The Turner Valley Formation has a lower or Elkton Member and an upper member formed of coarsely crystalline crinoidal limestone, locally altered to porous, coarsely crystalline dolomite. They are separated by a middle member of very fine grained silty, laminated, cherty dolomite. The Meramecian Mount Head Formation is divisible into six members, of which the Wileman, Salter, and Marston Members are mainly sandstone and silty dolomite, and grade westward into argillaceous and crinoidal limestone or eastward near their present truncated margins into anhydrite, evaporitic dolomite, and red sandstone. Intervening members, the Baril and Loomis, are mainly crinoidal limestone that grades eastward into porous dolomite. The uppermost member, the Carnarvon, is a persistent, dark argillaceous cryptocrystalline limestone, the lower part of which grades westward into shale and limestone inseparable from the Marston. The Mount Head and Turner Valley Formations pass northward into the Debolt Formation of southern Liard Trough and adjacent Peace River Embayment (Halbertsma, 1959). This unit, about 800 feet thick, consists of light yellowish brown, cherty, massive, bioclastic limestone and dolomite interbedded with shale in the lower part, and an upper part of light brown, very finely crystalline to dense, locally cherty dolomite with pink and white anhydrite. The Chesteran Etherington Formation consists of thin, cyclically alternating beds of green and red shale, and dense, silty, cherty, finely crystalline limestones and dolomites that grade westerly into thick, coarsely crystalline, bioclastic and dark argillaceous limestone.

East of Sweetgrass Arch on the northern flank of Williston Basin in Saskatchewan and Manitoba, the Mississippian sequence (Fig. VIII-26) has been truncated by pre-Mesozoic erosion so that progressively younger members appear downdip to the south towards the centre of the basin in North Dakota. The Osagian and Meramecian (Thomas, 1954) consist predominantly of carbonates in the west that grade into cyclical alternations of carbonates and evaporites, which, farther east, become progressively more evaporitic and contain more sandstone and siltstone lenses (Fig. VIII-26). They comprise the Mission Canyon and overlying Charles Formations of which a maximum of 1,000 feet has been preserved in the south. All Mission Canyon cycles resemble one another although varying somewhat in detail. The lowest cycle, the Tilston Beds, is typical. Cherty, crinoidal limestones at the base grade up to fine-grained, chalky limestones and finely crystalline, porous dolomites with oölite, pisolite, and algal zones prominent in the upper part (Member MC1 of Thomas). These are overlain by argillaceous silty dolomitic limestones with streaks of shale that grade eastward to anhydrite, dolomitic anhydrite, and mottled, red and grey, cryptocrystalline algal dolomite (Member MC2). From east to west and northeast to southwest the evaporites grade to argillaceous dolomites, and the oölitic, algal carbonates grade to fine-grained cherty limestones. These facies changes rise to successively higher levels westward, each succeeding cycle developing into a complete carbonate sequence near the central part of Williston Basin. The carbonate–evaporite cycles are interpreted by Thomas and Glaister (1960) as the deposits of a shallow-water shelf with marginal evaporites, from which the sea was retreating gradually but with a rhythmic inflow of marine waters. The Charles Formation as defined by Thomas and Glaister is restricted by erosion to southern Saskatchewan. It also comprises cycles of evaporites and dolomite. The evaporites are anhydrite, anhydritic dolomite, and finely crystalline dolomite. Salt occurs in the uppermost and lowermost units in the central part of the basin. The carbonates are similar to those of the Mission Canyon Formation.

The Chesteran Big Snowy Group, occurs mainly in the United States and as an erosion remnant only in southernmost Saskatchewan. The Kibbey Formation consists of sandstone with anhydrite and carbonate near the top, and the Otter Formation consists of variegated red and green shales.

In the southern Rocky Mountains, disconformably overlying the Mississippian carbonates of the Rundle Group and disconformably overlain by the Triassic Spray River Formation, are sandstone and dolomite of the Rocky Mountain Group of Early and Middle Pennsylvanian age and phosphatic beds and chert of the Ishbel Group, late Early and Late Permian in age (McGugan and Rapson, 1962). The succession is thickest and most continuous in southern Alberta Trough, the formations thinning rapidly eastward and northward through convergence and truncation at several disconformities. The sandstones of the Tyrwhitt, Storelk, Tobermory, and Tunnel Mountain Formations are massive or thinly bedded, dominantly fine- and even-grained, crossbedded and quartzose, and are probably easterly derived. They are overlain by the Kananaskis Formation, a maximum of 180 feet of silty and cherty dolomite. The disconformably overlying Johnson Canyon Formation of the Ishbel Group consists of thinly bedded, phosphatic quartzose siltstone conformably overlain by the sandy limestones of the Telford. The Ross Creek contains alternating thin and thick beds of silty cherty carbonate, siltstone, and chert. The uppermost unit, the Ranger Canyon chert, is

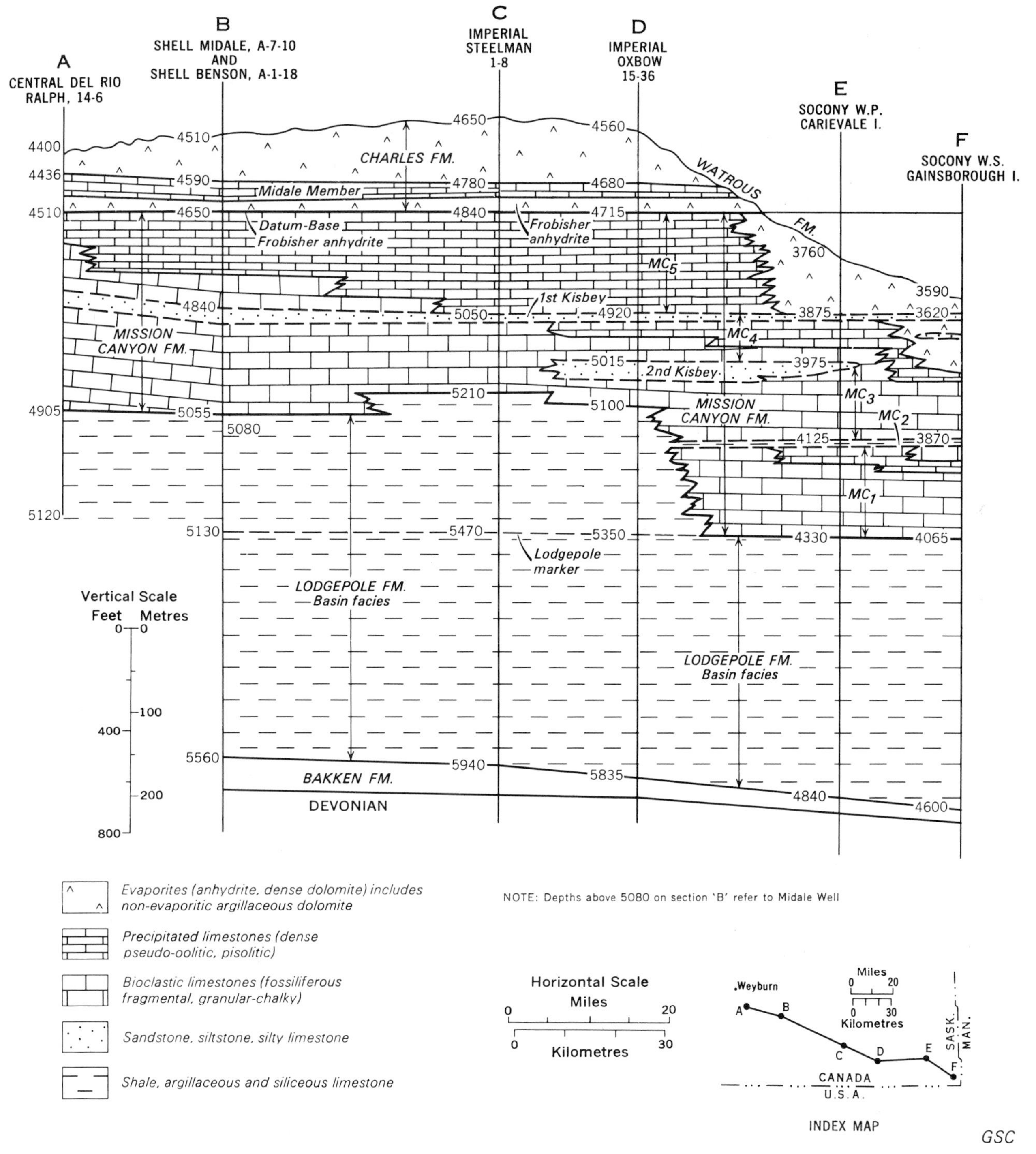

FIGURE VIII-26. Stratigraphic section through Mississippian rocks of Williston Basin in Saskatchewan (Edie, 1958).

a massive, persistent but thin bed that unconformably overlaps eastward, resting on the Mount Head Formation in the eastern Foothills. Locally, near Jasper, the uppermost Permian is represented by the Mowitch Formation, a coarse-grained sandstone that is glauconitic, phosphatic, and fish-bearing.

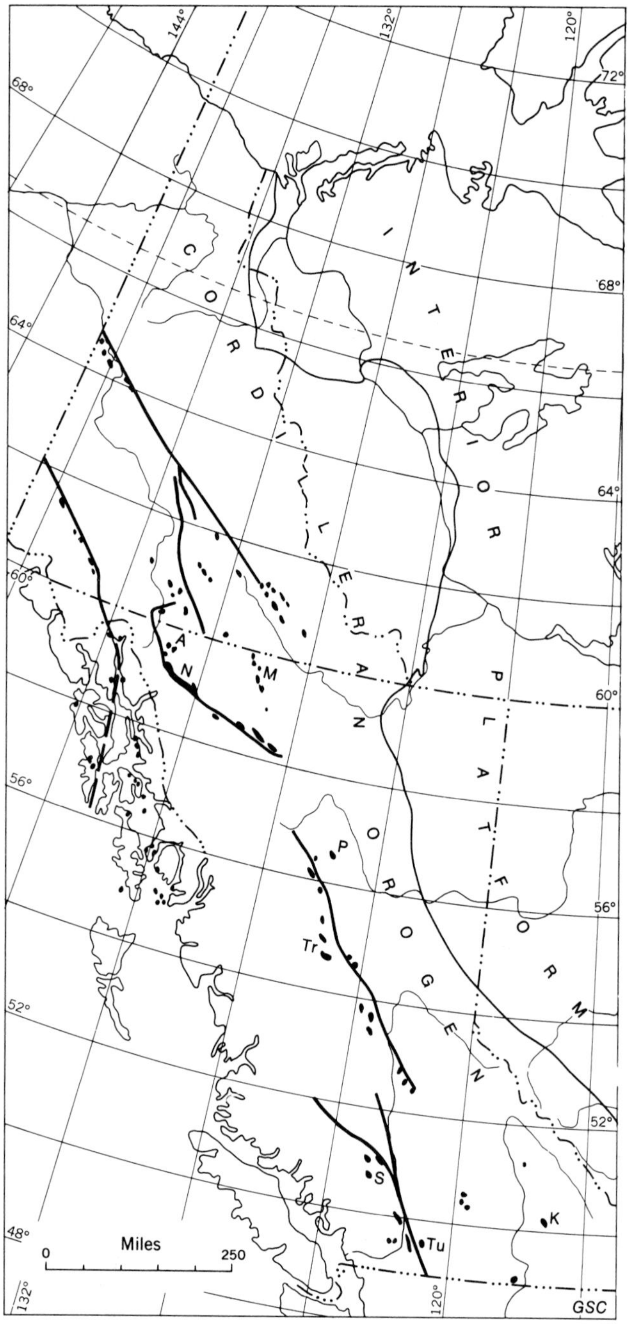

ULTRAMAFIC INTRUSIONS

Atlin. . . . . A	*Polaris. . . .* P
Kaslo. . . . . K	*Shulaps. . .* S
McDame. . . M	*Trembleur. .* Tr
Nahlin. . . . N	*Tulameen. .* Tu

Fault. . . . . ———

Fault (underwater). . . . . — —

FIGURE VIII-27. Distribution of ultramafic intrusions in the Cordilleran Orogen, British Columbia, Yukon Territory, and southeastern Alaska.

GRANITIC PLUTONS

1 Bayonne Batholith
2 Nelson Batholith
2a Coryell Intrusions
3 White Creek Batholith
4 Fry Creek Batholith
5 Kuskanax Batholith
6 Horsethief Batholith
7 Bugaboo Batholith
8 Ice River Complex
9 Adamant Batholith
10 Takomkame Batholith
11 Thuya Batholith
12 Guichon Batholith
13 Mt. Lytton Batholith and Eagle granodiorite
14 Copper Mountain Stock
15 Chilliwack Batholith
16 Coast Plutonic Complex
17 Galore Creek Pluton
18 Topley Intrusions
19 Hogem Batholith
20 Cassiar Batholith
21 Hotailuh Batholith
22 Marker Lake Batholith
23 Old Crow Batholith
24 Mt. Fitton Stock
25 Mt. Sedgwick Stock

METAMORPHIC COMPLEXES

C Custer Gneiss
Cc Coast Complex
H Horseranch Complex
M Malton Gneiss
S Shuswap Complex
T Tahtsa Complex
V Valhalla Complex
W Wolverine Complex
Y Yukon Complex

Granitic pluton . . . ///

Metamorphic complex . . . = \\ ||

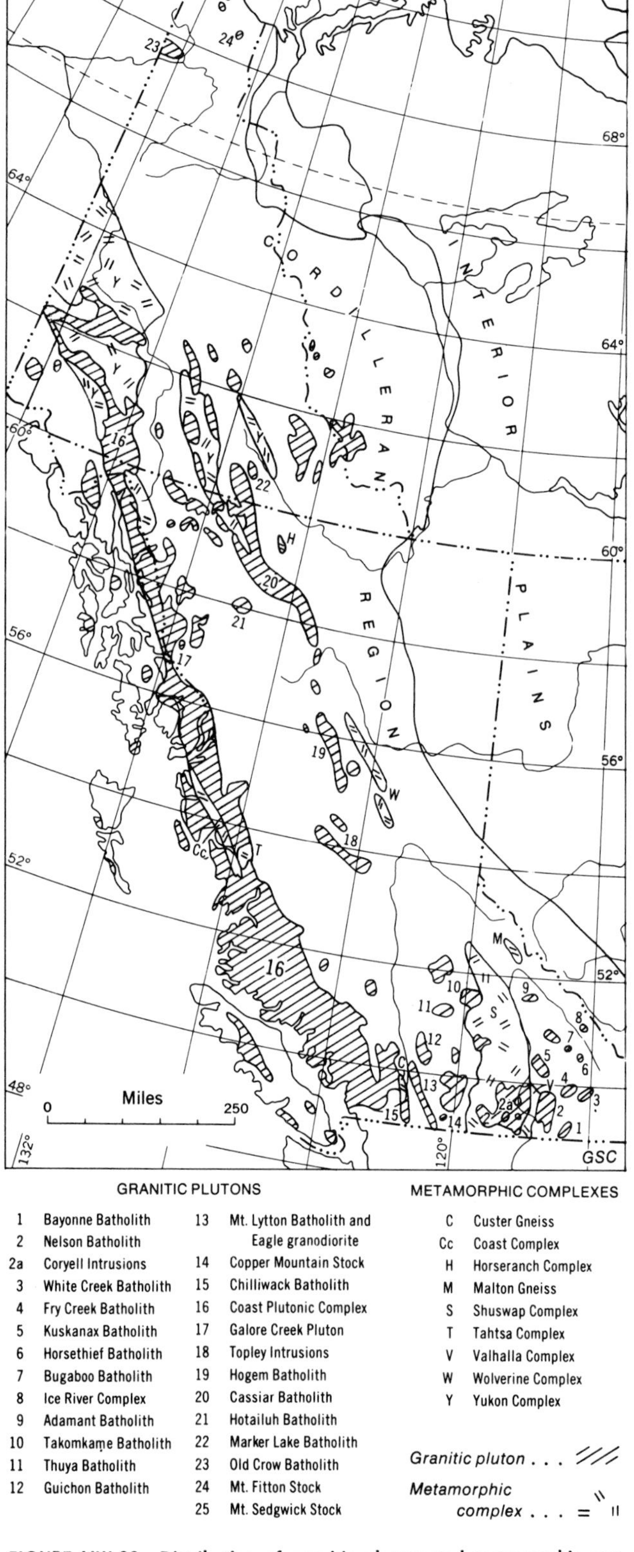

FIGURE VIII-28. Distribution of granitic plutons and metamorphic complexes of the Cordilleran Orogen.

ULTRAMAFIC ROCKS

Most of the known Cordilleran ultramafic intrusions (Fig. VIII-27) are alpine-type peridotites originally composed mainly of olivine and orthopyroxene (harzburgite). They characteristically occur as elongate bodies, commonly faulted, sheared, and highly serpentinized. The ultramafic rocks were emplaced at various times from the late Devonian to the early Jurassic, but mostly during the late Devonian to early Mississippian interval and the Pennsylvanian to late Middle Triassic interval. Several of the bodies, now largely serpentinite, have been re-intruded and squeezed tectonically into younger rocks during one or more of the orogenies that occurred after their initial emplacement as peridotites.

Some of the ultramafic intrusions are restricted largely to belts of thick greenstone, originally basalt and pyroxene andesite, and appear to be coeval with them. These are the McDame Intrusions within the Sylvester Group of Late Devonian and Mississippian age (Gabrielse, 1963), the Atlin Intrusions within the Pennsylvanian and Permian Cache Creek of Atlin Horst (Aitken, 1959), unnamed intrusions in the Triassic Kaslo Group (Cairnes, 1934), and perhaps also those in the lavas of the Lower Jurassic part of the Rossland Group (Little, 1960). Ultramafic rocks are not common in the pyroclastic-rich, younger Mesozoic volcanic sequences. The intimate association between the greenstone and ultramafic rocks suggests a community of origin similar to occurrences elsewhere in the world. Others, however, are intrusions into mixed assemblages of volcanic and sedimentary strata, for instance, the Trembleur Intrusions in the Pinchi Geanticline which cut Permian strata and supplied detritus to Upper Triassic formations (Armstrong, 1949), and the Shulaps body (Leech, 1953) which was emplaced into strata tentatively correlated with Upper Triassic formations and contributed detritus to sediments east of the Yalakom fault, that are possibly of late Early Jurassic age.

Some of the major faults of the western Cordillera, in particular the Pinchi, Shakwak, and Nahlin faults and the Yalakom–Fraser system, may have provided channelways for emplacement of a large amount of ultramafic and associated volcanic material in the Permian and Triassic. These faults, which were generated mainly in the zone between the crystalline rocks of the Coast and Omineca Geanticlines, penetrated to the mantle in the Permian and Triassic and permitted emplacement into the crust of the greatest amount of ultramafic rock in the history of the Cordillera. Subsequent movement along the faults has caused the ultramafic bodies to be displaced so that they now may be in fault contact with adjacent strata.

An exception to the alpine-type are the Tulameen and Polaris bodies. The former consists of a dunite core fringed by clinopyroxenitic rocks, in turn partly bordered by slightly older, undersaturated, alkalic gabbroic rocks similar to Copper Mountain stock, which is dated at 195 m.y. The Tulameen body has intruded the Upper Triassic Nicola Group and has yielded a K–Ar date of 186 m.y., that is, an early Jurassic age. The Polaris body is mainly dunite and olivine-rich peridotite (wehrlite) but it also includes clinopyroxenitic and hornblendic units characteristic of undersaturated ultramafic rocks. K–Ar dates of 164 and 152 m.y. on biotite and hornblende indicate that its age is Middle Jurassic. More than thirty-five similar intrusions in southeastern Alaska are aligned on a northwesterly trend. K–Ar dates from these range from 85 m.y. to 109 m.y. (Lanphere and Eberlein, 1966). Similar bodies may exist in St. Elias Mountains.

PLUTONIC ROCKS

The greatest concentration of plutonic rocks is in the Coast Plutonic Complex and the Omineca Crystalline Belt, especially in the former (Fig. VIII-28). Even though granitic intrusions are common elsewhere in the Cordilleran Orogen their abundance in no way compares to the great volume present in two crystalline belts. Throughout the history of the Cordilleran Geosyncline these geanticlinal belts have been essentially positive and mobile, particularly since the Triassic. They were the sites of repeated uplift and plutonism evidenced not only in the debris shed from time to time and deposited in the adjoining troughs, but also from radiometric data. Clearly, the plutonic rocks, particularly the moderate to high-grade metamorphic rocks, evolved for the most part not in deeply depressed troughs but in the intermittently persistent, uplifted belts marginal to them. Within these belts, then, there were greater concentrations of heat than elsewhere, and from time to time plutonic fronts arose.

Gabrielse and Reesor (1964) indicate that the composition of the plutons in the Omineca Geanticline changes with age from predominantly quartz diorite and monzonite in late Paleozoic, through intermediate types during the Mesozoic, to syenites and quartz monzonites in the Tertiary; furthermore, they conclude that the idea of a granitic series ranging from autochthonous granitized rocks through mobilized material and finally to intrusive granite does not hold. Instead, they consider the plutons to have evolved in successive pulses over a very long period of time. Roddick (1965) has also concluded that the southern part of the Coast Plutonic Complex progressively evolved with continually changing composition over a long period. It appears that many of the plutonic pulses are broadly synchronous with orogenic spasms. Plutonism accompanied the following orogenies: the Hadrynian East Kootenay; the Triassic Tahltanian; the Jurassic Nassian and Inklinian; the Jura-Cretaceous Columbian; and the late Cretaceous to early Tertiary Laramide. Evidence for plutonism accompanying the Devono-Mississippian Cariboan Orogeny is indecisive. Metamorphic rocks occur either as regionally metamorphosed terrane in which the stratigraphy can generally be recognized or as metamorphic complexes in which the stratigraphy is commonly in doubt. The less metamorphosed rocks occur throughout the Omineca Crystalline Belt, commonly exhibiting the Barrovian sequence of metamorphism (kyanite–sillimanite type) and attaining the upper grades of the almandine–amphibolite facies without the development of much granitic material. The metamorphic complexes, widespread in the Coast Plutonic Complex and underlying several large areas in the Omineca Crystalline Belt, include abundant granitic material, particularly in the cores of the gneiss domes. The regionally metamorphosed rocks commonly yield the youngest K–Ar dates, suggesting that the complexes were not only sites of more intense plutonic activity, but also sites of greater heat flow until relatively late in the history of the region.

Yukon Group

Regionally metamorphosed rocks comprising metasediments, metavolcanics, and paragneisses known as the Yukon Group, underlie large areas of Yukon Plateau. Along the boundary with Alaska these rocks are continuous with the Birch Creek Schist of Alaska. Where fossiliferous, the rocks have previously been described, but where the metamorphic grade is high local names are applied, such as Harvey Group in the Glenlyon area, Big Salmon Complex in the Teslin area, and Oblique Creek Formation in the Jennings area.

In the Dawson and McQuesten areas the grade of metamorphism is significantly higher southwest of Tintina Trench than to the northeast. Northeast of the Trench, in Mayo and McQueston areas, great thicknesses of quartzite and schist with some limestone are partly correlative with the Hadrynian. Southwest of Tintina Trench, in Dawson, Ogilvie, and McQuesten areas, a thick section of quartzites, micaceous quartzites, and quartz–mica schists form the Nasina Group. Sericitized and chloritized intrusive rocks of the Klondike Schist and granitic gneiss termed the Pelly Gneiss are probably in part equivalent to the less metamorphosed Hadrynian rocks to the northeast. Limestones associated with metasediments just south of Yukon River at the Alaska Boundary have yielded crinoid ossicles that indicate a Paleozoic age. In the Dawson area it seems probable that two main sequences of rocks are involved in the regional metamorphism: a lower one of Hadrynian age, and an upper one, including the ultramafic bodies, greenstone, and basic intrusions of Paleozoic age, and possibly in large part Devonian and Mississippian.

Along the Coast Geanticline in southwest Yukon Territory, the Yukon Group consists largely of quartz–mica schists, quartz–biotite–feldspar gneisses, crystalline limestones, slate, and quartzite. These metasedimentary rocks of possibly Precambrian age and later include minor hornblende and chlorite schist presumably derived from volcanic rocks.

Metamorphic rocks in southern Cassiar Mountains include strata as young as Mississippian and probably as old as Cambrian. The Oblique Creek Formation consists of thick sequences of quartz–albite–mica gneiss, albite–actinolite schist, meta-chert, conglomerate, greenstone, and meta-tuff in Jennings and Wolf Lake areas. To the northwest in Teslin area, the Big Salmon Complex includes intercalated crystalline limestones with Mississippian fossils. Farther north, quartz–mica schist and gneiss, granitic gneiss, quartzite, and crystalline limestone are the equivalent of Cambrian and younger strata.

Northeast of Tintina Trench in Finlayson Lake, Frances Lake, and Watson Lake areas, granitic gneisses, characterized by opalescent quartz grains, and associated schists and phyllites were evidently derived from Hadrynian clastic rocks.

K–Ar ages ranging from 178 to 222 m.y. suggest that the Yukon Group was regionally metamorphosed during the Tahltanian Orogeny, and at least locally during the Inklinian Orogeny. The general lack of metamorphism in Upper Triassic rocks suggests that much of the metamorphism took place in the earlier orogeny.

Horseranch Group

The Horseranch Group, in Cassiar Mountains, comprises regionally metamorphosed and locally granitized metasedimentary rocks similar to those of the Wolverine Complex but considerably less granitic (Gabrielse, 1963). It contains recrystallized and locally feldspathized quartzite, quartz–mica schist, granitic gneiss, augen gneiss, hornfels, skarn, and crystalline limestone. In places granitic pegmatite sills and dykes are common. The group is exposed in a fault-bounded, doubly plunging anticline about 30 miles long; stratigraphic relationships are unknown. In gross lithology the Horseranch Group most closely resembles the Lower Cambrian Atan Group. A K–Ar age of 57 m.y. was obtained on muscovite from granitic rocks at the north end of Horseranch Range but whether this dates the regional metamorphism is not known.

Wolverine Complex

The Wolverine Metamorphic Complex in Omineca Mountains is composed of highly metamorphosed and granitized rocks of Proterozoic and early Paleozoic age (Armstrong, 1949; Roots, 1954). It forms the eastern part of central Omineca Geanticline. Granitic material, zones of feldspathization, and pegmatite are concentrated along northeast-trending belts and domes. The domes and accompanying depressions result, in part, from the intersections of north-northwesterly and west-northwesterly

PLATE VIII-7
Veined gneiss of Shuswap Metamorphic Complex, intensely folded, in core of Thor-Odin Dome, central Monashee Mountains, British Columbia.

folds. The former trend, characterized by crenulations and wrinkle lineations of nearly constant orientation, are considered by Roots to have been deformed by the moderately open folds with the latter trend. Furthermore, because the isograds are apparently parallel with the stratigraphic succession and are folded by west-northwest-trending folds Roots argued that the metamorphism was developed during the earlier folding. Schistosity in the complex and adjoining less metamorphosed rocks of the Tenakihi and Ingenika Groups is also parallel with the bedding.

Roots considered that the plutonism took place in early Paleozoic as Wolverine debris occurs in a conglomerate he mapped as Mississippian. However, the conglomerate could be late Lower Cretaceous in which case the plutonism could be mid-Mesozoic and contemporaneous with that in the Shuswap Metamorphic Complex. Upper Jurassic dates on a muscovite–biotite pair of 139 m.y. and 143 m.y. have been obtained from the Misinchinka schist in the Rocky Mountain Trench adjacent to the Wolverine Complex, but the K–Ar dates from the Wolverine Complex fall into two groups, one ranging from 38 m.y. to 43 m.y. and the other 22 m.y. to 29 m.y.

Shuswap Complex

The Shuswap Metamorphic Complex, which underlies the southern culmination in the Omineca Geanticline, comprises rocks ranging in age from Proterozoic to early Mesozoic which are metamorphosed to upper almandine–amphibolite facies. Although many domes are present in the complex, it is dominated by three, paired gneiss domes occurring at 50 mile intervals along the eastern margin. These domes [Valhalla (Reesor, 1965; *Frontispiece*), Thor-Odin (Reesor, 1966), and Frenchman's Cap (Wheeler, 1965)] have cores of veined augen gneiss and granite gneiss (Pl. VIII-7) intertongued with and mantled by hybrid metasedimentary gneiss and schist, the outer part of which is riddled with pegmatite and leucogranite and surrounded by a fringing zone of low-grade rocks. Nowhere in the cores of the domes has an ancient crystalline basement been identified. On the contrary, Reesor (1966) concluded that the core of Thor-Odin Dome is composed of Windermere and lower Paleozoic strata. The pegmatite-rich zone is particularly extensive west and northwest of Frenchman's Cap Dome and west and south of Thor-Odin Dome. The fringe of low-grade rocks is commonly featured either by a zone of crushing and

PLATE VIII-8. Fold-mullion structures parallel with axes of recumbent folds in hybrid gneiss of Shuswap Metamorphic Complex mantling Valhalla Dome, southern Selkirk Mountains, British Columbia.

mylonitization, or by a rapid gradation from sillimanite–almandine–muscovite and staurolite-bearing rocks to greenschist. The distinctive structural style of the complex, apart from the development of domes, is an easterly trending lineation marked by mineral orientation and the axes of isoclinal and recumbent folds (Pl. VIII-8).

In the salient northeast of Revelstoke, the foliation within wedges of gneiss emplaced into Shuswap gneisses antedates the formation of the Shuswap gneissosity according to J. V. Ross. The earliest recognized structures belonging to the development of the Shuswap gneisses are large isoclinal recumbent folds. These, and the local, smaller isoclinal folds refolding them, probably result partly from flowage off rising and expanding easterly trending warps on the present sites of the domes and partly synchronously with subsequent diapirism. Following the movement that developed an easterly trending penetrative mineral lineation, the complex was redeformed resulting in superimposed northerly and northwesterly trending folds and lineations. This later deformation produced domes and depressions that formed at shallow levels and included the upward diapiric movement of the cores of the domes and possibly also upthrusting of gneiss wedges. As the metamorphism waned, movement along the eastern edge of the complex induced cataclasis, mylonitization, alteration, and late faulting with brecciation.

The petrogenic evolution within the Shuswap Complex has been established only in Valhalla Dome (Reesor, 1965) and is summarized in Table VIII-1 together with

TABLE VIII-1 *Summary of events in evolution of Valhalla Complex (Reesor, 1965)*

Stage		Structural Events	Petrogenic Events
Late Stage ↑	Locally confined	8. Late faulting in 'crushed zone'	8. Pyritization
		7. Minor faulting and jointing in complex	7. Basalt dyke intrusion in western Valhalla. Sericitization and epidotization in 'crushed zone' east of Valhalla Complex
		6. Igneous emplacement under regional tensional conditions	6. Intrusion of hornblende and/or augite monzonite both east and west of Valhalla Complex
Second Phase	Destructive	5. Diapiric upward movement of cores of Valhalla and Passmore Domes	5. Possibly some synchronous emplacement of massive leucogranite in zone west of Valhalla Complex
		4. Strong, penetrative, cataclastic flowage in all layers of all rock types of eastern part of Valhalla Complex. Easiest relief of stress vertically upward	4. Minor pegmatite and pegmatitic granite. Metamorphism in garnet-sillimanite subfacies of amphibolite facies
		Termination of principal constructional phase of evolution	
First Phase ↑	Constructive	3. Minor structural impulses, with gradual growth of antiformal masses. Shape and location of Passmore Dome dependent on formation of Valhalla Dome and thus slightly after	3. Leucogranite and early pegmatite in all layers of the complex. Grey granodiorite–gneiss in all layers
		2. Initial uplift of Valhalla Dome with original form determined in east-west elongate antiformal complex. Coincident flowage of 'hybrid gneiss' to the flanks of Valhalla Dome governed by shape of the confining space. Initial syntectonic movement confined so that easiest relief of stress horizontal	2. Metamorphism to perhaps hornblende granulite facies, with partial melting of pelitic and semi-pelitic rocks. Horizontal emplacement of quartz diorite and granodiorite of 'veined gneiss' in Valhalla Dome and upper layer ('mixed gneiss') of Passmore Dome
		1. Possible earlier structural episodes not recognized	1. Deposition of thick succession of pelites, semi-pelites, quartzite, minor limestone. Minor, conformable, basic igneous rocks

associated structural events. Reesor noted that " . . . no single process, and no single associated structural episode is responsible for the formations of the complex. It is, rather, the sum of many processes, structural and petrogenic, evolving successively through a long period." He noted that the early structural episode was characterized by horizontal movement of lenticular migmatitic lenses of augen granodiorite gneiss in the core. This was followed by accumulation of granitic and pegmatitic material. There had been accumulation and growth rather than compression and shortening. After stagnation, a second phase followed that was essentially deformational and expressed as upward diapiric movement. The least migmatized, though highly metamorphosed metasediments, are lowest in the structural succession and therefore neither simple magmatic emplacement from below nor simple granitization in situ is possible for the formation of the augen gneiss. Furthermore, at some levels, and at some localities, the amount of quartzo-feldspathic material is so low that even the melting or transforming of all the rocks would be insufficient to produce the amount of granite present. Reesor therefore concluded that some of the granitic material was derived from beyond the complex in a succession of impulses, although some may have originated from melting in situ.

PLATE VIII-9. Agmatite, Coast Plutonic Complex, Douglas Channel west of Kiltsuit River, British Columbia. Aplitic leucogranite veining and surrounding angular blocks of granular amphibolite and granodiorite.

Coast Plutonic Complex

The Coast Plutonic Complex extends the length of Coast Mountains for 1,100 miles, merging northward with the Yukon Crystalline Platform and terminating against the Cascade Fold Belt in the south. The complex is composed mainly of foliated and non-foliated granitoid plutonic rocks but also contains large areas of metamorphic rocks (Roddick, *et al.,* 1966) (Pl. VIII-9). An irregular belt of narrow, elongate, steep-walled roof pendants of metasedimentary rocks stretches southeastward from within the Wrangell–Revillagigedo gneiss belt on the west side of the complex in southeastern Alaska to near the eastern side, near Bella Coola. The metasedimentary rocks range from greenschist to almandine–amphibolite facies and comprise schist, quartzite, limestone, and conglomerate, locally carrying granitic clasts. East of the metasediments and apparently underlying them is a belt of gneiss and migmatite that has a gently dipping foliation over large areas and locally exhibits recumbent folds with easterly and northerly trending axes. The gneiss may be overlain and intruded by granitic rocks, or grade into them. East of Kemano the gneisses appear to underlie Permian metasediments and rocks forming part of the pre-Hazelton Tahtsa Complex (Stuart, 1960).

More or less homogeneous plutonic rocks form a large part of the complex between latitudes 52° and 55°. Quartz diorite and diorite are abundant west of the metasedimentary belt whereas granodiorite and quartz monzonite bodies occur throughout the complex. Granodiorite is characteristic of the composite plutons such as the northeast-trending apophyses near Skeena River, regarded by Duffell and Souther (1964) as forceful intrusions. The quartz monzonite bodies are distinct, young plutons, some forming the core of the granodiorite bodies. Syenite and granite are rare and occur only in small plutons in an east-northeast-trending belt west of Bella Coola. Roddick, *et al.* (1966) stated that a quartz diorite line cannot be drawn through the complex, but remarked that the potassium feldspar content east of the metasedimentary belt is greater than to the west. In southeastern Alaska, south of Stikine River, quartz diorite is dominant on both sides of the Wrangell–Revillagigedo gneiss belt but granodiorite and quartz monzonite are more common to the east.

Northwest of Stikine River the Coast Plutonic Complex contains narrow, steep-walled belts of metasediments and amphibolite but is composed mainly of an interlocking system of discrete plutons. Near the British Columbia–Yukon boundary leucogranite and granodiorite plutons intrude older foliated quartz diorite that now appears as a matrix between the younger plutons (Christie, 1957). Farther south, near Stikine River, the eastern part of the complex contains pre-Late Triassic foliated diorite plutons and metamorphic rocks and younger, steep-walled plutons of quartz monzonite, whereas the axial part is characterized by granodiorite.

The southernmost part of the complex has been studied in the greatest detail (Roddick, 1965). It is a heterogeneous complex of plutons ranging in composition from diorite and quartz diorite to granodiorite. Gabbro and granite are rare. The average composition is that of quartz diorite with hornblende exceeding biotite, and potassic feldspar totalling about 5 per cent. This part of the complex is characterized by diffuse interplutonic contacts, in contrast with those north of Stikine River, and contains steep-walled, generally northwesterly elongated roof pendants partly bounded by faults. There is no appreciable change in composition of either the pendant rocks or the adjoining plutons over a vertical range of 7,000 feet.

Opinions differ concerning the mode of origin of the plutonic rocks in the southernmost part of the complex. Bacon (1957) and others emphasize that the invaded rocks, which had previously been metamorphosed, have not been greatly disturbed by the emplacement of granitic rock and invoked the passive intrusion of andesitic magma. Roddick (1965) concluded that the granitic rocks formed from 'wet' pre-existing metamorphic rocks by evolution through a plutonic series, mainly from hornblende diorite towards biotite granite in the course of a long period of retrograde metamorphism during the gradual uplift of the Coast Geanticline. The evolution was accompanied by mass movement of plutonic rock partly bounded by synplutonic faults and partly as plastic, saltdome-like intrusions. Roddick has based this conclusion on numerous microscopic and megascopic data in which the occurrence of relict dykes is particularly striking (Roddick and Armstrong, 1959). The 'synplutonic' dykes intruded earlier consolidated plutons and were eventually partly transformed into granitic rock by continuing metasomatism. Locally this happened after the dykes were fractured, faulted, or deformed within remobilized plutons.

The Coast Plutonic Complex exhibits several periods of plutonism. It is not known when these began or whether the complex experienced the late Ordovician period of granitic emplacement known in southeastern Alaska or the pre-Devonian metamorphism and diorite intrusion evident in Cascade Mountains and on San Juan Islands. The earliest phase of plutonism for which there is evidence took place during the mid-Triassic Tahltanian Orogeny in the Stikine River region, followed there by the early Jurassic Inklinian Orogeny. Episodes of plutonism elsewhere, perhaps coeval in part with the Tahltanian or Inklinian phases, took place mainly in the southeastern part of the complex. K–Ar dates, ranging from 139 m.y. to 95 m.y., indicate episodes of plutonism in the western third of the complex during the early and middle phases of Columbian Orogeny. The K–Ar dates ranging from 77 m.y. to 42 m.y. come mainly from quartz monzonite and granodiorite plutons in the central and eastern parts of the complex. Some plutons intrude Upper Cretaceous strata and support radiometric evidence for granitic emplacement during latest Cretaceous and early Tertiary time. Many of the young plutons have been intruded along the eastern margin of the complex into regions where granitic rocks were emplaced in the early Mesozoic. Thus the Coast Geanticline, an uplifted zone that was emergent since the mid-Triassic, was for the same period a zone of repetitive plutonism.

Cascade Complex

In Cascade Fold Belt, clastic sediments as young as Albian are folded, faulted, and intruded by a granitic stock with a K–Ar date of 84 m.y. The deformation is referred, accordingly, to the late phase of the Columbian Orogeny. However, in the northwest steep reverse faults, dipping southwest or locally northeast, involve Upper Cretaceous volcanics, and some deformation also took place later. In western Cascade Mountains early Lower Cretaceous and older beds are involved in westerly and northwesterly directed recumbent folds and thrusts transported over an autochthone featured by a northeasterly trending, faulted anticline with pre-Devonian basement in its core (J. W. H. Monger). The recumbent structures are redeformed by northwesterly trending warps, faults, kink bands, and minor conjugate folds, and in Washington State are overlain unconformably by late Upper Cretaceous clastic sediments.

Cascade Fold Belt underwent various types of regional metamorphism at different times. In the core of the belt the migmatitic Custer gneiss developed from the late Paleozoic Hozameen Group (McTaggart and Thompson, 1967) during regional metamorphism of Barrovian type in latest Paleozoic or earliest Mesozoic time, contemporaneously with the Skagit metamorphism in Washington (Misch, 1966). Later, parts of the Hozameen Group were subjected to low pressure, regional or contact metamorphism featured by andalusite. Finally, in latest Cretaceous time, coeval with the emplacement of the tonalite and diorite of the Spuzzum Intrusions, dated at 76 m.y., the metamorphic rocks were raised to sillimanite grade.

The western part of the Cascade Fold Belt is characterized by regional metamorphism of glaucophane schist type which in Washington is considered by Misch to be of Permo-Triassic age. In the Cascade Mountains of Canada J. W. H. Monger has discovered lawsonite in Mesozoic clastic sediments but is uncertain whether it is of detrital or metamorphic origin.

MESOZOIC

Triassic

Tectonic Summary

Lower Triassic rocks are not known in the western parts of the Cordilleran Geosyncline in Canada although they are present a few miles south in Washington. Middle Triassic ribbon chert, argillite, greenstone, and possibly coeval ultramafic rocks, and minor limestone occur locally in the northwestern and central parts, apparently lying conformably on the Permian. In southernmost parts of the geosyncline, Middle Triassic sediments featured by sharpstone conglomerate, unconformably overlie late Paleozoic

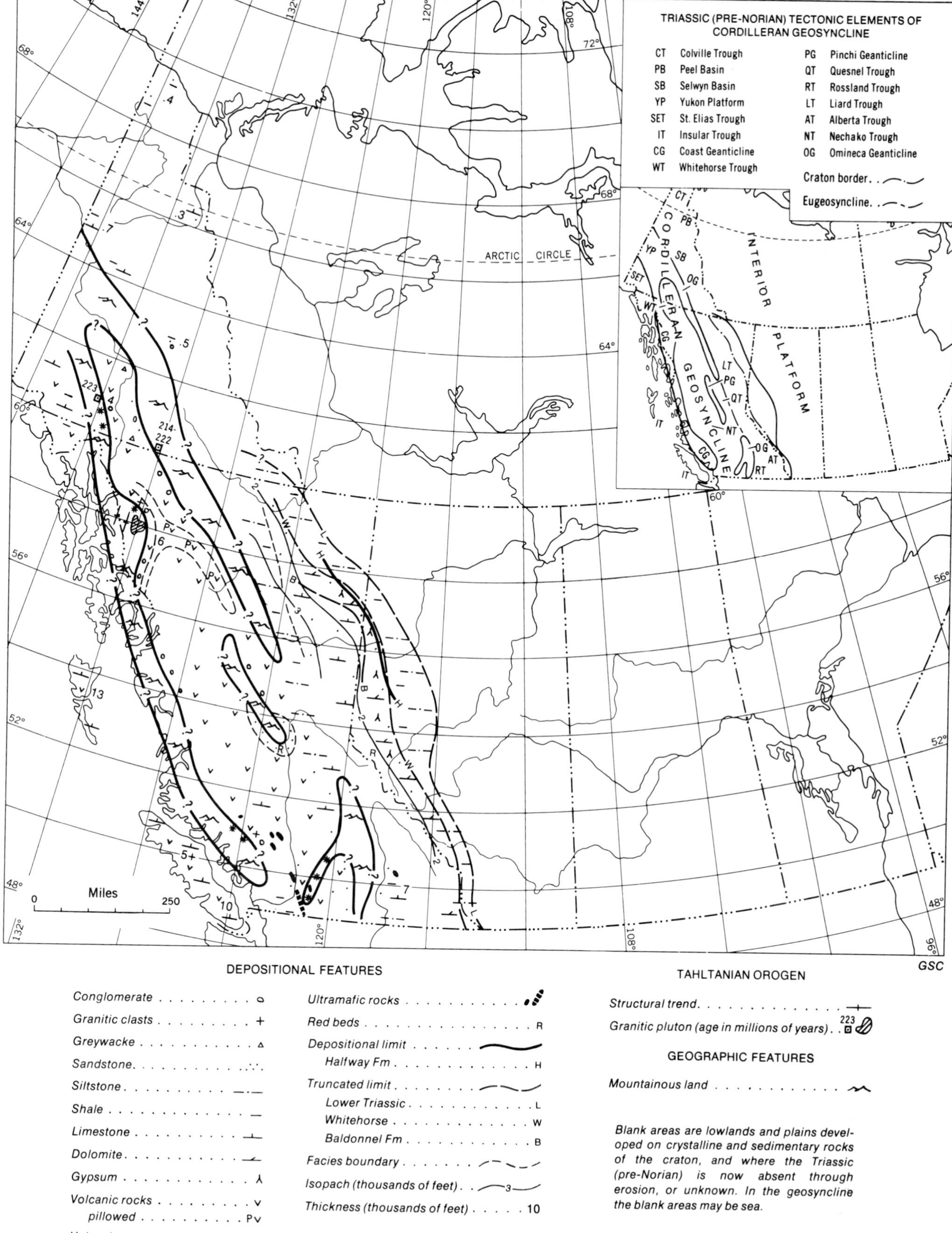

FIGURE VIII-29. Upper Triassic, Karnian, sedimentation and tectonism in Western Canada. Includes Lower and Middle Triassic sediments of Liard and Alberta Troughs and some features of the early and mid-Triassic Tahltanian Orogeny.

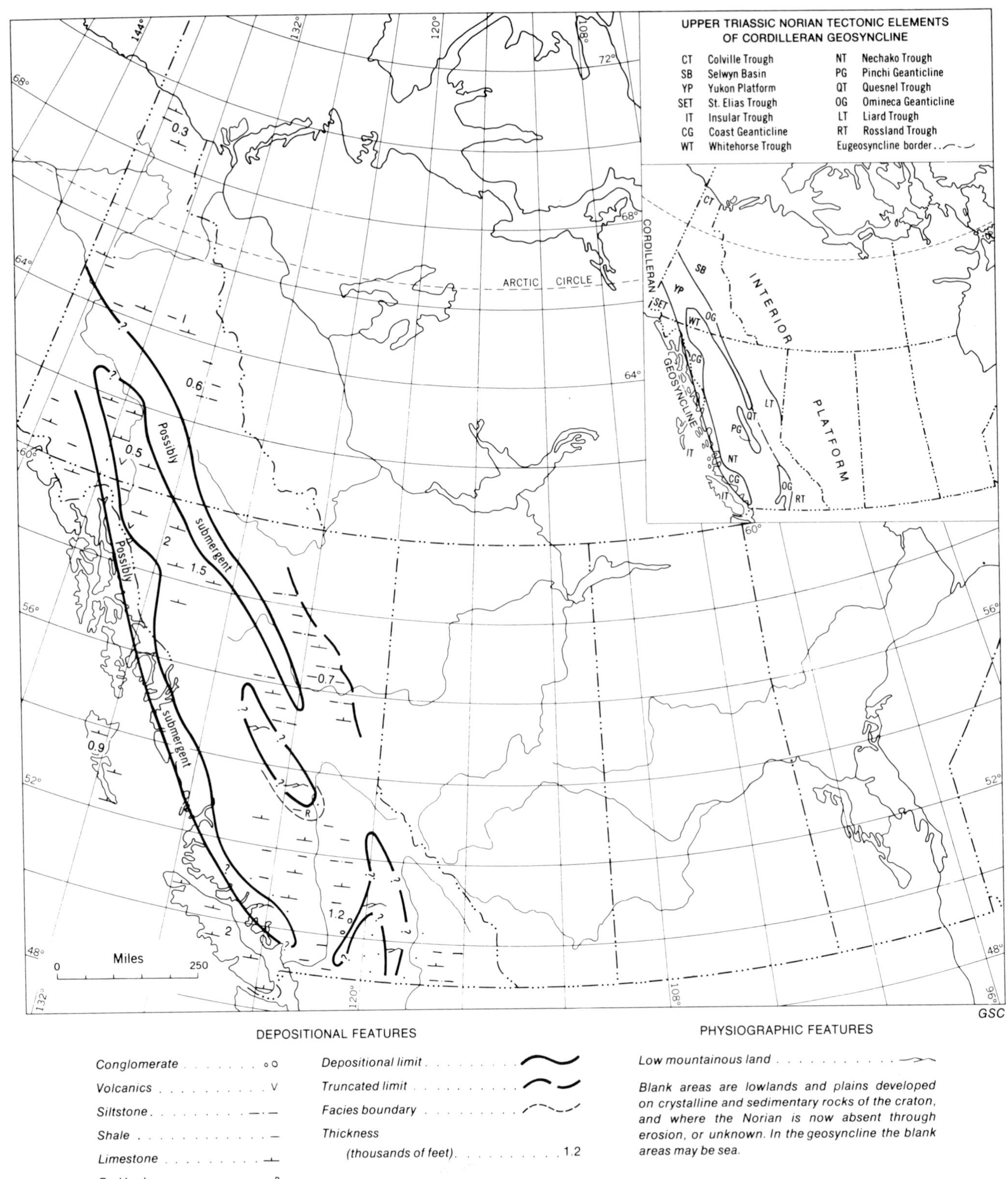
UPPER TRIASSIC NORIAN TECTONIC ELEMENTS OF CORDILLERAN GEOSYNCLINE
CT Colville Trough
SB Selwyn Basin
YP Yukon Platform
SET St. Elias Trough
IT Insular Trough
CG Coast Geanticline
WT Whitehorse Trough
NT Nechako Trough
PG Pinchi Geanticline
QT Quesnel Trough
OG Omineca Geanticline
LT Liard Trough
RT Rossland Trough
Eugeosyncline border
CORDILLERAN GEOSYNCLINE
INTERIOR PLATFORM
ARCTIC CIRCLE
Possibly submergent
Possibly submergent
0.3
0.6
0.5
2
1.5
0.7
0.9
1.2
2
Miles
0
250
GSC
DEPOSITIONAL FEATURES
Conglomerate
Volcanics
Siltstone
Shale
Limestone
Red beds
Depositional limit
Truncated limit
Facies boundary
Thickness (thousands of feet) 1.2
PHYSIOGRAPHIC FEATURES
Low mountainous land
Blank areas are lowlands and plains developed on crystalline and sedimentary rocks of the craton, and where the Norian is now absent through erosion, or unknown. In the geosyncline the blank areas may be sea.

FIGURE VIII-30. Upper Triassic, Norian, sedimentation and tectonism in Western Canada.

rocks. The western sequences represent generally quiescent eugeosynclinal conditions possibly prevailing from the Permian. The Omineca Geanticline, an intermittently emergent arch during most of the period, separates the eugeosyncline from the miogeosynclinal Alberta and Liard Troughs (Fig. VIII-29). Lower Triassic siltstone and shale in the troughs disconformably overlie the early Upper Permian, the hiatus increasing eastward on the craton through overlap and bevelling of the Permian and Carboniferous. The entire western margin of the craton was probably emergent and stable, these conditions prevailing throughout the period. Triassic red beds are known in Williston Basin in the northern United States, but if formerly they extended into Canada, they have been removed by pre-Jurassic erosion.

In the late Middle Triassic, parts of the Cordilleran Geosyncline underwent deformation and plutonic activity constituting the Tahltanian Orogeny. Uplift at the end of the orogeny established the main tectonic elements that prevailed until mid-Jurassic time. The early Upper Triassic, Karnian, is represented in Insular Trough mainly by a thick succession of submarine basaltic flows and in Whitehorse Trough principally by andesitic and basaltic flows, pyroclastics, and clastics containing volcanic and mid-Triassic and earlier debris. The latter for the most part were derived from islands and volcanoes forming Coast Geanticline and Stikine Arch. Similar volcanics and volcanic clastics accumulated during the Karnian in most of Nechako and Quesnel Troughs although some red beds were deposited around the fringes of Pinchi Geanticline. Quartzose clastics derived from southernmost Omineca Geanticline were laid down in eastern Quesnel and Rossland Troughs. In Liard and Alberta Troughs siltstone and sandstone accumulated, grading eastward, along the margin of the craton, into an evaporitic and red bed facies with basal shoreline and offshore sandbars.

In the late Upper Triassic, Norian (Fig. VIII-30), volcanism persisted in Whitehorse Trough adjacent to the Coast Geanticline and Stikine Arch, and in Nechako and Quesnel Troughs. Clastic sediments accumulated as red beds around the uplifted Pinchi Geanticline and were also derived from the southern part of the Coast Geanticline and parts of the Omineca Geanticline. The latter was locally covered by thin limestone. Clastics were deposited in Insular Trough. During the latest Norian carbonate deposition prevailed throughout much of the geosyncline, as the sections were remarkably thin but complete in the northern and eastern elements, and indicated quiescent conditions of deposition to the end of the Triassic.

Lower and Middle Triassic of Western Cordilleran Geosyncline

An assemblage of argillite, chert, greenstone, and minor limestone similar to that in the Cache Creek Group overlies apparently conformably the youngest Permian at several localities. This assemblage includes unfossiliferous rocks in the Atlin Horst, regionally metamorphosed beds yielding Ladinian *Daonella* in the Stikine Arch (Souther, 1959), and unmetamorphosed strata containing *Daonella* in St. Elias Trough. The Pavilion Group, containing hexacorals, occurs near Lillooet close to the southwestern end of the Pinchi Geanticline. Trettin (1961) considered the Pavilion Group to overlie the Upper Permian Marble Canyon Formation but Campbell and Tipper (1966) regard some of the Pavilion Group to be an older part of the Cache Creek Group that has been thrust over the Marble Canyon Formation. Near Greenwood an assemblage of sharpstone conglomerate, siltstone, and limestone with *Daonella* lies with angular unconformity on upper Paleozoic rocks of the southern Omineca Geanticline. The Fennell Formation of pillowed greenstone at the southeastern end of Quesnel Trough underlies fossiliferous Karnian beds. It and beds containing *Daonella* or *Halobia* along the eastern Coast Mountains near Skeena River and near Chilko Lake may be of Middle Triassic age. Near Skeena River the Triassic beds contain limestone boulders and chert-pebble conglomerate lying unconformably on Permian beds.

Tahltanian Orogeny

In the Middle Triassic, during the Tahltanian Orogeny, parts of the Cordilleran eugeosyncline were deformed, intruded by diorite and granodiorite, and uplifted (Fig. VIII-29). An early phase is evident in the southernmost Cordillera near Greenwood, where Middle and possibly Lower Triassic sharpstone conglomerate unconformably overlies upper Paleozoic rocks. A late phase in late Ladinian time affected ancestral Stikine Arch where Middle Triassic and earlier strata were folded along northerly trends and were more severely deformed and metamorphosed than the succeeding Upper Triassic and Lower Jurassic beds that were later folded along northwesterly trends. Plutonism during the Triassic in the Coast and Omineca Geanticlines is indicated by the following K–Ar dates: 206 and 227 m.y. from dioritic boulders in Lower Jurassic conglomerates on Stikine Arch, presumably derived from a nearby pluton (Fig. VIII-28); 223 m.y. from a hornblende–biotite granodiorite in the Coast Geanticline in southern Yukon Territory; 214 to 222 m.y. from muscovite–biotite–albite–epidote gneiss in the northern Omineca Geanticline; and 205 m.y. from greenschist and a granitic pluton in the southern Omineca Geanticline. Widespread uplift is inferred from the erosional unconformity between Upper and Middle Triassic beds in the northern Coast Geanticline and the southern Omineca Geanticline, and between the Upper Triassic and upper-Paleozoic along the flanks of the Pinchi Geanticline and in Cascade Mountains.

It is uncertain how much deformation of upper Paleozoic rocks in the Pinchi Geanticline took place during the Tahltanian Orogeny. The structures in these rocks are roughly parallel with the long axes of the geanticline and are characterized mainly by moderately tight, generally upright folds in relatively competent limestone beds and by more irregular and severe deformation in the argillaceous and cherty rocks. On the other hand the Mesozoic rocks of adjoining Nechako and Quesnel Troughs are gently folded, warped, and faulted and this contrast in tectonic style may indicate an orogeny in the Pinchi Geanticline. It may reflect, however, an earlier pulse in Late Pennsylvanian or Early Permian time or merely differences in structural behaviour as both successions were probably deformed during later Mesozoic orogenies.

Upper Triassic of Western Cordilleran Geosyncline

The stratigraphy of the Upper Triassic in the western Cordilleran Geosyncline is best known along the flanks of Whitehorse Trough and in Insular Trough. In these regions the Karnian and Norian rocks are fossiliferous and easily recognized, but in Nechako and Quesnel Troughs volcanic rocks are widespread and fossils scarce.

Whitehorse Trough. Karnian deposits along the western side of the Whitehorse Trough (Figs. VIII-28, -29, -31a) are included in the lower part of the Lewes River Group of southern Yukon (Tozer, 1958; Wheeler, 1961) and in the Stuhini Group and its eastern clastic facies, the King Salmon Formation, exposed along the eastern part of northern Coast Mountains (Fig. VIII-32a, b) (Souther and Armstrong, 1966). Along this belt Karnian beds are predominantly volcanic. The more westerly comprise andesitic flows, pyroclastics, and abundant volcanic clastics derived partly from the deposition of pyroclastics in water and partly from the erosion of volcanic rocks. Some of the volcanic rocks are apparently subaerial and the sequences contain disconformities resulting from local uplift and the building of volcanic cones. Gneiss and granodiorite clasts in the lower parts of the Stuhini Group suggest an early Karnian uplift in the western part of Stikine Arch and that the volcanic rocks were deposited on a terrain deformed and metamorphosed during the Tahltanian Orogeny. The Lewes River Group grades eastward into greenstone and graded-bedded volcanic arenite,

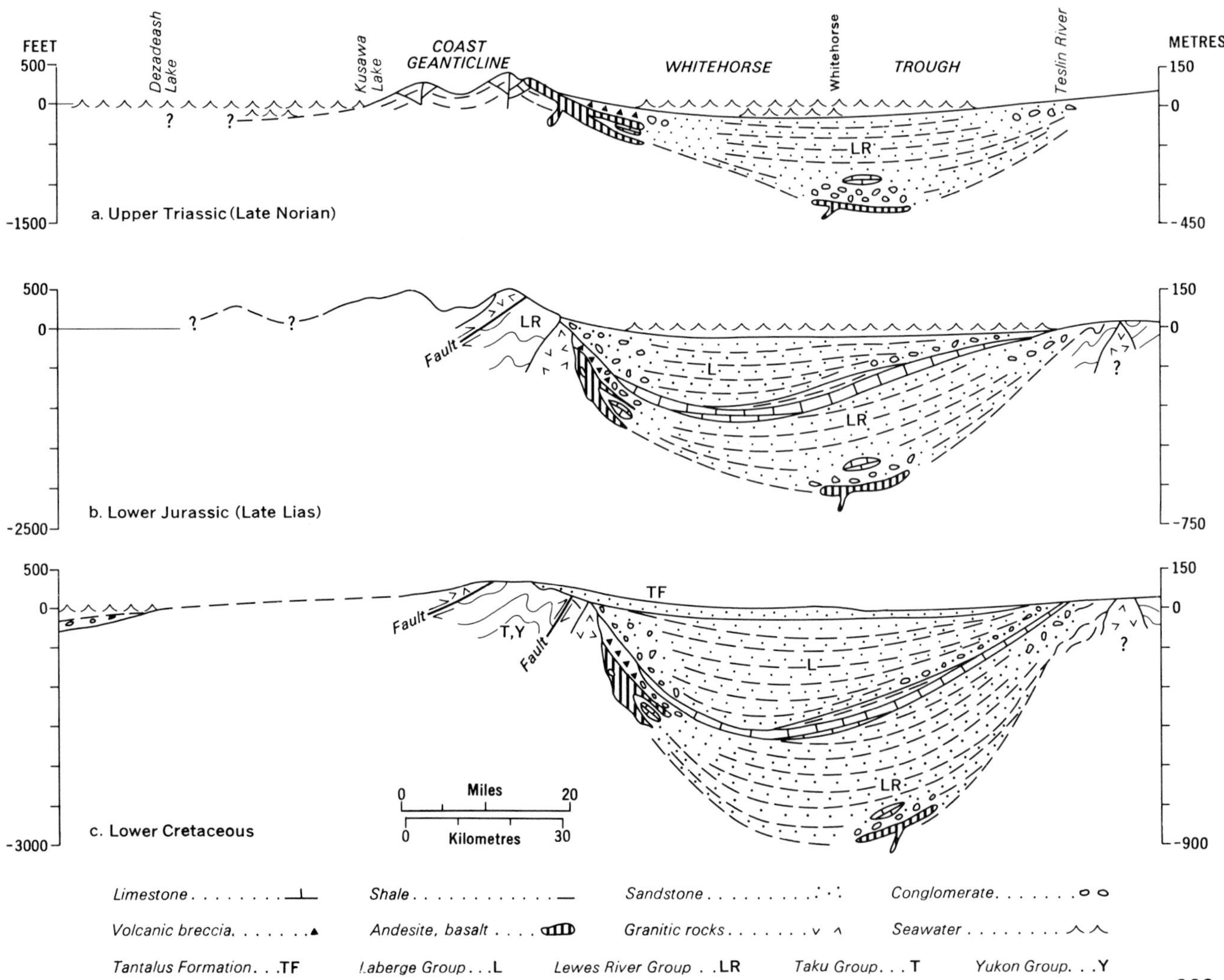

FIGURE VIII-31. Diagrammatic restored sections across Whitehorse Trough, Yukon Territory, during the Mesozoic era (Wheeler, 1961).

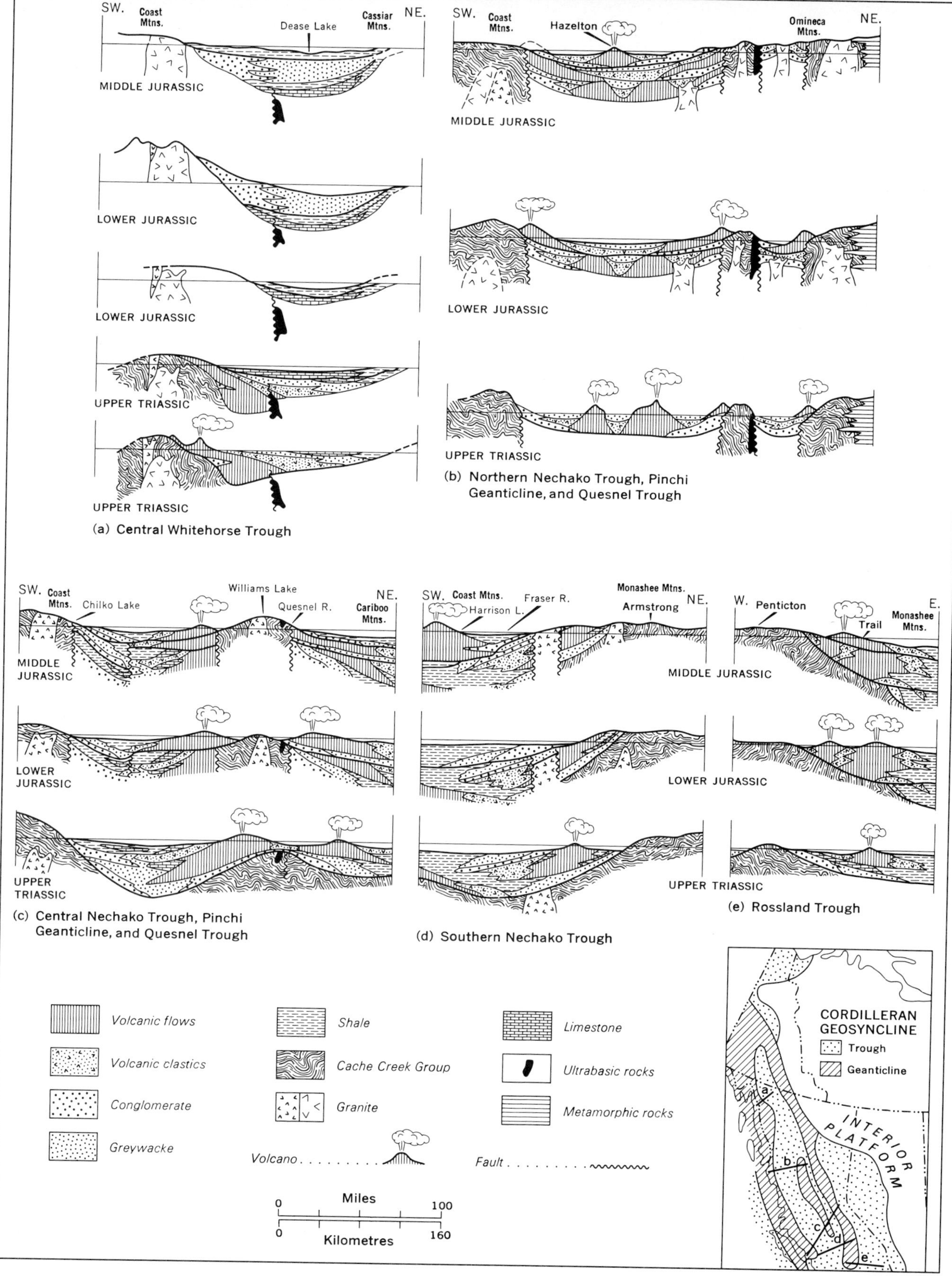

FIGURE VIII-32. Diagrammatic restored sections across Whitehorse, Nechako, Quesnel, and Rossland Troughs of the Cordilleran Geosyncline from Upper Triassic to Middle Jurassic times (Souther and Armstrong, 1966; Campbell, 1966).

whereas the more easterly outcrops of the Stuhini Group include spilitic pillowed basalt more than 6,000 feet thick that forms an arcuate belt. Still farther east volcanic clastic and fine-grained sedimentary rocks are predominant.

Volcanic rocks are much less extensive in the Norian than in the Karnian as they are restricted principally to the western exposures of the Lewes River Group where they overlie a mid-Norian *Halobia* fauna and underlie limestone carrying latest Norian *Spondylospira lewesensis.* The volcanic rocks comprise about 2,500 feet of andesitic and basaltic flows and pyroclastics. The latter carry fragments as long as 8 inches and were probably derived from sources no more than 5 or 10 miles to the west. The pyroclastics become finer eastward and, east of Yukon River, pass into graded-bedded volcanic arenite deposited in the central part of Whitehorse Trough. The arenite is overlain by late Norian argillite containing *Monotis subcircularis* succeeded by limestone yielding *Spondylospira.* These late Norian sediments grade farther northeastward, near Teslin River, into an assemblage of greywacke, limestone, and some pebble-conglomerate with greenstone and chert clasts deposited along the northeastern margin of Whitehorse Trough.

In Stikine Arch the upper part of the volcanic Stuhini Group may be partly Norian. The overlying sediments, principally limestones of the Sinwa Formation, are definitely Norian. This limestone extends discontinuously across the Whitehorse Trough to the Atlin Horst and indicates that the latest Norian was a period of tectonic quiescence within Whitehorse Trough.

Nechako and Quesnel Troughs. Much of the Interior Plateau of British Columbia and the southern Omineca Mountains is underlain by the poorly exposed and sparsely fossiliferous Upper Triassic and Lower Jurassic Takla and Nicola Groups and related strata that were deposited in the Nechako and Quesnel Troughs (Figs. VIII-29, 32c, d) (Cockfield, 1948; Tipper, 1959). The Upper Triassic rocks are predominantly dark grey to dark green basic andesite and basalt flows with augite phenocrysts, pyroclastics, and volcanic conglomerate and arenite. Intercalated within the volcanics are minor sedimentary rocks. Dark grey to black shaly limestones typically carry Karnian fauna in the south-central part of the region whereas grey limestone and dark shales commonly yield Norian fossils. The Takla Group fringing the Pinchi Geanticline near Prince George is composed of red and brown shales, black limestone, and coarse conglomerate. The latter contain clasts as large as 18 inches in diameter of andesite, porphyritic andesite, quartz, and chert, apparently derived from the Cache Creek Group as a result of uplift of the Pinchi Geanticline. Near Fort St. James the Takla Group contains clasts of serpentine in conglomerate and grains of chromite in the matrix that were derived from ultramafic intrusions emplaced into the Cache Creek Group of the Pinchi Geanticline (Armstrong, 1949).

Volcanic rocks of the Nicola Group are most abundant and the pyroclastics are coarsest along a north- to northeast-trending belt south of Kamloops where they probably represent an axis of late Triassic volcanism (Fig. VIII-29). To the east near Hedley, equivalent strata contain considerable quartzose clastic sediments (Rice, 1947) that must have had a siliceous source farther east, in the Omineca Geanticline. Furthermore, Nicola and equivalent strata apparently overlie older rocks with erosional unconformity west of Okanagan Valley (Cockfield, 1948). To the west the volcanic rocks of the Nicola Group pass into clastic rocks, as in western Cascade Mountains the Cultus shales disconformably overlie the Chilliwack Group. Farther north, near Bridge River, the Noel, Hurley, and Tyaughton Formations are principally clastics intercalated with some andesitic volcanics constituting the Pioneer Formation. The Tyaughton Formation ranges in age from Norian to Hettangian and contains Rhaetian fossils. It is featured by near-shore coquina-bearing limestone interbedded with red and green conglomerate, the clasts of which are mainly volcanic rocks, chert, some argillite, and rare granitic rocks (H. W. Tipper). This facies is indicative of the southwestern margin of Nechako Trough, as the sediments are derived from the uplifted Coast Geanticline.

Omineca Geanticline. Late Karnian or Norian limestone, 30 feet thick, lies on Permian (?) volcanic and sedimentary rocks on the east side of Cassiar Mountains (Gabrielse, 1963), the remnant indicating that during the late Triassic in this region the Omineca Geanticline was slightly depressed. To the southeast, near Prince George and in Rocky Mountain Trench fossiliferous Upper Triassic clastic rocks occur, along with volcanic rocks similar to the Takla Group. The regions east of Okanagan Valley now underlain by the Shuswap Metamorphic Complex and granitic plutons were probably a source not only for the quartzose clastics near Hedley but also for part of the Slocan Group that was deposited in Rossland Trough to the east.

Rossland Trough. Typical argillaceous flysch of the Slocan and Ymir Groups underlies the inner or western part of Kootenay Arc. Fossils dated only as Triassic have been obtained from the Slocan but none occurs in the Ymir. The thickness of the Slocan Group is controversial, estimates ranging from 6,800 feet to 37,000 feet. Nevertheless the thickness is considerable and it would appear that the sediments accumulated in a deeply subsiding trough that lay east of the Omineca Geanticline, roughly on the site of Lardeau Trough, first evident in the early Paleozoic (Fig. VIII-32e). The base of the Slocan Group contains debris of the underlying Kaslo Group. The Kaslo consists of pyroclastics and andesitic and dacitic lava within which lies a belt of serpentine. The Kaslo Group is regarded by Cairnes as lying unconformably on strata mapped as Milford Group but which contain Mesozoic fossils.

Insular Trough. The Upper Triassic strata of Queen Charlotte, Vancouver, and some of the smaller islands off the southern mainland were deposited in Insular Trough west of the Coast Geanticline. The Lower Karnian is represented by 10,000 to 14,000 feet of volcanic rocks of the Karmutsen Group and related formations that lie disconformably on the Permian Sicker Group. The volcanics are sodic basalt comprising massive submarine flows, pillow lava, pillow breccia, and aquagene tuff that resulted from the breaking up of glassy, vesicular submarine lava upon being quenched in sea water (Carlisle, 1963). The Upper Karnian and most of the Norian is represented by the limestone of the Kunga Formation in the Queen Charlotte Islands, and by the Quatsino on Vancouver Island. Upper Norian clastic sediments occur at the base of the overlying Bonanza Group, which near Cowichan Lake on Vancouver Island consist of arenite and conglomerate, with fossil logs (Fyles, 1955).

St. Elias Trough. In the St. Elias Mountains late Middle Triassic *Daonella*-bearing calcareous siltstones lie apparently disconformably on Permian strata and are overlain by volcanic rocks of the Mush Lake Group (Muller, 1967). The latter, in Kluane and Donjek Ranges, is probably correlative in part with the Nikolai greenstone of eastern Alaska that lies between the *Daonella* beds and Karnian limestone. Although near the Alaskan border the Upper Triassic consists mainly of volcanic rocks, farther southeast it comprises a Karnian limestone, equivalent to the Chitistone and Nizina limestones in Chitina Valley area of eastern Alaska (Moffitt, 1938), a lower Norian limestone, and upper Norian shales that contain *Monotis subcircularis* and are equivalent to the McCarthy shale in eastern Alaska.

Triassic of Northern Cordilleran Geosyncline

In *British Mountains,* about 1,000 feet of interbedded silty shale, argillaceous siltstone, and fine-grained sandstone with occasional carbonate beds occur near the Alaska–Yukon boundary (Mountjoy, 1967a). They are referred to the Ivishak Member of the Sadlerochit Formation that contains early Triassic (Griesbachian) ammonites in Alaska. Farther east in British Mountains these beds have not been recognized and Upper Triassic strata unconformably rest on Carboniferous and older strata. The Upper Triassic Shublik Formation comprises 270 to 300 feet of brown-weathering, pelecypod limestone coquina and overlying siltstone and fine-grained sandstone between Firth and Malcolm Rivers. The rocks appear to overlie pre-Mississippian strata of the Neruokpuk Formation with angular unconformity and locally a thin basal conglomerate is present. The moderately resistant Upper Triassic sequence is overlain by recessive weathering Jurassic shales.

Isolated remnants of Triassic strata outcrop along the eastern side of *Richardson Mountains* on Rat and Vittrekwa Rivers and near Caribou and Peel Rivers. On Rat River between 50 and 65 feet of carbonaceous shales with lenses of impure coal unconformably overlie undated chert and sandstone pebble-conglomerates that occur above Permian clastics. They are overlain conformably by Middle Jurassic sandstone. Spores and pollen from the carbonaceous strata indicate a Middle and/or Upper Triassic age. On Vittrekwa River, 90 feet of fine-grained calcareous sandstone and limestone of probable Upper Triassic age unconformably overlie the upper Devonian Imperial Formation and disconformably underlie Upper Jurassic sandstones. Farther south between Caribou Lake and Peel River about 300 feet of calcarenite with a few beds of silty limestone also contain a fauna of probable Upper Triassic age (Mountjoy, 1967a).

In the *Ogilvie Mountains* about 1,000 feet of recessive shales and platy, argillaceous limestones of the Shublik Formation occur in the trough of Monster syncline, disconformably overlying Permian strata and unconformably overlain by Upper Cretaceous rocks. Although this sequence has yielded only an Upper Triassic fauna, similar strata about 45 miles to the west in Alaska contain Middle Triassic Ladinian ammonites. About 1,000 feet of poorly exposed, thin-bedded, black shales and limestones on Rackla River are referred to the Shublik Formation.

Black shale and slate 2,000 feet thick occur in the Tombstone–Tintina area (Tempelman-Kluit, 1966). A basal member, 100 feet thick, of slaty, impure, fetid limestone contains Middle and Upper Triassic fossils. Much of the slate and shale could be of Jurassic age. More than 500 feet of interbedded micaceous sandstone and shale with minor conglomerate and concretionary shale containing an Upper Triassic fauna outcrops along Tay River (Roddick and Green, 1961b).

Triassic of Eastern Cordilleran Geosyncline and Interior Platform

Triassic rocks in the *Rocky Mountains* between the International Boundary and Smoky River are included in the Spray River Group. The group totals about 1,700 feet at North Saskatchewan River (Best, 1958), increasing to 2,800 feet near Smoky River (Gibson, 1968), and is relatively thin in the eastern Rockies and Foothills south of Bow River. The Spray River of southeastern British Columbia, attaining a maximum of about 1,500 feet, is mostly assigned to the Sulphur Mountain Formation which is divided into a lower recessive shaly siltstone, a blocky brown-weathering unit, and an upper dolomitic siltstone unit. Overlying light grey to buff weathering limestones and calcareous sandstone, 20 to 40 feet thick, are included in the Whitehorse Formation, which is restricted mainly to the Elk River and Wigwam Creek areas.

The same formations are recognized north of Bow River. The Sulphur Mountain Formation consists of dark grey-brown to rusty brown weathering siltstones, silty dolomites, shales, and fine-grained sandstone, and the Whitehorse Formation is a light grey to buff weathering assemblage of limestones, sandy limestones, dolostones, intraformational breccias, and evaporites. Between Bow and Smoky Rivers, the Sulphur Mountain is divisible into four members (Gibson, 1968). The Phroso Siltstone Member comprises 150 to 652 feet of shaly siltstones and silty shales with minor intercalations of dolomitic siltstone and sandstone, and contains *Claraia stachei* of Griesbachian age. Overlying dolomitic siltstone and shale, 118 to 442 feet thick with *Euflemingites* of Smithian age, are included in the Vega Siltstone Member. The Whistler Member of Anisian age is composed of recessive dark grey weathering dolomite with phosphatic pebble-conglomerate, 12 to 140 feet thick. The Llama Member of silty to sandy dolomite and siltstone, 9 to 145 feet thick, is also Anisian. Two members are recognized within the Whitehorse Formation between North Saskatchewan and Athabasca Rivers. The lower Starlight Evaporitic Member with a maximum thickness of 1,320 feet, contains buff to yellow limestone, collapse breccias, and gypsum. A prominent unit of well-indurated quartzitic sandstone, as much as 256 feet thick, occurs in the upper part in that region. The upper Winnifred Member contains sandy dolomite and limestone. Between Athabasca and Smoky Rivers, 11 to 205 feet of pelletoid fossiliferous limestone, lying between the Starlight and Winnifred Members, is termed the Brewster Limestone Member. In the mountain north of Smoky River, the lower Triassic shales and siltstones are overlain by sandstone and dolomite, and the upper part contains massive to shaly limestone. A remarkable fauna of large fossil fish is known from beds of Lower Triassic age at Wapiti Lake and has also been reported north of Peace River.

Sediments of the Sulphur Mountain Formation are postulated to have been laid down during minor marine transgressions and regressions in a deltaic-type environment. In contrast, sediments of the Whitehorse Formation were probably deposited in a more restricted shallow marine environment, with the occurrence of gypsum, collapse breccias, and red beds indicating deposition under subaerial and highly saline, evaporitic environments.

In the vicinity of Peace River (McLearn and Kindle, 1950), much of the lower part of the Triassic succession is not exposed, although several hundred feet of interbedded shale and siltstone are known near Halfway River. At Peace River, the lowest exposed beds, representing the Liard Formation, comprise the thinly bedded, calcareous, dark siltstones, 75 to 430 feet thick, with the Ladinian Meginae Zone. The succeeding Grey Beds, consisting of more than 2,000 feet of massive quartzitic sandstones, siltstones, reddish fine clastic sediments, limestones, anhydrite, dolomite, and breccias, represent depositional environments varying from marine to near-shore and evaporitic conditions. The Grey Beds contain a *Nathorstites* fauna (Sutherlandi Zone) near the base, the early Late Triassic Mahaffy Cliffs and Red Rock Spur fauna near the middle, and *Lima*? *poyana* fauna toward the top. The carbonate rocks of the upper Grey Beds and the Pardonet Formation were deposited during regional subsidence and renewed marine transgression in late Karnian and early Norian time. The Upper Triassic Pardonet beds of dark calcareous siltstones and shales with some dark limestones, although only 200 to 700 feet thick, contain a remarkably complete sequence of Upper Karnian and Norian ammonoid zones. They consist mainly of dark calcareous siltstone and shale with some dark coquinoid limestone.

Between the Liard and Halfway Rivers, the earliest Triassic seas transgressed slightly bevelled Paleozoic rocks. The Grayling Formation, at the base of the succession, consists of 350 to 1,500 feet of dark non-calcareous shales, minor limestones, with some sandstone, and contains *Claraia stachei* (Griesbachian). It is recognized only between Liard and Sikanni Chief Rivers, apparently grading southward into a siltstone facies generally included with the Toad Formation. The latter, 600 to 3,000 feet thick, comprises grey calcareous siltstones, calcareous shales, minor limestone, and sandstone with Dienerian, Smithian, Spathian, and Anisian ammonoid faunas (Pelletier, 1963).

Increased uplift during Middle Triassic resulted in an increased influx of sand and the deposition of the Liard Formation, which comprises as much as 600 feet of grey calcareous, crossbedded quartzitic sandstone and dark grey siltstone. The succeeding beds, with a maximum thickness of more than 2,000 feet, include fine- to coarse-grained sandstones, light grey to yellow limestone and dolomite, intraformational breccia, and bioclastic, bituminous limestones. Recent studies by Pelletier suggest that the dark calcareous siltstones were deposited in the most northwesterly region more or less continuously from Smithian (Lower Triassic) to Norian (latest Triassic) time, representing a coalescence of Toad and Pardonet facies without any intervening sandstone of Liard or Grey Beds type.

Triassic beds beneath the Peace River Plains have been placed (Hunt and Ratcliffe, 1959; Armitage, 1962) in the Montney and Doig Formations of the Daiber Group and in the Halfway, Charlie Lake, Baldonnel, and Pardonet Formations of the Schooler Creek Group. The Montney, similar to the Toad of the Foothills, grades upward from dark shale into argillaceous siltstones. The Doig, consisting of bituminous dolomitic siltstone with nodular phosphate at the base, may be more than 400 feet thick in the west. Its lower beds have been correlated with phosphatic beds of Anisian age in the Sulphur Mountain and Toad Formations. The Halfway Formation, containing well-sorted, fine- to medium-grained sandstone has been interpreted as near-shore sandbar deposits (Fig. IX-27). Its maximum thickness is more than 400 feet, decreasing eastward to a zero depositional edge. An interval of stability is indicated by the near-shore and evaporitic deposits of the overlying Charlie Lake Formation. The latter, ranging from 0 to more than 1,400 feet, consists of massive anhydrite, red dolomitic siltstone, dolomite, and minor salt, and contains the important oil-producing Boundary Lake Member of dolomitized skeletal limestone. The Charlie Lake beds grade laterally westward into sandstones and limestones similar to those of

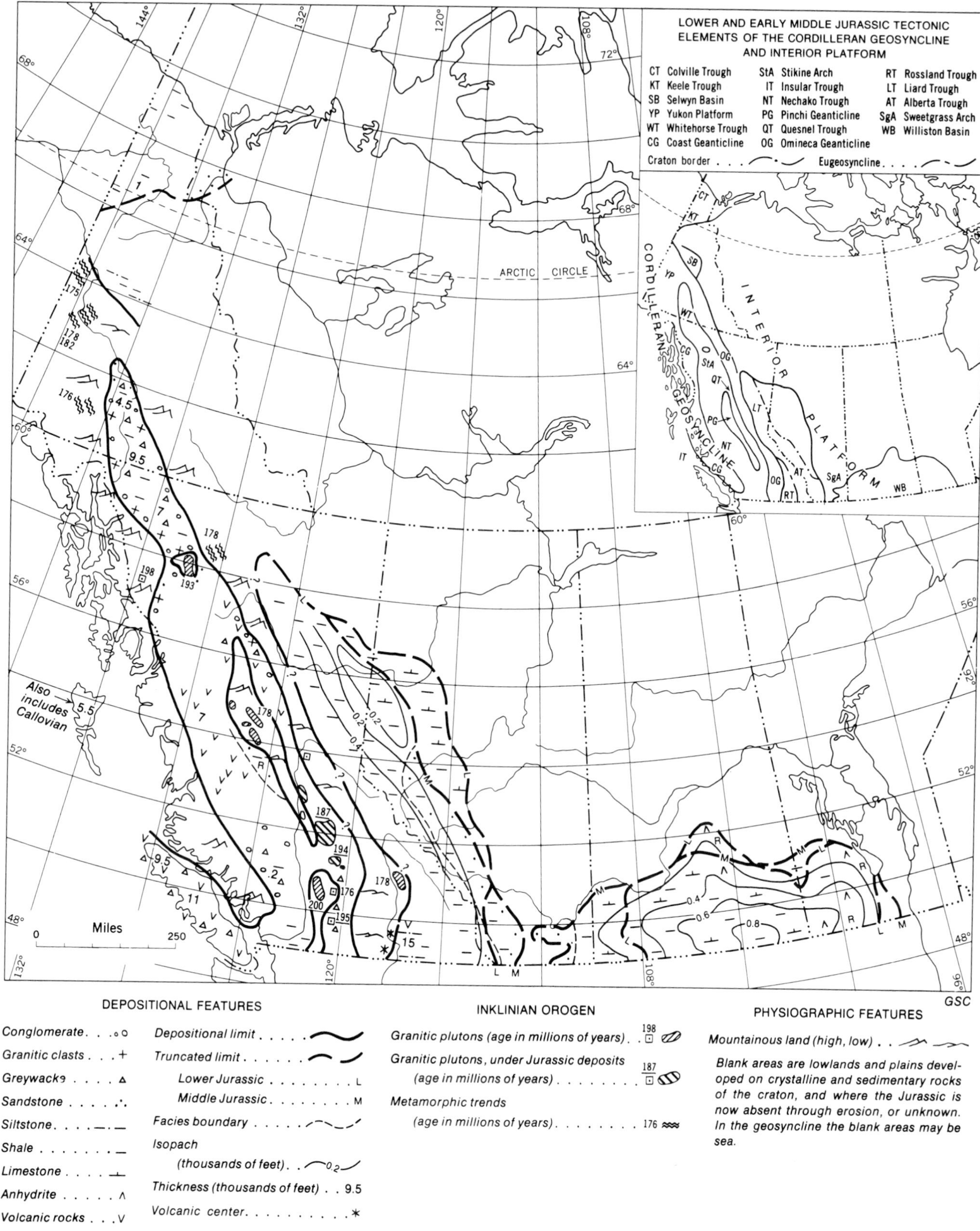

FIGURE VIII-33. Lower and early Middle Jurassic sedimentation and tectonism in Western Canada, and some features of the Lower Jurassic Inklinian Orogeny.

the Halfway and are probably represented in the Foothills by part of the Grey Beds and by evaporites of the Whitehorse Formation farther south. The Baldonnel Formation, as much as 300 feet thick and composed of dolomitized skeletal limestone, is the major gas reservoir. The Baldonnel is generally correlated with microcrystalline and fragmental limestone of the upper unit of the Grey Beds, although it is considered by some to be equivalent in part to the Pardonet Formation. The Pardonet is best known in the Foothills, as it was largely removed from more easterly areas by post-Triassic erosion.

The origin and correlation of the Halfway Formation is controversial. Although the Halfway, Liard, and lower Grey Beds contain similar near-shore sand deposits, neither their precise relationships nor their depositional history has been clearly established. Some attribute the Halfway to regression; others maintain that it resulted from widespread transgression and that it lies unconformably on earlier Triassic beds. The development of the Liard and Halfway sandbars and their gradation westward into a silty to shaly facies also suggest shorelines in the east (Pelletier, 1963). The northward increase in sand ratios and the direction of sediment transport deduced from primary sedimentary structures point to a northeasterly or northerly positive cratonic element, probably in southeast Yukon Territory or District of Mackenzie, as a source for some, at least, of the Triassic sediments in Liard Trough.

Jurassic

Tectonic Summary

The Jurassic System lies conformably on the Triassic in parts of Insular, Nechako, and Whitehorse Troughs and unconformably and disconformably on Triassic and older strata, or plutonic rocks, around the margins of the Coast, Pinchi, and Omineca Geanticlines as a result of uplift during the Inklinian Orogeny, and a general epeirogenic uplift of the craton (Fig. VIII-33). The orogeny is represented by emplacement of granitic plutons in Stikine Arch and the Pinchi and Omineca Geanticlines, and by regional metamorphism in Yukon Platform. These elements were progressively reduced in relief and adjoining troughs subsided strongly during the remainder of the Lower and early Middle Jurassic. Coarse conglomerates containing granitic, volcanic, and some metamorphic debris flank the uplifts. In the non-volcanic Whitehorse Trough the conglomerates grade into thick turbidites but in Quesnel and Nechako Troughs they are associated with abundant pyroclastic and volcanic clastic rocks. In western Rossland Trough andesitic and basaltic flows grade eastward into shales and siltstone. Possibly some ultramafic rocks were emplaced into the volcanic rocks in the Lower Jurassic. In the early Jurassic thick porphyritic pyroclastic andesite accumulated in southern Insular Trough. The northern part was stable and received limestone and shale, succeeded in early Middle Jurassic time by explosive, partly subaerial volcanic rocks. In Colville Trough of northern Yukon Territory, thin black shale was deposited with sandstone and siltstone flanking Aklavik Arch. These sediments represent an embayment of the Arctic Sea that lacked direct connections with seas in the south. In Alberta Trough, subsidence was slight and sedimentation was interrupted only by minor regressions. Thin euxenic shale, siltstone, and limestone were possibly contiguous across Purcell Arch with similar sediments in Rossland Trough. Along the margin of the craton the shales overlap eroded Triassic and upper Paleozoic strata and contain interbedded sandstone derived from Sweetgrass Arch. Lower Jurassic marginal red sediments were derived from the craton and grade into evaporites in the centre of Williston Basin, which was strongly autogeosynclinal throughout the Jurassic. The basin was connected with the geosyncline by a narrow seaway in the northern United States, more open circulation being established in the Middle Jurassic as southern Sweetgrass Arch was depressed.

Rocks of the Middle Jurassic Bathonian stage are unknown in the western Cordilleran Geosyncline, apparently the result of a general regression accompanying Nassian Orogeny. Granitic rocks were intruded along Skeena Arch transverse to Nechako and Whitehorse Troughs. Southern Whitehorse and northern Nechako Troughs were apparently deformed as the Upper Jurassic lies unconformably on Permian to Lower Jurassic strata. Faults bordering Atlin Horst and associated, southwest-directed thrusts and folds were probably produced at this time. Following Nassian Orogeny three discrete depositional basins developed, the Tantalus and Bowser Basins and Tyaughton Trough, and much of the older orogenic lands were broadened as positive elements, some under active erosion (Fig. VIII-34). Much of Insular Trough was emergent, thick clastic sediments being deposited along the western margin of the Insular Geanticline. Tyaughton Trough received considerable granitic debris from terrain along the western margin of the Pinchi Geanticline, now merged with the Omineca Geanticline. Bowser Basin received detritus, especially from Atlin Horst and Skeena Arch, but the sea was connected across a depressed central part of the Coast Geanticline with that of northern Insular Trough. Tantalus Basin was a landlocked basin in which siliceous clastic sediments and coal-forming plants accumulated. Deep, narrow foredeeps filled with intercalated sandstone and shale developed in Colville Trough bordering the uplifted Brooks Geanticline, which in Alaska was the site of orogenic disturbances and intrusion of granitic rocks. The effects of Nassian Orogeny are not evident in Alberta Trough, the subsidence being slight and intermittent. Minor hiatuses within late Middle Jurassic shales are marked by glauconitic shoreline sands derived from the east. Accompanying a general depression of the craton in the late Jurassic, shale and siltstone derived from the west was spread throughout Alberta Trough, across

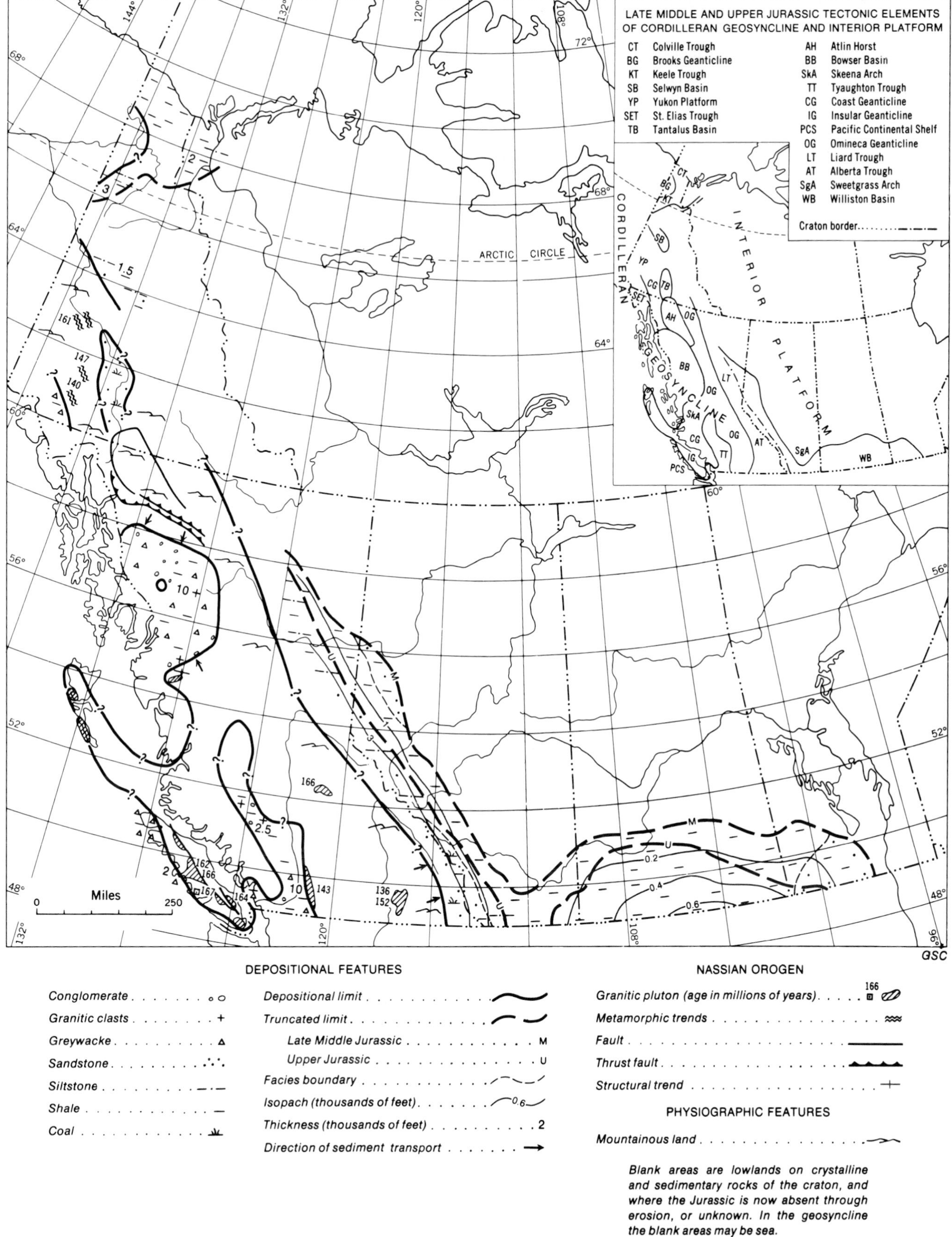

FIGURE VIII-34. Late Middle and Upper Jurassic sedimentation and tectonism in Western Canada, and some features of the Middle Jurassic Nassian Orogeny.

Sweetgrass Arch, and into Williston Basin. In the latest Jurassic, non-marine environments prevailed in southern Alberta Trough as it was filled with sands derived from the uplifted southern Omineca Geanticline during the initial phase of the Columbian Orogeny.

Inklinian Orogeny

A period of regional uplift, granitic intrusion, and locally, regional metamorphism, termed the Inklinian Orogeny, occurred in the Pinchi, Omineca, and northern Coast Geanticlines in latest Triassic and earliest Jurassic time. Lower Jurassic strata, commonly Sinemurian, occur along the eastern flank of the northern Coast Geanticline and around Stikine Arch, resting unconformably on beds of Middle and Upper Triassic age. Along the flanks of the Pinchi and Omineca Geanticlines they lie on Upper Triassic, Permian, Pennsylvanian, and Cambrian formations or on granitic plutons. The Lower Jurassic conglomerates commonly carry granodiorite, diorite, and quartz diorite debris which is particularly abundant in the thick wedges bordering the northern Coast Geanticline and Stikine Arch where uplift was greatest (Fig. VIII-33).

Several oval, biotite–hornblende granodiorite plutons in Stikine Arch and in the Pinchi and Omineca Geanticlines intrude Upper Triassic and older rocks that have undergone little or no metamorphism. They were rapidly unroofed and contributed debris to the Lower Jurassic conglomerates. Some of these plutons (Fig. VIII-28) and their oldest K–Ar dates are the Hotailuh (193 m.y.), Galore Creek (198 m.y.), Guichon (200 m.y.), Thuya (194 m.y.), and Takomkane (187 m.y.) batholiths and Copper Mountain stock (195 m.y.). Other plutons that may be partly of the same age are the granodiorite and pink granite phases of the Topley Intrusions and the aegirine–augite monzonite of the Kuskanax batholith. Both these plutons have yielded K–Ar dates up to 178 m.y. and the Topley pink granites occur as debris in Middle Jurassic sediments. K–Ar ages of about 180 m.y. from schists and gneisses of the Yukon Group near the Alaskan Boundary suggest that regional metamorphism took place in the Yukon Crystalline Platform during the early Jurassic, but no evidence of deformation at this time has been found elsewhere.

Lower and Early Middle Jurassic of Western Cordilleran Geosyncline

Whitehorse Trough. The Laberge Group of Early and early Middle Jurassic age underlies much of south-central Yukon Territory (Wheeler, 1961) and part of northwestern British Columbia northwest of Bowser Basin and south and west of the Atlin Horst (Souther and Armstrong, 1966). It lies upon the Upper Triassic with a disconformity that increases to the southwest. The Laberge Group consists of three facies: a southwestern, coarse clastic facies represented in British Columbia southwest of King Salmon thrust by the Takwahoni Formation, a central turbidite facies represented northeast of the thrust by the

PLATE VIII-10. Conglomerate of Lower Jurassic Laberge Group with well-rounded granite cobbles, southwest of Whitehorse, Yukon Territory.

Inklin Formation; and a local northeastern conglomeratic facies along Teslin River in Yukon Territory (Figs. VIII-31b, 32a).

The southwestern facies is interbedded conglomerate, greywacke, siltstone, and shale, more than 11,000 feet thick, and characterized by rapid facies changes, channelling, and local disconformities. The conglomerates are prevalent in the lower part of the group. Those in the Takwahoni Formation are associated with mid-Pliensbachian and early Toarcian ammonites whereas farther northwest conglomerates occur with early Sinemurian and early Toarcian ammonites. The conglomerates, which at several localities carry boulders nearly 4 feet across, must have been derived from sources nearby. They are composed essentially of clasts of volcanic rock, which predominate in the lower parts of the conglomerate sections or granitic rocks, which are most abundant in the upper sections (Pl. VIII-10). Metamorphic detritus is rare. The greywackes contain considerable quartz and potash feldspar (Pl. VIII-11). The conglomerates are most abundant to the southwest and individual beds, which are commonly lenticular, thicken rapidly in that direction suggesting that they were derived from granite-cored highlands in the Coast Geanticline that were uplifted at intervals during the early Jurassic. Known sources of granitic rocks are: the granodiorite and quartz diorite of the Coast Plutonic Complex southwest and northwest of Whitehorse, Yukon Territory; mid-Triassic diorites in Stikine Arch; and the post-Karnian, pink hornblende granodiorite of the Hotailuh batholith (Gabrielse and Reesor, 1964). Siltstones and shales are abundant in the early Middle Jurassic, upper part of the Laberge Group and suggest that by this time the highlands had been reduced to regions of low relief.

In Yukon Territory, the coarse clastic facies of the Laberge Group grades eastward into the turbidite facies of the Inklin Formation which is more than 9,000 feet thick. It is featured by graded-bedded greywacke, siltstone, and shale displaying slump structures, convoluted bedding, and intraformational breccia with but a few fossils and no ripple-marks. The sediments were deposited in the rapidly subsiding central part of Whitehorse Trough, presumably from turbidity currents that originated as slumps off the rapidly deposited deltas along the southwest margin of the trough.

The northeastern facies is characterized by a tabular sheet of conglomerate at the base of the Laberge Group that is extremely coarse locally, carrying 12-foot blocks of limestone, and therefore must have been derived from the east, from the Omineca Geanticline. The latter was uplifted only in earliest Jurassic time and considerably less than the Coast Geanticline.

The fauna from the Laberge Group (Frebold, 1964) lacks about eight ammonite zones, indicating two gaps possibly caused by non-deposition. One spans the upper Sinemurian and most of the lower Pliensbachian and the other is in the upper part of the Pliensbachian. The gaps occur elsewhere in western Canada and Frebold considered that they may represent periods of general regression. Locally, as in Rossland Trough, they coincide with times of strong volcanic activity, and in other areas with times of uplift.

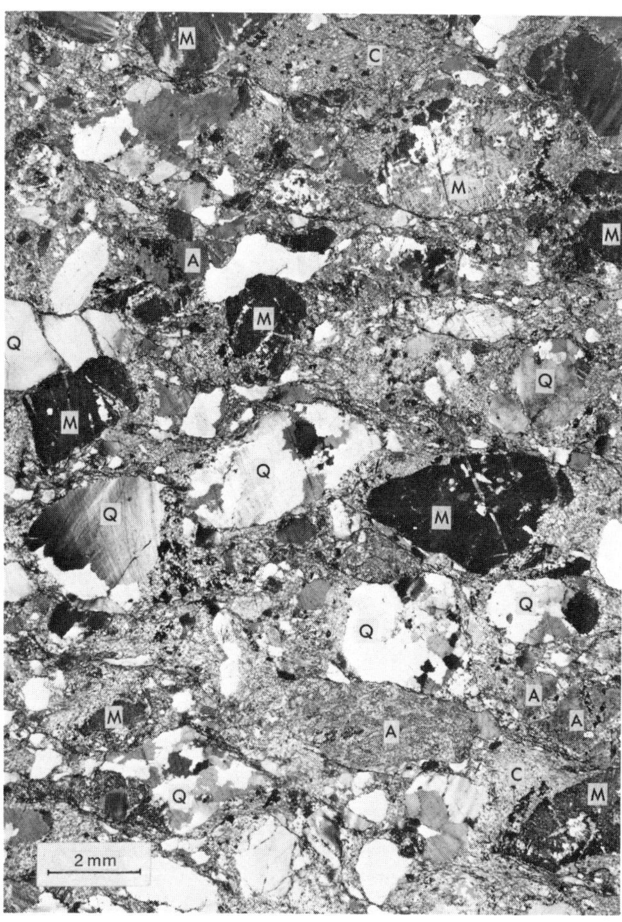

PLATE VIII-11. Photomicrograph of Lower Jurassic microcline-bearing greywacke from northern Cassiar Mountains, British Columbia. Q—quartz; M—microcline (stained); A—altered plagioclase; C—chert.

Nechako Trough. The unfossiliferous red beds of the Takla Group, derived from the erosion of the rising and expanding Pinchi Geanticline to the northeast, are overlain disconformably by the chert-pebble conglomerate unit at the base of the Hazelton Group and may therefore be partly Lower Jurassic (Fig. VIII-32c). The red beds apparently grade southwestward into marine volcanic rocks deposited in the central part of the Nechako Trough (Tipper, 1959). The conglomerate unit, which is both marine and non-marine, contains andesite and basalt flows and tuffs not unlike those in the Takla Group and also quartzite, shale, and siliceous speckled greywacke. The conglomerate clasts, averaging about an inch in diameter but locally as much as 3 feet, are quartz, chert, minor greenstone and argillite, and rare metamorphic and pink granitic rocks. The latter are typical of the nearby Topley Intrusions, which are composed of diorite and pink granitic phases, and cut the lower part of the Takla red beds thus indicating granitic emplacement during uplift and expansion of the Pinchi Geanticline in the early Jurassic. The conglomerate unit is overlain by the main unit of varicoloured andesitic and rhyolitic flows, breccia, and tuff and arkose, carrying early Middle Bajocian fossils.

Near Coast Mountains, the Hazelton Group is more than 11,000 feet thick and comprises two volcanic divisions separated by a mainly marine sedimentary division, all of which were deposited in the deeply subsiding Nechako Trough. The volcanic rocks are fine breccias or coarse tuffs with subordinate flows of red and green andesite and basalt with some rhyolite and dacite. No volcanic centres have been recognized although east of the Coast Mountains near Skeena River breccias contain fragments 2 feet or more in diameter (Duffell and Souther, 1964). Elsewhere along the east side of the Coast Mountains the breccias contain fragments of granitic rocks and metamorphic equivalents of the Hazelton Group lie with angular unconformity on a complex of greenstone and older plutonic rocks (Stuart, 1960). Near Bella Coola greenstone containing Bajocian or older fossils lies unconformably on foliated saussuritized granodiorite of the Coast Plutonic Complex (Baer, 1967). It is apparent, therefore, that the western margin of the volcanic Nechako Trough in late Lower or early Middle Jurassic time lay just west of the eastern edge of the present Coast Plutonic Complex.

Near Taseko Lakes, clastic sediments have yielded Norian, Rhaetian, and Hettangian fossils. This is the only region in the Cordilleran Geosyncline where the Jurassic can be demonstrated to lie conformably on the Triassic. The late Lower and early Middle Jurassic rocks are mainly shales, which implies remote or subdued source lands. North of the lakes a conglomerate, probably Lower Jurassic, contains boulders of Upper Triassic, Upper Paleozoic, and Devonian rocks. In the Cascade Mountains, the Lower Jurassic is represented by shales of the Cultus Formation and the Middle Jurassic by basaltic pillow lava, breccia, and tuff. In eastern Coast Mountains, the lower part of the Dewdney Creek Group contains Lower and Middle Jurassic volcanic greywacke and a few flows (Coates, 1967).

Quesnel Trough. The predominantly volcanic Takla Group, deposited in the northern part of Quesnel Trough, contains Lower Jurassic intercalated sediments, with green andesitic and basaltic flows, breccias, and tuffs. In the southern part of the trough, near Prince George, the volcanic rocks are similar but contain a purple analcite-bearing unit. The clastic rocks are derived mainly from the erosion of volcanic rocks. Some are metamorphosed to zeolite facies.

Coarse, clastic, Lower Jurassic rocks with granitic debris from recognizable sources occur along the edge of Quesnel Trough and lie unconformably on the Triassic, indicating uplift of the Omineca and Pinchi Geanticlines in the earliest Jurassic. The latter geanticline perhaps was also uplifted in the Middle Jurassic (Fig. VIII-32c, d). In southern Omineca Mountains *Harpoceras* is associated with coal-bearing and conglomeratic strata (Armstrong, 1949), presumably deposited along the margin of the Omineca Geanticline. Southeast of Prince George a conglomerate, probably Sinemurian, contains boulders of granite similar to that cutting Karnian beds (H. W. Tipper). At the north end of the belt of Cache Creek rocks, lying *en echelon* southeast of the Pinchi Geanticline, Sinemurian conglomerate contains boulders of older phases of Thuya batholith that intrudes Karnian rocks around Bonaparte Lake. Lower Jurassic rocks south of Quesnel contain boulders of granite similar to those exposed nearby in the Pinchi Geanticline and other Jurassic conglomerates contain granitic and Cache Creek debris (Campbell, 1961). At the south end of the Pinchi Geanticline, near Ashcroft, conglomeratic beds carrying granitic debris and associated with strata yielding Bajocian fossils (Crickmay, 1930) lie unconformably on the Guichon batholith, which intrudes the Karnian (Duffell and McTaggart, 1952). The upper part, above an upper granite-bearing conglomerate, contains Callovian fossils. Crickmay considered the succession conformable but elsewhere Callovian strata are separated from Bajocian and older beds by an unconformity reflecting the Nassian Orogeny. If an hiatus exists in this section it may be beneath the upper conglomerate.

Rossland Trough. The Rossland Group of andesite and basalt flows southwest of Kootenay Lake was deposited in western Rossland Trough (Fig. VIII-32e). The group is composed almost entirely of volcanic rocks in the west, containing Sinemurian fossils near the base and unconformably overlying the Pennsylvanian Mount Roberts Formation (Little, 1960). Northeastward, the lower part of the Lower Rossland Group intertongues with clastic sediments of the Sinemurian and (?)Hettangian Archibald Formation whereas higher beds become the Elise Formation. Volcanic clastic beds near the top of the Archibald Formation contain granitic pebbles. The Archibald presumably grades northeastward into the unfossiliferous Ymir Group that was probably deposited close to the axis of Rossland Trough. It appears that the Rossland lavas were extruded near the flexure between Rossland Trough and the southernmost Omineca Geanticline, which was uplifted in earliest Jurassic or latest Triassic time. The Lower Rossland Group is overlain by the Hall Formation which carries faunas ranging in age from early Toarcian near the base to Middle Bajocian or younger near the top (Frebold and Little, 1962). The Hall Formation is chiefly argillite, but contains siltstone, greywacke, and conglomerate towards the north and is overlain conformably by volcanics and sediments of the Upper Rossland Group.

Insular Trough. On Vancouver Island the Lower Jurassic is represented by explosive rocks of the Bonanza Formation ranging in age from late Karnian to Toarcian. They consist of porphyritic andesitic agglomerates and tuffs. Sequences 6,000 feet thick accumulated in some places. In northwestern Vancouver Island considerable quantities of volcanic arenite and argillite were deposited. No early Middle Jurassic (Bajocian) beds have been recognized on Vancouver Island. On Queen Charlotte Islands the Lower Jurassic is represented by the Upper Kunga shales and the Maude shale and sandstone, conformably succeeded by the Middle Jurassic Yakoun Formation. The Yakoun is composed of explosive volcanics as much as 6,000 feet thick and contains Bajocian and Callovian fossils. The basal beds are scoriaceous lapilli tuffs whereas higher in the section slightly sodic, andesitic, block agglomerates are interbedded with clastic sediments. Sutherland Brown (1966) considers that a chain of volcanoes formed along the east coast of present Queen Charlotte Islands, flanked on the west by a shallow marine basin in which coal accumulated, intercalated with volcanic arenite and tuff.

Nassian Orogeny

The Nassian Orogeny during mid-Jurassic (Bathonian) time resulted in granitic intrusion on Vancouver Island and regional uplift of the western Cordillera. Uplift of Atlin Horst and Skeena Arch segmented the Whitehorse and Nechako Troughs into Tantalus and Bowser Basins and Tyaughton Trough (Fig. VIII-34). The major southwesterly directed thrust faults and related structures on the southwest side of Atlin Horst were probably produced at this time. Souther and Armstrong (1966) suggest that the Lower Jurassic turbidite facies and associated rocks glided southwesterly off the rising horst as a gravity slide, the King Salmon thrust. In the Skeena Arch the Hazelton and older rocks were folded along northeasterly trends and were probably intruded by granitic plutons prior to the deposition of the Bowser Group in the earliest Upper Jurassic. This is suggested by intrusion of the Hazelton Group by the early, more easterly phases of the Coast

Plutonic Complex and by the presence of debris not unlike these early phases in the southwesternmost exposures of the Bowser Group, itself cut by still younger granitic intrusions.

Some deformation and plutonism also took place in Insular Trough. This is suggested by an unconformity on the west coast of Vancouver Island between Toarcian and Callovian beds, the presence of granitic clasts in the conglomerates, and the association of steep northwest-trending faults with northwesterly elongate, syntectonic and late syntectonic plutons intrusive into Lower Jurassic and older rocks. Several K–Ar dates on the granodiorite plutons range from 151 m.y. to 167 m.y. The deformation was mild, apparently consisting of the development of broad, northwesterly trending folds, in contrast to northerly trends within late Paleozoic rocks, and fracturing into elongate blocks along northwest-trending faults.

Elsewhere in the eugeosynclinal belt Middle Jurassic orogenic movements are more obscure but may be represented by the following features: absence of Bathonian fossils; an unconformity between early and late Middle Jurassic beds along the east side of the southern Coast Geanticline; the late Middle Jurassic granite-bearing conglomerates resting unconformably upon the Inklinian Guichon batholith; and a K–Ar date of 166 m.y. on the granite phase of the Thuya batholith.

Upper Jurassic of Western Cordilleran Geosyncline

Tantalus Basin. The Tantalus Formation in south-central Yukon Territory comprises quartz- and chert-bearing conglomerate and sandstone, shale, and coal apparently derived from siliceous rocks in the Coast and Omineca Geanticlines (Fig. VIII-31c). The sediments were deposited under non-marine conditions if one judges from the presence of coal and fossil plants of Neocomian or possible Portlandian age, and the lack of marine fossils. The Tantalus Formation lies apparently conformably on the Laberge Group in the north-central part of the basin near Carmacks but lies unconformably on siliceous metamorphic rocks in its southwesternmost outcrops and disconformably on mid-Lower Jurassic (Pliensbachian) in its southernmost exposures (Wheeler, 1961).

Bowser Basin. The Bowser Group is a thick succession of marine and non-marine shales, greywacke, and conglomerate that was deposited in the Bowser Basin. The group includes, in the east, the Oxfordian strata of the upper division of the Takla Group (Lord, 1948) and the Groundhog coal measures. Chert-pebble conglomerate is present mainly in the northwestern and northern parts of the basin. It occurs as huge, wedge-shaped channel-fills that apparently represent streams carrying Cache Creek chert debris derived from Atlin Horst and Stikine Arch (Souther and Armstrong, 1966). Conglomerate in the southwest occurs in Oxfordian shales and is composed of clasts, as large as a foot in diameter, of volcanic rocks from the Hazelton Group, or chert and granite. The granitic debris is not unlike some of the older phases of the Coast Plutonic Complex that cut Hazelton strata in Skeena Arch. The Bowser Group lies unconformably upon the Hazelton Group in Skeena Arch and on older Jurassic rocks in Stikine Arch. It appears to lie unconformably upon Permian strata in the Oweegee Mountains in the west-central part of Bowser Basin.

Tyaughton Trough. South of Skeena Arch and east of the Coast Mountains the Relay Mountain Group occurs in a fault-bounded belt along Fraser River and extends into the Cascade Mountains. The group in the northern part of the Tyaughton Trough (Jeletzky and Tipper, 1968) is composed of an essentially conformable sequence of clastic sediments that range in age from late Callovian to Barremian and contains fossils representing all intervening stages. The base of the group is not exposed. Shales and siltstones occupy the central part of the trough but grade laterally to the southwest and northeast into greywacke and locally conglomerate. Granitic detritus, derived from masses exposed to the northeast, is restricted to the northeastern exposures of the group and first appears in Upper Oxfordian beds carrying *Buchia concentrica.* The latter may lie disconformably on Lower Oxfordian shales with *Cardioceras.*

In eastern Cascade Mountains the lower part of the Ladner Group is mainly a slate containing belemnites. Around Harrison Lake, Callovian beds of the Mysterious Creek Formation are locally overlain disconformably by 3,000 feet of early Oxfordian conglomerate. The clasts are argillite, chert, quartzite, tuff, agglomerate, and the Middle Jurassic Harrison Lake porphyries and micropegmatite. Elsewhere early Lower Cretaceous beds lie disconformably on the Billhook Formation which conformably overlies the Mysterious Creek Formation. The southwestern flank of Tyaughton Trough accordingly appears to have been subjected to periodic uplift during the Late Jurassic. In southwest Cascade Mountains, the Nooksack Group is mainly slate (J. W. H. Monger), flysch-like in character, and commonly contains sand- or silt-sized volcanic clastic rocks or locally, in its uppermost part, beds of granite-bearing conglomerate.

Pacific Continental Shelf. Late Middle and Upper Jurassic clastic sediments are found only locally on the west coast of Vancouver Island near Esperanza Inlet. The lower unit, Division A of Jeletzky (1950), ranges in age from mid-Callovian to (?)early Kimmeridgian. It consists mainly of tuffaceous mudstone, siltstone, and greywacke with minor pebble-conglomerate which at one locality contains pebbles of granitic rocks and lies with angular unconformity on the Bonanza Group. The upper part, of Oxfordian age, is mainly a succession of greywacke beds, but the top is not exposed. The upper unit, Division B, not in contact with Division A, comprises Portlandian shale and sandstone. It is overlain disconformably by the early Lower Cretaceous One Tree Formation.

Jurassic of Eastern Cordilleran Geosyncline and Interior Platform

Colville Trough. In Aklavik Range of northern Richardson Mountains (Jeletzky, 1967), the Bug Creek Formation, late Sinemurian to possibly early Oxfordian in age, consists of about 600 to 800 feet of fine-grained quartzose sandstones and siltstones, probably derived from the east. The Upper Jurassic is represented by Husky shale, a succession some 1,300 feet thick of dark to brownish grey concretionary shale and siltstone with minor fine or pebbly sandstone and lenses of *Buchia* coquina. The uppermost 190 feet are lowermost Cretaceous and are transitionally overlain by Valanginian sandstones. Near Vittrekwa River the Husky grades southward into the North Branch conglomerate, 600 feet thick, a shoreline deposit on the northern flank of Aklavik Arch.

The Jurassic of British Mountains is not well known, but concretionary grey and black shales are similar to the Kingak shale of Alaska which is 4,000 feet thick. The shale lies disconformably on the Triassic and Carboniferous but unconformably on the Neruokpuk Formation. In southern Keele Range, 2,000 feet of black shale is succeeded by 2,400 feet of siltstone, shale, and quartzose sandstone, the uppermost part of which is of early Lower Cretaceous age (Frebold, *et al.,* 1967).

Selwyn Basin. At least 1,000 feet of black shale, slate, and siltstone containing Middle Bathonian, Lower Callovian, and Lower Oxfordian ammonites occurs in the hanging-wall of a major thrust fault in the Tombstone–Tintina region (Tempelman-Kluit, 1966).

Alberta and Liard Troughs. In the Foothills and Rocky Mountains of southeastern British Columbia and southwestern Alberta, the Jurassic is represented by the Fernie Formation. It is about 600 to 1,000 feet thick, and lies unconformably on eroded Triassic or Paleozoic rocks. In the Fernie area (Frebold, 1957), basal Jurassic beds containing the *"Arnioceras"* fauna consist of a few feet of black pelletoidal and nodular phosphate rock and shale overlain by at least 100 feet of black shales. Farther east, in the vicinity of Blairmore, the transgressive basal deposits are Toarcian sandstone and shales. The overlying Bajocian Rock Creek Member consists mainly of rusty weathering dark shale with siltstone and sandstone and is characterized by belemnite conglomerates and the *Teloceras* fauna. One of the major Jurassic inundations is represented by early Callovian Grey Beds, containing the *Corbula munda* and *Gryphaea* beds. Medium to light grey shales are present near Blairmore but calcareous sandstone and sandy limestone are more abundant farther west. Glauconitic sandstone and shale, with *Cardioceras,* of the Oxfordian Green Beds grade upward into the Passage Beds of interbedded fine-grained marine sandstone, siltstone, and black shale. These upper sandy sediments were deposited during the final retreat of the Fernie sea that accompanied the influx of clastics produced during the initial phase of Columbian Orogeny.

Toward the end of the Jurassic, non-marine conditions of deposition, which were established in the Crowsnest region, are represented by the Kootenay Formation. The Kootenay increases from an erosional edge on Interior Platform to more than 3,500 feet in the Fernie Basin. At Blairmore, the formation is divided into four members (Norris, D. K., 1959). The basal Moose Mountain Member is a quartz and chert sandstone transitionally overlying the Fernie shales. It contains a Portlandian ammonite near Fernie, B.C. The other three members, Adanac, Hillcrest, and Mutz, comprise a sequence of carbonaceous mudstones, siltstones, and sandstones, with several commercial coal seams. These beds are considered to be Jurassic on the basis of spore analysis although macrofloral evidence suggests a Cretaceous age (Bell, 1956). In the westernmost exposures, the upper beds of the Kootenay Formation include more than 1,400 feet of Elk conglomerate, composed mainly of chert, quartz, and quartzite, as large as 6 inches in diameter, that was derived from the rising southern Omineca Geanticline, expanding eastward during the Columbian Orogeny.

Marine deposits of Sinemurian age include coquina and conglomerate near Banff. Between Crowsnest Pass and Bow River they are locally absent, and the initial Jurassic transgression is represented by Toarcian limestones, sandstones, and black papery shales. The sequence is lithologically similar to that of the Crowsnest area, but also includes such prominent units as the easterly derived Bajocian Rock Creek sandstone in the vicinity of Highwood River (Douglas, 1959) and the Callovian Pigeon Creek sandstone at Mount Allan (Crockford, 1949). The latter appears to be a local sandy facies of the Grey Beds. The Kootenay attains a maximum thickness of 3,400 feet in the mountains southeast of Banff but to the east is eroded and thins rapidly to zero. The lower part contains fine-grained sandstone and coal-bearing beds. The upper part includes several thick, coarse-grained, sandstone beds, locally finely conglomeratic, interbedded with silty, carbonaceous shales. Those beds, termed the Pocaterra Creek Member, are probably a facies of the more massive Elk conglomerates.

Basal Fernie beds in the central Foothills of Alberta (Douglas, 1958; Mountjoy, 1962), between Bow and Athabasca Rivers, are included in the Nordegg Member, 30 to 100 feet of black, cherty, and phosphatic dolomite or limestone with siltstones and shales. They are overlain by 10 to 20 feet of dark papery fissile shales followed by the thin Rock Creek sandstone. In some areas, the Rock Creek is represented by dark grey shales with belemnite conglomerates overlying the Paper shales and underlying the dark to yellow-brown shales of the Grey Beds. In the more northerly areas, glauconitic, silty, concretionary shale comprising the Green Beds overlaps and truncates the Grey Beds in a northeasterly direction. This is probably the result of uplift of the margin of the craton at the end of the Middle Jurassic. At the top of the group, intercalated thin siltstones and silty shales grade into the overlying Nikanassin Formation. The latter, about 1,200 feet thick, consists of thick beds of fine- to medium-grained, quartzose sandstone interbedded with dark grey shale, thin siltstone, and a few thin coal seams. It occupies a stratigraphic position similar to that of the Kootenay Formation but lacks commercial coal. Late Jurassic *Buchia* occur near the base of the formation. The Nikanassin increases from 2,000 feet near Jasper to nearly 4,000 feet in western exposures near Smoky River. Similar strata, more than 6,000 feet thick north of Smoky River (Zeigler and Pocock, 1960), are included in the Minnes Formation, reported to contain Jurassic microfossils near the base and early Lower Cretaceous spores in the upper part.

In the Peace River Foothills (Stott, 1967), the basal Fernie beds, 56 to 209 feet thick, consist of phosphatic, calcareous, and cherty shales with some limestone and siltstones, overlain by black calcareous papery shale. The middle succession of 65 to 273 feet of rusty weathering sideritic marine shale with a persistent glauconitic siltstone marker, is equated on the basis of microfauna and lithology with the Rock Creek, Grey Beds, and Green Beds of more southerly regions. Interbedded sandstone and shale intertongue with and grade upward into fine- to coarse-grained, quartzose sandstone of the Monteith Formation which spans the boundary between the Jurassic and Cretaceous.

The Jurassic of the adjacent Interior Platform is lithologically similar to the Fernie Formation (Lackie, 1958). The northeastern limit is a highly irregular erosional edge (Fig. VIII-33). Black, calcareous shales of the Nordegg Member, formed as a shelf deposit, were later covered in central Alberta by a fairly extensive chert and locally by accumulations of pebbly sandstone derived from Paleozoic beds to the northeast (Springer, *et al.*, 1964). The dark platy Poker Chip shales are overlain by glauconitic arenaceous beds of the Rock Creek Member. Thick black shale, with abundant glauconite pellets, of the Green Beds grade upward into siltstone and sandstone of the Passage Beds. Farther south, toward Sweetgrass Arch, much of the Middle and Upper Jurassic is not present, due partly to non-deposition and partly to later erosion.

Sweetgrass Arch and Williston Basin. The region of the Sweetgrass Arch in southern Alberta, emergent in Lower Jurassic time, was depressed during the Middle and Upper Jurassic and received a maximum of more than 600 feet of sediments (Thompson and Crockford, 1958). The Middle Jurassic Bajocian Sawtooth Formation, 0 to 235 feet, comprises two quartzose sandstone members separated by green shale with belemnite conglomerates. It was deposited on the irregular erosion surface carved on Mississippian rocks around several islands that remained along the crest of the arch. The epineritic Sawtooth sandstones grade eastward into limy sandstone of the Shaunavon Formation and westward into black shales of the Rock Creek Member. The Callovian Rierdon Formation contains as much as 250 feet of alternating grey to green calcareous shale, brown limestones, and grey to green argillaceous siltstones. It was deposited over Sweetgrass Arch, grading laterally westward into the shales of the Grey Beds of Alberta Trough and eastward into the Lower Vanguard calcareous shales of Williston Basin. The Oxfordian Swift Formation, ranging from 0 to 75 feet, of non-calcareous shale and fine quartzose silty sands, in part glauconitic, appears to lie disconformably on the Rierdon, the result of positive movements of Sweetgrass Arch at the end of the Middle Jurassic. The Swift beds grade into the light coloured shales of the Upper Vanguard and westward into the Green Beds and Passage Beds. Erosion in the late Jurassic and earliest Cretaceous removed the Swift beds from the crest of the arch, truncating older beds in a northward direction.

In Williston Basin, Jurassic rocks have a maximum thickness of more than 1,400 feet (Milner and Blakslee, 1958; Springer, *et al.*, 1964). Lower Jurassic red beds of the Lower Watrous Formation composed of siltstone, shale, and sandstone lie unconformably on Mississippian and Devonian rocks, filling depressions on a highly irregular erosional surface. These sediments, overlapped by the remainder of Jurassic deposits, were deposited in an oxidizing environment along the margin of an evaporitic embayment centred in the northern United States. Continued subsidence resulted in an expansion of the basin and the deposition of upper Watrous anhydrite, dolomite, and shales. Along Sweetgrass Arch an extensive peninsula separated the evaporitic waters of Williston Basin and the open seas of Alberta Trough. During Middle Jurassic time, silty and dolomitic marine shales of the Gravelbourg Formation accumulated in the central part of Williston Basin and quartzose sandstone and shale were deposited under shallow near-shore conditions along the eastern margin. The Gravelbourg is overlain with minor disconformity by the Shaunavon Formation as a westward shifting of the centre of downwarp resulted in the deposition of widespread, fine-grained sandstone and oölitic limestone in the west, at the same time as shale with minor sandstone was deposited in the east. Interbedded shales and sandstone derived from the west and southwest comprising the upper Shaunavon suggest regression during the Middle Jurassic, and subsequently transgression is recorded by the shales of the lower Vanguard Formation. Sandstones within the middle Vanguard are unconformably overlain by upper Vanguard marine shales, the result of a general regression at the end of the Callovian and subsequent transgression in the Oxfordian. Emergence during latest Jurassic to early Cretaceous time resulted in general widespread erosion of the Jurassic rocks, particularly around the margin of the basin.

Cretaceous

Tectonic Summary

Lower Cretaceous. Sedimentation in the deeply subsiding troughs of the Cordilleran Geosyncline continued from the Jurassic into the early Lower Cretaceous (Fig. VIII-35).

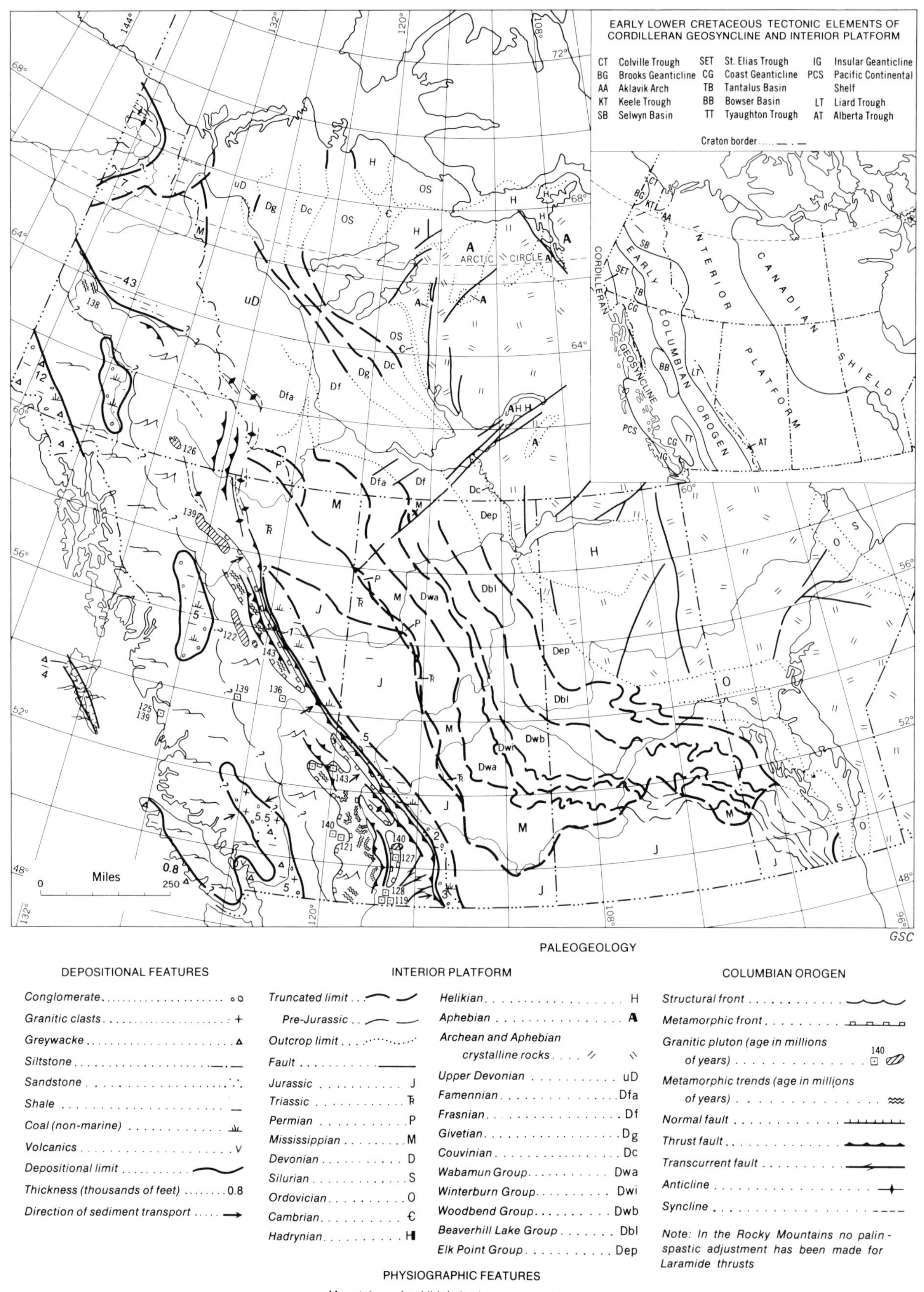

FIGURE VIII-35. Early Lower Cretaceous sedimentation and tectonism in Western Canada, and some features of the early phase of the Columbian Orogeny and of pre-Albian geology.

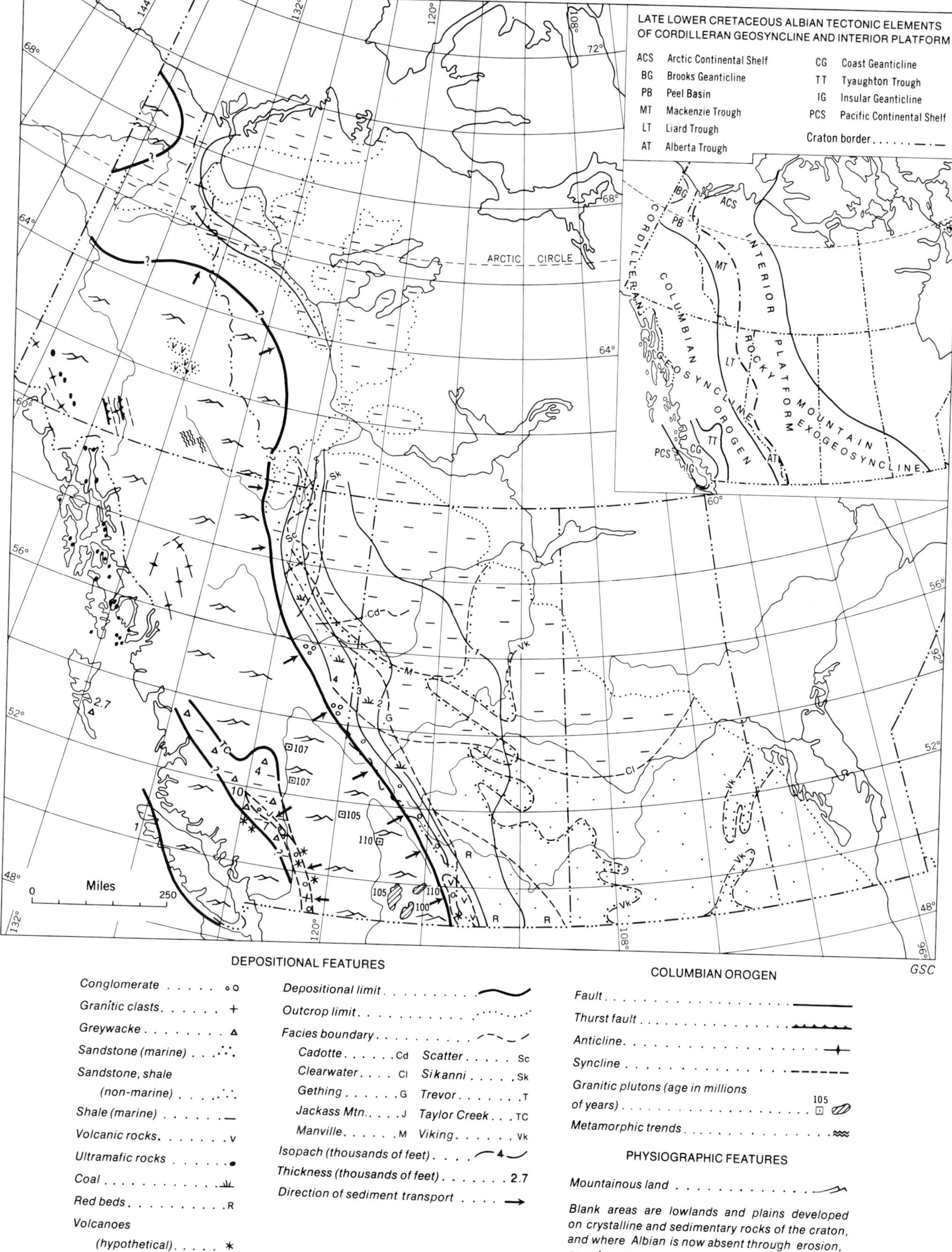

FIGURE VIII-36. Lower Cretaceous, Albian, sedimentation and tectonism in Western Canada, and some features of the middle phase of the Columbian Orogeny.

Some, such as Keele and Alberta Troughs, appear to have been foredeeps that were closely linked with adjacent rising geanticlinal welts and received thick clastic sediments deposited partly under non-marine conditions. In other elements, such as Bowser and Tantalus Basins and Tyaughton Trough, which lay between the geanticlines, deposition occurred contemporaneously with the early phase of Columbian Orogeny. Large granitic plutons were emplaced during the orogeny and extensive metamorphism occurred throughout the Omineca Geanticline. The orogeny and associated uplift were most intensive in the south and possibly also occurred in the Brooks Geanticline west of the Alaska Boundary. To what extent the orogeny affected the Coast Geanticline is not known but this belt was generally uplifted, much debris was supplied to St. Elias Trough and Pacific Continental Shelf, and the marine connection to Bowser Basin was greatly restricted. Sedimentation in Queen Charlotte Islands was restricted to a narrow, deeply depressed central graben. A boreal marine embayment, persisting from the late Jurassic, probably extended from the region of Keele Trough and Selwyn Basin into northern parts of Alberta Trough. By Aptian time, however, the sea had completely withdrawn from the craton and bordering troughs. Preserved beneath Albian sediments of the craton is a generally homoclinal succession of Paleozoic and early Mesozoic formations and many remnants of the topography that were established in the Aptian, or that persisted from earlier periods of cratonic uplift.

In the Albian (Fig. VIII-36) the central part of the western Cordilleran Geosyncline appears to have been land, marine conditions prevailing only in Tyaughton Trough and on the Pacific Continental Shelf. Tyaughton Trough was partly taphrogenic, and received much greywacke, shale, and volcanic rocks and some extremely coarse conglomerates that were derived from fault-bounded mountains to the east. Volcanism took place in the north, the basalt flows covering broad intermontane areas of moderate relief in central Yukon. East of the Columbian orogenic lands the early Albian sea transgressed rapidly southward over a plain of little relief. The adjacent basins and troughs were strongly depressed and the craton subsided evenly over broad areas. Peel Basin was partly exogeosynclinal, the clastic sediments derived from uplift of northern Columbian Orogen to the south. Mackenzie and northern Liard Troughs may have been more akin to foredeeps. In the south the vast Rocky Mountain Exogeosyncline developed and although much sediment was carried out over the craton, a substantial part was trapped in the strongly depressed linear Alberta Trough. The Albian clastic sediments were derived from the southern mountainous part of Columbian Orogen to the west and in small part from the east, from the Canadian Shield and its Paleozoic cover. The bulk was deposited under lacustrine, alluvial and neritic environments and formed a broad, low-lying, alluvial plain that bordered the Albian seas to the north. Variations in the rates of subsidence of the sea floor, of the influx of clastic material, and of uplift of the source region resulted in three major southward marine transgressions that alternated with three northward regressions and overlap of the marine shales by non-marine clastics, and also in several minor cyclical facies alternations. The non-marine facies do not extend beyond a northeast-trending hingeline that lies subparallel with the Devonian Peace River Arch, greater depression and marine shale facies prevailing to the north. Near the mountains, the alluvial plain was swampy and heavily forested by conifers in the early Albian and later also by angiosperms. The southwest was semi-arid and the site of small volcanoes. Tongues of sandstone of western source occur in northern Liard Trough, reflecting uplift of the central Omineca Geanticline, a prominent feature of Columbian Orogen in the early Upper Cretaceous. The latest of the Albian transgressions extended into the central United States joining the sea that had spread northward from the Gulf of Mexico.

Upper Cretaceous. Columbian Orogeny continued in the early Upper Cretaceous, the last phase represented by regional uplifts, minor folding and intrusion of post-orogenic granites (Fig. VIII-37). Synorogenic clastic sediments, including conglomerates, were deposited in the northern Rocky Mountain Exogeosyncline, Pacific Continental Shelf, Tyaughton Trough, and the northern elements of the geosyncline. These sediments conformably or disconformably succeed the Lower Cretaceous and are conformably succeeded by marine shales that reflect relative orogenic quiescence during the mid-Upper Cretaceous. A great deal of the Cordilleran Region was land, mainly mountains. In broad intermontane valleys and trenches, forming Sustut and Tyaughton Troughs and the Rocky Mountain and Tintina Trenches, non-marine clastic sediments accumulated and locally there was volcanism, partly pyroclastic and acidic. These rocks are not well dated; the age of the base of the successions probably varies generally, and may also be partly early Tertiary. In general, they lie nonconformably or with angular unconformity on older rocks, reflecting the effects of the local phase of Columbian Orogeny or the cumulative effect of all phases and older orogenies as well. The sequences are partly marine in Hecate and Georgia Basins and Tyaughton Trough. In Rocky Mountain Exogeosyncline the late Upper Cretaceous clastic sediments are very thick, representative of the widespread uplift of southern Columbian Orogen and the effects of the early phase of the Laramide Orogeny that continued into the Tertiary (Fig. VIII-44). The sediments grade from non-marine sandstone, shale, and conglomerate in the west to marine shale in the east and are conformably to unconformably overlain by the Tertiary. Regional uplift, including the northern part of the craton, resulted in the southward withdrawal of the seas from the continental interior.

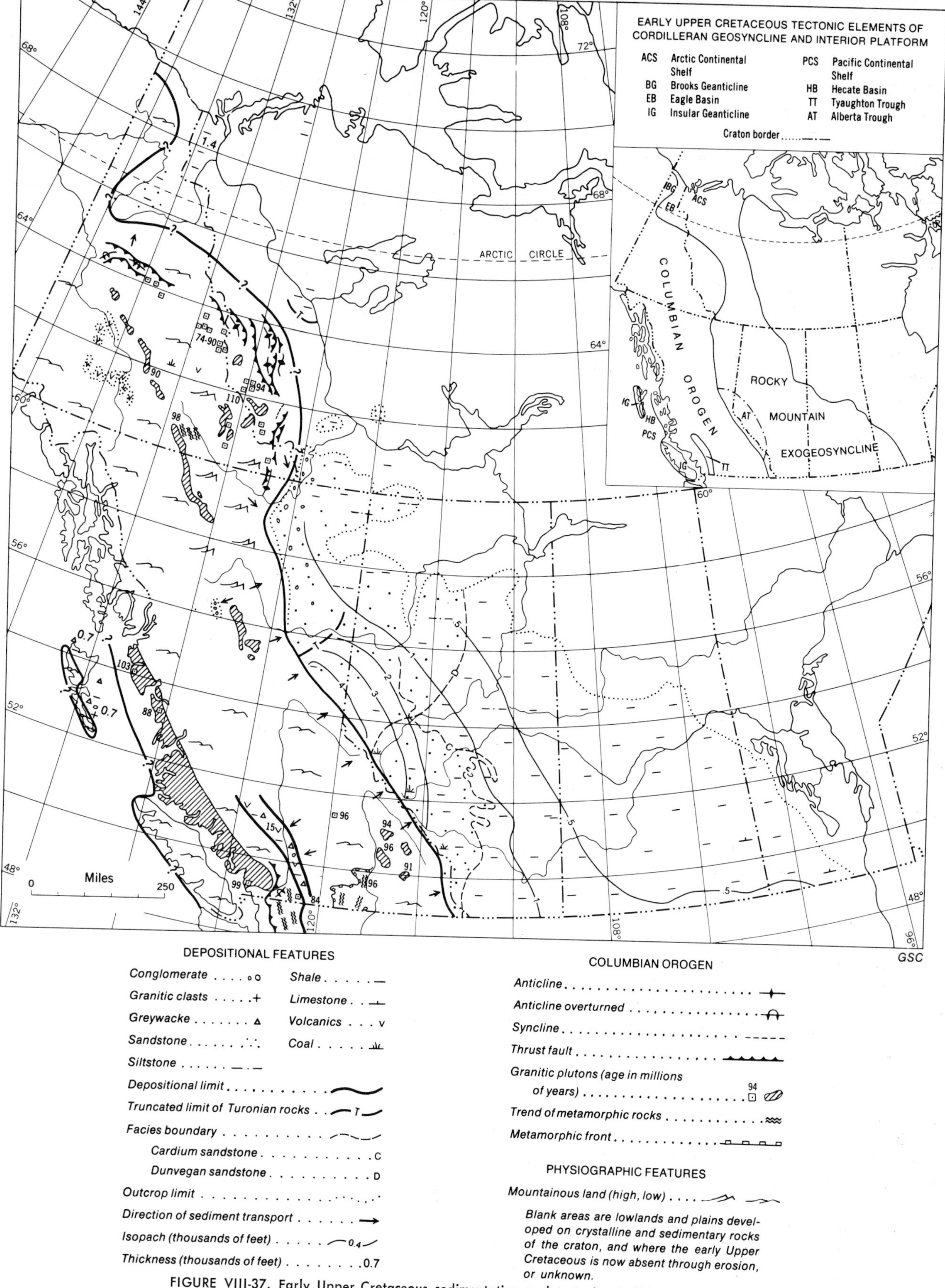

FIGURE VIII-37. Early Upper Cretaceous sedimentation and tectonism in Western Canada, and some features of the late phase of the Columbian Orogeny.

Columbian Orogeny

From Late Jurassic to earliest Upper Cretaceous time parts of the Cordilleran Geosyncline underwent major deformation, regional metamorphism, granitic intrusion, and uplift—the Columbian Orogeny—during which the following structural provinces were established: (1) *Eastern Columbides,* a northeasterly directed alpine-type orogen in the south, whose core zones of plutonic rocks constitute much of the Omineca Geanticline and in the north include the arcuate Selwyn Fold Belt and the eastern termination of Brooks Geanticline; (2) *Columbian Zwischengebirge,* characterized by a heterogeneous mosaic of northwesterly elongate, uplifted blocks with intervening troughs and successor basins; (3) *Western Columbides,* comprising the Coast, Cascade, Insular, and St. Elias segments, dominated by plutonic rocks and steeply dipping, southwesterly directed structures.

Columbian Orogeny consisted of three phases. The earliest, occurring in the latest Jurassic, was intense but restricted mainly to Omineca Geanticline. The middle phase, in Aptian and Albian time, was more widespread. The late phase in earliest Upper Cretaceous was manifested mainly by intrusion of granite bodies.

Eastern Columbides. While the syntectonic basins were receiving clastic deposits in latest Jurassic time, deformation and plutonism occurred in the Omineca Geanticline. The youngest rocks deformed are the Middle and Upper(?) Jurassic upper part of the Rossland Group whereas the oldest rocks, not involved, are those of the Uslika Formation, probably of Aptian age. Radiometric dates on metamorphic and granitic rocks in the southern Omineca Geanticline and southern Quesnel Trough and evidence from textural studies, such as alignment of metamorphic minerals parallel with the axes of early folds, indicate that the early Columbian deformation began in the Portlandian or Kimmeridgian. Two K–Ar ages of 140 m.y. and one of 135 m.y. have been obtained from metamorphic rocks of the Mount Ida Group in the western part of the Omineca Geanticline, and one age of 146 m.y. from northeast Selkirk Mountains. The latter appears to represent the time of growth of biotite poikiloblasts in a schist, the muscovite matrix of which gave an age of 205 m.y. Elongate, syntectonic or oval, late tectonic biotite–hornblende granodiorite plutons such as the Cassiar and Nelson batholiths, and the Porcupine, Ruby Range, and Glacier Creek stocks yield K–Ar dates ranging from 136 m.y. to 152 m.y. These plutons are locally foliated and in gross aspect parallel the structural grain. Furthermore, the discordant, post-tectonic biotite granodiorite plutons, roughly circular in plan, yield dates of less than 143 m.y.

The core zone of the Eastern Columbides contains several structural culminations and areas of high-grade metamorphism (Fig. VIII-28). The overall pattern of structural trends, as displayed by the long dimensions of the metamorphic complexes, the fault traces, and by the fold axes in the rocks adjoining them, is that of a gentle arc, convex eastward.

The deeper structural levels exposed within the culminations are featured by multiphase folding in which earlier attenuated isoclines have been redeformed by later folds to produce several huge, partly interdigitating and backfolded nappes with profiles resembling that of an anvil. The frontal parts of the nappes correspond to the horn and the backfolds to the rear of the anvil (Fig. VIII-38). The higher structural levels, well displayed in Cariboo Mountains, are characterized by single phase, broad, open folds and fault blocks.

In cross-section the anvil structures are characterized by broad undulating arches whose western parts have subsidiary northeast-dipping reverse faults and late parasitic folds, commonly asymmetrical or overturned to the southwest. The late folds in the western part of the Shuswap anvil structure, however, are upright whereas those in the northwesternmost part are tight with axial planes and associated cleavage progressively changing attitude westward from northeasterly dips to southwesterly. The eastern part of the Shuswap anvil structure is represented by the enveloping surface of the late folds in the Shuswap Complex which dips eastward under the back-folded part of the Selkirk anvil structure lying to the east. The axial planes of the late folds and attitudes of thrust faults in the Selkirk anvil structure are arranged in the form of a fan; those in the southwestern part dip northeast, pass through vertically along the fan axis, and then dip southwest in the northeastern part of the structure. Structures in the northeastern part are characterized by overturned and undulating recumbent folds that are part of thrust masses that truncate and override structures of the westernmost Rocky Mountains. The Selkirk anvil structure is probably largely allochthonous and westerly directed structures within it may have resulted from underthrusting of the nose of the Shuswap anvil structure into the back of the Selkirk anvil structure.

The Purcell anticlinorium is composed of several north-plunging segments separated by faults. In cross-section the anticlinorium is crudely anvil-shaped. The structures in its western part merge with those of the Kootenay Arc which are featured by complex repetitive folding whereas those in the north plunge under the eastern part of the Selkirk anvil structure. The central part is dominated by a broad, gently undulating anticline transected by southwest-dipping thrust faults, north-northwesterly trending normal faults, and smaller folds co-axial with those formed during the Hadrynian East Kootenay Orogeny. The Moyie, Hall Lake, and St. Mary's faults existed prior to the intrusion of the White Creek and Bayonne batholiths. Some of the early-formed faults acted as oblique thrusts as the intervening segments moved differentially eastward (Leech, 1962b).

In the western ranges of southern Rocky Mountains a thin sequence of lower Paleozoic carbonate, quartzite, and pelitic rocks is thrown into several southwesterly over-

PLATE VIII-12. Folds with steeply west-dipping axial plane cleavage in Cambrian, Arctomys and Waterfowl Formations, near Sullivan River, southern Rocky Mountains, British Columbia. Mount Tsar in right background.

turned and recumbent folds with southeast-dipping axial plane cleavage (Henderson, 1954). These folds are cut by the Redwall and other high-angle strike-slip faults, commonly marked by zones of breccia and mylonite. Between the faults the strata are imbricated by thrusts or segmented by small cross-faults.

To the northeast in western Main Ranges, across a fan-axis marked by vertical cleavage, the dominantly pelitic Cambro-Ordovician succession is intricately folded, the cleavage and axial planes dipping southwest. Comparable folds also occur locally in the alternating shale and limestone succession of the central Main Ranges (Pl. VIII-12). To the southeast the Columbide structural front is limited by the presence of Jura-Cretaceous clastic rocks in Fernie Basin (Fig. VIII-35).

About 20 miles north of the Big Bend of Columbia River, in a culmination in the main ranges of the Rocky Mountains, a mass of pre-Hadrynian gneiss is thrust over Lower Cambrian and Hadrynian strata (Fig. VIII-38a). The enveloping staurolite–kyanite, garnet, and biotite isograds gradually cut across the westernmost thrusts and folds of the main ranges. Post-kinematic, porphyroblastic biotite has yielded a K–Ar age of 111 m.y. which provides an upper limit on the time of formation of the structures (Price and Mountjoy, 1970).

The structures of the stratified rocks of Cassiar Mountains (Gabrielse, 1963) are extremely heterogeneous and certain ones are confined to the individual northwesterly trending blocks that are bounded by major steeply dipping faults (Fig. VIII-39b). In some blocks the folds are overturned to the northeast whereas in others they are upright or overturned southwest. Some faults bounding the blocks coincide with marked changes in thickness and facies of the Lower Paleozoic strata. Numerous small cross-faults contribute to the iscontinuous distribution of stratigraphic units. In southern Cassiar Mountains northeasterly overturned folds with steeply dipping axial planes occur with northeasterly directed thrust faults (Gabrielse, 1962b). The structures are not nearly as continuous as the thrusts and folds in western Rocky Mountains but otherwise their style is similar and they may have been produced during the same phase of deformation. In western Rocky Mountains this deformation predates deposition of the Sifton Formation of Paleocene and possibly Upper Cretaceous age in Rocky Mountain Trench, and in Cassiar Mountains predates deposition of the Santonian to Campanian continental sediments that occur in a northwesterly trending trench that forms an acute angle with Rocky Mountain Trench. Accordingly, the structures were formed during Columbian Orogeny, and could be as young as late Columbian.

The southern part of the Cassiar batholith from which a muscovite–biotite pair has yielded K–Ar ages of 123 m.y. and 139 m.y. lies subparallel with the regional structure but is intrusive into previously metamorphosed and deformed rocks. The Marker Lake batholith in northern Cassiar Mountains with a K–Ar date of 126 m.y. is possibly also related to the early phase of Columbian Orogeny. It is mainly a medium-grained uniform granodiorite or quartz monzonite.

In Pelly Mountains two areas of different structural style are separated by a major northeasterly directed thrust fault. Southwest of the thrust, the structure is characterized by moderately west-dipping homoclines and low-angle thrust faults, some of which are folded. Displacement is directed mainly to the northeast. Displacement on some steeply dipping thrust faults in the southwestern part of the region is southwesterly. Locally, crystalline rocks have been thrust northeasterly over Devono-Mississippian clastic strata. The thrust sheets have been broken subsequently by a north-northwesterly trending normal fault. Northeast of the main thrust and flanking Tintina Trench, structures are featured by steep dips, tight upright folds, and fault slices bounded by steeply dipping faults.

In Ogilvie Mountains and Stewart Plateau near Tombstone and Mayo, tightly folded, sheared, foliated and locally metamorphosed strata possibly as young as early Lower Cretaceous display a marked northwesterly and northerly directed structural asymmetry (Tempelman-Kluit, 1966). Two major thrust faults and numerous subsidiary thrust faults produce an imbrication of thrust slices above a basal *décollement.* The rocks are also involved in overturned folds (Fig. VIII-40). One major overturned syncline was later deformed by folds having northeasterly trending axes. Coarse- to medium-grained syenite, monzonite, and quartz diorite intrude the deformed sequence of Lower Cretaceous sediments and have K–Ar dates of 102 and 106 m.y. (Albian). K–Ar dates on the metamorphic rocks near Keno Hill range from 81 to

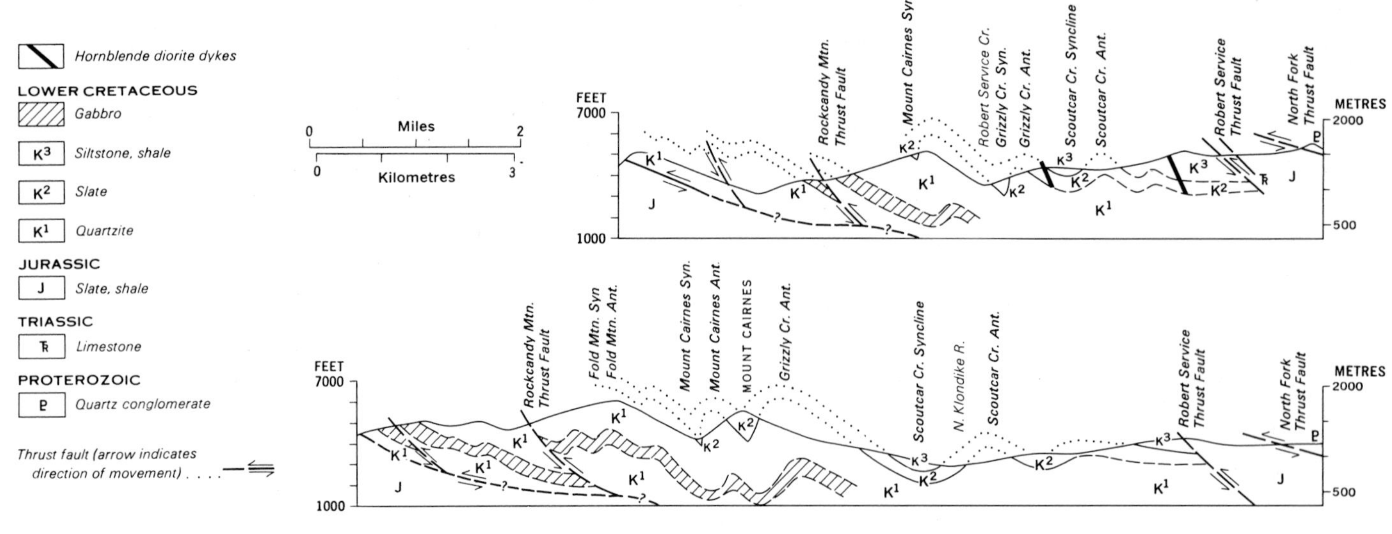

FIGURE VIII-40. Structure-section through southern Ogilvie Mountains near Tombstone, Yukon Territory (by D. J. Tempelman-Kluit).

93 m.y. and indicate a later metamorphic event that may be related to the early Laramide Orogeny.

Dacitic and basaltic flows on MacMillan Plateau dated at 100 and 117 m.y. lie with marked angular unconformity on Paleozoic strata that had been strongly deformed along northwesterly trending axes. The flows were apparently extruded on a surface of considerable relief. Similarly, strata beneath the Hutshi Group were strongly deformed along northwesterly trending axes before deposition of the volcanics. The numerous late-orogenic plutons in Selwyn Fold Belt northeast of Tintina Trench (Pl. VIII-13) are characteristically coarsely megacrystic, homogeneous, quartz monzonites. K–Ar ages from 74 to 110 m.y. suggest a considerable range in time of emplacement.

The extent of Columbian deformation in Selwyn and Mackenzie Mountains is difficult to assess. In Selwyn Fold Belt the structures are cut by plutons, some of which have yielded K–Ar dates as old as early Upper Cretaceous. In southern Mackenzie Fold Belt the Columbide structural front is limited by the presence of Albian clastic rocks and Cenomanian conglomerates (Figs. VIII-36 and 37). Major deformation in northern Mackenzie and Wernecke Mountains preceded deposition of the late Cretaceous to early Tertiary sediments of Bonnet Plume Basin but had not occurred in the region of Monster syncline in southwestern Porcupine Plateau. Probably then, the deformation in Selwyn and much of Mackenzie Mountains took place during the Columbian Orogeny.

Columbian Zwischengebirge. The Mesozoic formations in the zwischengebirge have structural characteristics that are related partly to their lithology, and hence are dependent on their competency, and partly to the behaviour of adjoining geanticlines and fault blocks. In the Mesozoic rocks of the Nechako and Quesnel Troughs the structures of the competent predominantly volcanic and volcanic-clastic rocks are broad folds, warps, and steep faults, and generally reflect relatively little shortening. They trend northwesterly or north-northeasterly in the Nicola Group at the south end of the Pinchi Geanticline and northeasterly across Skeena Arch. Tight folds and the local development of cleavage occur near the Pinchi fault and other faults bounding the Pinchi Geanticline. More tightly compressed folds are probably related to the movements between the major fault blocks, which, in the case of the Pinchi fault, continued until the mid-Tertiary.

The early Mesozoic formations of Whitehorse Trough and the Upper Jurassic and Lower Cretaceous beds of Tantalus Basin were closely folded and faulted, probably during the mid-Columbian phase, prior to being bevelled and overlain unconformably by the Upper Cretaceous Hutshi Group. The intensity of the folding is governed partly by their lithology, as tight folds are characteristic of the turbidite facies of the Laberge Group and broad, open folds are typical of the conglomerate, near-shore facies. Regional metamorphism within Columbian Zwischengebirge was slight. The Mesozoic and older rocks are generally of low greenschist facies or less. Zeolite and prehnite–pumpellyite facies occur locally and glaucophane schist facies is developed in the late Paleozoic volcanics near Pinchi fault and in Atlin Horst. The age of the latter metamorphism is uncertain and could be contemporaneous with the associated Permo-Triassic ultramafic intrusions.

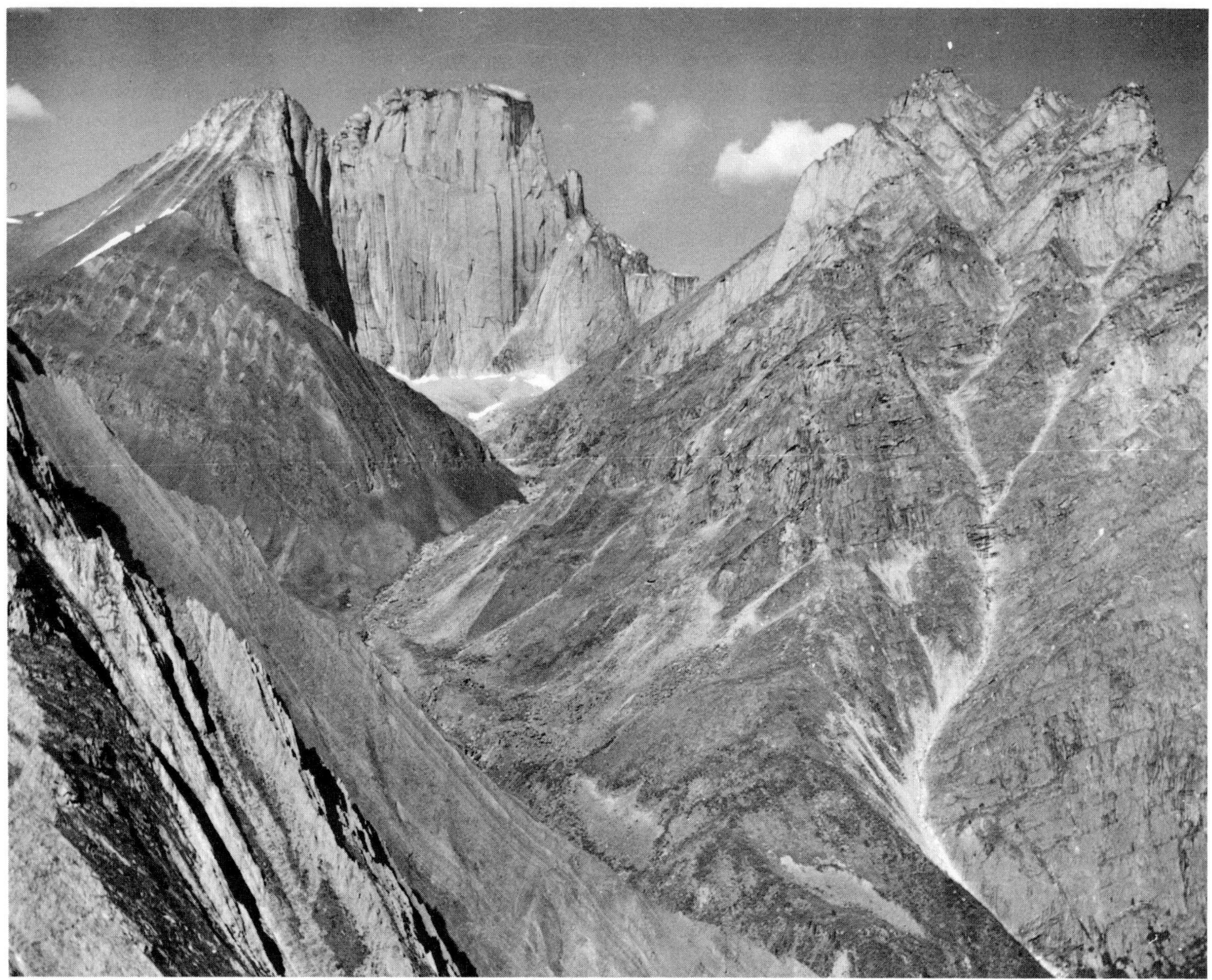

PLATE VIII-13. Late Columbian (Cretaceous) granitic pluton, forming peaks, intrusive into dark weathering Ordovician and Silurian Shales and Upper Cambrian carbonates (foreground), Ragged Range, Selwyn Mountains, Yukon Territory.

Western Columbides

The effects of Columbian Orogeny in the Coast and Cascade Mountains and Yukon Plateau have not generally been separated from those of other orogenies. They are described in the section on Plutonic Rocks.

Lower Cretaceous of Western Cordilleran Geosyncline

Tyaughton Trough. The early Lower Cretaceous, Berriasian to Barremian, part of the Relay Mountain Group has about the same facies and distribution as the Upper Jurassic part. Shaly rocks occur in the central part of the trough, and greywacke occurs on the flanks. In the northeast, the group is conformably overlain by the non-marine Jackass Mountain Group of Aptian to early Albian age. A thick lower division of greywacke and shale is overlain by a middle division of 2,000 to 3,000 feet of granite-bearing boulder conglomerate, succeeded by an upper division of several hundred feet of greywacke. The conglomerate was apparently derived from uplift to the northeast, in the southwest part of Columbian Orogen (Fig. VIII-35). In the southwest, the Relay Mountain Group is overlain by a shale and greywacke unit that is overlain conformably by the marine, late Aptian and Albian Taylor Creek Group. The basal conglomerate of the latter contains no granitic material and, although approximately equivalent in age to the conglomerate division of the Jackass Mountain Group, was probably derived from Coast Geanticline southwest of the trough. The western facies of the Taylor Creek Group is tuff and volcanic breccia with abundant black shale conformably overlain by the Upper Cretaceous Kingsvale Group.

In Fraser Valley, equivalents of the Valanginian part of the Relay Mountain Group are the Lillooet and Brew Groups (Duffell and McTaggart, 1952). Granite-bearing conglomerate occurs in the upper part of the latter. Farther south, the Dewdney Creek Group consists of several thousand feet of interbedded siltstone, volcanic arenite, greywacke, and conglomerate containing Hauterivian and Barremian fossils. A conglomerate, as much as 2,000 feet thick, occurs 300 feet above the Barremian fossils and is probably of Aptian age. It contains granitic detritus which is dissimilar to the Mount Lytton batholith and Eagle granodiorite outcropping a short distance to the northeast; the source is unknown. The Albian part is marine siltstone. The predominantly non-marine Pasayten Group to the east contains Albian plants and is interbedded with eastward protruding tongues of the marine Albian strata of the Dewdney Creek Group (J. A. Coates).

In the Coast Mountains, near Harrison Lake, Lower Cretaceous strata contain much pyroclastic debris. The Peninsula and Brokenback Hill Formations are early Berriasian to Hauterivian and lie disconformably on Middle and Upper Jurassic rocks. The Fire Lake Group farther northwest occurs as roof pendants in the Coast Plutonic Complex. It is a heterogeneous assemblage of andesitic volcanic rocks, argillite, greywacke, and granite-bearing conglomerate with Berriasian fossils. Similar roof pendants on the west side of the complex are referred to the Gambier Group (Roddick, 1965). As the debris is coarser in southernmost Coast Mountains than farther northeast the source area appears to be islands within the southernmost Coast Geanticline composed of granitic and metamorphic terrain and explosive volcanoes.

Mainly non-marine volcanic rocks of the Spences Bridge and Kingsvale Groups occur northeast of the belt of sedimentary strata deposited in Tyaughton Trough. The Spences Bridge Group comprises varicoloured porphyritic lavas of andesite, dacite, basalt, and porphyritic rhyolite and pyroclastics with blocks a foot to 2 feet wide and fragments of plant stems and twigs. Associated clastic sediments contain Aptian plants (Duffell and McTaggart, 1952). The group lies unconformably on the Cache Creek Group or the Guichon batholith and is in turn unconformably overlain by the Kingsvale Group. The basal beds of the latter are characterized by coarse clastic sediments as much as 1,000 feet thick. They contain Albian fossil plants and clasts of the Nicola Group and granitic rocks. The main part is basaltic and andesitic lavas and pyroclastic rocks that are relatively undeformed.

Two isolated occurrences of late Lower Cretaceous rocks were possibly deposited in a northern extension of Tyaughton Trough. Marine and non-marine Aptian and Albian clastic sediments were encountered in drillholes beneath Tertiary strata in the Interior Plateau west of Quesnel (H. W. Tipper). Marine Albian shales occur east of the Coast Mountains near Ootsa Lake. They are not in contact with older formations and are overlain by 2,000 to 3,000 feet of arkose succeeded by andesitic and basaltic volcanic rocks probably equivalent to the Kingsvale Group (Duffell, 1959).

Tantalus and Bowser Basins. Clastic sediments of Lower Cretaceous age occur in the upper part of the mainly Jurassic Tantalus Formation and Bowser Group. Near Hazelton, in southeastern Bowser Basin the alternating marine and non-marine Red Rose Formation, equivalent to part of the Bowser Group, is overlain conformably by the Brian Boru Formation of porphyritic andesite flows, breccias, tuff, and volcanic arenite (Sutherland Brown, 1960).

Omineca Geanticline. The Uslika Formation, which occurs in a fault-slice in Omineca Mountains, contains conglomerate with clasts as large as 10 inches in diameter of andesite and diorite (Roots, 1954; Armstrong, 1949). The sources of the latter are the early phases of the Omineca Intrusions that outcrop about 20 miles to the west. Fossil plants provisionally assigned to the Aptian occur in argillites associated with the conglomerate. Gently folded dacitic, andesitic, and basaltic flows with an aggregate thickness of more than 5,000 feet underlie a large area northeast of Tintina Trench, south of Tay River (Roddick and Green, 1961a, b). Individual flows range in thickness from 10 to 300 feet. The volcanic sequence unconformably overlies deformed Paleozoic strata and the flows are thought to have been extruded onto an erosion surface of moderate relief. Two samples of porphyritic dacite have given K–Ar dates of 117 m.y. and 100 m.y.

Pacific Continental Shelf. The One Tree Formation, which outcrops on islands off the west coast of Vancouver Island, lies disconformably on Upper Jurassic strata (Jeletzky, 1950). It is composed of clastic sediments containing marine fossils ranging in age from early Berriasian to mid-Valanginian. Near Quatsino Sound, greywacke and conglomerate contain fossils of late Valanginian to Hauterivian age and lie unconformably on the Bonanza Group or Jurassic granite. The Hauterivian is absent in the east where coquina limestone of possible early Barremian age lies disconformably or possibly unconformably on older Cretaceous rocks. The limestone is succeeded by late Barremian siltstone and sandstone which in the eastern part of Quatsino Sound are overlain by 2,000 feet of conglomerate. The conglomerate intertongues westward with quartzose sandstones. It is derived from the east and reflects uplift of the Insular Geanticline on Vancouver Island during the middle phase of the Columbian Orogeny. It is overlain by marine shales and sandstone similar to those in the Albian Haida Formation of Queen Charlotte Islands.

Late Valanginian to late Barremian clastic sediments on Queen Charlotte Islands form the Longarm Formation (Sutherland Brown, 1966). The lower part contains greywacke, conglomerate, and some volcanic rocks and the upper part consists principally of graded-bedded calcareous siltstone and greywacke that were deposited in a graben-like trough. It lies unconformably on the Jurassic Yakoun Formation and older rocks but is faulted against the Haida Formation and overlain, possibly unconformably, by the Upper Cretaceous Honna Formation. The Haida Formation comprises a lower sandstone member with Albian fauna and an upper shale member with Cenomanian and

Turonian marine fossils. It contains granitic detritus and lies unconformably on all older rocks except the Longarm Formation. Aptian beds are apparently absent on the Queen Charlotte Islands.

St. Elias Trough. The Dezadeash Group in St. Elias Mountains is composed of thick successions of graded-bedded greywacke, siltstone, and shale (Kindle, 1953). The lower beds in the eastern exposures contain coal and conglomerate with granitic clasts apparently derived from the Coast Geanticline to the northeast. The group has yielded marine fossils ranging from late Tithonian to middle Valanginian.

Selwyn and Keele Troughs. An apparently conformable sequence of clastic rocks of possible Lower Cretaceous age occurs in the Tintina–Tombstone area, Yukon Territory (Tempelman-Kluit, 1966). The succession comprises: a lower member of thick-bedded quartzite and minor black slate about 1,200 feet thick; a middle member of pale green and bright red cherty slate 100 to 200 feet thick; and an upper member of crosslaminated, lime-cemented siltstone with interbedded black slate at least 1,500 feet thick. These rocks may conformably overlie Jurassic strata and are tentatively correlated with similar sequences in part of Valanginian age, in Kandik Basin of Alaska and southern Keele Range, Yukon Territory (Frebold, *et al.*, 1967). A tholeiitic diabase and gabbro sill, 300 to 800 feet thick, intrudes the quartzite member.

Lower Cretaceous of Northern Cordilleran Geosyncline

Keele Trough. A generally conformable sequence of shale and sandstone, partly non-marine, Valanginian to Aptian in age, 4,000 to 6,000 feet thick, conformably overlies Upper Jurassic–Berriasian shales and is disconformably succeeded by Albian shales. These rocks, which were deposited in an embayment of Arctic Sea, are thought to have been derived mainly from uplift of the Brooks Geanticline during Columbian Orogeny, and partly from cratonic land adjacent to southern Richardson Mountains. In northern Richardson Mountains the lowermost Albian, 350 feet of buff, fine-grained, thinly bedded, hard, quartzose sandstone, is overlain by about 350 feet of whitish grey, fine- to coarse-grained, quartzose sandstones and associated carbonaceous siltstone, sandstone, shale, and coal. In central Richardson Mountains the North Branch conglomerate, 600 feet thick, marks the northern flank of Aklavik Arch during the Valanginian and Hauterivian. Dark grey concretionary Barremian shales and siltstones, 3,000 feet thick, conformably succeed and overlap southerly the older strata and are in turn overlain and overlapped southerly by about 600 feet of light grey, buff, fine- to medium-grained, well-sorted quartzose and micaceous sandstones. In southern Keele Range and Eagle Plain the succession is comparable to that of northern Richardson Mountains but considerably thicker.

Peel Basin. On Peel Plateau, the Albian comprises four units: a basal glauconitic sandstone as much as 350 feet thick; black to brownish grey, soft, fissile, concretionary shale with *Cleoniceras, Beaudanticeras,* and *Lemuroceras,* about 500 feet thick; some 500 to 1,000 feet of dark grey silty and bentonitic shale; and an upper silty shale and glauconitic siltstone at least 500 feet thick (E. W. Mountjoy). A fine-grained calcareous sandstone, 1,200 feet thick, in part laterally equivalent, grades northwards into the upper units. The sandstone unit contains *Gastroplites* and is overlain by 400 feet of undated silty dark brown shale and dark bluish grey concretionary shale. The Albian shales of Anderson Plain, northern Richardson Mountains, and Eagle Plain are similar and generally lie disconformably or with regional unconformity on strata as old as the Precambrian.

Mackenzie Trough. In Mackenzie Plain, between Franklin and Mackenzie Mountains, the Sans Sault Group lies unconformably on Devonian strata. It varies from 1,000 to almost 4,000 feet in thickness and consists of a basal sandstone, a middle shaly member, and an upper sandstone, all of Albian age. The overlying Slater River Formation is about 1,500 feet of marine shale, and is succeeded by the Little Bear Formation of conglomerate, sandstone, and coal, tentatively considered to be late Albian.

Lower Cretaceous of Rocky Mountain Exogeosyncline

Pre-Albian (Fig. VIII-35). Lowermost Cretaceous strata, dominantly alluvial sandstones, and shales in southern Alberta, grade northwesterly into marine mudstones and siltstones near Peace River and transitionally overlie the Jurassic Fernie Formation (Fig. VIII-41). They are bevelled in an easterly and northerly direction by a regional erosional unconformity beneath the Albian and do not extend far beneath the plains nor beyond Muskwa River in the Foothills (Figs. VIII-42, 43). The unconformity represents a major erosional interval related to epeirogenic uplift during the early phase of Columbian Orogeny.

Although partly Jurassic, the Kootenay and Nikanassin Formations probably include Lower Cretaceous strata in the more westerly and thickest sections. In southern Rocky Mountains near Fernie and Banff, coal-bearing beds and thick conglomerates with chert and quartz clasts occur at the top of the Kootenay. Carbonaceous sediments characterize the upper Nikanassin in the vicinity of Smoky River (Irish, 1951). The Minnes Formation, between Smoky and Pine Rivers, comprises sandstones, shales, and carbonaceous mudstones, 6,000 feet thick (Ziegler and Pocock, 1960). The lower part includes much quartzose sandstone considered to be marine and late Jurassic in age. The upper part, including a thick succession of coal-bearing beds similar to those of the Kootenay and Nikanassin, appears to be dominantly non-marine and contains early Lower Cretaceous spores.

In the Carbon Creek synclinorium between Pine and Peace Rivers and to the north, almost to Prophet River, the Jurassic Fernie shales and siltstones grade upward into quartzose marine sandstone of the Monteith Formation (Mathews, 1947), which is dated as late Jurassic to early

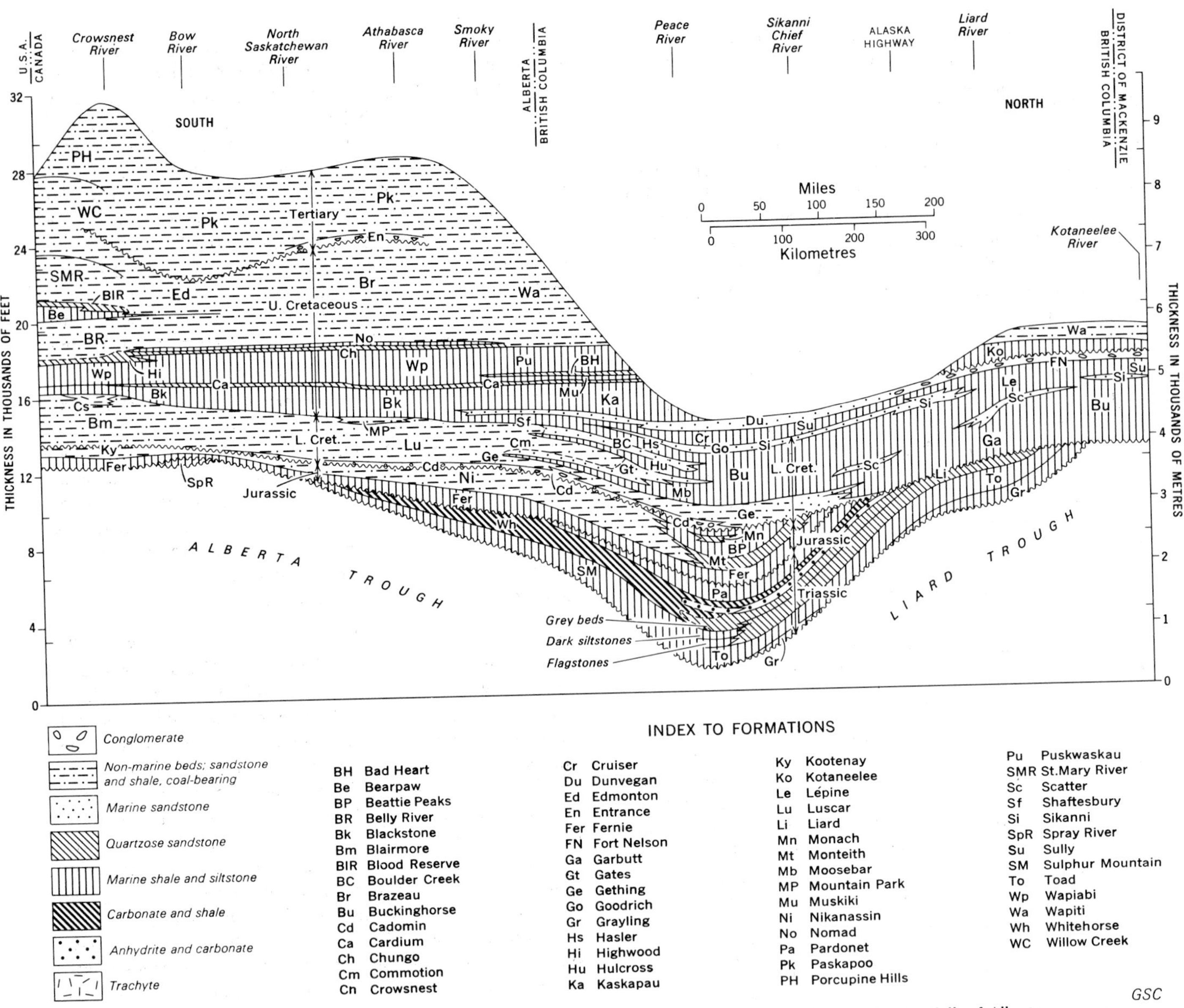

FIGURE VIII-41. Restored longitudinal stratigraphic section of Mesozoic and Tertiary rocks along the Foothills of Alberta and British Columbia (by D. F. Stott).

Valanginian. Those beds and the overlying Beattie Peaks Formation are considered to be equivalent to most of the Minnes strata north of Smoky River. The Monteith sandstones, best developed near Peace River, grade northwesterly into marine shales and siltstones similar to the overlying Beattie Peaks. The latter contains a succession of silty marine mudstones with many channel sandstones and a Valanginian fauna of *Buchia*. The middle to late Valanginian Monach Formation contains medium- to coarse-grained sandstones near Pine River which are not present north of Peace River but may be represented by some fine-grained sandstones. The uppermost beds of the succession, unnamed, include interbedded mudstone, fine-grained sandstone, and locally, thin coal seams. The southern limit of the dominantly marine, lowermost Cretaceous sediments lies along the line of Peace River Arch.

Albian (Fig. VIII-36). The Blairmore Group of the southern Foothills of Alberta is 2,500 feet thick in the west, thinning to 1,300 feet in the east. It is 6,500 feet thick in Fernie Basin in southern Rocky Mountains. The group comprises a thick wedge of non-marine detrital strata that is divisible into three formations (Mellon, 1967). The Gladstone Formation, 250 feet in more easterly exposures, comprises a widespread basal siliceous conglomerate of quartzite, chert, and argillite, or a quartzose sandstone locally termed Dalhousie sandstone, a middle unit of non-marine, dark grey, green, and red shales interbedded with calcareous siltstone, and fine-grained sandstone, and an upper "calcareous" member of dark grey, calcareous shale and silty limestone with abundant freshwater pelecypods, gastropods, and ostracods. The middle Blairmore, or Beaver Mines Formation, consists of 800 to

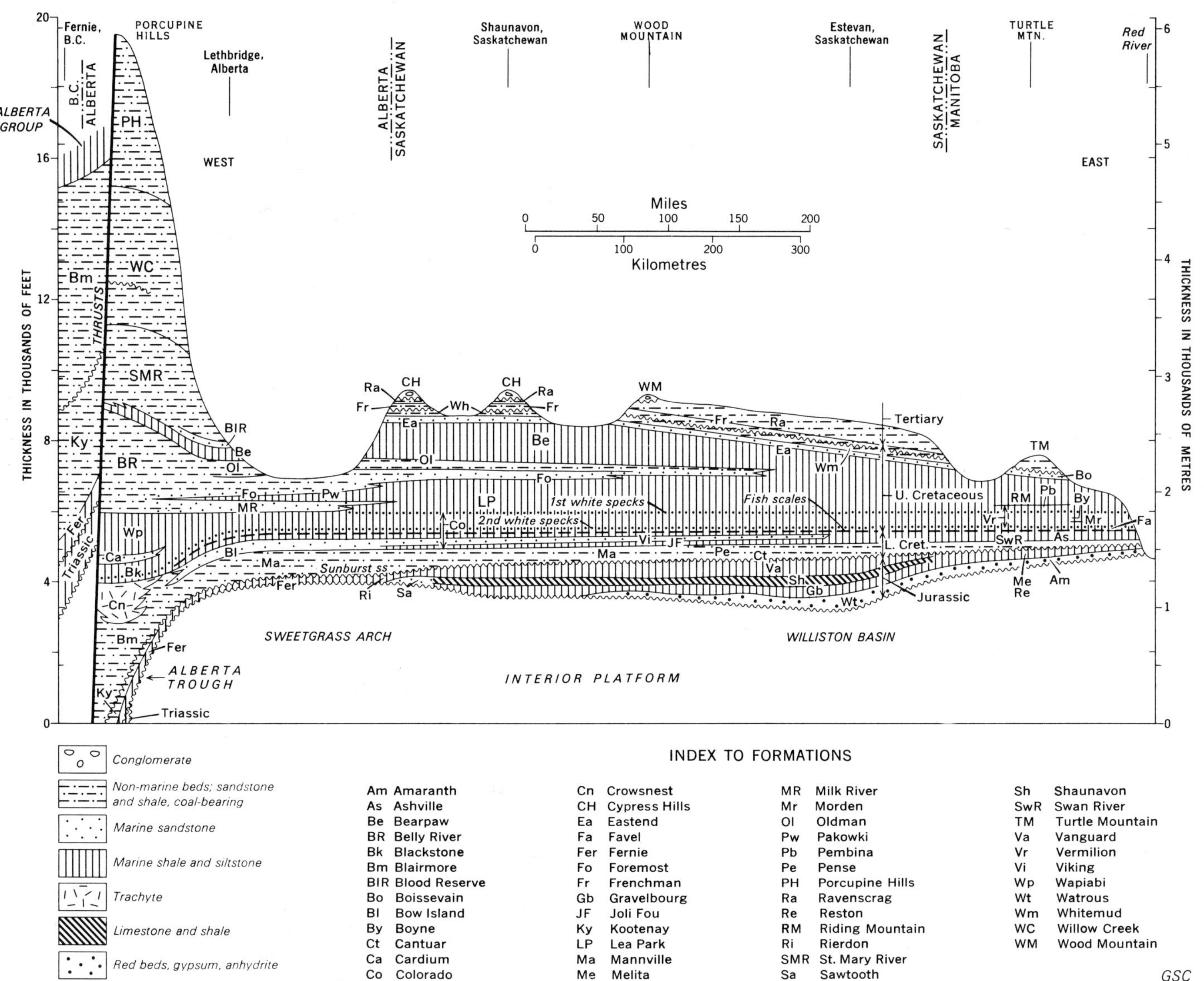

FIGURE VIII-42. Stratigraphic section of Mesozoic and Tertiary rocks from Fernie, British Columbia, across southern Alberta and Saskatchewan to Manitoba (by D. F. Stott).

1,200 feet of non-marine, varicoloured shales and green feldspathic sandstone, such as the local McDougall–Segur, that contain abundant volcanic detritus and chlorite cement, and conglomerates with igneous pebbles derived from the unroofing of the batholiths of the Omineca Geanticline to the west. A non-dicotyledonous flora, termed the Lower Blairmore flora, from Gladstone and Beaver Mines strata heretofore has been considered Aptian but recently has been found to extend upward into rocks of middle Albian age. The upper beds of the Blairmore Group in the southern Foothills differ from the lower ones, both in composition of the sandstone and in floral content. In the Crowsnest Pass region, the Mill Creek Formation, 580 feet thick, comprises quartzose cherty sandstone and green and red mottled shale that grade upward into trachytic tuff and agglomerate of the Crowsnest Formation. Near Coleman, the pyroclastic beds attain a maximum thickness of 1,600 feet but thin to the north and east, becoming interbedded with and grading into the cherty quartzose sandstone and varicoloured shales of the Mill Creek. Sanidine from the Crowsnest Formation has yielded a K–Ar date of 96 m.y. A predominantly dicotyledonous flora comprises the Upper Blairmore or Mill Creek flora. It occurs in both the sedimentary and pyroclastic beds, and is of Albian age.

In the Foothills between North Saskatchewan and Smoky Rivers, strata equivalent to the Blairmore are included in the Cadomin, Luscar, and Mountain Park Formations, which are equivalent to the Gladstone and Beaver Mines Formations of Mellon (1967). In that region, the Blairmore equivalents total 900 to 2,000 feet in thickness. The basal Cadomin conglomerate, 35 to 40 feet thick, is composed of well-indurated pebbles of quartz, chert, quartzite, and argillite. It is overlain by the lower

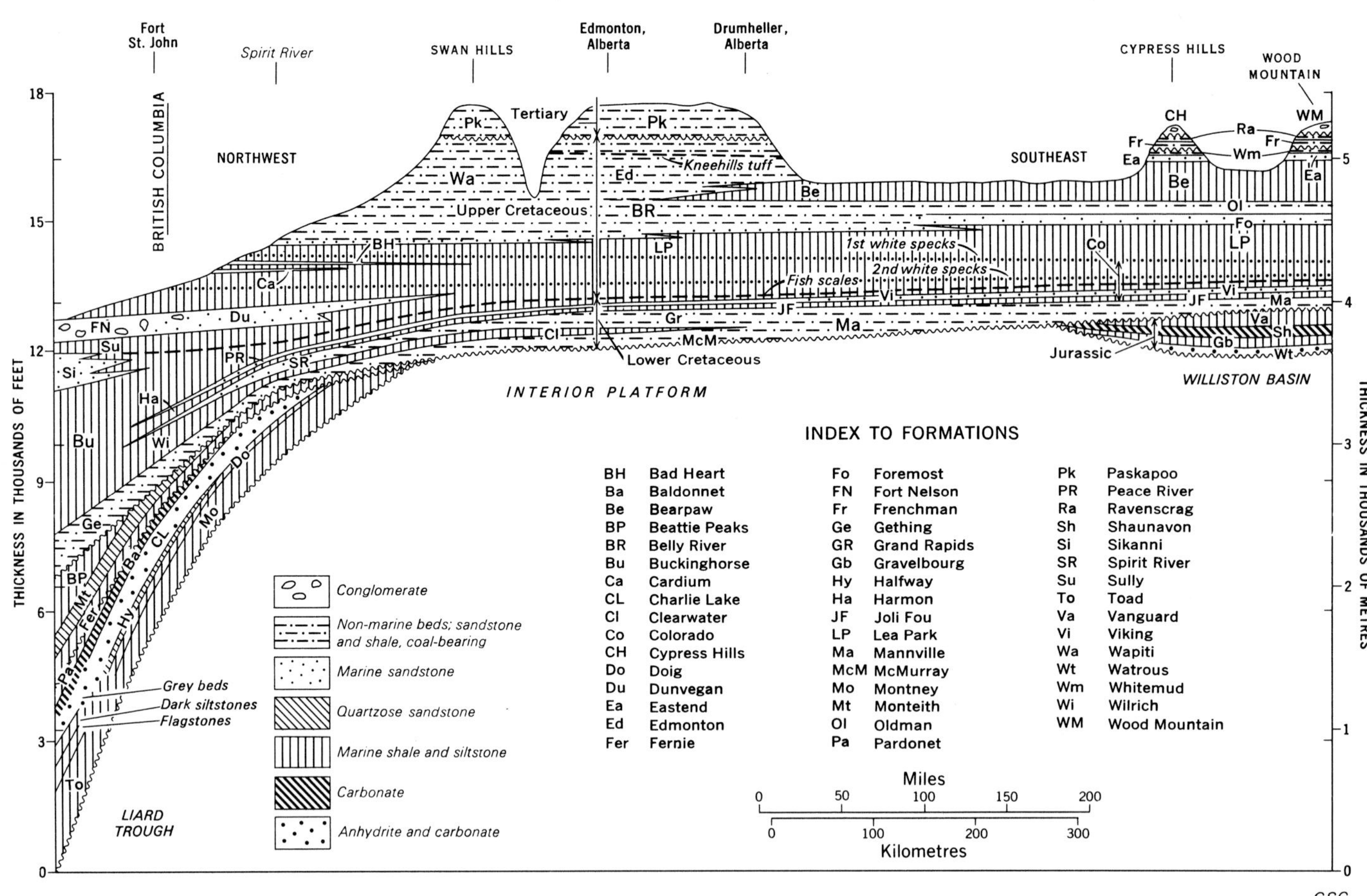

FIGURE VIII-43. Stratigraphic section of Mesozoic and Tertiary rocks from Fort St. John, northeastern British Columbia, southeastward to Saskatchewan (by D. F. Stott).

Luscar Formation equivalent of the Gladstone Formation, comprising thin-bedded, dark grey, carbonaceous shale, siltstone, and fine-grained sandstone, with 15 to 20 feet of dark grey shale with ostracods at the top. Basal Beaver Mines equivalents include 20 feet of dark grey concretionary marine shale with foraminifera correlative with that of the Moosebar Formation and Clearwater shales. The remainder of the Beaver Mines Formation consists of two facies: one previously referred to as the upper Luscar Formation, characterized by pale to medium grey rocks, cemented by illite or kaolinite and quartz, and containing commercial coal beds; and the other, the Mountain Park Formation, of green to greenish grey shales and sandstone, cemented in part by chlorite and locally conglomeratic. Beds equivalent to the Mill Creek Formation are absent in the central Foothills, owing to non-deposition or erosion.

Between Smoky and Peace Rivers, beds equivalent to the Blairmore Group are represented by sediments of the Bullhead and Fort St. John Groups, their combined thickness more than 6,000 feet (Stott, 1968). The Cadomin Formation, consisting of piedmont gravels and conglomerates, interfingers eastward with sediments of the alluvial plain, represented by the Gething Formation. The overlying marine Fort St. John shales were deposited conformably or with only a minor hiatus. The intertonguing of near-shore sandstones of the Commotion Formation with alluvial plain sediments on the one side and marine shales on the other shows that the sea was relatively shallow. The Cadomin conglomerate attains a maximum thickness of 600 feet and grades laterally northward and eastward into fine marine sandstones and argillaceous siltstones. The Gething Formation, about 1,800 feet thick on Peace River, thins rapidly eastward. It contains brown siltstones, silty and carbonaceous sandstones, grey to brown carbonaceous mudstones, and some commercial coal. The overlying Moosebar shale, merging northward with the Buckinghorse Formation, represents a major marine incursion. It thins southward to Smoky River, and is replaced by the chert sandstones of the Gates and lower Commotion Formations. The Commotion Formation contains numerous coal seams, chert sandstones, and carbonaceous shales. The lower Commotion or Gates Formation is dated as early to middle Albian and also contains the Lower Blairmore flora. The dark grey, silty marine shales of the Hulcross Member of the Commotion are overlain by and are in part laterally equivalent to the Boulder Creek deposits of well-sorted chert sandstone, carbonaceous sediments, and conglomerate deposited on an alluvial deltaic plain. The upper Commotion, with the middle Albian ammonite *Gastroplites,* contains an angiosperm flora possibly slightly older than the typical Upper Blairmore flora. The northeasterly trend of marine and non-marine facies boundaries is subparallel with the trend of faults bordering the Devonian Peace River Arch which suggests differential subsidence in the depositional basin. Marine sediments deposited during late Albian time are the dark grey, concretionary marine shales included in the Hasler Formation, the fine-grained marine sandstones of the Goodrich Formation, and the dark grey marine shales of the Cruiser Formation. The Goodrich sandstones disappear eastward and southward resulting in one continuous succession of dark grey, concretionary, silty, marine shales known as the Shaftesbury Formation. The shales overlap the non-marine beds southeastward along the Foothills. Their thickness correspondingly decreases until they are not represented in the southernmost Foothills.

Lower Cretaceous rocks between Tetsa and La Biche Rivers lie unconformably on Triassic to Mississippian sediments (Stott, 1968b). They comprise a thick succession of intertonguing deltaic and marine sandstone and shale and grade transitionally upward into the alluvial and deltaic conglomeratic sandstones of the Dunvegan Formation. The basal Garbutt dark grey, concretionary and silty marine shales, about 900 feet thick, are succeeded by the Scatter Formation, a 1,200-foot wedge comprising two major units of fine-grained, glauconitic sandstones separated by a thick shale member. The Scatter is approximately equivalent to the Commotion Formation farther south, including and overlain directly by beds containing the middle Albian *Gastroplites* fauna. The Scatter Formation is overlain transitionally by 3,000 feet of concretionary shales and thin argillaceous siltstone of the Lepine Formation. The Sikanni Formation of fine-grained nearshore sandstone is about 1,000 feet thick at Muskwa River but grades northward and eastward into silty shale and platy grey siltstone. The overlying Sully Formation comprises 1,000 feet of silty mudstone with sideritic concretions, fissile black shales, and mudstone with interbedded silty sandstone and siltstone.

The Albian succession in the Peace River region is similar to that of the Foothills to the west (Rudkin, 1964). The Cadomin extends eastward as a thin fine pebble-conglomerate or coarse-grained sandstone. The Gething coal-bearing beds are much reduced in thickness and the upper part grades laterally into glauconitic marine sandstones and shales of the Bluesky Formation. Within the overlying Spirit River Formation, the basal Wilrich marine shales gradually replace alluvial and deltaic sandstones and shales of the Falher Member. The upper Notikewin Member of well-sorted sandstone is equivalent to upper beds of the Gates Formation. The Harmon shales of the Peace River Formation represent the late middle Albian marine transgression. Well-sorted sandstones of the Cadotte and the coarse-grained sandstone and carbonaceous sediments of the Paddy Member are part of the nearshore and alluvial deltaic plain sediments associated with the transgression. They are overlain by 400 to 900 feet of Shaftesbury marine shale.

In the central and southern Interior Platform, the Albian comprises, in ascending order, the Mannville Group, Joli Fou Formation, Viking Formation, and an unnamed shale beneath the Fish Scale beds which are considered to mark the base of the Upper Cretaceous. All these beds above the Mannville are commonly included in the lower part of the Colorado Group.

The Mannville Group, ranging from 200 to 1,000 feet in thickness, has recently been subdivided in central Alberta into the McMurray and Fort Augustus Formations (Mellon, 1967). The McMurray Formation lies unconformably on Mississippian and Devonian carbonates over most of the central Alberta Plains, overlapping older Cretaceous or Jurassic detrital strata in the western part of the region. The thickness, controlled by relief on the underlying erosion surface, varies from zero to about 400 feet. The McMurray comprises three members: the basal or Deville Member, not always present, is a residual detritus formed of red and green waxy shale, chert fragments, dark brown shale, siltstone, and sandstone; the middle or Ellerslie Member consists of dark grey, silty shale, siltstone, and white kaolinitic quartz sandstone; and the upper or "calcareous" member of hard dark grey, calcareous shale and siltstone with abundant ostracods. The Fort Augustus Formation can be traced into the Beaver Mines Formation of the Foothills. The lower or Wabiskaw Member of the Fort Augustus is marine, dark grey, glauconitic shale and fine-grained, glauconitic sandstone, containing a Clearwater foraminiferal assemblage. The remainder of the Fort Augustus is of shoreline and non-marine origin, consisting of laminated shale and siltstone, and fine- to medium-grained, feldspathic sandstone, and containing a "Lower Blairmore" megaflora. The marine beds thicken to the north, grading into the Clearwater and Loon River Formations, whereas the overlying non-marine beds thin and grade laterally in the northern plains into shoreline beds, such as the Grand Rapids and Notikewin sandstones. In east-central Alberta, the basal quartzose sandstone of the Mannville was previously termed the Dina Member. It is overlain by the Cummings Member, a marine shale that includes equivalents of the Ostracod zone. In that area, the upper Mannville was divided into Islay, Tovell, Borradaile, and O'Sullivan Members on the basis of small differences in sandstone composition (Nauss, 1945).

In northeastern Alberta, the McMurray sediments were derived from the Canadian Shield to the east. They consist of 100 to 200 feet of well-sorted quartzose sandstone that is impregnated with heavy oil over a wide area, and constitutes the Athabasca Oil Sands (Fig. IX-29). A thin shale, equivalent to the Ostracod zone separates the basal beds from the glauconitic Wabiskaw sandstone. The overlying Clearwater marine shales are transitionally succeeded by carbonaceous sandstones and shales of the Grand Rapids Formation. These upper Mannville sandstones, in the Cold Lake area of Alberta, contain heavy hydrocarbons, transitional in properties between the bitumen of the Athabasca Oil Sands to the north and heavy crude oil of Lloydminster area to the south.

The Joli Fou marine shales, 60 to 110 feet thick, are widely distributed throughout the Interior Plains but disappear westward into the non-marine beds of Mill Creek Formation of the Blairmore Group. The Viking sandstone, 50 to 100 feet thick, grades eastward into siltstone and shale and into the marine shales of the Ashville Formation in Manitoba. The Viking is correlated also with the Pelican sandstone of northeastern Alberta. In southwestern Alberta, the Viking sandstones grade into dark marine shales and sandstones of the Bow Island Formation that attains a thickness of more than 400 feet. Those beds and tuffaceous beds with heulandite in the extreme southwest are equivalent to the Mill Creek or upper Blairmore and Crowsnest strata of the Foothills. The relationship of the Joli Fou and Viking Formations of the Plains with the Peace River Formation is controversial. Although stratigraphic evidence strongly favours their correlation, micropaleontological evidence suggests that the Viking and Joli Fou are slightly younger.

In southeastern Saskatchewan, the non-marine Cantuar and Pense Formations are overlain by the Ashville Group. Coarse-grained sandstones and accumulations of chert detritus occur locally at the base. In southwestern Saskatchewan the Roseray quartzose, fine- to medium-grained sandstones lying unconformably on Jurassic sediments may be of late Jurassic or early Cretaceous age. Sandstones of the Cantuar, ranging from greywacke to quartzose sandstone, are interbedded with silt, grey and green shale, coal, and variegated clay. The Pense comprises fine-grained sandstone with some interstitial white clay and interbedded silt and dark grey shale. The Ashville succession of grey marine shale is divided by the Viking sandstone into the Joli Fou shale below and an unnamed shale above. Two other sands are recognized, the Spinney Hill near the base and the widespread but lenticular Fish Scales near the top. The latter beds, although easily recognized on electric and gamma-neutron logs, have only minor lithological expression, as they are composed of shale with some sand and fish remains.

In Manitoba, the Swan River Group includes all the sandstone in the lower part of the succession. The basal part consists of discontinuous fine- to coarse-grained quartzose sandstones and light coloured clay. Shaly glauconitic sandstone, presently included in the upper part in the Swan River region, appears equivalent in part to the Viking and Joli Fou Formations of the Ashville Group farther south and west.

The latest Albian marine shales are included in the Shaftesbury Formation of Peace River Plains, the lower Colorado Group of the western Plains, and the upper Ashville Group of Manitoba. The boundary between Lower and Upper Cretaceous beds is taken as the base of the Fish Scale Sand which probably coincides with the uppermost range of the late Albian ammonite *Neogastroplites*.

Upper Cretaceous of Western Cordilleran Geosyncline

Pacific Continental Shelf. On eastern Queen Charlotte Islands the Lower Cretaceous Haida Formation is succeeded, generally conformably, by the coarse clastic Honna Formation that contains granite-bearing conglomerates and by the shales of the Skidegate Formation. These sediments totalling 6,000 feet, and a granite-bearing conglomerate near Bella-Bella, were deposited in Hecate Basin which probably extended southeast of Queen Charlotte Islands, and formed slightly earlier than Georgia Basin.

The Nanaimo and Comox Groups in Georgia Basin on Vancouver Island consist of marine and intertonguing marine, shoreline, and coal-bearing non-marine clastic sediments that were derived from the erosion of the mountains in central Vancouver Island (Buckham, 1947). The rapidly subsiding basin formed between Coast and Insular Geanticlines, on the site of the present Strait of Georgia and western Coast Mountains. Non-marine tongues are typically represented by conglomerate and sandstone units, and the marine facies by shales. The sediments, which range from late Santonian to late Maestrichtian in age, lie with angular unconformity or nonconformity upon older rocks and Jurassic plutons.

In the eastern part of Georgia Basin, in the Mount Garibaldi region north of Vancouver, a conglomeratic basal unit, the Cheakamus Formation, containing Campanian marine fossils rests unconformably on altered quartz diorite of the Coast Plutonic Complex (Mathews, 1958). The total thickness of the Cheakamus and overlying Empetrum and Helm Formations may be more than 20,000 feet. They occur in a fault block and are intruded by later phases of the Coast Plutonic Complex. Near Vancouver the base of the Burrard Formation is a conglomerate, with granitic boulders, which lies unconformably on the Coast Plutonic Complex. Fossil plants and microflora from the lower part of the Burrard Formation are mainly Campanian, whereas the upper part is possibly early Tertiary. In a drillhole on Fraser Delta the Burrard Formation is 14,000 feet thick and lies on granitic rocks.

Columbian Zwischengebirge. The lower part of the Ootsa Lake Group which lies unconformably on all older rocks may contain Upper Cretaceous strata. Freshwater molluscs from the base of the andesitic unit near Ootsa Lake may be Upper Cretaceous age although associated fossil plants are regarded as Paleocene (Tipper, 1963).

The Sustut Group comprises non-marine clastic sediments with abundant granitic detritus derived from the Omineca Intrusions to the northeast (Lord, 1948). In places the group is separable into a lower division of conglomerate and pebbly sandstone and an upper division of sandstone and shale, with several thin bands of white-weathering dacitic tuff near the base. It forms a northwest-trending belt and was apparently deposited in a broad intermontane valley or trench. The group has yielded fossil plants probably of Cenomanian age and others that are Paleocene. It lies unconformably on older rocks in the valleys but occurs also as upland remnants in northern Omineca Mountains.

The Hutshi Group in southwestern Yukon Territory overlies Lower Cretaceous and older strata with marked angular unconformity and is intruded by granodiorite and pink granophyric quartz monzonite. The group comprises gently folded flows and flow breccias that range from basalt to rhyolite, with agglomerate, tuff, and minor clastic sedimentary rocks. Conglomerates and breccias commonly occur at the base. Locally, the group is more than 3,000 feet thick.

Eastern Columbides. Near Rossland in the Monashee Mountains, the Sophie Mountain Formation of quartzitic conglomerate and minor argillite contains fossil plants of Cenomanian to Campanian age. The formation is not observed in contact with other units but probably rests unconformably on older rocks. It contains no fragments of the nearby Nelson batholith and the source of the quartzite pebbles is unknown.

The Upper Cretaceous and Paleocene Sifton Formation and related rocks in northern Rocky Mountain Trench comprise conglomerate, sandstone, shale, and minor coal. Most of the clasts in the conglomerate are limestone with some sandstone, quartzite, chert, dolomite, and argillite that appear to have been derived from the east. In places the conglomerates become coarser and more abundant towards the east. Some with coarse, angular clasts along the eastern margin of outcrop may be in part of fanglomeratic origin.

In Cassiar Mountains, two northwesterly trending trench-like valleys bounded by major faults are underlain by gently dipping sandstones, conglomerates, and shales, variably carbonaceous, and locally containing seams of coal. Near Turnagain River a flora, dated as Santonian–Campanian, has been found.

Upper Cretaceous of Northern Cordilleran Geosyncline

The Eagle Plain Formation lies unconformably on Albian shales and the Mississippian. It consists of 2,000 feet of fine- to medium-grained sandstone, light brownish grey and arkosic, with crossbedding indicating a generally northeasterly direction of sediment transport (Mountjoy, 1967b). These strata are overlain by 1,200 feet of silty shale with thin interbeds of siltstone and sandstone and plants of Cenomanian age *Inoceramus* ex gr. *dunveganensis* have been collected.

Soft, dark grey shales of Cenomanian and Turonian age occur in northern Richardson Mountains (Jeletzky, 1961). They are about 1,000 feet thick, weather orange or bluish grey, and rest unconformably on Aptian sandstone. The shales are the youngest rocks cut by dextral wrench faults bounding Richardson Mountains, some displacement having taken place during the Laramide Orogeny. Grey marine Turonian shales occur in a fault slice at Fort Norman in Franklin Mountains.

In northern Yukon Territory and northwestern District of Mackenzie late Upper Cretaceous and early Tertiary non-marine clastic strata are present in several small areas. These strata may be of various ages as most available plant material is not diagnostic, but all lie with angular or regional unconformity on deformed or disturbed strata and are deformed to various degrees as the result of the late phase of Laramide Orogeny in early Tertiary. They are considered to be post-orogenic or synorogenic. It is improbable that the remnants were part of a once continuous sheet of sediments, although those of Arctic Coastal Plain may be, and, accordingly, would grade offshore into marine equivalents on the Arctic Continental Shelf and the Mackenzie Delta. The Monster Formation, in Ogilvie Mountains, is composed of 4,000 feet of dark brownish grey, medium- to coarse-grained, crossbedded arkosic sandstone (Mountjoy, 1967b). Thick beds alternate with covered intervals that are presumed to be argillaceous rocks. Some beds are conglomeratic, the pebbles of quartz and chert being well rounded and as large as 3 inches in diameter. Upper Cretaceous plants are present in the lower half. These are the youngest rocks in the region and rest with regional unconformity on the Triassic and Permian. The lithologically similar Bonnet Plume Formation on Peel River rests with angular unconformity on deformed lower Paleozoic strata. It may lie in a fault-bounded basin. The lignite, with late Cretaceous or early Tertiary spores, lies near the top of the formation which has a maximum thickness of 5,000 feet. The Moose Channel Formation west of Mackenzie Delta includes a 7-foot, sub-bituminous coal seam, utilized locally. The formation is more than 200 feet thick and consists mainly of feldspathic, coarse-grained sandstone.

Upper Cretaceous of the Rocky Mountain Exogeosyncline

Upper Cretaceous strata immediately underlie much of the Interior Platform, extending from within the Foothills almost to the Canadian Shield (Figs. VIII-37, -44). At the western limit of their exposure, they attain a maximum of 12,000 feet but thin rapidly to less than 4,000 feet in the east (Figs. VIII-42, -43). The sediments, mostly sandstone and shale, were derived mainly from late Columbian and early Laramide uplifts in the Cordilleran Geosyncline; a small amount of detrital material was probably contributed by the Shield. The rocks of Cenomanian to Santonian age are, except for the deltaic deposits of the Dunvegan Formation, almost entirely marine and constitute the Alberta, Smoky, and Colorado Groups (Fig. VIII-41). Extensive alluvial sediments deposited after mid-Campanian time are found in the Belly River and Edmonton Formations.

The Alberta Group extends along the Foothills from Montana to Athabasca River (Stott, 1963). Within it, the Blackstone and Wapiabi Formations, consisting of

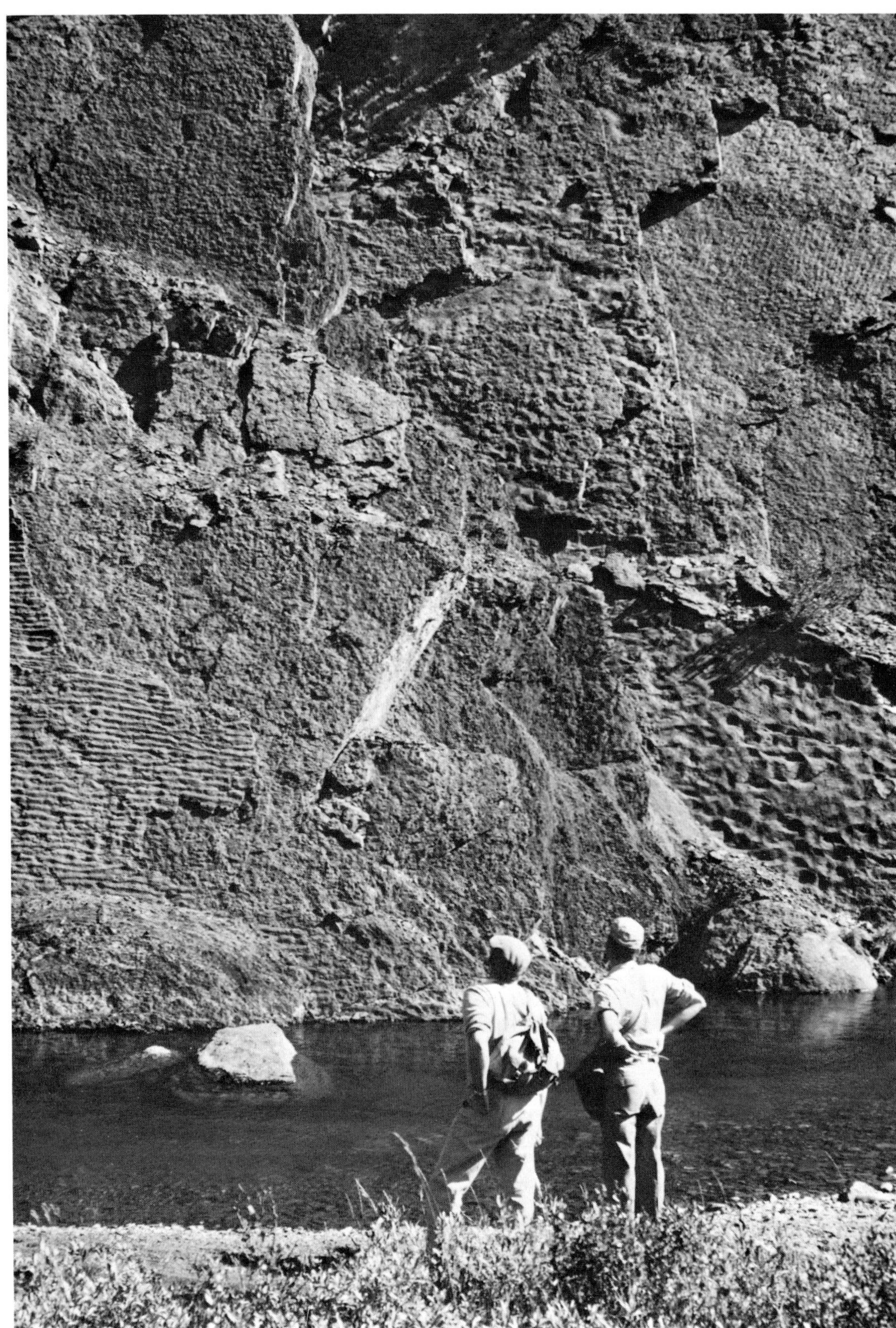

PLATE VIII-14
Ripple-marks on several bedding surfaces on sandstones of Upper Cretaceous Sunkay Member, Blackstone Formation, Burnt Timber Creek, Foothills of Alberta.

marine shales, are separated by arenaceous epineritic and shoreline beds of the Cardium Formation. The Blackstone Formation is characterized by fossil zones of Cenomanian to Turonian age. The basal Sunkay Member, which includes the Fish Scale beds in the central Foothills, overlaps the Blairmore Group in a southerly direction, disappearing almost completely in southwestern Alberta where the Blackstone disconformably overlies the Crowsnest volcanic rocks. The Sunkay Member, representing a marine transgression, has a thin layer of chert pebbles at the base and contains sideritic, rusty weathering, silty shale, mudstone and sandstone (Pl. VIII-14). The Vimy Member, developed during the inundative phase, contains shales that are calcareous to dolomitic, gypsiferous, and pyritic. The Haven and Opabin Members, formed by regressive sediments similar to the transgressive deposits, grade upward into thick-bedded, fine- to medium-grained sandstone. In the central Foothills, the relatively thin Cardium Formation contains littoral marine beds of thick-bedded, well sorted, fine-grained cherty sandstone; the basal unit extends eastward beneath the Plains and at Pembina oil field forms one of the largest reservoirs in Canada (Fig. IX-24d). The Cardium also includes marine shales and lagoonal and marsh deposits of carbonaceous shales, siltstones, argillaceous sandstone, and some coal. The Cardium sandstones grade laterally eastward into shaly siltstones and shales. The overlying marine shales of the Wapiabi Formation include several zones of *Scaphites* ranging from Coniacian to Santonian. The transgressive deposits of rusty weathering sideritic shales and siltstones are included in the Muskiki, Marshybank, and Dowling Members. The inundative facies is represented by calcareous shales of the Thistle Member. A major regression is recorded in the blocky to rubbly, silty mudstones of the Hanson Member and in the overlying fine-grained sandstone to argillaceous siltstone of the Chungo Member. A non-marine facies of greyish green shales with thin coal beds occurs in the Chungo at a few places along the western Foothills. A short-lived transgression, probably related to Lea Park of the Plains, is represented by dark grey shales, thin siltstones, and sandstones of the Nomad Member. South of Highwood River, beds equivalent to the upper three members of the Wapiabi contain much sandstone and are included in the Belly River Formation of the Foothills.

North of Athabasca River, some shales and siltstones of the Sunkay Member of the Blackstone Formation grade into massive sandstone that constitutes the Dunvegan Formation. The overlying marine strata form the Smoky Group and the marine shales between the Blairmore Group and the Dunvegan Formation are the Shaftesbury Formation (Stott, 1967). The Dunvegan Formation contains interbedded marine and non-marine shales and sandstones of Cenomanian age that thicken northward to more than 1,200 feet. Several major sandstone lobes extend from the Peace River Foothills into the Plains of British Columbia and Alberta forming a complex delta. The formation averages about 500 feet in thickness north of Peace River and becomes conglomeratic.

The Smoky Group is divided into the Kaskapau, Bad Heart, and Puskwaskau Formations. Along the Foothills, the Kaskapau contains much siltstone in the lower and middle parts that grades northward near Peace River into several prominent sandstones. These near-shore sandstones may be related to the underlying Dunvegan Formation and may also be associated with a broadening of the uplift of the central part of the Omineca Geanticline to the west. Sideritic shales of the upper Haven and Opabin Members of the Kaskapau grade upward into epineritic sandstones of the Cardium Formation. The Cardium Formation is present in the Foothills below the Bad Heart sandstone and the intervening shale is called Muskiki. The Cardium Formation grades laterally eastward into silty shales and is represented on lower Smoky River only by a pebble bed. The Bad Heart Formation of the Foothills contains well-sorted sandstone similar to that of the Cardium. In the Plains, it is highly glauconitic and is succeeded by sideritic and calcareous shales of the Dowling and Thistle Members of the Puskwaskau Formation. The upper beds of the Puskwaskau are transitional with overlying coarse-grained sandstones and coal-bearing beds of the Wapiti Formation. As in the Wapiabi Formation of the southern Foothills, the uppermost marine shales of the Puskwaskau intertongue westward with arenaceous sediments, grading laterally into non-marine strata of the Wapiti Formation.

In the Liard River region, the Dunvegan Formation, formerly referred to as the Fort Nelson Formation, consists of 500 to 600 feet of massive conglomerate, coarse-grained sandstone, carbonaceous shales, and a few thin coal seams (Stott, 1960). A regional disconformity, representing the Turonian stage, separates it from the overlying Kotaneelee marine shales. The hiatus is possibly related to uplifts associated with the late Columbian Orogeny, the intrusion of the Cassiar batholith, and the granitic bodies in Yukon Territory (Fig. VIII-37). The Kotaneelee dark grey, sideritic shales, exposed in only a few localities, grade upward into the Wapiti Formation of dominantly continental sandstones, shales, and minor coal.

In the Plains, marine beds above the Mannville Group are generally assigned to the Colorado Group, the lower part of which is Lower Cretaceous (Williams and Burk, 1964). Equivalent beds are the Lloydminster shale in eastern Alberta and the La Biche shales of northeastern Alberta. They are dark grey, bentonitic and concretionary shales, and include the Fish Scale marker horizon toward the base and two units of calcareous shale, termed the Second (Lower) and First (Upper) White Specks. In southern Alberta, the Colorado shales grade upward into well-sorted sandstones of the Milk River Formation that in turn are overlain by marine shales of the Pakowki Formation. The Milk River sandstones merge westward with the lower part of the Belly River Formation and, in east-central Alberta, grade into about 1,000 feet of grey marine shales constituting the Lea Park Formation. The Belly River Group of the Plains, averaging about 900 to 1,000 feet, comprises the Foremost and Oldman Formations (Russell and Landes, 1940). In eastern Alberta, nine members representing tongues of marine shales and deltaic sediments are recognized within strata equivalent to the Foremost (Shaw and Harding, 1954). Throughout most of southern Alberta and as far north as Edmonton, the Belly River is overlain by marine shale of the

Bearpaw Formation (Lines, 1963). Progressively younger shales occur at the top of the Bearpaw from west to east in southeastern Alberta and Saskatchewan, and the thickness of the formation ranges from less than 100 feet near the Foothills to as much as 1,200 feet in the east.

The Belly River Formation and its equivalents form a thick wedge of clastic sediments that extends from the Foothills into Saskatchewan. These continental beds, several thousands of feet thick in the west, thin to a few hundred feet in the east and grade laterally into marine rocks (Fig. VIII-42). In the southern Foothills, the Belly River Formation, about 2,000 feet of green sandstone and shale with some coal, is overlain by 800 feet of marine shales included in the Bearpaw Formation. These beds lie below 2,500 feet of non-marine, hard sandstone and shale of the St. Mary River Formation (Douglas, 1950). Well-sorted marine sandstone immediately overlying the Bearpaw is locally known as the Blood Reserve Formation. The Willow Creek Formation, lying transitionally above the St. Mary River is about 4,000 feet thick. The lower part comprises grey-weathering sandstone with interbedded varicoloured shales that grade into the upper part of massive buff-weathering sandstone and brown shale. No hiatus is recognized within the formation although the lower part contains Upper Cretaceous non-marine invertebrates and the upper part contains a typical Paleocene fauna (Tozer, 1956).

The Edmonton Formation of central Alberta, 1,100 to 2,500 feet thick, includes all Cretaceous non-marine beds equivalent to the Bearpaw shale, or lying above it. (Ower, 1960; Williams and Burk, 1964). It consists of soft sandstones, bentonitic and silty shales. Coal seams are common in the lower and upper parts and a marine limestone tongue, the Drumheller Member, occurs locally in the lower part. The Kneehills Tuff, the most distinctive and persistent marker, is in dark bentonitic shales underlain by white clay and sandstone near the middle of the formation. An abundant dinosaurian fauna has been obtained from the formation in the Drumheller badlands.

The marine shales of the Bearpaw Formation of southwestern and central Alberta are not recognized in the central and northern Foothills, and separation of Belly River strata from similar non-marine beds of the younger Edmonton Formation is not possible, the entire succession being included in the Brazeau or Wapiti Formations. The lower beds of the Brazeau, 800 to 1,500 feet thick, include quartz pebble sandstone and conglomerates. The remainder of the formation consists of about 5,000 feet of interbedded, medium- to coarse-grained, greenish grey sandstone with interbedded shale, some tuff, and thin coal seams. It is overlain by the Entrance basal conglomerate and thick deposits of Paleocene age. The Wapiti Formation, approximately equivalent to the Brazeau has been divided into five members (Allan and Carr, 1946). The equivalent to the Kneehills Tuff, a widespread time and stratigraphic marker, occurs near the base of the uppermost member.

In the Cypress Hills of southeastern Alberta and southwestern Saskatchewan, the Bearpaw shales are overlain by very fine grained marine sandstones of the Eastend Formation. The succeeding Whitemud, 15 to 75 feet thick, includes white to light grey refractory clays, siltstones, and sandstones. The Battle Formation contains dark grey to purplish bentonitic shale with the Kneehills Tuff occurring near the top. In southwestern Saskatchewan, the Battle, Whitemud, and Eastend Formations are bevelled beneath *Triceratops*-bearing beds of the Frenchman Formation which grade transitionally upward into the Paleocene Ravenscrag (Furnival, 1946). The Frenchman consists of about 200 feet of medium-grained sandstone with carbonaceous and bentonitic shales.

Upper Cretaceous rocks of eastern Saskatchewan and Manitoba, about 1,800 feet thick, are dominantly marine shales (Wickenden, 1945). The Fish Scale beds are in the Ashville Group which extends stratigraphically to the top of the Second White Specks shale. The latter forms the Keld Member of the Favel Formation. The Vermilion River Formation, lying above the Favel with apparent conformity, consists of the Morden, Boyne, and Pembina Members. The Boyne includes the First White Specks shale. The Pembina dark grey, non-calcareous shales are post-Colorado in age. The Riding Mountain Formation probably contains beds equivalent to most of the Milk River, Pakowki, Foremost, Oldman, and Bearpaw Formations. It consists of green clays, grey siliceous shales, and dark grey bentonitic shales, and ranges in thickness from 700 feet in southern Manitoba to 1,500 feet in southern Saskatchewan. The succeeding Boissevain Formation, about 100 feet thick, contains greenish grey sandstone.

CENOZOIC

Tertiary

Tectonic Summary

In the Tertiary almost all of western Canada was land. The mountain belts formed during Columbian Orogeny were rejuvenated and new mountain belts were produced by the Laramide Orogeny, the early phase of which began in the late Upper Cretaceous and the late phase ended probably early in the Oligocene (Fig. VIII-44). The principal effects of the orogeny were the development of most of the easternmost and northernmost structural elements of the Cordilleran Region: the linear Rocky Mountain Thrust Belt, the arcuate Mackenzie Fold Belt, and the Northern Yukon Fold Complex. The structures

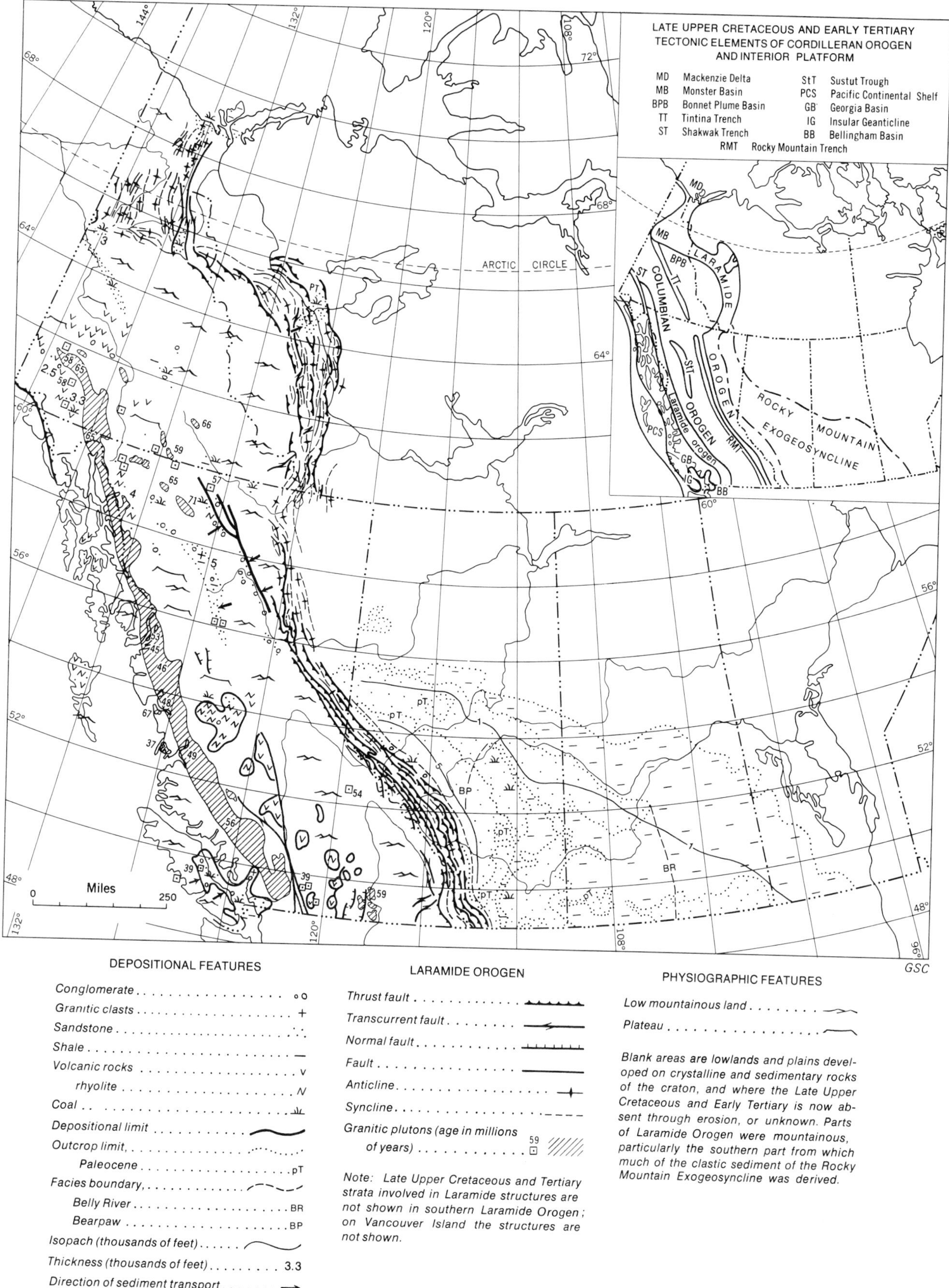

LATE UPPER CRETACEOUS AND EARLY TERTIARY TECTONIC ELEMENTS OF CORDILLERAN OROGEN AND INTERIOR PLATFORM
MD Mackenzie Delta
MB Monster Basin
BPB Bonnet Plume Basin
TT Tintina Trench
ST Shakwak Trench
StT Sustut Trough
PCS Pacific Continental Shelf
GB Georgia Basin
IG Insular Geanticline
BB Bellingham Basin
RMT Rocky Mountain Trench
COLUMBIAN OROGEN
LARAMIDE OROGEN
ROCKY MOUNTAIN EXOGEOSYNCLINE
ARCTIC CIRCLE
Miles
0
250
DEPOSITIONAL FEATURES
Conglomerate
Granitic clasts
Sandstone
Shale
Volcanic rocks
rhyolite
Coal
Depositional limit
Outcrop limit,
Paleocene
Facies boundary,
Belly River ... BR
Bearpaw ... BP
Isopach (thousands of feet)
Thickness (thousands of feet) ... 3.3
Direction of sediment transport
LARAMIDE OROGEN
Thrust fault
Transcurrent fault
Normal fault
Fault
Anticline
Syncline
Granitic plutons (age in millions of years)
Note: Late Upper Cretaceous and Tertiary strata involved in Laramide structures are not shown in southern Laramide Orogen; on Vancouver Island the structures are not shown.
PHYSIOGRAPHIC FEATURES
Low mountainous land
Plateau
Blank areas are lowlands and plains developed on crystalline and sedimentary rocks of the craton, and where the Late Upper Cretaceous and Early Tertiary is now absent through erosion, or unknown. Parts of Laramide Orogen were mountainous, particularly the southern part from which much of the clastic sediment of the Rocky Mountain Exogeosyncline was derived.
GSC

FIGURE VIII-44. Late Upper Cretaceous and early Tertiary sedimentation and tectonism in Western Canada, and some features of the Laramide Orogeny.

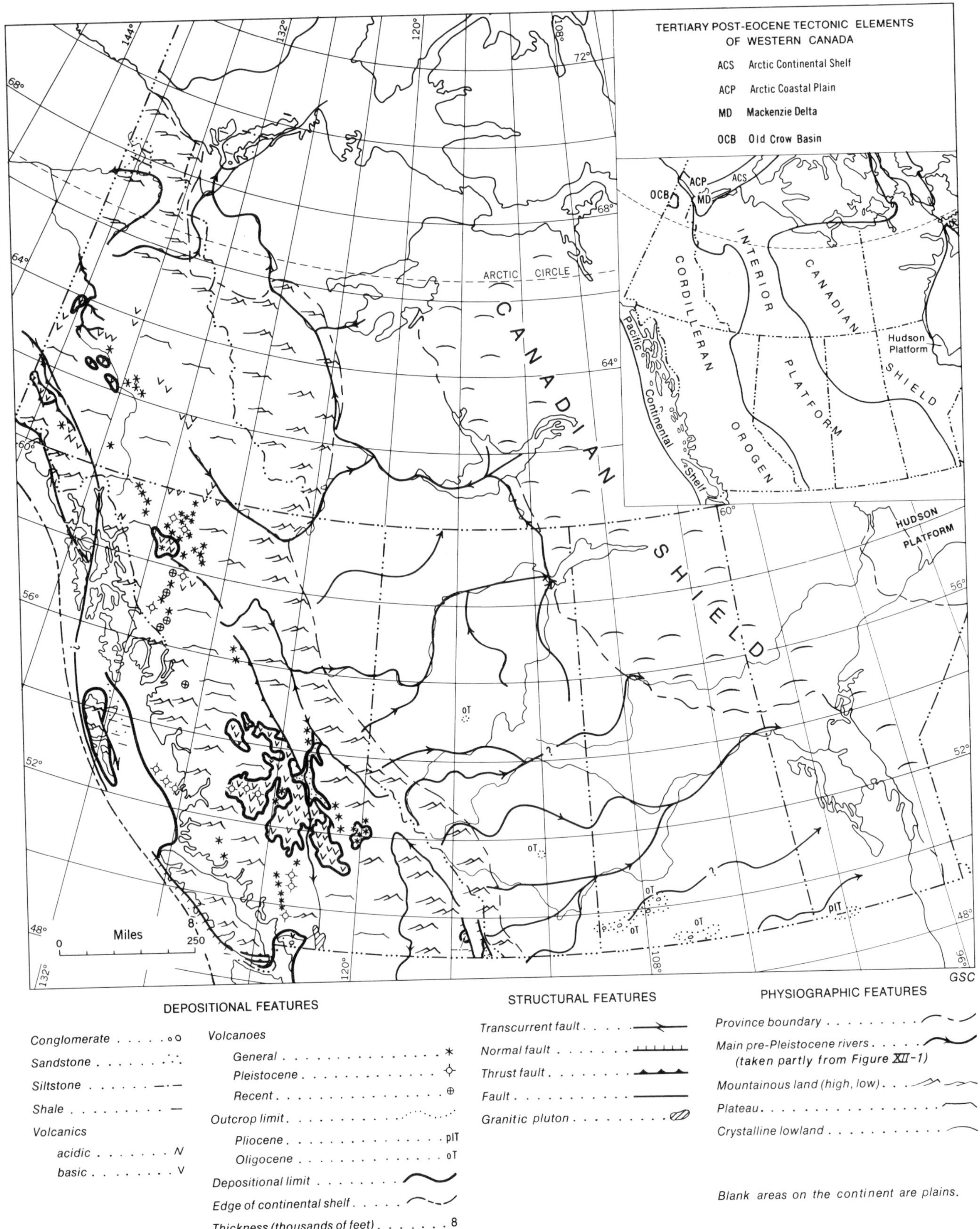
TERTIARY POST-EOCENE TECTONIC ELEMENTS OF WESTERN CANADA
ACS Arctic Continental Shelf
ACP Arctic Coastal Plain
MD Mackenzie Delta
OCB Old Crow Basin
CORDILLERAN OROGEN
INTERIOR PLATFORM
CANADIAN SHIELD
Hudson Platform
Pacific Continental Shelf
ARCTIC CIRCLE
CANADIAN SHIELD
HUDSON PLATFORM
Miles
0
250
GSC
DEPOSITIONAL FEATURES
Conglomerate
Sandstone
Siltstone
Shale
Volcanics
acidic
basic
Volcanoes
General
Pleistocene
Recent
Outcrop limit
Pliocene
Oligocene
Depositional limit
Edge of continental shelf
Thickness (thousands of feet)
STRUCTURAL FEATURES
Transcurrent fault
Normal fault
Thrust fault
Fault
Granitic pluton
PHYSIOGRAPHIC FEATURES
Province boundary
Main pre-Pleistocene rivers (taken partly from Figure XII-1)
Mountainous land (high, low)
Plateau
Crystalline lowland
Blank areas on the continent are plains.

FIGURE VIII-45. Tertiary, post-Eocene, sedimentation and tectonism in Western Canada.

of the Columbian and older orogens were slightly modified and some movement took place on previously formed faults. Scattered, discordant bodies of quartz monzonite, granite, syenite, and quartz diorite were intruded in the western Cordillera. They include small stocks and sills related to volcanic extrusives in Columbian Zwischengebirge and Insular Fold Belt, small batholiths in the southeastern Columbides, and several batholiths of the eastern Coast Plutonic Complex that were accompanied by faulting and minor folding.

During the early Tertiary, deposition continued in most of the negative tectonic elements that were established during the latest Upper Cretaceous: the Rocky Mountain Exogeosyncline, the Pacific and Arctic Continental Shelves, and the intermontane valleys and trenches of the Cordilleran interior. The deposits were mainly non-marine, synorogenic, clastic sediments. Succeeding volcanic sequences are mainly Eocene. They are mostly subaerial, occurring contemporaneously with tilting and faulting, or related to the intrusion of some of the Laramide granitic stocks. They form several distinct provinces: partly marine basalt and rhyolite that accumulated on the Pacific Continental Shelf; basalt and rhyolite of the St. Elias Mountains; dacite and rhyolite of the central Interior Plateau; andesite, and trachyandesite of the southern Interior Plateau.

During the mid-Tertiary erosion was dominant, both in the Cordilleran Region and on the Interior Plains (Fig. VIII-45). Widespread surfaces of low relief and peneplains were produced, and some of the larger elements of the present drainage system were established, but little of the debris produced is preserved except possibly on the Arctic and Pacific Continental Shelves. Some gravels occur on the southern Interior Plains. In the mountains, faulting contributed to the formation of small intermontane basins where fluviatile and lacustrine sediments accumulated. Marine clastic sediments were deposited on the Pacific Continental Shelf along the west coast of Vancouver Island and along the east coast of northern Queen Charlotte Islands. In the late Tertiary, basalt and olivine basalt erupted from fissures and shield volcanoes. The flows covered large parts of the undulating erosion surfaces of the Interior Plateau and penetrated into the valleys of Columbia Mountains. Some thrusting and folding took place in St. Elias Mountains. Transcurrent movements occurred on many of the major faults, and on some displacement has continued to the present. Plutonism occurred in the core of Cascade Fold Belt. Differential uplift in the Pliocene resulted in the elevation of Coast Mountains, parts of the Interior Plateau, and Rocky Mountains. Many small volcanoes formed, some apparently aligned along faults or zones of weakness. The activity continued locally into the Pleistocene, eruption taking place beneath or on top of the ice sheets.

Laramide Orogeny

During the Laramide Orogeny the layered miogeosynclinal and exogeosynclinal sequences on the eastern and northern elements of the Cordilleran Geosyncline were deformed and many of the structural features of the Eastern Cordilleran Orogen were produced (Fig. VIII-44). The orogeny is herein considered to have taken place during and immediately subsequent to the deposition of the late Upper Cretaceous and early Tertiary non-marine clastic

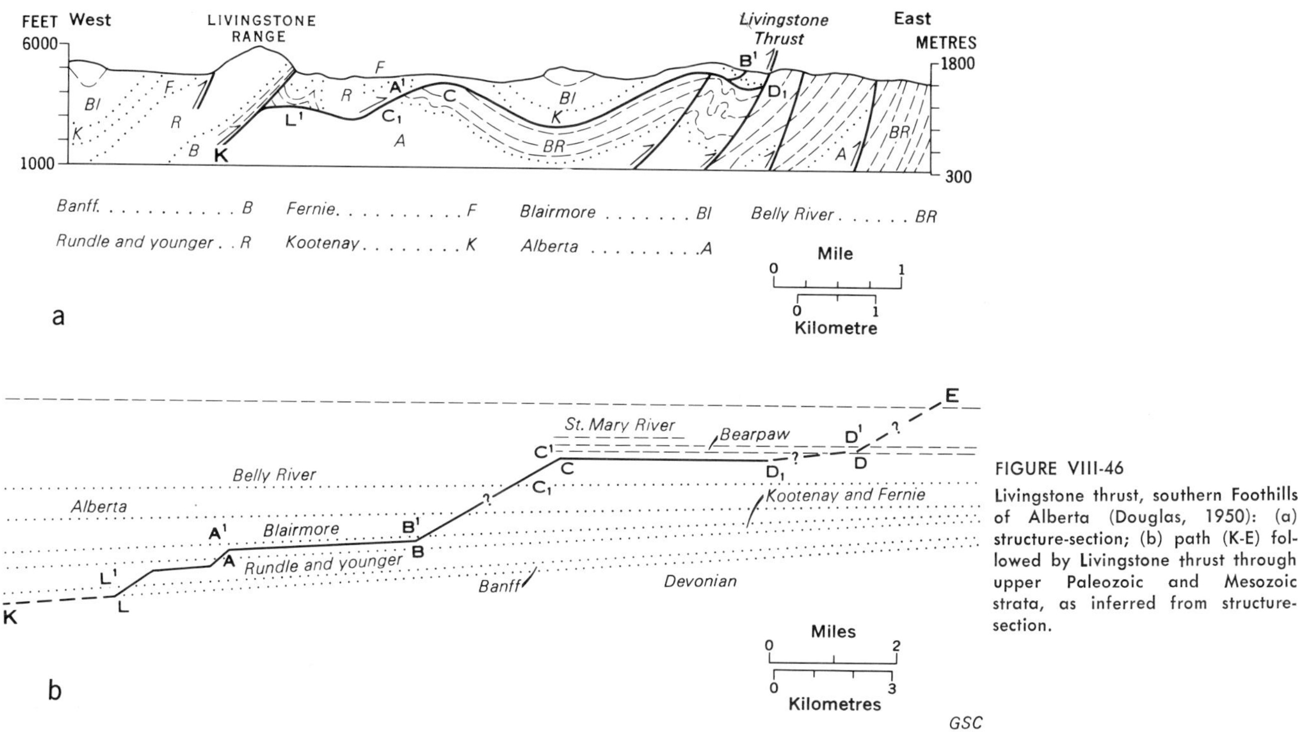

FIGURE VIII-46
Livingstone thrust, southern Foothills of Alberta (Douglas, 1950): (a) structure-section; (b) path (K-E) followed by Livingstone thrust through upper Paleozoic and Mesozoic strata, as inferred from structure-section.

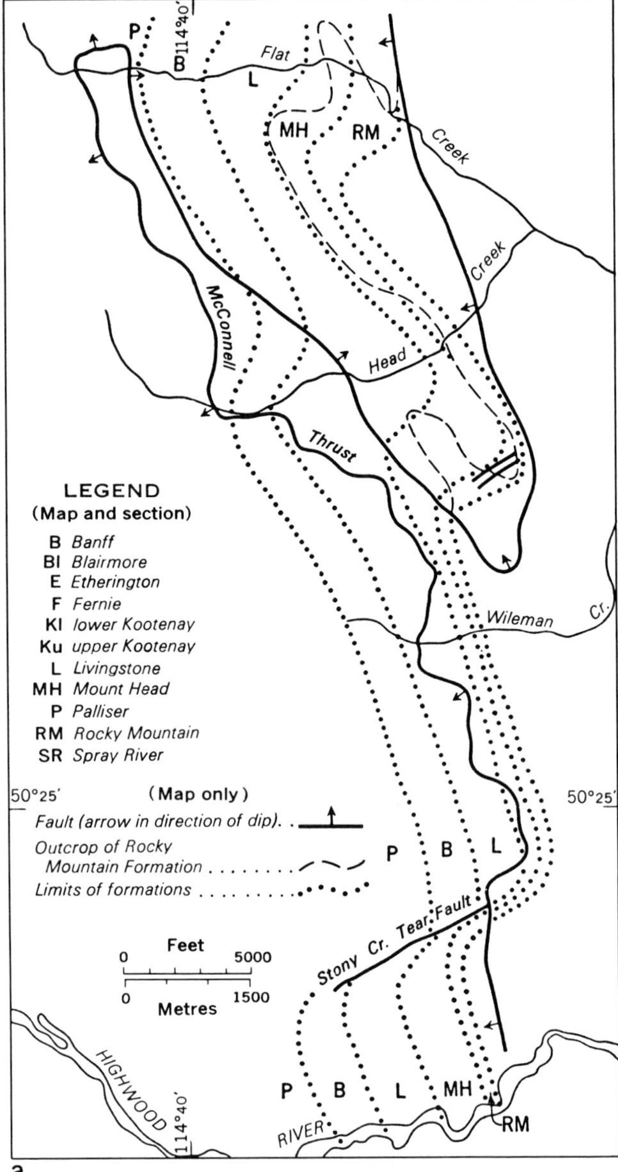

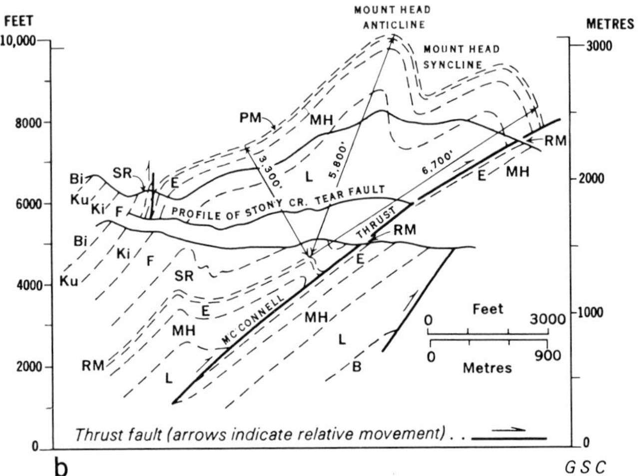

FIGURE VIII-47. Limits of formations above McConnell thrust plane and association with tear faults, southern Rocky Mountains of Alberta (Douglas, 1958).

sequences that are involved in the structures of the southern Rocky Mountains and Foothills and are partly post-orogenic in northwestern Mackenzie and southern Richardson Mountains. The Oligocene and Miocene beds are post-orogenic (Fig. VIII-45). In the western Cordillera, in the mountainous region produced during the Columbian Orogeny, the effects of the Laramide Orogeny appeared to have been limited to transverse and normal faulting, the intrusion of small granite plutons and batholithic intrusions in the Cascade Mountains.

Rocky Mountain Thrust Belt. The Rocky Mountains and Foothills are segmented into three gentle salients separated by shallow re-entrants. The loci of these features are related to the presence of Precambrian basement buttresses that were positive tectonic elements in the early Paleozoic: the Liard, Peace River, and Sweetgrass Arches. The youngest rocks outcrop in the Foothills and the oldest formations in the cores of the salients. Thus, the Foothills are underlain mainly by Mesozoic strata with outliers of Tertiary and inliers of Paleozoic rocks; the more easterly ranges of the Rocky Mountains are formed of Paleozoic and early Mesozoic strata; and the main and westernmost ranges consist of Paleozoic and Proterozoic formations.

The southern Rocky Mountains and Foothills are formed of several large, west-dipping thrust sheets, each of which has been displaced relatively eastwards many miles (Fig. VIII-38a). The strata within the thrust sheets are broken by many closely spaced, subparallel, steeply dipping faults of small displacement, and the folds are complex and disharmonious. In the extreme south total displacement is about 100 miles, representing a shortening of 50 per cent (Bally, *et al.*, 1966), and the thrust belt, as indicated by seismic data, is allocthonous above an undeformed, gently westerly dipping basement of Precambrian crystalline rock (Fig. IX-32). Many of the more westerly structures are considered to have formed in the Columbian Orogeny and to have been modified slightly in the Laramide.

The more westerly thrusts are considered to have originated first, initially as fractures low within the Proterozoic and Paleozoic successions (Fig. VIII-46) and then to have been extended, preferentially following the bedding in zones of easy gliding such as shale or coal, upwards through the Mesozoic and Tertiary strata to the surface and laterally in both directions along the strike (Douglas, 1950). New breaks formed and the extensions of the various thrusts either interlock, merge, or are connected by subsidiary faults. Tear faults are present where the strata initially are transversely cut off by the thrust, the locus being a fault or fracture zone that was produced in the rocks at an earlier time (Fig. VIII-47). The great lateral displacements of the thrust sheets are produced by the riding out of little deformed sheets of rock, the lower zones of gliding being brought into juxtaposition with higher zones. The maximum known displacement is that of the Lewis thrust which has a minimum displacement of more than 45 miles. Initial folds are

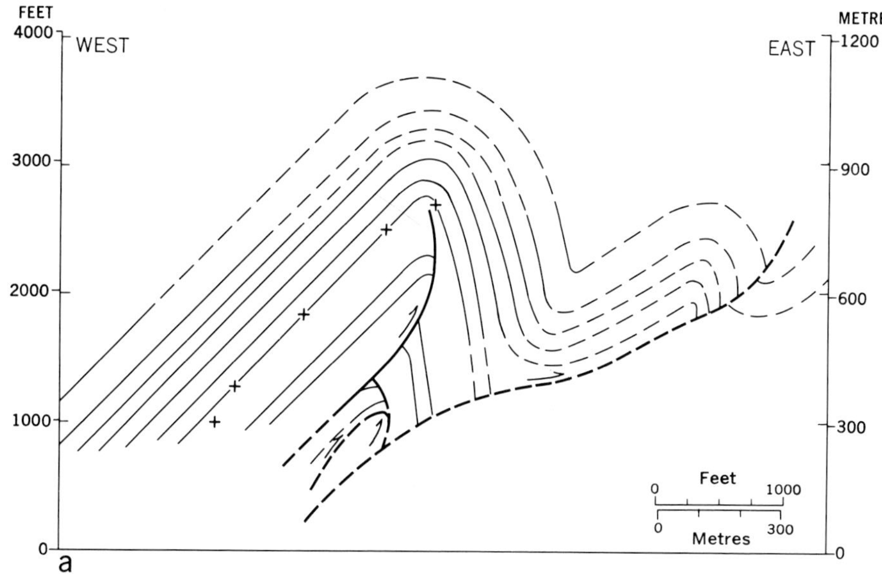

Right section through Centre Peak anticline (left) and Green Creek syncline and anticline (right) at Green Creek, Livingstone Range, Alberta. All three concentric folds have developed above a detachment surface that is a west-dipping 'stepped' thrust fault, and above inflection points in the path of this fault through the stratigraphic layering. The axis of curvature or focal line for the upper level of Centre Peak anticline lies along the terminus of an axial thrust fault that rises out of a surface of interstratal slip.

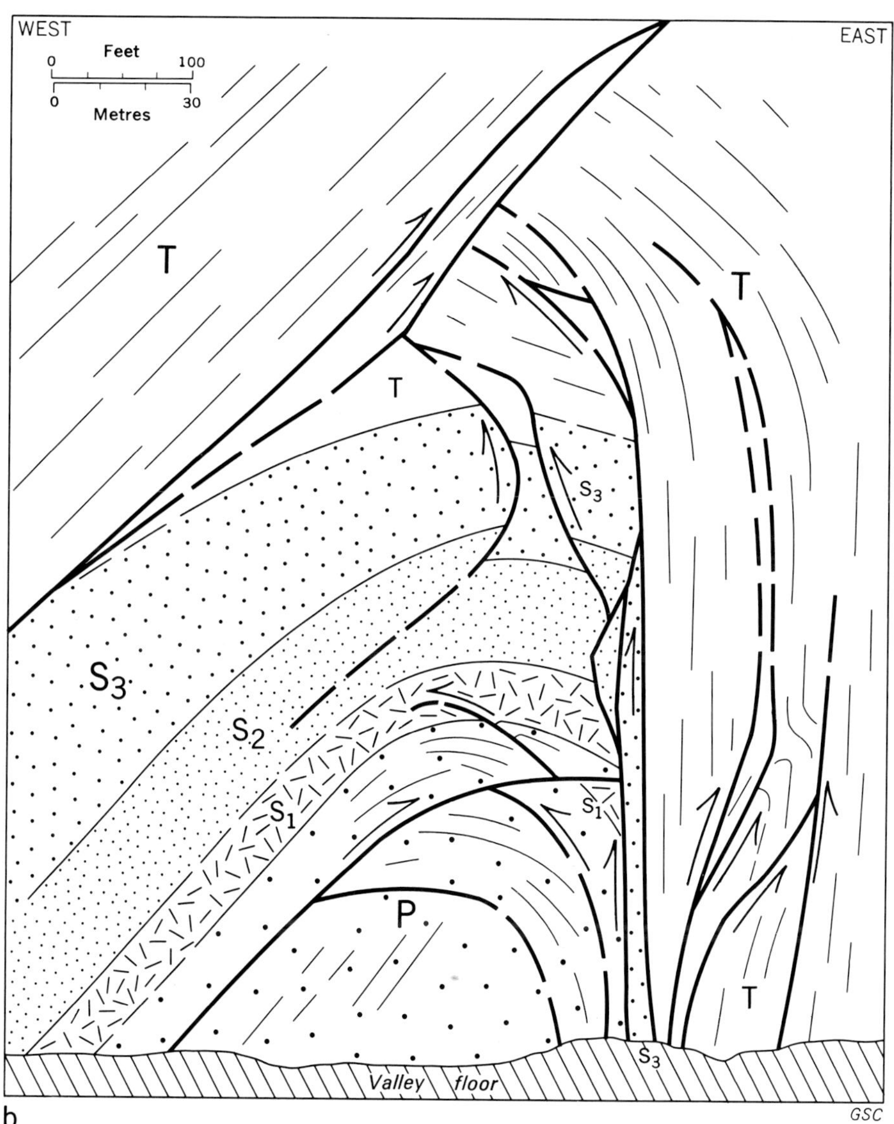

Detail of axial region of Centre Peak anticline. Heavy lines are faults; dashed lines are bedding. P-Pekisko Member; S_1 S_2 S_3 – Shunda Member; T-Turner Valley Member. The thrust fault in upper left is that which terminates as an axis of curvature for Centre Peak anticline, shown in (a). The vertical faults in the centre of the figure are older axial faults that have been rotated in conjunction with the external rotation of bedding produced by continued folding. The normal faults on the right are contraction faults (thrust faults) that have been rotated into an overturned position.

FIGURE VIII-48. Flexural-slip folds in southern Foothills of Alberta (Price, 1964c).

induced concomitantly with displacement of the strata and sequentially, drag-folds are developed with *décollement* at the thrust plane. Splays from the initial thrust plane, sigmoidal in cross-section, merge asymptotically downwards with the thrust and upwards with an earlier formed thrust. The successions of thin thrust slices or imbrications so produced are considered to have formed in sequence from east to west within the overthrust mass, the easternmost slices being detached and over-ridden by the main overthrust mass along the newly formed splay. Where associated with folds some faults occur on the less steeply dipping or back-limb of the anticline rather than the forelimb, and dip subparallel with the strata. Collapse of the core of the folds and the concave character of the fault plane impart rotation to the strata even to the extent of overturning (Pl. VIII-15). Displacement on a new fault in the footwall strata of a fault results in an induced anticline, a superimposed anticline in both the hangingwall strata and the fault plane itself, the formation of another fault on the back-limb of this anticline, and cessation of displacement on the folded portion of the first fault. The sequence of faulting and folding of strata and fault planes is considered to be the result of a continuous, self-perpetuating process (Douglas, 1958), or the result of two stages of deformation, firstly the formation of several fault slices and subsequently the folding of them as a group (Scott, 1951).

Folds within the more southerly thrust sheets are essentially concentric and flexural-slip (Price, 1964c). Individual folds are attenuated vertically along their axial surfaces by thrust faults that originate as surfaces of interstratal slip on one limb, and which lie, at their upper terminus, in the constricted core of the overlying concentric fold (Fig. VIII-48).

In the southern Foothills of Alberta the thick late Upper Cretaceous and Paleocene formations are involved in the easternmost structures, mainly as steeply west-dipping homoclinal slices. In the central Foothills, these strata are compressed into long narrow synclines, the upturning of the western flanks of which was consequent upon the development of east-dipping thrust faults. Between these faults and other, west-dipping thrusts are wedge-like zones of greatly thickened, fissile marine shales and sandstones. The thickening is accomplished by the production of many, very closely spaced thrusts which are generally folded concordantly with the strata.

In southern Rocky Mountains are several post-orogenic normal faults that strike subparallel with the thrusts. Most have small displacements, west side down (Pl. VIII-16). They are generally considered to flatten downward and merge with the pre-existing thrusts (Bally, *et al.*, 1966). The Flathead fault in the Flathead River region (Price, 1966) is large and forms part of a graben system that postdates Laramide structures in Lewis thrust sheet, and that formed while the late Eocene to early Oligocene Kishenehn Formation was being deposited. A deep well has been drilled close to the Fording River fault,

PLATE VIII-15. Westerly overturned folds in Miette Range, near Jasper, Front Ranges of southern Rocky Mountains, Alberta. Northern end of vertically dipping McConnell thrust lies beneath dark band on right; folds in Cambrian and Devonian carbonates and shales to left are rotated into overturned position by displacement on concave, upward steepening thrust surface. In background, tree-covered valleys in Mesozoic clastics separate parallel ranges of Paleozoic thrust sheets.

a northern element of the system (Dahlstrom, *et al.*, 1962). The interpretation that the Fording River fault merges with the Lewis thrust is shown on Figure VIII-49; alternatively, the normal fault offsets the thrust at depth.

Normal faults also border Rocky Mountain Trench, particularly the southernmost segment (Leech, 1966). The trench is a major, linear topographical feature (Pl. VIII-17), which is partly underlain by the easterly derived, fault-bounded, late Cretaceous and early Tertiary Sifton Formation in the north, and by Miocene silts in the south. Although the loci of many longitudinal faults are speculatively considered to have been produced by transcurrent faulting, certain structural and stratigraphic elements extend from Purcell Mountains into southern Rocky Mountains without offset other than that by the normal faults. The trench transects structures produced in the Columbian Orogeny and terrain that is allocthonous with respect to the Precambrian crystalline basement. It is thought by Leech to mark an old, deep, fracture zone that reasserted itself through the allocthonous veneer. Price and Mountjoy (1970) suggest that the site of the trench corresponds with the locus of the hinge zone that bordered the Cordilleran Geosyncline prior to the thrusting.

In northern Rocky Mountains, very broad, long, and high-amplitude folds have gently dipping west flanks and vertical or faulted eastern flanks (Fig. VIII-39b). They are cored by a thick west-dipping sequence of Helikian strata, gently folded by the Racklan Orogeny (Pl. VIII-2), and cut by numerous, northerly trending gabbro dykes. According to G. C. Taylor, west-dipping thrusts in the Paleozoic strata pass into *décollement* surfaces parallel

PLATE VIII-16

Normal fault in Paleozoic carbonates, Cirrus Mountain, Main Ranges of southern Rocky Mountains, Alberta. Ml—Mississippian, Livingstone; Mb—Banff; Dp—Devonian Palliser; Df—Fairholme; Omw—Ordovician, Mount Wilson; Ooc—Owen Creek; Osk—Skoki.

PLATE VIII-17. Rocky Mountain Trench. Looking south across a central part of the trench near the junction of Fraser and Torpy Rivers. Cariboo Mountains are on the right; Rocky Mountains on the left with Mount Robson, elevation 12,972 feet, on skyline beneath wing tip.

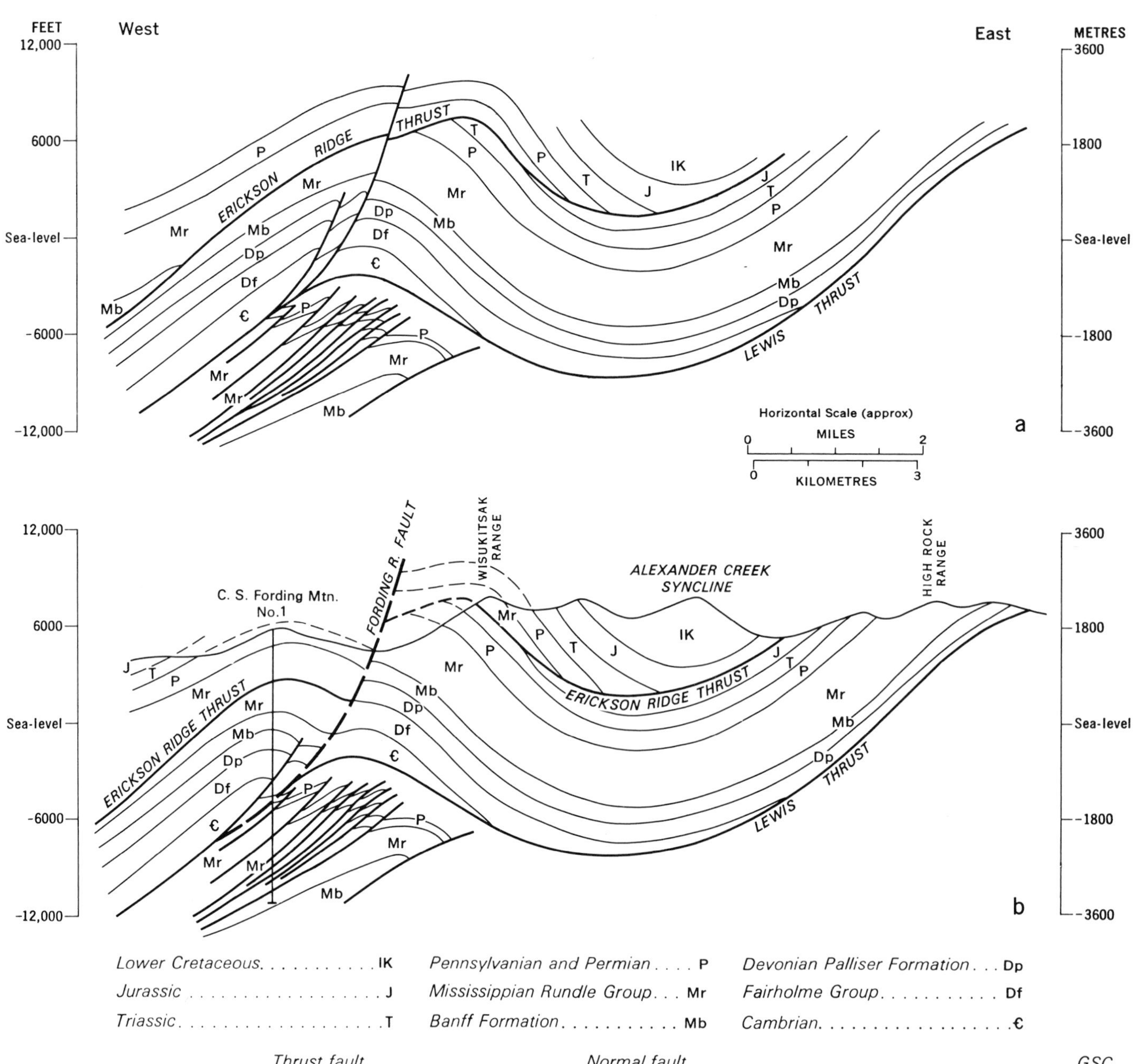

FIGURE VIII-49. Cross-section through Lewis thrust sheet and California Standard, Fording River No. 1 well, southern Rocky Mountains; (a) Structure before normal faulting; (b) Structure after normal faulting, the Fording River normal fault decreasing dip at depth and merging with the Lewis thrust (Dahlstrom, Daniel, and Henderson, 1962).

with the bedding of Silurian dolomites or at the unconformity at the base of the Silurian where it lies in contact with the Helikian. The main thrust belt lies west of the broad folds, involving pelitic facies of the lower Paleozoic and the Hadrynian. Structures in the Mesozoic rocks of the Foothills are long, narrow, tightly compressed similar folds in Triassic sandstones, broken by fore-limb thrust faults. The folds are steeply inclined and in the overlying Cretaceous shales become less persistent and more numerous. They are considered to lie discordantly above the structures of the Paleozoic carbonates, the zone of *décollement* being in the Devono-Carboniferous black shales of the Besa River Formation (Fitzgerald and Braun, 1965).

Mackenzie Fold Belt. The Mackenzie Fold Belt is composed of broad, short folds, the crests and troughs nearly flat with sharply upturned and faulted flanks (Fig. VIII-39a). Some folds are long, narrow, and tightly compressed with faults lying on either or both flanks and in the axial region. Some of the broad anticlines are cored with Helikian and Hadrynian strata in northern and western Mackenzie Mountains and Franklin Mountains and with phyllite in Wernecke Mountains and Taiga Ranges. The lower Paleozoic contains much carbonate, the contact of the uppermost, generally Middle Devonian massive beds with the overlying, mainly Upper Devonian shales forms extensive stripped bedding surfaces that sharply delimit the flanks of the anticlinal mountain ranges and the intervening synclinal valleys (Pl. VIII-4). In the extreme south, in Liard Plateau, a low east-facing homocline dominates the structure. It is bounded on the west by east-dipping thrust faults and extends for a width of 50 miles interrupted only by a few gentle folds, asymmetrical westward. To the north anticlinal mountain ranges appear right hand *en echelon*. In the southern part of Mackenzie Fold Belt the folds are markedly segmented. The individual segments are oriented along west, northwest, and northeast lines and are commonly broken by faults with a small amount of thrust or normal displacement that also have the same trend. A fracture system appears to have been present in the rocks as faults or zones of small fractures prior to the Laramide deformation. Old faults with normal displacement may have been rotated along strike into attitudes where thrust displacement occurs. In western Mackenzie Mountains some tightly folded anticlines are broken by what appears to be two episodes of folding, manifested by faulting of older faults and by overturning of the folds to the east or west in the opposite direction to an earlier overturning. These structures may represent some of the easternmost elements of Columbian Orogen. Most thrust faults are associated with folds and with their middle or fore-limb. The amount of deplacement is small; shortening across the Mackenzie and Franklin Mountains is only about 10 per cent. The thrust faults dip either eastward or westward and commonly end at a small tear fault which is oriented in the direction of the old fracture system, or which may be linked by a short segment of it. On these segments little horizontal displacement has occurred; rather, the beds have undergone only rotational translation. Thrust faults with homoclinal hanging-wall and footwall strata are rare. Generally, subsidiary structures indicate some dextral motion in addition to the dip-slip where the trend of the thrust is northeasterly, and sinstral where northwesterly.

In the Mackenzie River valley near Fort Norman, non-marine beds, poorly dated as Eocene, are involved in the folding and thrusting, particularly near Mackay Range. As the beds lie with strong regional unconformity on Lower Cretaceous to Middle Devonian strata, some tilting, warping, and possibly also folding and faulting may have taken place during the early phase of the Laramide Orogeny or earlier. Some small complex structures in Mackenzie Plain and Franklin Mountains appear to have been produced with *décollement* at the level of the Cambrian salt and anhydrite. The larger structures, particularly the major anticlines with cores of Helikian and Hadrynian strata probably formed with *décollement* close to the crystalline basement.

Northern Yukon Fold Complex. In the vicinity of Bonnet Plume Basin where the Richardson and Mackenzie Mountains merge, very gently folded and tilted non-marine beds of the late Upper Cretaceous or early Tertiary Bonnet Plume Formation lie with angular unconformity on deformed Paleozoic and Proterozoic rocks (Fig. VIII-50), the bulk of the orogenic deformation having taken place prior to their deposition. The structural grain around the periphery of the basin is considered by R. A. Price in terms of two sets of structural elements whose antecedents have controlled patterns of deformation and sedimentation since the Precambrian. The structure of southern Richardson Mountains is dominated by northerly and northwesterly trending faults, most or all of which have a large right-hand separation. These faults bound a complex horst and broad, north-plunging anticlinorium that forms the core of the mountains. In northwestern Mackenzie Mountains and southern Porcupine Plateau the dominant system of east-west trending folds and faults is associated with a less conspicuous system of northerly and northwesterly trending, right-hand faults and folds that join those of Richardson Mountains. The anisotropy inherited from the structural elements that were produced in the Hadrynian and Paleozoic exerted a strong influence on the character of the structures produced during the early phase of Laramide Orogeny. The older faults were reactivated and assumed new kinematic roles related to their orientation relative to the direction of maximum principal stress. For example, the western sides of the faults bounding eastern Richardson Mountains were downthrown during the Paleozoic, particularly during deposition of the Lower Cambrian and the Middle Devonian. The faults now have the northeast side downthrown and have been subjected to right-hand transcurrent displacement. In northern Mackenzie Mountains they merge along strike with easterly trending thrust faults downthrown to the north. The kinematic roles of both easterly and northerly trending faults can be integrated in terms of a single deformation arising from a north-south shortening in conjunction with relative tectonic transport northward. In northernmost Richardson Mountains near Aklavik some displacement on the wrench faults on the east side can be seen to be later than mid-Upper Cretaceous. Albian shales are involved in the folds fronting northwestern Mackenzie Mountains. Inasmuch as these structures are considered to be kinematically related and are in part older than the late Upper Cretaceous Bonnet Plume Formation, a large part of the structures of the northern part of the Eastern Cordilleran Orogen are considered to be early Laramide.

Long broad open anticlines and synclines, some displaying *en echelon* linkage are present on Eagle Plain and Nahoni Range. There, northerly trending structures appear to be truncated against a major thrust on the southeast side of Keele Range. Culminations and depressions mark their intersection with the west-trending structures in the Taiga Ranges.

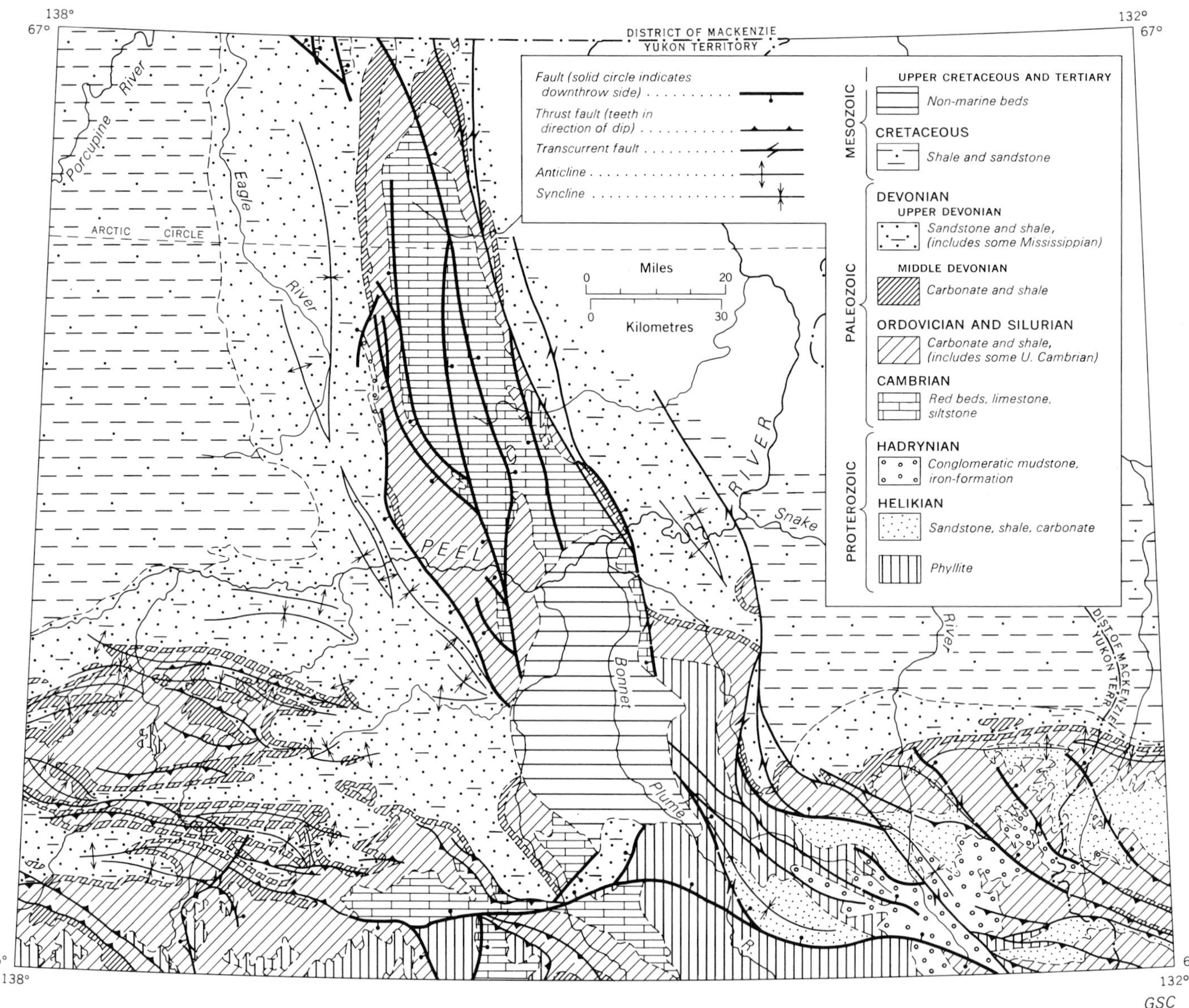

FIGURE VIII-50. Geology, provisional, in the vicinity of Bonnet Plume Basin, northern Yukon Territory, showing early Laramide structures of southern Richardson and northwestern Mackenzie Mountains (by R. A. Price and D. K. Norris).

Yukon Plateau. In the northern Coast and Omineca Geanticlines and in the intervening area, large, sharply cross-cutting bodies of quartz monzonite and alaskite or miarolitic granite were emplaced near the end of the Cretaceous. The granites are characterized by highly variable texture from fine to very coarse grained, and in places porphyritic, abundant smoky quartz, low mafic-mineral content, and dull creamy colour of the feldspars. Small pegmatitic streaks and clots are common and drusy cavities are abundant. Traces of fluorite and apatite are widespread whereas allanite and topaz are rare. Tourmaline and axinite are locally abundant in one batholith. The quartz monzonites are similar to the miarolitic granites but contain less potash feldspar and more mafic minerals. These granitic rocks were apparently emplaced at relatively shallow depths during a time of crustal tension and no significant regional deformation appears related to them.

St. Elias Fold Belt. The time of pre-Tertiary deformation in the Canadian part of the St. Elias Mountains is not known. However, Paleocene and later volcanic and sedimentary rocks are displaced by thrust and counterthrusts (Muller, 1967) and possible tillites in easternmost Alaska equivalent to part of the St. Clare Group are tilted and gently folded. The age of the 'tillites' is not known, but they may be equivalent to marine tillites of Miocene and Pliocene(?) age on the Gulf of Alaska that were involved in latest Pliocene or earliest Pleistocene deformation. Movement along faults on the southwest side of the St. Elias Mountains continues to the present day, if one judges by the strong earthquakes of 1899 and the last decade. The central crystalline core of St. Elias Mountains with fault blocks of Lower Cretaceous sediments is

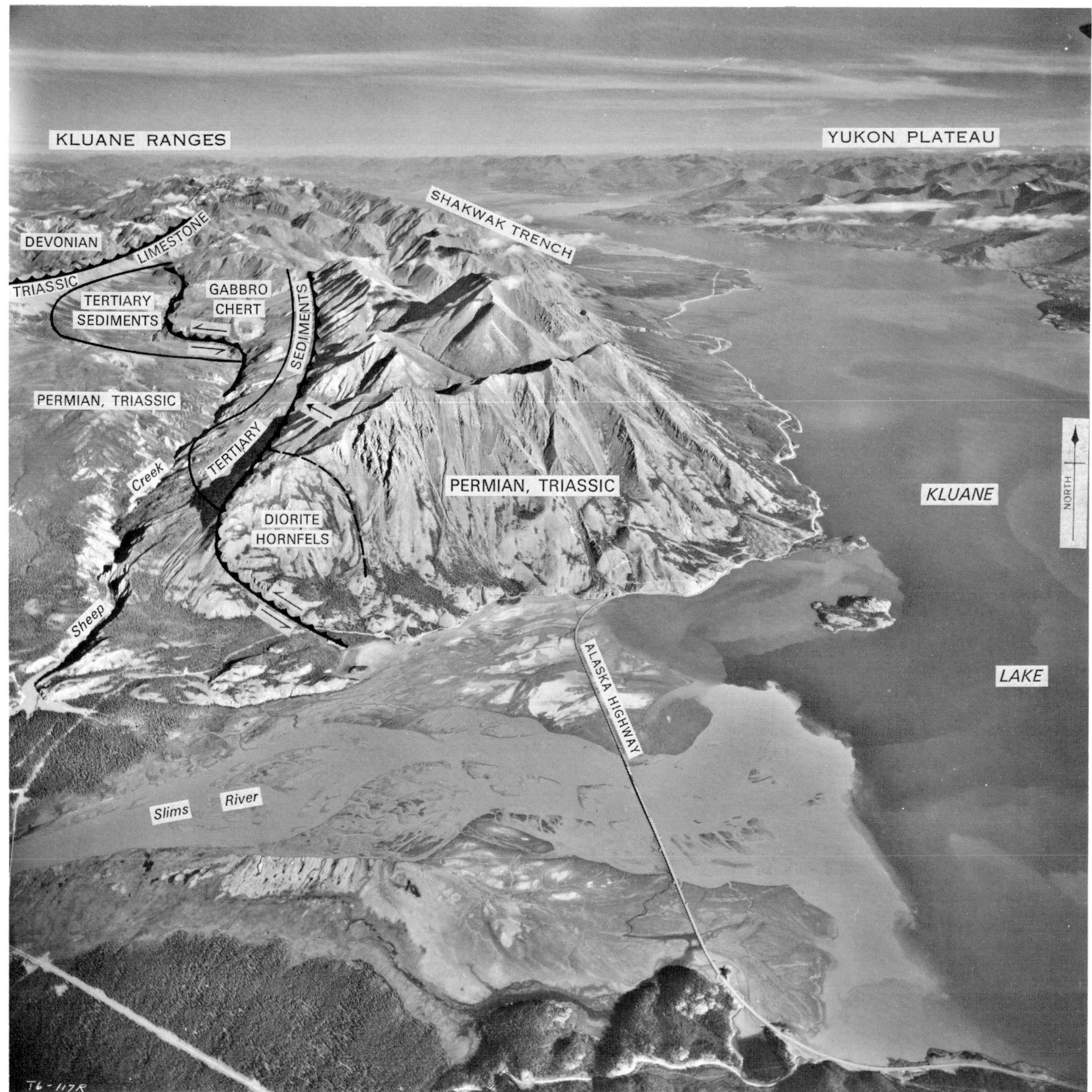

PLATE VIII-18. Late Tertiary thrusts in Kluane Ranges, St. Elias Mountains, Yukon Territory. Shakwak Trench, floored with Pleistocene deposits, separates the younger rocks of St. Elias Fold Belt from Yukon Crystalline Platform which is underlain by early Paleozoic and late Precambrian metamorphic rocks and granitic plutons of Mesozoic and Tertiary ages.

bounded on both sides by inward-dipping faults that separate it from adjacent regions that are characterized by folds and thrust faults directed away from the axial region of the fold belt. On the northeastern side, the Duke River thrust zone is marked by numerous lenses of gypsum and converges southeastward with the Shakwak fault that bounds the fold belt on the northeast. The intervening zone is intensely deformed and has at least two counter-thrusts directed to the southwest (Pl. VIII-18).

Insular Fold Belt. Structures in Upper Cretaceous rocks of Georgia Basin, produced in the early Tertiary, appear to reflect movements on faults in the basement and are related to two prominent, steep northwest-trending faults on which beds are downdropped on the southwest. The Upper Cretaceous rocks are intruded by sills and stocks of quartz diorite with K–Ar dates of 35 to 59 m.y. At the south end of Vancouver Island, folds in the Tertiary formations trend easterly and are associated with the north-dipping, east-trending thrust on which displacement took place in the Oligocene. On Queen Charlotte Islands gentle warps in the Tertiary volcanics may merely represent sagging above an evacuated magma chamber. The faults that affect Tertiary rocks are generally steep and trend northwesterly, parallel with the prevailing fault and fold trends in older rocks. On Queen Charlotte Islands they have been active since at least the Lower Cretaceous and combine right-hand wrench movement with an east-side down displacement. On Vancouver Island the northwesterly faults were established in Middle Jurassic time but the nature of their subsequent history is unknown except that movement on those along the west coast downdropped Tertiary sediments in post-Miocene time.

The northwest-trending faults also include one on the continental margin off the west coast of the Queen Charlotte Islands (Fig. VIII-51). This fault is considered by Sutherland Brown (1966) to dip steeply under the continent and by Wilson (1965) to be one of a series of transform faults within the San Andreas–Denali linkage. It separates northwesterly trending continental structures to the northeast from a region on the ocean floor to the southwest that is characterized by north to northeasterly trending magnetic anomalies (Fig. VIII-52). Vine (1966) considered that the oceanic crust has spread laterally away from the axis of the East Pacific Rise in the region of the Juan de Fuca ridge. He estimated that the rate of spreading may have decreased within Pliocene time from a rate of 4 or 5 to 2.9 cm/yr for the last 5 m.y.

Interior Plateau. Early Tertiary structures are extensional features such as normal faults and dyke-filled fractures superimposed on Columbian structures. Movement along the faults took place partly contemporaneously with the deposition of the early Tertiary sediments and volcanic rocks, and partly later. The normal faults have a zig-zag pattern in southwestern Monashee Mountains. Tertiary strata in the horsts, grabens, and half-grabens are locally folded and commonly tilted eastward. The fault system controlled the direction of basalt and lamprophyre dyke swarms and influenced the distribution of the Coryell Intrusions. Northerly trending topographical elements in the poorly exposed Tertiary volcanics of the central Interior Plateau may also reflect similar northerly trending block faults. More variable trends and attitudes of tilting and folding occur in the northern part near Stikine Arch. Some reverse movement took place on Pinchi fault subsequent to the deposition of the Upper Cretaceous to Paleocene Sustut Formation.

Cascade and Coast Mountains. Recurrent movements on the Fraser River fault zone that transects the core of the southern Cascade Mountains resulted in the localization of Eocene continental clastics and their subsequent deformation prior to the emplacement of Chilliwack batholith in the mid-Tertiary. Similar events affected the southern part of Coast Mountains where late Upper Cretaceous beds are tilted, faulted, and intruded by granitic plutons.

Paleocene and Eocene (Fig. VIII-44)

Pacific Continental Shelf. In Bellingham Basin beneath the lower Fraser River Delta, the upper beds of non-marine sandstones and conglomerate comprising the Burrard Formation are early Tertiary. The conformably overlying Kitsi-

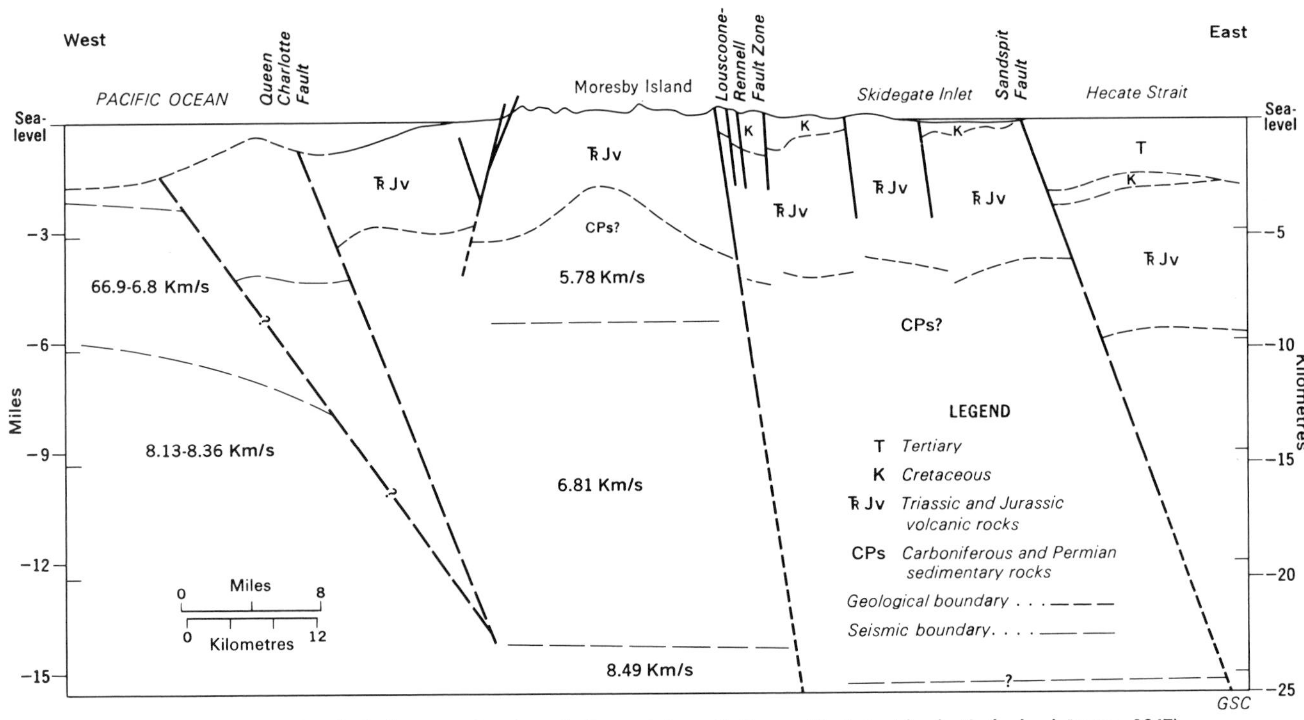

FIGURE VIII-51. Hypothetical cross-section through the crust beneath Queen Charlotte Islands (Sutherland Brown, 1967).

lano Formation and the equivalent Huntingdon Formation contain a Middle Eocene flora. In Washington, on the southern margin of the basin, the Huntingdon Formation lies unconformably on the Chuckanut Formation, the lower part of which is equivalent to the upper Nanaimo Group. At the southern end of Vancouver Island the Eocene Metchosin Formation comprises 7,500 feet of submarine pillow basalt, minor pyroclastics, and sediments. It lies unconformably on the Lower Cretaceous on Olympic Peninsula of Washington. On southern Queen Charlotte Islands the Massett Formation has several distinctive facies (Sutherland Brown, 1966). The Dana Inlet facies comprises subaqueous pyroclastic breccias with mixed rhyolitic and basaltic clasts. The subaerial equivalent, the Kootenay Inlet facies, consists of rhyolitic ash flows, tuffs, and breccias, and dacitic and basaltic flows. The Tartu Inlet facies of subaerial volcanics in northern Queen Charlotte Islands is composed of three members totalling 18,000 feet in thickness. The lowest member is a mixture of basalt breccias and flows and rhyolite ash flows, tuff, and flows. The middle member is mainly rhyolitic flows and ash. The upper member consists of slightly sodic columnar basalt flows. Mica from a sill related to the lower member yielded a K–Ar date of 62 m.y.

Cascade Mountains. Conglomerates of local derivation lie unconformably on the Custer gneiss and granitic and metamorphic rocks along Fraser River south of Lillooet (McTaggart and Thompson, 1967). They are also faulted against similar rocks to the east thus indicating faulting along Fraser River during and after the Eocene. Along the same trend south of Hope remnants of Eocene conglomerate are engulfed by the Miocene Chilliwack batholith that yields K–Ar dates of 18 m.y.

Interior Plateaux. Subaerial volcanic rocks with subordinate clastic rocks are 5,000 feet thick in the interior of British Columbia. They are preserved in isolated structural basins and fault troughs, or occur as upland remnants lying with angular unconformity on older rocks.

In the southernmost Interior Plateau the Kamloops and Princeton Groups, and the Springbrook, Marron,

a

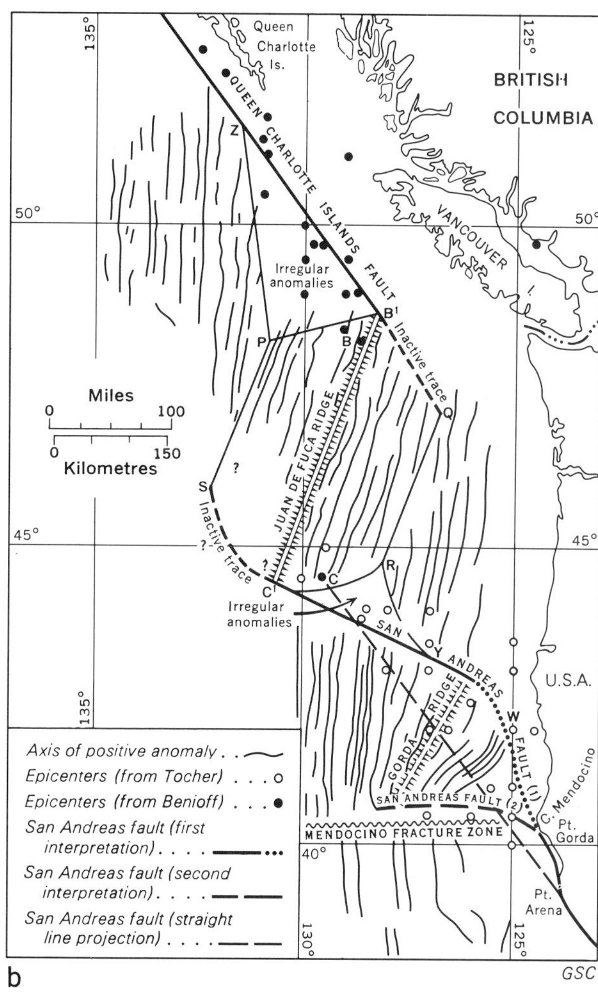

FIGURE VIII-52. Magnetic anomalies southwest of Vancouver Island: a) Total magnetic field: areas of positive anomaly shown in black; straight lines indicate faults (Vine, 1966); b) Interpretation of transform faults (Wilson, 1965).

White Lake, and Kettle River Formations are considered Middle Eocene on the basis of flora from the sediments of the Kamloops and Princeton Groups and the Kettle River Formation, and mammal teeth near Princeton. The volcanic rocks have yielded K–Ar dates ranging from 45 m.y. to 49 m.y. (Rouse and Mathews, 1961). They are mainly andesites and trachy-andesites with subordinate basalt and rhyolite that occur as lenticular flows and pyroclastic sheets. The felsic types commonly are ash flows. Tilting and faulting took place contemporaneously with the deposition of sediments and eruption of the volcanic rocks. The Kettle River Formation increases in thickness towards some bordering faults. Feeder dykes for the middle Marron lavas have the same trends as normal faults, and also appear to be related to the Coryell Intrusions.

The Ootsa Lake Group of the central Interior Plateau is composed principally of spherulitic, perlitic rhyolite, and subordinately of andesite, basalt, and clastic sediments. Flows are about as common as pyroclastic rocks. Some volcanic rocks, particularly felsic types, originally mapped with the younger Endako Group (Armstrong, 1949) have yielded K–Ar dates of 53 m.y. in common with early Tertiary volcanics of the Ootsa Lake Group and those in southern British Columbia (Mathews, 1964).

The Sloko Group (Aitken, 1960) of northern British Columbia is mainly pyroclastic dacite and rhyolite with subordinate andesite and basalt, and contains poorly preserved plants of Cretaceous or Tertiary age. The pyroclastic rocks range from coarse explosion breccias, some of which consist entirely of granitic fragments, to delicate vitric tuffs and ignimbrites. Flows are rare. The associated sediments are derived from nearby volcanic material and contain coal, plant fragments, and logs. The Sloko strata are flat or gently tilted and are commonly bounded by normal faults or ring fractures. Some dykes follow the faults or form parallel swarms, suggesting that volcanism was contemporaneous with faulting and locally accompanied by cauldron subsidence. Some of the trachytic volcanics are apparently genetically related to quartz monzonite plugs, one of which has a K–Ar date of 69 m.y. Locally, the pyroclastics grade downward to felsite and thence to quartz monzonite through a difference in elevation of less than 5,000 feet.

In southwestern Yukon Territory the Carmacks and Skukum Groups contain sediments of Paleocene and Eocene age, overlain by volcanic rocks, mainly basalt, but including trachyte, rhyolite, andesite, and pyroclastic rocks. The rocks are tilted and truncated by an erosion surface probably of Miocene(?) age.

St. Elias Mountains. Southwest of Shakwak Trench in Kluane area Paleocene sandstone and conglomerate with minor shale and coal are as much as 2,500 feet thick. They have been involved in middle or late Tertiary thrusting. In Dezadeash area flat-lying and gently dipping beds of conglomerate, sandstone, and shale, 3,500 feet thick, lie unconformably on porphyritic granite or on Mesozoic volcanics and sediments. The strata are cut by a stock and numerous sills of soda syenite. In the Squaw Creek–Rainy Hollow area (Watson, 1948) gently to moderately dipping conglomerates, sandstones, and shale overlie porphyritic rhyolite flows in a down-faulted block. The sedimentary and volcanic units, each about 1,500 feet thick, are in part intercalated and both are considered Paleocene.

Coal seams are present in well-stratified Paleocene or upper Eocene conglomerates, sandstones, and siltstones along northwestern Tintina Trench and also in the Carmacks area. Similar rocks, lacking coal, are present along Pelly River in Tintina Trench and along MacMillan River to the northeast. Lignitic coal seams occur with typical Tertiary clastic rocks on Liard and Coal Rivers in southeastern Yukon Territory and along Rapid River near McDame.

Arctic Coastal Plain. West of Mackenzie Delta the Moose Channel Formation consists of 1,200 feet of non-marine sandstone, loosely consolidated, fine- to coarse-grained, feldspathic, greenish grey to brown, and ripple-marked, interbedded with silty grey shale (Mountjoy, 1967). A seam of sub-bituminous coal 7 feet thick occurs on Moose Channel. Microflora indicate a general Upper Cretaceous to early Tertiary age. East of the delta, the Paleocene to Eocene Reindeer Formation, more than 700 feet thick, contains non-marine silty shales, siltstone, common sandstone, quartzite, and chert conglomerate and coal.

Mackenzie Plain. In the vicinity of Fort Norman Paleocene or Eocene shales, forming a small basin, rest with regional unconformity on Lower Cretaceous to Middle Devonian strata. The lower part, 4,000 feet thick, comprises soft sandstones, shales, and lignite. The upper part, capping hills south of Little Bear Lake, is 2,000 feet of massive conglomerate.

Rocky Mountain Exogeosyncline. The Paleocene of the Interior Plains and Rocky Mountain Foothills ranges from more than 5,000 feet in the west to only a few hundred feet in southwestern Manitoba. Massive buff-weathering sandstones, included in the Paskapoo Formation of central Alberta and in the Ravenscrag in Saskatchewan, overlie the Cretaceous coal- and dinosaur-bearing beds. An erosional unconformity apparently separates the Edmonton and Paskapoo Formations although deposition may have been continuous in southern Saskatchewan and Alberta. In the southern Foothills, the boundary between the Cretaceous and the Paleocene lies within the apparently conformable sequence of the Willow Creek Formation.

The Willow Creek Formation consists of soft, medium-grained grey sandstone and variegated shales overlain by buff-weathering beds. It contains two molluscan faunas (Tozer, 1956), the older being correlated with that in the upper Edmonton Formation. The younger fauna is correlated with that in the Paskapoo and Ravenscrag Formations. The Willow Creek is more than 4,000 feet

PLATE VIII-19. Sandstone channel-filling in mudstones of Tertiary Paskapoo Formation, Burnt Timber Creek, Foothills of Alberta.

thick near Castle River and thins northward, the lower part merging with the upper Edmonton, and the upper part bevelled beneath the unconformably overlying Porcupine Hills Formation (Douglas, 1950). The Porcupine Hills include about 4,000 feet of coarse-grained, massive, crossbedded, grey and green sandstone and grey and brown shales.

The Paskapoo Formation is 3,000 feet thick in the southern Foothills and more than 6,500 feet in the central Foothills (Pl. VIII-19). It contains massive, crossbedded, coarse-grained, brown sandstone, grey and green shales, and some limestone. The thin, lenticular Entrance conglomerate commonly occurs at the base between North Saskatchewan and Athabasca Rivers. Thick coal seams of economic importance occur near Edmonton. The Paleocene age has been established by a well-preserved molluscan fauna, mammalian remains, and plants.

In the Cypress Hills along the Alberta–Saskatchewan border, Paleocene beds with a mammalian fauna are included in the Ravenscrag Formation (Furnival, 1946). The base is drawn below the lowest commercial coal seam and appears to be conformable with the underlying, dinosaur-bearing Frenchman Formation. The Ravenscrag is a cyclic succession of silts, clays, and lignite that ranges in thickness from about 500 feet to 250 feet, thinning eastward across southern Saskatchewan.

The Turtle Mountain Formation in southern Manitoba is considered to be early Tertiary, and probably Paleocene in age. The formation, estimated to be about 100 feet thick, contains fine sand, silt, clay, and thin coal seams. Paleocene foraminifera from the Cannonball Formation, which occurs on the west flank of Turtle Mountain in North Dakota, indicate that marine strata may lie between the Turtle Mountain Formation and the Cretaceous Boissevain Formation. This short-lived Cannonball Sea had connections with the Gulf of Mexico and perhaps with the Arctic Ocean. It may be possibly related to the post-Ravenscrag subsidence of Williston Basin.

Oligocene and Younger (Fig. VIII-45)

Pacific Continental Shelf. Clastic marine sediments of the middle and Upper Oligocene Carmanah Formation and of the Lower Miocene Sooke Formation occur along the west coast of Vancouver Island. They unconformably overlie older rocks and are unconformably overlain by the Pleistocene. The beds strike parallel with the coast and dip west, oceanward. The Skonun Formation of Miocene and Pliocene age on northern Queen Charlotte Islands comprises intertonguing marine and non-marine sands and shales, 6,000 feet thick in the east. It overlaps Lower Tertiary volcanics westward (Sutherland Brown, 1966).

Interior Plateaux. Miocene silts, sands, and gravels occur along the major valleys such as that of the Fraser River and its tributaries near Prince George (H. W. Tipper), Thompson River (Campbell and Tipper, 1966), and southernmost Rocky Mountain Trench (Leech, 1966). These occurrences indicate that the major drainage routes were established by the Miocene and preceded by a long interval of erosion.

The flat-lying Plateau Basalts of central British Columbia and southern Yukon Territory have yielded K–Ar dates of 10, 12, and 13 m.y. They overlie and interfinger with clastic sediments containing late Miocene flora and locally include diatomite deposits. The Plateau basalts and olivine basalts and their equivalents, the andesites and basalts of the Endako Group, were erupted from fissures and shield volcanoes onto a gently undulating erosion surface that had a relief of 1,500 to 2,000 feet. In the east, the lavas apparently flowed as wide sheets into the valleys bordering Columbia Mountains (Campbell and Tipper, 1966). In the west, however, in the Coast Mountains, the basalts, in response to differential uplift in the Pliocene now lie at elevations of as much as 8,000 feet. Volcanic rocks in northwestern British Columbia equivalent to the Plateau Basalts are the earliest flows of the Mount Edziza volcanic cone (Fig. VIII-53), the basalt flows of the Level Mountain Formation, and the interfingering rhyolitic and dacitic pyroclastics of the Heart Peaks Formation that have yielded a K–Ar date of 15 m.y.

Near Alsek River in St. Elias Mountains, volcanic rocks possibly of Miocene age are varicoloured agglomerate, breccia, tuff, rhyolite, dacite, andesite, and basalt about 3,500 feet thick. These rocks are believed to overlie Paleocene and older strata unconformably and to have been extruded onto a surface having more than 2,000 feet relief. Farther northwest in Kluane Ranges, about 1,600 feet of massive and columnar basalt and andesite are

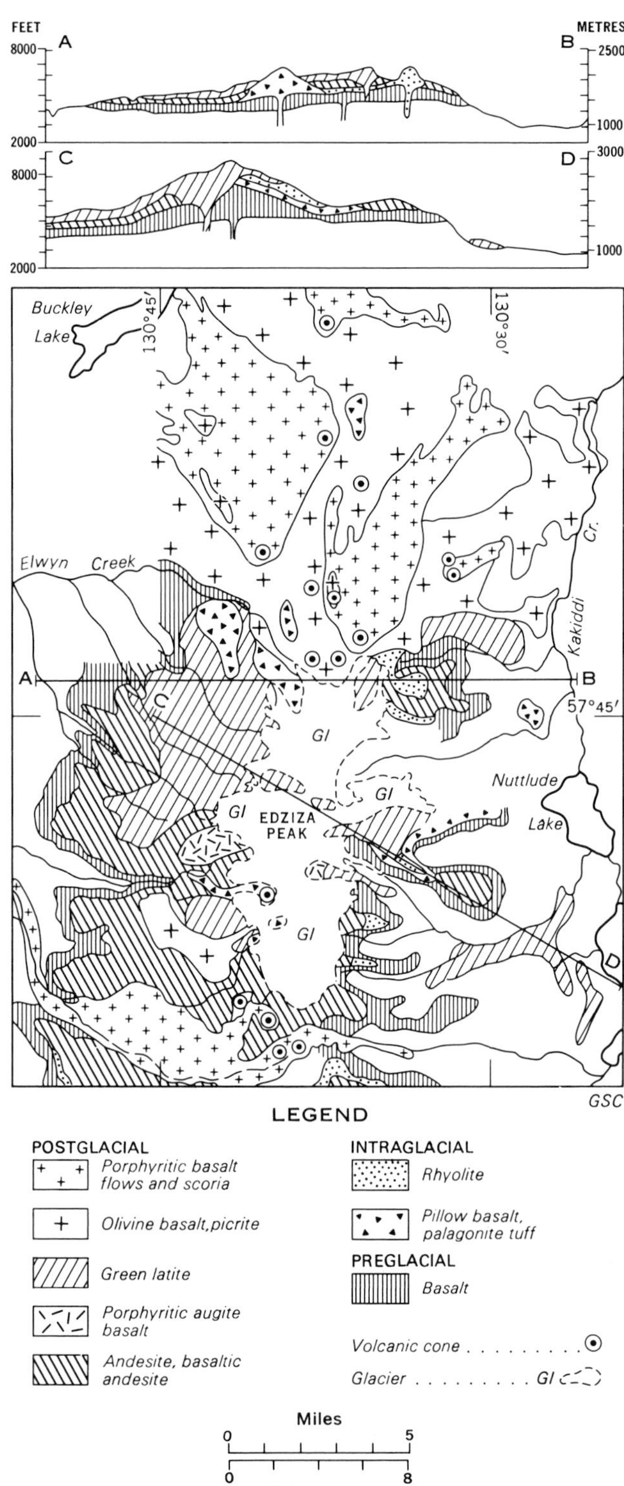

FIGURE VIII-53. Mount Edziza volcanic complex, northwestern British Columbia (Souther, 1966).

intercalated with sand, shale, and coal at the base, and contain intercalated layers of tuff and ash near the top. They are overlain by 350 feet of coarse volcanic conglomerate.

PLATE VIII-20. Cinder cone, 500 feet high, on post-glacial basalt of north flank of Mount Edziza volcanic complex, British Columbia. Partly eroded cones in middle distance.

Lavas of the Selkirk Group and related rocks in southwestern Yukon Territory and northern British Columbia range from Pliocene to Recent. They were extruded onto an erosion surface similar to the present one, and many flows were confined to the present valleys. The Tuya Formation in northern British Columbia includes a great deal of volcanic ash that is intercalated with flows near the centres of eruption. In several places volcanic cones consisting predominantly of ash are capped by flat-lying flows thought to have been emplaced at a time when the region was covered by ice. The "Valley" olivine basalts of the southern Interior Plateau occur as benches and in valleys carved into the plateau surface. Many of the volcanic cones or centres are shown on Figure VIII-45.

Rocky Mountains. In upper Flathead River valley, the Kishenehn Formation of latest Eocene or earliest Oligocene age was deposited in a structural basin along the downthrown side of the Flathead normal fault. Two main facies are recognized by Price (1966): conglomerates and breccias adjacent to the fault derived locally from the Paleozoic and Precambrian rocks of the upthrown side, and a basinal facies of fine clastic material, marl, and lignite. Sedimentation took place simultaneously with displacement on the fault as the sequence of rock types that occur as clasts is the inverse of their normal stratigraphic order in the hanging-wall succession. About 6,600 feet of sediments are present. The Kishenehn lies with angular unconformity on strata deformed by the Laramide Orogeny, and establishes an upper limit for dating the underlying structures of the southern Rocky Mountains.

Interior Plains. Gravels derived from Precambrian and Cambrian rocks of the western and main ranges of southern Rocky Mountains are included in the late Eocene Swift Current Creek beds and the early Oligocene Cypress Hills Formation of southwestern Saskatchewan and southeastern Alberta. The latter, capping the Cypress Hills, consists of varying amounts of sands and gravels and has a maximum thickness of 300 feet. The pebbles are mainly quartzite and chert with some trachyte and other porphyritic rocks. The formation has yielded a large vertebrate fauna, especially mammals. Other remnants of fluvial deposits representing erosion of the Rocky Mountains are the Miocene Wood Mountain gravels of southern Saskatchewan and the Miocene or Pliocene conglomerates and gravels capping Swan Hills, Hand Hills, and Saddle Hills in central Alberta.

Quaternary

Almost all the Cordilleran Region and Interior Plains were glaciated during the Pleistocene (*see* Chapter XII and Map 1253A). In the unglaciated part of Yukon Plateau, the gold-bearing stream deposits of the Klondike including the "White Channel" gravels and related deposits were preserved. They may be latest Tertiary. Elsewhere, a great variety of glacial and fluvioglacial deposits are present and in some of the pre-glacial valleys attain great thicknesses and may include earliest Pleistocene and latest Tertiary sediments. Large snowfields and numerous active glaciers are present in the Coast, St. Elias, Selkirk, and Rocky Mountains. Some other ranges have a few small glaciers, the largest of which are in southeastern Selwyn Mountains. Several small volcanoes near Mount Edziza, on lower Iskut River, and north of Terrace have been active within the last 2,000 years, erupting since the last retreat of the ice (Pl. VIII-20).

SELECTED REFERENCES

General

British Columbia Department of Mines and Petroleum Resources; Annual Reports.

Gabrielse, H., and Reesor, J. E.
1964: Geochronology of plutonic rocks in two areas of the Canadian Cordillera; *Roy. Soc. Can.*, Spec. Publ. No. 8, Geochronology in Canada, pp. 96–138.

Gabrielse, H., and Wheeler, J. O.
1961: Tectonic framework of southern Yukon and northwestern British Columbia; *Geol. Surv. Can.*, Paper 60-24.

Geological Survey of Canada:
Age determinations and geological studies; Annual papers on K–Ar age determinations—Papers 60-17 to 67-17. Report of Activities—Papers 63-1 to 67-1.

Gunning, H. C., editor
1966: Tectonic history and mineral deposits of the Western Cordillera, A Symposium; *Can. Inst. Mining Met.*, Spec. vol. 8.

McCrossan, R. G., and Glaister, R. P., editors
1964: Geological history of Western Canada; *Alberta Soc. Petrol. Geol.*

Roedder, D. H.
1967: Rocky Mountains; Band 5 Beiträge Zur Region alen Geologie Dar Erde; *Gebrüder Borntraeger*, Berlin-Nikolassee.

White, W. H.
1959: Cordilleran tectonics in British Columbia; *Bull. Am. Assoc. Petrol. Geol.*, vol. 43, no. 1, pp. 60–100.

Northern Cordilleran Orogen and Interior Platform

Aitken, J. D.
1960: Atlin map-area, British Columbia; *Geol. Surv. Can.*, Mem. 307.

Blusson, S. L.
1968: Geology and tungsten deposits near the headwaters of Flat River, Yukon Territory, and southwestern District of Mackenzie, Canada; *Geol. Surv. Can.*, Paper 67-22.

Bostock, H. S.
1936: Carmacks District, Yukon; *Geol. Surv. Can.*, Mem. 189.
1952: Geology of northwest Shakwak Valley, Yukon Territory; *Geol. Surv. Can.*, Mem. 267.

Brabb, E. E.
1967: Stratigraphy of the Cambrian and Ordovician rocks of east-central Alaska; *U.S. Geol. Surv.*, Paper 559-A.

Brosgé, W. P., Dutro, J. T. Jr., Mangus, M. D., and Reiser, H. N.
1962: Palaeozoic sequence in eastern Brooks Range, Alaska; *Bull. Am. Assoc. Petrol. Geol.*, vol. 46, pp. 2174–2198.

Campbell, R. B.
1967: Glenlyon map-area, Yukon Territory; *Geol. Surv. Can.*, Mem. 352.

Christie, R. L.
1957: Bennett, Cassiar District, British Columbia; *Geol. Surv. Can.*, Map 19-1957.

Churkin, M. Jr., and Brabb, E. E.
1965: Ordovician, Silurian and Devonian biostratigraphy of east-central Alaska; *Bull. Am. Assoc. Petrol. Geol.*, vol. 49, pp. 172–185.

Douglas, R. J. W., and Norris, D. K.
1961: Camsell Bend and Root River map-areas, District of Mackenzie, Northwest Territories; *Geol. Surv. Can.*, Paper 61-13.
1963: Dahadinni and Wrigley map-areas, District of Mackenzie, Northwest Territories; *Geol. Surv. Can.*, Paper 62-33.

Frebold, H.
1964: Lower Jurassic and Bajocian ammonoid faunas of northwestern British Columbia and southern Yukon; *Geol. Surv. Can.*, Bull. 116.

Frebold, H., Mountjoy, E. W., and Tempelman-Kluit, D. J.
1967: New occurrences of Jurassic rocks and fossils in central and northern Yukon Territory; *Geol. Surv. Can.*, Paper 67-12.

Gabrielse, H.
1962a: Cry Lake map-area, British Columbia; *Geol. Surv. Can.*, Map 29-1962.
1962b: Kechika map-area, British Columbia; *Geol. Surv. Can.*, Map 42-1962.
1962c: Rabbit River map-area, British Columbia; *Geol. Surv. Can.*, Map 46-1962.
1963: McDame map-area, Cassiar District, British Columbia; *Geol. Surv. Can.*, Mem. 319.

Gabrielse, H., and Souther, J. G.
1962: Dease Lake, British Columbia; *Geol. Surv. Can.*, Map 21-1962.

Gabrielse, H., Roddick, J. A., and Blusson, S. L.
1965: Flat River, Glacier Lake, and Wrigley Lake, District of Mackenzie and Yukon Territory; *Geol. Surv. Can.*, Paper 64-52.

Green, L. H., and Roddick, J. A.
1961: Nahanni, Yukon Territory and District of Mackenzie; *Geol. Surv. Can.*, Map 14-1961.
1962: Dawson, Larsen Creek and Nash Creek map-areas, Yukon Territory; *Geol. Surv. Can.*, Paper 62-7.

Green, L. H., Roddick, J. A., and Wheeler, J. O.
1960a: Quiet Lake map-area, Yukon Territory; *Geol. Surv. Can.*, Map 7-1960.
1960b: Finlayson Lake map-area, Yukon Territory; *Geol. Surv. Can.*, Map 8-1960.

Harker, P.
1963: Carboniferous and Permian rocks, southwestern District of Mackenzie; *Geol. Surv. Can.*, Bull. 95.

Hume, G. S.
1954: The Lower Mackenzie River area, Northwest Territories and Yukon; *Geol. Surv. Can.*, Mem. 273.

Jackson, D. E., and Lenz, A. C.
1962: Zonation of Ordovician and Silurian graptolites of N. Yukon, Canada; *Bull. Am. Assoc. Petrol. Geol.*, vol. 46, pp. 30–45.

Jeletzky, J. A.
1961: Eastern slope, Richardson Mountains: Cretaceous and Tertiary structural history and regional significance. Geology of the Arctic, Proc. 1st. Internat. Symposium, Arctic Geol.; vol. 1, *Univ. Toronto Press*, pp. 532–583.
1967: Jurassic and (?) Triassic rocks of the eastern slope of Richardson Mountains, northwestern District of Mackenzie; *Geol. Surv. Can.*, Paper 66-50.

Kindle, E. D.
1953: Dezadeash map-area, Yukon Territory; *Geol. Surv. Can.*, Mem. 268.

Lanphere, M. A., and Eberlein, G. D.
1966: Potassium-argon ages of magnetite-bearing ultramafic complexes in southeastern Alaska; (Abstract) *Geol. Soc. Am.*, Spec. Paper No. 87, p. 94.

Martin, L. J.
1959: Stratigraphy and depositional tectonics of north Yukon–lower Mackenzie area, Canada; *Bull. Am. Assoc. Petrol. Geol.*, vol. 43, No. 10, pp. 2399–2455.

Moffitt, F. H.
1938: Geology of the Chitina Valley and adjacent areas, Alaska; *U.S. Geol. Surv.*, Bull. 844.

Monger, J. W. H.
1968: Atlin Horst Project: *In* Report of Activities, Part A, May to October, 1967; *Geol. Surv. Can.*, Paper 68-1.

Mountjoy, E. W.
1967a: Triassic stratigraphy of northern Yukon Territory; *Geol. Surv. Can.*, Paper 60-19.
1967b: Upper Cretaceous and Tertiary stratigraphy, northern Yukon Territory, and northwestern District of Mackenzie; *Geol. Surv. Can.*, Paper 66-16.

Muller, J. E.
1967: Kluane Lake map-area, Yukon Territory; *Geol. Surv. Can.*, Mem. 340.

Mulligan, R.
1955: Teslin map-area, Yukon Territory; *Geol. Surv. Can.*, Mem. 326.

Norford, B. S.
1964: Reconnaissance of the Ordovician and Silurian rocks of northern Yukon Territory; *Geol. Surv. Can.*, Paper 63-39.

Norris, A. W.
1967: Description of Devonian sections in northern Yukon Territory and northwestern District of Mackenzie; *Geol. Surv. Can.*, Paper 66-39.

Norris, D. K., Price, R. A., and Mountjoy, E. W.
1963: Northern Yukon Territory and northwestern District of Mackenzie; *Geol. Surv. Can.*, Map 10-1963.

Poole, W. H., Roddick, J. A., and Green, L. H.
1960: Wolf Lake map-area; *Geol. Surv. Can.*, Map 10-1960.

Roddick, J. A., and Green, L. H.
1961a, b: Sheldon Lake and Tay River; *Geol. Surv. Can.*, Maps 12-, 13-1961.

Souther, J. G.
1959: Chutine, Cassiar District, British Columbia; *Geol. Surv. Can.*, Map 7-1959.
1960: Tulsequah, Cassiar District, British Columbia; *Geol. Surv. Can.*, Map 6-1960.
1967: Cordilleran volcanic study: *In* Report of Activities, Part A; *Geol. Surv. Can.*, Paper 67-1.

Stott, D. F.
1960: Cretaceous rocks in the region of Liard and Mackenzie Rivers, Northwest Territories; *Geol. Surv. Can.*, Bull. 63.

Tempelman-Kluit, D. J.
1968: Geological setting of the Faro, Vangorda and Swim base metal deposits, Yukon Territory; *In* Report of Activities, Part A; *Geol. Surv. Can.*, Paper 68-1.
1970: The stratigraphy and structure of the Keno Hill quartzite in the Tombstone River–Upper Klondike River map-areas, Yukon Territory; *Geol. Surv. Can.*, Bull. 180.

Tozer, E. T.
1958: Stratigraphy of the Lewes River Group (Triassic), central Laberge area, Yukon Territory; *Geol. Surv. Can.*, Bull. 43.

Watson, K. de P.
1948: The Squaw Creek Rainy Hollow area, northern British Columbia; *B.C. Dept. Mines,* Bull. 25.

Watson, K. de P., and Mathews, W. H.
1944: The Tuya-Teslin area, northern British Columbia; *B.C. Dept. Mines,* Bull. 19.

Wheeler, J. O.
1961: Whitehorse map-area, Yukon Territory; *Geol. Surv. Can.*, Mem. 312.
1963: Kaskawulsh, Yukon Territory; *Geol. Surv. Can.*, Map 1134-A.

Ziegler, P. A.
1959: Frühpalaozoische tillite im östlichen Yukon Territorium (Kanada); *Eclogae Geologicae Helvet.*, vol. 52, no. 2, pp. 735–741.

Southwestern Cordilleran Orogen

Armstrong, J. E.
1949: Fort St. James map-area, Cassiar and Coast Districts, British Columbia; *Geol. Surv. Can.*, Mem. 252.

Bacon, W. R.
1957: Geology of Lower Jervis Inlet, British Columbia; *B.C. Dept. Mines,* Bull. 39.

Baer, A. J.
1967: Bella Coola and Laredo Sound map-areas, British Columbia; *Geol. Surv. Can.*, Paper 66-25.

Buckham, A. F.
1947: The Nanaimo coal field; *Trans. Can. Inst. Mining Met.*, vol. 50, pp. 460–472.

Cairnes, C. E.
1934: Slocan mining camp, British Columbia; *Geol. Surv. Can.*, Mem. 173.

Campbell, R. B.
1961: Quesnel Lake map-area, west half, British Columbia; *Geol. Surv. Can.*, Map 3-1961.
1963: Adams Lake, British Columbia; *Geol. Surv. Can.*, Map 48-1963.
1967: McBride map-area, British Columbia; *In* Report of Activities, Part A; *Geol. Surv. Can.*, Paper 67-1.

Campbell, R. B., and Tipper, H. W.
1966: Bonaparte River, British Columbia; *Geol. Surv. Can.*, Map 3-1966.

Carlisle, D.
1963: Pillow breccias and their aquagene tuffs, Quadra Island, British Columbia; *J. Geol.*, vol. 71, pp. 48–71.

Coates, J. A.
1967: Manning Park area, Cascade Mountains; *In* Report of Activities, Part A; *Geol. Surv. Can.*, Paper 67-1.

Cockfield, W. E.
1948: Geology and mineral deposits of Nicola map-area, British Columbia; *Geol. Surv. Can.*, Mem. 249.

Crickmay, C. H.
1930: Jurassic rocks of Ashcroft, British Columbia; *Univ. Calif. (Berkeley) Publ., Bull. Dept. Geol. Sci.*, vol. 19, no. 2, pp. 23–74.

Danner, W. R.
1964: Permian: Western Cordilleran region; *Alta. Soc. Petrol. Geol.*, Geological history of western Canada, pp. 109–110.

Duffell, S.
1959: Whitesail Lake map-area, British Columbia; *Geol. Surv. Can.*, Mem. 299.

Duffell, S., and McTaggart, K. C.
1952: Ashcroft map-area, British Columbia; *Geol. Surv. Can.*, Mem. 262.

Duffell, S., and Souther, J. G.
1964: Geology of Terrace map-area, British Columbia; *Geol. Surv. Can.*, Mem. 329.

Frebold, Hans, and Little, H. W.
1962: Palaeontology, stratigraphy, and structure of the Jurassic rocks in the Salmo map-area, British Columbia; *Geol. Surv. Can.*, Bull. 81.

Fyles, J. T.
1955: Geology of the Cowichan Lake area, Vancouver Island, British Columbia; *B.C. Dept. Mines,* Bull. 37.

Fyles, J. T., and Eastwood, G. E. P.
1962: Geology of the Ferguson area, Lardeau District, British Columbia; *B.C. Dept. Mines Petrol. Resources,* Bull. 45.

Hyndman, D. W.
1968: Mid-Mesozoic multiphase folding along the border of the Shuswap Metamorphic Complex; *Bull. Geol. Soc. Am.,* vol. 79, pp. 575–588.

Jeletzky, J. A.
1950: Stratigraphy of the west coast of Vancouver Island between Kyuquot Sound and Esperanza Inlet, British Columbia; *Geol. Surv Can.,* Paper 50-37.

Jeletzky, J. A., and Tipper, H. W.
1968: Upper Jurassic and Cretaceous rocks of Taseko Lakes map-area and their bearing on the geological history of southwestern British Columbia; *Geol. Surv. Can.,* Paper 67-54.

Jones, A. G.
1959: Vernon map-area, British Columbia; *Geol. Surv. Can.,* Mem. 296.

Leech, G. B.
1953: Geology and mineral deposits of the Shulaps Range, southwestern British Columbia; *B.C. Dept. Mines,* Bull. 32.
1962a: Metamorphism and granitic intrusions of Precambrian age in southeastern British Columbia; *Geol. Surv. Can.,* Paper 62-13.

Little, H. W.
1960: Nelson map-area, west half, British Columbia; *Geol. Surv. Can.,* Mem. 308.

Lord, C. S.
1948: McConnell Creek map-area, Cassiar District, British Columbia; *Geol. Surv. Can.,* Mem. 251.

Mathews, W. H.
1958: Geology of the Mount Garibaldi map-area, southwestern B.C., Canada; *Bull. Geol. Soc. Am.,* vol. 69, pp. 161–178.
1964: Potassium-argon age determinations of Cenozoic volcanic rocks from British Columbia; *Bull. Geol. Soc. Am.,* vol. 75, pp. 465–468.

McTaggart, K. C., and Thompson, R. M.
1967: Geology of part of the northern Cascades in southern British Columbia; *Can. J. Earth Sci.,* vol. 4, pp. 1199–1228.

Misch, P.
1966: Tectonic evolution of the northern Cascades of Washington State; *Can. Inst. Mining Met.,* Spec. Vol. No. 8, Tectonic history and mineral deposits of the western Cordillera, pp. 101–148.

Park, C. F. Jr., and Cannon, R. S. Jr.
1943: Geology and ore deposits of the Metaline Quadrangle, Washington; *U.S. Geol. Surv.,* Prof. Paper 202.

Reesor, J. E.
1957: The Proterozoic of the Canadian Cordillera in southeastern British Columbia and southwestern Alberta; *Roy. Soc. Can.,* Spec. Publ. No. 2, Proterozoic in Canada, pp. 150–177.
1965: Structural evolution and plutonism in Valhalla gneiss complex, British Columbia; *Geol. Surv. Can.,* Bull. 129.
1966: The Thor-Odin Gneiss Dome, Monashee Mountains, southern British Columbia; *In* Report of Activities; *Geol. Surv. Can.,* Paper 66-1.

Rice, H. M. A.
1947: Geology and mineral deposits of the Princeton map-area, British Columbia; *Geol. Surv. Can.,* Mem. 243.

Roddick, J. A.
1965: Vancouver north, Coquitlam, and Pitt Lake map-areas, British Columbia; *Geol. Surv. Can.,* Mem. 335.

Roddick, J. A., and Armstrong, J. E.
1959: Relict dykes in the Coast Mountains near Vancouver, B.C.; *J. Geol.,* vol. 67, pp. 603–613.

Roddick, J. A., Baer, A. J., and Hutchison, W. W.
1966: Coast Mountains project; *In* Report of Activities; *Geol. Surv. Can.,* Paper 66-1.

Roots, E. F.
1954: Geology and mineral deposits of Aiken Lake map-area, British Columbia; *Geol. Surv. Can.,* Mem. 274.

Rouse, G. E., and Mathews, W. H.
1961: Radioactive dating of Tertiary plant-bearing deposits; *Science,* vol. 133, pp. 1079–1080.

Souther, J. G.
1966: Cordillera volcanic study; *In* Report of Activities, May to October, 1965, pp. 87–89; *Geol. Surv. Can.,* Paper 66-1.

Souther, J. G., and Armstrong, J. E.
1966: North-central belt of the Cordillera of British Columbia; *Can. Inst. Mining Met.,* Spec. Vol. No. 8, Tectonic history and mineral deposits of the western Cordillera, pp. 171–184.

Stuart, R. A.
1960: Geology of the Kemano-Tahtsa area; *B.C. Dept. Mines Petrol. Resources,* Bull. 42.

Sutherland Brown, A.
1957: Geology of the Antler Creek area, Cariboo District, British Columbia; *B.C. Dept. Mines,* Bull. 38.
1960: Geology of the Rocher Deboule Range; *B.C. Dept. Mines Petrol. Resources,* Bull. 43.
1963: Geology of the Cariboo River area, British Columbia; *B.C. Dept. Mines Petrol. Resources,* Bull. 47.
1966: Tectonic history of the Insular Belt of British Columbia; *Can. Inst. Mining Met.,* Spec. Vol. No. 8, Tectonic history and mineral deposits of the western Cordillera, pp. 83–100.

Tipper, H. W.
1959: Revision of the Hazelton and Takla Groups of central British Columbia; *Geol. Surv. Can.,* Bull. 47.
1963: Nechako River map-area, British Columbia; *Geol. Surv. Can.,* Mem. 324.

Trettin, H. P.
1961: Geology of the Fraser River valley between Lillooet and Big Bar Creek; *B.C. Dept. Mines Petrol. Resources,* Bull. 44.

Vine, F. J.

1966: Spreading of the ocean floor: new evidence; *Science,* vol. 154, pp. 1405–1415.

Wheeler, J. O.

1965: Big Bend map-area, British Columbia; *Geol. Surv. Can.,* Paper 64-32.

1966a: Eastern tectonic belt of western Cordillera in British Columbia; *Can. Inst. Mining Met.,* Spec. Vol. No. 8, Tectonic history and mineral deposits of the western Cordillera, pp. 27–45.

1966b: Lardeau (west half) map-area, British Columbia; *In* Report of Activities; *Geol. Surv. Can.,* Paper 66-1.

Wilson, J. T.

1965: Transform faults, oceanic ridges, and magnetic anomalies southwest of Vancouver Island; *Science,* vol. 150, pp. 482–485.

Yole, R. W.

1963: An Early Permian fauna from Vancouver Island, British Columbia; *Bull. Can. Petrol. Geol.,* vol. 11, pp. 138–149.

Southeastern Cordilleran Orogen and Interior Platform

Aitken, J. D.

1966: Middle Cambrian to Middle Ordovician cyclic sedimentation, southern Rocky Mountains, Alberta; *Bull. Can. Petrol. Geol.,* vol. 14, pp. 405–411.

1968: Cambrian sections in the easternmost southern Rocky Mountains and the adjacent subsurface, Alberta; *Geol. Surv. Can.,* Paper 66-23.

Aitken, J. D., and Norford, B. S.

1967: Lower Ordovician Survey Peak and Outram Formations, southern Rocky Mountains of Alberta; *Bull. Can. Petrol. Geol.,* vol. 15, pp. 150–207.

Allan, J. A.

1954: Ice River Complex; *Alta. Soc. Petrol. Geol.,* 4th Ann. Field Conf. Guidebook, pp. 141–145.

Allan, J. A., and Carr, J. L.

1946: Geology and coal occurrences of Wapiti-Cutbank area, Alberta; *Alta. Research Council,* Rept. 48.

Andrichuk, J. M.

1958a: Stratigraphy and facies analysis of Upper Devonian reefs in Leduc, Stettler and Redwater areas, Alberta; *Bull. Am. Assoc. Petrol. Geol.,* vol. 42, pp. 1–93.

1958b: Cooking Lake and Duvernay (late Devonian) sedimentation in Edmonton area of central Alberta, Canada; *Bull. Am. Assoc. Petrol. Geol.,* vol. 42, pp. 2189–2222.

1960: Facies analysis of Upper Devonian Wabamun Group in west-central Alberta, Canada; *Bull. Am. Assoc. Petrol. Geol.,* vol. 44, pp. 1651–1681.

1961: Stratigraphic evidence of tectonic and current control of Upper Devonian reef sedimentation in the Duhamel area; *Bull. Am. Assoc. Petrol. Geol.,* vol. 45, pp. 612–632.

Armitage, J. A.

1962: Triassic oil and gas occurrences in northeastern British Columbia, Canada; *J. Alta. Soc. Petrol. Geol.,* vol. 10, pp. 35–56.

Baillie, A. D.

1955: Devonian system of the Williston Basin; *Bull. Am. Assoc. Petrol. Geol.,* vol. 39, pp. 575–629.

Bally, A. W., Gordy, P. L., and Stewart, G. A.

1966: Structure, seismic data and orogenic evolution of southern Canadian Rocky Mountains; *Bull. Can. Petrol. Geol.,* vol. 14, pp. 337–381.

Bassett, H. G.

1961: Devonian stratigraphy, central Mackenzie River region, Northwest Territories, Canada: Proceedings of First Internat. Symp. on Arctic Geol.; *Alta. Soc. Petrol. Geol.,* pp. 481–498.

Beales, F. W.

1956: Conditions of deposition of Palliser (Devonian) limestone of southwestern Alberta; *Bull. Am. Assoc. Petrol. Geol.,* vol. 40, pp. 848–870.

Bell, R. T.

1968: Proterozoic stratigraphy of northeastern British Columbia; *Geol. Surv. Can.,* Paper 67-68.

Bell, W. A.

1956: Lower Cretaceous floras of western Canada; *Geol. Surv. Can.,* Mem. 285.

Belyea, H. R.

1958: Distribution and lithology of organic carbonate unit, Upper Devonian Fairholme Group, Alberta; *Trans. Can. Inst. Mining Met.,* vol. 41, pp. 40–48.

1959: Devonian Elk Point Group, central and southern Alberta; *Geol. Surv. Can.,* Paper 59-2.

1960: Distribution of some reefs and banks of the Upper Devonian Woodbend and Fairholme Groups in Alberta and eastern British Columbia; *Geol. Surv. Can.,* Paper 59-15.

1962: Upper Devonian formations, southern part of Northwest Territories, northeastern British Columbia and northwestern Alberta; *Geol. Surv. Can.,* Paper 61-29.

Belyea, H. R., and Norford, B. S.

1967: The Devonian Cedared and Harrogate Formations in the Beaverfoot, Brisco and Stanford Ranges, southeastern British Columbia; *Geol. Surv. Can.,* Bull. 146.

Belyea, H. R., and Norris, A. W.

1962: Middle Devonian and older Palaeozoic formations of southern District of Mackenzie and adjacent areas; *Geol. Surv. Can.,* Paper 62-15.

Best, E. W.

1958: The Triassic of the North Saskatchewan-Athabasca Rivers area; *Alta. Soc. Petrol. Geol.,* Guidebook, 5th Ann. Field Conf., pp. 39–49.

Burwash, R. A., Baadsgaard, H., and Peterman, Z. E.

1962: Precambrian K/Ar dates from the Western Canada sedimentary basin; *J. Geophys. Res.,* vol. 67, pp. 1617–1625.

Colquhoun, D. J.
1962: Triassic stratigraphy in the vicinity of Peace River Foothills, British Columbia; *Edmonton Geol. Soc.*, Guidebook, 4th Ann. Field Conf., pp. 57–88.

Crockford, M. B. B.
1949: Geology of Ribbon Creek area, Alberta; *Alta. Research Council,* Rept. 52.

Dahlstrom, C. D. A., Daniel, R. E., and Henderson, G. G. L.
1962: The Lewis Thrust at Fording Mountain, British Columbia; *J. Alta. Soc. Petrol. Geol.*, vol. 10, pp. 373–395.

Douglas, R. J. W.
1950: Callum Creek, Langford Creek and Gap map-areas, Alberta; *Geol. Surv. Can.*, Mem. 255.
1958: Chungo Creek map-area, Alberta; *Geol. Surv. Can.*, Paper 58-3.
1959: Mount Head map-area, Alberta; *Geol. Surv. Can.*, Mem. 291.

Edie, R. W.
1958: Mississippian sedimentation and oil fields in southeastern Saskatchewan; *Bull. Am. Assoc. Petrol. Geol.*, vol. 42, no. 1, pp. 94–126.
1959: Middle Devonian sedimentation and oil possibilities, central Saskatchewan, Canada; *Bull. Am. Assoc. Petrol. Geol.*, vol. 43, pp. 1026–1057.

Fitzgerald, E. L., and Braun, L. T.
1965: Disharmonic folds in Besa River Formation, northeastern British Columbia; *Bull. Am. Assoc. Petrol. Geol.*, vol. 49, pp. 418–432.

Frebold, H.
1957: The Jurassic Fernie Group in the Canadian Rocky Mountains and Foothills; *Geol. Surv. Can.*, Mem. 287.

Fuller, J. G. C. M.
1956: Mississippian rocks in the Saskatchewan portion of the Williston basin—a review; *North Dakota Geol. Soc., Saskatchewan Geol. Soc.*, First Internat. Williston Basin Symp., pp. 29–35.

Fuller, J. G. C. M., and Porter, J. W.
1962: Cambrian, Ordovician and Silurian Formations of the Northern Great Plains, and their regional connections; *J. Alta. Soc. Petrol. Geol.*, vol. 10, pp. 455–485.

Furnival, G. M.
1946: Cypress Lake map-area, Saskatchewan; *Geol. Surv. Can.*, Mem. 242.

Fuzesy, L. M.
1960: Correlations and subcrops of the Mississippian strata in southeastern and south-central Saskatchewan; *Sask. Dept. Min. Res.*, Rept. 51.

Gibson, D. W.
1968: Triassic stratigraphy between the Athabasca and Smoky Rivers of Alberta; *Geol. Surv. Can.*, Paper 67-65.

Grayston, L. D., Sherwin, D. F., and Allan, J. F.
1964: Middle Devonian *in* Geological history of Western Canada; *Alta. Soc. Petrol. Geol.*

Halbertsma, H. L.
1959: Nomenclature of Upper Carboniferous and Permian strata in the subsurface of the Peace River area; *J. Alta. Soc. Petrol. Geol.*, vol. 7, pp. 109–118.

Henderson, G. G. L.
1954: Geology of the Stanford Range, Kootenay District, B.C.; *British Columbia Dept. Mines,* Bull. 35.

Hughes, J. E.
1963: Summary account of Devonian sections mile 390 to mile 520, Alaska Highway; *British Columbia Dept. Mines Petrol. Res.*

Hunt, A. D., and Ratcliffe, J. D.
1959: Triassic stratigraphy, Peace River area, Alberta and British Columbia, Canada; *Bull. Am. Assoc. Petrol. Geol.*, vol. 43, pp. 563–589.

Irish, E. J. W.
1951: Pierre Greys Lakes map-area, Alberta; *Geol. Surv. Can.*, Mem. 258.

Jackson, D. E., Steen, G., and Sykes, D.
1965: Stratigraphy and graptolitic zonation of the Kechika and Sandpile Groups in northeastern British Columbia; *Bull. Can. Petrol. Geol.*, vol. 13, pp. 139–154.

Jones, L.
1965: The Middle Devonian Winnipegosis Formation of Saskatchewan; *Sask. Dept. Min. Res.*, Rept. 98.

Kidd, F. A.
1963: The Besa River Formation; *J. Alta. Soc. Petrol. Geol.*, vol. 11, pp. 369–372.

Klovan, J. E.
1964: Facies analysis of the Redwater reef complex, Alberta, Canada; *Bull. Can. Petrol. Geol.*, vol. 12, pp. 1–100.

Lackie, J. H.
1958: Subsurface Jurassic of the Peace River area; *in* Jurassic and Carboniferous of Western Canada; *Am. Assoc. Petrol. Geol.*

Lane, D. M.
1965: Souris River Formation in southern Saskatchewan; *Sask. Dept. Min. Res.*, Rept. 92.

Leech, G. B.
1962b: Structure of Bull River valley near latitude 49°35′; *J. Alta. Soc. Petrol. Geol.*, vol. 10, pp. 396–407.
1964: Kananaskis (west half) map-area; *in* Report of Activities; *Geol. Surv. Can.*, Paper 64-1.
1966: The Rocky Mountain Trench; *Geol. Surv. Can.*, Paper 66-14, pp. 307–329.

Lines, F. G.
1963: Stratigraphy of Bearpaw Formation of southern Alberta; *Bull. Can. Petrol. Geol.*, vol. 11, pp. 212–227.

Mackenzie, W. S.
1965: Upper Devonian carbonates of the Southesk Cairn Complex and associated strata, eastern Rocky Mountain Foothills, Alberta; *Bull. Can. Petrol. Geol.*, vol. 13, pp. 457–481.

Macqueen, R. W., and Bamber, E. W.
1967: Stratigraphy of the Banff Formation and the Lower Rundle Group (Mississippian), southwestern Alberta; *Geol. Surv. Can.*, Paper 67-47.

Manko, E. M.
1960: The Triassic of the Rock Lake area; *Edmonton Geol. Soc.*, Guidebook, 2nd Ann. Field Conf., pp. 25–42.

Mathews, W. H.
1947: Geology and coal resources of the Carbon Creek–Mount Bickford map-area, British Columbia; 1946 *B.C. Dept. Mines,* Bull. 24.

McGugan, A., and Rapson, J. E.
1962: Permo-Carboniferous stratigraphy, Crowsnest area, Alberta and British Columbia; *J. Alta. Soc. Petrol. Geol.*, vol. 10, pp. 352–368.

McLaren, D. J.
1955: Devonian formations in the Alberta Rocky Mountains between Bow and Athabasca Rivers; *Geol. Surv. Can.*, Bull. 35.

McLearn, F. H., and Kindle, E. D.
1950: Geology of northeastern British Columbia; *Geol. Surv. Can.*, Mem. 259.

Mellon, G. B.
1967: Stratigraphy and petrography of the Lower Cretaceous Blairmore and Mannville Groups, Alberta Foothills and Plains; *Alta. Research Council,* Bull. 21.

Milner, R. L., and Blakslee, G. W.
1958: Notes on the Jurassic of southwestern Saskatchewan: *in* Jurassic and Carboniferous of western Canada–a Symposium; *Am. Assoc. Petrol. Geol.*

Mountjoy, E. W.
1962: Mount Robson (southeast) map-area, Rocky Mountains of Alberta and British Columbia; *Geol. Surv. Can.*, Paper 61-31.
1965: Stratigraphy of the Devonian Miette reef complex and associated strata, eastern Jasper National Park; *Geol. Surv. Can.*, Bull. 110.

Mountjoy, E. W., and Aitken, J. D.
1963: Early Cambrian and late Precambrian paleocurrents, Banff and Jasper National Parks; *Bull. Can. Petrol. Geol.*, vol. 11, pp. 161–168.

Murray, J. W.
1965: Stratigraphy and carbonate petrography of the Waterways Formation, Judy Creek, Alberta, Canada; *Bull. Can. Petrol. Geol.*, vol. 13, pp. 303–326.

Nauss, A. W.
1945: Cretaceous stratigraphy of the Vermilion area, Alberta, Canada; *Bull. Am. Assoc. Petrol. Geol.*, vol. 29, pp. 1605–1629.

Norford, B. S., Gabrielse, H., and Taylor, G. C.
1966: Stratigraphy of Silurian carbonate rocks of the Rocky Mountains, northern British Columbia; *Bull. Can. Petrol. Geol.*, vol. 14, pp. 504–519.

Norris, A. W.
1963: Devonian stratigraphy of northeastern Alberta and northwestern Saskatchewan; *Geol. Surv. Can.*, Mem. 313.
1965: Stratigraphy of Middle Devonian and older Paleozoic rocks of the Great Slave Lake region, Northwest Territories; *Geol. Surv. Can.*, Mem. 322.

Norris, D. K.
1959: Type section of the Kootenay Formation, Grassy Mountain, Alberta; *J. Alta. Soc. Petrol. Geol.*, vol. 7, no. 10, pp. 223–233.

Norris, D. K., and Price, R. A.
1966: Middle Cambrian lithostratigraphy of southeastern Canadian Cordillera; *Bull. Can. Petrol. Geol.*, vol. 14, pp. 385–441.

North, F. K., and Henderson, G. G. L.
1954: Summary of the geology of the southern Rocky Mountains of Canada; *Alta. Soc. Petrol. Geol.*, 4th Ann. Field Conf. Guidebook, pp. 15–81.

Oliver, T. A., and Cowper, N. W.
1963: Depositional environments of the Ireton Formation, central Alberta; *J. Alta. Soc. Petrol. Geol.*, vol. 11, pp. 183–202.

Ower, J. R.
1960: The Edmonton Formation; *J. Alta. Soc. Petrol. Geol.*, vol. 8, pp. 309–323.

Pelletier, B. R.
1963: Triassic stratigraphy of the Rocky Mountains and Foothills, Peace River district, British Columbia; *Geol. Surv. Can.*, Paper 62-26.

Penner, D. G.
1959: Mississippian of south-central Alberta; *Alta. Soc. Petrol. Geol.*, Guidebook 9th Ann. Field Conf., pp. 104–112.

Porter, J. W., and Fuller, J. G. C. M.
1964: Ordovician and Silurian: *in* Geological history of Western Canada; *Alta. Soc. Petrol. Geol.*

Price, R. A.
1964a: The Precambrian Purcell system in the Rocky Mountains of southern Alberta and British Columbia; *Bull. Can. Petrol. Geol.*, vol. 12, pp. 399–426.
1964b: The Devonian Fairholme-Sassenach succession and evolution of reef-front geometry in the Flathead-Crowsnest area, Alberta and British Columbia; *Bull. Can. Petrol. Geol.*, vol. 12, pp. 427–451.
1964c: Flexural-slip folds in the Rocky Mountains, southern Alberta and British Columbia; seminars in Tectonics, Queen's University, Kingston.
1966: Flathead map-area, British Columbia and Alberta; *Geol. Surv. Can.*, Mem. 336.

Price, R. A., and Mountjoy, E. W.
1970: Geologic structure of the Canadian Rockies between Bow and Athabasca Rivers, a Progress Report; *Geol. Assoc. Can.*, Special Paper No. 6.

Rudkin, R. A.
1964: Lower Cretaceous: *in* Geological history of Western Canada; *Alta. Soc. Petrol. Geol.*

Russell, L. S., and Landes, R. W.
1940: Geology of the southern Alberta Plains; *Geol. Surv. Can.*, Mem. 221.

Scott, J. C.
1951: Folded faults in Rocky Mountain Foothills of Alberta, Canada; *Bull. Am. Assoc. Petrol. Geol.*, vol. 35, pp. 2316–2347.

Shaw, E. W., and Harding, S. R. L.
1954: Lea Park and Belly River Formations of east-central Alberta; *in* Western Canada sedimentary basin; *Am. Assoc. Petrol. Geol.*, pp. 297–308.

Sinclair, A. J.
1966: Anomalous leads from the Kootenay Arc, British Columbia; *in* Tectonic history and mineral deposits of the western Cordillera; *Can. Inst. Mining Met.*, Special Vol. No. 8.

Slind, O. L., and Perkins, G. D.
1966: Lower Palaeozoic and Proterozoic sediments of the Rocky Mountains between Jasper, Alberta, and Pine River, British Columbia; *Bull. Can. Petrol. Geol.*, vol. 14, pp. 442–468.

Springer, G. D., MacDonald, W. D., and Crockford, M. B. B.
1964: Jurassic: *in* Geological history of Western Canada; *Alta. Soc. Petrol. Geol.*

Stanton, M. S.
1958: Stratigraphy of the Lodgepole Formation, Virden-Whitewater area, Manitoba; *in* Jurassic and Carboniferous of Western Canada—a symposium; *Am. Assoc. Petrol. Geol.*, pp. 372–390.

Stearn, C. W.
1956: Stratigraphy and palaeontology of the Interlake Group and Stonewall Formation of southern Manitoba; *Geol. Surv. Can.*, Mem. 281.

Stott, D. F.
1963: The Cretaceous Alberta Group and equivalent rocks, Rocky Mountain Foothills, Alberta; *Geol. Surv. Can.*, Mem. 317.
1965: The Cretaceous Smoky Group, Rocky Mountain Foothills, Alberta and British Columbia; *Geol. Surv. Can.*, Bull. 132.
1967: The Fernie and Minnes strata north of Peace River, Foothills of northeastern British Columbia; *Geol. Surv. Can.*, Paper 67-19.
1968a: Lower Cretaceous Bullhead and Fort St. John Groups, between Smoky and Peace Rivers, Rocky Mountain Foothills, Alberta and British Columbia; *Geol. Surv. Can.*, Bull. 152.
1968b: Cretaceous stratigraphy between Tetsa and Labiche Rivers, northeastern British Columbia; *Geol. Surv. Can.*, Paper 68-14.

Thomas, G. E.
1954: The Mississippian of the northeastern Williston Basin; *Bull. Can. Inst. Mining Met.*, vol. 47, pp. 136–142.

Thomas, G. E., and Glaister, R. P.
1960: Facies and porosity relationships in some Mississippian carbonate cycles of Western Canada Basin; *Bull. Am. Assoc. Petrol. Geol.*, vol. 44, pp. 569–588.

Tozer, E. T.
1956: Uppermost Cretaceous and Paleocene non-marine molluscan fauna of western Alberta; *Geol. Surv. Can.*, Mem. 280.

Thompson, R. L., and Crockford, M. B. B.
1958: The Jurassic subsurface in southern Alberta: *in* Jurassic and Carboniferous of Western Canada; *Am. Assoc. Petrol. Geol.*

van Hees, H.
1956: The Elk Point Group. Notes on a subsurface cross-section extending from east-central Alberta through Saskatchewan to western Manitoba; *J. Alta. Soc. Petrol. Geol.*, vol. 4, pp. 29–39.
1965: Cambrian: *in* Geological history of Western Canada; *Alta. Soc. Petrol. Geol.*

Wickenden, R. T. D.
1945: Mesozoic stratigraphy of the eastern plains, Manitoba and Saskatchewan; *Geol. Surv. Can.*, Mem. 239.

Williams, G. D., and Burk, C. F., Jr.
1964: Upper Cretaceous: *in* Geological history of Western Canada; *Alta. Soc. Petrol. Geol.*

Wonfor, J. S., and Andrichuk, J. M.
1956: The Wabamun Group in the Stettler area, Alberta; *J. Alta. Soc. Petrol. Geol.*, vol. 4, pp. 99–111.

Ziegler, W. H., and Pocock, S. A. J.
1960: The Minnes Formation; *Edmonton Geol. Soc.*, Guidebook, 2nd Ann. Field Conf., pp. 43–71.

IX. Economic Minerals of Western Canada

INTRODUCTION

The economic minerals of Western Canada are numerous and diverse (Table IX-1) as the region embraces a great many geological environments that range from those of the complexly deformed rocks in the mountains of the Western Cordillera to those of less disturbed and flat sedimentary sequences of the Eastern Cordillera and Interior Plains (*see* Chap. VIII). In 1966 the region yielded 93.6 per cent of all fuels produced in Canada, valued at $1,080 million, some 30 per cent of the industrial minerals and materials valued at $249 million, and about 15 per cent of the metals valued at $302 million. Total value of the economic minerals and materials produced in 1966 was $1,631 million representing 41 per cent of that for Canada as a whole. Most important commodities produced, in order of their total cumulative values, are oil, coal, natural gas, lead, gold, copper, silver, and zinc. Other products small in value yet not produced elsewhere in Canada are tin, mercury, and potash.

Mineral production, which began in 1836 with the mining of coal on Vancouver Island, was small until the discovery of placer gold on Pend-d'Oreille and Fraser Rivers from 1855 to 1860. Placer gold was foremost in production until 1884 when it was again surpassed by coal. In the late 19th and early 20th centuries the numerous lode gold and base metal mines developed in the Cordilleran Region dominated production for many years. Natural gas was first discovered at Medicine Hat in 1890, natural gas and naphtha at Turner Valley in 1913, and crude oil at Norman Wells in 1920. During 1953 the value of crude oil produced in Canada, largely from Western Canada, exceeded for the first time that of any other single commodity; nickel, gold, and copper were the leaders in previous years.

The Cordilleran Region, in comparison with other metal-bearing parts of Canada, has produced about 90 per cent of the lead, more than half the zinc, nearly half the silver, and nearly one fifth the copper produced to date. With recent development of several large copper deposits the proportion of Cordilleran production may well rise. Conversely, with only two major gold mines in operation the value of Cordilleran gold, which formerly represented more than a fifth of Canadian production, is decreasing whereas that from the Canadian Shield in Ontario and Quebec is increasing relatively. The Cordilleran Region provides the greater part of the antimony, bismuth, cadmium, and tungsten produced in Canada, and all the tin and mercury. Platinum, magnesium, palladium, molybdenite, chromite, manganese, cobalt, and selenium have also been produced in the past. Iron has become important recently through development of contact metamorphic deposits of magnetite. Since 1958, nickel valued at more than a million dollars annually has been produced.

The fuels—petroleum, natural gas, and coal—are found in considerable abundance in Western Canada, the region yielding some 98 per cent of the oil and gas, and 44 per cent of the coal produced in Canada during 1965.

[1] Authorship responsibilities for sections of this chapter are: Mineral provinces and metallic deposits by H. W. Little; Coal by B. A. Latour; Paleozoic and Mesozoic oil and gas fields by H. R. Belyea and D. F. Stott, respectively; Foothills oil and gas fields by R. J. W. Douglas. The accounts of non-metallic minerals were prepared by H. W. Little, D. F. Stott, and H. R. Belyea, or taken from previous editions.

IX Economic Minerals of Western Canada

H.W. Little, H.R. Belyea, D.F. Stott, B.A. Latour, and R.J.W. Douglas[1]

Ironsides pit of Phoenix Copper mine, British Columbia.

The oil and gas occur mainly in the southern parts of the Interior Plains, the Devonian, Cretaceous, and Mississippian systems being most prolific, and from the thrust sheets of the Foothills of the Eastern Cordillera. Coal, of Cretaceous and Tertiary age, occurs at many places through the Cordillera and Plains, but the largest deposits and most mines are in the Eastern Cordillera and southern Plains.

Of the industrial minerals, the most valuable are asbestos, potash, sulphur, salt, and gypsum, whereas those of lesser importance are barite, fluorite, bentonite, sodium and magnesium sulphate, and diatomite. Large quantities of structural material such as cement, lime, sand and gravel, crushed rock, building stone, firebrick, common brick, and other clay products have been produced.

MINERAL PROVINCES

The economic minerals of the Cordilleran Region and Interior Plains include many of the metallic and industrial minerals, natural gas, petroleum, and coal. The region is divisible into two geologically distinct provinces—the Eastern and Western Mineral Provinces. Their boundary in the south is Rocky Mountain Trench and in the north follows close to the western boundary of the Eastern Cordilleran system (*see* Fig. IX-1 and Mineral Deposits of Canada, Map 1252A). The Eastern Province includes the Interior Plains, the Rocky Mountains and Foothills, Mackenzie Mountains, and much of Selwyn and Ogilvie Mountains; the Western Province embraces the remainder of the Canadian Cordillera.

Although similarities in stratigraphy and structure persist in places for some distance across the border between these provinces and similar types of mineral deposits are known in both, the differences between them are impressive. The Eastern Province is characterized by carbonate, sandstone, shale, and evaporites, unmetamorphosed or of very low grade metamorphism. In the eastern part, beneath the Interior Plains, the strata overlying the Precambrian crystalline basement are virtually undisturbed, comprising remnants of several depositional basins. In the smaller, western part, which forms the Eastern Cordillera, the sediments are folded and faulted and a few small intrusive bodies occur.

In contrast, the Western Province had a most complex history. The Proterozoic and early Paleozoic rocks which are exposed almost entirely in the eastern part are mainly miogeosynclinal facies. The late Paleozoic and early Mesozoic rocks are, however, of typical eugeosynclinal facies. In Coast and Omineca geanticlines the rocks are for the most part intensely folded and highly metamorphosed. Elsewhere intense deformation and high grade metamorphism are local, but the regional grade of metamorphism, although low, is generally much higher than that of the Eastern Province.

Orogenic movements occurred throughout and plutonic activity is recorded in the late Proterozoic, mid-Paleozoic, throughout the Mesozoic, and the early Tertiary. In the Mesozoic, linear basins of deposition were formed, some of which, towards the close were intermontane and continental, followed in the Tertiary by the extrusion of plateau basalt and the formation of volcanic cones.

TABLE IX-1 *Mineral production of Western Canada in 1966, and cumulative totals*

Western Mineral Province			Eastern Mineral Province		
	1966 (thousands)	Cumulative totals (thousands)		1966 (thousands)	Cumulative totals (thousands)
FUELS			FUELS		
Coal	31 tons $ 300	83,690 tons $ 337,442	Coal	6,607 tons $ 22,131	440,707 tons $ 1,543,952
			Liquid petroleum gases	51,190 bbl. $ 99,908	* $ 418,790
			Natural gas	1,326,195 Mcf $ 171,598	9,299,045 Mcf $ 1,110,663
			Petroleum crude	319,266 bbl. $ 787,256	3,158,806 bbl. $ 7,311,831
METALS			METALS		
Antimony	1,406 lb. $ 745	48,592 lb. $ 13,982			
Bismuth	47 lb. $ 199	6,203 lb. $ 11,192			
Cadmium	1,257 lb. $ 3,222	37,549 lb. $ 63,285	Cadmium	125 lb. $ 301	377 lb. $ 937
Chromite	— —	1 ton $ 32			
Cobalt	— —	2 lb. $ 0.4			
Copper	105,006 lb. $ 56,014	3,560,054 lb. $ 702,428			
Gold, lode	119 oz. $ 4,476	16,559 oz. $ 486,295	Gold, lode	— —	0.06 oz. $ 2
Gold, placer	42 oz. $ 1,554	16,262 oz. $ 357,287	Gold, placer	0.18 oz. $ 7	41 oz. $ 983
Iron concentrates	2,152 tons $ 20,779	18,102 tons $ 159,330			
Lead	226,438 lb. $ 36,656	15,335,202 lb. $ 1,259,190	Lead	211,687 lb. $ 31,640	492,394 lb. $ 66,904
Magnesium	— —	205 lb. $ 88			
Manganese	— —	2 tons $ 33			
Mercury	— —	4,171 lb. $ 10,445			
Molybdenum	17,306 lb. $ 28,072	24,655 lb. $ 40,570			
Nickel	3,622 lb. $ 3,104	28,231 lb. $ 22,427			
Platinum and palladium	— —	2 oz. $ 167			
Selenium	— —	1 lb. $ 1			
Silver	9,712 oz. $ 13,554	606,768 oz. $ 423,980	Silver	22 oz. $ 31	940 oz. $ 620
Tin	711 lb. $ 917	16,837 lb. $ 13,974			

TABLE IX-1 *Mineral production of Western Canada in 1966, and cumulative totals (conc.)*

Western Mineral Province

	1966 (thousands)	Cumulative totals (thousands)
Tungsten (WO_3)	4,185 lb. $ 5,000	20,236 lb. $ 43,691
Zinc	314,395 lb. $ 49,065	13,354,409 lb. $ 1,232,880
Industrial Minerals		
Arsenious oxide	— —	22,019 lb. $ 273
Asbestos	89 tons $ 15,071	591 tons $ 104,772
Barite	22 tons $ 176	252 tons $ 2,942
Diatomite	0.07 ton $ 4	4 tons $ 144
Fluorspar	0.15 ton $ 5	36 tons $ 792
Gypsum and anhydrite	— —	1,247 tons $ 6,323
Hydro-magnesite	— —	2 tons $ 28
Iron oxide and ochre	— —	18 tons $ 155
Jade	12 lb. $ 13	238 lb. $ 109
Mica	— —	12,822 lb. $ 186
Perlite	— —	1 ton $ 11
Sodium carbonate and magnesium sulphate	— —	24 tons $ 373
Talc	— —	2 tons $ 35
Structural Materials		
Cement	708 tons $ 15,959	10,190 tons $ 159,543
Clay products	$ 4,100	$ 60,093
Lime and limestone	1,484 tons $ 2,696	* $ 41,105
Sand and gravel	24,320 tons $ 21,960	* $ 164,267
Stone	77 tons $ 215	1,154 tons $ 9,080

Eastern Mineral Province

	1966 (thousands)	Cumulative totals (thousands)
Zinc	380,513 lb. $ 57,459	748,646 lb. $ 102,666
Industrial Minerals		
Phosphate rock	— —	4 tons $ 17
Potash	1,990 tons $ 62,665	5,029 tons $ 173,917
Salt	235 tons $ 3,877	2,752 tons 54,448
Sodium sulphate	405 tons $ 6,472	5,411 tons $ 73,909
Sulphur, elemental	2,041 tons $ 40,238	* $ 332,226
Gypsum and anhydrite	340 tons $ 1,004	6,559 tons $ 28,884
Structural Materials		
Cement	1,545 tons $ 30,870	25,780 tons $ 425,498
Clay products	$ 5,305	$ 134,002
Lime and limestone	129 tons $ 2,256	3,154 tons $ 41,082
Sand and gravel	30,876 tons $ 21,195	522,526 tons $ 320,778
Stone	2,167 tons $ 3,962	17,909 tons $ 35,676

Sources: Dominion Bureau of Statistics, British Columbia Department of Mines, and Mineral Resources Branch of Department Energy, Mines and Resources.

— No production

* Quantity not available

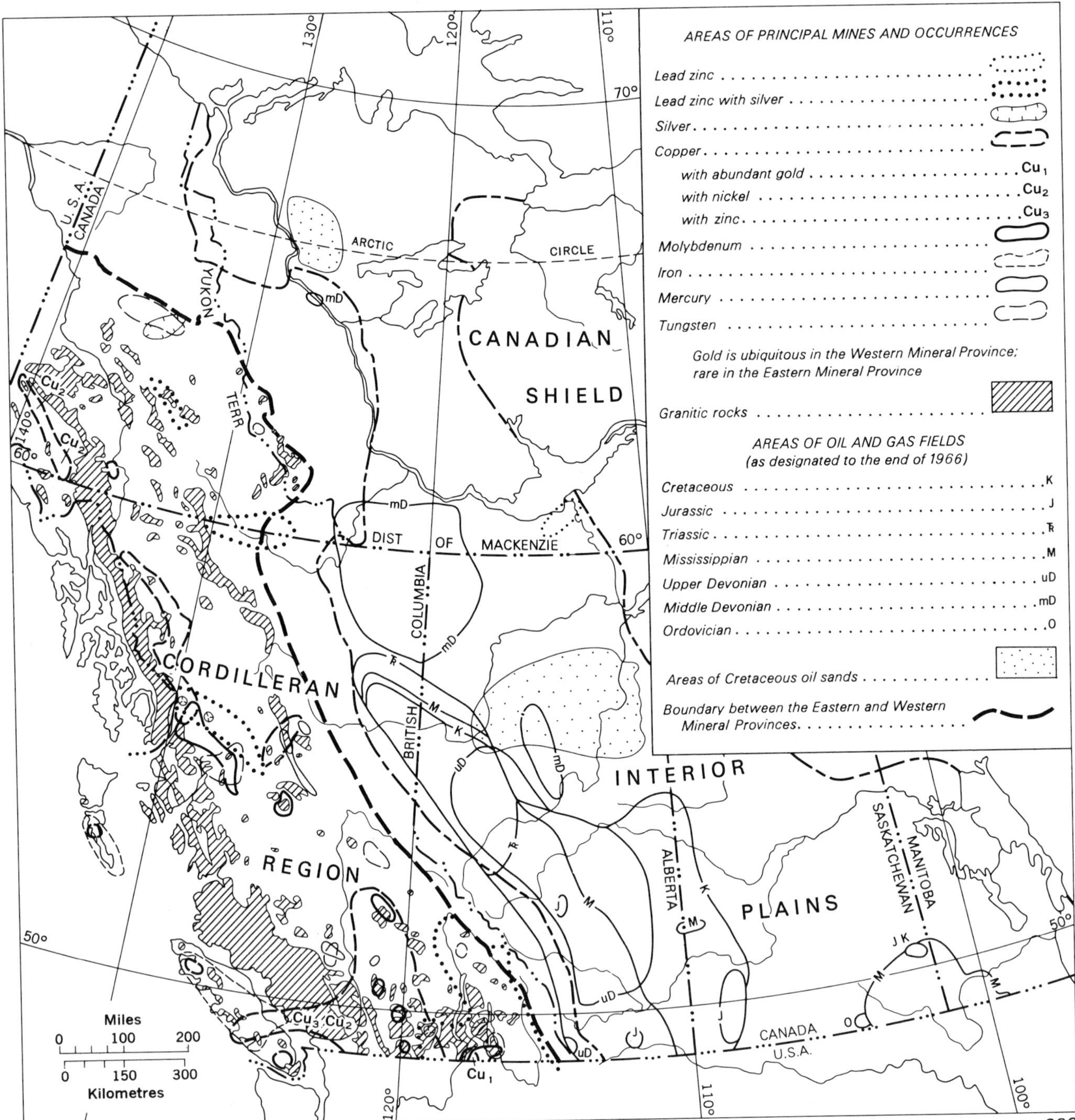

FIGURE IX-1. Mineral provinces of Western Canada.

METALLIC DEPOSITS

Eastern Mineral Province

Deposits of this province are typical of an environment reflecting an epeirogenic tectonic history, simple deformation, and only local metamorphism and plutonism. Contact metamorphic, magmatic segregation, and hypothermal deposits are unknown, and mesothermal deposits are rare. Non-ferrous metallic deposits are epithermal veins or low temperature replacements in limestone or shale, and ferrous deposits are of sedimentary origin. The great bulk of the economic minerals (Table IX-1) are petroleum, natural gas, and coal, and non-metallic deposits such as evaporites, saline lake deposits, or structural materials such as building and crushed stone, sand, gravel, cement, and bentonite.

Metallic mineral deposits with the important exception of Pine Point lie in the western part of the province. They are few in number, widely separated, and are not assigned to specific metallogenic provinces or epochs. Mineral properties and their production up to and including 1966 are given in Table IX-2.

Lode Deposits

Lead–Zinc–Silver

Lead–zinc–silver deposits (Fig. IX-2), some of which contain minor cadmium and gold, are classified as concordant or transgressive according to their relationships with the country rock.

Concordant Deposits

These are represented by Pine Point (10)[1], Monarch and Kicking Horse (98), and the Kootenay King (Fig. IX-2) mines.

The *Pine Point* region on the south shore of Great Slave Lake, District of Mackenzie, has a total of twenty-eight known orebodies ranging from a few thousand to 3 million tons and occurring in a belt 2 to 4 miles wide and 22 miles long (Fig. IX-3). To date, all production has come from two orebodies, each about 1,600 by 600 feet and 100 feet or more thick; a third is stripped in preparation for mining. Production began late in 1964, and by the end of 1965 more than 379 thousand tons of crude ore had been shipped to Trail, British Columbia and Kellogg, Idaho. Crude ore averaged nearly 50 per cent lead and zinc and the milling ore graded nearly 12 per cent.

The region is underlain by about 1,000 feet of Middle Devonian carbonates that rest on Precambrian crystalline basement and are succeeded unconformably by green, calcareous Upper Devonian shale. The carbonates grade northward into black shales and southward into evaporites. Regional dip is westerly at about 20 feet per mile (Campbell, 1957). Locally the beds have been folded into gentle flexures whose limbs are a few hundred to a few thousand feet long and dip up to 125 feet per mile. The fold axes plunge roughly S65°W, subparallel to the trace of faults in the Precambrian basement evident on aeromagnetic maps. Although post-Devonian movement on the faults cannot be proven, it is thought some small displacement may be responsible for the folds.

The ore occurs in the Presqu'ile Formation, in saccharoidal, vuggy dolomite that may have replaced reefal limestone. Some ore also occurs in a fine-grained granular dolomite that may underlie the Presqu'ile Formation but is mainly its stratigraphic equivalent. Other partly equivalent facies such as gypsiferous Nyarling Formation to the southeast and the limestones of the Sulphur Point Formation to the northwest are not mineralized. Primary ore at Pine Point (Schiller and Hornbrook, 1964) consists of disseminations, banded encrustations, and vug fillings of sphalerite and galena with minor marcasite, native sulphur, and bitumen. Secondary minerals are cerussite, smithsonite, and limonite (Bell, 1931) and occur to a depth of 100 feet. Bell suggests that the ore occupies zones of jointing along anticlinal crests, but Campbell (1957) considers the data to be too sparse to draw any firm conclusions as to structural control. In general, the orebodies lie in a narrow zone parallel to the fold axes, but primary control is the porosity of the dolomites of the Presqu'ile Formation.

Four processes for the formation of the ore have been suggested by Bell: chemical precipitation during sedimentation; lateral secretion from cold meteoric waters; leaching of deep-seated rocks by artesian waters; and deposition from hydrothermal solutions of magmatic sources. The syngenetic origin is unlikely as lead isotope ages obtained by Folinsbee indicate ages for the ore of 200 to 300 million years—much younger than the Middle Devonian age of the Presqu'ile Formation. No igneous rocks are known to intrude the Paleozoic strata within many miles of the deposits. Bell and Campbell favour a hydrothermal origin, but Campbell indicates that some solution and redeposition by meteoric waters has occurred.

Monarch and Kicking Horse deposits (98), which occur near Field in the Rocky Mountains, contain zinc, lead, silver, and cadmium. They are concordant bodies within dolomite of the Middle Cambrian Cathedral Formation (Ney, 1957), but whether the dolomite is primary or related to the mineralization is not known. Ore minerals occur most commonly disseminated in the matrix of grey dolomite breccia and also in veinlets cutting white and black dolomite. Mineralization is confined between two horizons 200 feet apart in the lower part of the formation, and mainly within gentle anticlinal folds. The ore is apparently unrelated to intrusive rocks, the nearest of which comprise the Ice River complex some 12 miles to the south and furthermore are of mid-Paleozoic age, much older than the ore which seemingly is related to folds produced during Laramide Orogeny. Similar mineral occurrences are reported at about the same stratigraphic horizon to the east on Mount Eisenhower and Copper Mountain (J. D. Aitken).

Transgressive Deposits

The *Estella* mine (106) is near Wasa east of Rocky Mountain Trench. The ore occurs in replacement veins and fissure fillings and contains zinc, lead, silver, cadmium, gold, and some cobalt. The Estella and the Kootenay King, a nearby small concordant deposit, occur in the Aldridge Formation in the lower part of the Helikian Purcell succession. This region also contains a num-

[1] Number is that assigned the deposit on Mineral Deposits of Canada, Map 1252A.

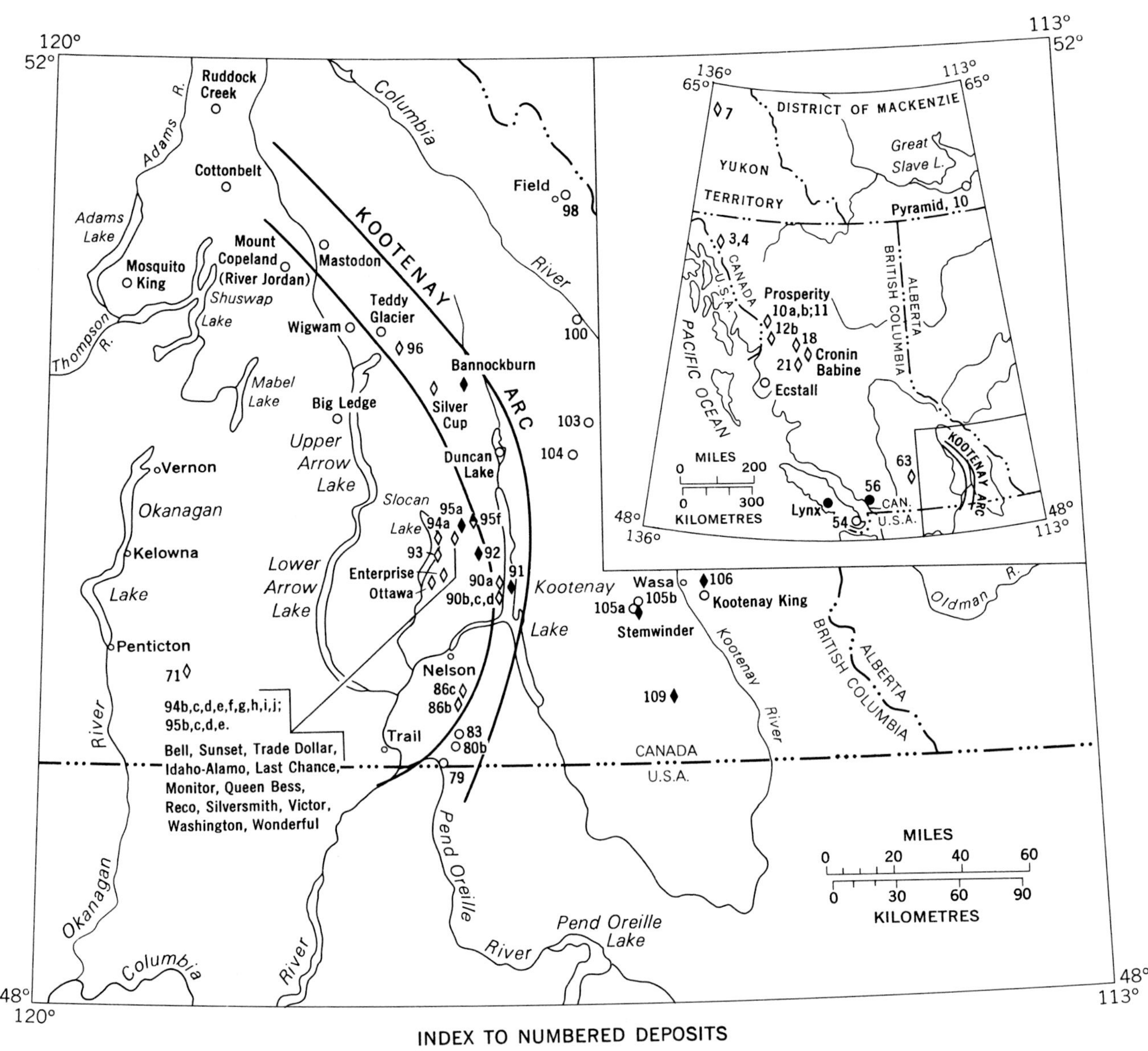

INDEX TO NUMBERED DEPOSITS

10. Pine Point
7. United Keno
3. Tulsequah Chief
4. Big Bull
10a. Premier Border
10b. Silbak Premier
11. Dunwell
12b. Toric
18. Silver Standard
21. Duthie
54. Tyee
56. Britannia
63. Nicola (Planet)
71. Highland-Bell
79. Reeves-MacDonald
80b. Jersey
83. H.B.
86b. Yankee Girl
86c. Ymir
90a. Florence (Ainsmore)
90b. Highland
90c. Number One
90d. Yale (Highlander)
91. Bluebell
92. Cork-Province
93. Galena Farm
94a. Bosun
94b. Hewitt
94c. Ivanhoe
94d. Mammoth
94e. Richmond-Eureka
94f. Ruth-Hope
94g. Silversmith and Slocan Star
94h. Standard
94i. Van Roi
94j. Violamac (Victor)
95a. Lucky Jim
95b. Noble Five
95c. Payne
95d. Rambler-Cariboo
95e. Surprise
95f. Whitewater
96. Spider
98. Monarch and Kicking Horse
100. Silver Giant
103. Paradise
104. Mineral King
105a. North Star
105b. Sullivan
106. Estella
109. St. Eugene

Concordant dissemination . . . . ○ *Non-concordant dissemination . . . .* ● *Transgressive (veins) . . . .* ◊

Transgressive (veins with considerable replacement) . . . . ♦

Notes: Numbers are those assigned to deposits shown on Map 1252A; others are named on figure. Properties from which lead and zinc are the principal product are underlined. *GSC*

FIGURE IX-2. Lead–zinc deposits of Western Canada, classified according to type (by H. W. Little).

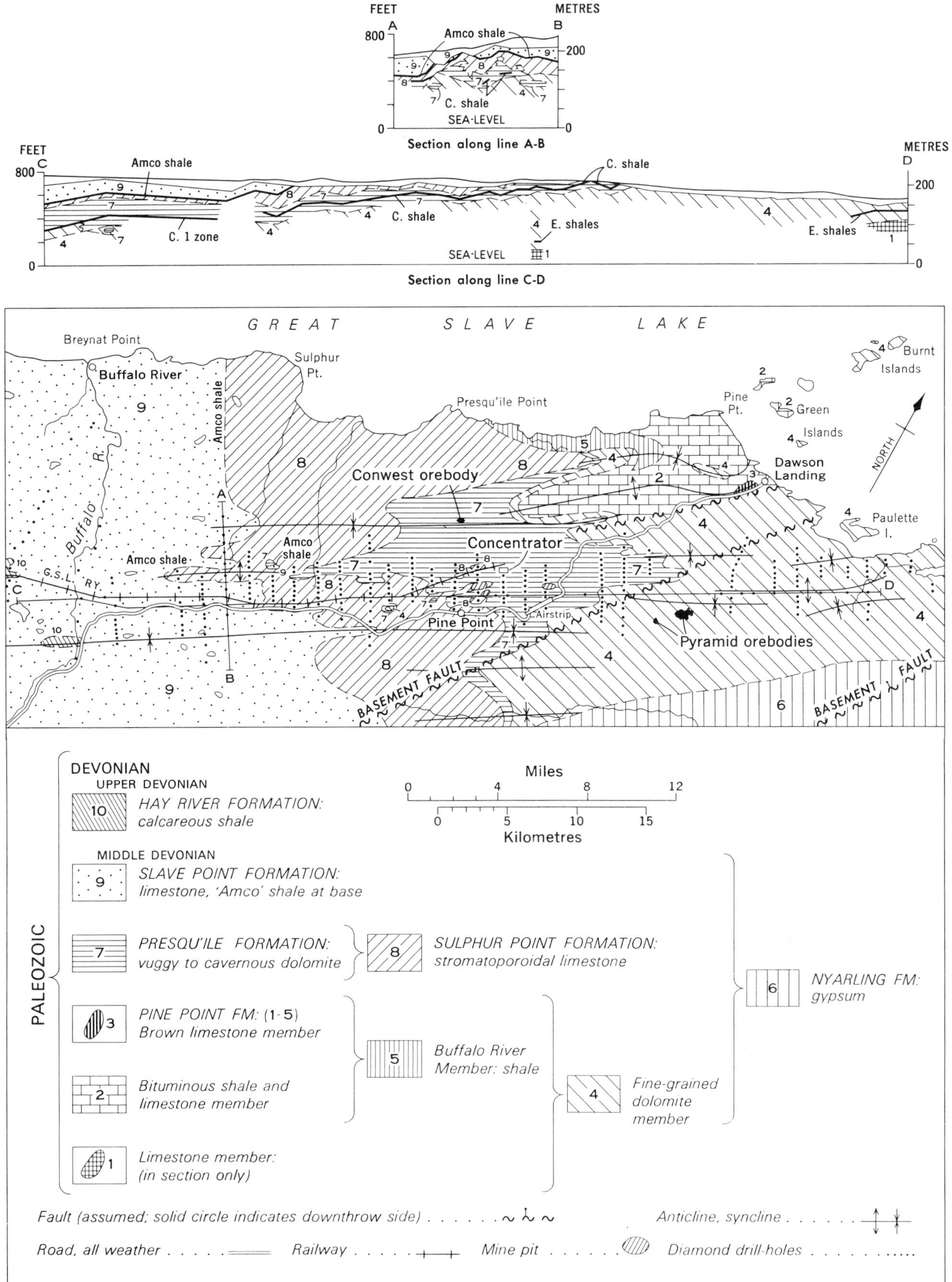

FIGURE IX-3. Geology in the vicinity of Pine Point lead–zinc deposits, District of Mackenzie (after A. W. Norris).

ber of sparsely mineralized quartz veins. The age of the base metal deposits is not known, but some quartz veins occur in late Lower Cretaceous, or possibly younger, syenitic rocks.

Copper

Concordant Deposits

The *Redstone* deposit (Fig. IX-9) in Mackenzie Mountains (Green and Godwin, 1964) is a bedded copper deposit. It occurs (J. A. Coates) mainly in three persistent green carbonate-rich beds within a sequence of Hadrynian mudstone and siltstone. The sequence, which strikes north and dips steeply west, is disrupted by two major west-dipping thrust faults and numerous normal faults of small displacement. In decreasing order of abundance, ore minerals consist of pyrite, chalcopyrite, bornite, chalcocite, covellite, tennantite, and galena. Supergene malachite, azurite, native copper, and limonite are present in various amounts. The mineralization has been traced laterally for at least 4 miles. Grade averages 2.30 per cent copper across 6.5 feet at the north end and 3.74 per cent across 5.5 feet at the south end, but less than 1 per cent in the central part.

Sedimentary Deposits

Iron

The *Clear Hills* deposits are mainly oölitic hematitic sandstone and shale occurring in the marine Upper Cretaceous Kaskapau Formation at Clear Hills, Alberta. The largest deposit is estimated at more than 1,000 million tons with an average grade of 31 per cent iron; another deposit of slightly higher grade exceeds 100 million tons. Other deposits are smaller and of lower grade. Tests are being made to determine if a marketable concentrate can be produced by beneficiation. The main deposit, near Swift Creek, is 3 to 30 feet thick, underlies an area about 13 by 3 miles, and is covered by up to 200 feet of overburden (Kidd, 1959). The ferruginous sandstone contains oölites formed of concentric shells of goethite and quartz in a matrix of quartz, goethite, siderite, and chamosite (?), with a little apatite and sericite.

The *Snake River* deposit in northern Mackenzie Mountains (Green and Godwin, 1964) occurs in the Hadrynian Rapitan Formation. The iron-formation, which is 137 feet thick, consists of jasper and hematite, with thin intercalations of mudstone. Ore is estimated at 20 billion tons of which about 5 billion tons can be mined by open-pit methods. The grade averages 46 per cent Fe, not allowing for dilution by waste interbeds. The phosphorus content of 0.35 per cent is due to the presence of apatite.

Surficial Deposits

Gold

Placer gold has been produced on South Saskatchewan, Peace, McLeod, Athabasca, Bow, Oldman, and other rivers, but North Saskatchewan has been the chief source. It was at first presumed to be derived from the Precambrian Shield to the east through concentration from glacial till. In 1887, however, Tyrrell proposed a western source, the Selkirk Mountains, for the Cretaceous sediments of western Alberta, and implied that the gold placers resulted from reconcentration during erosion of the Cretaceous rocks. Placer mining in Alberta began in 1859 or 1860, reached peak production in 1896, and is still operating on a minor scale. Total recorded gold production is about 19,000 ounces.

Western Mineral Province

Deposits of the Western Mineral Province are diverse, as is characteristic of areas of great geological complexity (Table IX-1). Metallic deposits containing a great variety of metals, several of which may occur in a single deposit, are widespread. Many types are represented, including pyrometasomatic, vein, magmatic segregation, and replacement deposits ranging from hypothermal to epithermal. In the descriptions of properties only one or two examples of each class and type are given because of space limitations. Pegmatites containing beryl, muscovite, or lepidolite are known, but of these only mica has been produced. Deposits of gypsum and bentonite are rare. Production data are shown in Table IX-2.

Although basic contributions to the concept of metallogenic provinces and epochs were made more than 40 years ago by Schofield (1919) and Brock (Brock and Schofield, 1928), much remains to be done before a valid and detailed metallogenic picture can be drawn. Only recently has the complexity of the tectonic history of the Canadian Cordillera been fathomed. Dating many of the mineral deposits and relating each to some phase of this complex history remains to be done.

Metallogenic maps of Canada for uranium, beryllium, molybdenum, iron, manganese, and tin have been published, but compilation of other metals has been published only in preliminary form at small scale by Lang (1961). Lang concluded that other than a division into eastern and western Cordilleran provinces no subdivision was as yet justified. He pointed out that in the western province gold is widely distributed, copper nearly so, and lead and zinc occur in many scattered areas, although mainly in the southeast. Minor nickel, cobalt, and iron occurrences are fairly numerous in southern British Columbia, and iron is abundant on Vancouver Island.

More recent studies by R. Mulligan indicate that in the eastern part of the Western Mineral Province

TABLE IX–2 *Total production from main lode metal mines and industrial mineral properties of Western Canada, to 1966 inclusive*

No.[1]	Property[2]	Area or Camp	Location[3]	Years of Production[4]	Ore or Mineral Thousand tons	Gold Thousand oz.	Silver Million oz.	Copper Million lb.	Lead Million lb.	Zinc Million lb.	Other metals or minerals Million lb. (mlb) or million tons (mt)
	District of Mackenzie										
1	Canada Tungsten	Flat River, N.W.T.	61°128°NE	1962-66	327	—	—	a	—	—	WO_3 8.29 mlb
10	Pine Point	Great Slave Lake	60°114°NE	1964-66	2,197	—	a	—	382	676	Cd 1.26 mlb
	Yukon Territory										
7	United Keno	Mayo, Yukon	63°135°NE	1913-66	2,748[5]	—	146.7	—	464	274	Cd 3.59 mlb
9, 10	Whitehorse Copper Belt (Pueblo, etc.)	Whitehorse, Yukon	60°135°NW	1897-1930	300	—	—	13	—	—	
	British Columbia										
2	Polaris-Taku	Taku River	58°133°NW	1938-51	753	231	a	a	—	—	
3, 4	Tulsequah Chief and Big Bull	Taku River	58°133°NW	1951-57	1,029	94	3.4	27	26	125	Cd 0.45 mlb
5	Cassiar Asbestos	McDame Creek	59°129°SW	1952-66	6,033	—	—	—	—	—	Asbestos 0.59 mt
9	Big Missouri	Portland Canal	56°130°SE	1927-42	848	58	0.1	—	a	a	
10a	Premier Border	Portland Canal	56°130°SE	1950-53	42	3	0.1	—	4	4	
10b	Silbak-Premier	Portland Canal	56°130°SE	1918-66	4,664	1,813	40.9	4	59	16	Cd 0.18 mlb
11	Dunwell	Portland Canal	55°129°NW	1926-41	50	10	0.3	a	2	2	
12a	Dolly Varden	Portland Canal	55°129°NW	1919-40	37	a	1.4	a	a	—	
12b	Toric	Portland Canal	55°129°NW	1928-59	1,379	a	18.6	—	10	1	
13	Outsider	Portland Canal	55°130°NE	1906-28	139	a	a	5	—	—	
14	Bonanza	Portland Canal	55°129°SW	1928-35	724	3	0.3	32	—	—	
15a	Golskeish	Portland Canal	55°129°SW	1918-29	51	5	a	—	—	—	
15b	Granby Point	Portland Canal	55°129°SW	1917-38	62	6	0.2	a	a	—	
15c	Hidden Creek	Portland Canal	55°129°SW	1914-36	23,948	121	6.6	709	—	—	
18	Silver Standard	Hazelton	55°127°SW	1913-65	216	15	7.4	a	17	26	Cd 0.33 mlb
19	Rocher Déboulé	Hazelton	55°127°SW	1915-52	53	4	a	6	a	a	
20	Red Rose	Hazelton	55°127°SW	1942-54	118	a	a	a	—	—	WO_3 2.21 mlb
21	Duthie	Smithers	54°127°NE	1923-53	65	3	1.6	a	6	5	Cd 0.01 mlb
22	Granisle	Babine Lake	54°126°NE	1966	206	1	a	2	—	—	
23	Pinchi Lake	Fort St. James	54°124°NE	1940-44	692	—	—	—	—	—	Hg 4.0 mlb
24	Surf Point	Porcher Island	54°130°SW	1919-39	68	20	a	a	—	—	

TABLE IX–2 *Total production from main lode metal mines and industrial mineral properties of Western Canada, to 1966 inclusive (cont.)*

No.[1]	Property[2]	Area or Camp	Location[3]	Years of Production[4]	Ore or Mineral Thousand tons	Gold Thousand oz.	Silver Million oz.	Copper Million lb.	Lead Million lb.	Zinc Million lb.	Other metals or minerals Million lb. (mlb) or million tons (mt)
26	Jedway	Moresby Island	52°131°SE	1962-66	3,296	—	—	—	—	—	Fe conc. 1.80 mt
27	Surf Inlet	Princess Royal Island	53°128°SW	1902-43	1,012	389	0.2	6	—	—	
28	Endako	Endako	54°125°SE	1965-66	7,848						Mo 5.15 mlb
31	Aurum (Island Mountain)	Wells, Cariboo	53°121°SW	1934-66	1,056	486	0.7	—	—	—	
32	Cariboo Gold Quartz	Wells, Cariboo	53°121°SW	1933-58	1,855	705	0.6	—	—	—	
33	Boss Mountain	100 Mile House	52°120°SW	1965-66	658	—	—	—	—	—	Mo 3.53 mlb
34	Minto	Bridge River	50°122°NW	1934-40	89	18	0.1	a	a	—	
35	Wayside	Bridge River	50°122°NW	1915-37	43	5	a	—	—	—	
36	Bralorne-Pioneer	Bridge River	50°122°NW	1899-1966	7,558	3,954	0.9	—	—	—	Minor WO_3
37	Iron Mike	Sayward, V.Is.	50°125°SW	1966	150	—	—	—	—	—	Fe conc. 0.09 mt
38	Coast Copper (Old Sport)	Benson River, V.Is.	50°127°SE	1962-66	1,275	83	0.1	41	—	—	Fe conc. 0.16 mt
39	Yreka	Quatsino, V.Is.	50°127°SW	1902-66	79	1	0.1	5	—	—	
40	Empire	Benson River, V.Is.	50°127°SE	1957-66	3,611	—	—	—	—	—	Fe conc. 1.76 mt
41	Nimpkish	Nimpkish Lake, V.Is.	50°126°SW	1959-63	2,392	—	—	—	—	—	Fe conc. 1.0 mt
42	Zeballos Iron (F.L.)	Zeballos, V.Is.	50°126°SW	1962-66	1,227	—	—	—	—	—	Fe conc. 0.94 mt
43a	Mount Zeballos	Zeballos, V.Is.	50°126°SW	1933-44	82	57	a	a	a	a	
43b	Privateer	Zeballos, V.Is.	50°126°SW	1934-53	314	172	a	a	—	—	
44a	Central Zeballos	Zeballos, V.Is.	50°126°SW	1938-47	58	42	a	a	a	a	
44b	Spud Valley	Zeballos, V.Is.	50°126°SW	1936-51	210	54	a	a	a	a	
45	Hualpai	Nootka Sound, V.Is.	49°126°NE	1959	62	—	—	—	—	—	Fe conc. 0.02 mt
46	Argonaut (Iron Hill)	Campbell River, V.Is.	49°125°NW	1951-57	4,109	—	—	—	—	—	Fe conc. 2.16 mt
47	Domineer (Mount Washington)	Courtenay, V.Is.	49°125°NE	1961-66	373	4	0.2	7	—	—	
48a	Cornell	Texada Island	49°124°NW	1897-1919	45	15	a	3	—	—	
48b	Marble Bay	Texada Island	49°124°NW	1899-1929	314	50	0.4	15	—	—	
48c	Vananda (Little Billie)	Texada Island	49°124°NW	1896-1952	70	12	a	2	—	—	
49	Texada	Texada Island	49°124°NW	1885-1966	12,181	14	0.2	19	—	—	Fe conc. 6.21 mt
51	Indian Chief	Clayoquot, V.Is.	49°126°SE	1904-38	81	1	0.1	2	—	—	
52	Brynnor	Kennedy Lake, V.Is.	49°125°SE	1962-66	3,915	—	—	—	—	—	Fe conc. 2.94 mt
53	Blue Grouse	Cowichan Lake, V.Is.	48°124°NE	1917-60	275	a	a	15	—	—	
54	Tyee	Mount Sicker, V.Is.	48°123°NE	1901-51	221	27	0.5	14	a	4	Cd 0.01 mlb
55	Sunro	Jordan River, V.Is.	48°124°SE	1962-66	520	3	a	15	—	—	

57	Craigmont	Merritt	50°120°SW	1961-66	8,634	—	a	266	—	—	
58	Bethlehem	Merritt	50°120°SW	1963-66	7,242	9	0.4	95	—	—	Mo 0.04 mlb
59	Vidette	Clinton	51°120°SW	1933-40	54	30	a	a	a	—	
60	Windpass	Kamloops	51°120°SE	1916-44	103	34	a	a	—	—	
61	Iron Mask	Kamloops	50°120°NE	1901-28	182	4	a	5	—	—	
62	Falkland Gypsum	Kamloops	50°119°SW	1925-56	1,247	—	—	—	—	—	Gypsum 1.25 mt
63	Nicola (Planet)	Merritt	50°120°SE	1926	79	8	0.2	a	2	1	Minor Bi
64	Pride of Emory	Hope	49°121°SW	1958-66	2,370	a	a	14	—	—	Ni 31.45 mlb
65	Copper Mountain	Princeton	49°120°SW	1917-62	34,775	188	4.4	613	—	—	
66a	Hedley Mascot	Hedley	49°120°SE	1936-49	682	223	a	2	—	—	
66b	Nickel Plate	Hedley	49°120°SE	1904-58	3,315	1,359	0.1	2	—	—	
67	French	Hedley	49°120°SE	1954-61	62	33	a	—	—	—	
69	Dividend-Lakeview	Osoyoos	49°119°SE	1907-49	123	16	a	a	a	a	
70	Fairview (Morning Star)	Fairview	49°119°SW	1933-41 1947-61	122	14	0.2	a	a	a	0.37 mt silica flux containing low values in Au
71	Highland-Bell	Beaverdell	49°119°SE	1901-66	387	11	27.0	—	19	23	Cd 0.08 mlb
72	Cariboo-Amelia	McKinney	49°119°SE	1894-1962	137	82	a	—	a	a	
73a	Mother Lode	Greenwood	49°118°SW	1900-62	4,317	173	0.7	77	—	—	
73b	Sunset	Greenwood	49°118°SW	1900-18	120	5	a	2	—	—	
74a	B.C.	Greenwood	49°118°SW	1900-19	103	1	a	9	—	—	
74b, f, g, h	Phoenix Copper (Knob Hill-Ironsides, Idaho, Brooklyn-Stemwinder, Snowshoe, Rawhide)	Greenwood	49°118°SW	1900-66	19,855	830	4.9	404	a	—	
74c	Dentonia	Greenwood	49°118°SW	1900-48	133	38	0.2	—	a	a	
74d	Emma	Greenwood	49°118°SW	1901-21	256	7	a	5	—	—	
74e	Oro Denero	Greenwood	49°118°SW	1903-17	136	3	a	4	—	—	
74i	Winnipeg	Greenwood	49°118°SW	1900-40	59	12	a	a	—	—	
75	Rock Candy	Grand Forks	49°118°NW	1918-42	36	—	—	—	—	—	Fluorspar 0.04 mt
76	Union	Franklin	49°118°NE	1913-46	189	55	1.4	a	a	1	
77	Velvet	Rossland	49°117°SW	1901-64	98	20	a	3	a	a	
78a	Centre Star group (Centre Star, War Eagle, Le Roi, Josie)	Rossland	49°117°SW	1893-1942	5,915	2,706	3.3	118	—	—	
78b	Red Mountain (Coxey)	Rossland	49°117°SW	1966	79	—	—	—	—	—	Mo 0.53 mlb
79	Reeves-Macdonald	Salmo	49°117°SE	1949-66	5,365	—	0.4	—	108	376	Cd 2.21 mlb
80a	Emerald, Dodger, and Feeney	Salmo	49°117°SE	1944-58	1,067	—	—	—	—	—	WO_3 13.74 mlb
80b	Jersey	Salmo	49°117°SE	1949-66	6,246	—	0.6	—	231	490	Cd 3.73 mlb
81	Bayonne	Kootenay Lake	49°116°SW	1935-51	89	42	0.1	—	a	a	
82a	Gold Belt	Salmo (Sheep Creek)	49°117°SE	1934-51	257	80	a	—	—	—	

TABLE IX–2 *Total production from main lode metal mines and industrial mineral properties of Western Canada, to 1966 inclusive (conc.)*

No.[1]	Property[2]	Area or Camp	Location[3]	Years of Production[4]	Ore or Mineral Thousand tons	Gold Thousand oz.	Silver Million oz.	Copper Million lb.	Lead Million lb.	Zinc Million lb.	Other metals or minerals Million lb. (mlb) or million tons (mt)
82b	Kootenay Belle	Salmo (Sheep Creek)	49°117°SE	1904-50 1961-65	333	110	a	—	—	—	Silica flux 0.03 mt
82c	Reno	Salmo (Sheep Creek)	49°117°SE	1906-50	430	232	0.2	—	—	—	
82d	Sheep Creek	Salmo (Sheep Creek)	49°117°SE	1902-50 1961-62	719	304	0.1	—	—	—	Silica flux 0.04 mt
83	H.B.	Salmo	49°117°SE	1912-66	5,249	a	0.8	—	86	456	Cd 3.76 mlb
84a	Arlington	Salmo	49°117°SE	1900-66	60	53	0.1	—	2	1	
84b	Second Relief	Salmo	49°117°SE	1902-59	228	99	a	a	a	a	
85	Hunter V and Double Standard	Ymir	49°117°SE	1902-29	63	1	0.3	—	—	—	
86a	Centre Star (Wesko)	Ymir	49°117°SE	1936-50	57	12	0.1	—	2	1	
86b	Yankee Girl	Ymir	49°117°SE	1907-51	408	124	0.7	—	14	14	Cd 1.88 mlb
86c	Ymir	Ymir	49°117°SE	1899-1950	367	110	0.5	—	11	2	
87a	Athabasca	Nelson	49°117°SE	1898-1943	46	20	a	a	a	a	
87b	Granite Poorman	Nelson	49°117°SE	1890-1954	200	65	a	a	a	a	
87c	Silver King	Nelson	49°117°SE	1889-1958	222	a	4.4	15	a	a	
88	Queen Victoria	Nelson	49°117°SE	1907-61	49	a	a	2	—	—	
89	Molly Gibson	Nelson	49°117°NE	1899-1950	62	a	1.0	—	5	a	
90a	Florence (Ainsmore)	Ainsworth	49°116°NW	1899-1960	223	a	0.4	—	25	6	Cd 0.02 mlb
90b	Highland	Ainsworth	49°116°NW	1890-1954	98	a	0.3	—	21	1	Minor Cd
90c	Number One	Ainsworth	49°116°NW	1889-1929	40	a	2.0	—	a	—	
90d	Yale (Highlander)	Ainsworth	49°116°NW	1889-1964	436	a	0.9	—	46	11	Minor Cd & Sb
91	Bluebell	Kootenay Lake	49°116°NW	1895-1966	4,078	—	5.5	4	400	419	Cd 1.92 mlb
92	Cork-Province	Kaslo	49°117°NE	1900-66	211	a	0.5	—	13	20	Cd 0.15 mlb
93	Galena Farm	Slocan	49°117°NE	1900-66	90	a	0.6	—	6	10	Minor Cd
94a	Bosun	Slocan	49°117°NE	1898-1962	70	a	1.9	—	11	7	Minor Cd
94b	Hewitt	Slocan	49°117°NE	1900-66	117	a	1.8	—	4	5	Minor Cd
94c	Ivanhoe	Slocan	49°117°NE	1895-1935	44	a	0.5	—	5	1	
94d	Mammoth	Slocan	49°117°NE	1925-66	94	a	1.0	—	7	10	Cd 0.04 mlb
94e	Richmond-Eureka	Slocan	49°117°NE	1896-1961	40	a	0.8	—	5	2	Minor Cd
94f	Ruth-Hope	Slocan	49°117°NE	1895-1962	66	a	2.5	—	22	4	Minor Cd
94g	Silversmith and Slocan Star	Slocan	49°117°NE	1893-1965	391	1	7.3	—	71	26	Cd 0.04 mlb
94h	Standard	Slocan	49°117°NE	1905-58	806	a	8.7	—	83	108	Cd 0.13 mlb

94i	Van Roi	Slocan	49°117°NE	1893-1958	314	a	2.8	—	18	17	Cd 0.04 mlb
94j	Violamac (Victor)	Slocan	49°117°NE	1923-66	163	2	4.1	—	47	31	Cd 0.18 mlb
95a	Lucky Jim	New Denver	50°117°SE	1893-1959	1,175	a	0.6	—	8	176	Cd 0.43 mlb
95b	Noble Five	Slocan	49°117°NE	1893-1956	44	a	0.5	—	5	4	Minor Cd
95c	Payne	Slocan	50°117°SE	1893-1939	122	—	3.7	—	38	2	
95d	Rambler-Cariboo	Slocan	50°117°SE	1895-1951	209	a	3.5	a	24	6	Cd 0.01 mlb
95e	Surprise	Slocan	49°117°NE	1893-1929	49	a	1.9	—	12	8	
95f	Whitewater	Kaslo	50°117°SE	1892-1956	501	2	3.5	—	31	51	Cd 0.08 mlb
96	Spider	Lardeau	50°117°NW	1911-58	140	12	1.7	a	24	25	Cd 0.13 mlb Sb 0.02 mlb
97	Meridian	Lardeau	50°117°NW	1903-41	98	17	a	—	—	—	
98	Monarch and Kicking Horse	Field	51°116°SE	1888-1953	813	—	0.8	—	102	157	Cd 0.06 mlb
99	Parson	Spillimacheen	51°116°SW	1940-65	199	—	—	—	—	—	Barite 0.20 mt
100	Silver Giant	Spillimacheen	50°116°NE	1908-57 1959-66	927	a	0.6	a	65	7	Cd 0.02 mlb Sb 0.04 mlb Barite 0.04 mt
101	Brisco	Spillimacheen	50°116°NE	1945-66	—	—	—	—	—	—	Barite 0.09 mt
102	Western Gypsum	Windermere	50°115°SW	1950-66	1,951	—	—	—	—	—	Gypsum 1.95 mt
103	Paradise	Toby Creek	50°116°SE	1901-52	71	a	0.7	—	16	8	Minor Cd
104	Mineral King	Toby Creek	50°116°SE	1954-66	2,202	—	1.7	1	77	184	Cd 0.63 mlb Barite 0.02 mt
105a	North Star	Kimberley	49°115°NW	1895-1929	68	—	1.3	—	48	a	
105b	Sullivan	Kimberley	49°115°NW	1900-66	99,371	4	217.2	6	13,035	11,278	Sn 17.41 mlb Cd 1.72 mlb Iron Sinter 0.55 mt
106	Estella	Cranbrook	49°115°NW	1951-66	80	a	0.1	—	8	16	Cd 0.01 mlb
108	Mayook	Cranbrook	49°115°SW	1926-54	111	—	—	—	—	—	Gypsum 0.11 mt
109	St. Eugene	Cranbrook	49°115°SW	1899-1929	1,062	3	5.9	—	249	32	

Most data have been supplied by the British Columbia Department of Mines and Petroleum Resources

[1] Number of property is from Map 1252A, Mineral Deposits of Canada (in folio)

[2] Production includes all known production by all owners, past and present

[3] Latitude and longitude of southeast corner of one-degree quadrangle and quarter of quadrangle in which property is situated

[4] Years of earliest and latest recorded production

[5] Tonnage prior to 1947 is not included

a Less than one-half of smallest unit shown in column

— No production

and in the Eastern Mineral Province zinc is almost everywhere associated with lead. In the central and western parts of the Western Mineral Province, however, zinc is much less abundant, lead even less so, and in some deposits zinc is affiliated with copper rather than lead. Copper, on the other hand, is minor in the eastern lead–zinc province, but widespread and abundant in the volcanic, eugeosynclinal region.

Mulligan (1966) has outlined a tin–beryllium–tungsten–molybdenum metallogenic province of lithophile affinity that occupies a belt lying west of Rocky Mountain Trench between the International Boundary and the Yukon. In the northwest tin and tungsten are also present, associated with small granitic intrusions that extend many miles eastward from Clear Creek, Yukon (Bostock *in* Little, 1959).

In central and western British Columbia the association of large, low-grade molybdenum deposits with late, leucocratic biotitic quartz monzonite facies of granitic intrusive complexes is apparent. This association is also evident for porphyry copper deposits. The age of the older facies of these complexes ranges from Jurassic to Upper Cretaceous, but that of the late leucocratic facies has not yet been established except in Tulsequah area where it is related to flows and pyroclastics of the late Upper Cretaceous and Early Tertiary Sloko Group (J. G. Souther).

Lode Deposits

Lead–Zinc–Silver

A great number of lead–zinc deposits that occur in southeastern British Columbia (Fyles, 1966) form part of a productive area also embracing Idaho and western Montana (Fig. IX-2). In the Purcell anticlinorium the Sullivan (105b), North Star (105a), and St. Eugene (109) deposits are of Precambrian age. Others considered to be Mesozoic occur along the Kootenay Arc from Salmo area in the south to the Big Bend of Columbia River in the north. Lead–isotope ratios indicate they have been contaminated by material derived from the Precambrian deposits (Sinclair, 1966). Muraro (1966) has also shown that lead–zinc deposits of the Kootenay Arc were formed before folding and metamorphism occurred, the folding having affected their shape in areas where flowage took place, and the metamorphism altering their texture. Deposits on the eastern flank of Kootenay Arc are for the most part concordant replacement, whereas those in the inner or concave part are mainly vein deposits most of which, in Slocan district, carry a much higher content of silver than the concordant types.

North of the Kootenay Arc from the Big Bend of Columbia River to northern British Columbia lead–zinc deposits are sparse. Veins with lead and zinc occur at Rancheria and Logjam Creek near the Yukon border. Replacement deposits occur farther north at Ketza River and Ross River, and at Keno Hill the veins, rich in silver, mark the north end of the lead–zinc belt.

Lead and zinc also occur in western British Columbia in complex vein deposits that yield mainly silver, the Toric (12b), Silver Standard (18), and Highland–Bell (71) mines, or with gold, silver, and copper as at Silbak Premier (10b). Zinc, with relatively little lead, is affiliated with copper in a few deposits—Britannia (56), Tyee (54), Tulsequah Chief (3), and Big Bull (4).

Fyles (1966) has classified lead–zinc deposits into concordant and transgressive types, but pointed out that both types may be represented in the same deposit, as in the Whitewater mine of the Slocan area.

Concordant Deposits

Except for Pine Point and a few deposits in Aiken Lake area, concordant lead–zinc deposits occur in the southeastern metallogenic province. Fyles subdivided the concordant deposits into Sullivan, Metaline, Salmo, and Shuswap subtypes which are, respectively, hypothermal replacements of argillaceous beds; mesothermal replacements of dolomitized limestone affected only by broad folding and faulting; mesothermal replacements of dolomitized limestone isoclinally folded and sheared; and replacements of marble and schist in complexly folded regions of high grade regional metamorphism.

The *Sullivan subtype* is unique, represented only by the *Sullivan* (105b) mine, the largest lead–zinc mine in the Cordillera (Table IX-2), which alone has produced nearly one half the metal wealth of British Columbia. It is of Precambrian age and comprises high temperature replacement of thin-bedded argillite of the Helikian Aldridge Formation. The orebody lies on the east side of the Purcell anticlinorium, whose limbs are characterized by gentle dips and minor warps (Freeze, 1966). The hanging-wall sediments are albitized and locally chloritized and tourmalinized. The footwall sediments contain a few conglomerate lenses and are heavily tourmalinized (Fig. IX-4). The ore preferentially replaces certain argillaceous members, but in places exhibits marked cross-cutting relationships. The orebody lies between the Kimberley and Hidden Hand faults which strike easterly, dip north, and have normal displacement, the former having a stratigraphic throw of about 10,000 feet. Steep north-trending normal faults displace the orebody a few tens of feet.

Based on the Houtermans lead-evolution model, the age of Sullivan lead was estimated to be 1,250 m.y. by Leech and Wanless (1962) and 1,340 m.y. by Sinclair (1966). As the lead–isotope ratios are virtually constant throughout the orebody a single period of mineralization from a single source is indicated, although some later redistribution may have occurred. Like Swanson and Gunning (1945), Leech and Wanless, and Sinclair favour an epigenetic source related to the source magma of Moyie Intrusions. Freeze (1966) believes that evidence indicates that the Sullivan is hydrothermal rather than syngenetic reconstituted by regional metamorphism. Although high

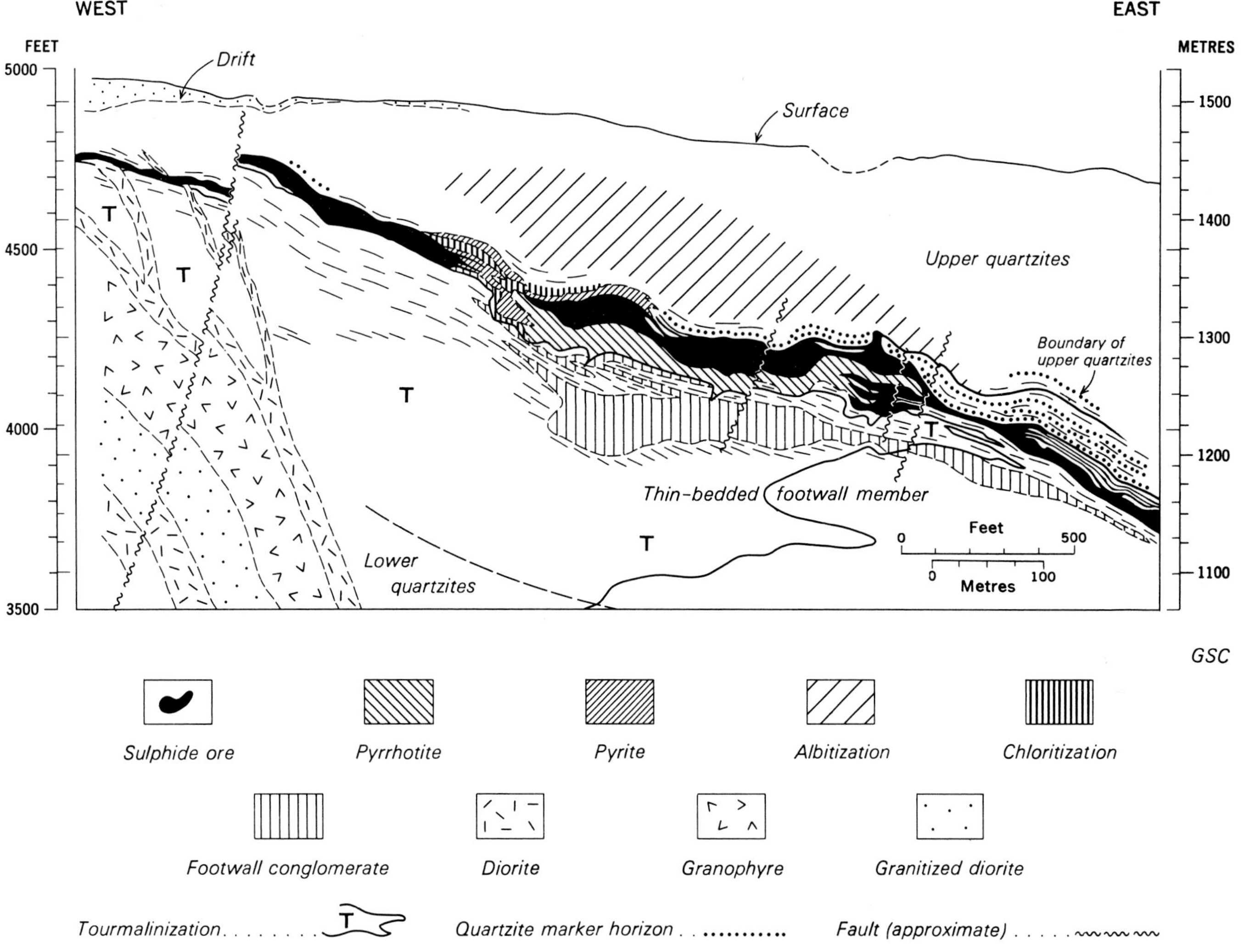

FIGURE IX-4. Cross-section showing conformable nature of Sullivan orebody, British Columbia (after A. C. Freeze).

temperature minerals such as garnet, tremolite, scapolite, and cordierite occur in the orebody and minimum temperatures of formation of 460°C for deposition of the sphalerite have been determined, the sediments barely a few feet away have reached only the chlorite–albite stage of regional metamorphism. Tourmalinization preceding mineralization is apparently younger than the Moyie sills. A lamprophyre dyke dated as 765 m.y. old intruded the ore zone during the rather lengthy period of mineralization.

The central part of the ore zone consists of a mass, roughly rectangular, dominantly of pyrite in the west and pyrrhotite in the east. Around this "iron core" the orebody is for the most part comparatively rich in lead, silver, tin, and arsenic, but towards the periphery zinc and antimony predominate. Boulangerite and other minor antimony minerals are disseminated mainly in the main ore zone but also in intersecting open fissures. Antimony is a substantial byproduct of the Sullivan mine. Cassiterite occurs, with iron sulphides and minor galena and sphalerite, in a vein that strikes northerly and dips 80 to 85°E, and intersects the main ore zone. However, cassiterite is found also at the base of the main orebody about the "iron core." The contact relationships between the vein and the orebody are vague. About 600 tons per year of tin concentrate is produced.

Metaline subtype is named after Metaline District, Washington. Deposits, which are concordant, occur in unmetamorphosed carbonate rocks either gently folded and faulted or brecciated. Examples are the Monarch and Kicking Horse (98), and Pine Point (10) mines in the Eastern Province.

Salmo subtype occurs in an environment of isoclinal folding with superimposed folding and shearing, and low greenschist facies grade of regional metamorphism. An example is the *Jersey* (80b). The host rock is Lower Cambrian limestone in a miogeosynclinal succession of pelitic, arenaceous, and calcareous rocks. The orebodies are encased in dolomitic envelopes within the limestone and commonly skarn forms the footwall. The limestone and adjacent sediments are recumbently folded and disrupted by thrust faults and small normal faults (Whishaw, 1954). The orebodies comprise sphalerite and galena with pyrite and some pyrrhotite, the iron sulphides being a little less abundant than the ore minerals. They form irregular pods (Fig. IX-5) the position of which is controlled by subsidiary coaxial folds on the limbs of the recumbent folds, and occur mainly in the anticlinal crests of the subsidiary folds and only on the upright limb of the fold. Trackless mining has been used successfully because of the generally flat lying nature of the orebodies.

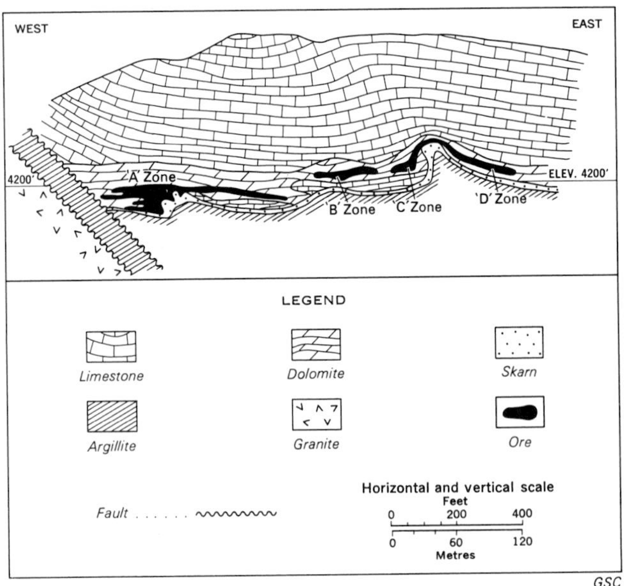

FIGURE IX-5. Diagrammatic cross-section of Jersey lead–zinc deposit, Salmo, British Columbia (after Q. G. Whishaw).

Other deposits of this type are the H.B. (83), Reeves–MacDonald (79), and Duncan Lake, all occurring along Kootenay Arc in dolomitized limestone of Lower Cambrian age.

Shuswap subtype. The Big Ledge, Wigwam, Cottonbelt, Ruddock Creek, and Mount Copeland deposits all occur in mainly calcareous layers in the schist, marble, and paragneiss sequences of the Shuswap Complex that mantle complexly folded domes with cores of granite gneiss and have undergone high grade regional metamorphism. The age of the host rock is generally unknown but may be Lower Cambrian in part. All deposits are large, low grade, and as yet not exploited.

Mount Copeland (Fig. IX-2) deposit was formerly known as River Jordan (Riley, 1961). Two bedded lodes comprising galena, sphalerite, pyrite, pyrrhotite, and minor chalcopyrite, with quartz, calcite, and some barite, occur on both limbs of a rudely conical synform that is overturned to the southwest and plunges southeast. The lodes are thought to occur in the same bed of drag-folded and brecciated impure limestone. They are estimated to contain nearly 3 million tons of ore grading more than 5 per cent each of lead and zinc and 1 ounce silver per ton.

Transgressive Deposits

Transgressive deposits are scattered throughout the Cordillera, ranging in type from replacements in or near shear and fracture zones to veins with very little wall-rock replacement. These relationships are largely dependent on the susceptibility to replacement of the host rock. Transgressive deposits commonly contain copper minerals or sulphosalts and in general have a higher silver content than concordant deposits.

The *Bluebell* mine (91) on Kootenay Lake is a replacement of limestone in isoclinally folded schists (Irvine, 1957). Three ore zones, each consisting of clusters of orebodies, are spaced at 1,500-foot intervals along the strike of Lower Cambrian limestone. The orebodies occur along narrow cross-fractures in the limestone bed.

Silver

Most silver produced from the Cordilleran Region is obtained as a byproduct from lead–zinc ores, the Sullivan mine being the greatest source (Table IX-2). From several mines, however, the primary product is silver, among them United Keno (7), Dolly Varden (12a), Toric (12b), Silver Standard (18), Duthie (21), Hunter V and Double Standard (85), Number One (90c), Molly Gibson (89), Silver King (87c), and several mines in the Slocan camp. Most produce lead and zinc and a few, gold. The Silver King is unique in that it yielded only copper and silver, the latter occurring largely as the mineral stromeyerite. Silbak Premier mine (10b) was also a noteworthy producer of silver, but the complex ore also yielded much lead, zinc, copper, cadmium, and gold, only the gold being greater in value than the silver.

In the *Keno Hill–Galena Hill* area of the Yukon, United Keno (7) is the largest silver producing mine in Canada. The area (Fig. IX-6) is underlain by metamorphosed sedimentary rocks that have been intruded by pods of basic rock, now altered to greenstone (McTaggart, 1960; Boyle, 1965). The strata trend easterly and dip gently to moderately southward, the apparent succession consisting of "Lower Schist", "Central Quartzite", and "Upper Schist" units. On Keno Hill, the "Lower Schist" unit contains a band of quartzite, the "No. 9", lithologically similar to the "Central Quartzite." Recent work indicates that the "Lower Schist" and "Central Quartzite" are of Mesozoic age whereas the age of the "Upper Schist" unit and its relationship to the other two remain questionable.

Because rock exposures are few, the structure in the Keno and Galena Hills area is not fully understood.

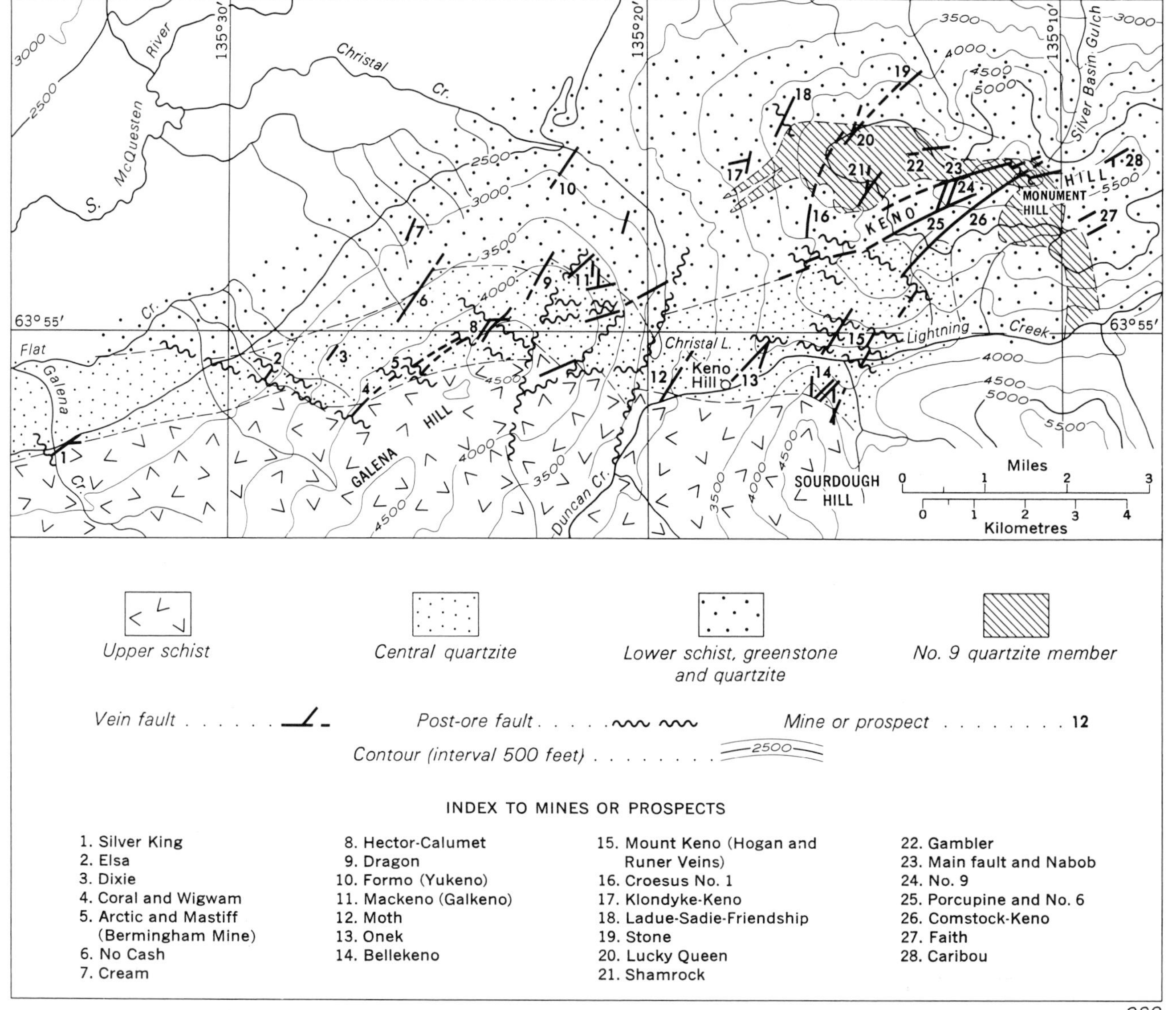

FIGURE IX-6. Geology of Keno Hill–Galena Hill, Yukon Territory, showing location of silver mines and prospects (after R. W. Boyle).

McTaggart regarded it as highly complex with an early stage of overthrusting to the north, producing bedding faults and tight, recumbent folds, followed later by north-westerly open folding, then vein-faults, and still later by low-angle bedding and cross-faults. Most vein-faults strike north to N70°E and dip steeply east to southeast. Boyle concluded that the ore shoots are localized in brecciated zones of early quartz, which was precipitated in the vein-faults with pyrite, arsenopyrite, and minor sulphosalts prior to galena, freibergite, and associated sulphides and carbonates, where the vein-faults traverse competent quartzite members of the "Lower Schist" and "Central Quartzite" or the greenstone bodies. Later cross-faults, which strike northwesterly and dip about 60°SW displace the vein-faults horizontally from a few feet to 500 feet. Primary ore minerals are galena, sphalerite, pyrite, and freibergite in a gangue of quartz and siderite. Supergene enrichment of lead and silver occurs in the upper part of the veins.

Gold

Gold occurrences are scattered throughout the Western Province. The larger producers, however, are more restricted; those that have produced more than 18,000 ounces are shown in Figure IX-7. Rising costs have forced many mines to close as the price of gold has remained fixed. In recent years only two major gold mines have been operating, the Cariboo Gold Quartz (32), which ceased operations in 1967, and the Bralorne–Pioneer (36). These mines yielded 53 per cent of the 1966 Cordilleran lode gold production, the balance being derived as a byproduct mainly of copper mines (Table IX-2).

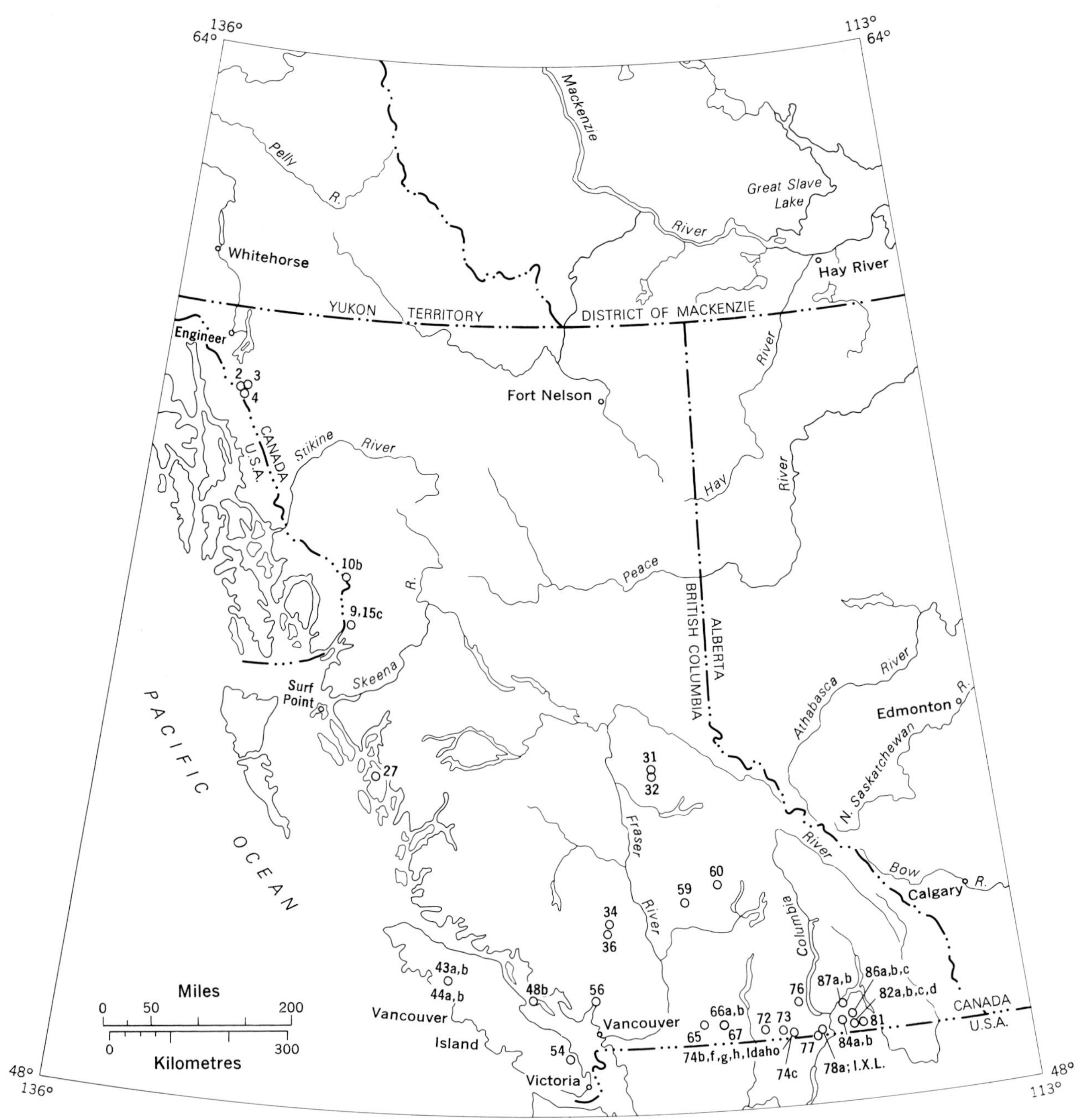

INDEX TO NUMBERED DEPOSITS

2. Polaris-Taku
3. Tulsequah Chief
4. Big Bull
9. Big Missouri
10b. Silbak Premier
15c. Hidden Creek
27. Surf Inlet
31. Aurum (Island Mountain)
32. Cariboo Gold Quartz
34. Minto
36. Bralorne-Pioneer
43a. Mount Zeballos
43b. Privateer
44a. Central Zeballos
44b. Spud Valley
48b. Marble Bay
54. Tyee
56. Britannia
59. Vidette
60. Windpass
65. Copper Mountain
66a. Hedley Mascot
66b. Nickel Plate
67. French
72. Cariboo Amelia (McKinney)
73. Mother Lode

PHOENIX COPPER

74b. Brooklyn-Stemwinder
74f. Knob Hill-Ironsides
74g. Rawhide
74h. Snowshoe
— Idaho

———

74c. Dentonia
76. Union
77. Velvet
78a. CENTRE STAR GROUP

Centre Star
Le Roi
War Eagle
Josie

———

— I.X.L.

81. Bayonne
82a. Gold Belt
82b. Kootenay Belle
82c. Reno
82d. Sheep Creek
84a. Arlington
84b. Second Relief
86a. Centre Star (Wesko)
86b. Yankee Girl
86c. Ymir
87a. Athabasca
87b. Granite Poorman

Deposit . . . O

Notes: Numbers are those assigned to deposits shown on Map 1252A, other deposits are named on figure. Properties from which gold is the principal product are underlined.

GSC

FIGURE IX-7. Lode gold deposits of the Cordilleran Region (by H. W. Little).

Nearly all deposits are mesothermal quartz veins with carbonate. Metallic minerals consist of native gold, tellurides, pyrite, arsenopyrite, pyrrhotite, sphalerite, and galena. Gold is often associated with the galena, particularly in high grade ores. Host rocks are commonly quartzites or granitic rocks, perhaps more susceptible to veining because of their competency.

The *Bralorne–Pioneer* mine (36), the most productive gold mine in the Canadian Cordillera, was formed in 1959 by the amalgamation of the Bralorne and Pioneer mines. The geology has been described by C. E. Cairnes, Joubin (1948), and Poole (1955). Impure cherts of the Fergusson Group, possibly of Permian age, are overlain successively by argillaceous sediments of the Noel, the Pioneer greenstone, and argillaceous beds of the Hurley Formations, all possibly of Upper Triassic age. These rocks trend west-northwesterly and were apparently folded into two anticlines separated by the Cadwallader shear zone. The southern limit of the northern anticline has been injected by an ultrabasic to acidic intrusive complex, the intrusions being less abundant south of the shear zone.

The veins occur between the Cadwallader shear zone and the Fergusson reverse fault to the north (Fig. IX-8). Two vein systems have been identified, the King, which occurs in the King section of the mine, and the Pioneer, which occurs in the Crown, Empire, and Pioneer sections. All veins are of fractured quartz and some ribboned, within which are disseminated native gold, gold telluride, several sulphides, and scheelite. The most westerly veins of the mine comprise the King vein system, from which the early production was obtained. Veins of the King system trend westerly, dip north, and are offset dextrally more than 200 feet by each of two steep north-trending faults, in the more westerly of which a mineralized vein occurs. The veins and ore shoots occur within and near the western end of an augite diorite body.

In the Pioneer vein system the ore-bearing quartz veins occur mainly in greenstone, according to Joubin, but Poole regards diorite as the most important host-rock. Ore shoots occur in all rock types except serpentine, but the richest ore occurs near serpentine, perhaps due to damming of the mineralizing solutions. The longest and most productive veins strike west to west-northwest and dip from 65°N to vertical. Two are several thousand feet long, and branches up to several hundred feet long are also ore bearing. There is only one major fault, which is between the Crown and Empire sections of the mine, and that strikes N20°W and dips 54°W. It is an oblique slip fault; the dip-slip is 370 feet, the hanging-wall having moved up, and the strike slip 240 feet. Displacement of the veins is also dextral.

Cariboo Gold Quartz mine (32) as now constituted comprises the old Cariboo Gold Quartz property, which has been inactive since 1959, and the nearby Aurum, formerly Island Mountain, mine (31), which was acquired in 1954 and from which all the ore supplying the concentrator has been derived in recent years (Guiguet, 1961). Impure quartzite, phyllite, slate, argillite, and minor grey limestone of the Midas and Snowshoe Formations of the Cariboo Group, the lower part of which is of Lower Cambrian age, form the northeast limb of an anticlinorium that trends northwest and is overturned to the southwest (Sutherland Brown, 1957). Most faults trend northerly and dip steeply east, the hanging-wall side having moved

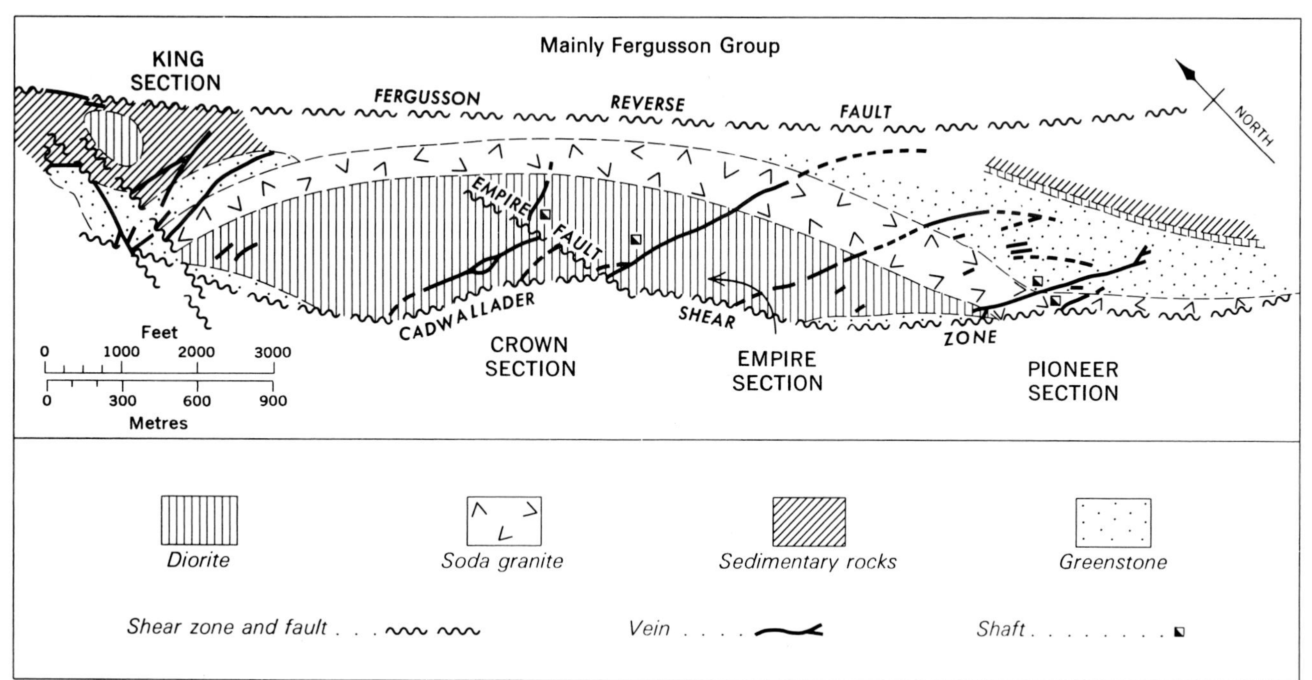

FIGURE IX-8. Bralorne–Pioneer gold mine, British Columbia; plan at 3,200-foot elevation (modified from F. R. Joubin).

southward and downward. The largest fault has horizontal and dip-slip components of about 1,400 feet each.

Four types of veins are recognized: transverse, diagonal, northerly, and strike veins. Transverse veins occupy *ac* joints whereas the diagonal and northerly veins occupy conjugate faults that also were developed during folding. The strike veins are the longest, but are commonly barren or sparsely mineralized. They occupy faults apparently unrelated to the foregoing structural pattern. Only one strike vein has been of mineable grade. The transverse veins strike N30° to 55°E and dip mainly 70 to 90°SE. They are small but so numerous that they provided most of the ore from the Cariboo Gold Quartz section. The diagonal veins, which strike N70°E to east and dip steeply south, are up to 5 feet wide and average about 150 feet long. Many tributary branches are of the transverse type. The northerly veins strike N20°E to north and dip 50 to 70°E.

In recent years, however, most ore has come from replacement bodies in limestone beds. On the limbs of folds they are tabular bodies parallel to the bedding, but on the crests of the folds they are cigar-shaped, the long axes being parallel to the regional plunge, 20°NW, of folds on the limb of the anticlinorium. Metallic minerals consist of pyrite and associated free gold with minor galena, sphalerite, cosalite, bismuthinite, scheelite, pyrrhotite, arsenopyrite, and chalcopyrite. Gangue minerals are quartz, ankerite, and muscovite in the veins, and ankerite with some quartz in the replacement bodies.

Hedley Camp, one of the larger gold camps on the Cordillera, contains the *Hedley Mascot* (66a), and *Nickel Plate* (66b) mines. These are unusual in that the ore occurs in skarn near the contact with unaltered Upper Triassic limestone. Early workers believed the ore to be related to the gabbro sills which produced the skarn, but Billingsley and Hume (1941) showed that the ore was spacially related to a single sheet, the "Midway" dyke, and to small folds subsidiary to the major ones, to zones of brecciation in skarn near the "Midway" dyke, and to transverse dykes which effected a damming of mineralizing solutions. Because the transverse dykes were emplaced after the formation of skarn but before mineralization, the ore is not derived from the "Midway" dyke but is related to a later period of mineralization, possibly from nearby granodiorite intrusions.

Copper

Copper deposits are found in four principal regions —south–central, southwestern, and northwestern British Columbia, and southwestern Yukon (Fig. IX-9). They are closely related to basic volcanic rocks, particularly those of Triassic age where invaded by granitic rocks. Copper ranks fourth in value of metal produced in the Western Mineral Province (Table IX-1); more than 3½ billion pounds valued at more than $600 million has been produced to date.

The largest copper deposits are replacement bodies which are subdivided according to the type of host rock as contact metamorphic, shear zone replacement, and porphyry deposits, the last being the replacement or fracture filling of brecciated intrusive rocks. Vein deposits of copper, such as those at Rossland, commonly show replacement of wall-rock adjacent to the veins, but at Rossland, although important amounts of copper were produced, the value of gold was greater.

Contact metamorphic deposits. These are represented by Pueblo (9), Big Chief–Little Chief (10), Craigmont (57), Phoenix (74 b, f, g, h), Mother Lode (73a), Sunset (73b), Marble Bay (48b).

The *Phoenix* deposits are the most productive of the contact metamorphic type. Chert and greenstone comprising the Knob Hill Formation of Carboniferous or Permian age is overlain unconformably by chert sharpstone 'conglomerate', a peculiar mainly bedded rock composed largely of chert fragments that was formerly regarded as jasperoid, but later shown by Seraphim (1956) to be a sedimentary breccia. The sharpstone conglomerate is overlain by Middle Triassic Brooklyn limestone and an upper sharpstone conglomerate which may be younger or the same repeated by folding or low-angle faulting. The strata are warped into a basin-like structure (Fig. IX-10) much of the eastern part of which is covered by Lower Tertiary sedimentary and volcanic rocks dipping east and terminated by a normal fault.

The limestone is converted to skarn generally near the base, but sometimes well above it, although no large intrusive bodies are known nearby. The closest is a Cretaceous granodiorite more than 2 miles distant. Around the periphery the structure seems simple with moderate to steep inward dips, but in the central part the limestone beds dip vertically and are apparently tightly folded being cut off on the north by a south-dipping reverse fault. Most orebodies lie within the skarn around the southern and western parts of the basin. The Stemwinder, however, occurs in a lens of limestone breccia or conglomerate that may form the core of the synclinal basin and may be Norian.

The largest orebodies are exposed in the Knob Hill–Ironsides pit (*Frontispiece*). The skarn, together with interbedded green argillite, lenses of sharpstone conglomerate, and a little quartzite, has been silicified and impregnated with chalcopyrite, pyrite, specular hematite, and some magnetite and pyrrhotite. This forms the 'lower ore band' which trends northerly and dips gently eastward. Above, also trending northerly but dipping more steeply eastward, is the 'upper ore band' which lies below the upper sharpstone conglomerate. Host rock for this orebody is mainly marble, with minor sharpstone conglomerate, skarn, and green argillite.

Shear zone replacement deposits. These are massive sulphide deposits and include the Britannia (56), Sunro (55), Hidden Creek (15c), Granduc, Tyee (54) mines and others.

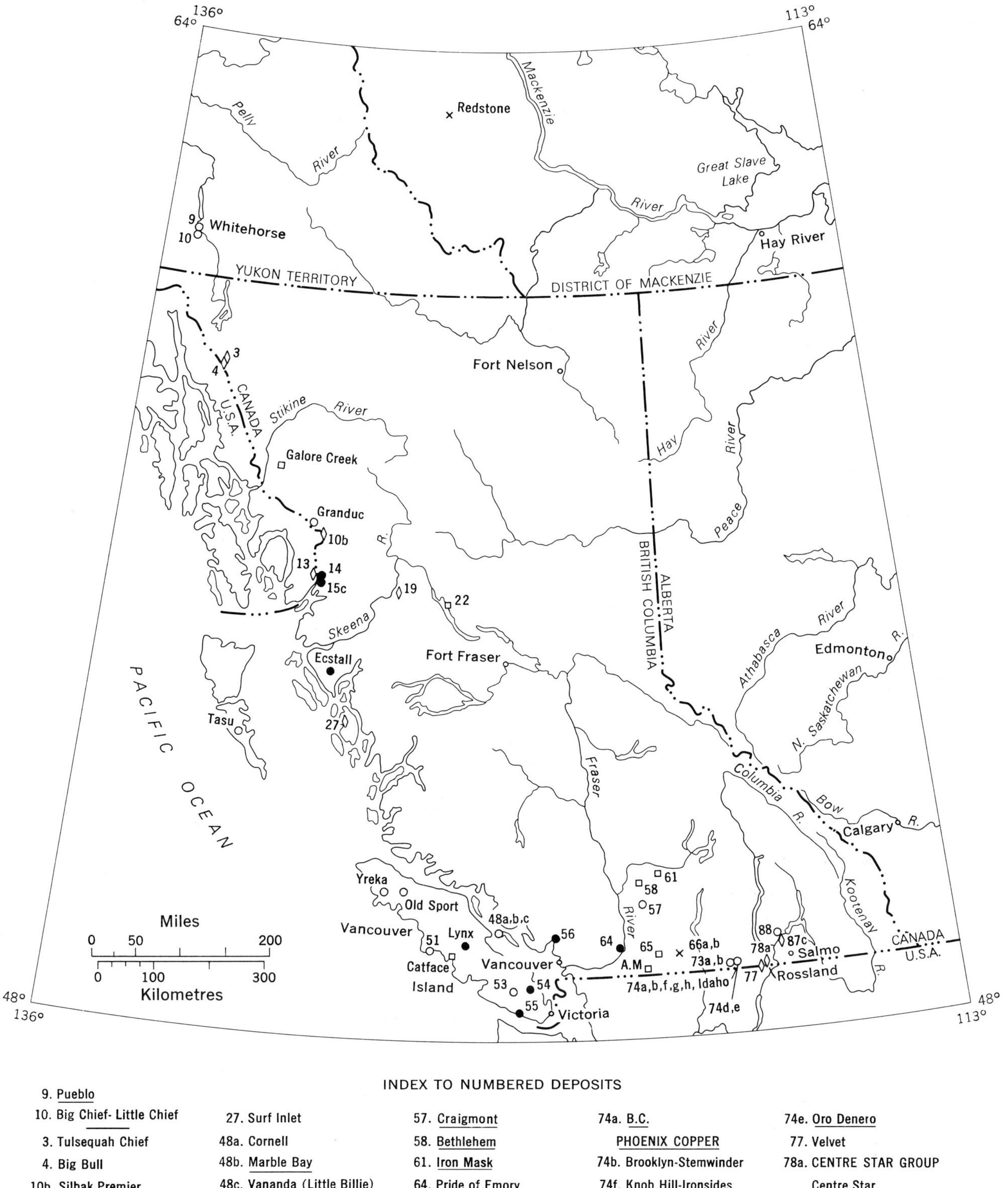

INDEX TO NUMBERED DEPOSITS

9. Pueblo				
10. Big Chief- Little Chief	27. Surf Inlet	57. Craigmont	74a. B.C.	74e. Oro Denero
3. Tulsequah Chief	48a. Cornell	58. Bethlehem	PHOENIX COPPER	77. Velvet
4. Big Bull	48b. Marble Bay	61. Iron Mask	74b. Brooklyn-Stemwinder	78a. CENTRE STAR GROUP
10b. Silbak Premier	48c. Vananda (Little Billie)	64. Pride of Emory	74f. Knob Hill-Ironsides	Centre Star
13. Outsider	51. Indian Chief	65. Copper Mountain	74g. Rawhide	Le Roi
14 Bonanza	53. Blue Grouse	66a. Hedley Mascot	74h. Snowshoe	War Eagle
15c. Hidden Creek	54. Tyee	66b. Nickel Plate	Idaho	Josie
19. Rocher Déboulé	55. Sunro	73a. Mother Lode		87c. Silver King
22. Granisle	56. Britannia	73b. Sunset	74d. Emma	88. Queen Victoria

Pyrometasomatic. . . ○ Replacement. . . ● 'Porphyry' and stockwork. . . □ Vein. . . ◊ Unclassified. . . ×

Notes: Numbers are those assigned to deposits shown on Map 1252A, other deposits are named on figure. Properties from which copper is the principal product are underlined.

GSC

FIGURE IX-9. Copper deposits of the Cordilleran Region, classified according to type (by H. W. Little).

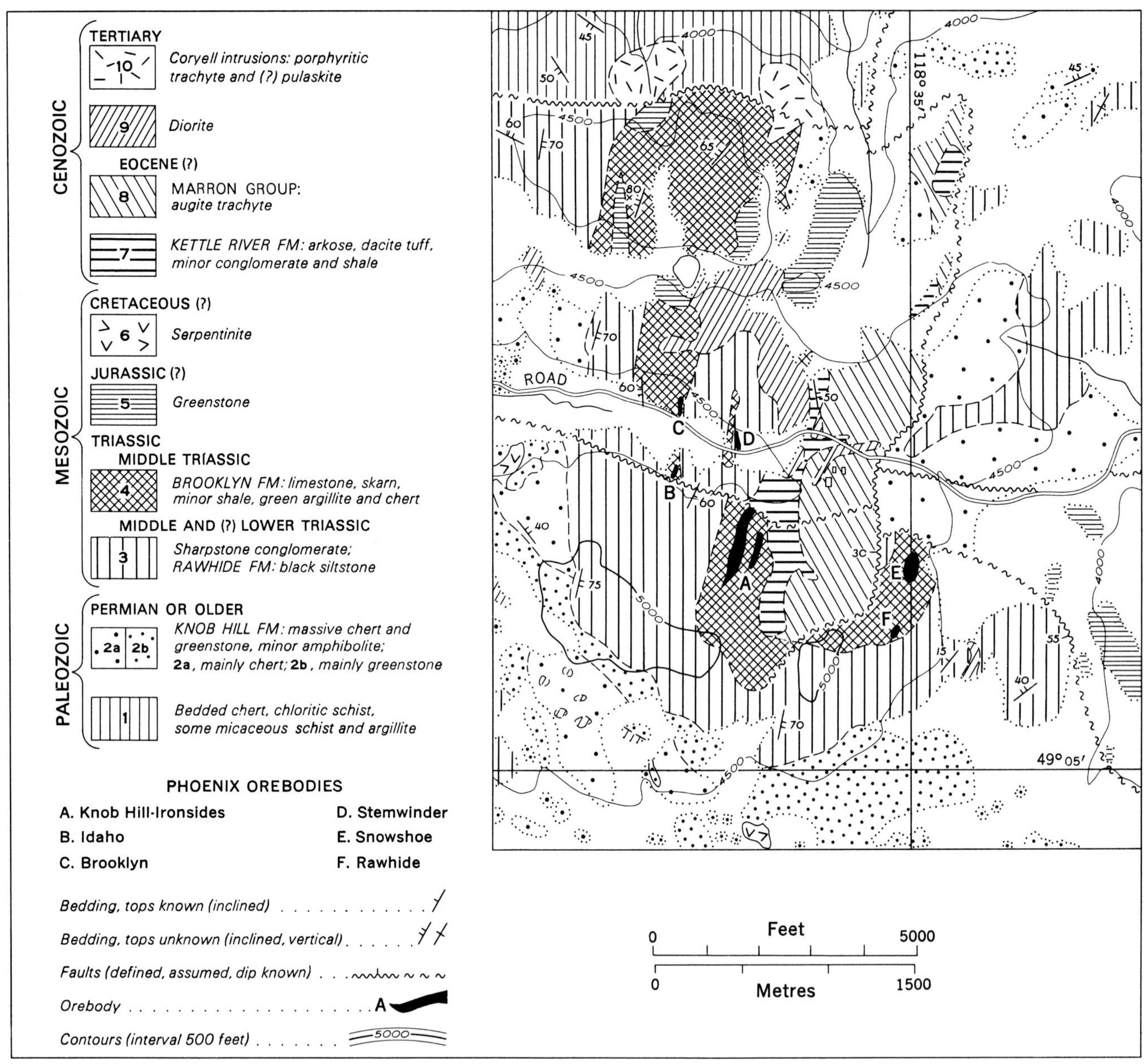

FIGURE IX-10. Geology in the vicinity of Phoenix copper deposits, British Columbia (by H. W. Little).

Britannia, the largest copper deposit mined to date in the Canadian Cordillera, occurs in a large roof pendant in the Coast batholith 20 miles north of Vancouver. The host rocks are steeply dipping quartzites, slates, cherts, and green tuffaceous sediments and volcanic clastics of the Britannia Formation, the lower part of the Gambier Group, of probable Upper Jurassic and Lower Cretaceous age. The rocks are intensely sheared along a zone 2,000 feet wide striking northwest and dipping steeply southwest into fissile sericite schist and, locally, talc or chlorite. The orebodies occur in the hanging-wall of a thrust fault near the footwall of the major shear zone (Irvine, 1948). Eight orebodies are known, which occur at intervals for 1½ miles of the 5-mile-long shear zone. They comprise huge lenticular to sheet-like masses formed of quartz, pyrite, and, locally, sphalerite, that were subsequently brecciated and then mineralized by chalcopyrite. Mining is by underground methods.

Porphyry copper deposits. Copper Mountain (65), Bethlehem (58), Catface, Granisle (22), and Galore Creek.

The *Bethlehem* mine (58) has recently come into production (White, Thompson, and McTaggart, 1957; Carr, 1960). The deposit occurs within the Guichon quartz diorite batholith of Early Jurassic age. The older quartz diorite on the Bethlehem property is intruded by a complex of granite, quartz diorite, dacite porphyry, and

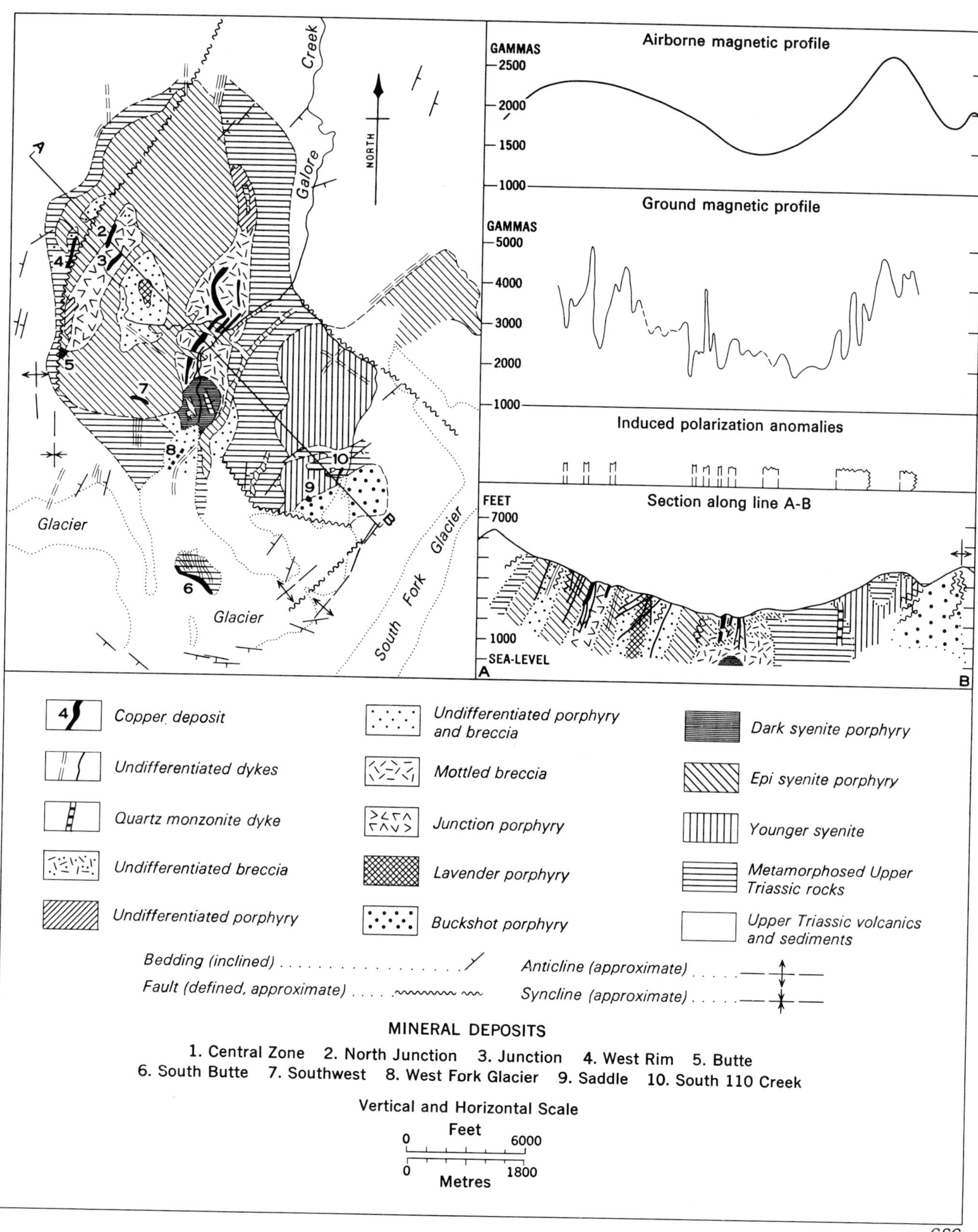

Creek
Galore
NORTH
Glacier
Glacier
South Fork Glacier
A
B
Airborne magnetic profile
GAMMAS
2500
2000
1500
1000
Ground magnetic profile
GAMMAS
5000
4000
3000
2000
1000
Induced polarization anomalies
Section along line A-B
FEET
7000
1000
SEA-LEVEL
Copper deposit
Undifferentiated dykes
Quartz monzonite dyke
Undifferentiated breccia
Undifferentiated porphyry
Undifferentiated porphyry and breccia
Mottled breccia
Junction porphyry
Lavender porphyry
Buckshot porphyry
Dark syenite porphyry
Epi syenite porphyry
Younger syenite
Metamorphosed Upper Triassic rocks
Upper Triassic volcanics and sediments
Bedding (inclined)
Fault (defined, approximate)
Anticline (approximate)
Syncline (approximate)
MINERAL DEPOSITS
1. Central Zone 2. North Junction 3. Junction 4. West Rim 5. Butte
6. South Butte 7. Southwest 8. West Fork Glacier 9. Saddle 10. South 110 Creek
Vertical and Horizontal Scale
Feet
0
6000
0
1800
Metres
GSC

FIGURE IX-11. Geology and cross-section of Galore Creek copper deposits, British Columbia (after D. A. Barr).

PLATE IX-1

Open pit and mill of Endako molybdenum mine, British Columbia.

quartz diorite porphyry. Explosion breccia is associated with the porphyry bodies. The breccia, host to the ore, contains fragments mainly of porphyry in abundant fine matrix. The breccia is silicified, sericitized, and has undergone argillic alteration. It also contains tourmaline, amphiboles, biotite, albite, epidote, chlorite, calcite, and zeolites. Three principal bodies of breccia, known as the Iona, Jersey, and East Jersey, are mineralized, mainly in their more altered parts, by chalcopyrite, bornite, and minor pyrite and molybdenite. Initial mining is by open pit.

Galore Creek copper deposits (Fig. IX-9) lie within a mountainous area 2 by 3½ miles east of Stikine River on the south flank of Stikine Arch (Barr, 1966), and though characteristically porphyry copper type they are in part pyrometasomatic. The area is underlain by volcanic and sedimentary rocks of probable Upper Triassic age which are rudely domed about a complex body of epidotized syenite porphyry (Fig. IX-11). Within the complex are zones of cataclastic breccia that occur mainly along facies contacts and which are hydrothermally altered and mineralized with chalcopyrite, bornite, pyrite, and magnetite in a gangue of biotite, potash feldspar, gypsum, garnet, chlorite, and carbonate. Secondary minerals, such as chalcocite, cuprite, native copper, malachite, and azurite occur as much as 100 feet from the surface.

Ten deposits are known of which the largest, the 'Central Zone', is 6,500 feet long and trends north-northeast. The copper minerals are disseminated throughout, but several sections of higher grade material are formed by swarms of veinlets and replacement masses.

Molybdenum

To the end of 1966 production of molybdenum in the Western Mineral Province was 24,655 pounds, valued at $40,570, and derived from a few small, high grade deposits. Recent exploration has established large deposits of low grade ore on the Endako (28), Boss Mountain (33), Red Mountain (78b), Lime Creek (16), and Glacier Gulch properties. The first three were in production in 1966; the others were under development.

The distribution of molybdenum deposits is similar to that of copper deposits; indeed they are commonly associated. Vokes (1963) has shown that molybdenum deposits are spacially and genetically related to the Nelson Intrusions in southeastern British Columbia, and to the Guichon batholith and Topley Intrusions in central British Columbia. The Glacier Gulch deposit on Hudson Bay Mountain and the Lime Creek deposit on Alice Arm appear to be related to leucocratic Tertiary acidic intrusions.

The *Endako* (28), in central British Columbia near Fort Fraser, is the largest molybdenum mine in Canada. Mining by open pit (Pl. IX-1) was begun in 1965, and 22,000 tons is now milled per day. Ore reserves are stated to exceed 90 million tons grading 0.20 per cent MoS_2.

The region is underlain by a batholith of the Topley Intrusions, considered to be Lower Jurassic although some parts may be younger. South of the mine, on the shore of François Lake, altered lavas probably of the Takla Group underlie a small area, but contacts with Topley Intrusions are not exposed. A few miles to the west, the batholith is overlain unconformably by the late Tertiary Ootsa Lake Group.

Carr (1966) established fourteen distinct facies, nine of which he referred to as quartz monzonite, one as granodiorite, and four as quartz diorite. Because bedrock exposures are poor the relationships of only a few units have been established—the others have to be deduced by indirect evidence. The orebody lies within the Endako quartz monzonite, an early phase of the Topley Intrusions. It is pinkish grey, medium grained with biotite and minor hornblende and contains numerous small phenocrysts of red orthoclase and a few of plagioclase and quartz and, in many places, clusters of more basic biotite-rich inclusions. To the north lies the generally finer grained leucocratic Casey biotite quartz monzonite, an elongate, sigmoid body oriented mainly in an east–west direction. The relative age of the two intrusions has not been established.

At the surface the orebody is more than 5,000 feet long and 1,000 feet wide, trends west-northwesterly, and appears to plunge gently west. The orebody is more than 500 feet deep in the central part and grades outward into sub-ore. Along a small part of its southern boundary, however, the orebody terminates against an east-striking fault that dips steeply north. The host rock has undergone, to various intensity, silicification, sericitization, and potash metasomatism. Ilmenite, leucoxene, and sphene are unusually abundant. The altered quartz monzonite has been intruded by numerous pre-ore dykes up to 50 feet wide of aplite and feldspar porphyry, and narrower post-ore dykes of lamprophyre. All rocks except the lamprophyre are traversed by predominantly gently dipping sinuous quartz veins from a fraction of an inch to 5 feet wide and as much as 400 feet or more along strike and down dip. The larger veins, however, in the western part of the orebody more commonly trend east-northeast and dip south. A few major faults trend east, northeast, and northwest, and numerous small lineaments trend north. The ages of these faults have not been determined, but as no mineralized quartz veins have been seen in them, they are probably post-ore. However, some molybdenite does occur in the gouge.

Molybdenite occurs mainly in the quartz veins and in fractures in aplite; much of it is fine grained, but coarse flakes do occur. According to C. W. Ball there appear to be three stages of mineralization. The first consists of molybdenite in a few early quartz veins and in adjacent altered wall-rock. The main mineralization is fine-grained molybdenite along the margins of narrow quartz stringers. It is accompanied by pyrite more extensive than the molybdenite orebody. The pyrite comprises less than 1 per cent of the orebody and occurs both in the quartz veins and disseminated in the wall-rocks. The final mineralization is coarse-grained molybdenite associated with calcite. Minor magnetite and specularite are present; chalcopyrite is rare.

Iron

The productive iron deposits of the Western Mineral Province are entirely on the coastal islands of British Columbia. They consist of pyrometasomatic magnetite deposits adjacent to diorite or granodiorite intrusions formed in skarn at the base of Upper Triassic limestone overlying basaltic pillow lavas. The Tasu (25) and Jedway (26) mines are on Moresby Island, the Empire (40), Nimpkish (41), Zeballos Iron (42), Iron Mike (37), Brynnor (52), and Argonaut (46) are on Vancouver Island, and the Texada (49) is on Texada Island. The Tasu and Texada deposits also contain considerable copper ore. It is conjectured (Eastwood, 1965) that the basalts, which contain as much as 14 per cent iron, may be the source of iron in these deposits since chemical conditions for an ion exchange from silicate to oxide are favourable at the contact with limestone. About 2 million tons per year of iron ore concentrate is produced and exported to Japan.

About 100,000 tons of pig iron per year is obtained at Trail and Kimberley from iron sulphide tailings produced in the milling of lead–zinc ores.

Tungsten

Tungsten deposits of the Western Mineral Province are somewhat scattered but appear to form three distinct provinces. The first, a beryllium–tin–tungsten–molybdenum province, extends along Omineca geanticline, mainly on the west side (Mulligan, 1966); the second is within the multi-metallogenic province centred about Hazelton; the third is related to granitic intrusions that form an east–west belt centred at Keno Hill, Yukon (Bostock *in* Little, 1959). Two types of lode deposits are of economic importance: quartz fissure veins and contact metamorphic.

The quartz fissure veins commonly carry pyrrhotite, chalcopyrite, and molybdenite, with wolframite or ferberite more common than scheelite. The *Red Rose* (20) is in a tungsten-bearing vein cutting a diorite body which is probably a cupola of the granodiorite stock forming the core of Rocher Déboulé Mountain (Kindle *in* Little, 1959), but at depth the vein follows the contact between the diorite and metamorphosed Lower Cretaceous argillite, quartzite, and greywacke (Sutherland Brown, 1960). The

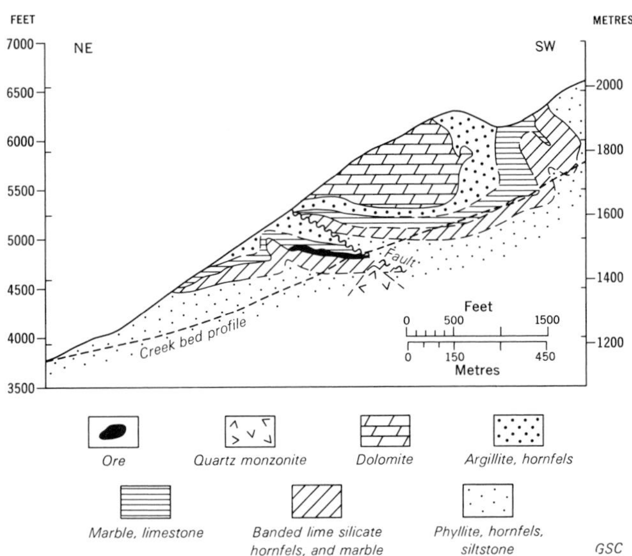

FIGURE IX-12. Cross-section through Canada Tungsten mine, Flat River, District of Mackenzie (by S. L. Blusson).

vein strikes N30°to 45°W and dips 40° to 75°SW. Within it, the two ore shoots rake steeply northwest, and consist of quartz with feldspar, biotite, hornblende, ankerite, tourmaline, apatite, scheelite, ferberite, molybdenite, and chalcopyrite. The Red Rose produced tungsten concentrate during World War II.

Contact metamorphic deposits occur as irregular replacement bodies in pyroxene–garnet skarn and to a lesser degree in adjacent limestone and granite. Such bodies are usually cut by tungsten-bearing quartz veins. Scheelite is the most abundant ore mineral and is usually accompanied by abundant pyrrhotite. Former producers are the Emerald (80a), Dodger, and Feeney mines near Salmo, British Columbia. In 1965 at the *Canada Tungsten* mine (1) at Flat River, District of Mackenzie, 108,000 tons of ore averaging 2.53 per cent WO_3 was milled. Ore reserves, prior to mining, were reported to be 1,320,000 tons grading 2.51 per cent WO_3 and 0.45 per cent copper (Green and Godwin, 1963). The scheelite (S. L. Blusson) is disseminated in a dark green pyroxene and garnet skarn forming a tabular replacement body at the base of a massive Lower Cambrian limestone (Fig. IX-12). The skarn occurs only on the lower, flat-lying limb of an overturned syncline which is intruded by quartz monzonite and cut by pre-ore faults. These faults and an intrusive cupola about 100 feet below the deposit are thought to localize the ore within the limestone host rock. The ore consists of scheelite, pyrrhotite, and minor chalcopyrite, enriched locally by coarse-grained scheelite–microcline–quartz veins and later veinlets of fine-grained biotite, quartz, scheelite, and sulphide.

Mercury

Mercury deposits of the Western Mineral Province occur in two subprovinces (Stevenson, 1940). The more southerly extends from Kamloops westward to Bridge River and the other is along Pinchi fault. An isolated occurrence is known at Sechart, Vancouver Island. In both subprovinces mercury occurs as cinnabar replacing carbonate rocks adjacent to faults. The carbonate rocks are either dolomitized limestone or carbonated serpentinite. A few minor deposits occur in altered volcanic or sedimentary rocks. The host rocks range in age from Permian to early Tertiary.

Of the two deposits along the Pinchi fault, the *Pinchi Lake* mine (23) was the main source of mercury for the allies during World War II, when 4.2 million pounds of mercury valued at more than $10 million was recovered at the two properties. Cinnabar, minor pyrite, and minor stibnite occur as veinlets and blebs in dolomite of Permian age, although one orebody is in carbonatized brecciated serpentine. Quartz and calcite are gangue introduced with the cinnabar into cracks and cavities near the Pinchi fault zone.

Nickel

The *Pride of Emory* mine (64) is to the present the only source of nickel ore in the Cordilleran Region. Although discovered in 1923 it did not reach major production until 1958. The host rocks comprise a complex of peridotite, pyroxenite, and hornblendite which, except for a zone of schist on the south, is surrounded by diorite and minor norite of the Coast Intrusions of post-Paleozoic, pre-Eocene age. Twelve orebodies are known (James and Eastwood, 1964) ranging from 50 to 150 feet in diameter and from 250 to 1,000 feet long. They plunge steeply north or west, most within or near a plane that strikes N75°W. It is uncertain why they are so localized. The ore shoots are disseminated and massive sulphides consisting mainly of nickeliferous pyrrhotite, pentlandite, and chalcopyrite, with small amounts of other sulphides of iron, nickel, cobalt, and copper. It has not been clearly established whether magmatic segregation or hydrothermal action was the primary process by which the ore was emplaced.

Minor Metals

Other metals produced in the Western Mineral Province are cadmium, antimony, tin, and bismuth, each valued at more than $10 million, platinum at more than $100,000, and manganese, chromium, palladium, and cobalt valued at less than $100,000 each (Table IX-1). Uranium is reported in several deposits. Cadmium, antimony, tin, and bismuth are obtained as byproducts in lead–zinc mines. Antimony is also obtained from stibnite-bearing veins.

Sedimentary Deposits

Unlike the Eastern Mineral Province, there are no metallic deposits of sedimentary origin that are currently of economic value in the Western Mineral Province. Of interest are germanium-bearing coaly beds in sediments of Eocene age near Powell River and extensive magnetite-bearing Lower Cambrian quartzite up to 8 feet thick in Salmo area.

Surficial Deposits

Metallic minerals occurring in surficial deposits are placer and chemical precipitates. Of the latter the bog iron deposits are the most important, but none has yet been exploited. On a tributary of Zymoetz River east of Terrace more than half a million tons of ore assaying more than 50 per cent iron rests on a pyrite-bearing porphyritic rock. Similar deposits occur at the head of Taseko Creek northwest of Lillooet.

Gold

Gold placer mining superseded the fur trade as the important spur to industrial development of the Canadian Cordillera. This impetus occurred in the southern part in 1858 and in the Yukon fifty years later. As the placer fields became depleted the attention of prospectors and miners turned to the discovery and development of lode mines. In addition to gold and an appreciable amount of silver (average fineness 861 in British Columbia and about 700 in the Klondike), placer mining has yielded minor amounts of tin and tungsten minerals and some platinum metals. Early operations consisted almost entirely of working shallow deposits by hand, but as early as 1880 hydraulic methods were introduced. Later, bucket-line and suction dredges were used, and were in operation until 1966 in the Yukon where permafrost requires thawing of the gravels.

More than 5 million ounces of placer gold worth nearly $100 million has been produced in British Columbia, whereas Yukon placers have yielded nearly 11 million ounces valued in excess of $250 million. In the past decade nearly all placer gold in Canada was from operations in Klondike area, Yukon.

The alluvial deposits formed for the most part during the Tertiary. Deep decay of rocks under moderate to semitropical conditions occurred in the early Tertiary. Uplift in the late Tertiary led to concentration of gold in stream gravels along with such minerals as magnetite, pyrite, platinum, osmiridium, cassiterite, scheelite, rutile, and monazite. Although glaciation destroyed many deposits, those in deep, narrow canyons escaped scouring by ice. Western Yukon, however, was not glaciated partly due to the aridity of the climate during the Pleistocene, with the result that the Klondike district was one of the richest placer fields in the world.

The *Klondike* district (3) near Dawson was the source of more than half the placer gold of Western Canada. Bedrock is mainly the Klondike schist of sedimentary origin, containing albite, quartz, chlorite, and calcite. Bodies of sheared quartz-feldspar porphyry may also be present. Some rocks resemble those of late Proterozoic or Cambrian age that lie some distance to the northeast, but the age is not known.

Numerous quartz veins, mostly small, occur in the Klondike schist and contain pyrite, a little chalcopyrite, galena, and free gold. Most gold is concentrated by erosion in the pre-Pleistocene creek channels, known as the 'white channel.' Subsequent stream action has reworked these auriferous gravels to form new placers in present stream beds, at various levels as much as 300 feet below the 'white channel' paystreak (McConnell, 1905).

The *Cariboo* district (30) was at one time the most productive placer gold field in British Columbia. As records are incomplete for the years prior to 1874 total production is not known. It is estimated to be more than 2.5 million ounces, valued at more than $50 million. Williams and Lightning Creeks, the two most celebrated, are reported to have yielded gold to the value of some $20 million.

The region is one of moderate relief deeply dissected by stream erosion underlain by phyllite, quartzite, argillite, and limestone of the early Paleozoic Cariboo Group. Within the main productive belt these rocks form two anticlinoria and an intervening synclinorium striking northwest (Sutherland Brown, 1957). Decomposition by weathering of auriferous quartz veins during the late Cretaceous or early Tertiary probably caused concentration and enrichment of the gold by alternate solution and deposition (Johnston and Uglow, 1926). Uplift in the late Tertiary resulted in rejuvenation of streams and concentration of the gold in stream gravels. Subsequent glaciation apparently was limited in destructive effect because of stagnation of the ice in the narrow valleys so that some Tertiary placers were preserved. Elsewhere reconcentration of gold from the glacial till was accomplished by recent stream action.

Other placer fields, each of which has yielded $1 million to $40 million in gold are Atlin, Fraser River, Omineca, Dease Creek, and Tulameen in British Columbia, and Sixtymile River, Haggart, Livingstone, Burwash, Henderson, and Clear Creeks in Yukon.

Hydrothermal and Metamorphic Deposits

Asbestos

Many asbestos deposits are known in the Western Mineral Province, but of these only that at Cassiar is in production.

At *Clinton Creek,* near Dawson, Yukon, cross-fibre asbestos up to one quarter inch long occurs in a small ultrabasic body enclosed by phyllites, argillites, and quartzites. Production from this property commenced in late 1967. *Cassiar Asbestos* (5) is on Mount McDame about 3 miles north of Cassiar. It lies within a 500-by-1,700-foot ultrabasic body of Mississippian (?) age. The asbestos occurs as cross-fibre veins in dark green serpentine, commonly one half to one inch wide and up to 15 feet long. Gabrielse (1963) concluded that the asbestos was formed long after serpentinization occurred, during the deformation accompanying emplacement of Cassiar Batholith during the Columbian Orogeny under metamorphic conditions represented by the upper part of the greenschist facies.

Barite, Witherite, Fluorite

Barite is produced only in upper Columbia Valley south of Golden. That from the Silver Giant mine (100) near Spillimacheen is recovered from tailings whereas that from the Mineral King mine (104) near Invermere is a byproduct of lead–zinc mining. Barite veins are mined at Brisco (101), Parson (99), and Larrabee. The mineral also occurs as gangue in the Britannia copper mine (56) but none is recovered.

Witherite occurs near the lower crossing of Liard River by Alaska Highway in British Columbia and is reported near the crossing of Pelly River by Canol Road in the Yukon. Both occurrences are replacements of limestone cut by narrow veins.

The largest known deposit of fluorite in the Cordillera is the *Rock Candy* (75), a lenticular stockwork of veins composed of fluorite, barite, quartz, and calcite in early Tertiary Coryell syenite. Near Birch Island, the Rexspar property, in recent years also a uranium prospect, contains over a million tons of material containing 20 per cent fluorite and 15 per cent celestite.

Magnesite

Extensive beds of magnesite, possibly of sedimentary rather than hydrothermal origin, are known in eastern Purcell Mountains. In the Lower Cambrian Cranbrook Formation near Cranbrook, the magnesite bed is 25 to 55 feet thick, and intermittently exposed over 18,000 feet. It is interbedded with quartzite into which it grades through zones 75 to 150 feet thick of alternating thin quartzite and carbonate strata. A similar but smaller deposit occurs in the same formation several miles farther west. Recently magnesite has been discovered in the Proterozoic Mount Nelson Formation near Brisco. The deposits are pod-like bodies and apparently were formed by hydrothermal alteration of dolomite. The largest deposits, reported in 1966, occur in the Middle Cambrian Cathedral Formation on the west flank of Mount Brussilof, near the junction of Cross and Mitchell Rivers. None of the magnesite deposits of the Cordillera has been exploited.

Perlite

Perlite of early Tertiary age intercalated with rhyolite occurs at François Lake in central British Columbia and was first noted by Dawson in 1876. About 1,112 tons of the volcanic glass was mined and shipped in 1953, but there has been no additional production.

Talc

Talc is common in the serpentinites of the Western Mineral Province, but few deposits have been worked. Production was mostly from southern Vancouver Island, and small amounts from the vicinity of Lillooet.

Jade

Within the last 10 years the collection of jade, which occurs as alluvial boulders (some up to 10 tons), has developed into a substantial minor industry. Jade has been reported in lower Fraser Valley near Hope and from many places in the interior of British Columbia from the International Boundary to Wheaton Creek. The most productive region is in the Fraser Canyon north of Hope and along the tributary Bridge and Yalakom Rivers. The jade is nephrite variety. Although the host-rock of jade is serpentinite, little jade has been found in place.

Evaporites

Gypsum

Gypsum is used in the manufacture of wallboard, plaster, and portland cement. Only one deposit, at *Falkland* (62), has been worked in the Western Mineral Province, more than a million tons having been quarried. Pods of anhydrite and gypsum occur in argillaceous sediments of the Permian Cache Creek Group, closely associated with faults. The deposits have been regarded as hydrothermal, but recently Baird (1964) suggested that they are sedimentary evaporites squeezed upwards along faults and emplaced by plastic flow.

Devonian gypsum was quarried from 1945 to 1958 at Mayook (108) in Rocky Mountain Trench east of Cranbrook. Large deposits occur in the Eastern Mineral Province in the Middle Devonian Burnais Formation, currently exploited at two quarries near Windermere. Elsewhere in the Eastern Mineral Province gypsum has been reported at many places, the largest deposits being in Manitoba. It is mined at Amaranth (17) from a bed 40 feet thick in the Jurassic Amaranth Formation occurring 100 feet below the surface, and at Silver Plains (22) from a bed 30 to 50 feet thick lying at 150 feet depth. At Gypsumville (15), Manitoba, it occurs as isolated ridges arising above swamp and although situated within the outcrop belt of Silurian rocks, its age is not definitely known.

Other occurrences are known in southern Yukon in the Rainy Hollow area of northwestern British Columbia, and in the Triassic Whitehorse Formation at Mowitch Creek in Jasper Park. It occurs also on the banks of Slave and Salt Rivers north and west of Fort Fitzgerald.

Sodium and Magnesium Sulphate

Sodium sulphate (Glauber's salt) is found in many closed drainage basins of southern Saskatchewan in the form of brines and intermittent or permanent crystal beds. A large industry has been built for its recovery; reserves are estimated at 200 million tons, over 4 million tons having been produced. The sodium sulphate is mined from dried or frozen lake deposits but recently the bulk is obtained by evaporation of brine from the alkali lakes. About 95 per cent of production is used in the pulp and paper industries. Plants are in operation at Palo, Chaplin Lake, Bishopric, Ormiston, and Gladmar. Production in 1965 totalled 323,000 tons valued at more than $5 million.

Sodium carbonate, sodium sulphate, and magnesium sulphate (epsom salt) are obtained from several small basins in the semi-arid Interior Plateau of British Columbia where the salts are precipitated in undrained lakes during times of abundant evaporation or cold weather. The precipitates form bowl-like masses of crystals embedded in mud. Total production is about 14,000 tons of magnesium sulphate and more than 10,000 tons of sodium carbonate.

Salt

Salt (halite) occurs in both the Middle and Upper Devonian strata in Western Canada. It is produced commercially from the Prairie Formation of the Middle Devonian Elk Point Group. This salt horizon occurs on a west-dipping homocline that extends from northeastern Alberta to Manitoba at depths varying from 600 feet at McMurray to over 5,000 feet between Edmonton and southern Saskatchewan. Thin layers of anhydrite and clay are common in the salt sequence, and the pure salt grades laterally to anhydrite and clastics. At Lindbergh salt for domestic and industrial consumption is produced from brine from a section 700 feet thick at a depth of 3,600 feet, and from a section 400 feet thick at a about 3,700 feet depth near Unity, Saskatchewan. At Duvernay brine is used to make caustic soda, chlorine, and hydrochloric acid. At Neepawa, Manitoba, brine is obtained from a porous zone in the Upper Devonian Souris River Formation at 1,160 feet and from the Winnipegosis Formation at 1,453 feet depth. The brine contains 170,000 to 180,000 ppm of dissolved salts of which 85 per cent is sodium chloride.

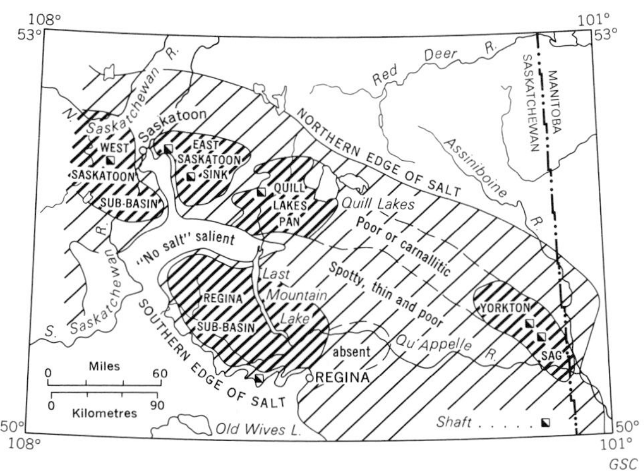

FIGURE IX-13. Potash occurrences in the Prairie evaporite basin, Saskatchewan (after A. M. Klingspor).

Potash

Potash occurs in the upper 300 feet of the Prairie Formation of the Middle Devonian Elk Point Group of Saskatchewan (Fig. IX-13). The potash-rich units (Klingspor, 1966), designated K-1, K-2, and K-3 zones, from base to top, are probably continuous across the basin but areas high in sylvinite and carnallite are separated by areas thin and poor in these minerals and with a high insoluble mineral content. The latter areas seem to correspond with high reef growth in the Winnipegosis Formation. Each zone consists of a variable succession of indistinctly bedded units of halite and lenticular unbedded masses of sylvinite (sylvite and halite), carnallite, and halite. The sylvinite contains the highest proportion of potassium but occurs only as thin zones. The percentage of potash in each zone increases gradually upwards until terminated abruptly by a clastic layer, generally of red anhydritic or halitic clay. The K-1 layer is the most coarsely crystalline and purest ore. The crystals range from 1 inch to 2 inches in the K-1 zone, whereas they range from 0.3 inch to 1.3 inches in the K-2 zone, and from 0.1 to 0.6 inch in the K-3 zone. Individual zones may be as much as 20 feet thick.

It is estimated that potash can be mined economically to depths of 3,500 feet. Commercial grade potash

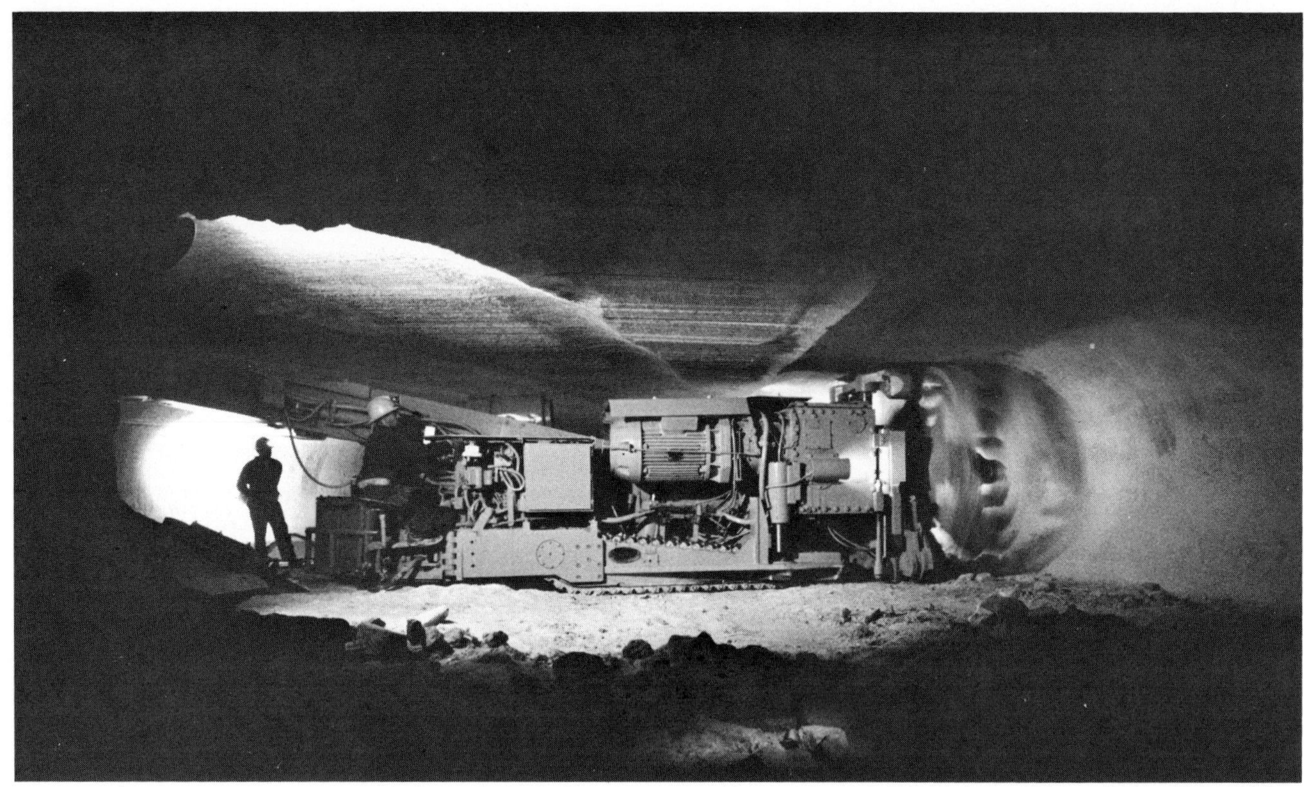

PLATE IX-2. Mining potash underground at Esterhazy, Saskatchewan.

is between 25 and 35 per cent K_2O. Recoverable reserves to a depth of 3,500 feet and grading 25 per cent or better with bed thicknesses of 5 to 10 feet have been estimated at 6.4 billion tons. Mines in operation by 1969 are at Patience Lake (12), Belle Plaine (13), Esterhazy (14), Lanigan, Viscount, Allan, and Vanscoy. At Belle Plaine the potash is obtained by solution of strata lying at over 5,000 feet depth. This plant is the only one in the world where potash is mined in this way. Salt is precipitated from the concentrated solutions and the residual solutions are fed to a crystallizer to precipitate the potash.

Other Sedimentary Deposits

Limestone, Dolomite

Limestone is one of the most valuable of the non-metallic minerals; it is used mainly in the production of cement. The Fort Whyte plant, Manitoba, uses limestone, 95 to 96 per cent $CaCO_3$, from the Devonian Elm Point Formation near Steep Rock and clay from surficial deposits nearby. High calcium limestone is obtained from the Devonian Point Wilkins Member of the Manitoba Group near Mafeking and shipped to the cement plant at Regina. In Alberta, the Upper Devonian Palliser limestone is quarried at Exshaw and Cadomin. At Bamberton on Vancouver Island, limestone is quarried from the Permian Sicker Group and shale is obtained from the Upper Cretaceous Nanaimo Group. The plant on Lulu Island near Vancouver obtains limestone from the Triassic Marble Bay Formation on Texada Island.

Lime is produced in Alberta from the Mississippian Loomis Member of the Mount Head Formation at Kananaskis, the plant formerly utilizing Cambrian limestone. The best bed is 70 feet thick, 95 to 99 per cent $CaCO_3$, and up to 2 per cent $MgCO_3$. Limestone from the Mississippian Livingstone Formation containing 97 per cent $CaCO_3$ and 2 per cent $MgCO_3$ is quarried for lime at Crowsnest Lake. This plant also produces crushed limestone for glass-making, poultry grit, stucco dash, coal-washing, and stock feed. The Devonian Elm Point Formation is quarried for lime at Spearhill, Manitoba. High magnesia lime and dolomite are quarried from the Ordovician Stonewall and Stony Mountain Formations and from the Silurian in Manitoba for crushed stone, rubble, curbstone, lime, and terrazzo. There are many excellent deposits of limestone throughout the Cordillera that are not at present being worked.

In Manitoba, a mottled dolomitic limestone containing large cephalopods and gastropods, known as Tyndall building stone, is obtained from the Ordovician Red River Formation, and a strikingly decorative mottled greenish and purplish grey dolomite building stone is obtained from the Stony Mountain Formation.

PLATE IX-3

Natural gas processing plant, Pincher Creek, Alberta.

Clay

In southern Saskatchewan clay for china, ball, fire, and stoneware products is obtained from the late Upper Cretaceous Whitemud Formation. Drain and sewer pipe, stone and household ware are manufactured from similar clay at Medicine Hat. Non-marine shales of Cretaceous and Tertiary age are used for local brick and tile industries. Shale from the Eocene Huntingdon Formation on Vedder Mountain in the lower Fraser Valley is the principal source of clay for the large tile, brick, pipe, and other clay products plants located nearby. Clay from surficial deposits has been used but is largely of inferior quality.

Bentonite

Bentonite is used for the production of well drilling mud, foundry moldings, and pellets. Non-swelling (calcium) bentonite is mined at Morden, Manitoba, from the Vermilion River Formation and is used in the purification of mineral and vegetable oils. Other deposits are known in the Battle Formation of southern Saskatchewan, in the Bearpaw and Edmonton Formations of south-central Alberta. The better types of swelling (sodium) bentonite are in the Edmonton and Bearpaw Formations of central Alberta and mining operations are located near Onoway and Rosalind. Semi-swelling bentonite is found in the Ravenscrag and Battle Formations in southern Saskatchewan. A little bentonite has been mined near Princeton, British Columbia, where it occurs in beds 3 and 11 feet thick separated by four inches of lignite, in the coal-bearing part of the Eocene Princeton Group. A seam of white bentonite 9 feet thick occurs in coaly shales of the same age near Quilchena.

Diatomite

Diatomite has been mined 8 miles north and 24 miles south of Quesnel, British Columbia. The diatomite is of Upper Miocene age, rests upon clay, sand, and gravel, and is in places overlain by basalt flows. Maximum thickness of the deposits is about 83 feet.

Phosphate

Phosphate rock of Mississippian to Jurassic age occurs in the southern Rocky Mountains near Fernie,

Michel, and Crowsnest. That near the base of the Banff and Exshaw Formations is oölitic and nodular. Brecciated dolomite partly cemented by apatite lies in the upper part of the Rocky Mountain Group. Phosphatic sandstone occurs near the base of both the Spray River Formation and the Fernie Formation. These phosphate beds are thin and of too low grade to be developed at present.

Marl

Many small lakes in British Columbia contain deposits of marl which has been used locally for agricultural purposes. Probably the largest of these deposits lies in Cheam Lake near Chilliwack, where the marl is 4 to 12 feet thick and covers about 4 acres. In recent years 25,000 to 40,000 tons per year has been obtained by dragline dredging.

Hydrocarbon Associates

Sulphur

Sulphur is obtained from the hydrogen sulphide in sour natural gas during the normal preparation of the gas for use as fuel. Most sulphur produced is from Alberta and is obtained from Mississippian rocks in the Foothills fields of Waterton, Pincher Creek, and Jumping Pound, and from the Devonian Leduc Formation at Redwater, Innisfail, and Rimbey, the Nisku Formation at Nevis and the Wabamun Group at Okotoks, and Calgary. In 1965 reserves were estimated at 99 million long tons; production was 1,538,428 long tons.

Helium and Nitrogen

Helium has been produced since 1963 from two wells near Swift Current, Saskatchewan, from the Upper Cambrian Deadwood Formation. The reservoir is finely porous, silty to sandy dolomite, dolomitic siltstone and sandstone that overlie knobs of Precambrian rhyolite rising several hundred feet above the general basement surface. The gas is over 90 per cent nitrogen and up to 2 per cent helium. Net pay thicknesses in the two wells are 108 and 168 feet with recoverable reserves being estimated at 2 billion cubic feet and an annual capacity of 12 million cubic feet. Helium also occurs at Wood Mountain but is not produced. There the Cambrian sands are thinner and helium content lower.

FUELS

Coal

Coal deposits are widely distributed in Western Canada (Fig. IX-14), the largest being in the Foothills and southern Rocky Mountains. Most coal mined comes from beds of Lower Cretaceous and Upper Cretaceous age and some from Tertiary strata. Coal production reached an all time high of 7.0 million tons in 1949, gradually declined to 5.1 million tons in 1963, but increased to 6.8 million tons in 1967. Of the last, 0.9 million ton was mined in the Alberta Foothills, 2.7 million tons from the Alberta Plains, 2.0 million tons from Saskatchewan, and 1.2 million tons from the Cordilleran Region of British Columbia and the Yukon. Coal production from Western Canada in 1967 accounted for 60 per cent of the total Canadian output of 11.4 million tons.

Western Cordilleran Region

On Vancouver Island the coal-bearing strata belong to the Nanaimo Group of Upper Cretaceous age. The Nanaimo is about 7,000 feet thick; the upper part is non-marine and the lower part consists of intertonguing marine and coal-bearing beds. The coal is of high volatile bituminous rank. The strata were deposited in basins on a deeply eroded, uneven surface of Mesozoic sedimentary, volcanic, and plutonic rocks. The seams are floored by sandstone which rarely contains the roots of vegetation from which the coal was derived. Accordingly, it has been suggested that the greater part of the coal was derived from driftwood deposited in lagoons. Mining commenced in the Nanaimo and Comox fields in 1852, and nearly all recoverable coal has been extracted. Production has dwindled rapidly with only 375 tons being produced in 1967. Coal deposits of the same age occur farther north at Suquash and on Graham Island, the most northerly of the Queen Charlotte Islands. Lignitic coal of Tertiary age is also found on Graham Island.

Coal seams of Upper Jurassic or Lower Cretaceous age occur in rocks included with the Hazelton Group in Bulkley River valley and in Kispiox area north of Hazelton. The coal-bearing strata are cut by minor igneous intrusions and in places lie near younger volcanic rocks. As a result, the coal ranges in rank from low grade bituminous to low grade anthracite, depending on proximity to igneous rocks. Seams are as much as 14 feet thick, but have been folded and crushed. In 1967 production from the Telkwa coalfield near Telkwa amounted to 16,000 tons. The strata of the remotely situated Groundhog coalfield at the headwaters of Skeena River are presumably of the same age. The seams are closely folded and faulted. The coal is sheared, of semi-anthracite rank, but very high in ash.

The principal coal mining area in Yukon is at Carmacks where about 1,900 tons was mined in 1967. Production is from a seam 9 feet thick in the Tantalus Formation of early Lower Cretaceous age. This formation occurs in several small, isolated areas between Carmacks and Whitehorse. A little Tertiary coal has been mined about 40 miles north of Dawson.

Coals of Tertiary age are widely distributed over the Western Cordillera. The principal producing areas have been in the south near Princeton and Merritt where production ceased in 1961 and 1963 respectively. At Hat Creek the seams are exceptionally thick, totalling 466 feet. The coal is very dirty but may be, in part, recoverable by stripping.

Rocky Mountains and Foothills

In the southern Rocky Mountains and Foothills, coal deposits occur mainly in the Kootenay Formation of Lower Cretaceous age. The coal is mostly bituminous and locally semi-anthracite. Much is sheared and the strata may be highly inclined, closely folded, and repeated by

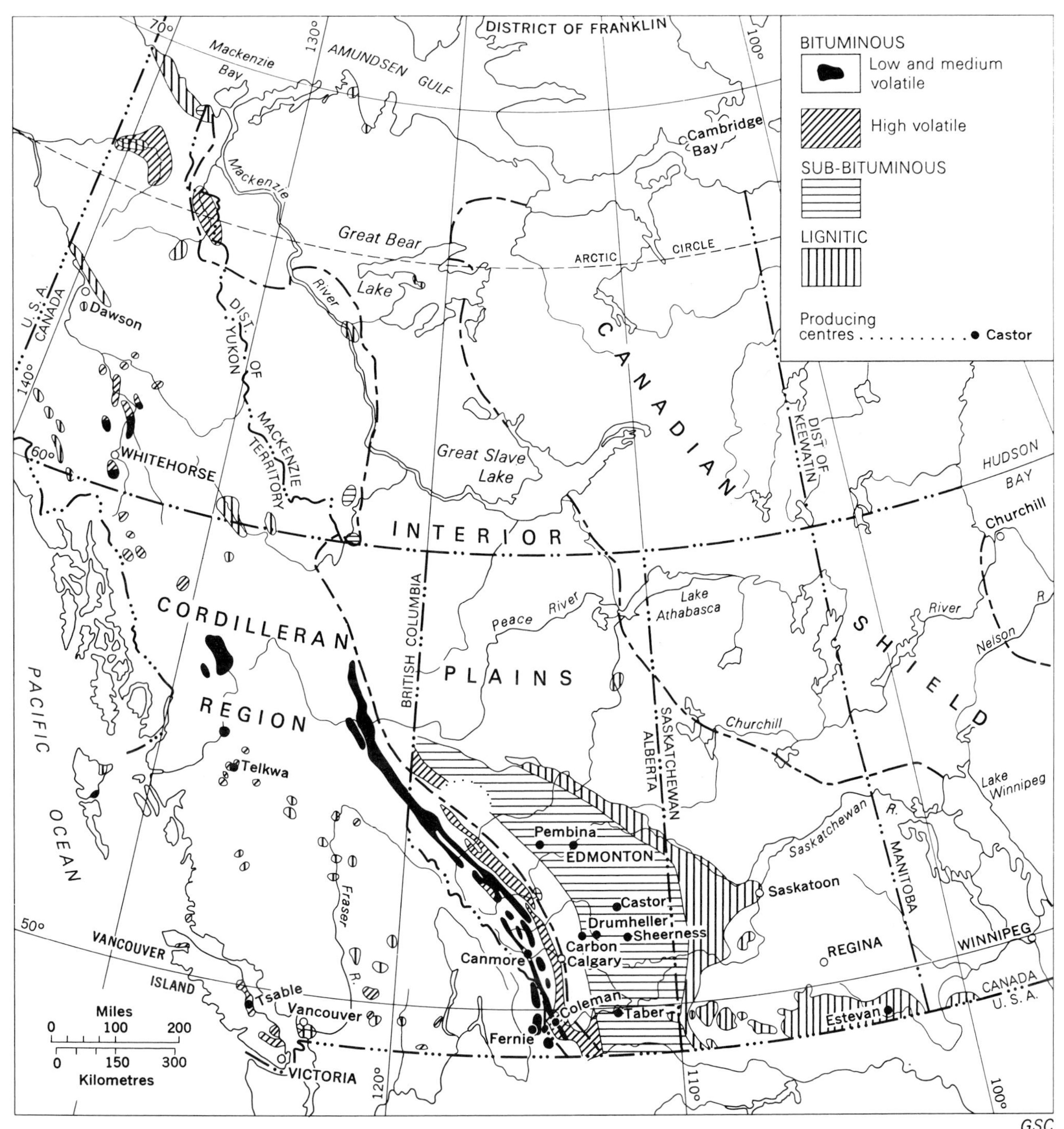

FIGURE IX-14. Coal-bearing areas of Western Canada, classified according to rank (by B. A. Latour).

thrust faults. Some is hard and blocky where the seams are less disturbed.

In southeastern British Columbia, Crowsnest coalfield comprises three areas, namely: the undeveloped upper Elk River area to the north; the central Crowsnest area in which there is large production at Michel; and the undeveloped Flathead River area to the south. In the Crowsnest area the Kootenay is about 3,500 feet thick and contains 22 seams with an aggregate thickness of 150 feet. At Michel, Corbin, and Tent Mountain the strata have been folded and faulted and the coal squeezed from the limbs into pockets on the crests and troughs of the folds where it is several times thicker than normal. Where such conditions occur near surface the coal can be economically recovered by strip mining. In 1967 the Crowsnest area produced 1.2 million tons and a cumulative production of 62 million tons. The coal is of medium volatile bituminous rank and has excellent coking qualities. Probable recoverable reserves of the Crowsnest coalfield are estimated at 5 billion tons.

In the Crowsnest coal area of Alberta the Kootenay Formation decreases in thickness from 800 feet at Coleman where five seams aggregate 47 feet, to 430 feet at Bellevue where three seams total 37 feet. The coal has been obtained from underground and strip mines, but at present only the Vicary mine near Coleman is producing. The coal is of medium and low volatile, bituminous rank and can be used for the production of coke. Production in 1967 totalled 621,000 tons; probable recoverable reserves are 3.0 billion tons.

Along Bow River valley in the vicinity of Canmore, coal from the Kootenay Formation has been mined continuously since 1888. The coal measures are about 1,000 feet thick, dip steeply west, and lie within the Paleozoic strata of the Front Ranges. The coal is of low volatile, bituminous rank with small pockets of semi-anthracite. Coal of coking quality is being mined at Canmore. Production in 1967 was 289,000 tons; probable recoverable reserves are 1.1 billion tons. Between Canmore and Crowsnest Pass much coal is known, principally along Kananaskis, Sheep, Highwood, and Oldman Rivers, and forms a large reserve estimated to be 3.3 billion tons. Some small operations have been carried out, but as the area can not be reached by rail development is in the prospecting stage.

In the central Foothills of Alberta, coal has been mined from the Luscar Formation of Lower Cretaceous age at Luscar, Mountain Park, Cadomin, and Nordegg. The Luscar Formation is about 1,000 feet thick and contains several seams. In its upper part two seams, 6 and 40 feet thick, have been mined. The coal is of low and medium volatile, bituminous rank. Mining ceased in 1956.

The basal beds of the Tertiary Paskapoo Formation are coal-bearing at Mercoal, Sterco, Coalspur, Hinton, and Saunders. Four seams lie on the flanks of broad folds or are contorted and thickened by minor folds and faults into large masses of sheared coal. The coal is of high volatile, bituminous rank. Production ceased in 1965; probable reserves of recoverable coal are 2.4 billion tons.

In the Peace River area, coal deposits are found in the Lower Cretaceous Gething Formation of the Bullhead Group. Considerable reserves are known nearby in the Carbon Creek basin and on Hasler Creek. Along Liard River at the south end of Mackenzie Mountains, and in the Mackenzie River valley, coal seams of Cretaceous and Tertiary ages occur but are undeveloped.

Interior Plains

Coal has been mined in many parts of the Interior Plains. Annual production from Saskatchewan (all lignite) has been constant at about 2 million tons since 1954; that from the plains area of Alberta has fluctuated between 2.0 and 2.6 million tons. In Saskatchewan coal is produced from the Tertiary Ravenscrag Formation near Estevan. Production in 1967 was 2,008,147 tons; the coal was used mainly for generation of electricity.

The coal deposits of the Alberta Plains occur mostly in Upper Cretaceous formations, but a few mineable beds are found in Paleocene formations. Most important Upper Cretaceous formations are the Foremost, Oldman, and Edmonton. Coal seams in the Foremost are mined at Taber and Milk River as well as at smaller mines as far east as Medicine Hat. At Lethbridge and Magrath the Oldman contains several coal seams. These are a good grade of high volatile, bituminous coal in contrast to the sub-bituminous rank of most other coal of this age on the plains. Beds equivalent to the Foremost and Oldman also contain mineable coal seams in the Peace River region. The Edmonton Formation is the main source of coal in central Alberta, the principal producing centres being Wabamun, Castor, and Drumheller. Five workable seams are known in the Drumheller area where production is mainly from underground mines. The coal is sub-bituminous, non-coking, and tends to be friable. Total production in 1967 from the Alberta Plains area was 2,664,000 tons.

Petroleum and Natural Gas

Ordovician Fields

Ordovician oil is produced from the Red River Formation from a single well near South Alma, Saskatchewan. Some 70,000 barrels have been recovered to date from a reservoir of bryozoan, non-skeletal calcarenite. It grades up-dip into dense dolomite and is capped by anhydrite and shale. A well at Hummingbird produced oil for a short time.

Devonian Fields

The major producing system in Western Canada is the Devonian, the province of Alberta yielding by far the

TABLE IX–3 *Proved recoverable reserves of crude oil in Western Canada to December 31, 1966, by province and geological age of reservoir (thousands of barrels of 34.97 gallons at 60° F).*

	Reservoir	Alberta	Sask.	Man.	B.C.	N.W.T.	Total	%
	Upper Cretaceous	1,460,096					1,460,096	17.9
Lower Cretaceous	Viking*	21,719	36,823				58,542	0.7
Lower Cretaceous	Mannville*	129,462	38,285		8,496		176,243	2.2
	Jurassic	33,620	233,779				267,399	3.3
	Triassic	17,562			245,826		263,388	3.2
	Permian				337		337	—
	Mississippian	148,086	672,313	58,330	13,090		891,819	11.0
Upper Devonian	Wabamun*	8,167					8,167	0.1
Upper Devonian	Nisku*	256,998					256,998	3.2
Upper Devonian	Leduc*	1,760,181					1,760,181	21.7
Upper Devonian	Beaverhill Lake*	2,105,064					2,105,064	25.9
Middle Devonian	Kee Scarp					47,125	47,125	0.6
Middle Devonian	Slave Point	4,280					4,280	0.1
Middle Devonian	Keg River	298,313					298,313	3.7
Middle Devonian	Gilwood, Granite Wash	347,156					347,156	4.3
	Ordovician		33				33	—
	Unclassified	170,028			1,081		171,109	2.1
	Totals	6,760,732	981,233	58,330	268,830	47,125	8,116,250	100.0
	%	83.3	12.1	0.7	3.3	0.6	100.0	

* Includes stratigraphic equivalents

TABLE IX–4 *Proved recoverable reserves of natural gas in Western Canada to December 31, 1966, by province and geological age of reservoir (billions of cubic feet at 14.65 psi and 60° F).*

	Reservoir	Alberta	Sask.	Man.	B.C.	N.W.T.	Total	%
	Upper Cretaceous	3,056	304				3,360	7.3
Lower Cretaceous	Viking*	4,463	520		15		4,998	10.8
Lower Cretaceous	Mannville*	5,539	89		375		6,003	13.0
	Jurassic	497	33				530	1.1
	Triassic	230			4,172		4,402	9.5
	Permian	85			115		200	0.4
	Mississippian	12,379	13		100		12,492	27.0
Upper Devonian	Wabamun*	2,966			67		3,033	6.6
Upper Devonian	Nisku*	878					878	1.9
Upper Devonian	Leduc*	5,345					5,345	11.6
Upper Devonian	Beaverhill Lake*	1,384					1,384	3.0
Upper Devonian	Other							
	Middle Devonian	64			2,213	117	2,394	5.2
	Gilwood	260					260	0.6
	Unclassified	967					967	2.0
	Totals	38,113	959		7,057	117	46,246	100.0
	%	82.4	2.1		15.3	0.2	100.0	

* Includes stratigraphic equivalents

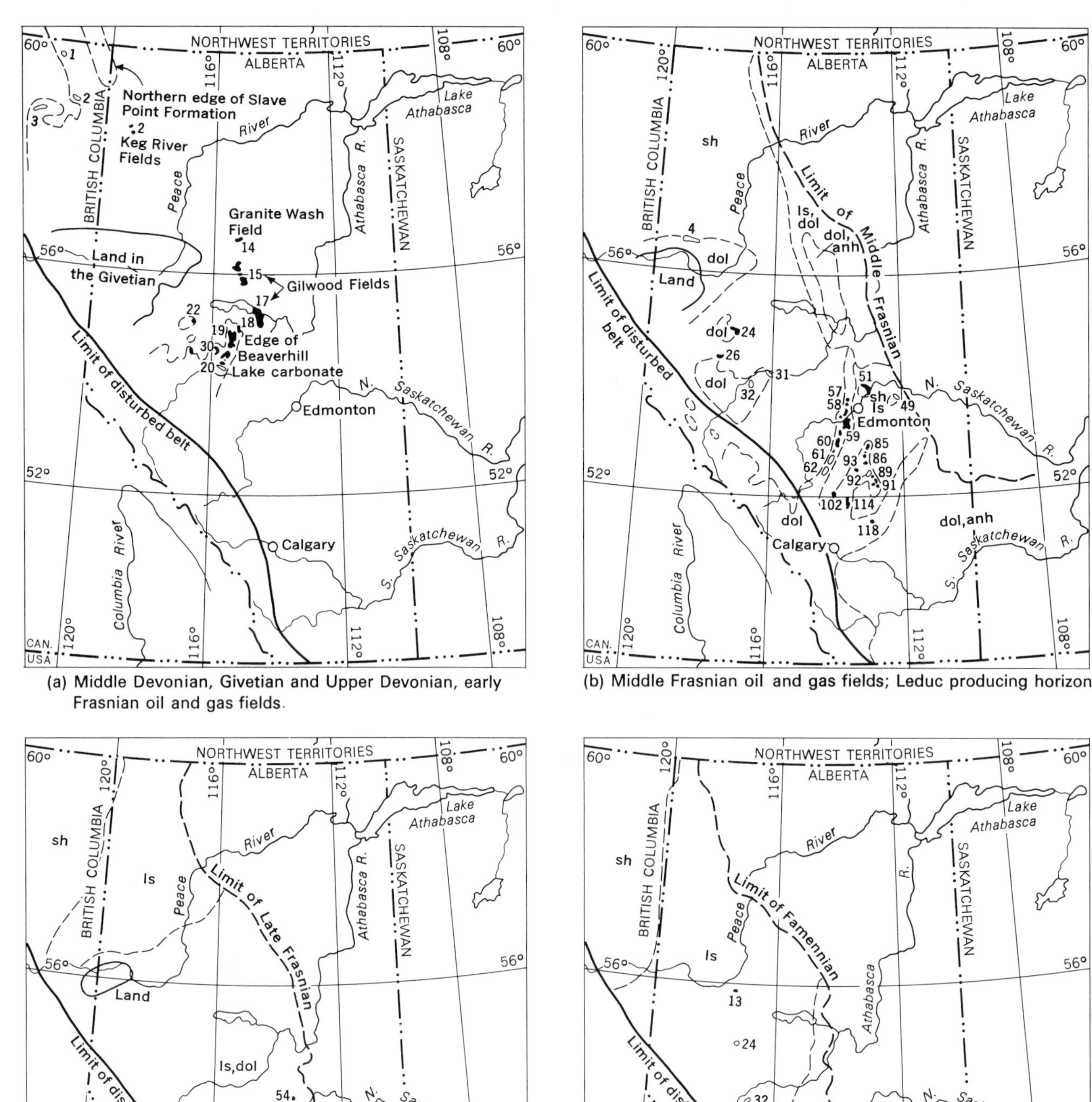

(a) Middle Devonian, Givetian and Upper Devonian, early Frasnian oil and gas fields.

(b) Middle Frasnian oil and gas fields; Leduc producing horizon.

(c) Late Frasnian oil and gas fields; Nisku and Camrose producing horizons.

(d) Famennian oil and gas fields; Wabamun producing horizon.

GSC

Scale: 1 inch to 190 miles or 305 kilometres

FIGURE IX-15. Devonian oil and gas fields of Western Canada. Oil fields shown as solid black areas, gas fields shown as open areas; fields numbered according to Map 1252A, data to end of 1965 (by B. MacLean).

most and containing the greatest reserves. Many different horizons are productive; some in the Middle Devonian and others, containing the bulk of the oil and gas, are in the Upper Devonian. The Devonian contains 59.6 per cent of the oil in Western Canada and 28.9 per cent of the gas (Tables IX-3 and 4). Production in 1966 was 140 million barrels of oil, 43 per cent of the total, and 510 million Mcf of gas, 32 per cent of the total for Western Canada.

Middle Devonian Fields

Granite wash. Basal Devonian sandstones commonly called 'granite wash' (Fig. IX-15a) fill irregularities on the Precambrian surface in northern Alberta. The sandstones are quartzose to arkosic with some dolomitic or anhydritic cement. Some are the near-shore equivalents of Elk Point carbonates and evaporites, but some may be older. In the Red Earth field (14) porosity is about 13 per cent, and the oil of 38 degrees A.P.I. is produced from 4,700 feet depth. In 1966 the granite wash yielded 2,759,159 barrels of oil and 120,375 Mcf of gas.

The *Keg River Formation* in northwestern Alberta was found productive of oil in 1965. The Rainbow (2), Rainbow South (3), Zama Lake (1), and Zama North areas include many separate fields and numerous discoveries, each in an apparently separate pool. The main producing horizon is the Rainbow Member of the Keg River Formation which forms pinnacle reefs or mounds that rest on the lower Keg River fine-grained crinoidal limestone platform. The reservoir commonly is a stromatoporoid and coral bioherm, overlain by laminites, presumably algal. The Keg River is commonly dolomitized to extremely coarsely crystalline white dolomite. Non-porous dolomite, anhydrite, and halite of the Muskeg Formation lie adjacent to and overlie the carbonate mounds. Production is from depths of 5,700 to 6,000 feet through 200 to 400 feet of strata at the Rainbow A, B, and F pools. Porosity ranges from 4 to 13 per cent, and horizontal permeability varies from 50 to 780 md. The oil has gravities of 40 to 42 degrees A.P.I. and 34 to 35 degrees A.P.I. in various pools.

Slave Point and Sulphur Point Formations. Gas occurs in the Slave Point Formation in the Petitot (1), Kotcho Lake (2), and Clarke Lake (3) fields of northeastern British Columbia (Figs. IX-15a, -16). The reservoir is a grey and white mottled, coarsely crystalline, vuggy dolomite resulting from several periods of dolomitization, that completely obscured the original lithology (Pl. IX-4b). The undolomitized deposits consist of a rubble of coarse stromatoporoid fragments set in a fine- to coarse-grained limestone matrix or cemented by sparry calcite. The reefs and associated porous rocks occur along the front of a carbonate platform flanked by greenish grey shales. Dips of carbonate beds at the front are 25 to 35 degrees. Porosity and permeability are greatest at

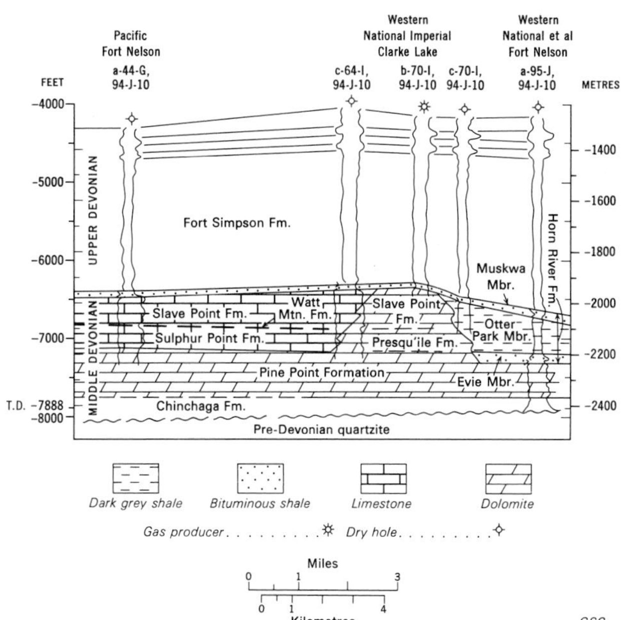

FIGURE IX-16. Cross-section through Middle Devonian Clarke Lake field, British Columbia (after Gray and Kassube).

the carbonate front and decrease with increasing distance from it. The porosity resulting from early and intermediate dolomitization is predominantly intercrystalline, averaging 10 to 12 per cent and reaching as high as 17 per cent; the permeability is less than 100 md. Later dolomitization increases porosity somewhat but also the voids may be filled by late precipitation of dolomite. The gas is trapped by a facies change to impermeable limestone. Maximum net gas pay is about 360 feet and depth to production is about 6,200. Production in 1966 was 42.6 million Mcf of gas.

In the Rabbit Lake gas field of southern District of Mackenzie the Sulphur Point reservoir is a stromatoporoid-coral limestone with good intergranular porosity. The accumulation occurs on the crest of an anticline on the northwest upthrown side of a small northeast-trending normal fault.

Gilwood Formation. The Mitsue (17) and Nipisi fields (15) produce oil from the Gilwood sandstones of the Elk Point Group (Fig. 15a). They are quartzose sandstones with scattered feldspar grains, poorly sorted, angular to subrounded, and interbedded with green pyritic shales. Porosity is 13 to 14 per cent. The oil is trapped by an up-dip pinchout of sand. Pay thickness varies from 10 to 40 feet at depths of about 4,900 feet. The oil at Mitsue is 42.9 degrees A.P.I. In 1966, 7,684,686 barrels of oil and 3.05 million Mcf of gas were produced.

Kee Scarp Formation. The Norman Wells field (1), discovered in 1920, produces from the Kee Scarp Formation on the homoclinal west flank of Norman Range of

Franklin Mountains. The producing horizon is the upper Kee Scarp reef, a light grey and buff limestone composed of abundant stromatoporoids and corals in a matrix composed largely of coarse, grain-supported, skeletal debris, much derived from stromatoporoids. The lower member of the Kee Scarp forms an extensive limestone platform overlying Hare Indian black shale. Bituminous shales of the Canol Formation cap the reef. The oil is 34.4 degrees A.P.I., 749,653 barrels being produced in 1965.

Upper Devonian Fields

Beaverhill Lake Formation. Oil of 41 to 45 degrees A.P.I. is produced from the Swan Hills Member of the Beaverhill Lake Formation in several fields south of Peace River Arch (Fig. IX-15a). Production in 1966 was 54,283,011 barrels of oil and 59.4 million Mcf of gas. The oil is trapped in reef-fringed banks covered and separated from one another by shale and shaly limestone. The banks, 400 to 500 feet thick, lie near the margins of the Beaverhill Lake carbonate platform. The facies developed in the Judy Creek (19) field (Murray, 1966) are a typical example of the reservoirs (Fig. IX-17). The platform carbonates are predominantly brown, fine-grained limestones, dolomitic limestones, coral beds and fine- to coarse-grained, largely skeletal, limestones carrying stromatoporoid and *Amphipora* fragments, and skeletal calcarenites. Porosity in the platform beds is largely restricted to lenses of grain-supported skeletal limestones. The banks resting on the platform are made of a central core of lime mudstone which contains patches of non-skeletal, pelletoid limestone with a little porosity. Dendroid stromatoporoids, *Amphipora,* ostracods, and gastropods are common organisms. Towards the margin of the banks the fine-grained limestones intertongue with stromatoporoid-algae reefs consisting of tabular, dendroid, and massive stromatoporoids in a skeletal calcarenite matrix that is largely derived from stromatoporoids and has excellent to good porosity. Coarse, porous, calcirudites and bedded calcarenites are associated with the reefs and overlie the major part of the bank. They have good intergranular porosity and together with the reef facies form the best producing zones of the Swan Hills Member. The banks grade laterally to and are overlain by impermeable shales and fine-grained shaly limestones of the Beaverhill Lake Formation.

The *Leduc Formation* of the Woodbend Group contains some of the major oil and gas fields of Alberta (Fig. IX-15b). The fields are too numerous to list. In 1966 they produced 52,788,795 barrels of oil and 285.4 million Mcf of gas. The oil and gas have accumulated in stratigraphic traps formed by reef complexes covered and separated by impervious greenish grey shales. The reefs developed on shoals composed predominantly of biostromal, stromatoporoid-rich beds and skeletal lime sands comprising the Cooking Lake platform. Commercial production from Cooking Lake has been obtained only at Skaro.

The reservoir of the Redwater (51) oil and gas field (Klovan, 1964) is one of the few that are undolomitized and provides an excellent example of the internal constitution of Devonian reef complexes (Figs. IX-18, -19). Other fields of this type are Golden Spike (59b) and Duhamel (85a). The upper, producing part of the reef complex is composed of organically bound massive stromatoporoid reef limestones, 3 to 30 feet thick, interbedded with coarse, skeletal calcarenites derived largely from stromatoporoid debris. Calcilutites occur sporadically on the northeast front of the Redwater complex

PLATE IX-4. PHOTOMICROGRAPHS OF TYPICAL DEVONIAN CARBONATE ROCKS:

a. Stromatoporoid growth enveloped by calcarenite (boundstone), granular calcite cement. Middle Devonian Sulphur Point Formation, Imperial Sun Arrowhead Aurora I-46, I-46-60-50-122-15, at 6,338 feet depth. Natural size. GSC 113782-C.

b. Dolomite pseudo-breccia caused by several stages of dolomitization; vuggy porosity. Middle Devonian Presqu'ile Formation, Clarke Lake gas field, B.C. Natural size. (Gray and Kassube, 1963).

c. Lime mudstone with more than 10 per cent comminuted skeletal debris (wackestone); gastropods, ostracods. Middle Devonian Slave Point Formation, California Standard Steen River 2-22, 2-22, 117-5 W 6, at 4,332 feet depth; x5. GSC 113781-E.

d. Non-skeletal calcarenite (grainstone), poorly sorted, bedded; a few algal-coated stromatoporoid and coral fragments; intergranular, intrafossil and small vug porosity. Middle Devonian Slave Point Formation, Pan-American Shell Kakisa F-35, F-35-61-00-117-15, at 1,718 feet depth. Natural size. GSC 113782-B.

e. *Amphipora* and non-skeletal grains in lime mud matrix (packstone). Upper Devonian Swan Hills Member (lagoonal facies), Beaverhill Lake Formation. Home Swan Hills A-10-20, 10-20-67-10 W 5, at 8,113 feet depth; x⅔. (R. W. Edie, 1961)

f. Skeletal calcirudite with lime mud matrix (skeletal lime packstone containing stromatoporoids, corals, ostracods, foraminifera). Upper Devonian Leduc Formation. Canadian Superior Holt 15-36, 15-36-44-22 W 4, at 4,875 feet depth; x5. GSC 113781-L.

g. Non-skeletal calcarenite (grainstone): grains and lumps of calcilutite, some coated; granular calcite cement. Upper Devonian Peechee Member, Southesk Formation. B.A. Hand Hills No. 1, 7-14-30-17 W 4, at 5,942 feet depth; x5. GSC 113781-G.

h. Massive stromatoporoid fragments in coarse-grained skeletal calcarenite matrix with intergranular porosity. Upper Devonian Leduc Formation, Imperial Golden Spike No. 11, 11-23-51-27 W 4, at 5,367 feet depth. Natural size. GSC 113782-A.

i. *Amphipora* limestone (wackestone). *Amphipora* in lime mud matrix with comminuted skeletal debris. Upper Devonian Leduc Formation, Imperial Redwater 56, 9-18-57-21 W 4, at 3,297 feet depth; x5. GSC 113781-K.

j. Crystalline dolomite; anhydrite partly fills intercrystalline voids; crossed nicols. Upper Devonian Nisku Formation, B.A. Pyrcz No. 1, 12-25-50-26 W 4, at 4,907 feet depth; x5. GSC 113781-F.

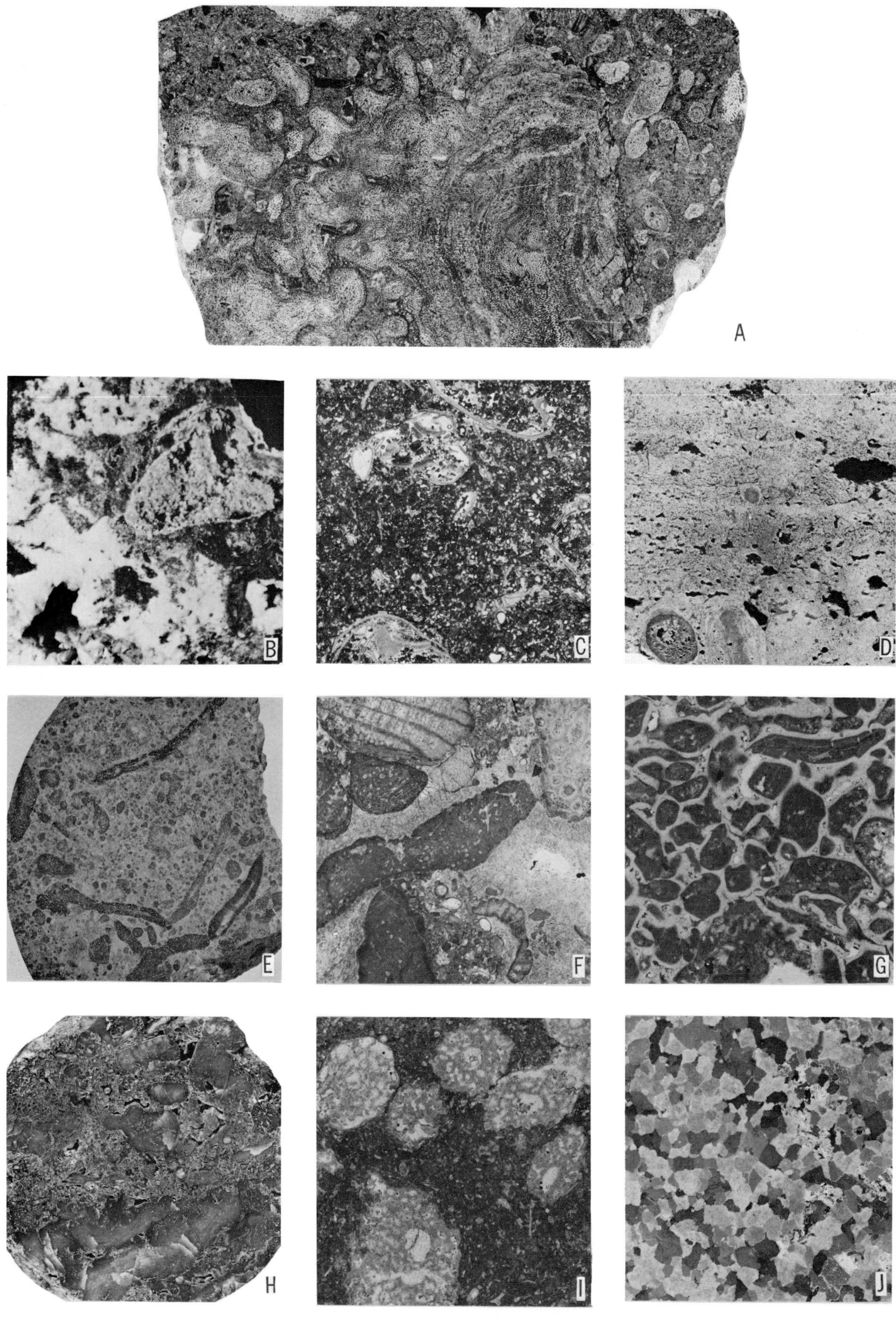
A
B
C
D
E
F
G
H
I
J

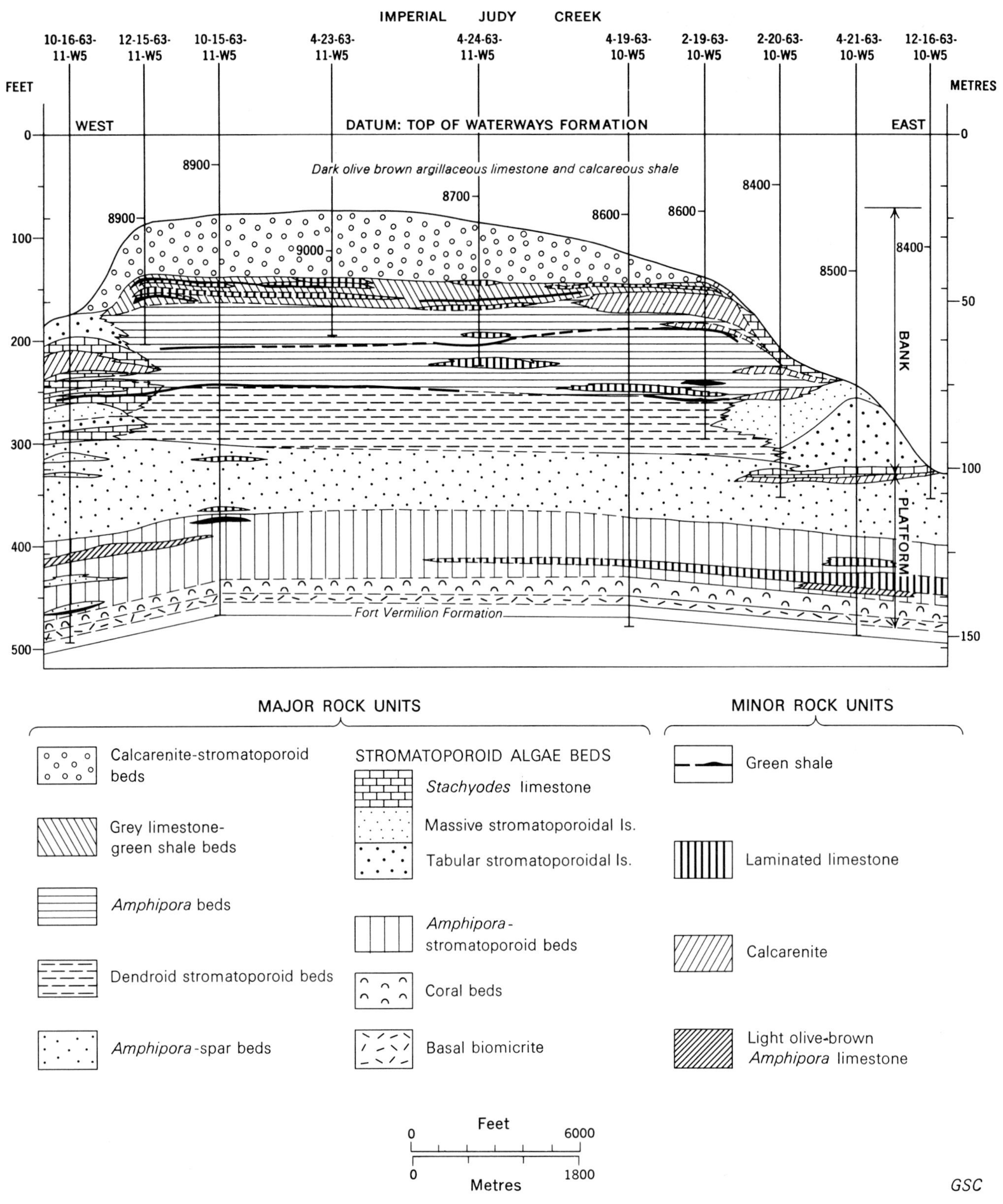

FIGURE IX-17. Cross-section through Upper Devonian, Swan Hills reef, south Judy Creek field, Alberta (after J. W. Murray).

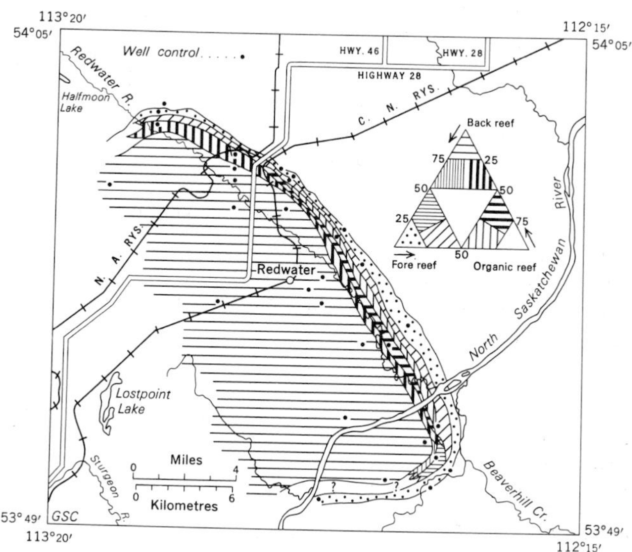

FIGURE IX-18. Distribution of major facies in upper Leduc Formation, Redwater reef complex, Alberta (after J. E. Klovan).

at least 25 to 50 feet below its highest part. In the fore-reef talus there is a progressive change in fauna from fragmented massive stromatoporoids to tabular stromatoporoids, colonial corals, dendroid stromatoporoids, *Megaladon,* and tabulate and rugose corals set in a coarsely fragmented matrix. Oncolites and algal coatings on fossil fragments are common. Farther off-reef the sediments become finer and dips reach 20 degrees. Within the reef complex, the organic facies intertongue with cleanly washed, porous, skeletal sands, in places containing large stromatoporoid fragments, or composed of finely comminuted grain-supported debris and lime mudstone. In the interior of the complex are laminated limestones, lime mudstone with *Amphipora,* and non-skeletal calcarenites containing pellets, lumps, and coarse structureless grains of various shapes and sizes largely cemented by sparry calcite but with some scattered intergranular porosity. The best porosity, both intergranular and vuggy, occurs in the grain-supported skeletal calcarenites and in the organically bound reefs or in the coarse skeletal calcarenites and calcirudites of the talus slopes dipping into the basin. Porosity is also present in the non-skeletal calcarenites and *Amphipora* calcarenites and calcilutites. Oil of 34 to 36 degrees A.P.I. gravity has accumulated on the up-dip northeast flank of the structure. Porosity averages 6.53 per cent and permeability is excellent in the producing zones, maximum oil zone thickness being 220 feet and average 100 feet.

In most oil and gas fields the Leduc Formation is composed of fine to medium crystalline dolomite with intercrystalline and vuggy porosity. The trap is a mound-shaped structure enclosed and covered by greenish grey impervious marine shales, and it is generally assumed that the initial internal constitution of these dolomite bodies was the same as that of the Redwater reef complex described above. The platform beds of the Cooking Lake Formation are similar to those at Redwater and the location of the mounds is similarly controlled by build-up of stromatoporoid-rich shoals where dolomitization has failed to destroy the stromatoporoid structure completely. Some production has been obtained from the lower part of Leduc in some fields along the Rimbey–Meadowbrook reef chain. The upper part, in which most oil and gas accumulations occur, is light grey to buff, medium to coarsely crystalline dolomite, with vuggy porosity and some

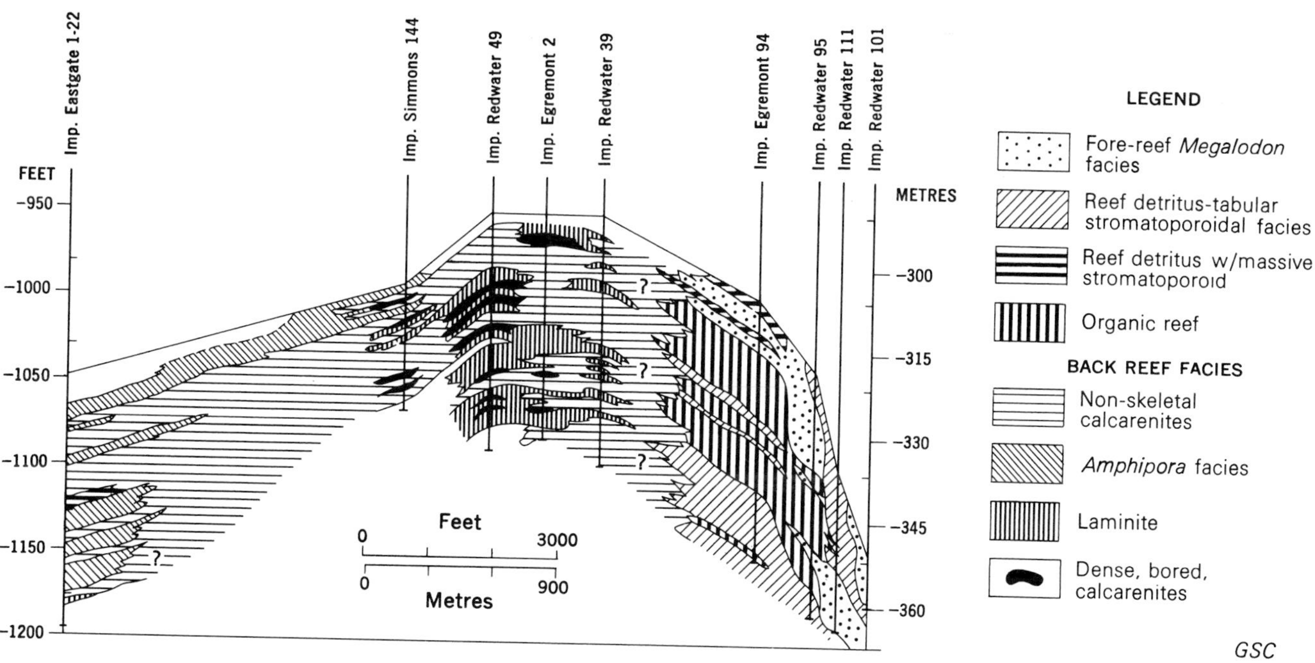

FIGURE IX-19. Composite cross-section through the upper Leduc Formation, Redwater reef complex, Alberta (after J. E. Klovan).

intercrystalline porosity and fractures. Dolomitization has completely destroyed all vestiges of the original structure except for occasional ghosts of stromatoporoids and corals. Fields along the Rimbey–Meadowbrook reef chain (Fig. IX-20) produce both oil and gas, the thickness of the gas cap increasing towards the south. Porosity in these fields ranges from 4 to 10 per cent and permeability is good. Gravity of the oil ranges from 27 degrees at Fairydell (52) to 44 degrees A.P.I. at Westerose (61). In the Bashaw (86) carbonate complex from which the Malmo-Duhamel (85) chain extends north-northeast and in the Stettler and Big Valley fields to the southeast pay thicknesses are generally less than in the Rimbey–Meadowbrook chain but in other respects they are similar. Porosities range from 5 to 8 per cent and gravity of oil from 27.7 to 43.3 degrees A.P.I.

West of the Rimbey–Meadowbrook reef chain production is largely gas. Light grey crystalline dolomite with vuggy and intercrystalline porosity forms reef complexes and banks enclosed by shale and resting on a widespread stromatoporoid-rich carbonate. Depths to production are great and the area has not yet been completely

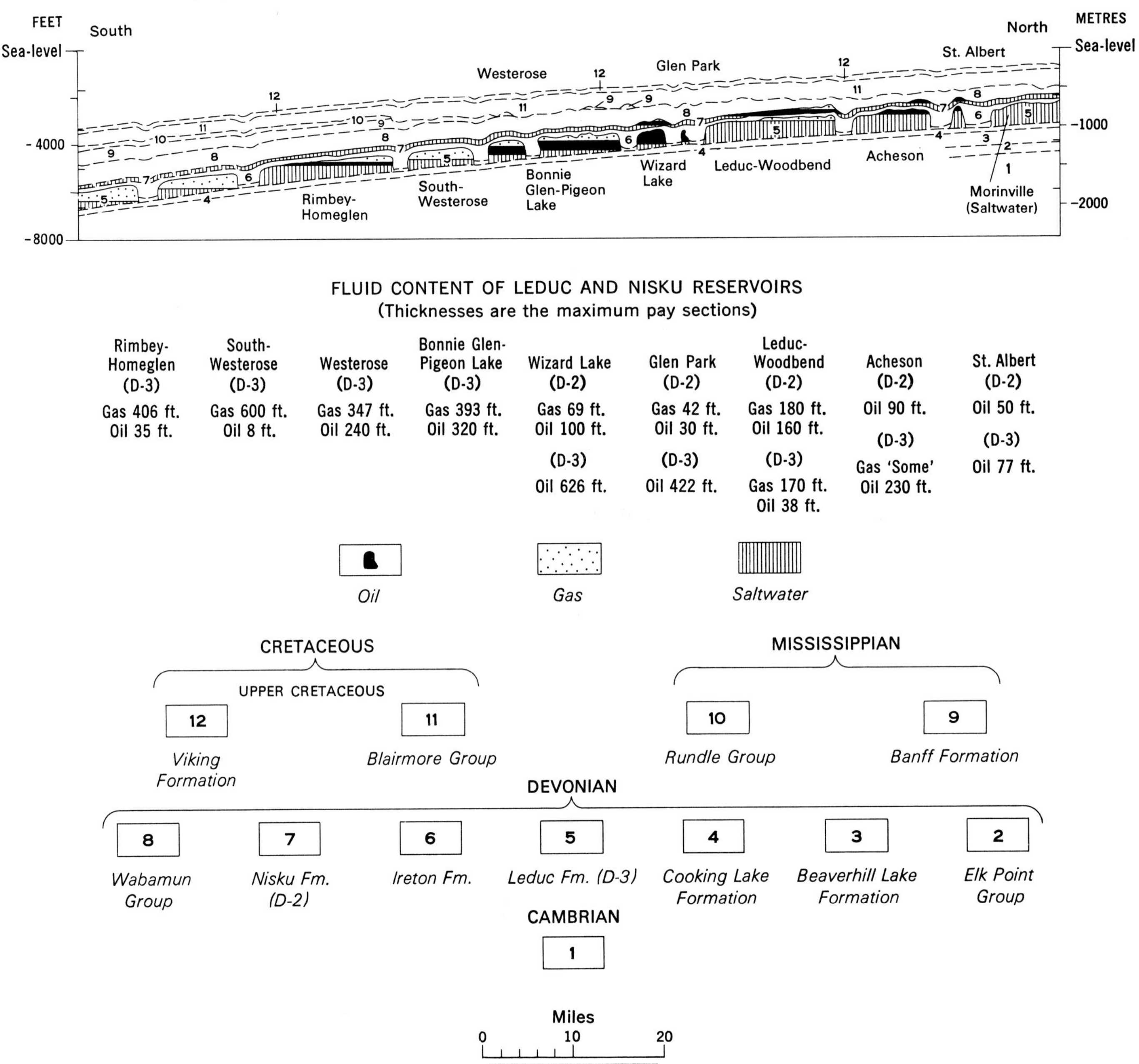

GSC

FIGURE IX-20. Fluid content of Upper Devonian Leduc and Nisku reservoirs, Bonnie Glen–Wizard Lake reef trend, Alberta (after W. C. Gussow).

explored: 8,700 feet at Windfall (31), 11,460 feet at Simonette (26), and 12,500 feet at Berland River. Pay zones vary from 142 to 350 feet, porosities from 4.5 to 7.9 per cent, and gravity of the oil from 37 to 48 degrees A.P.I.

Dolomite considered to have originated from reefs fringing the Peace River landmass produced gas at Worsley (4) and oil from 169 feet of pay at Normandville (13a). A gas pool at the up-dip eroded edge of the Grosmont Formation has been partly explored at Craigend. Porosity averaging 10.7 per cent in the form of vugs and fractures occurs in finely crystalline and sucrosic weathered dolomites. They have a tarry oil stain and are overlain by shales of Cretaceous age.

The *Nisku Formation* of the Woodbend Group is productive of oil and gas where overlying Leduc fields of the Rimbey–Meadowbrook reef chain north of Bonnie Glen, and together with the subjacent Camrose Formation where overlying those of the Bashaw complex, and other more easterly fields (Fig. 15c). The Nisku reservoirs are light grey dolomite with good vuggy and fracture porosity. East of the Leduc chain the upper part of the Nisku grades to anhydrite and the lower Nisku and underlying brown coral-stromatoporoid-rich dolomite of the Camrose form the reservoirs. Porosity is partly filled with anhydrite and distribution is irregular. The traps are partly stratigraphic, partly structural due to draping over the underlying Leduc reefs (Fig. IX-20). Pay zones vary to a

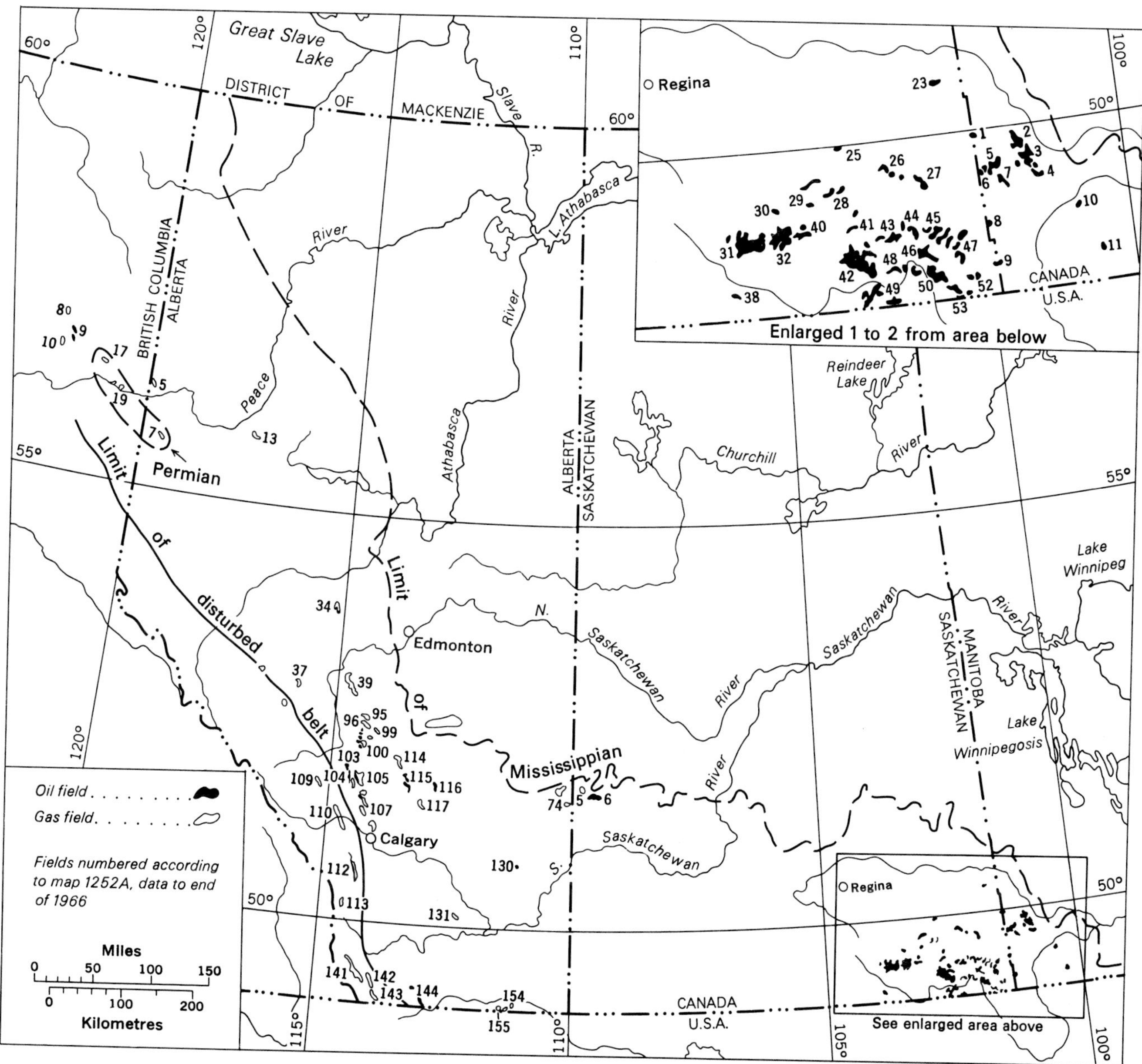

FIGURE IX-21. Mississippian and Permian oil and gas fields of Western Canada (by B. MacLean). GSC

maximum of 119 feet, porosity is generally from 3 to 5 per cent, and the gravity of the oil is 30 to 40 degrees A.P.I. In 1966, some 12,984,866 barrels of oil was produced from the Nisku and 36.5 million Mcf of gas.

Wabamun Group. Sour gas is produced from the Crossfield dolomite of the Wabamun Group at a number of fields that trend northwesterly between Okotoks (111) and Olds (106b) in Alberta (Fig. IX-15d). The gas occurs in the intercrystalline and pin-point porosity of fine to medium crystalline dolomites which grade eastward up-dip into non-permeable dolomite and anhydrite. A number of small fields and discoveries produce gas from the up-dip edge of the Wabamun truncated at the pre-Cretaceous surface. The hydrocarbons occur in crystalline sugary dolomites with good intercrystalline porosity and from vuggy brecciated dolomites and limestones. Porosity has been increased by leaching and weathering of the dolomite at the erosion surface. Gas with no associated oil or water occurs in porous vuggy dolomite in the lower part of the Wabamun at Simonette (26), Pine Creek (32a), and South Sturgeon Lake (21b). The gas is trapped in the dolomite against overlying fine-grained tightly cemented Wabamun limestone. In 1966, the Wabamun produced 68,451 barrels of oil and 76.3 million Mcf of gas.

Mississippian Fields

The Mississippian is the second most productive system in Western Canada, in 1966 yielding 74,186,392 barrels of oil and 484.5 million Mcf of gas, some 22.7 and 29.8 per cent respectively of the oil and gas produced in Western Canada. It is third in gas and oil reserves, accounting for 11 per cent of the oil and 27 per cent of the gas (Tables IX-3, -4). Productive Mississippian regions are, however, more extensive than Devonian (Figs. IX-1, -21).

Williston Basin

Oil of 27 to 38 degrees A.P.I. with very little gas is produced from Mississippian strata on the northeast flank of Williston Basin in southeastern Saskatchewan and southwestern Manitoba (Fig. IX-21). In 1966, 5,230,904 barrels were produced in Manitoba and 60,245,964 barrels in Saskatchewan. The oil is trapped in cyclically alternating porous and non-porous limestones, and some has accumulated where the porous beds are truncated at the pre-Jurassic or pre-Cretaceous erosion surface. As a result, the fields form a series of belts trending west to northwest, producing from successively higher strata down-dip to the southwest.

The Bakken sandstones produce a little 36-degree A.P.I. oil at Coleville–Smiley (6), Saskatchewan. The Souris Valley Formation produces in Manitoba in the Daly (5) and Virden (2, 3) areas where the porous Virden–Whitewater Lake crinoidal and oölitic limestones are truncated. The Nottingham field (47) produces 30- to 37-degree A.P.I. oil from the Alida-Tilston beds and the Parkman field (28) produces 34-degree A.P.I. oil from the Tilston and Souris Valley zones. The traps are topographic or structural highs at the erosion surface. Thirteen fields produce from the Frobisher–Alida beds, the largest being Hastings (46), Willmar (43), and Workman (52b), and ten from the Midale beds the largest being Steelman (42a), Weyburn (36b), and Midale (39). In these fields most traps are the result of porous car-

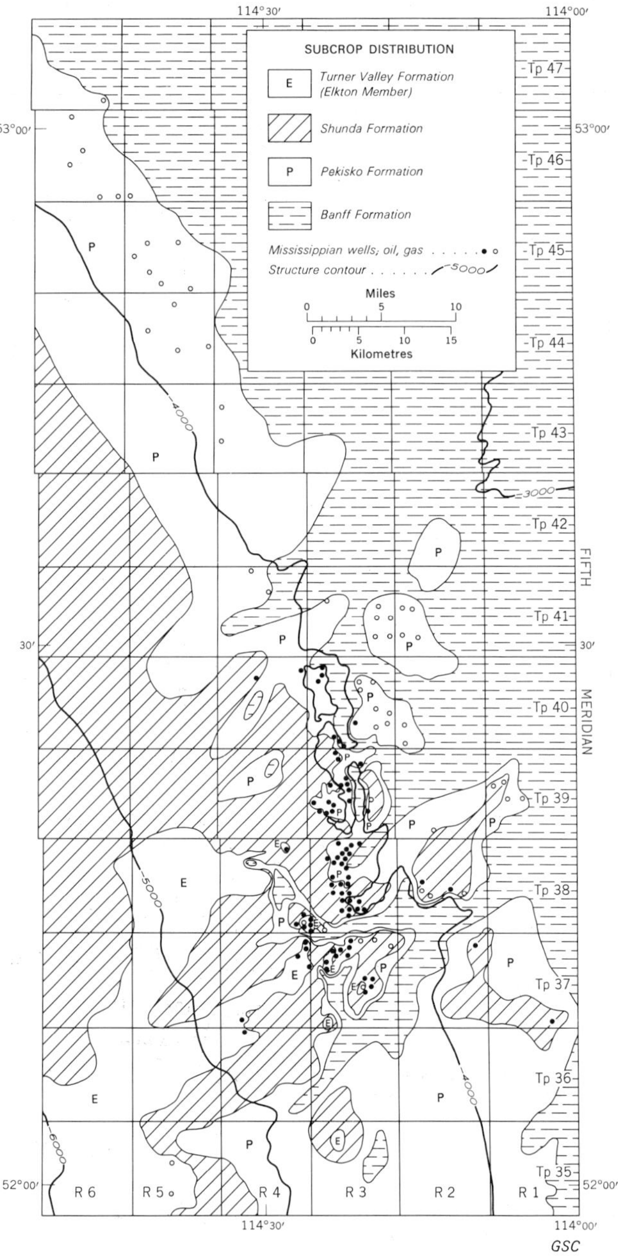

FIGURE IX-22. Mississippian oil and gas fields, Sylvan Lake–Minnehik trend, Alberta, showing paleogeology of the pre-Jurassic and pre-Albian erosion surface (by H. Martin).

bonates grading to non-porous carbonates or anhydrite, but in some the oil is trapped at the erosion surface.

Thomas (1962) and Fuzesy (1966) point out that production is largely controlled by porosity and permeability which in turn are dependent on the original constitution of the rock. The best reservoir rocks are oölite-pisolite, cryptocrystalline to microcrystalline limestones, encrinites, spergenites, algal oölitic-pisolitic limestones, and crinoidal limestone. All have less than 10 per cent matrix and good to excellent intergranular porosity. The presence of fine-grained limestone matrix decreases permeability, but dolomitization of the matrix to form sucrosic dolomite results in good intercrystalline porosity and a productive reservoir. Interconnecting vuggy porosity is developed in algal, oölitic, and pisolitic limestones where their matrix is leached and cavities enlarged by solution. Cavities in fossils account for a considerable proportion of the total porosity, lessened in places by infilling of the pore spaces by calcite, anhydrite, or silica.

Anhydrite and fine-grained, argillaceous, non-porous limestones underlie the reservoirs. The cap rock may be primary anhydrite with hard very finely crystalline argillaceous limestone, or result from secondary infilling of original porosity by anhydrite or chert at the post-Mississippian erosion surface, or be the argillaceous beds of the Jurassic Watrous Formation.

Alberta and British Columbia

Mississippian oil and gas produced in Alberta exclusive of that from the Foothills is from stratigraphic traps at the up-dip eroded edge of the Mississippian carbonates where deeply incised by pre-Mesozoic stream valleys (Fig. 22). Most production is from the Elkton Member of the Turner Valley Formation in west-central Alberta but the Pekisko and Banff Formations also produce (Fig. 23). The Elkton Member consists of buff and grey, fine to medium crystalline dolomite ghosts of corals and crinoids and with good vuggy and intercrystalline porosity. The dolomite grades laterally into and is interbedded with fine- to medium-grained crinoidal limestone with little or no porosity. The traps are formed partly by the up-dip change from porous dolomite to non-porous limestone and partly by truncation of the Elkton with sealing by impervious overlying beds. In places stratigraphic traps are modified by structural nosing along a north-northwest trend. Gravity of the oil ranges from 30 to 40 degrees A.P.I. Porosity ranges from 5 to 10 per cent and pay thickness from 40 to 55 feet in these fields. Fields along the Elkton trend from Harmattan (104) to Sundre (103) produce at depths of 9,000 feet to 10,000 feet. A few small gas fields occur where the Pekisko Formation is truncated at the erosion surface or where it occurs as outliers. Producing zones are dolomite with intercrystalline and leached vuggy porosity and incompletely cemented crinoidal limestones that grade laterally into tightly cemented limestones. Production from the Mississippian in Alberta in 1966, excluding Foothills fields, was 7,810,156 barrels of oil and 456.1 million Mcf of gas.

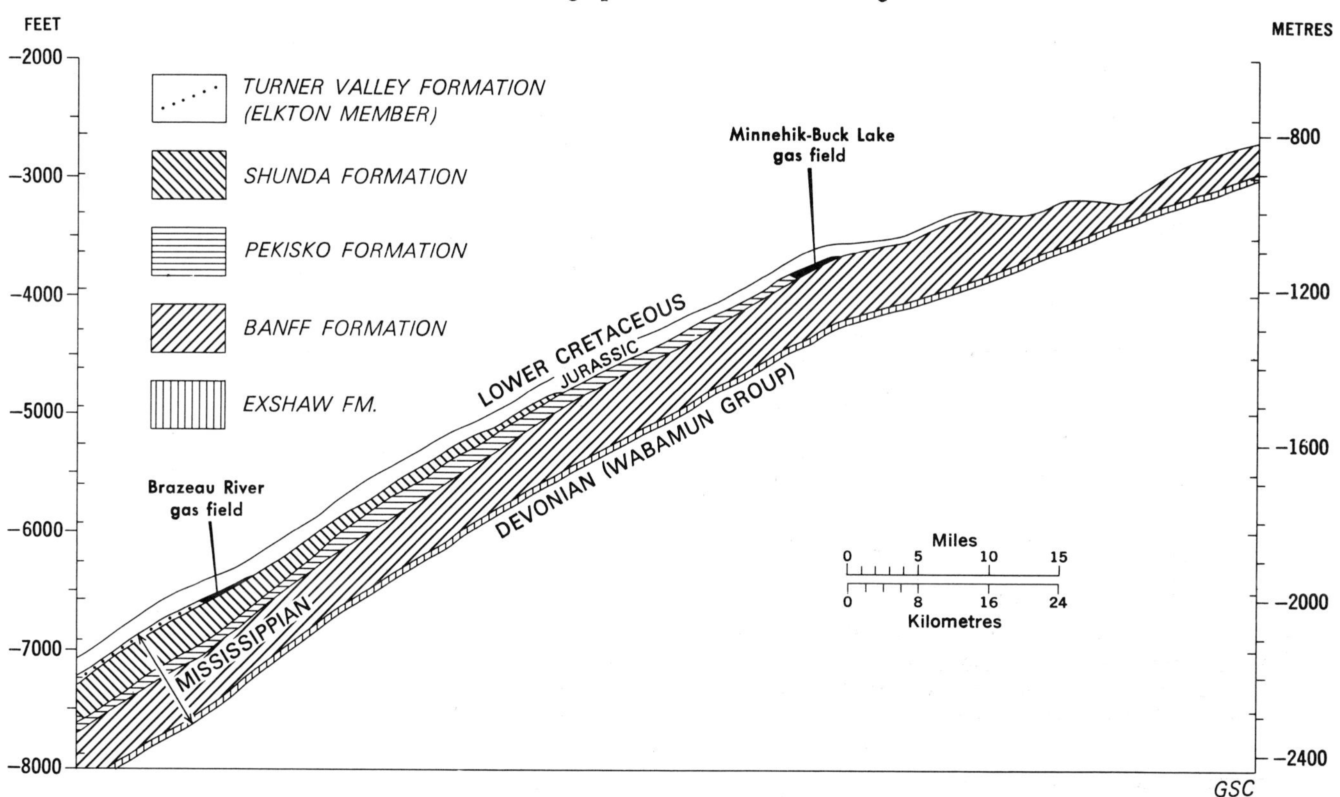

FIGURE IX-23. Cross-section through the Mississippian from Brazeau River field to Minnehik–Buck Lake field, Alberta (by H. Martin).

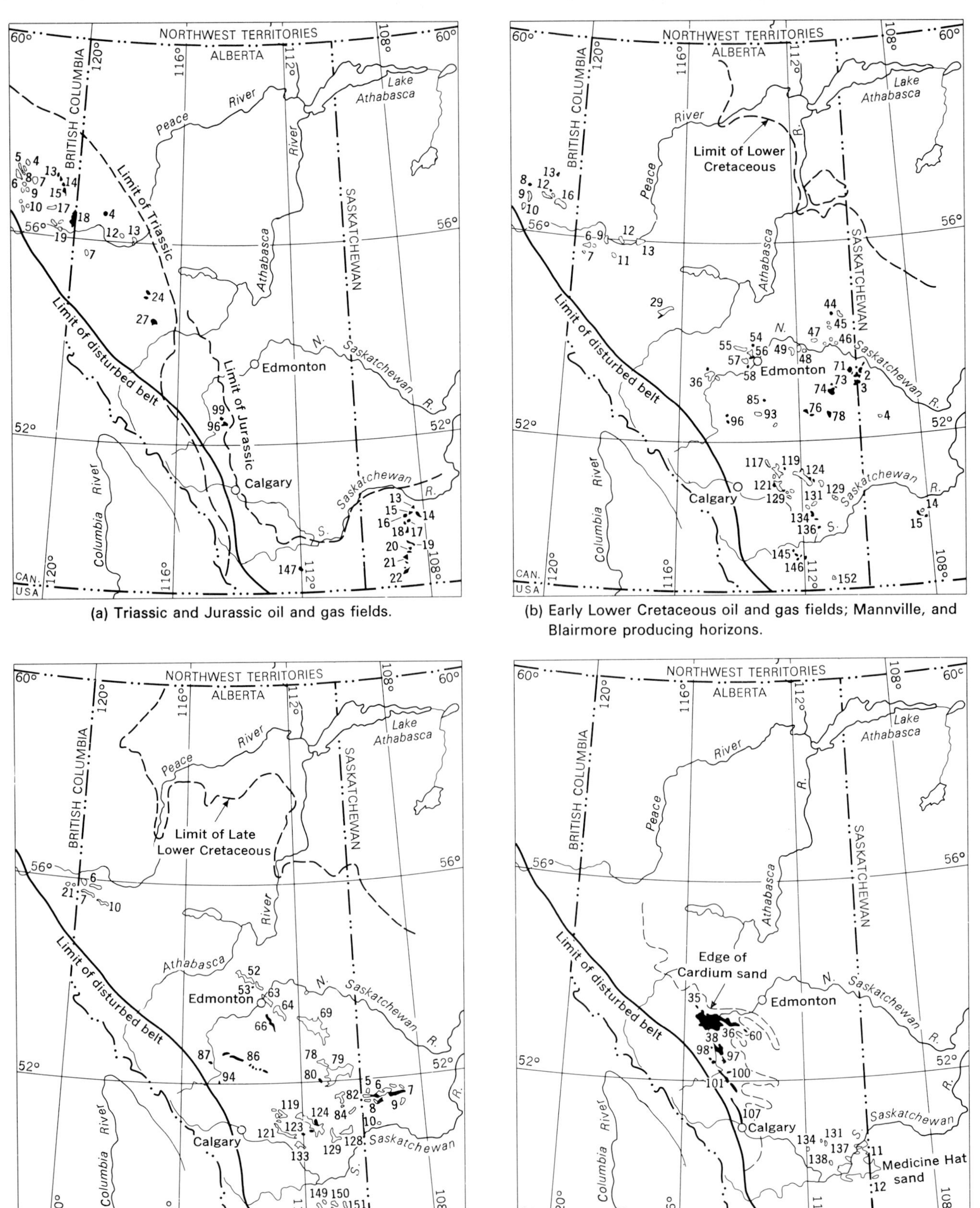

(a) Triassic and Jurassic oil and gas fields.

(b) Early Lower Cretaceous oil and gas fields; Mannville, and Blairmore producing horizons.

(c) Late Lower Cretaceous oil and gas fields; Viking, Cadotte and Bow Island producing horizons.

(d) Upper Cretaceous oil and gas fields; Cardium and Medicine Hat producing horizons.

GSC

Scale: 1 inch to 190 miles or 305 kilometres

FIGURE IX-24. Mesozoic oil and gas fields of Western Canada. Oil fields shown as solid areas, gas fields shown as open areas; fields numbered according to Map 1252A, data to end of 1965 (by B. MacLean).

In northeastern British Columbia the Blueberry oil field (9) and a number of gas fields produce from the Debolt Formation. The reservoir is generally brown, cherty, bioclastic limestone partly replaced by dolomite with intercrystalline and solution cavity porosity. The fields occur along the up-dip eroded margin of the Debolt and accumulation is partly the result of erosion and sealing of the beds at the pre-Mesozoic erosion surface and partly due to porosity pinchout from porous dolomite to limestone. Lenticular sandstones of the Kiskatinaw Formation produce gas at Boundary Lake South. Production from the Mississippian of British Columbia in 1966 was 899,368 barrels of oil and 3.8 million Mcf of gas.

Permian

The Belloy Formation produces gas at several small fields in British Columbia and Alberta (Fig. IX-21). The reservoir is a porous sandstone interbedded with dense limestones and cherty limestones. In 1966 production totalled 13.5 million Mcf.

Triassic Fields

Triassic sediments contain the greater part of the oil and gas reserves of British Columbia but only a small part of those of Alberta (Tables IX-3, -4). The system is productive in northeastern British Columbia and nearby Alberta (Fig. IX-24a). In 1966, 109 million Mcf of gas and 17,000,347 barrels of oil were produced.

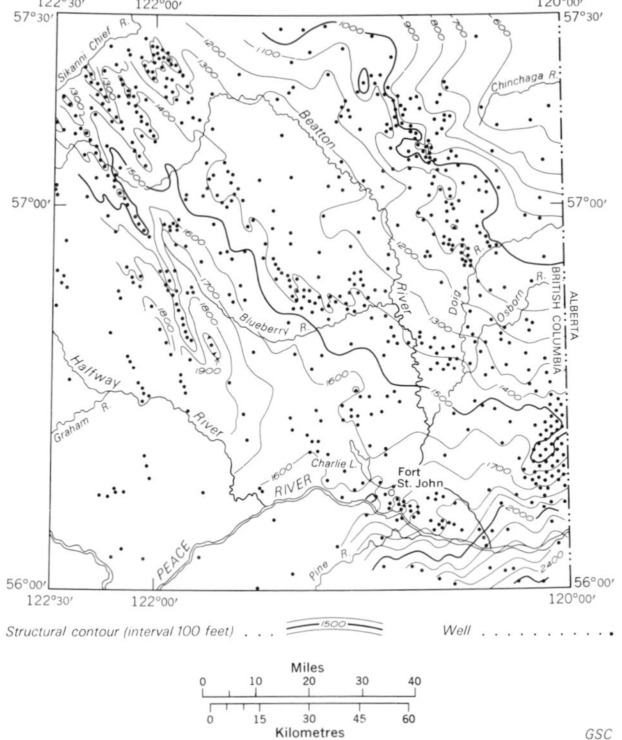

FIGURE IX-25. Structural contours on top of the Triassic system, Fort St. John area, British Columbia (by R. M. Procter).

In British Columbia the accumulations of oil and gas are controlled by a close interrelationship of folding, facies, and porosity, and pre-Albian topography. Most structural closures are on northwest-trending Laramide anticlines but some are on northeasterly flexures related to faults along the north side of the Devonian Peace River Arch (Fig. IX-25). Production is obtained at about 5,000 feet. Gas fields within the Baldonnel Formation (Fig. IX-26) include the Fort St. John (19), Nig Creek (7), Blueberry (9), Beg (6), Bubbles (5a), Jedney (5b), and and Laprise Creek (4) fields. The porosity occurs mainly as interstitial voids in an allochthonous limestone composed of fragmented pelecypods, brachiopods, and crinoids. In the Jedney and Laprise fields, the carbonate was deeply eroded in early Cretaceous time. Some gas is present in the sandstone of the Halfway Formation in the Fort St. John and Jedney fields. A major Triassic gas discovery was made in 1965 near Sukunka River in the Foothills west of Dawson Creek. In Alberta, gas is produced from dolomitic coquina and sandstone of the Montney Formation in the Tangent field and from the Baldonnel at Saddle Hills. Production has been obtained also at Kaybob South, Braeburn, Clear Hills, Fox Creek, Whitelaw, Snipe Lake, Mountain Park, and Nordegg River. Most oil produced is obtained from the Boundary Member of the Charlie Lake Formation at Boundary Lake field (17). The reservoir is similar to the Baldonnel, being composed of dolomitized skeletal limestone. Oil is also produced from Halfway sandstone at Beatton River (13a), Milligan Creek (13c), Wildmint (14), and Peejay (15c) fields. The oil in the Halfway is trapped stratigraphically by variations in porosity of the sandstone which formed as near-shore sand bars (Fig. IX-27). The gravity ranges from 26 degrees A.P.I. near the subcrop edge to nearly 50 degrees A.P.I. adjacent to the Foothills (Hitchon, 1964).

In Alberta, oil and gas are obtained from the Sturgeon Lake (24) area where individual sand lenses in the lower part of the succession are truncated at the post-Triassic erosional surface.

Jurassic Fields

Jurassic rocks contain only a small proportion of the oil and gas reserves of Western Canada, the producing fields occurring mostly in southern Alberta and Saskatchewan (Fig. IX-24a). Total production in 1966 was 1.8 million barrels of oil and 11.2 million Mcf of gas from Alberta, and 24.5 million barrels of oil and 7.2 million Mcf of gas from Saskatchewan.

In Alberta, the largest gas reserves are in the Nordegg Member in Medicine River (96), Gilby (95), and Paddle River (34) fields in central and west-central parts of the province. In the southeast, a small amount of gas is produced from the upper Shaunavon sandstone. Oil is

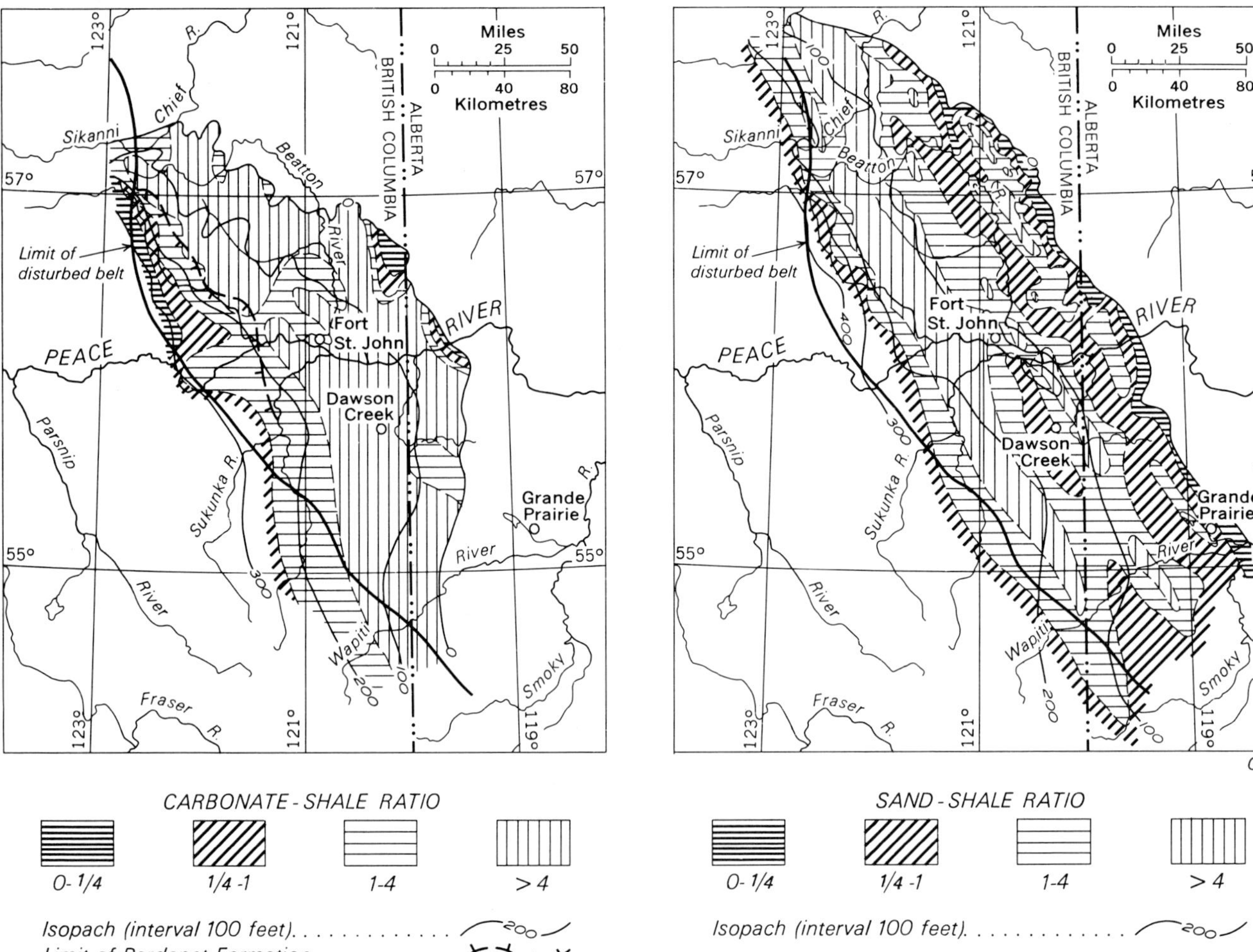

FIGURE IX-26. Isopachs and facies of the Triassic Pardonet and Baldonnel Formations, Fort St. John area, British Columbia (after Barss, et al.).

FIGURE IX-27. Isopachs and facies of Triassic Halfway Formation, Fort St. John area, British Columbia (after Barss, et al.).

produced from quartzose sandstone and belemnite conglomerate of the upper Sawtooth Formation at Skiff, Conrad (147), Glenphyll, and Burdett. The gravity of the oil is about 25 degrees A.P.I.

In Saskatchewan, oil of about 22 degrees A.P.I. is produced from dolomitic sandstones and bioclastic limestone of the Shaunavon Formation in a combination of stratigraphic and structural traps. Of these, the Rapdan (22), Dollard (21), Bone Creek–Instow (19) fields represent beach and channel-fill deposits, in part controlled by pre-existing topography (Christopher, 1964). The Gull Lake (18), Eastend (21b), and Leon Lake (20b) fields are developed on anticlines and the Leitchville–Shaunavon (20) field on the flank of a southeasterly plunging syncline. Several small fields find production in the middle Vanguard sandstone over the Swift Current Arch, a post-Jurassic structure in which the sandstone is truncated by pre-Albian erosion, trapping the oil stratigraphically.

The Wapella field (24) in southeastern Saskatchewan produces oil of 26 degrees A.P.I. gravity from fine-grained sandstone of Jurassic or Cretaceous age. In western Saskatchewan in the Fosterton field (15b), oil of 21 degrees A.P.I. is obtained from Roseray sandstones lying unconformably between rocks of known Jurassic and Cretaceous age.

Cretaceous Fields

Cretaceous rocks particularly those of Alberta (Fig. IX-24) contain a major portion of the oil and gas reserves of Canada (Tables IX-3, -4). In Alberta, Cretaceous sediments contain more than 13,000 million Mcf cubic feet of gas, about one third of the known marketable gas, and to end of 1966 have produced about one half of the marketed gas. Oil reserves in 1966, over 1,500 million barrels, account for about one quarter of the recoverable crude oil of Alberta. In 1966, production of natural gas from the Lower Cretaceous totalled 391 million Mcf or 24 per cent of that of Western Canada, and 97.8 million Mcf from the Upper Cretaceous, 6 per cent of the total. Oil production totalled 24.3 million barrels from the Lower

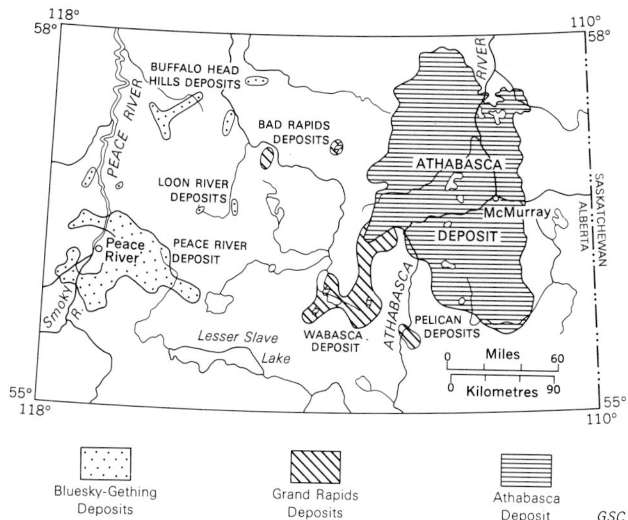

FIGURE IX-28. Oil sands of northern Alberta evaluated by the Oil and Gas Conservation Board, 1963 (after Pow, et al.).

Cretaceous in 1966, some 7.4 per cent of total from Western Canada, and 43.8 million barrels or 13.4 per cent from the Upper Cretaceous.

Athabasca Oil Sands

Of the known oil reservoirs in the world, the Athabasca oil sands of northeastern Alberta (Figs. IX-28, -29) is one of the largest, if not the largest. It is estimated (Pow, *et al.,* 1963) to contain more than 626 billion barrels of heavy oil in place, 369 billion barrels of recoverable raw oil-sands oil, and 266 billion barrels of recoverable up-graded synthetic crude oil. The evaluated sands extend over an area of 5¾ million acres and are well exposed along the banks of Athabasca River. The deposits were first reported by explorers as early as 1778, but only in recent years has their recovery been considered economically feasible by such methods as open-strip mining and injection of steam and aqueous solutions. The oil impregnation occurs in fluviatile, lacustrine, and lagoonal sands of the McMurray, Clearwater, and Grand Rapids Formations. The McMurray sandstones, containing the largest reserves, consist predominantly of quartz and are very lenticular. They lie on a highly irregular erosion surface carved on Devonian rocks in pre-Cretaceous time and are in part draped over some of the higher features.

Lower Cretaceous Fields

In the lower Mannville Formation (Fig. IX-24b) basal well-sorted quartzose sandstones were deposited as shoreline sediments or as channel-fills in part controlled by the topography of the underlying erosional surface. Structural traps are also found in these and higher sands of the lower Mannville where draped over Upper Devonian reefs as a result of differential compaction of the surrounding shale. Oil fields are numerous but small, the largest being Bellshill Lake (76a). Gas fields are also numerous, the largest being Kaybob (29), Princess (131), and Cessford (124a). Gas has been discovered also within the older Nikanassin sandstones south of Dawson Creek in British Columbia. In the upper Mannville, stratigraphic traps formed in part by intertonguing of sandstones and shales. Oil, having a gravity ranging from 10 to 18 degrees A.P.I. is found in numerous small fields near Lloydminster (71) and along the Alberta–Saskatchewan border.

Reservoirs in beds equivalent to the Lower Colorado are found in sandstone of the Peace River, Viking, and Bow Island Formations (Fig. IX-24c). Variation in the porosity of the lenticular Viking sands, related to winnowing and current action, together with up-dip loss of permeability, produce many stratigraphic traps. In general, the reservoirs are elongate sandbars, trending northwesterly in central Alberta. The Joarcam–Joseph Lake (66) trend extends for 30 miles, the oil and gas field being 2 to 4 miles wide. The Joffre–Gilby (94, 95) oil and gas field is 45 miles long and 1 to 1½ miles wide. The Viking gas reserves, including the largest fields of Viking-Kinsella (69), Provost (79), and Bindloss (128), are estimated at 9,200 million cubic feet, about 17 per

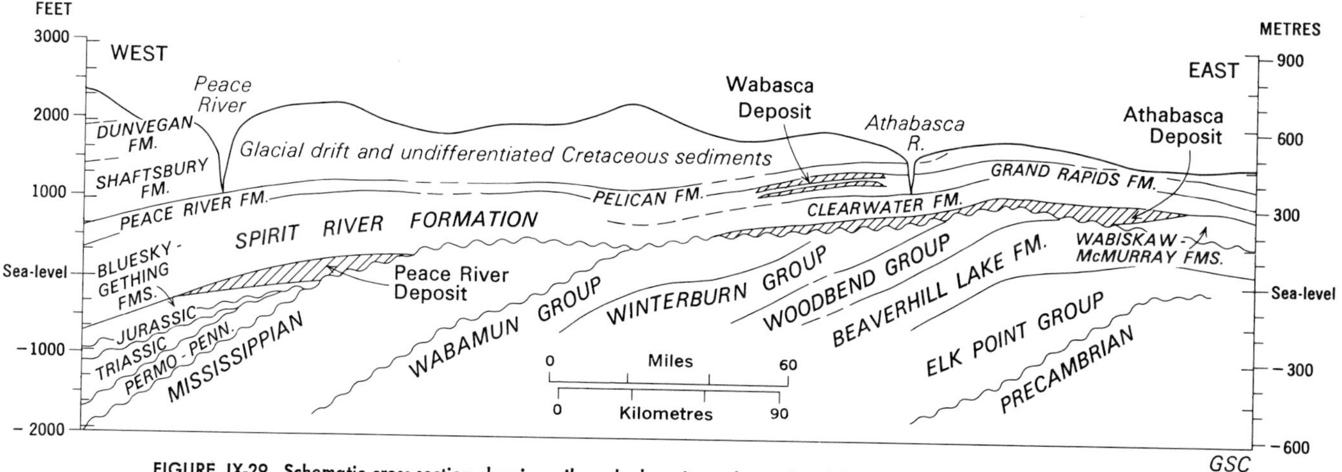

FIGURE IX-29. Schematic cross-section showing oil sands deposits and associated formations, Alberta (after Pow, et al.).

cent of total gas reserves of Western Canada. In Saskatchewan, the Viking produces oil at Coleville-Smiley (6) and gas at Brock (9). Basal Colorado sands are productive at Cessford (124a), Alberta. Gas is obtained from the Cadotte sandstone of the Peace River Formation in the Pouce Coupe field (6b) and other nearby fields of northern Alberta. The Cadotte is of near-shore origin and is associated with deltaic sediments. Gas accumulations are present in southern Alberta in the Bow Island sandstones at Pendant d'Oreille (152) and Foremost (149a) fields. The Bow Island Formation includes a succession of intertonguing sandstone and shale, the sandstone being of similar origin to the Viking. The former Bow Island field is now used for gas storage.

Upper Cretaceous

The Pembina (36b) field contains a considerable proportion of the recoverable oil reserves of Canada, being areally one of the largest known in North America and accounting for nearly 20 per cent of the oil reserves of Western Canada (Fig. IX-24d). The reservoir is found in barrier and epineritic sandstones of the Cardium Formation which has a regional dip to the southwest. The oil, of 37-degree A.P.I. gravity, is trapped by the up-dip change from sandstone to shale. A number of smaller Cardium oil fields with some gas, such as Crossfield (107), Garrington (101), and Willesden Green (38), extend southeasterly from Pembina.

Marine sandstones at the base of the Belly River Formation produce oil and gas in Pembina and Willesden Green fields. The sandstones are well sorted and are similar to the Cardium, having been formed as beaches and epineritic sand bars during a major regression of the Cretaceous seas.

About 5 per cent of Western Canada's recoverable gas reserves are present in the Medicine Hat sandstone in the combined Medicine Hat field (137) of southeastern Alberta and Hatton field (12) southwestern Saskatchewan, the largest single Cretaceous reserve of gas. Gas has been reported also from Dunvegan, Edmonton, Brazeau, and Wapiti strata.

Foothills Fields

In the late Cretaceous and Tertiary Laramide Orogeny, the eastern parts of Cordilleran Geosyncline were deformed. A series of folds and thrust sheets were produced which constitute the main control for entrapment of

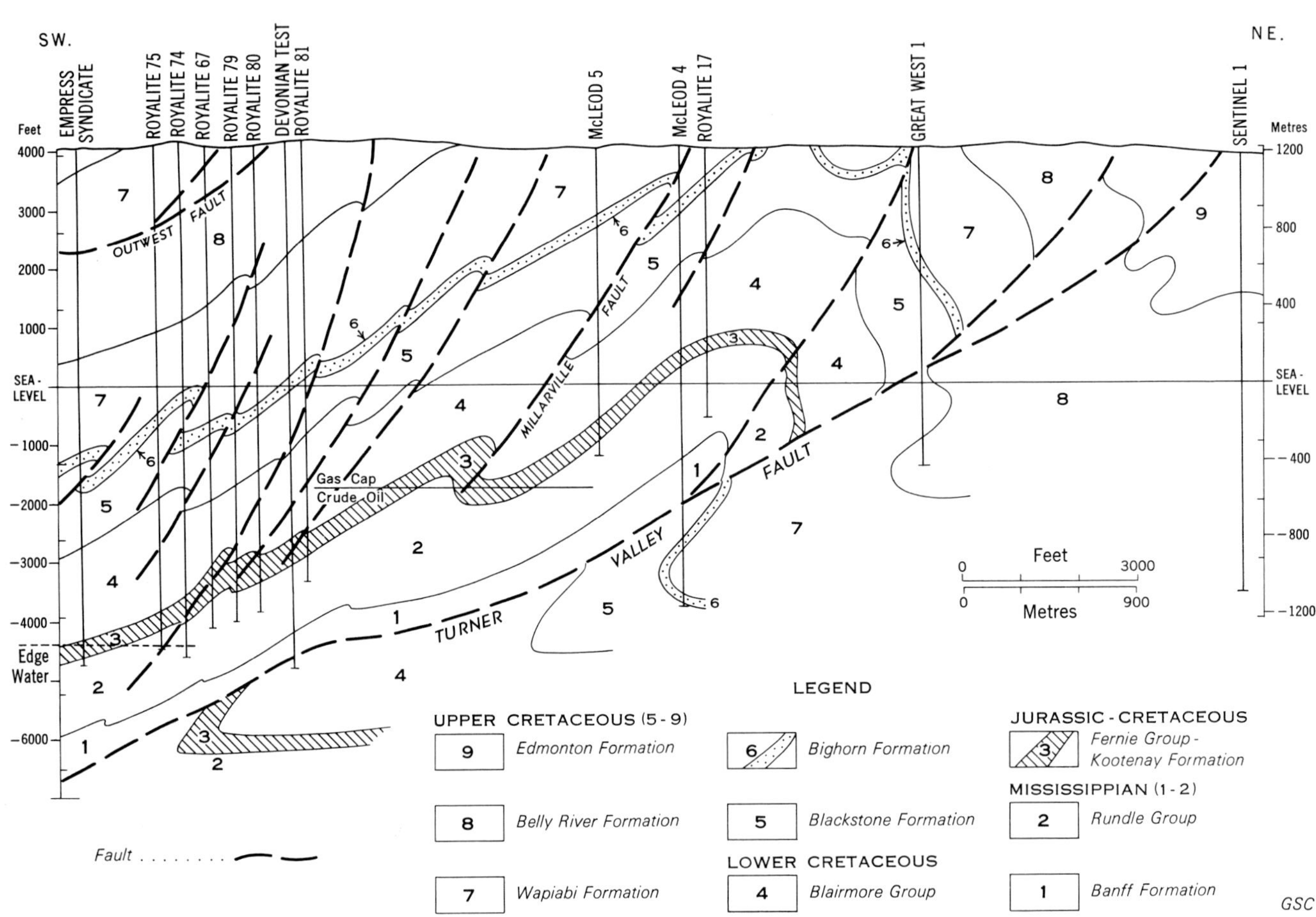

FIGURE IX-30. Structure-section through the central part of the Turner Valley oil and gas field, Alberta (after W. B. Gallup).

PLATE IX-5. Drilling rig, Shell Waterton #1 well.

hydrocarbons in the Eastern Cordillera (Figs. IX-30, -31, and -32). The natural gas fields of the southern Foothills of Alberta, which produce mainly from the Mississippian are described in this section. Some other fields in the Eastern Cordillera are only partly structurally controlled and have been described according to the age of their producing horizons. These are the Norman Wells field producing oil from the Middle Devonian Kee Scarp reef, and several fields in British Columbia producing from Triassic dolomites and sand bars. Natural gas has been discovered in Middle Devonian carbonates in the cores of Kotanelee and Pointed Mountain anticlines of Liard Plateau, Yukon and British Columbia, and light gravity oil has been found in Pennsylvanian sandstones beneath Eagle Plain, northern Yukon.

Reserves of the Foothills fields, established to end of 1966, were 5,000 million Mcf of gas, 116.2 million barrels of natural gas liquids, and 5.8 million barrels of oil. The fields also contain about 333 million long tons of recoverable elemental sulphur, one third of the total reserves. During 1966 production was 130 million Mcf of gas, 5.8 million barrels of natural gas liquids, and a million barrels of crude oil.

Producing fields are Waterton (141), Pincher Creek (142), Turner Valley (112), Jumping Pound (110a), Savanna Creek (113), Sarcee, and Lookout Butte (143), the seven fields accounting for 75 per cent of the gas reserves, most of the natural gas liquids, and all the crude oil. The principal reservoirs are in the Mississippian Turner Valley Formation of the Rundle Group. They consist of fine- to medium-crystalline dolomite with fine intergranular and vuggy porosity, or of coarsely crystalline, vuggy, crinoidal limestones. Much of the permeability is the result of fracturing in the brittle carbonates. The gas commonly contains dissolved light oil, especially the deeper fields, such as Waterton, Jumping Pound, and Pincher Creek where the reservoirs are 10,000 to 12,000 feet deep. Hydrogen sulphide content is generally between 5 and 15 per cent, but is 25 per cent in the Waterton field and up to 87 per cent in the Panther River wells. The reservoirs for the latter gas are in the upper Devonian

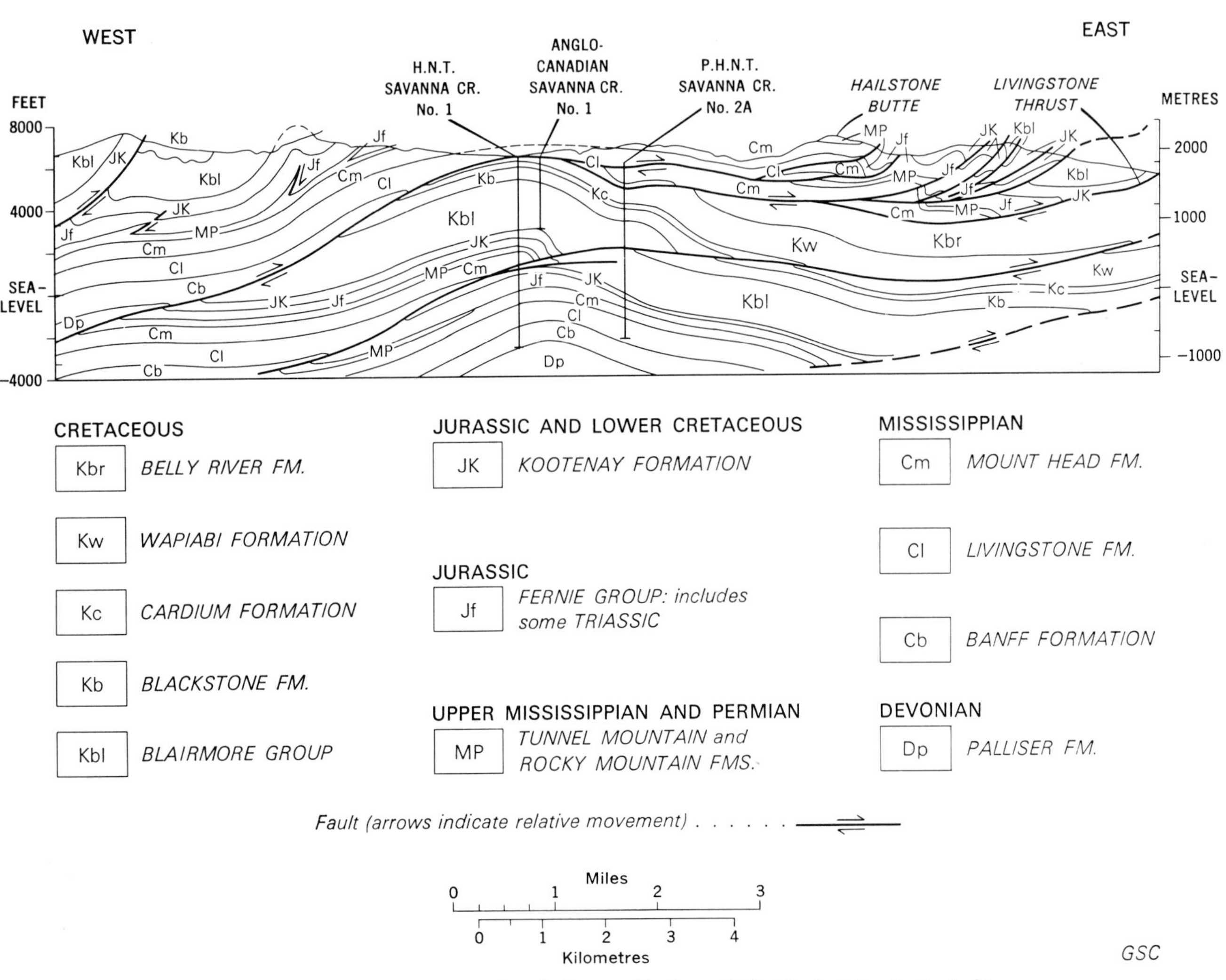

FIGURE IX-31. Structure-section through Savanna Creek gas field, Alberta (after Scott, et al.).

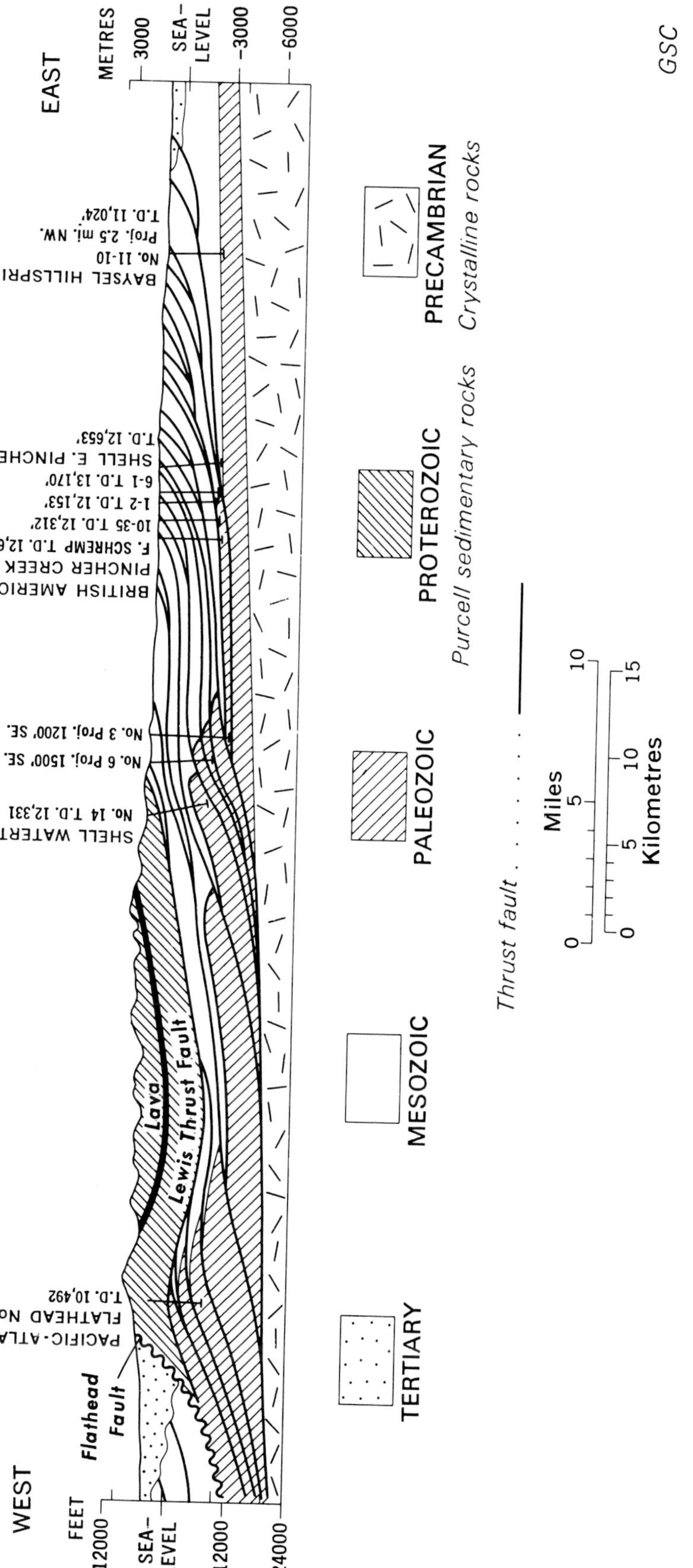

FIGURE IX-32. Structure-section through Waterton and Pincher Creek gas fields, Alberta (after Bally, et al.).

Nisku Formation and Wabamun Group; the remaining 13 per cent consists of inert gas, mainly nitrogen and a little methane. The Wabamun is productive of natural gas only in the Waterton field. In several small non-productive fields gas is encountered in Triassic dolomites as well as in the Mississippian. In the Turner Valley field some light oil is found in Lower Cretaceous sandstones but the bulk of the crude oil, 38 to 42 degrees A.P.I., is in the Mississippian.

The hydrocarbon accumulations occur where the Mississippian reservoirs are cut off by underlying thrusts, either in simple anticlines, west-dipping homoclines, or in multiple slices and more complicated folds. The surface structure may be cored with Mississippian strata as in the anticline at Turner Valley (Fig. IX-30), but in the other fields the reservoir lies beneath one or more thrust sheets (Figs. IX-31, -32). Oil and gas accumulations are considered to have been present in gently west dipping undisturbed Mississippian rocks prior to the Laramide Orogeny and to have migrated again into structurally high and salient parts of the thrust sheets during the orogeny.

SELECTED REFERENCES

General

Alberta Oil and Gas Conservation Board:
- Summary of monthly statistics, Alberta oil and gas industry.
- Schedule of wells drilled for oil and gas; annually since 1949.

Alberta Society of Petroleum Geologists:
- Geological history of western Canada.
- Oil fields of Alberta, 1960 (and supplement, *in press*).
- Gas fields of Alberta (*in press*).

British Columbia Department of Mines and Petroleum Resources:
- Annual reports.
- Schedule of wells drilled for oil and gas.

Department of Northern Affairs and National Resources:
- Schedule of wells for Northwest Territories, Yukon Territory and Canada Lands not within the Provinces; annually since 1960.

Saskatchewan Department of Mineral Resources:
- Monthly oil and gas reports.
- Petroleum and natural gas reservoir annual.

Metallic Deposits

Barr, D. A.
1966: The Galore Creek copper deposits; *Bull. Can. Inst. Mining Met.*, vol. 59, No. 651, pp. 841–853.

Bell, J. M.
1931: The genesis of the lead–zinc deposits at Pine Point, N.W.T.; *Econ. Geol.*, vol. 26, No. 6, pp. 611–624.

Billingsley, P., and Hume, C. B.
1941: The ore deposits of Nickel Plate Mountain, Hedley B.C.; *Trans. Can. Inst. Mining Met.*, vol. 44, pp. 524–590.

Boyle, R. W.
1965: Geology, geochemistry, and origin of the lead–zinc–silver deposits at the Keno Hill–Galena Hill area, Yukon Territory; *Geol. Surv. Can.*, Bull. 111.

Brock, R. W., and Schofield, S. J.
1928: Geological history and metallogenic epochs in the Western Cordillera of Canada; *Pan-Pacific Sci. Congr.*, Tokyo, 1926, Proc., pp. 591–606.

Campbell, Neil
1957: Stratigraphy and structure of Pine Point area, N.W.T., *in* Structural geology of Canadian ore deposits; vol. II, *Can. Inst. Mining Met.*, pp. 161–174.

Carr, J. M.
1960: Porphyries, breccias, and copper mineralization in Highland Valley; *Can. Mining J.*, vol. 81, No. 11, pp. 71–73.
1966: The geology of the Endako area; *B.C. Minister of Mines*, Ann. Rept. 1965.

Eastwood, G. E. P.
1965: Replacement magnetite on Vancouver Island, British Columbia; *Econ. Geol.*, vol. 60, pp. 124–128.

Freeze, A. C.
1966: On the origin of the Sullivan orebody, Kimberley, B.C., *in* Tectonic history and mineral deposits of the Western Corillera; *Can. Inst. Mining Met.*, Spec. vol. No. 8, pp. 263–294.

Fyles, J. T.
1966: Lead-zinc deposits in British Columbia, *in* Tectonic history and mineral deposits of the Western Cordillera; *Can. Inst. Mining Met.*, Spec. vol. No. 8, pp. 231–238.

Green, L. H., and Godwin, C. I.
1963, 1964: Mineral industry of Yukon Territory and southwestern district of Mackenzie, Northwest Territories 1962 and 1963; *Geol. Surv. Can.*, Papers 63-38 and 64-36.

Guiguet, M.
1961: Cariboo gold quartz; *Western Miner*, vol. 34, No. 7, pp. 37–44.

Irvine, W. T.
1948: Britannia Mine, *in* Structural geology of Canadian ore deposits; *Can. Inst. Mining Met.*, Jubilee Vol., pp. 105–109.

1957: The Bluebell Mine, *in* Structural geology of Canadian ore deposits; *Can. Inst. Mining Met.*, vol. II, pp. 95–104.

James, A. R. C., and Eastwood, G. E. P.
1964: Pride of Emory (Giant Mascot Mines Ltd.); *B.C. Minister of Mines,* Ann. Rept. 1964, pp. 137–142.

Johnston, W. A., and Uglow, W. L.
1926: Placer and vein gold deposits of Barkerville, Cariboo district, British Columbia; *Geol. Surv. Can.,* Mem. 149.

Joubin, F. R.
1948: Bralorne and Pioneer Mines, *in* Structural geology of Canadian ore deposits; *Can. Inst. Mining Met.,* Jubilee Vol., pp. 168–177.

Kidd, Donald J.
1959: Iron occurrence in the Peace River region, Alberta; *Res. Council Alta.,* Geol. Div., Prel. Rept. 59-3.

Lang, A. H.
1961: A preliminary study of Canadian metallogenic provinces; *Geol. Surv. Can.,* Paper 60-33.

Leech, G. B., and Wanless, R. K.
1962: Lead isotope and potassium-argon studies in the East Kootenay district of British Columbia, *in* Petrological studies (Buddington Vol.); *Geol. Soc. Am.,* pp. 241–279.

Little, H. W.
1959: Tungsten deposits of Canada; *Geol. Surv. Can.,* Econ. Geol. Ser. No. 17.

McConnell, R. G.
1905: Klondike gold fields; *Geol. Surv. Can.,* Ann. Rept., vol. 14, 1901, pt. B, pp. 1–71.

McTaggart, K. C.
1960: The geology of Keno and Galena Hills, Yukon Territory; *Geol. Surv. Can.,* Bull. 58.

Mulligan, R.
1966: Geology of Canadian tin occurrences; *Geol. Surv. Can.,* Paper 64-54.

Muraro, T. W.
1966: Metamorphism of lead–zinc deposits in southeastern British Columbia, *in* Tectonic history and mineral deposits of the Western Cordillera; *Can. Inst. Mining Met.,* Spec. vol. No. 8, pp. 239–247.

Ney, C. S.
1957: Monarch and Kicking Horse Mine, *in* Structural geology of Canadian ore deposits, vol. II; *Commonwealth Mining Met. Congr. 6th,* pp. 143–152.

Poole, A. W.
1955: The geology and analysis of vein and fault structure of the Bralorne Mines; *Trans. Can. Inst. Mining Met.,* vol. 58, pp. 433–437.

Riley, C.
1961: The River Jordan lead–zinc deposit, Revelstoke Mining division, B.C.; *Trans. Can. Inst. Mining Met.,* vol. 64, pp. 268–272.

Schiller, E. A., and Hornbrook, E. H.
1964: Mineral industry of District of Mackenzie, 1963; *Geol. Surv. Can.,* Paper 64-22.

Schofield, S. J.
1919: The Mesozoic period of mineralization in British Columbia; *Trans. Can. Min. Inst.,* vol. 21, 1918, pp. 422–427.

Seraphim, R. H.
1956: Geology and copper deposits of the Boundary district, British Columbia; *Trans. Can. Inst. Mining Met.,* vol. 80, pp. 384–394.

Sinclair, A. J.
1966: Anomalous lead from the Kootenay Arc, British Columbia, *in* Tectonic history and mineral deposits of the Western Cordillera; *Can. Inst. Mining Met.,* Spec. vol. No. 8, pp. 249–262.

Stevenson, J. S.
1940: Mercury deposits of British Columbia; *B.C. Dept. Mines,* Bull. No. 5.

Sutherland Brown, A.
1957: Geology of the Antler Creek area, Cariboo district, British Columbia; *B.C. Dept. Mines,* Bull. No. 38.

Swanson, C. O., and Gunning, H. C.
1945: Geology of the Sullivan Mine; *Trans. Can. Inst. Mining Met.,* vol. No. 48, pp. 645–667.

Vokes, F. M.
1963: Molybdenum deposits of Canada; *Geol. Surv. Can.,* Econ. Geol. Rept. No. 20.

Whishaw, Q. G.
1954: The Jersey lead–zinc deposit, Salmo, B.C.; *Econ. Geol.,* vol. 49, No. 5, pp. 521–529.

White, W. H., Thompson, R. M., and McTaggart, K. C.
1957: The geology and mineral deposits of Highland Valley, B.C.; *Trans. Can. Inst. Mining Met.,* vol. 60, pp. 273–289.

Non-Metallic Deposits

Baird, D. M.
1964: Origin of gypsum-anhydrite deposits at Falkland, British Columbia; *Can. J. Earth Sci.,* vol. 1, No. 1, pp. 1–9.

Gabrielse, H.
1963: McDame map-area, Cassiar district, British Columbia; *Geol. Surv. Can.,* Mem. 319.

Klingspor, A. M.
1966: Cyclic deposits of potash in Saskatchewan; *Bull. Can. Petrol. Geol.,* vol. 14, pp. 193–207.

Fuels

Bally, A. W., Gordy, P. L., and Stewart, G. A.
1966: Structure, seismic data, and orogenic evolution of southern Canadian Rocky Mountains; *Bull. Can. Petrol. Geol.,* vol. 14, pp. 337–381.

Barss, D. L., Meyers, N., and Berr, E. W.
1965: Triassic; *in* Geological history of western Canada; *Alta. Soc. Petrol. Geol.,* pp. 113–136.

Christopher, J. E.
1964: Sedimentation patterns within the Middle Jurassic Upper Shaunavan Member, southwestern Saskatchewan; *Third Intern. Williston Basin Symp.,* pp. 133–141.

Douglas, R. J. W., Norris, D. K., Thorsteinsson, R., and Tozer, E. T.
1963: Geology and petroleum potentialities of northern Canada; *Geol. Surv. Can.,* Paper 63-31.

Fuzesy, L. M.
1966: Geology of the Frobisher–Alida beds, southeastern Saskatchewan; *Sask. Dept. Mineral Res.,* Rept. 104.

Gallup, W. B.
1951: Geology of Turner Valley oil and gas field, Alberta; *Am. Assoc. Petrol. Geol. Bull.,* vol. 35, pp. 797–871.

Gray, F. F., and Kassube, J. R.
1963: Geology and stratigraphy of Clarke Lake gas field, British Columbia; *Bull. Am. Assoc. Petrol. Geol.,* vol. 47, pp. 467–483.

Gussow, W. C.
1954: Differential entrapment of oil and gas; A fundamental principle; *Bull. Am. Assoc. Petrol. Geol.,* vol. 38, pp. 816–853.

Hitchon, B.
1964: Formation fluids, *in* Geologic history of western Canada; *Alta. Assoc. Petrol. Geol.,* pp. 201–217.

Klovan, J. E.
1964: Facies analyses of the Redwater reef complex, Alberta, Canada; *Bull. Can. Petrol. Geol.,* vol. 12, pp. 1–100.

MacKay, B. R.
1947: Coal reserves of Canada; reprint of Chap. one and Appendix A of Report of the Royal Commission on coal, 1946, Ottawa.

Murray, J. W.
1966: An oil-producing reef-fringed carbonate bank in the Upper Devonian Swan Hills Member, Judy Creek, Alberta; *Bull. Can. Petrol. Geol.,* vol. 14, pp. 1–103.

Pow, J. R., Fairbanks, G. H., and Zamora, W. J.
1963: Descriptions and reserve estimates of the oil sands of Alberta, *in* Athabasca Oil Sands, K. A. Clark Volume; *Res. Council Alta.*

Scott, J. C., Hennessey, W. J., and Lamon, R. S.
1957: Savanna Creek gas field, Alberta; *Alta. Soc. Petrol. Geol.,* Guidebook 7th Ann. Field Conf., pp. 113-130.

Thomas, G. E.
1962: Textural and porosity units for mapping purposes, *in* W. E. Ham, *ed.* Classification of carbonate rocks; *Am. Assoc. Petrol. Geol.,* Mem. 1, pp. 193–223.

X. Geology of the Arctic Archipelago

INTRODUCTION

The geology of that part of the Arctic Archipelago that lies north of the Canadian Shield is dealt with in this chapter. The archipelago includes a land area of about 300,000 square miles underlain for the most part by rocks of Phanerozoic age. Precambrian rocks of other parts of the archipelago, particularly of Baffin, Somerset, and Victoria Islands, are treated in Chapter IV. Rocks of all Paleozoic and Mesozoic systems and of Cenozoic age are present. They are mainly sedimentary, but some plutonic and volcanic rocks are also found. Several intervals of Paleozoic orogeny affected parts of the area. The Mesozoic was not a time of orogenic activity, but in the Cenozoic some deformation occurred.

The area is divisible into seven major geological provinces (Fig. X-1): The *Arctic Lowlands,* formed of little disturbed, mainly lower Paleozoic rocks overlying the Precambrian basement; *Boothia Uplift,* a feature characterized by north-trending structures, mainly of Paleozoic age, with a Precambrian core exposed in the south dividing Arctic Lowlands into eastern and western parts; *Franklinian Geosyncline,* folded in the Paleozoic; *Sverdrup Basin,* which in late Paleozoic and Mesozoic time was superimposed on the folded Franklinian Geosyncline and was itself folded in the Cenozoic; *Prince Patrick Uplift,* an area of intermittent tectonic elevation in Mesozoic and Cenozoic time; *Arctic Coastal Plain,* composed of gently seaward dipping late Cenozoic strata, probably concealing the extensions of the Prince Patrick Uplift; and *Arctic Continental Shelf,* the seaward extension of Arctic Coastal Plain.

The structural provinces are described followed by a chronological account of the sedimentary, volcanic, plutonic, and tectonic events that have affected the area. Correlations of stratigraphic units and tectonic events are shown on Chart IV.

1 R. Thorsteinsson prepared the account of the geology of the Paleozoic and Precambrian; E. T. Tozer prepared the parts treating the Mesozoic and Cenozoic. When acknowledging, reference should be made to individual author and page number.

GEOLOGICAL PROVINCES

Arctic Lowlands

The Arctic Lowlands include the terrains where the Precambrian basement is overlain by flat-lying or little disturbed sedimentary strata for the most part of Cambrian to Late Devonian age. In the western part, Cretaceous and early Cenozoic sediments form the surface. The lowlands represent the northern continuation of the Interior Plains of the continental mainland. They may also be

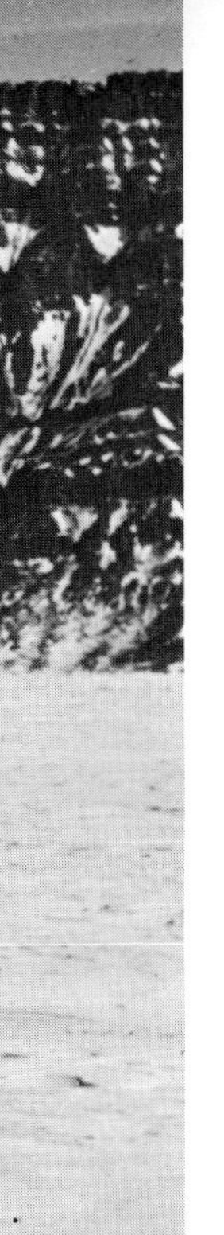

X

Geology of the Arctic Archipelago

R. Thorsteinsson and E. T. Tozer[1]

Triassic Blaa Mountain shales with gabbro sills on Raanes Peninsula, east side of Eureka Sound, Ellesmere Island.

regarded as the northern part of the North American Craton.

The lowlands are divided into segments by north- and northeasterly-trending uplifted belts and inliers of Precambrian rocks. The segments between the inliers appear to be basins that have experienced substantial subsidence. Aeromagnetic data suggest that the sedimentary thickness is more than 10,000 feet. Boothia Uplift, which bisects the lowlands, is so large and has experienced such a complex history that it is treated as a separate geological province. Foxe Basin represents the eastern part of the lowlands.

In the western lowlands a 250-mile-long inlier of Precambrian rocks flanked by gently inclined Paleozoic strata is known as the Minto Arch. This is essentially a northeasterly trending and plunging anticline with a structural relief of more than 3,000 feet. The strike parallels that of the exposed Precambrian rocks. Northeasterly trending gravity faults dislocate the Paleozoic rocks throughout the greater part; at the west end there is at least one north-trending fault. These faults indicate that the Minto Arch has characters of a horst as well as those of an arch.

Precambrian rocks forming inliers on southern Victoria Island have been termed the Wellington Arch. Adjacent Paleozoic rocks appear to be horizontal; the inliers seem to represent monadnocks on the basement surface rather than exposed parts of an area that has experienced uplift in Paleozoic or later times. On the other hand, the strike of Archean rocks at the head of Hadley Bay near the middle of Victoria Island coincides with those of the Slave Province of the Canadian Shield, which lies immediately south of the island. This suggests that much of southern Victoria Island may be underlain by an extension of the Slave Province, which has been resistant to subsidence since Precambrian time.

Boothia Uplift

This uplift is composed of Precambrian rocks flanked by a Cambrian to Lower Devonian sedimentary sequence and characterized by north-trending structures. Outliers of Middle and Upper Devonian and Cenozoic rocks are also present. Boothia Uplift as used here includes both the "Boothia Arch" and the "Cornwallis Fold Belt" of earlier accounts (Thorsteinsson, 1959; Kerr and Christie, 1965).

Both folding and faulting have contributed to the uplift. Most of the tectonic activity took place in the Devonian but faulting also occurred in the Cenozoic. The uplift strikes north, is 600 miles long, and about 125 miles wide at its widest point. Precambrian crystalline and sedimentary rocks in the southern two thirds form a conspicuous salient, penetrating Arctic Lowlands. Folded and faulted Paleozoic rocks flank the Precambrian core on Prince of Wales and Somerset Islands. The maximum structural relief expressed in terms of the level of the basement surface is about 25,000 feet. In Peel Sound the Precambrian rocks disappear beneath the Paleozoic formations. To the north, across Parry Channel, Boothia Uplift is expressed as a belt of northerly trending folds,

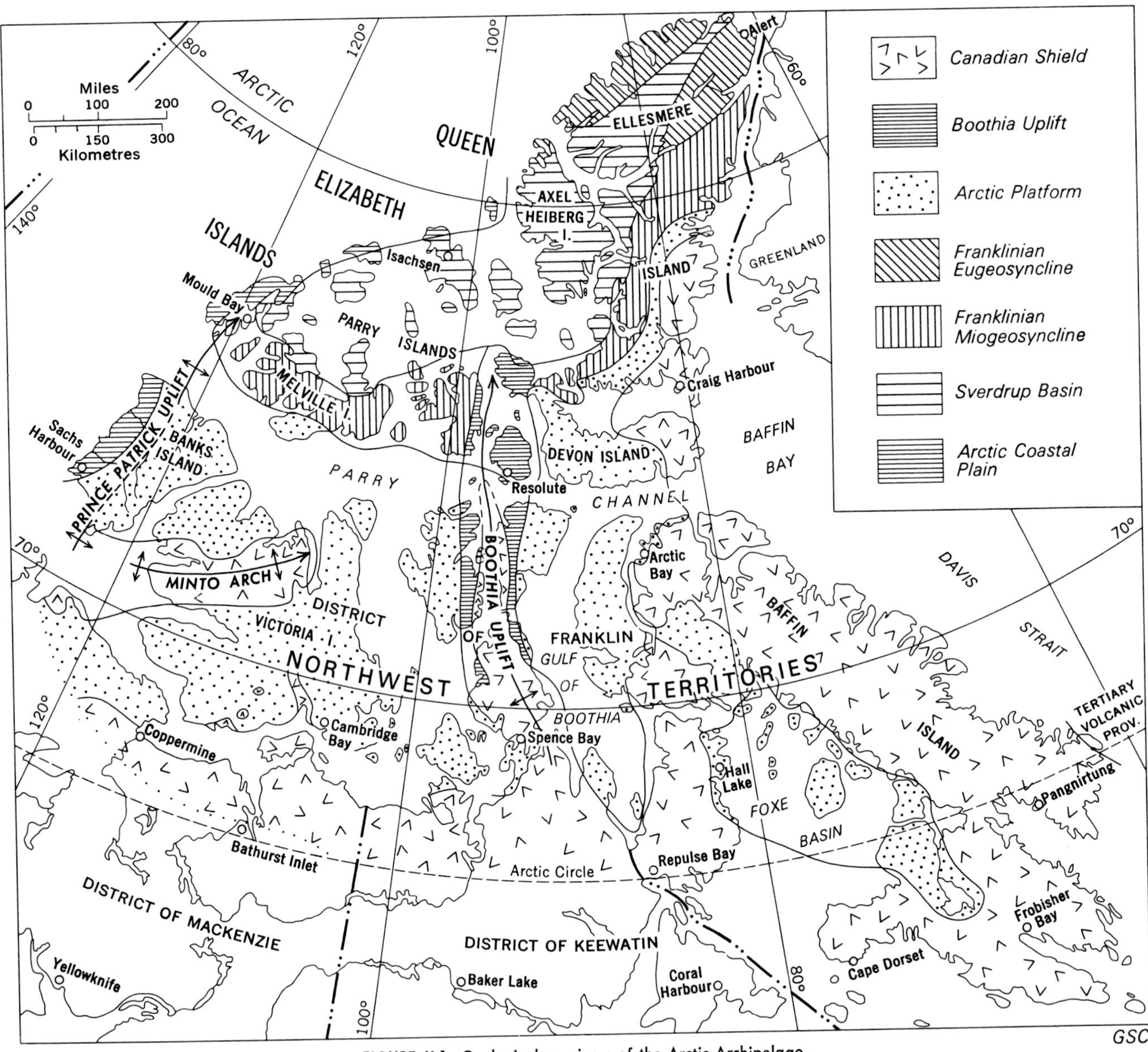

FIGURE X-1. Geological provinces of the Arctic Archipelago.

with linear grabens bounded by normal and transcurrent faults, forming a block interrupting the east–west folds of Franklinian Geosyncline. This northern part of the uplift is known as the Cornwallis Fold Belt, where the folds are characterized by generally steep flanked anticlines and broad open synclines. North of Grinnell Peninsula at Belcher Channel the Paleozoic rocks of the Boothia Uplift disappear beneath the younger formations of Sverdrup Basin, and a major anticlinal feature, the Cornwall anticline, lies on strike with the uplift.

Five unconformities within the environs of the uplift attest to episodes of deformation that range from Devonian to Cenozoic time. 1. The oldest is a Lower Devonian angular unconformity of regional extent. It is most precisely dated in eastern Bathurst Island where it is bracketed between the Bathurst Island and Stuart Bay Formations, both of Early Devonian age. Comparable unconformities occur within the Peel Sound Formation on Prince of Wales Island and within the Snowblind Bay Formation on Cornwallis Island. 2. An angular unconformity in eastern Bathurst Island separates the Lower Devonian Stuart Bay Formation from the early Middle Devonian, Disappointment Bay Formation. On Cornwallis Island, the latter formation unconformably overlies the Cornwallis Group and Cape Phillips Formation. 3. The Middle Devonian Bird Fiord Formation and the Upper Devonian Griper Bay Formation are separated by an angular unconformity on eastern Bathurst Island. 4. An episode of broad upwarping of the Boothia Uplift is indicated by a disconformity that separates Carboniferous and Lower Permian rocks along the northern extremity of the uplift. 5. Late Cretaceous or Cenozoic volcanism and faulting have also affected the uplift on Bathurst and Cornwallis Islands.

Franklinian Geosyncline

This geosyncline was the site of more or less continuous, heavy sedimentation between late Precambrian and Late Devonian times. It is now the site of a complex fold belt that can be traced from Melville Island on the west to the central part of the archipelago, and thence northeasterly through Ellesmere Island to the northern part of Greenland—a distance of some 1,300 miles. Extensions of the fold belt probably underlie Sverdrup Basin and the Arctic Continental Shelf, extending southwest to join with the British Mountains of northern Yukon.

Rocks of Franklinian Geosyncline that border the Arctic Lowlands are miogeosynclinal in character; carbonates, quartzose sandstones, and shales are dominant facies. The total thickness of sedimentary rocks is about 40,000 feet. The northwesternmost exposures are of eugeosynclinal facies, mainly volcanic and volcanic-derived rocks, together with slate, chert, and impure limestone. The boundary between the miogeosyncline and eugeosyncline, as drawn on Figure X-1, is placed where the dominantly carbonate–shale–sandstone sequence is replaced by sections dominated by clastic rocks. Volcanic rocks are known only in the northern part of the eugeosyncline, adjacent to the Arctic Ocean.

The most extensive and profound tectonic event to affect the Franklinian Miogeosyncline was the Ellesmerian Orogeny of Late Devonian or Early Carboniferous age which produced the Parry Islands, Central Ellesmere, and Northern Ellesmere Fold Belts. The age of the clastic wedge deposits in the miogeosyncline suggests that the eugeosyncline was affected by orogeny and uplift prior to the Middle Devonian, and no doubt the eugeosyncline was folded during the Ellesmerian Orogeny as well.

Sverdrup Basin

Sverdrup Basin is a regional depression, superimposed on the Franklinian Geosyncline. It contains an essentially concordant succession of formations ranging in age from Lower Carboniferous (Viséan) to Upper Cretaceous. In places early Cenozoic beds form the youngest part of the concordant sequence; elsewhere they unconformably overlie the older beds. The relations of these beds show that in Cenozoic times Sverdrup Basin had ceased to be a simple, continuously subsiding area. Partly during but mainly after the deposition of the Cenozoic beds the basin experienced Eurekan Orogeny, which involved folding, thrust faulting, and the emplacement of piercement bodies composed of Carboniferous evaporites.

Originally a simple crustal depression, as a result of Eurekan Orogeny the basin today is a great synclinorium, the axis of which extends northeast for 600 miles from northern Melville Island to northern Ellesmere Island. Apparently this structural axis was also the depositional axis, for it more or less marks the site of heaviest sedimentation for much of the history of the basin.

The maximum thickness of sediment in any one part of the basin is about 35,000 feet; the aggregate thickness of all the formations is more than 50,000 feet, but it is unlikely that this amount accumulated in any one area. The rocks are mainly sedimentary, but upper Paleozoic and Cretaceous basalts are present and thick gabbroic sills intrude much of the sequence. In the axial area, as time progressed the depocentres migrated westward: from Ellesmere Island in the upper Paleozoic, to eastern Axel Heiberg Island in the Triassic, to western Axel Heiberg Island in the Cretaceous. On the margins of the basin the sections are much thinner, partly through thinning of individual formations, and partly through the disappearance of beds.

From the thickness and lithology of the rock sequences there is no doubt that present south and east margins of the basin (Fig. X-1) lie close to the original limits. The northwestern edge is concealed by late Cenozoic beds of the Arctic Coastal Plain. Adjacent to the plain the basin exposures show that the regional dip is to the southeast, and the beds thicken down-dip. Rocks of shallow-water facies are found at some levels, suggesting that an intermittently elevated sill separated Sverdrup Basin from the Arctic Ocean during the upper Paleozoic and Mesozoic. Prince Patrick Uplift is probably an exposed remnant of this sill.

Prince Patrick Uplift

On the west side of the archipelago, adjacent to the coast, a series of inliers indicate uplifted areas. They include the Nelson Head Proterozoic inlier and Cape Crozier anticline, respectively forming the north and south capes of Banks Island, and the area of Devonian rocks that forms much of southern Prince Patrick Island. These inliers are characterized by north-trending faults, mostly of Cenozoic age. They are on strike with one another and are presumably related structural features. Collectively termed the Prince Patrick Uplift they probably represent culminations on a largely buried structural elevation. A smaller, complementary feature is the Eglinton Graben.

In Paleozoic time the east boundary of the uplift may have been the locus of dextral strike-slip faults. This implies that during the Paleozoic the uplift lay south of its present position and would account for the absence of the Ellesmerian structures of Parry Islands Fold Belt. These are well developed on western Melville Island, 40 miles to the east. The Devonian rocks of Prince Patrick Island lie directly on strike but are devoid of similar structures. The fold belt may end abruptly in the vicinity of the Eglinton Graben; alternatively it is truncated by faults. An abrupt ending for the Parry Islands Fold Belt is difficult to reconcile with the widely held theory that the Franklinian Orogen is related to the Paleozoic orogenic belt of northern Yukon. This justifies favouring the alternative that the fold belt is truncated by a strike-slip fault, or faults. The locus of the Devonian inlier of Cape M'Clure, with structural features related to those of Prince Patrick Island rather than to those of the Parry Islands Fold Belt, renders it unlikely that the folds are displaced to the south by transcurrent movement. This leaves displacement to the north, or dextral movement, as the only alternative. According to this interpretation, the Parry Islands Fold Belt is truncated by a dextral fault and displaced to the north.

In late Paleozoic and Mesozoic time Prince Patrick Uplift appears to have been resistant to subsidence and as such defined the western boundary of heavy sedimentation in Sverdrup Basin. There is no evidence that wrench faulting continued into the Mesozoic, but vertical movements probably occurred. The local unconformity between the Wilkie Point and Mould Bay Formations suggests that movement occurred in the Upper Jurassic. Movement also took place in the early Cenozoic and again in the late Cenozoic or Pleistocene. Parts of Prince Patrick Island are seismically active suggesting that movement on the faults is continuing.

Arctic Coastal Plain

Arctic Coastal Plain comprises a narrow strip of little disturbed sediments that extends the coast of the Arctic Ocean from Banks Island to Meighen Island. The sediments are Pliocene or Pleistocene, unconformably blanketing the rocks of Prince Patrick Uplift and Sverdrup Basin. In general these late Cenozoic beds appear to dip gently northwest, towards the sea, but on Ellef Ringnes Island the dip is apparently to the northeast. On Prince Patrick Island the beds have been dislocated by faults of small displacement. The southern faults, near the exposed part of the Prince Patrick Uplift, strike north as do those of the uplift. Farther north the faults strike northeast.

Northwest of the Arctic Coastal Plain the *Arctic Continental Shelf* is about 100 miles wide. The continental slope is also about the same width, and lies between 600 and 3,000 metres depth and the Canada Basin. Analysis of the magnetic properties of Canada Basin (King, *et al.*, 1966) suggests that it is underlain by rocks similar to those of the Canadian Shield and not by typical oceanic crust.

PRECAMBRIAN

Late Proterozoic sedimentary rocks are brought to the surface in parts of Franklinian Miogeosyncline, and metamorphosed rocks, probably of Proterozoic age, occur in the eugeosyncline. In northeastern Ellesmere Island, Hadrynian dolomite, shale, and sandstone disconformably underlie Lower Cambrian strata (Fig. X-2). At Ella Bay it is more than 5,600 feet thick, but towards the south it is much thinner, and near Bache Peninsula is absent, the Cambrian resting directly upon basement gneisses (Christie, 1967).

In northern Ellesmere and Axel Heiberg Islands, metamorphic rocks of uncertain age are exposed. The Rens Fiord Complex of northern Axel Heiberg Island (Fricker and Trettin, 1962; Trettin, 1964) includes slate, phyllite, sandstone, chert, dolomite, greenschist, spilitic volcanic flows, quartzite, hornfels, and marble. The Cape Columbia Group of northern Ellesmere Island (Blackadar, 1954; Christie, 1964) is composed of a variety of gneissic and schistose rocks, equivalents of which are unconformably overlain by Ordovician Wilderness strata. Apart from stromatolites collected in the Rens Fiord Complex, neither that complex nor the Cape Columbia Group has yielded fossils. A K–Ar radiometric age of 550 ± 35 m.y. has been obtained from gneiss of the Cape Columbia Group and 535 ± 35 m.y. from a schistose sandstone of the Rens Fiord Complex. These ages suggest a period of metamorphism in Cambrian or Hadrynian time. The rocks themselves are presumably Cambrian or older.

LOWER AND MIDDLE PALEOZOIC

Cambrian

In the Arctic Lowlands, Lower and Middle Cambrian rocks are discontinuously exposed along the contact with the Canadian Shield (Pl. X-1); in the Franklinian Geosyncline they are represented only in the miogeosynclinal belt of Ellesmere Island. In both provinces the Cambrian rocks are separated from the Precambrian by a regional unconformity. Rocks of Upper Cambrian age are unknown in the archipelago, and a regional disconformity separates Cambrian and Lower Ordovician rocks.

Arctic Lowlands and Franklinian Miogeosyncline

Lower and Middle Cambrian rocks of eastern Devon Island aggregate 900 feet thick (Kurtz, *et al.*, 1952). The Lower Cambrian Rabbit Point Formation consists of 20 to 30 feet of sandstone, variably argillaceous, arkosic and quartzitic, and containing *Olenellus*. It is separated from the overlying Middle Cambrian Bear Point Formation by a sharp yet conformable contact that may be a disconformity. The Bear Point contains *Glossopleura*, and consists mainly of dolomite, intraformational con-

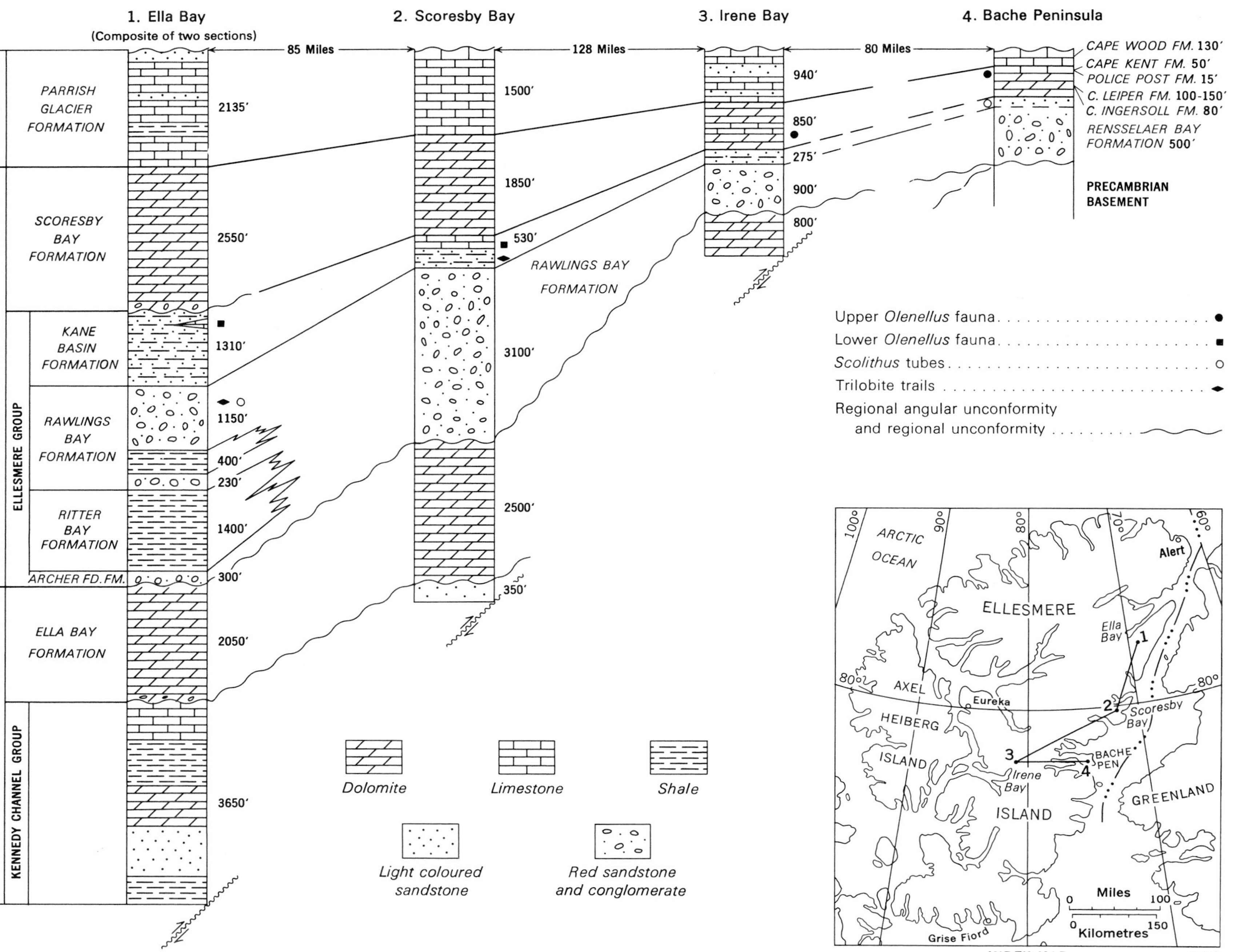

FIGURE X-2. Columnar sections, Proterozoic and Cambrian rocks, central-eastern Ellesmere Island (by J. W. Kerr).

PLATE X-1. Lower Paleozoic strata overlying Precambrian crystalline rocks, south coast of Devon Island.

glomerate, and minor dolomitic limestone up to 520 feet thick. The Ooyahgah Formation with Middle Cambrian brachiopods is composed of relatively soft weathering dolomite and minor intraformational conglomerate, 210 to 400 feet thick.

The Middle Cambrian of Boothia Peninsula and Somerset Island consists of about 300 feet of weakly cemented, brownish weathering sandstone, interbedded with dolomite that is variably shaly and quartzose, and intraformational breccia and conglomerate (Blackadar and Christie, 1963). It rests nonconformably on Precambrian crystalline rocks and is unconformably overlain by Ordovician carbonates.

The basal Paleozoic beds on Victoria Island are red and green sandstone, with minor shale, siltstone, and dolomite, up to 400 feet thick, unconformably overlying various Proterozoic formations (Thorsteinsson and Tozer, 1962). Lower Cambrian olenellids have recently been discovered in these rocks.

Two formations tentatively assigned to the Cambrian mark the base of the Paleozoic succession of northwestern Baffin Island (Trettin, 1965). The Gallery Formation was deposited in a southeasterly trending basin and rests with regional unconformity on various formations of Proterozoic age. It includes reddish sandstone with minor siltstone, conglomerate, breccia, and shale.

The greatest known thickness (1,125 feet) is near Arctic Bay; to the northeast and south it thins to zero. The attitude of crossbedding indicates that the sediment came from these directions. A sharp contact, probably representing a minor disconformity, defines the base of the overlying Turner Cliffs Formation, composed of dolomite, quartzose and dolomitic sandstone, intraformational conglomerate, and minor siltstone and shale. The maximum thickness of 1,000 feet is attained in Navy Board Inlet and, like the Gallery, the Turner Cliffs Formation thins to the north and disappears to the south. The depocentres of the Gallery lie to the west of that of the Turner Cliffs Formation. The Gallery lacks diagnostic fossils; *Lingulella* has been obtained from the Turner Cliffs. The exact age of these beds is uncertain but they are older than mid-Ordovician.

At Bache Peninsula, Ellesmere Island, Precambrian crystalline rocks are overlain by the Rensselaer Bay Formation comprising about 500 feet of dominantly clastic rocks divisible into three members (Christie, 1967). The lower is sandstone and stromatolitic dolomite, intruded by diabase sills; the middle is unfossiliferous arkose and conglomerate; and the upper is a sandstone with *Scolithus*-like tubes. Both the middle and upper members overlap westward and at the east entrance to Sverdrup Pass the upper member rests directly on the crystalline rocks. The Rensselaer Bay beds are succeeded by five formations, cumulatively 450 feet thick, dominantly carbonate. The Cape Leiper and Cape Ingersoll are unfossiliferous dolomites overlain by 15 feet of Police Post limestone with *Olenellus* and other Lower Cambrian trilobites. The succeeding Cape Kent limestone has not yielded fossils on Bache Peninsula but is correlated with the type Cape Kent in Greenland, which contains *Olenellus*. The highest Cambrian beds, the Cape Wood Formation, composed of dolomite, sandstone, and limestone, have yielded Middle Cambrian *Glossopleura* (Troelsen, 1950). Opinions differ regarding the position of the base of the Cambrian in the Bache Peninsula succession. Troelsen regarded all the beds below the Police Post limestone as "Eo-cambrian," and correlated them with the Thule Group of Inglefield Land, on the Greenland side of Kane Basin. Kerr (1967) suggests that the transgressive *Scolithus*-bearing beds at the top of the Rensselaer Bay are Lower Cambrian (Fig. X-2). Christie (1967) accepts the Cambrian dating for the *Scolithus* beds, and suggests that the two underlying members of the Rensselaer Bay Formation, which thicken to the east and disappear to the west, are possibly Precambrian.

Thick Lower and Middle Cambrian miogeosynclinal deposits occur northwest and northeast of Bache Peninsula in northeastern Ellesmere Island (Kerr, 1967). Figure X-2 shows the salient characters of three Proterozoic and Cambrian sections studied by Kerr, and his correlations with the thin Lower and Middle Cambrian platform deposits of Bache Peninsula.

Ordovician, Silurian, and Lower Devonian

Attention has already been drawn to the widespread disconformity between Middle Cambrian and early Ordovician strata. The next younger widespread Paleozoic unconformity in Arctic Archipelago occurs between Lower and Middle Devonian rocks. Ordovician to Early Devonian time is marked by general tectonic quiescence and more or less continuous sedimentation in the Arctic Lowlands, and the Franklinian Miogeosyncline (Fig. X-3). In these regions neither the Ordovician–Silurian boundary nor the Silurian–Devonian boundary is marked by unconformities.

On the Arctic Lowlands the rocks are mainly carbonates, with some evaporites. In Franklinian Miogeosyncline two principal facies were deposited: carbonates and evaporites, similar to those of the lowlands, but thicker; and graptolitic shales and argillaceous limestone. Commonly the graptolitic beds overlie the carbonates but on northwest Melville Island the section is almost entirely of graptolitic facies. On Melville and Ellesmere Islands there are thick carbonates which probably formed as banks within the troughs that accommodated the graptolitic sediment.

In Franklinian Eugeosyncline a great variety of rocks is present, mainly fine clastic rocks, some graptolitic, volcanic rocks, and locally carbonates. A very thick succession of clastic rocks, the Cape Rawson Formation, perhaps as old as Late Ordovician and certainly Silurian and Early Devonian, is transitional between the typical miogeosynclinal and eugeosynclinal sequences (Fig. X-1).

In the eugeosyncline orogenic activity probably started in the Silurian. On the Boothia Uplift tectonic elevation started in the Early Devonian. Adjacent to these areas the Silurian and Lower Devonian rocks include a variety of clastic sediments, both marine sandstone and beds of "Old Red Sandstone" facies.

Lower Ordovician, Canadian

Carbonate rocks of Canadian age are not widely exposed. On the Arctic Lowlands they are known from Devon and Ellesmere Islands; on Boothia Uplift from Cornwallis Island; and within the miogeosyncline, from Ellesmere and Melville Islands. In the southern lowlands their presence has been proved only by an isolated occurrence of limestone with shaly interbeds, containing Arenigian graptolites, on Jens Munk Island in Foxe Basin (Blackadar, 1963).

On Devon Island rocks of Canadian age disconformably overlie Middle Cambrian strata (Kurtz, *et al.*, 1952). The Mingo River Formation is 260 feet thick, predominantly limestone in the east but grades to dolomite in the west, with minor sandstone, intraformational conglomerate, and chert. The overlying Nadlo Point Formation comprises 590 feet of limestone and dolomitic limestone. Both formations are dated by the presence of *Hystricurus*.

The Canadian on Bache Peninsula is represented by three formations: the Cass Fiord, about 1,500 feet of

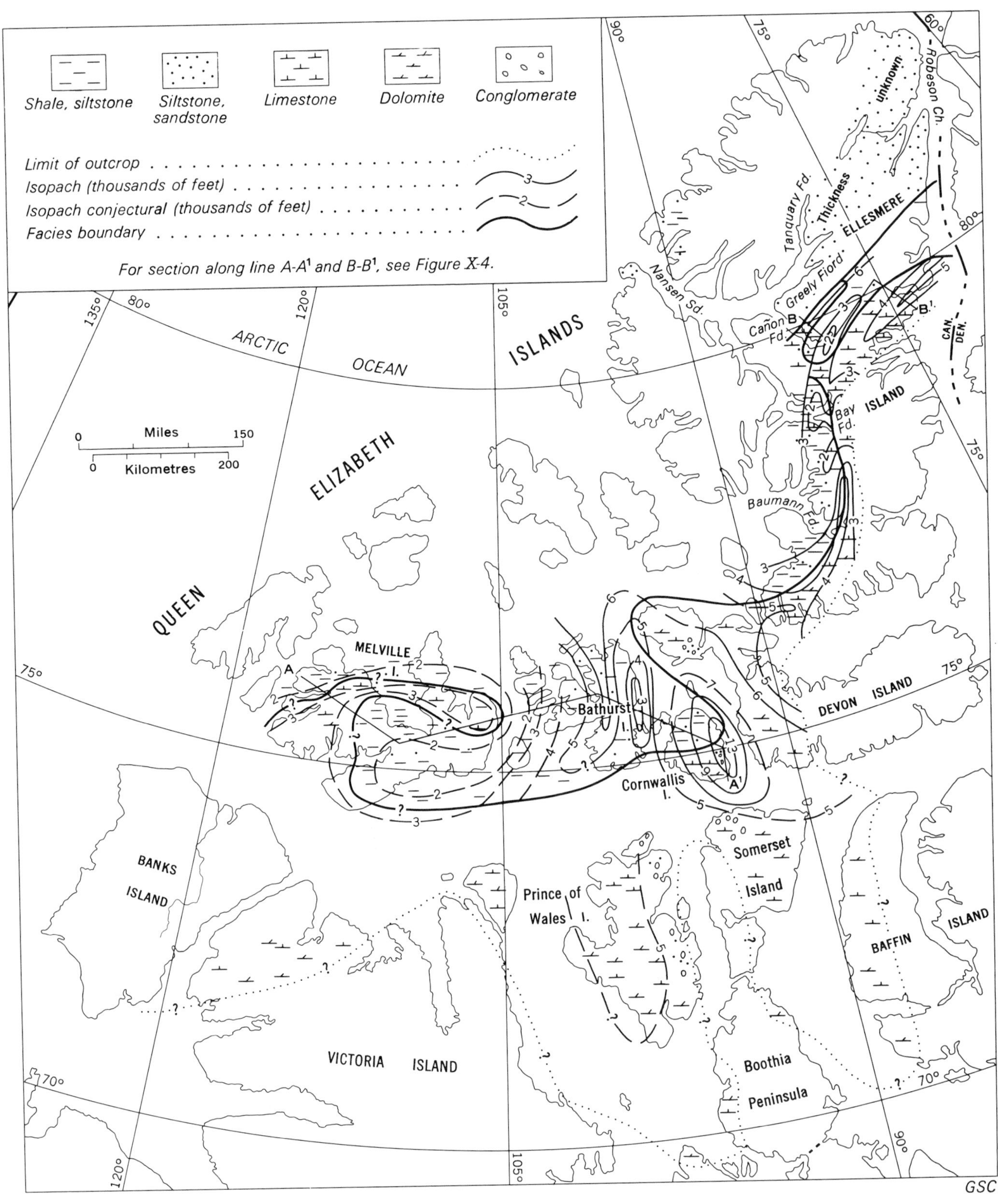

FIGURE X-3. Distribution of Upper Ordovician to Lower Devonian rocks in Arctic Archipelago (by R. Thorsteinsson).

limestone, dolomitic limestone, and intraformational conglomerate, with minor anhydrite and containing undescribed trilobites; the Cape Clay, about 300 feet of porous dolomite with gastropods, cephalopods, and trilobites; and an unnamed formation comprising about 300 feet of dolomitic limestone, limestone, and intraformational conglomerate.

The unfossiliferous Copes Bay Formation outcrops extensively on Ellesmere Island and includes 1,800 to 4,800 feet of thin-bedded impure limestone with anhydrite and limestone autobreccia as a minor but conspicuous component. Baumann Fiord Formation overlies both the Copes Bay and also Canadian rocks on Bache Peninsula. It consists of recessive weathering anhydrite, anhydritic limestone, and limestone from zero to 2,500 feet thick. Fossils are rare but *Hystricurus* is known from Flagler Fiord. This formation is exposed in the core of the Centre anticline on Cornwallis Island.

Conformably above the Baumann Fiord is the Eleanor River Formation composed mainly of resistant, thick-bedded limestone, from 800 to 2,700 feet thick. On Ellesmere Island the lower part contains *Ceratopea,* and on Cornwallis Island ostracods of Canadian or possibly younger age. The beds assigned to the Eleanor River Formation at Burnett Inlet, Devon Island, contain corals and cephalopods that have been dated as post-Canadian.

The Canrobert Formation of northwestern Melville Island consists of at least 1,000 feet of limestone and dolomite with intraformational conglomerate, calcarenite, and calcareous sandstone. Arenigian graptolites occur in the uppermost part; the base is nowhere exposed.

Mid-Ordovician and Silurian Carbonates and Evaporites

The Cornwallis Group is widely distributed in the Franklinian Miogeosyncline, in the northern part of Boothia Uplift, and in the adjacent lowland areas north of Parry Channel. It rests conformably on the Eleanor River Formation. South of Parry Channel correlative rocks are wholly carbonates and are assigned to several formations. Three formations are now distinguished within the Cornwallis Group: (1) The lower Bay Fiord Formation (780 to 1,800 feet of recessive weathering) is mainly thin-bedded limestone in part silty, shaly, and quartzose, and contains *Gonioceras* of Wilderness age. Locally the lower third consists of anhydrite. (2) The Thumb Mountain Formation comprises 1,000 to 2,800 feet of thick-bedded, resistant limestone, with some dolomite containing corals, brachiopods, and *Receptaculites,* probably of Barneveld age. (3) The uppermost formation, the Irene Bay, is a recessive unit of thin-bedded, shaly limestone with greenish grey shale partings, 120 to 675 feet thick. Cephalopods and other fossils of the Arctic Ordovician fauna of about Maysville age are abundant.

In northwest Baffin Island the sequence comprises, in ascending order, the Ship Point, Baillarge, and Cape Crauford Formations (Trettin, 1965). The Ship Point beds consist mainly of dolomite, in part shaly, silty, and sandy, with lesser dolomitic shale, siltstone, and sandstone. The lower beds may be as old as Arenigian, for graptolites occur in possible Ship Point correlatives in Foxe Basin. Fossils of about Wilderness age occur in higher beds. Disconformably above the Ship Point is the Baillarge Formation, divided into two members: Member A, up to 450 feet of limestone and dolomite, in part laminated and shaly, from which no fossils have been obtained; Member B, 1,140 feet of dolomitized cliff-forming limestone, with recessive units of shaly limestone. The lower 200 feet of this member contains corals and gastropods that indicate a correlation with the Thumb Mountain Formation of Ellesmere Island. This is overlain by 80 feet of green, shaly limestone with a fauna similar to that of the Irene Bay Formation; still higher beds in Member B contain Niagaran corals and brachiopods. The Cape Crauford Formation conformably overlies Baillarge and consists of up to 1,340 feet of dolomitic limestone, calcareous dolomite, and evaporite solution breccias. This formation, the youngest Paleozoic unit in northwest Baffin Island, also contains Niagaran fossils.

Ordovician shale and limestone with faunas of Wilderness, Barneveld, and probably also Richmond age, occur on the east and north margins of Foxe Basin. At Putnam Highland, southern Baffin Island, these rocks are at least 600 feet thick. Silurian (Niagaran) limestone and dolomitic limestone is preserved in the middle of the basin, on Prince Charles and adjacent islands.

In the western part of Arctic Lowlands from Somerset Island to Victoria Island all Ordovician rocks and part of the Silurian succession form a remarkably uniform and drab sequence consisting almost wholly of dolomite, dense to porous and vuggy, and fine to coarse grained. Chert, dolomitic shale and sandstone, and intraformational breccia are minor constituents, especially near the base. This sequence overlies Lower Cambrian strata paraconformably or rests nonconformably on Precambrian rocks. Rough estimates of the thickness vary from about 1,000 feet on Somerset Island to about 3,000 feet on Stefansson and Victoria Islands. The lower beds are unfossiliferous and of uncertain age. Higher beds contain a *Gonioceras* fauna of Wilderness age, the somewhat younger Arctic Ordovician fauna, and in the upper half Niagaran fossils are known. Ashgillian graptolites are known from one locality, a thin shale on Falsen Island off the east coast of Victoria Island.

Upper Ordovician, Silurian, and Lower Devonian Carbonates

Complex facies relationships, mainly within Franklinian Miogeosyncline and near Boothia Uplift, characterize the Upper Ordovician to Lower Devonian rocks (Figs. X-3, -4). The Allen Bay Formation (Upper Ordovician to Middle Silurian) and overlying Read Bay Formation (Middle Silurian to Lower Devonian) are carbonates that grade laterally into graptolitic shale and siltstone of the Cape Phillips Formation (Upper Ordovician to Lower

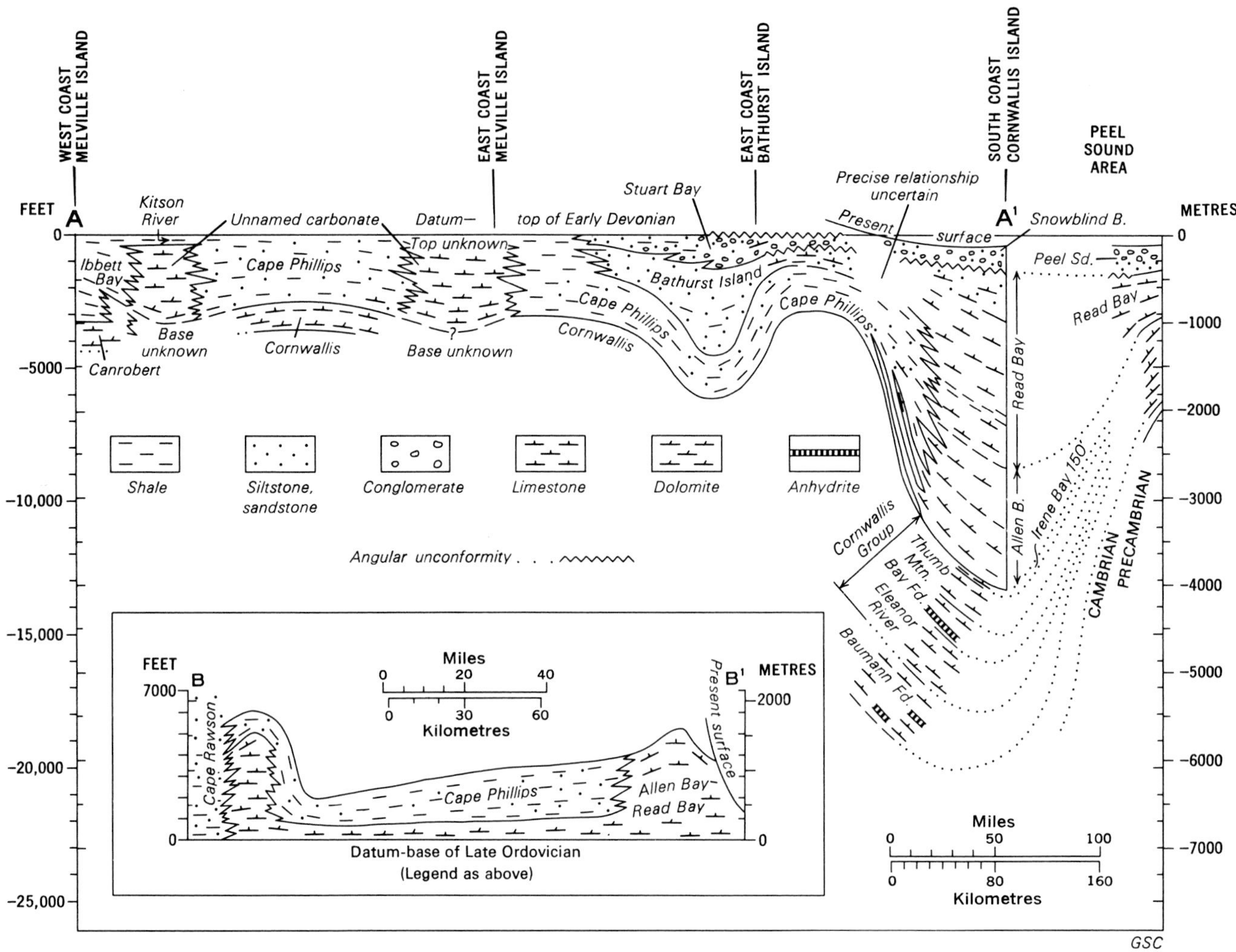
FIGURE X-4. Diagrammatic restored sections of Upper Ordovician to Lower Devonian rocks of Arctic Archipelago; (a) along line A–A′, Figure X-3; (b) along line B–B′, Figure X-3 (by R. Thorsteinsson).

Devonian). In northern regions of the Franklinian Geosyncline the Cape Phillips Formation passes laterally into sandstones and siltstones of the Cape Rawson Formation.

The Allen Bay Formation rests with sharp yet conformable contact on the Cornwallis Formation. In the type section on Cornwallis Island it is a uniform sequence, predominantly yellowish dolomite, about 5,500 feet thick (Thorsteinsson, 1959). Highly porous and massive beds, presumably representing biostromal reefs, are commonly impregnated with solid bitumen. Subordinate limestone and dolomitic limestone comprise 10 per cent of the formation. Elsewhere limestone and dolomitic limestone increase in proportion. South of Parry Channel rocks correlative with the Allen Bay Formation are present in the Baillarge and Cape Crauford Formations and in the unnamed dolomite of the western part of the lowlands. Ordovician, probably Richmondian, fossils occur in the lower beds of the Allen Bay Formation and Wenlockian ostracoderms in the upper part.

The Read Bay Formation is a varied assemblage of limestone, sandstone, dolomite, siltstone, and shale. In some parts of the archipelago it has the rank of a group. The basal contact is conformable, variably sharp or gradational. The formation outcrops in northern Victoria, Stefansson, Prince of Wales, Somerset, Devon, and southwestern Ellesmere Islands, and on Boothia Peninsula. It also outcrops in the Franklinian Miogeosyncline from Cornwallis Island, through northwestern Devon Island and Ellesmere Island. North of Baumann Fiord, the Allen Bay and Read Bay equivalents are indivisible although both limestone and dolomite occur in the lower part and limestone predominates above.

The type section of Read Bay Formation on Cornwallis Island (Thorsteinsson, 1959) is divisible into four members, in ascending order as follows: Member A, 1,875 feet of mainly thin bedded argillaceous limestone alternating with generally thick bedded biostromal and fossil fragmental limestone; Member B, 60 to 100 feet of shale and minor sandstone; Member C, 3,775 feet of beds similar to Member A, but with biostromal and biohermal developments that are thicker and commonly dolomitized; Member D, about 1,800 feet of alternating red calcareous sandstone and argillaceous limestone. The greater part of Member A contains the late Wenlockian to Ludlovian fauna characterized by *Atrypella scheii.* Higher beds of Member A contain *Monograptus bohemicus* of Lower Ludlovian age; Member C contains fossils that probably indicate a Lower Devonian age; Member D has not yielded diagnostic fossils.

On northwestern Devon Island the Read Bay Group (Thorsteinsson, 1963) embraces the Douro Formation, about 1,300 feet of interbedded thin-bedded argillaceous limestone and skeletal limestone with *Atrypella scheii*; the Devon Islands Formation, about 480 feet of shale containing the *Monograptus ultimus* Zone, which is provisionally regarded as Lower Devonian; the Sutherland River Formation, about 500 feet of medium-bedded, fine-grained dolomite with minor limestone and sandstone, containing a fauna formerly dated as Upper Silurian (Boucot, *et al.*, 1960); and the Prince Alfred Bay Formation, about 700 feet of unfossiliferous, thin- to medium-bedded, fine-grained sandstone with lesser limestone and dolomite. A somewhat similar sequence occurs in southwestern Ellesmere Island (Greiner, 1963, p. 292). On the north coast of Stefansson Island three unnamed formations are included in the Read Bay Group (Thorsteinsson and Tozer, 1962): the lower, about 400 feet of limestone and lesser dolomite with *Atrypella scheii*; the middle, about 125 feet of shale with lower Ludlovian graptolites; and the upper, about 150 feet of thin-bedded unfossiliferous dolomite. The Prince Alfred Bay Formation and the upper dolomite of Stefansson Island have not yielded diagnostic fossils. Their age is uncertain and they may be younger than the highest beds in the type section of the Read Bay Formation.

Carbonate banks occur north and west of the main belt of graptolitic shales on Ellesmere Island and Melville Island (Kerr, 1962; Tozer and Thorsteinsson, 1964). That of Ellesmere Island is about 5,000 feet thick and occurs as an apophysis of the main mass of Allen Bay and Read Bay rocks (Fig. X-3). It is bordered on the northwest by the Cape Rawson Formation and on the southeast by the graptolitic Cape Phillips Formation. The spatial relationship of the carbonate bank on Melville Island is uncertain owing to the nature of the exposures. This bank is situated north of a belt of Cape Phillips Formation and is possibly isolated. The thickness is estimated at 6,000 feet, but this figure probably includes about 3,000 feet of beds correlative with the upper part of the Cornwallis Group.

Graptolitic Rocks of Franklinian Miogeosyncline

Rocks of graptolitic facies are widely distributed in Franklinian Miogeosyncline, but the span of time covered by this type of sedimentation varies considerably from place to place. The longest span, recorded by the Ibbett Bay Formation on northwestern Melville Island, extends from the Arenigian (Lower Ordovician) to the Lower Devonian. The most widespread formation is the Cape Phillips, the basal beds of which are Upper Ordovician, Ashgillian, and locally the upper beds are Lower Devonian. On the west side of Boothia Uplift the Lower Devonian Bathurst Island and Stuart Bay Formations, characterized by fine-grained sandstone and graptolitic shale, overlie the Cape Phillips strata. Where graptolitic rocks overlie the carbonate banks they record only a short span of time, as shown by the 300-foot Lower Devonian Kitson Formation of Melville Island and by analogous deposits of uppermost Silurian age on Ellesmere Island.

The Ibbett Bay Formation comprises about 3,000 feet of black shale, with minor dolomite, chert, siltstone, and limestone. It is exposed only in the Canrobert Hills of northwest Melville Island, an area that represents the inner part of Franklinian Miogeosyncline. Graptolites indicate beds of Arenigian, Caradocian, Ashgillian, Llandoverian, Ludlovian, and Early Devonian age. It conformably overlies the Canrobert Formation, and is disconformably overlain by the Blackley Member of the Weatherall Formation.

The Cape Phillips Formation, predominantly graptolitic shale and siltstone, was defined originally on Cornwallis Island (Thorsteinsson, 1959). It outcrops in a linear belt that follows much of the Franklinian Miogeosyncline from Melville Island to Ellesmere Island. The transition zone from Allen Bay and Read Bay carbonate to the Cape Phillips Formation shale and siltstone is narrow and sharply defined on Cornwallis Island (Fig. X-4a). There the Cape Phillips Formation embraces the combined time span of the Allen Bay and Read Bay Formations, that is, Ashgillian to Emsian. On Ellesmere Island carbonate sequences of variable time spans and thicknesses, but which are invariably equivalent to the lower part of the Allen Bay Formation, extend northwesterly into regions predominantly of Cape Phillips facies. Beds of limestone, variably argillaceous and cherty, and chert, are common constituents in the Ashgillian and Llandoverian part, especially on Cornwallis and Bathurst Islands. On these islands dolomite is also common in the Ashgillian part. Shale and siltstone comprise the younger parts of the Cape Phillips Formation.

Where Cape Phillips beds represent a time span from Ashgillian to Lower Devonian, the thickness ranges from about 1,400 to more than 8,500 feet. The formation thickens to the south towards the line of facies change, with minimal thickness in medial regions of the miogeosynclinal belt. It also thickens gradually northward changing into the Cape Rawson facies. In general the Upper Silurian and Lower Devonian parts of the Cape Phillips Formation account for more than half of the thickness.

On Bathurst Island the graptolitic Lower Devonian is represented by the Bathurst Island and Stuart Bay Formations (McLaren, 1963b; Kerr and Temple, 1965). The Bathurst Island Formation comprises up to 3,410 feet of very fine grained sandstone, variably argillaceous and calcareous, calcareous and silty mudstone, and minor dolomitic siltstone. The typical Stuart Bay rocks comprise 1,220 feet of calcareous, argillaceous, fine-grained sandstone with some mudstone, siltstone, and minor bioclastic limestone, and thin limestone and chert conglomerate beds at the base. In eastern Bathurst Island, Stuart Bay beds contain a greater proportion of limestone, and include conspicuous reefoid masses and conglomerates. The contact of the Bathurst Island Formation with the underlying Cape Phillips beds is transitional, but nevertheless appears to be approximately isochronous wherever observed. On the other hand, the contact between the Bathurst Island and Stuart Bay beds is markedly diachronous. West and north of the type locality, the Bathurst Island Formation thickens gradually at the expense of Stuart Bay beds, entirely replacing the latter. South and east of the type locality the relationships are reversed and further complicated by an unconformity at the base of the Stuart Bay Formation, beneath which the Bathurst Island Formation is deeply eroded and in places cuts out entirely. This angular unconformity within the Lower Devonian marks the first major movement of Boothia Uplift within the Paleozoic. In central Bathurst Island the Stuart Bay Formation is overlain, presumably disconformably, by the Middle Devonian Eids Formation. In eastern Bathurst Island, the Disappointment Bay Formation, a dolomite equivalent to the lower part of the Eids Formation rests with angular unconformity on Stuart Bay and older beds. The second movement of Boothia Uplift is thus narrowly bracketed in time by late Lower and Middle Devonian rocks. Although the main source for the Bathurst Island and Stuart Bay sediments appears to have been from the north, a secondary source, particularly for the coarse clastic rocks in the Stuart Bay Formation, was Boothia Uplift.

Clastic and Volcanic Rocks of the Franklinian Eugeosyncline

On Ellesmere Island a thick sequence of Ordovician (?) to Devonian clastic rocks extends in a belt from the head of Trold Fiord, through central Canyon Fiord, northeast to Archer Fiord. These rocks, known as the Cape Rawson Formation, form a transition between sequences characteristic of the miogeosyncline to the southeast and the eugeosyncline to the northwest. Cape Rawson rocks are also exposed northwest of Archer Fiord, where they are characterized by more intense folding and low rank metamorphism. Northwest of Archer Fiord the base is not exposed, but at the head of the fiord the Cape Rawson overlies the Ordovician Cornwallis Group, and to the south in Canyon and Trold Fiords it rests gradationally on the Silurian part of the Cape Phillips Formation.

The Cape Rawson consists mainly of sandstone and siltstone in the regions of facies change to the Cape Phillips and Eids Formations. To the north it is composed of greywacke, subgreywacke, impure sandstone, chert, micaceous gritty shale, phyllite, and impure sandstone (Christie, 1964). The top has not been recognized, and it is possible that upper beds are equivalent to the Upper Devonian Okse Bay Formation.

Although great thicknesses of sediments are probably represented, the complexity of structures has precluded accurate measurements. About 15,000 feet of Cape Rawson beds is estimated to occur in Canyon Fiord. Cape Rawson rocks are generally barren of fossils; nevertheless, three collections obtained indicate Lower Silurian, Upper Silurian, and Lower Devonian rocks. It is possible that rocks described by Blackadar (1954) on the north coast of Ellesmere Island as the Mount Disraeli, Sail Harbour, and View Creek Groups are equivalent to the Cape Rawson Formation.

In M'Clintock Inlet, on the north coast of Ellesmere Island, seven formations have recently been distinguished by Trettin (1966) within the rocks classed as the M'Clintock and Challenger Groups by Christie (1964). The total thickness probably exceeds 12,000 feet. The oldest rocks are Ordovician carbonates with *Gonioceras* of Wilderness age, resting unconformably on slates and phyllites that are probably equivalents, at a lower metamorphic rank, of the Cape Columbia gneiss. Above the Wilderness carbonates are red sandstones, succeeded by several thousand feet of volcanic flows, in turn overlain by carbonates with Richmondian Arctic Ordovician fauna and graptolitic beds and carbonates with *Climacograptus* cf. *latus* Elles and Wood of Ashgillian age. The Ashgillian rocks are succeeded by more than 750 feet of sandstone and conglomerate believed on lithological grounds to be correlative with the Imina Group, which contains Llandovery graptolites farther to the west. Finally, above the Imina equivalent there is at least 1,300 feet of limestone and calcareous sandstone, with *Conchidium,* of Late Silurian age.

Silurian rocks are also known farther to the west, in northwestern Ellesmere Island (Trettin, 1964). The Imina Group comprises several thousand feet of beds, predominantly lithic arenite and siltstone with lesser shale and conglomerate, and contains Llandoverian graptolites in the upper part. Between 3,000 and 6,000 feet of slaty shale and slaty siltstone apparently overlies the Imina, locally with volcanic flows of keratophyric or quartz keratophyric composition (especially in the upper part) and containing graptolites of Llandoverian or Wenlockian, and Ludlovian age. The succeeding 5,000 feet of siltstone, shale, sandstone, and conglomerate carries Ludlovian graptolites; these rocks unlike the underlying volcanic-derived formation are composed mainly of chert and quartz, laminated and thin bedded with low-angle crossbedding and evidence of soft sediment deformation.

On northern Axel Heiberg Island there is at least 3,000 feet of slate and siltstone with some lithic arenite, tuffaceous arenite, and tuff containing Wenlockian graptolites. As on Ellesmere Island, the volcanic material is chiefly keratopyhric and quartz keratophyric. Groove casts indicate southeasterly to easterly current directions. These rocks lie in fault contact with the Rens Fiord Complex and are overlain unconformably by the Lower Devonian Stallworthy Formation. This is the only locality known within Franklinian Eugeosyncline where there is evidence for an unconformity within the Silurian–Devonian sequence.

Lower Devonian Red Beds of the Boothia Uplift

In the Boothia Uplift widespread Lower Devonian red beds reflect the onset of tectonic elevation. The Snowblind Bay Formation on Cornwallis Island comprises up to 1,500 feet of red limestone-conglomerate, dolomite, siltstone, limestone, dolomitic limestone, and dolomitic siltstone and sandstone. On the east coast of the island these beds appear to overlie the Read Bay Formation conformably. In the interior there is an unconformity within the Snowblind Bay sequence. There the upper Snowblind Bay beds rest with angular unconformity on the lower beds and also on older formations. Ostracoderms indicate a Gedinnian age. Invertebrate fossils from clasts in the limestone-conglomerate attest to a provenance of eroded Read Bay and Allen Bay Formations. The Snowblind Bay Formation evidently represents a syntectonic deposit, essentially correlative with the Stuart Bay Formation of Bathurst Island. The angular unconformity within the Snowblind Bay Formation is correlated with the unconformity at the base of the Stuart Bay beds.

A sedimentary environment and tectonic history comparable to that of the Snowblind Bay beds is attributed to the approximately correlative Peel Sound Formation of Somerset and Prince of Wales Islands. Adjacent to the Precambrian exposures of the uplift the Peel Sound beds contain large boulders of Precambrian crystalline rocks. In western Prince of Wales Island, Peel Sound beds are relatively fine grained and intergrade and intertongue with the uppermost part of the Read Bay Formation; they are eventually replaced by a purely marine sequence devoid of red beds and conglomerate.

Lower Devonian Red Beds and Volcanic Rocks of the Eugeosyncline

In the eugeosynclinal terrane of northern Axel Heiberg Island a sequence of Lower or Middle Devonian red beds, the Stallworthy Formation, is abruptly but concordantly succeeded by the Svartevaeg volcanic rocks (Fricker and Trettin, 1962; Trettin, 1964). The Stallworthy Formation is divisible into three members. Member A at the base comprises up to 3,000 feet of beds. A basal pebble-conglomerate and sandstone is overlain by red siltstone, sandstone, and shale. Member B includes 1,000 to 2,500 feet of conglomerate, breccia, sandstone, and minor siltstone. Member C comprises 8,000 feet of red and green siltstone, sandstone, conglomerate, breccia, and calcareous and tuffaceous arenite with Lower or early Middle Devonian ostracoderms. Chert and quartz are the dominant constituents of all the sedimentary rocks. The Svartevaeg Formation comprises turbidites and volcanic rocks, about 10,000 feet of volcanic arenite, tuff, keratophyric and spilitic flows, siltstone, shale, conglomerate, and breccia. Silurian brachiopods occur in limestone boulders in a basalt, but autochthonous fossils are unknown. The Svartevaeg Formation is overlain unconformably by the Viséan Emma Fiord Formation.

Middle and Upper Devonian

Middle and Upper Devonian rocks are widely distributed in the Franklinian Miogeosyncline and occur as outliers within the Boothia Uplift (Fig. X-5). They are also exposed in the western part of the Arctic Lowlands, where they show close similarities with the succession on the mainland (Chap. VIII). Throughout Franklinian Miogeosyncline Middle Devonian rocks succeed the Lower Devonian conformably, but in the region of Boothia Uplift an angular unconformity separates the Middle Devonian from older rocks. The Middle and Upper Devonian rocks are divisible into two gross lithologic units, the lower of which is dominantly carbonate and shale and the upper mainly terrigenous sediments representing a clastic wedge derived from the north. In the inner part of the miogeosyncline, adjacent to the eugeosyncline, both the Middle and Upper Devonian are dominated by clastic rocks.

The lower part of the sequence in the outer part of the miogeosyncline includes dominantly carbonate formations (Disappointment Bay and Blue Fiord); drab coloured shales, siltstones, and fine-grained sandstones (Goose Fiord and Eids Formations); and red and green clastics with evaporites. Most or all of these rocks are of early Middle Devonian (Eifelian) age. The upper part of the sequence shows the initiation of clastic sedimentation throughout the whole of the miogeosyncline and the western part of the lowlands. Except for some isolated Frasnian reefs on Banks Island, carbonate formations are completely absent. Initially the sedimentation was mainly marine; later it was almost entirely non-marine. The principal marine formations are the Bird Fiord and the greater part of the Weatherall, both of Givetian age. The younger, mainly non-marine, formations are the Okse Bay and its approximate equivalents the Hecla Bay and Griper Bay Formations. Intercalated marine bands of Frasnian age occur on Prince Patrick Island and of Famennian age on Melville and Cameron Islands.

In the inner parts of the miogeosyncline the two divisions are not discernible, but are represented by the Cape Rawson Formation, a clastic wedge deposit which may range from Upper Ordovician to Middle or even Upper Devonian. Parts of the Devonian succession of northwestern Melville Island resemble the Cape Rawson Formation, but there the oldest thick clastics (Blackley Member of Weatherall Formation) are probably early Middle Devonian.

Deposition of clastic rocks of northerly derivation in the miogeosyncline commenced with the Upper Ordovician or Silurian Cape Rawson Formation, and continued until possibly the Upper Devonian. By the early Middle Devonian they had spread to areas such as northwest Melville Island, and Trold and Canyon Fiords on Ellesmere

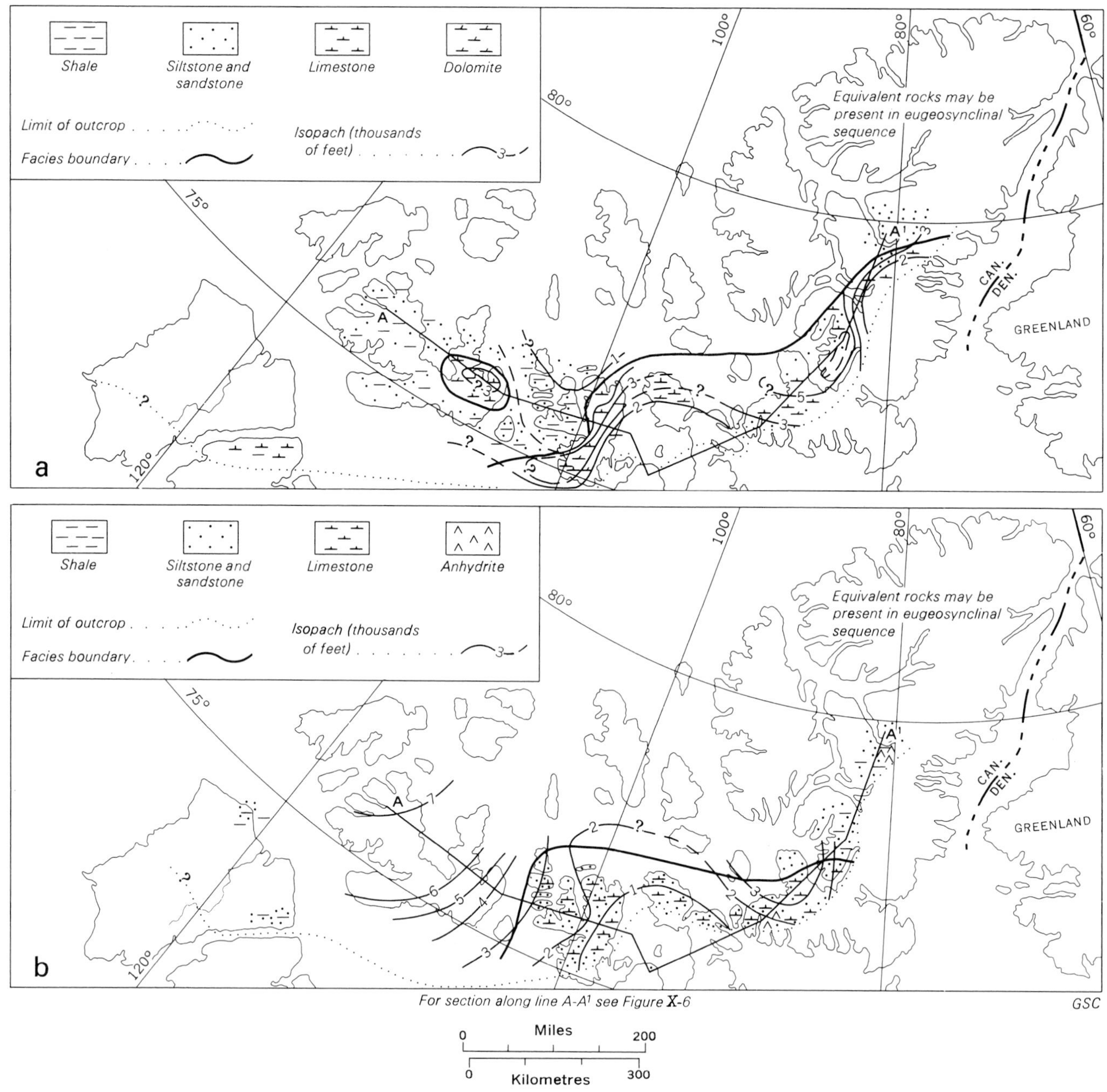

FIGURE X-5. Distribution of Middle Devonian rocks in Arctic Archipelago; (a) Eifelian, (b) Givetian (by R. Thorsteinsson).

Island. In late Middle Devonian (Givetian) time the clastic beds achieved their greatest extent by covering the miogeosyncline and spreading beyond, south of Parry Channel, to the lowlands. These conditions persisted until latest Devonian (Famennian) time.

Early Middle Devonian (Eifelian)

The early Middle Devonian rocks of the miogeosyncline include a great variety of carbonate, clastic, and evaporitic rocks. The Disappointment Bay Formation where originally defined on Cornwallis Island comprises about 280 feet of porous dolomite with basal sandstone and conglomerate overlying Silurian rocks with angular unconformity (Thorsteinsson, 1959). The upper contact of the formation is not preserved on Cornwallis Island. Rocks previously assigned to the Sherard Osborn and Driftwood Bay Formations on eastern Bathurst Island by Thorsteinsson and Glenister (1963) have been consigned by J. W. Kerr to the Disappointment Bay Formation. On Bathurst Island, the Disappointment Bay includes 700 to 2,100 feet of beds primarily resistant, generally porous dolomite, including a local basal sandstone and pebble-

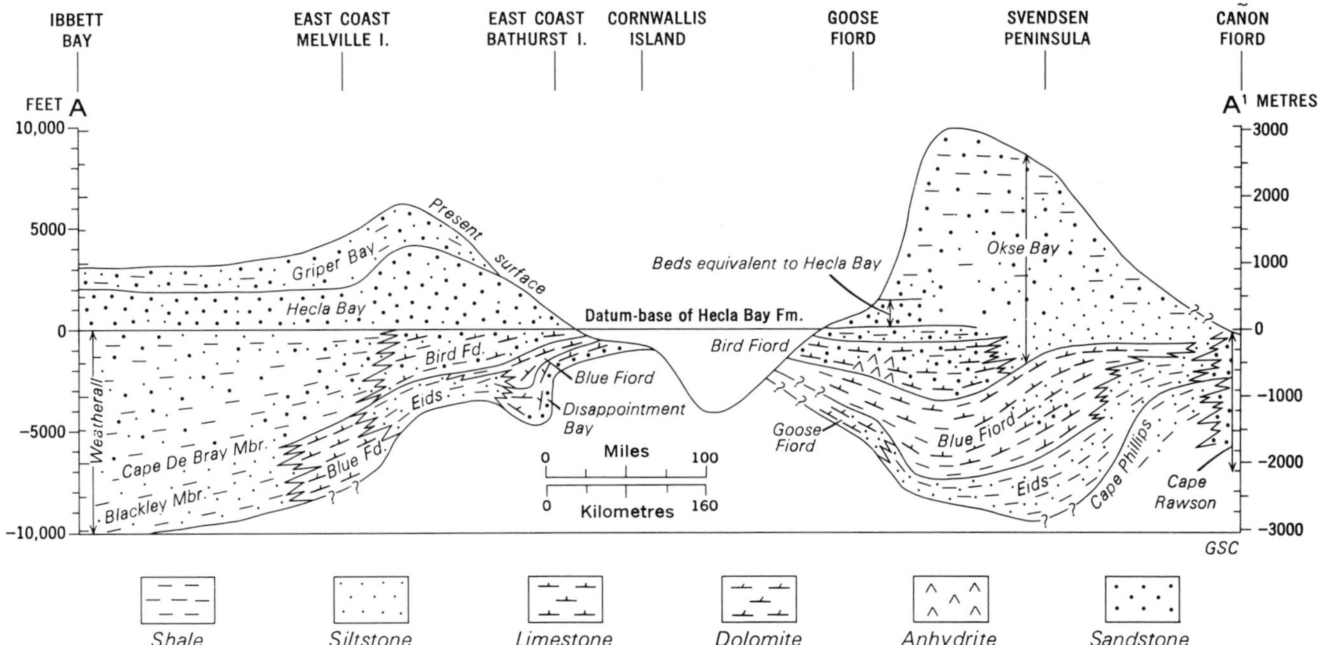

FIGURE X-6. Diagrammatic restored section of Middle and Upper Devonian rocks of Arctic Archipelago along line A–A′ of Figure X-5 (by R. Thorsteinsson).

conglomerate, formerly considered to represent the Driftwood Bay Formation. The Disappointment Bay Formation is overlain with sharp yet conformable contact by limestones of the Blue Fiord Formation. The thickest sections of Disappointment Bay occur in southern Bathurst Island where the formation includes numerous interbeds of dolomitic sandstone. In eastern Bathurst Island it rests with angular unconformity upon various Ordovician to Lower Devonian formations. To the west the angular unconformity passes into a disconformity with Disappointment Bay rocks overlying the Stuart Bay Formation. Still farther west the Disappointment Bay Formation grades laterally into the lower part of the Eids Formation through a transition zone characterized by a gradual decrease in dolomite and corresponding increase in siltstone.

The Eids Formation is composed of thin-bedded, recessive rocks, 600 to more than 3,000 feet thick, mainly of medium grey siltstone, variably shaly and calcareous, and minor calcareous, locally gypsiferous shale. The base of the Eids is a disconformity approximating a time-stratigraphic surface. The upper contact however is diachronous, overlain on Ellesmere Island with gradational contact by carbonate rocks of the Blue Fiord Formation. The Eids is developed in western Bathurst Island but eastward it grades laterally into the Disappointment Bay and Blue Fiord Formations. Correlation of the Eids Formation with the Blue Fiord and Weatherall Formations of Melville Island is speculative, as faunal evidence is lacking and exposures are discontinuous.

The Goose Fiord Formation comprises 1,010 feet of dolomitic siltstone and sandstone, silty dolomite and dolomite preserved in southwestern Ellesmere Island where it lies with an abrupt yet conformable contact on the Read Bay Group (Greiner, 1963). It is overlain with similar contact relationships by the Blue Fiord Formation. Goose Fiord rocks have not yielded diagnostic fossils but they probably represent a relatively sandy facies equivalent to the more argillaceous Eids Formation that occurs to the north, in the axial part of the miogeosyncline.

The Vendom Fiord Formation is confined to parts of the Arctic Lowlands and Franklinian Miogeosyncline on Ellesmere Island (Fig. X-7). It comprises up to 600 feet of red and green, thin-bedded, variably calcareous and silty sandstone, with quartz-pebble conglomerate, siltstone, and anhydrite as minor constituents. These rocks outcrop as a narrow belt that extends from Vendom Fiord where they grade into the Eids Formation, to the head of Canyon Fiord where they merge with the Cape Rawson Formation. They rest disconformably on either the Allen Bay–Read Bay Formations or the Cape Phillips Formation, and are conformably overlain by the Blue Fiord Formation. Their distribution and facies relationships indicate that these sediments, unlike other Devonian clastic formations, were probably derived mainly from an eastern source.

From interfingering relationships and stratigraphic position it appears that the Disappointment Bay, Eids, and Goose Fiord Formations, and also the red and green beds between Vendom and Canyon Fiords, are essentially correlative. Most of these rocks are devoid of diagnostic fossils but the Eids contains trilobites of Eifelian age (Ormiston, *pers. com.*), and it is therefore presumed that the other formations are also Eifelian.

The Blue Fiord Formation is characteristically developed as a resistant, microcrystalline and fossil frag-

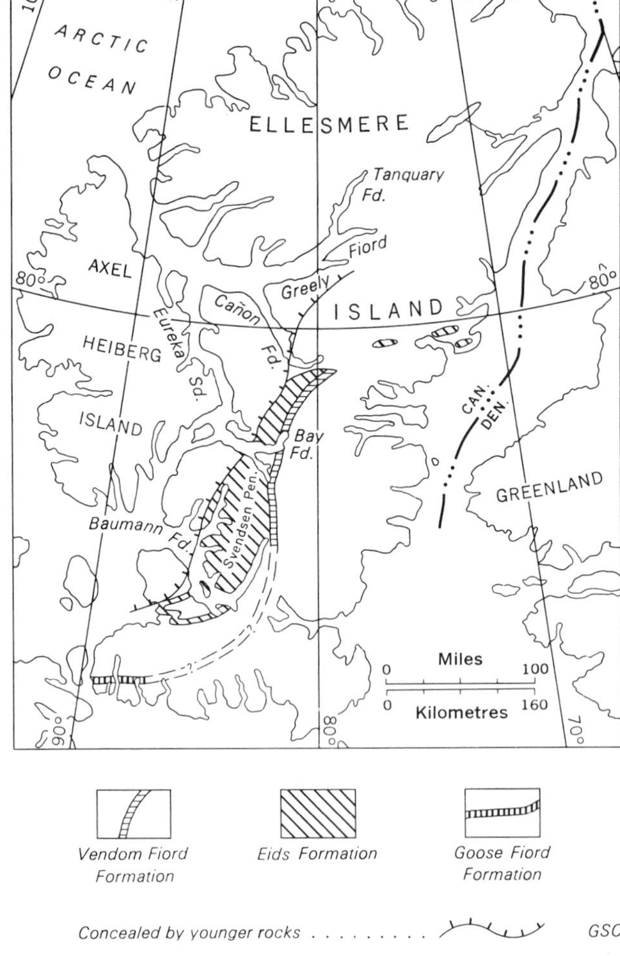

FIGURE X-7. Outcrop of Middle Devonian, Vendom Fiord, Eids, and Goose Fiord Formations, Ellesmere Island (by R. Thorsteinsson).

mental limestone, with lesser dolomite, shale, and siltstone (Figs. X-5a and 6). Dolomite forms a conspicuous constituent and locally is dominant. Outcrops of Blue Fiord rocks are distributed as an irregular belt along the southeastern and southern margins of the Franklinian Miogeosyncline from Ellesmere Island, northwestern Devon Island, Bathurst Island, and Melville Island. In northeastern Melville Island the formation includes about 2,500 feet of limestone and dolomite. There the formation is interpreted as representing an isolated carbonate bank and may include rocks correlative with the Disappointment Bay Formation. The Blue Fiord Formation outcrops in the Arctic Lowlands of northwestern Victoria Island, where neither the base nor the top of the formation is exposed. The formation is characterized by highly variable thicknesses; from zero where it has graded into correlative formations, to a maximum of more than 4,500 feet between Vendom and Bay Fiords on Ellesmere Island. It contains a rich fauna of Eifelian corals, brachiopods, and trilobites.

Late Middle Devonian (Givetian) and Non-Marine Clastic Rocks

The Givetian is represented by the Bird Fiord Formation on Ellesmere, Devon, and Bathurst Islands, and by the Weatherall Formation of eastern Melville Island (Figs. X-5b, -6). The Weatherall of western Melville Island includes a basal member (Blackley) that is probably of early Middle Devonian age.

The Bird Fiord Formation is composed of light greenish grey calcareous sandstone and quartzose limestone with interbeds of dark green shale and siltstone. Corals, bivalves, brachiopods, and trilobites are common. The contact with the underlying Blue Fiord carbonates is sharp but conformable.

On northeastern Melville Island the Weatherall Formation abruptly and conformably overlies the Blue Fiord Formation. It is divisible into (1) a lower sandstone, siltstone, and shale sequence, some 700 feet thick, and variably calcareous and drab weathering with marine Givetian fossils; and (2) an upper sandstone, siltstone, and shale sequence, about 3,900 feet thick, devoid of marine fossils and probably of non-marine deposition. Carbonaceous fragments occur throughout, but especially characterize the upper member. On northwestern Melville Island the lower part of the Weatherall Formation includes the Blackley Member, which rests with abrupt and probably disconformable contact on the Lower Devonian graptolitic beds of the Ibbett Bay Formation. It comprises about 2,300 feet of apparently unfossiliferous grey micaceous shale with interbeds of siltstone. The succeeding Cape de Bray Member comprises about 2,000 feet of grey to black micaceous shale with siltstone interbeds, in which Givetian brachiopods occur. The Cape de Bray Member is followed by about 6,000 feet of beds that closely resembles the typical Weatherall rocks of eastern Melville Island. Givetian corals, brachiopods, trilobites, and bivalves are common in the beds above the Cape de Bray Member, but towards the top of the Weatherall marine fossils become increasingly rare. In the absence of fossil evidence, the correlation of the Blackley Member with the Disappointment Bay and Blue Fiord Formations is tentative. However, if this interpretation is correct the Weatherall Formation of western Melville Island is both Eifelian and Givetian whereas in the eastern part of the Island it is only Givetian.

Late Middle (?) and Upper Devonian

The Devonian rocks that succeed the Weatherall and Bird Fiord Formations are mainly non-marine. East of Grinnell Peninsula they are known as the Okse Bay Formation, and on Bathurst Island and to the west they are represented by the Hecla Bay and Griper Bay Formations of the Melville Island Group (Pl. X-2). These rocks, in which the youngest dated beds are Famennian, are the youngest deposited in Franklinian Geosyncline. Their upper contact is everywhere a profound angular unconformity.

PLATE X-2. Upper Devonian rocks and late Cenozoic fault, Blue Hills, southwestern Melville Island, view eastward. H–Hecla Bay Formation; G–Griper Bay Formation.

The Hecla Bay Formation is a uniform succession 1,200 to about 4,000 feet thick, of light grey to white sandstone that is generally thick bedded and cross-stratified. Carbonaceous beds characterize the formation which is also relatively resistant to weathering and of distinctive colour. The contact with the Weatherall Formation is abrupt on eastern Melville Island, but becomes transitional to the west. On Bathurst Island and Grinnell Peninsula it gradationally overlies the Bird Fiord Formation. Although the Hecla Bay Formation has not yielded diagnostic fossils, its age is limited by the Givetian and Famennian ages of underlying and overlying formations.

The Griper Bay Formation is mainly sandstone, siltstone, and shale with thin coal seams and conglomerate as minor constituents. The rocks are characterized by green and greyish colours with units of white sandstone like those of the Hecla Bay Formation. Up to 4,000 feet of Griper Bay rocks outcrop in the Franklinian Miogeosyncline on Melville and Bathurst Islands, where they rest concordantly on the Hecla Bay sandstones. They also occur on Boothia Uplift where they overlie with angular unconformity various older formations, the youngest being Givetian. This unconformity attests to the third period of movement of Boothia Uplift. The greater part of the

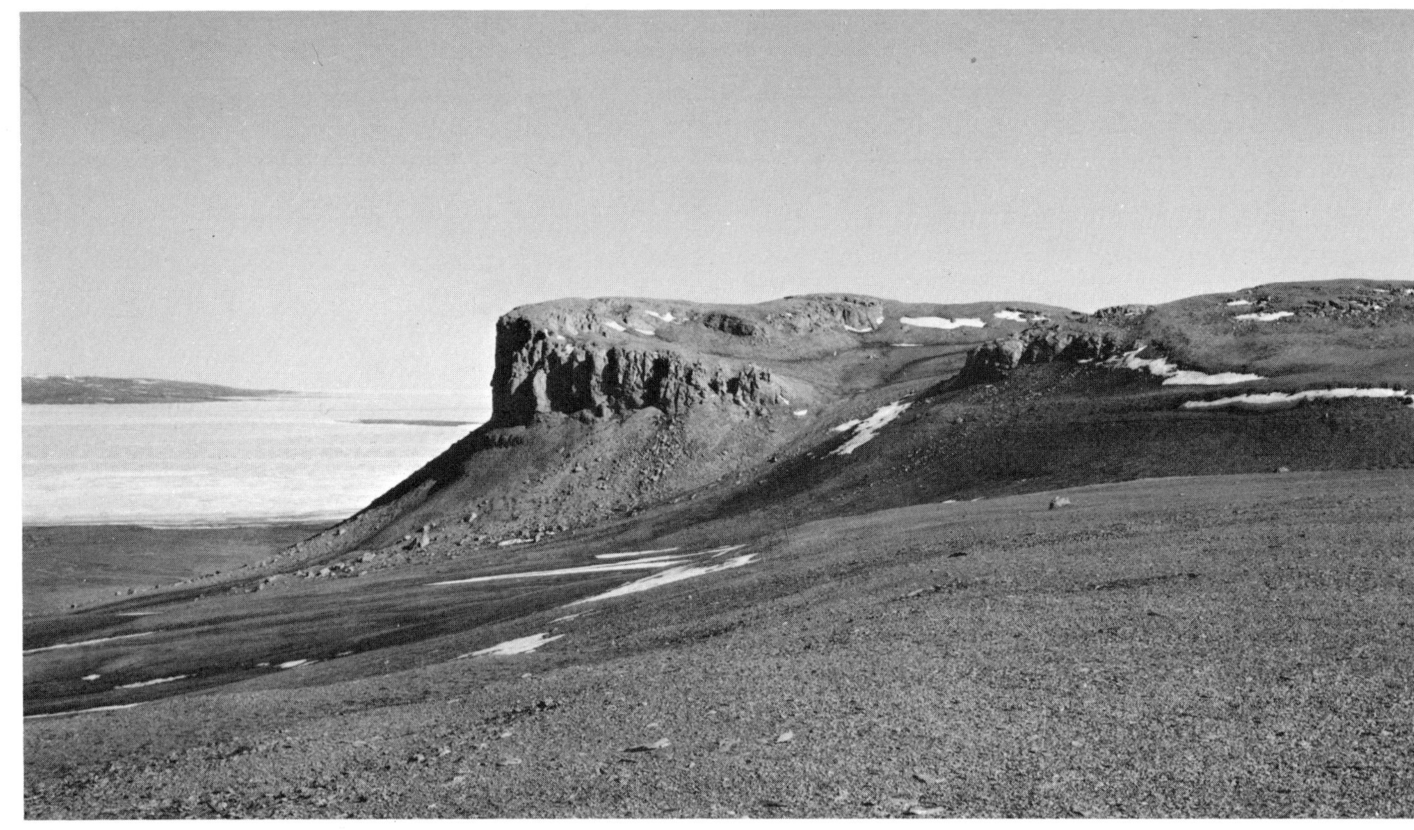

PLATE X-3. Upper Devonian Frasnian Gyrfalcon Bluffs, northern Banks Island.

Griper Bay was evidently deposited under non-marine conditions but thin beds with Famennian brachiopods occur about 2,000 feet above the base on Melville and Bathurst Islands (Kerr, *et al.,* 1965). Estherians, fragments of armoured fish and spores, have also been described from the Griper Bay of Melville and Bathurst Islands. The rocks assigned to this formation on Prince Patrick Island comprise about 4,500 feet of beds with no base exposed. Thin-bedded sandstone and siltstone with Frasnian brachiopods and corals form the lower part of the section; thick-bedded, light coloured non-marine sandstone, with thin coals, characterizes the upper part. The marine Frasnian beds have no known counterparts on the island to the east. Strata more or less equivalent to the Griper Bay are also present on Banks Island where they include considerable sandstone and siltstone but also some isolated Frasnian limestone reefs (Pl. X-3), the only known Upper Devonian reefs within the archipelago.

The Okse Bay Formation on Ellesmere Island (McLaren, 1963a) includes at least 10,000 feet of sandstone, siltstone, and shale with thin coal seams. They have yielded plant and fish fossils not dated more precisely than Upper Devonian. The formation has four members: a lower sandstone, a lower sandstone and shale, an upper sandstone, and an upper sandstone and shale. Two subdivisions are recognizable in the lower sandstone member, a lower unit of red and green sandy shale, and an upper unit comprising 1,350 feet of thick-bedded to massive sandstone, which appears to be the equivalent of the Hecla Bay Formation. Presumably the upper three members of the Okse Bay Formation are correlative with the Griper Bay Formation. North of the latitude of Vendom Fiord on Ellesmere Island the lower part of the Okse Bay Formation is believed to be older than to the south, and to include equivalents of the Bird Fiord and Blue Fiord Formations.

Ellesmerian Orogeny

The main interval of folding during the Ellesmerian Orogeny was between the Famennian and the Viséan. This is shown by the occurrence of Famennian rocks at the top of the essentially concordant sequence in the Franklinian Miogeosyncline, and by the local occurrence of Viséan strata at the base of the sequence in the Sverdrup Basin, which unconformably overlies the folded rocks of the Franklinian Geosyncline.

In the Franklinian Miogeosyncline the principal structures produced by the Ellesmerian Orogeny are the Parry Islands and Central Ellesmere Fold Belts. The eugeosyncline evidently experienced a long sequence of tectonic events. Some movement certainly preceded the deposition of Lower Devonian rocks. However, from available evidence it would appear that the principal period of orogenic activity within the eugeosyncline, as in the miogeo-

PLATE X-4. Parry Islands Fold Belt, northwest Melville Island, view eastward. Dark rocks in cores of anticlines are Ordovician, Silurian, and Devonian conformable sequences folded during the Ellesmerian and Melvillian Orogenies unconformably overlain by the Upper Carboniferous Canyon Fiord Formation (C) in the synclines, folded in the Melvillian Disturbance. In the distance are gently dipping Permian and Mesozoic beds (M) of southern Sverdrup Basin.

syncline, was between the Devonian and the Viséan.

The Parry Islands Fold Belt of Melville and Bathurst Islands is characterized by long, narrow, more or less symmetrical anticlines separated by broad, shallow synclines (Pl. X-4). A few steeply dipping thrust faults of small horizontal displacement parallel the regional strike of the folds. The major structural features of Parry Islands Fold Belt suggest a *décollement,* probably within the evaporitic sequence of the Ordovician Cornwallis Group.

The east–west strike of Parry Islands structures is nearly at a right angle to the north–south regional trend of structures of Boothia Uplift. On eastern Bathurst Island the two trends meet in an area of structural complexity. It is characterized chiefly by close, northerly trending folds as well as by northerly striking faults, several of which have strike-slip components. Certain folds within the Boothia Uplift adjacent to Parry Islands structures have undergone a second episode of folding as a result of the Ellesmerian Orogeny; however, the greater part of the uplift appears to have acted as a buttress that was little affected by the orogeny.

The Central Ellesmere and the Parry Islands Fold Belts bear similar structural relationships to the Boothia Uplift. Structures of Central Ellesmere Fold Belt strike southeasterly from Grinnell Peninsula across northwestern Devon Island proper, whence they curve northeasterly into southwestern Ellesmere Island and continue diagonally across the island. From Grinnell Peninsula to about the latitude of Baumann Fiord characters of the Central Ellesmere Fold Belt are analogous to those of the greater part of the Parry Islands Fold Belt. The generally simple fold patterns displayed there suggest that the southwestern part of the Central Ellesmere Fold Belt was affected by the Ellesmerian period of orogeny only.

Between Baumann Fiord and Kane Basin the Central Ellesmere Fold Belt experienced a long, complex, structural history. Folds, thrust faults, and normal faults, all striking northeast, are present. The thrust faults, commonly *en echelon,* generally dip northwest at moderate to steep angles and extend for more than a hundred miles. Two episodes of deformation, the Ellesmerian and Eurekan in the Cenozoic, are clearly in evidence in this region. This is shown by the presence of numerous outliers of the Cenozoic Eureka Sound Formation, resting with angular unconformity on rocks of early Paleozoic age but nevertheless folded and overridden by thrust faults. The relative effects of the two orogenies is difficult to assess. Many folds and normal faults, but no thrusts, are demonstrably older than the deposition of the Eureka Sound Formation, suggesting that the structures of the Ellesmerian Orogeny were predominantly folds. Several thrust faults demonstrably postdate the Eureka Sound Formation and many normal faults postdate both the Eureka Sound Formation and thrust faults. Probably the major episode of thrust faulting resulted from the Eurekan Orogeny whereas the normal faults represent a still later structural event.

The orogenic history of the Franklinian Eugeosyncline is more complex than that of its complementary miogeosyncline. The Franklinian Eugeosyncline had undergone several orogenic episodes, possibly in the Lower Cambrian in northern Ellesmere and northern Axel Heiberg Islands from the evidence provided by radiometric ages, and between the Middle Silurian and Lower Devonian in northern Axel Heiberg Island. The principal orogeny however was the Ellesmerian as shown by the widespread angular unconformity below rocks of Carboniferous age. The youngest unequivocally dated rocks below this unconformity are of Lower or Middle Devonian age. Consequently, the question of whether the Ellesmerian Orogeny or a somewhat older orogeny of about Middle or early Late Devonian affected the Franklinian Eugeosyncline cannot be answered on the basis of available evidence.

On northwestern Ellesmere Island small granitic plutons range in composition from quartz monzonite to granodiorite, quartz diorite, and diorite (Trettin, 1964). They are variously massive to foliate, and concordant to discordant. Radiometric age determinations from a pluton on Axel Heiberg Island and another from Ellesmere Island yielded ages of 360 ± 25 m.y. (late Devonian) and 335 ± 25 m.y. (early Carboniferous) respectively. The youngest rocks intruded are probably of Early Silurian age. In all probability the emplacement of these plutons was related to the Ellesmerian Orogeny. Accordingly it is unlikely that the unconformity between rocks of Middle Silurian and Lower or Middle Devonian in northern Axel Heiberg Island reflects the principal orogeny in the eugeosyncline. In the sedimentary record of the miogeosyncline, however, there is evidence that the orogenic events and uplift in the eugeosyncline preceded the Ellesmerian Orogeny of the miogeosyncline. This is shown by the clastic deposits that first appeared in the Upper Ordovician or Lower Silurian, and gradually became more extensive, reaching their maximum extent in the late Middle and Upper Devonian.

UPPER PALEOZOIC AND MESOZOIC

The end of the Ellesmerian Orogeny in late Devonian or early Carboniferous time marks a complete change in the régime of sedimentation and tectonism in the Arctic Archipelago. Following this orogeny a new cycle of sedimentation was initiated that lasted from the Carboniferous to the Upper Cretaceous. This cycle was terminated by the Eurekan Orogeny in early Cenozoic time.

The principal site of sedimentation from the Carboniferous to the Upper Cretaceous was Sverdrup Basin. In the Upper Carboniferous it is possible that small detached basins may also have existed south of the main area of subsidence, for example on northwest Melville Island. Cretaceous rocks also extend beyond the basin, most extensively in the western part of the lowlands. The Carboniferous and Permian rocks include clastics of varied grain size, carbonates, evaporites, and volcanic rocks, resting with angular unconformity on the bevelled structures of the Franklinian Orogen. The Lower Carboniferous deposits are non-marine; Upper Carboniferous and Permian beds are mainly marine.

In the Mesozoic a more monotonous suite is encountered. Nearly all rocks are medium- to fine-grained quartzose sandstone, siltstone, and shale with minor amounts of conglomerate and some basalts in the Cretaceous. Marine and non-marine deposits alternate in about equal volume. Biogenic carbonate rocks and evaporites are totally absent. Possibly cooler climatic conditions prevailed than in the Paleozoic.

There was relatively little tectonic activity between the Ellesmerian and Eurekan Orogenies, except on the margins of the Sverdrup Basin. The Melvillian Disturbance, of about Early Permian age, produced folds and faults near the south and east margins. At the western margin, defined by the Prince Patrick Uplift, movement on gravity faults was probably initiated in the Late Jurassic. All the margins were relatively resistant to subsidence and show incomplete sequences with many disconformities and gentle discordances for the Carboniferous to Upper Cretaceous interval. In the axial part of the basin, on the other hand, the sequence from the Upper Carboniferous to the Upper Cretaceous is essentially concordant. In places the concordant sequence even includes beds of early Cenozoic age. From a regional standpoint, however, there is no doubt that early Cenozoic time marks the end of uniform subsidence within the Sverdrup Basin.

Gabbroic dykes and sills intrude most of the Carboniferous to Cretaceous formations. They were probably emplaced in Cretaceous time.

UPPER PALEOZOIC

Carboniferous and Permian

For the Carboniferous and Permian the record of sedimentation includes beds of the following ages: Lower Carboniferous (Viséan); Upper Carboniferous (Bashkirian, Moscovian, Gzhelian or Zhigulevskian, and Orenburgian); and Permian (Asselian, Sakmarian, Artinskian, and Guadalupian). Earliest Carboniferous (Tournaisian), mid-Carboniferous (Namurian), and latest Permian (Dzhulfian) rocks are unknown and probably absent.

The Viséan rocks are all non-marine and are separated from the younger beds by a regional unconformity.

The Bashkirian to Guadalupian sequence is one of great complexity with intertonguing formations of conglomerate, sandstone, shale, limestone, and evaporites (Fig. X-8). Volcanic rocks also occur locally. In general the carbonate rocks, in part reefoid, intertonguing with dark shales and associated with evaporites characterize the sequence within the axial part of Sverdrup Basin. On the south and east margins sandstone and conglomerate dominate. However a substantial unit of sandstone and conglomerate also forms the base of the sequence in the axial part, and tongues of limestone extend into the marginal areas at several levels. For purposes of description the Bashkirian to Guadalupian sequence is divided into two major units; an older unit extending from the Bashkirian to the early Artinskian and a younger unit of late Artinskian and Guadalupian rocks. In the axial part of Sverdrup Basin the whole sequence is essentially concordant. There appears to be, however, a widespread disconformity within the Artinskian and this permits the discrimination of the two major units. A contemporary break is also encountered on the south and east margins of the basin. On the margins, however, there is clearly more than one break in the succession because there are overlapping formations underlain by disconformities in the Sakmarian and Guadalupian as well as in the late Artinskian.

The Upper Carboniferous and Permian formations have been dated by their fusulinacean and ammonoid faunas. Thorsteinsson has determined the fusulinaceans, W. W. Nassichuk the ammonoids. Study of these faunas is incomplete but the following provides an indication of the scope of the faunas and of the way in which the stage names are interpreted.

The oldest rocks are dated as Bashkirian (Morrowan). Rocks of this age have been positively identified on the basis of ammonoids only in reef limestone masses brought to the surface in piercement domes on Axel Heiberg and Melville Islands. Faunas of Moscovian and younger age are widely distributed. Lower Moscovian (Atokan) is proved by the presence of *Profusulinella* and *Eofusulina* and also a rich ammonoid fauna that includes *Winslowoceras*. Younger Moscovian beds are recognized by a zone with *Wedekindellina* and a second zone with *Fusulina*. The Gzhelian (Zhigulevskian) Stage is characterized by *Quasifusulina, Triticites,* and *Fusulinella;* Orenburgian by schwagerinids that indicate the Russian Zone of *Pseudofusulina*; Asselian by characteristic species of *Schwagerina*; Sakmarian by a zone with *Monodiexodina* and *Pseudoschwagerina*. Two fusulinacean zones are recognized in the lower part of the Artinskian; the lower with *Parafusulina,* the upper with *Schwagerina hyperborea* (Salter). The later Artinskian and Guadalupian rocks lack fusulinaceans and are dated by ammonoids that represent at least three stratigraphic levels. The older two, characterized successively by *Metalegoceras* and *Spirolegoceras* are dated as Artinskian; the youngest ammonoid, *Neogeoceras,* provides evidence for the recognition of Guadalupian strata.

Lower Carboniferous

The Emma Fiord Formation rests unconformably on folded rocks of the Franklinian Geosyncline and is the oldest in the Sverdrup Basin (Kerr and Trettin, 1962). Outcrops are sporadic and occur only in a belt extending from Svartevaeg on northern Axel Heiberg Island to M'Clintock Inlet in northern Ellesmere Island. The formation includes at least 1,000 feet of dark grey carbonaceous siltstone and fine-grained sandstone, variable shaly, with minor light grey sandstone, and thin coal seams with fossil plants and a microflora of Viséan age. The upper contact with the younger Carboniferous strata is invariably a disconformity.

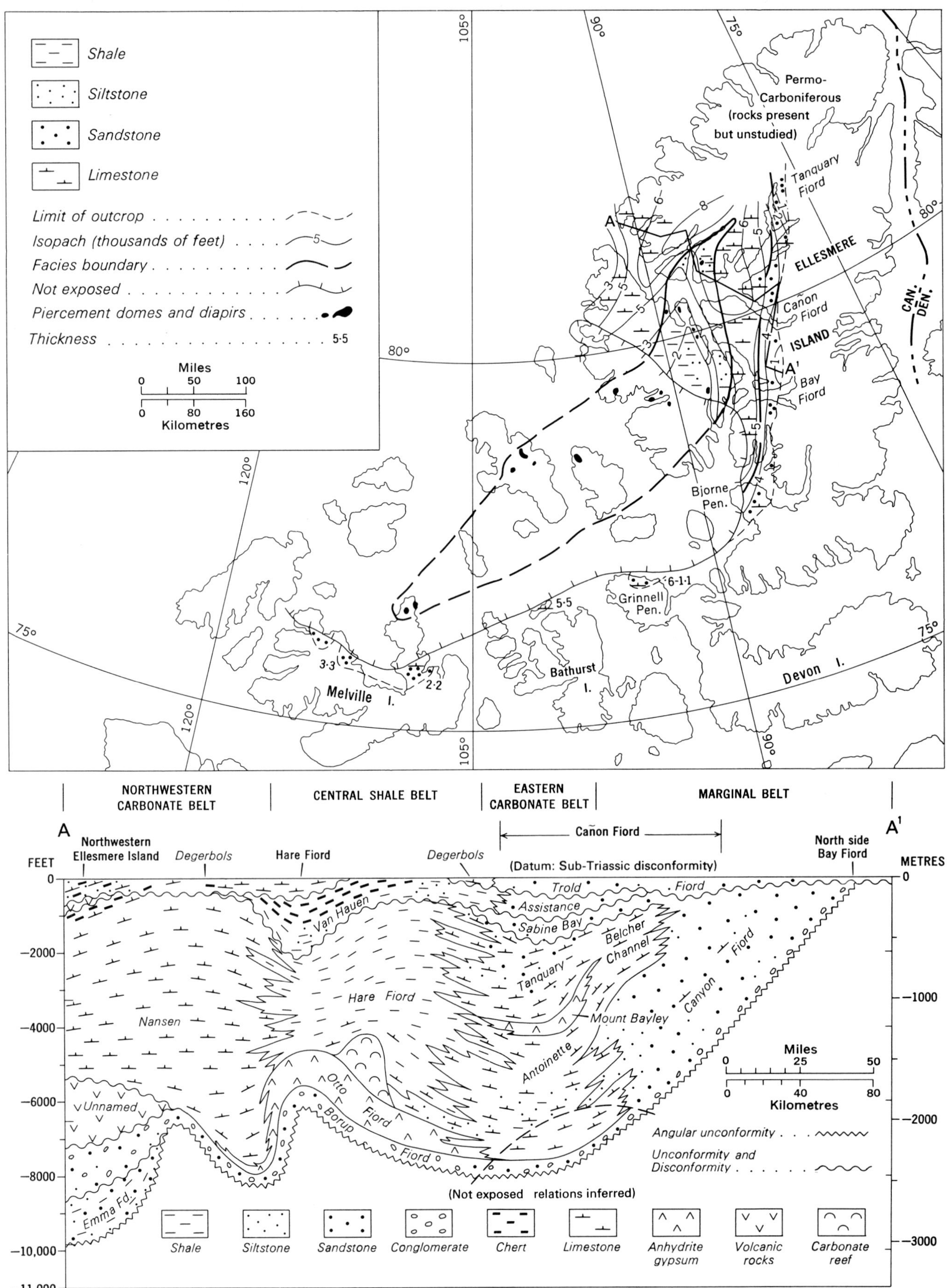

FIGURE X-8. Distribution and restored section of Pennsylvanian and Permian rocks in Arctic Archipelago (by R. Thorsteinsson).

Upper Carboniferous and Early Permian

The Bashkirian, Moscovian, Orenburgian, Gzhelian, Asselian, and Sakmarian Stages, and the early part of the Artinskian, are well represented in the Sverdrup Basin by an essentially conformable succession. Higher in the Permian, within the Artinskian, there is an unconformity throughout the basin. The late Artinskian and Guadalupian rocks that occur above this unconformity are described later.

The basal beds of the Bashkirian to early Artinskian sequence, virtually everywhere, are red conglomerate and sandstone. These rocks are represented by the Borup Fiord Formation and by the lower conglomeratic part of the Canyon Fiord Formation. The higher and greater part of the Bashkirian–early Artinskian succession is developed in four facies belts. These belts are arranged parallel to the northeasterly trending axis of the Sverdrup Basin (Fig. X-8a). From southeast to northwest the belts are as follows: (1) a marginal facies belt developed on the south and east sides of the Sverdrup Basin characterized by the clastic and carbonate rocks, respectively the Canyon Fiord and Belcher Channel Formations; (2) an eastern carbonate belt, in which the principal rock units are the Antoinette, Mount Bayley, Tanquary, and Belcher Channel Formations; (3) a central shale belt where the rocks known as the Hare Fiord Formation are mainly shale and siltstone; (4) a northwestern carbonate belt, in which the Nansen Formation is the principal rock-unit. Evaporitic rocks occur in the eastern carbonate, central shale, and northwestern carbonate belts. The eastern and northwestern carbonate belts merge east of the head of Hare Fiord in northern Ellesmere Island. The marginal facies belt with both clastic and carbonate formations marks the southern and eastern margins of the Sverdrup Basin, and is exposed as a narrow band of outcrops traceable from Melville Island to the north coast of Ellesmere Island, a distance of about 1,000 miles. Extensions of the eastern carbonate belt, central shale belt, and the northwestern carbonate belt probably underlie the central and western parts of the Sverdrup Basin.

The Borup Fiord Formation is a heterogeneous, dusky red weathering assemblage of conglomerate, conglomeratic sandstone, and sandstone, with minor siltstone and shale, that form the basal beds of the sequence in the central shale belt and adjacent carbonate belts. It varies in thickness from zero to about 1,300 feet. The formation is widely exposed in the northern parts of Axel Heiberg and Ellesmere Islands, and grades laterally into the basal conglomerate of the Canyon Fiord Formation of the marginal facies belt. The Borup Fiord lies either with disconformity upon the sporadically distributed Emma Fiord Formation or with angular unconformity upon older rocks. Throughout much of their extent the Borup Fiord and Canyon Fiord Formations constitute the oldest rocks of Sverdrup Basin. Borup Fiord lacks diagnostic fossils but is dated tentatively as Bashkirian.

The Otto Fiord Formation occurs in the central shale belt and the adjacent carbonate belts. It is composed mainly of medium- to thick-bedded anhydrite and minor interbeds of limestone, and ranges in thickness from zero to nearly 1,200 feet. The contact with the underlying Borup Fiord Formation is gradational. In the axial region of Sverdrup Basin it is approximately coextensive with, though somewhat more extensive than, the immediately younger Hare Fiord Formation. It grades laterally into the basal limestone beds of the Nansen Formation northwest and north, and into the basal limestones of the Antoinette Formation to the southeast.

The Nansen Formation typically developed in the northwestern carbonate belt is a uniform succession of limestone, 4,000 to more than 7,000 feet thick. It is widely exposed in northern Axel Heiberg Island and northwestern Ellesmere Island. It is also exposed at the edge of the marginal facies belt on Raanes Peninsula in central Ellesmere Island where the upper beds are reefoid. The basal contact of the Nansen Formation is variable. In the vicinity of facies change with correlative rocks of the Hare Fiord Formation, the Nansen gradationally overlies the Otto Fiord evaporites, but where the evaporites are missing it gradationally overlies the Borup Fiord Formation (Fig. X-8b). At the northwestern extremity of Ellesmere Island about 1,800 feet of volcanic flows and pyroclastic rocks is intercalated between the Nansen and Borup Fiord Formations. The Nansen Formation evidently attains its greatest thickness where it grades laterally into the shale of the Hare Fiord Formation. In such areas, for example, reefoid development is common in the lower part of the Nansen Formation. On Raanes Peninsula the Nansen rocks contain much interbedded quartzose sandstone and chert is important in the upper part on Axel Heiberg Island. The Nansen contains abundant fusulinaceans that range in age from Lower Moscovian to early Artinskian.

The eastern carbonate belt is best represented between Bay and Tanquary Fiords where the characteristic succession is four, or locally, three formations. From oldest to youngest these are: the Canyon Fiord Formation which consists mainly of reddish terrigenous clastic rocks, and includes conglomerate like that in the Borup Fiord Formation. It ranges from Bashkirian or Moscovian to early Orenburgian. The Antoinette Formation consists mainly of limestone and sandstone, 1,400 to over 2,600 feet thick, intertonguing with and overlying the Canyon Fiord Formation. Where overlying the Canyon Fiord it is late Orenburgian to Asselian but at East Cape in Canyon Fiord it includes equivalents of the Canyon Fiord Formation ranging in age from Moscovian to Asselian. The Mount Bayley Formation includes up to 820 feet of anhydrite with minor limestone. It lies gradationally on the Antoinette Formation and is probably Asselian. The overlying Tanquary Formation comprises 800 to 2,200 feet of Sakmarian to early Artinskian limestone and sandstone. The formation is everywhere underlain by the Mount Bayley Formation, the contact being gradational.

The Hare Fiord Formation, the characteristic unit of the central shale belt, includes 1,000 to more than 4,000 feet of beds, mainly grey siltstone and shale with lesser amounts of impure limestone and chert, resting gradationally on the Otto Fiord evaporites. Limestone bioherms, a few tens of feet to more than 1,500 feet thick, containing a brachiopod and ammonoid fauna of lower Moscovian age (Nassichuk, 1965) occur in the lower part. The non-reef parts of the Hare Fiord Formation contain fusulinacean and ammonoid faunas of Moscovian to early Artinskian age. The Hare Fiord Formation outcrops between Whitsunday Bay on Axel Heiberg Island and the head of Hare Fiord on Ellesmere Island, grading laterally into carbonate rocks. The conjectured distribution of the Hare Fiord Formation in southwestern regions of the Sverdrup Basin where Permian–Carboniferous rocks are hidden beneath younger rocks (Fig. X-8a) is based upon extrapolation of the geological relationships evident on Axel Heiberg and Ellesmere Islands and the occurrence of anhydrite diapirs which are derived from the Otto Fiord Formation. Inclusions of reef-like limestone in the anhydrite contain ammonoids of Bashkirian age. The large intrusions occur only where the Otto Fiord evaporites are overlain by incompetent siltstone and shale beds of the Hare Fiord Formation, for example on Svartefjeld Peninsula. In northwest Axel Heiberg Island where Otto Fiord evaporites are overlain by competent carbonate beds of the Nansen Formation only small bodies of intrusive anhydrite are found. Furthermore, the Mount Bayley Formation which outcrops in western Ellesmere Island is lithologically similar to the Otto Fiord Formation and the two formations attain comparable maximum thickness, but the Mount Bayley rocks are invariably overlain by competent limestone and sandstone beds and do not form diapirs.

The sequence of formations in the marginal facies belt is particularly variable owing to the presence of several disconformities and an angular unconformity. The lower beds are clastics of the Canyon Fiord Formation and the upper parts are carbonates of the Belcher Channel Formation. The latter limestones are, in places, entirely represented by clastics inseparable from the Canyon Fiord Formation and accordingly are included in it. On Ellesmere Island the Canyon Fiord Formation consists mainly of reddish sandstone and conglomerate with thin beds of limestone. It is thickest, at least 5,200 feet, in central Canyon Fiord and contains Moscovian to Sakmarian fusulinaceans, the upper part here being equivalent to the Belcher Channel carbonates. Between Canyon and Bay Fiords the thickness is much less mainly the result of bevelling prior to the deposition of the Lower Cretaceous Isachsen Formation. Farther south near the head of Trold Fiord the formation is 1,750 feet thick and ranges from Moscovian to Orenburgian. At least 1,000 feet of Canyon Fiord beds are present north of Eids Fiord.

On Melville Island the Canyon Fiord rocks occur in two tectonic situations. On eastern Melville Island about 2,000 feet of sandstone and conglomerate, with Bashkirian or Moscovian brachiopods, form the lower part of the Sverdrup Basin sequence, and are overlain concordantly but disconformably by Permian rocks. On northwestern Melville Island, south of Sverdrup Basin, Canyon Fiord rocks are preserved in isolated synclines. South of Raglan Range about 4,000 feet of sandstone, conglomerate, and minor limestone with Moscovian fusulinaceans occurs, but a few miles to the north, on the north side of the range, these rocks are absent and the Guadalupian Trold Fiord Formation rests directly on the Devonian. The present isolation of the Canyon Fiord rocks is partly related to the Melvillian disturbance described later, but it is also probable that some Canyon Fiord rocks of northwestern Melville Island were deposited in depressions separate from Sverdrup Basin.

The Belcher Channel Formation which outcrops throughout much of the marginal facies belt consists mainly of limestone, in part quartzose and bioclastic, and minor sandstone. The formation is most complete on Ellesmere Island between Bjorne Peninsula and Canyon Fiord, where 1,000 to 1,900 feet is present, resting with gradational contact on the Canyon Fiord Formation, and ranging in age from Orenburgian to early Artinskian. On Grinnell Peninsula it includes about 600 feet of Sakmarian and early Artinskian limestone which lies either with disconformity on the Canyon Fiord Formation, or with angular unconformity on rocks of lower Paleozoic age (Nassichuk, 1965). On Helena Island the formation includes some 600 feet of beds of uncertain age resting with angular unconformity on lower Paleozoic rocks. Belcher Channel rocks in northeastern Melville Island disconformably overlie the Canyon Fiord Formation and are entirely early Artinskian.

The sub-Belcher Channel disconformity is apparently responsible for the absence of Canyon Fiord rocks from northern Bathurst Island and parts of Grinnell Peninsula. It is probable that this disconformity reflects late Paleozoic movement of Boothia Uplift.

Melvillian Disturbance

In at least two areas on the margin of Sverdrup Basin folding and faulting termed herein the Melvillian Disturbance took place during the interval between deposition of Upper Carboniferous and Upper Permian rocks. The effects are best displayed in northwest Melville Island between Raglan Range and Canrobert Hills. There, the Upper Carboniferous Canyon Fiord Formation was folded along the same east–west axis first established during the Ellesmerian Orogeny (Pl. X-4). Nearby the Guadalupian Trold Fiord Formation rests unconformably upon the Canyon Fiord rocks and shows no sign of Melvillian folds. At the head of Trold Fiord, Ellesmere Island, an angular unconformity separates the Canyon Fiord and Trold Fiord Formations; the Upper Carboniferous rocks were faulted against Ordovician limestones prior to deposition of the Permian beds.

Late Permian

The Permian rocks representing the late Artinskian and Guadalupian are approximately co-extensive with those of the Bashkirian to early Artinskian interval, but parts of the late Permian succession are transgressive. Two regional facies belts may be distinguished. The basinal facies is composed of fine-grained clastics and chert; the van Hauen Formation is overlain by carbonates and chert of the Degerbols Formation. The marginal facies, indicating near-shore conditions on the south and east edges of Sverdrup Basin, consists of glauconitic sandstone divided into the Sabine Bay, Assistance, and Trold Fiord Formations. Regional disconformities mark the base and top of most of these formations, and at various localities one or more may have been removed by erosion, so that various formational sequences occur. All the formations except the Sabine Bay are entirely marine. The marine beds contain abundant brachiopods, bryozoans, and rare ammonoids. Fusulinaceans so abundant in the underlying Moscovian–early Artinskian rocks are completely unrepresented in these younger Permian faunas.

The Sabine Bay Formation consists of mainly nonmarine, light coloured sandstone, conglomeratic sandstone, and conglomerate of late Artinskian age (Tozer and Thorsteinsson, 1964; Nassichuk, 1965). On northeastern Melville Island where the thickness varies between 20 and 400 feet it lies between the Belcher Channel and Assistance Formations. On western Ellesmere Island the Sabine Bay is exposed in a narrow belt from south of Canyon Fiord to Tanquary Fiord varying in thickness from a feather edge to 640 feet and resting on the Belcher Channel Formation or the Tanquary Formation. The formation is overlain by either the Assistance or the Trold Fiord Formation. Sabine Bay rocks are believed to pinch-out towards the northwest, and to have no equivalents within the basinal facies of Sverdrup Basin.

The Assistance Formation is composed principally of greyish sandstone and siltstone, variably glauconitic, commonly poorly consolidated, replete with brachiopods. It ranges in thickness from zero to 1,200 feet and contains late Artinskian ammonoids. It is distributed discontinuously along south and east margins of the Sverdrup Basin, from northeastern Melville Island to Greely Fiord on Ellesmere Island and is apparently equivalent to the van Hauen Formation of the basinal facies.

The Trold Fiord Formation is mainly glauconitic sandstone with minor chert and limestone, variably consolidated and as much as 1,000 feet thick. Fossils are abundant, mainly brachiopods and at one locality the Guadalupian ammonoid *Neogeoceras* (Nassichuk, *et al.*,

PLATE X-5. Lower Devonian Eids Formation (E), folded during the Ellesmerian Orogeny unconformably overlain by 100 feet of Permian glauconitic sandstone of the Trold Fiord Formation (T) and the Lower Triassic Bjorne Formation (B). View north of Trold Fiord, Ellesmere Islands.

1965). It transgresses south and southeast, and overlies several formations: the Sabine Bay, Assistance, and Canyon Fiord, and the lower Paleozoic (Pl. X-5).

The van Hauen Formation of the basinal facies belt is most commonly black siltstone and shale, variably calcareous and non-calcareous, and up to 2,460 feet thick. Bedded black chert, apparently an alteration product of siltstone, forms a conspicuous constituent in the upper part of some sections. Van Hauen rocks have not yielded diagnostic fossils but are dated as late Artinskian because they grade laterally into the Assistance Formation on Bjorne Peninsula of Ellesmere Island.

The Degerbols Formation, the youngest Permian formation of the basinal facies, comprises up to 1,100 feet of predominantly cherty and fossiliferous limestone. The formation outcrops extensively in northern Axel Heiberg and Ellesmere Islands where it commonly rests on the van Hauen Formation. It appears to be at least approximately the same age as the Trold Fiord Formation and is therefore tentatively dated as Guadalupian. In some places, however, the Degerbols rests directly on the Nansen Formation, and it would appear that the van Hauen beds are truncated. The Degerbols of northern Axel Heiberg Island is mainly light coloured, fossiliferous chert, with minor siltstone. This chert is apparently altered limestone. About 120 feet of basaltic flows and pyroclastic rocks are locally present between the Nansen and Degerbols Formations on northeast Axel Heiberg Island. On southern Ellesmere Island and Melville Island the marginal and basinal sequences evidently intertongue as bioclastic limestone of the Degerbols type is associated with the marginal sandstone formations. On Bjorne Peninsula at least 465 feet of white limestone overlies the Assistance Formation, this limestone forms the classical outcrops of Great Bear Cape, discovered by Per Schei. A similar limestone on Sabine Peninsula, Melville Island, lies between beds of Assistance and Trold Fiord facies (Nassichuk, 1965).

MESOZOIC

In the Arctic Archipelago the principal site of Mesozoic sedimentation was Sverdrup Basin (Pl. X-6). Cretaceous rocks occur south and east of the basin as outliers resting on the folded rocks of the Franklinian Geosyncline, and they also form an extensive cover over the little disturbed Paleozoic rocks on Banks Island of the western Arctic Lowlands.

In the axial part of Sverdrup Basin Mesozoic strata from the Triassic to the Upper Cretaceous are structurally conformable as are the Permian and Triassic rocks. Dis-

PLATE X-6. Mesozoic rocks north of Blaa Mountain, Ellesmere Island, folded during the Eurekan Orogeny. Formations are: Triassic, H–Heiberg; Jurassic, B–Borden Island; S–Savik; A–Awingak; Lower Cretacous, I–Isachsen; dark cuesta capped by Cretaceous basalt. Recessive Jura-Cretaceous Deer Bay Formation, not visible, occurs between Awingak and Isachsen Formations.

conformities occur however beneath the Triassic and at several levels in the Jurassic. On the margins many formations overstep. Such known formations are: Triassic: Karnian (Schei Point), Norian (Heiberg); Jurassic: Sinemurian (Borden Island), Toarcian (Wilkie Point), and Volgian (Mould Bay); mid-Lower Cretaceous (Isachsen).

During the Mesozoic the archipelago was unaffected by orogeny. In many areas the rocks are folded, but the folding took place during Eurekan Orogeny in Cenozoic time.

The Mesozoic rocks consist mainly of fine- to medium-grained quartzose sandstone, siltstone, and shale. Conglomerate is volumetrically unimportant. Basalt flows are interbedded with Cretaceous sedimentary rocks in northern Sverdrup Basin. Marine and non-marine sediments alternate. Commonly the marine Mesozoic formations consist of shale in central Sverdrup Basin, with contemporaneous sands on the south and east margins. The non-marine beds are frequently crossbedded, ripple-marked, and contain coal at several horizons. Shallow-water features are also common in the marine formations. It follows that most of the sediment was deposited in relatively shallow water, upon a surface characterized by low gradients. The non-marine beds were presumably deposited on deltas. During the three principal periods of deltaic development (Triassic Heiberg Formation, Jurassic Awingak Formation, and Lower Cretaceous Isachsen Formation) thin, widely distributed marine beds are interbedded with the non-marine sediments, indicating periodical marine transgressions over the deltas. The wide distribution of these marine beds indicates that the deltas were of very low relief.

The volume of Mesozoic sediment originally deposited in the Sverdrup Basin was large, probably more than 150,000 cubic miles. The boundary between the shale and sand facies belts suggests that the source of most of this sediment lay east and south of the basin. Minor amounts of sediment were derived from the north in Lower Triassic time and from the north or northwest in the Upper Triassic (Karnian) and possibly also the Middle Jurassic Callovian). The Lower Triassic rocks of northern origin were probably derived by uplift of the metamorphic complex of northern Axel Heiberg Island. These sources were probably volumetrically unimportant, the main source of the great volume of clastic sediments, mainly fine-grained and commonly quartzose, lay to the south and west; the precise provenance is uncertain. Some sediments may have been derived from the denudation of the folded Paleozoic rocks. However, the area embraced by the Franklinian Geosyncline was largely denuded by Upper Carboniferous time. The large volume and fine-grained nature of the Mesozoic sediment suggest that much came from distant sources, such as the west slope of the East Greenland Caledonides or the west slope of the Appalachian Mountains. Sediment from the latter would have been transported by a major drainage system traversing the Canadian Shield. Such a drainage system would be analogous to the Missouri–Mississippi System of today, feeding sediment from distant uplifted areas, across extensive lowlands, into the Gulf of Mexico.

The distribution of sand and conglomeratic beds in the Triassic, Jurassic, and early Lower Cretaceous marine formations (up to the Valanginian) suggests that the shorelines during these periods were not far from the east and south limits of their outcrop. This is also suggested by the complete absence of marine Triassic and Jurassic rocks south and east of Sverdrup Basin. The Triassic, Jurassic, and early Lower Cretaceous faunas are closely related to contemporary assemblages in Spitsbergen, East Greenland, and northern Siberia. These faunas presumably entered Sverdrup Basin from the northwest, and their close relationship with those of other arctic areas suggests that a marine area, probably an oceanic basin, existed on the site of the Arctic Ocean during Triassic, Jurassic, and Cretaceous time, as has been suggested by Diener, Haug, Arkell, Frebold, and Sachs.

The Albian transgression in the arctic islands was much more widespread, but, as in earlier Mesozoic time, the Albian seas probably did not extend far beyond the southeast limit of Sverdrup Basin, although they did extend beyond the basin on Melville and Banks Islands, and were undoubtedly continuous with the Albian sea that covered western Canada.

In the Upper Cretaceous at the time of deposition of the Kanguk Formation in Sverdrup Basin marine strata were deposited not only in western Canada but also on the east shore of Baffin Bay, Greenland. The Upper Cretaceous rocks of west Greenland nonconformably overlie Precambrian rocks and they are the oldest and only marine Mesozoic sediments in the Baffin Bay area. For this period it is possible, as suggested by Teichert and Birkelund, that there was a direct marine connection between the region of Sverdrup Basin and Baffin Bay. The connection could probably have been in the vicinity of southern Ellesmere Island where Cenozoic non-marine beds apparently rest unconformably upon Paleozoic formations. It is possible that Upper Cretaceous rocks were originally present, but removed prior to the deposition of the Cenozoic strata.

Triassic

Triassic rocks of the Sverdrup Basin are exposed on Ellesmere, Axel Heiberg, Cornwall, Table, Exmouth, Cameron, Melville, Prince Patrick, Brock, and Borden Islands. Their distribution and facies are shown on Figures X-9 and X-10.

Permian–Triassic Boundary

In the axial part of Sverdrup Basin and in parts of the marginal area Lower Triassic rocks rest disconformably upon Permian strata. In places the younger Permian rocks are Guadalupian; elsewhere they are late Artinskian. Latest Permian (Dzhulfian or Ochoan) strata are unknown

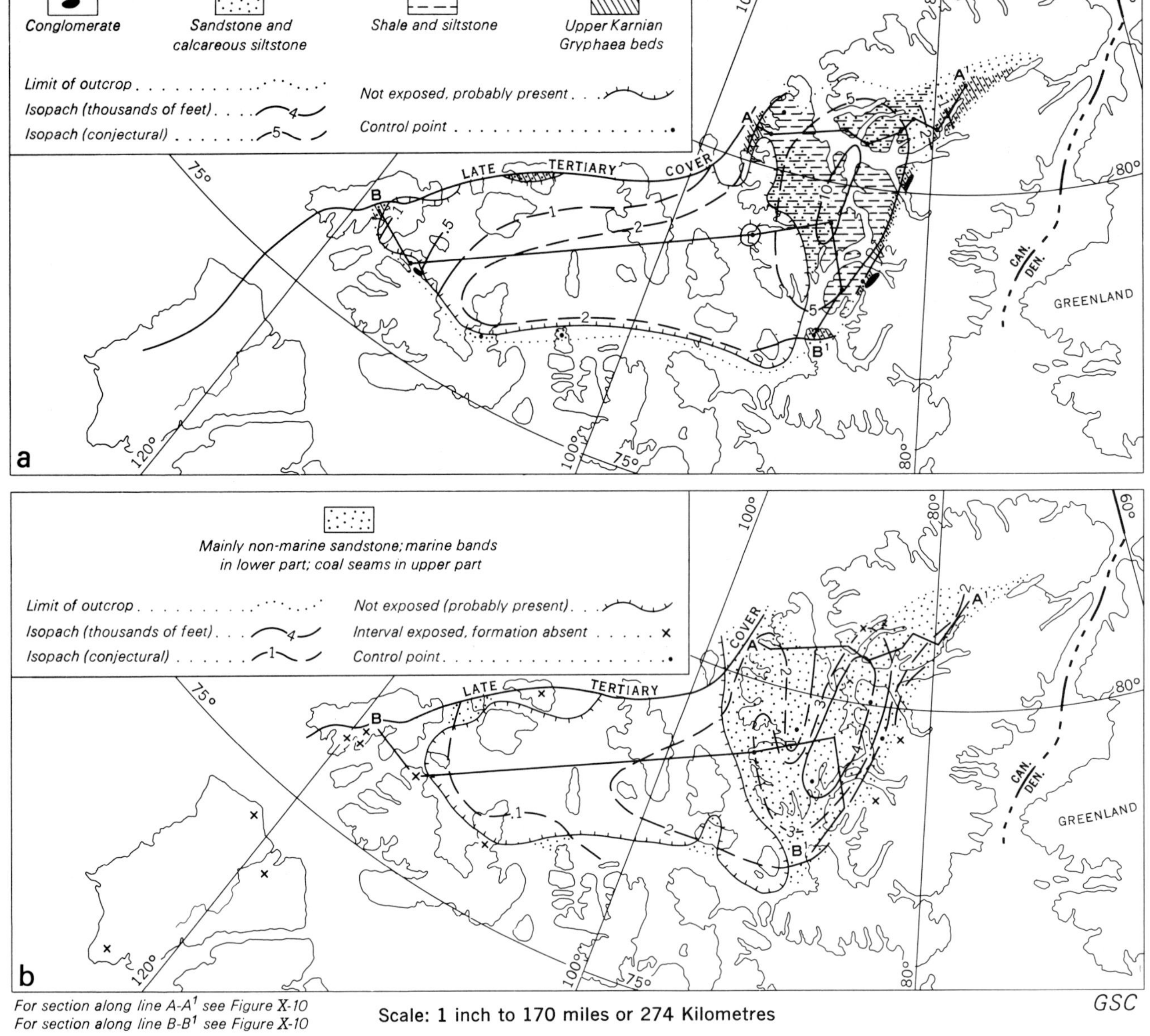

FIGURE X-9. Distribution of Triassic rocks in Arctic Archipelago; (a) Griesbachian to Karnian, (b) Norian, Heiberg Formation (by E. T. Tozer).

in the archipelago. The oldest Triassic beds are Lower Griesbachian, as old as any Triassic rocks known. The contact between the Permian and Triassic rocks is invariably well marked by lithological change but not marked by physical evidence of erosion. From the available evidence it appears that the Permian–Triassic boundary is paraconformable, marks a hiatus, and that the gap in the sedimentary record is within the latest Permian and not in the Triassic.

Marine Rocks

Marine conditions prevailed throughout the axial part of Sverdrup Basin from the earliest Triassic (Griesbachian) to the early Upper Triassic (Karnian). Some of the Lower Triassic beds on the margins were probably deposited in a non-marine environment. For this interval the sections on the margins of Sverdrup Basin differ from those of the axis both in thickness and lithology. Most of the rock on the south and east margins consists of sandstone and calcareous siltstone (Bjorne and Schei Point Formations); in the axial part it is shale and siltstone (Blind Fiord and Blaa Mountain Formations). On the northwest margin of the basin the sections are of mixed character. For Griesbachian, Smithian, Spathian, Anisian, and Ladinian the rocks are mainly shale and siltstone but in the Dienerian and Karnian the sections include sandstone and conglomerate.

The Bjorne Formation disconformably overlies Permian strata and consists mainly of quartzose, commonly crossbedded sandstone, with conglomeratic interbeds on

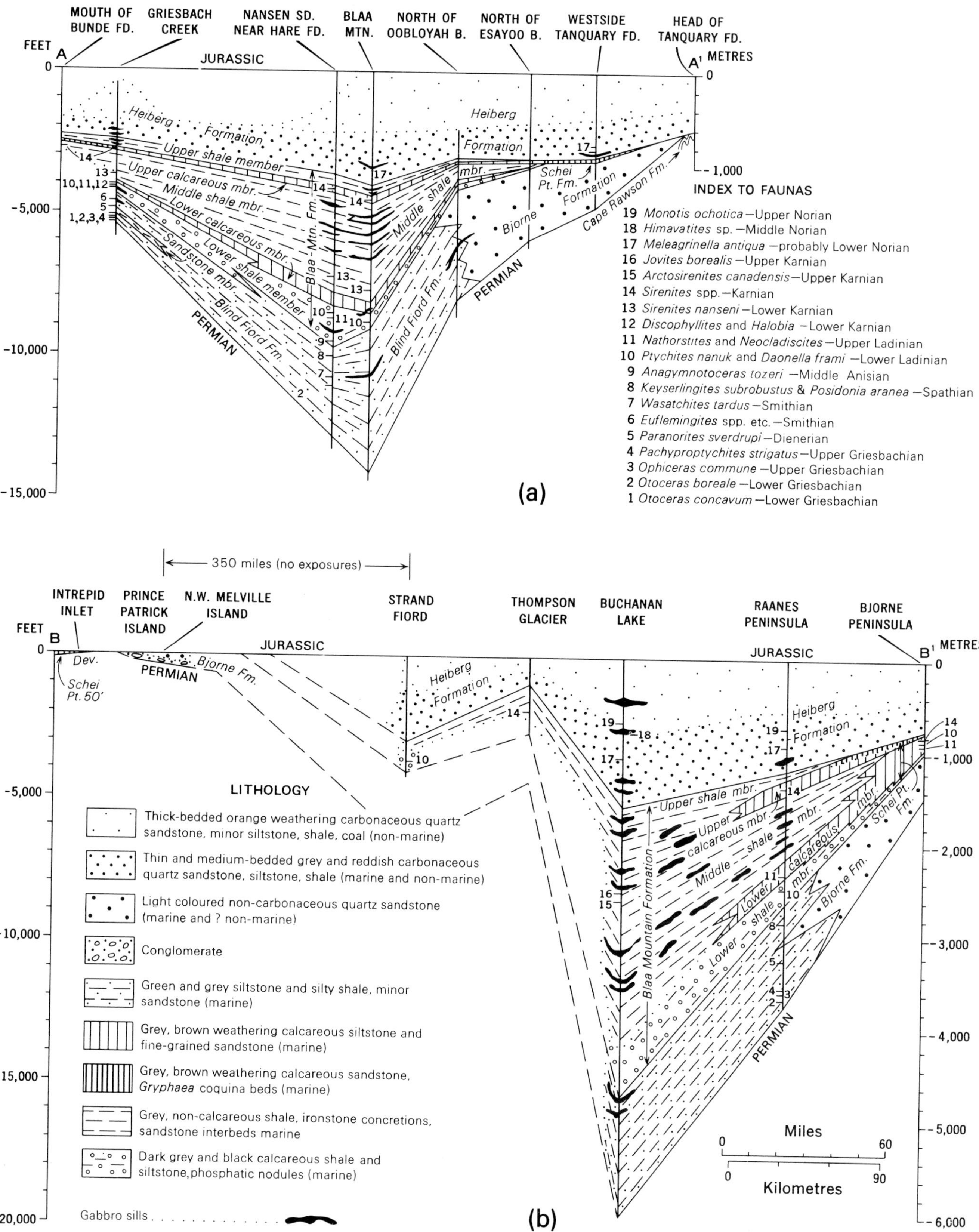
MOUTH OF BUNDE FD.
GRIESBACH CREEK
NANSEN SD. NEAR HARE FD.
BLAA MTN.
NORTH OF OOBLOYAH B.
NORTH OF ESAYOO B.
WESTSIDE TANQUARY FD.
HEAD OF TANQUARY FD.
FEET
A
A'
METRES
JURASSIC
Heiberg Formation
Upper shale member
Upper calcareous mbr.
Middle shale mbr.
Lower calcareous mbr.
Lower shale member
Sandstone mbr.
Blind Fiord Fm.
PERMIAN
Blaa-Mtn. Fm.
Middle shale mbr.
Blind Fiord Fm.
Schei Pt. Fm.
Bjorne Formation
Cape Rawson Fm.
0
-5,000
-10,000
-15,000
-1,000
INDEX TO FAUNAS
19 Monotis ochotica—Upper Norian
18 Himavatites sp.—Middle Norian
17 Meleagrinella antiqua—probably Lower Norian
16 Jovites borealis—Upper Karnian
15 Arctosirenites canadensis—Upper Karnian
14 Sirenites spp.—Karnian
13 Sirenites nanseni—Lower Karnian
12 Discophyllites and Halobia—Lower Karnian
11 Nathorstites and Neocladiscites—Upper Ladinian
10 Ptychites nanuk and Daonella frami—Lower Ladinian
9 Anagymnotoceras tozeri—Middle Anisian
8 Keyserlingites subrobustus & Posidonia aranea—Spathian
7 Wasatchites tardus—Smithian
6 Euflemingites spp. etc.—Smithian
5 Paranorites sverdrupi—Dienerian
4 Pachyproptychites strigatus—Upper Griesbachian
3 Ophiceras commune—Upper Griesbachian
2 Otoceras boreale—Lower Griesbachian
1 Otoceras concavum—Lower Griesbachian
(a)
350 miles (no exposures)
INTREPID INLET
PRINCE PATRICK ISLAND
N.W. MELVILLE ISLAND
STRAND FIORD
THOMPSON GLACIER
BUCHANAN LAKE
RAANES PENINSULA
BJORNE PENINSULA
FEET
B
B'
METRES
JURASSIC
Dev.
Schei Pt. 50'
PERMIAN
Bjorne Fm.
Heiberg Formation
Upper shale mbr.
Upper calcareous mbr.
Middle shale mbr.
Lower calcareous mbr.
Lower shale
Blaa Mountain Formation
Schei Pt. Fm.
Bjorne Fm.
PERMIAN
LITHOLOGY
Thick-bedded orange weathering carbonaceous quartz sandstone, minor siltstone, shale, coal (non-marine)
Thin and medium-bedded grey and reddish carbonaceous quartz sandstone, siltstone, shale (marine and non-marine)
Light coloured non-carbonaceous quartz sandstone (marine and ? non-marine)
Conglomerate
Green and grey siltstone and silty shale, minor sandstone (marine)
Grey, brown weathering calcareous siltstone and fine-grained sandstone (marine)
Grey, brown weathering calcareous sandstone, Gryphaea coquina beds (marine)
Grey, non-calcareous shale, ironstone concretions, sandstone interbeds marine
Dark grey and black calcareous shale and siltstone, phosphatic nodules (marine)
Gabbro sills
Miles
0
60
0
90
Kilometres
(b)
GSC

FIGURE X-10. Restored sections, Triassic formations of Arctic Archipelago; (a) along lines A–A′, (b) along lines B–B′ of Figure X-9 (by E. T. Tozer).

the extreme margins of the basin, for example in Canyon Fiord and northeast of Trold Fiord on Ellesmere Island, and on Melville Island. Bjorne rocks weather bright red, orange, yellow, brown, and white. Fossils are rare, but *Otoceras* (Griesbachian) occurs near the base at Trold Fiord, and poorly preserved younger Lower Triassic ammonoids are known from other localities. Marine fossils are unknown in the beds on the south margin of Sverdrup Basin. The Bjorne is overlain by Anisian strata and is thus fairly well dated as Lower Triassic. The contemporary rocks exposed on the western coast of Ellesmere Island and on eastern and northern Axel Heiberg Island are the Blind Fiord Formation, which consists of green and grey siltstone, fine-grained sandstone, and shale. The Blind Fiord beds are well dated by ammonoid faunas. On Raanes Peninsula, eastern Axel Heiberg Island, and near Hare Fiord, they span the Lower Triassic, from the Griesbachian to the Spathian. Around Otto Fiord and on northern Axel Heiberg Island the uppermost beds are Smithian and the boundary between the Lower and Middle Triassic lies within the overlying Blaa Mountain Formation. On northern Axel Heiberg Island a sandstone member of Dienerian age occurs within the Blind Fiord Formation. This member consists of hard green and red sandstone, with some conglomerate and beds of *Myalina* coquina. The sandstones of this member become increasingly fine grained towards the south.

The Schei Point and Blaa Mountain Formations are essentially contemporaneous and of Anisian, Ladinian, and Karnian age. Around Otto Fiord and on northern Axel Heiberg Island latest Lower Triassic (Spathian) beds are included within the Blaa Mountain Formation. Typical Schei Point rock is grey, brown weathering, highly calcareous siltstone and fine-grained sandstone, with bioclastic layers composed of brachiopod and bivalve shells in the upper part. Shale is the typical Blaa Mountain lithology. Two prominent tongues of Schei Point lithology interfinger with the Blaa Mountain shales throughout western Ellesmere Island and on northern Axel Heiberg Island. These tongues divide the Blaa Mountain Formation into five members, in ascending order: the Lower Shale, Lower Calcareous, Middle Shale, Upper Calcareous, and Upper Shale. The Lower and Upper Calcareous Members are tongues of Schei Point facies. The Lower Shale is commonly black and calcareous, with calcareous and phosphatic concretions. The higher shales are noncalcareous, commonly with red weathering clay ironstone concretions. Shales equivalent to the Lower and Middle Shale Members are recognizable in Schei Point sections at some localities; notably on Fosheim and Raanes Peninsulas.

Throughout central Ellesmere Island, the top of the Schei Point Formation is marked by the Upper Karnian "Gryphaea Bed": 100 feet of calcareous sandstone with coquinoid layers of *Gryphaea* and *Plicatula,* which on Raanes Peninsula and north of Greely Fiord can be traced laterally into the Upper Calcareous Member of the Blaa Mountain Formation. This bed is of unusual interest. In Tanquary Fiord it oversteps the Lower Triassic Bjorne Formation. Comparable beds are also present on the west side of the Sverdrup Basin, on Prince Patrick and Borden Islands. At Intrepid Inlet, Prince Patrick Island, the Schei Point *Gryphaea* bed rests unconformably upon Devonian rocks; on Borden Island it represents the oldest exposure. A similar and apparently contemporary *Gryphaea* bed in the Blaa Mountain Formation of northwestern Axel Heiberg Island occupies the position of the Upper Calcareous Member. Upper Karnian *Gryphaea* beds are thus widely distributed on the margins of the Sverdrup Basin and their occurrence probably indicates an interval of shoal water conditions along the border of Sverdrup Basin following uplift.

The Blind Fiord and Blaa Mountain Formations of the axial part of Sverdrup Basin were laid down some considerable distance from shore. In the Triassic there were two sources of sediment, one essentially continuous feeding sediment to the south and east margins of the basin, and the other an intermittent source (or sources) providing sediment to the north and northwest margins of the basin. Formation of the Dienerian sandstone member was perhaps related to uplift of the lower Paleozoic massif of northern Axel Heiberg Island. The Upper Karnian *Gryphaea* beds of northern Axel Heiberg and Borden Islands probably reflect uplift of the marginal sill of Sverdrup Basin. Beyond the sill there was probably open Arctic Ocean, because the presence of the cosmopolitan marine faunas that entered Sverdrup Basin throughout Triassic time demands a circum-Arctic migration route. The postulated shoal or sill on the northwest margin of Sverdrup Basin does not appear at any time to have constituted a barrier to the movement of these faunas.

Upper Triassic Deltaic Rocks

The youngest Triassic formation in Sverdrup Basin is the Heiberg, which consists mainly of non-marine, carbonaceous sandstone, with marine beds at several levels in the lower part. The lower marine beds with *Meleagrinella antiqua* are probably Lower Norian, the higher marine strata include Middle Norian beds and strata with the cosmopolitan Upper Norian *Monotis ochotica.* The beds above those with *Monotis* are entirely non-marine, with fossil plants and thin coal seams. They may be partly Jurassic, but if so, they are not younger than Sinemurian. The Heiberg normally overlies the Blaa Mountain Formation or the Schei Point Formation, but at the head of Tanquary Fiord the Heiberg overlaps Cape Rawson beds.

The Heiberg Formation indicates that in late Triassic time the level of sedimentation in Sverdrup Basin rose above strandline, at first intermittently, later continuously. From the Griesbachian to the Karnian the Triassic depocentre apparently lay on eastern Axel Heiberg Island and in latest Triassic time there were at least two such centres, one on eastern and the other on western Axel Heiberg Island. They were separated by a structure on strike with the Lower Paleozoic massif at the north of the island.

Jurassic

Triassic–Jurassic Boundary

As already mentioned, it is possible that beds of earliest Jurassic age occur in the upper, non-marine part of the Heiberg Formation, but for this there is no proof. If the uppermost Heiberg beds are Jurassic they are not yet separable by lithological criteria from the lower, undoubtedly Triassic, part of the formation. The top of the uppermost Heiberg sandstone commonly forms a prominent, easily recognized bedding plane throughout the Sverdrup Basin. The next younger beds are marine Jurassic strata; in places they are Sinemurian, the Borden Island Formation; elsewhere they are Toarcian, the Savik, Wilkie Point, and Jaeger Formations. Marine Hettangian rocks are unknown and are probably absent. Both Sinemurian and Toarcian rocks overstep locally and in places a basal conglomerate occurs beneath Toarcian beds. The contact between the Heiberg and succeeding Jurassic formations is evidently a paraconformity.

Lower Jurassic (Sinemurian) Marine Rocks

The oldest known Jurassic rocks, the Sinemurian Borden Island Formation, are exposed on Borden and Melville Islands, also on eastern Axel Heiberg and western Ellesmere Islands (Fig. X-11). The formation comprises up to 200 feet of grey and green glauconitic sand and is particularly characterized by thin beds of hard, red, ferruginous sandstone. On Ellesmere and Axel Heiberg Islands the Borden Island beds overlie the Heiberg Formation. In the western islands they overlap, resting on Schei Point strata on Borden Island and upon the Bjorne Formation on Melville Island. The Borden Island Formation has not been recognized in the axial part of the Sverdrup Basin. Possibly the lowermost beds of the Savik shale are Sinemurian and equivalent to the Borden Island sands, but for this there is no evidence. The distribution of Sinemurian beds in the Sverdrup Basin is unusual, for throughout the Mesozoic it is the general rule that all beds on the margins of the basin are represented in the axial part; for the Sinemurian this does not apply. Rocks of the next Jurassic stage, the Pliensbachian, are unknown throughout the archipelago. Possibly Pliensbachian time was one of gentle uplift and erosion, and the present Sinemurian beds are remnants of a former more extensive deposit.

Later Jurassic (Toarcian–Oxfordian) Marine Rocks

Toarcian sand and sandstone on the margins of Sverdrup Basin are represented by shale in the axial region. The facies interfinger on Mackenzie King and Ellef Ringnes Islands and in the Eureka Sound area. The Lower Wilkie Point sands on Prince Patrick and Melville Islands and the Jaeger beds of Cornwall and western Ellesmere Islands are quartzose, grey and yellow or glauconitic and green. Hard red ferruginous beds and phosphatic nodules are common features. The shales of the Savik Formation on Axel Heiberg Island are light grey, argillaceous, and charged with clay ironstone concretions. The Oxfordian shales are black and silty.

The régime of marginal marine sand and axial shale deposition persisted from the Toarcian through the Bajocian and Bathonian into the Lower Callovian. Ammonite faunas of all these stages occur in the sands on the south side of the basin, and in shale on western Axel Heiberg Island.

Middle (?) and Upper Jurassic Deltaic Rocks and Marine Equivalents

In the Middle (?) and Upper Jurassic non-marine beds are widely distributed in the Sverdrup Basin (Fig. X-11a). In some areas marine strata are intercalated and the non-marine beds can be accurately dated; elsewhere they have been dated only in terms of the age of the underlying and overlying marine rocks.

On Prince Patrick and Melville Islands non-marine quartzose sands of the Upper Wilkie Point Formation lie between the Lower Bathonian *Arcticoceras* beds and the Lower Volgian Mould Bay Formation. On Cornwall Island comparable non-marine strata are assigned to the Awingak Formation which overlies Lower Callovian marine beds. The mainly non-marine Awingak Formation of Ellesmere and Axel Heiberg Islands has some marine intercalations. The formation consists of alternating units of hard pale coloured quartzose sandstone, and dark recessive silty shale and sandstone. On eastern Axel Heiberg Island the Awingak is underlain by Lower Oxfordian beds of the Upper Savik. In several areas, *Amoeboceras* of Upper Oxfordian or Lower Kimmeridgian age occurs within the formation, and on Fosheim Peninsula and near Li Fiord Lower Volgian *Buchia* beds occur in the uppermost strata. In Bunde Fiord of northwest Axel Heiberg Island the Awingak Formation is absent but *Amoeboceras*-bearing shales suggest that equivalents are present. The Awingak delta probably was formed of sediment derived from the south and east and northwest Axel Heiberg Island evidently lay beyond the edge of the delta.

Deltaic rocks are absent in the Jurassic section of Mackenzie King Island and probably on Ellef Ringnes Island. Whether the Jurassic deltas extended to these islands is not known, for disconformities probably occur in these sections.

Middle (?) and Upper Jurassic Unconformities and Disconformities

On the margins of Sverdrup Basin the Jurassic sequence is locally interrupted by unconformities and disconformities. The most profound is on southern Prince Patrick Island where the Lower Volgian Mould Bay Formation progressively truncates beds of the Wilkie Point Formation and eventually rests unconformably upon Devonian rocks. This unconformity probably reflects elevation of the Prince Patrick Uplift. On Mackenzie King Island, Oxfordian or Kimmeridgian shales of the Lower Mould Bay Formation rest directly but apparently con-

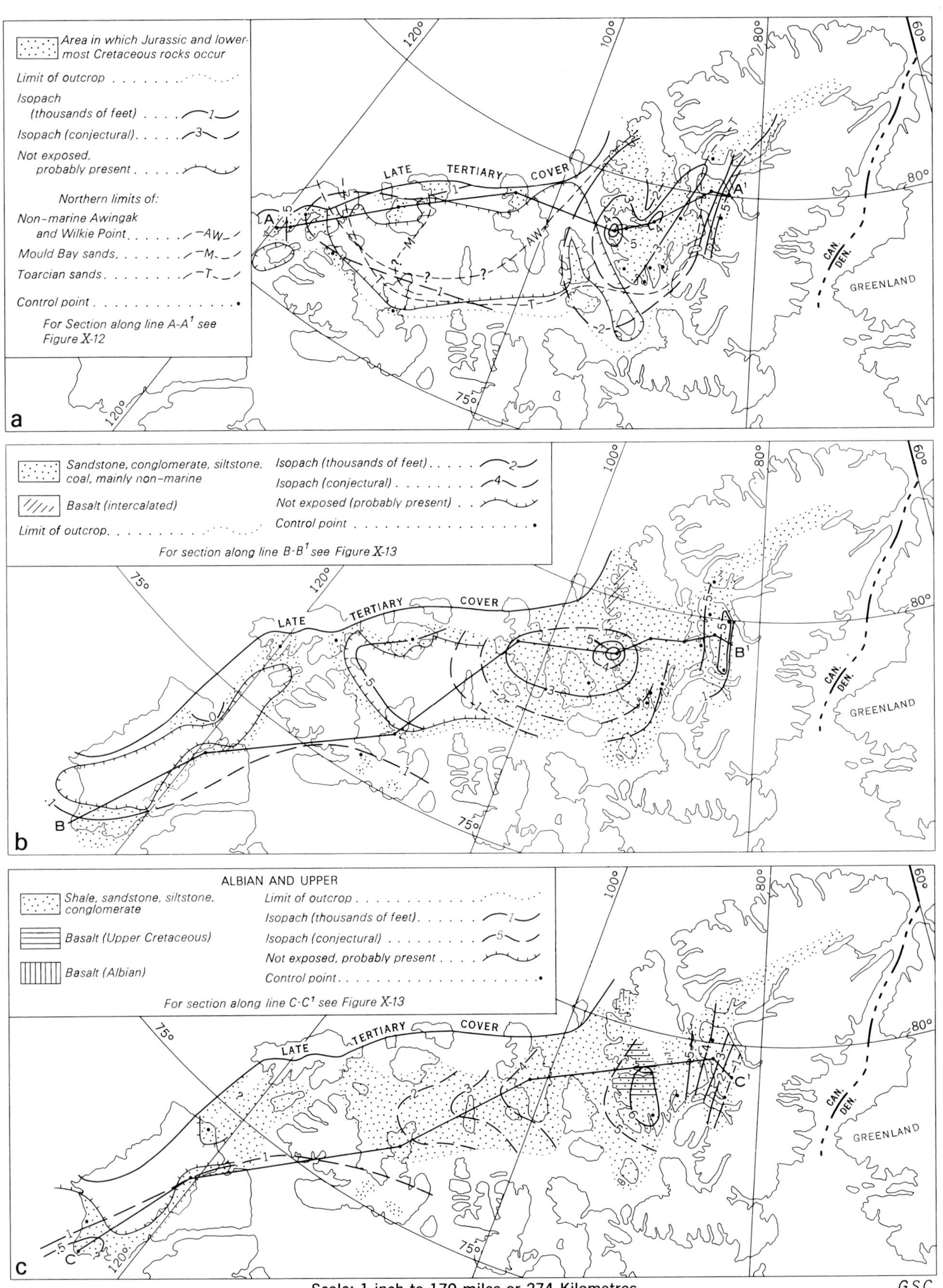

FIGURE X-11. Distribution of Jurassic and Cretaceous rocks in Arctic Archipelago; (a) Jurassic and lowermost Cretaceous, (b) Lower Cretaceous, Isachsen Formation, (c) Lower Cretaceous, Albian, and Upper Cretaceous (by E. T. Tozer).

formably upon Lower Bajocian beds of the Wilkie Point Formation. Upper Bajocian, Bathonian, and Callovian beds are unknown and apparently absent through disconformity.

On Ellef Ringnes Island no rocks are known that span the interval between the Lower Callovian and the Valanginian. Possibly such rocks are present, but the close proximity of Callovian sands to the Valanginian Deer Bay shale suggests that most or all of the Upper Jurassic is missing and that there is a disconformity.

At Buchanan Lake, eastern Axel Heiberg Island, the black, silty Upper Savik shales with Oxfordian *Cardioceras* rest directly on Lower Bajocian light grey clay shales of the Lower Savik. The lithological boundary between the Lower and Upper Savik is abrupt and probably indicates non-deposition during Upper Bajocian, Bathonian, and Callovian time. On Fosheim Peninsula the Lower Savik includes the Upper Bajocian or Lower Bathonian *Arkelloceras* beds, which have escaped truncation by the pre-Oxfordian disconformity that forms the lower boundary of the Upper Savik.

The unconformities presumably indicate positive activity on the margins of Sverdrup Basin. Probably the sections on southwestern Axel Heiberg Island are devoid of these unconformities as substantial thickness of unfossiliferous rock occurs between beds of Callovian and Volgian age.

Latest Jurassic and Earliest Cretaceous Marine Rocks

Sedimentation was widespread, the pattern of facies distribution (Fig. X-11a) resembling that for the Triassic and Jurassic. Sands and sandstone of the Mould Bay Formation occur on the southwest margin and grey shale and siltstone of the Deer Bay Formation in the axial area. Interfingering relationships are seen on Mackenzie King and southern Axel Heiberg Islands.

In the Deer Bay Formation, a homogeneous shale devoid of any evidence of physical breaks, ammonoid faunas of Upper Volgian, Berriasian, and Valanginian age indicate that sedimentation was continuous throughout the late Jurassic and early Lower Cretaceous. The Mould Bay Formation of Mackenzie King, Prince Patrick, and

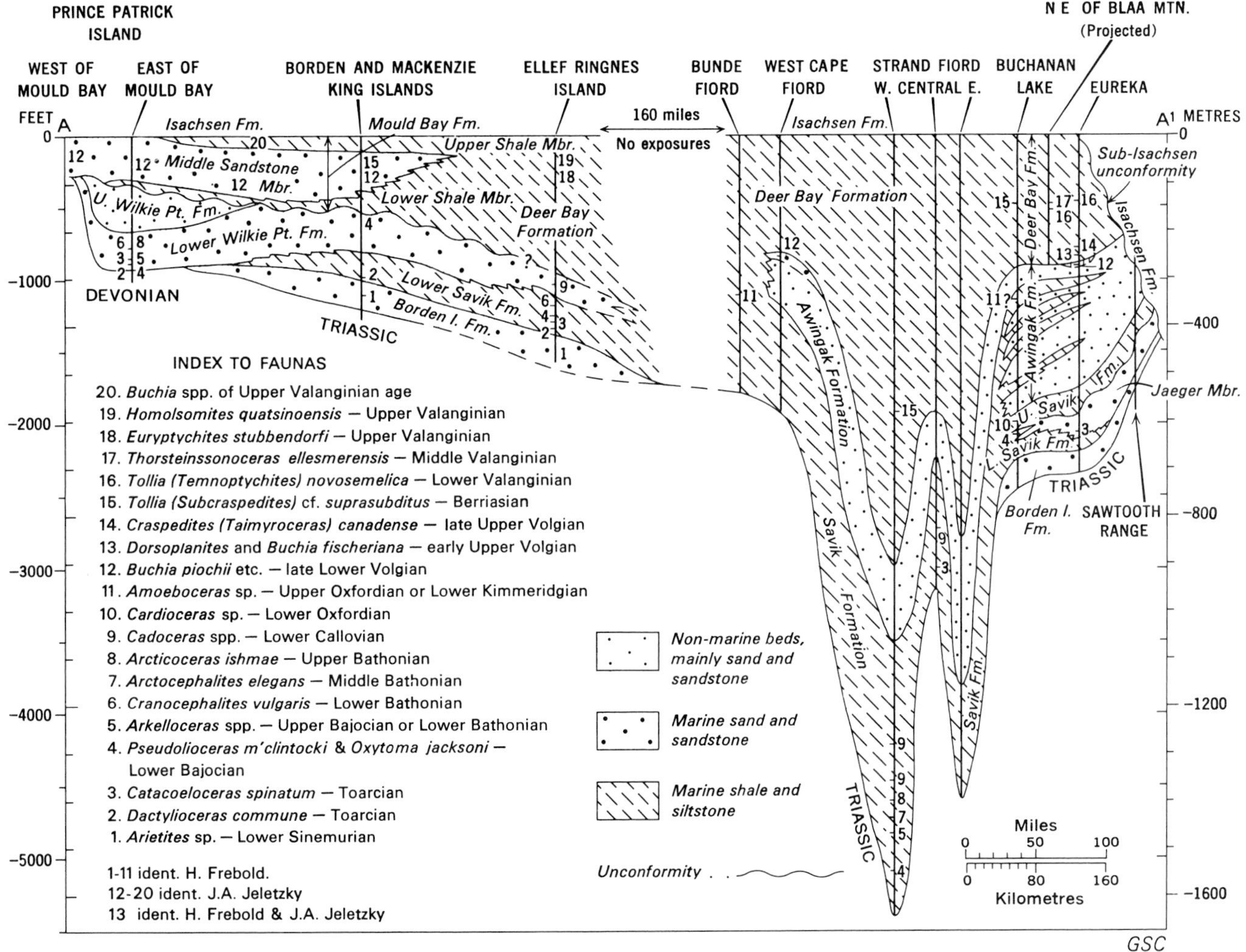

FIGURE X-12. Restored sections, Jurassic and lowermost Cretaceous rocks of Arctic Archipelago, along line A–A′ of Figure X-11 (by E. T. Tozer).

Melville Islands includes strata older than any part of the Deer Bay Formation. In the south and southwest the beds are mainly sand with some conglomerate. Tongues of shale that thicken to the northeast also occur. The Lower Shale Member on Mackenzie King Island has Oxfordian or Kimmeridgian *Amoeboceras* and the Mould Bay beds of all areas contain *Buchia* species of Lower Volgian age. The fossil record for the Mould Bay Formation of Prince Patrick Island is far less complete than that for the Deer Bay shales for it includes only Lower Volgian and Upper Valanginian. Upper Volgian, Berriasian, and much of Valanginian time are not demonstrably represented. For this period, as in the earlier Mesozoic, the margins of the Sverdrup Basin were relatively resistant to subsidence and preserve an incomplete sedimentary record.

Cretaceous

Mesozoic rocks of Triassic to the lowermost Cretaceous are found only in Sverdrup Basin. Beginning with the Isachsen Formation, the later Cretaceous rocks are more widespread and occur not only in the basin but also as outliers unconformably overlying the folded Devonian rocks and as extensive tracts in western Arctic Lowlands, lying on rocks as old as Precambrian (Figs. X-11b and X-11c).

Lower Cretaceous

The mainly non-marine Isachsen Formation conformably overlies the Deer Bay Formation on Axel Heiberg and Ellef Ringnes Islands. The relationship is essentially transitional, as shown both by the concordance of the strata and the occurrence at Good Friday Bay and near Isachsen of marine Valanginian *Buchia* beds in the lower part. On the margins of Sverdrup Basin the Isachsen beds overlap and rest on various Paleozoic and Mesozoic rocks. On Ellesmere Island, on the west side of Fosheim Peninsula Isachsen beds overlie the Deer Bay shale abruptly and concordantly, but probably disconformably. Towards the east Isachsen beds rest on progressively older Mesozoic beds: on the Awingak Formation in Sawtooth Range; on the Heiberg in central Vesle Fiord and northwest of Trold Fiord; on the Schei Point at the head of Vesle Fiord and north of Trold Fiord; on the Bjorne Formation in Canyon Fiord. Finally, northeast of Vesle Fiord and around Strathcona Fiord, the Isachsen rests on Devonian and older Paleozoic rocks. Where the Isachsen rests on upper Paleozoic or Mesozoic beds the contact is structurally conformable. On the other hand, the Devonian and older rocks that underlie the Isachsen have been folded and the contact is one of angular unconformity. On the northwest edge of Sverdrup Basin the formation abruptly and probably disconformably overlies Mould Bay strata. Beyond Sverdrup Basin, Isachsen beds occur on Banks Island and southeast Melville Island. Coal-bearing beds that occur near Pond Inlet, northern Baffin Island, possibly represent an outlier of the Isachsen resting on Precambrian crystalline rocks.

The Isachsen Formation normally consists of light coloured, quartzose sandstone, grit and conglomerate, with interbeds of dark siltstone, shale, and coal. Crossbedding is common. Lower Cretaceous leaves and plant microfossils are known from several localities. A non-marine environment of deposition is indicated for all but the thin marine beds near the base. In northwestern Axel Heiberg Island basalts are interbedded. The exact age of the Isachsen is uncertain. In places the basalt beds are Valanginian and marine Albian, and possibly also Aptian beds overlie. The greater part is probably Hauterivian and Barremian, but Aptian beds may be present.

Following deposition of the Isachsen Formation, marine transgression led to deposition of the Christopher Formation within Sverdrup Basin and on southern Melville Island and Banks Island. Christopher rocks are mainly grey shale, with calcareous septaria and concretions and small amounts of siltstone and sandstone. On Elles-

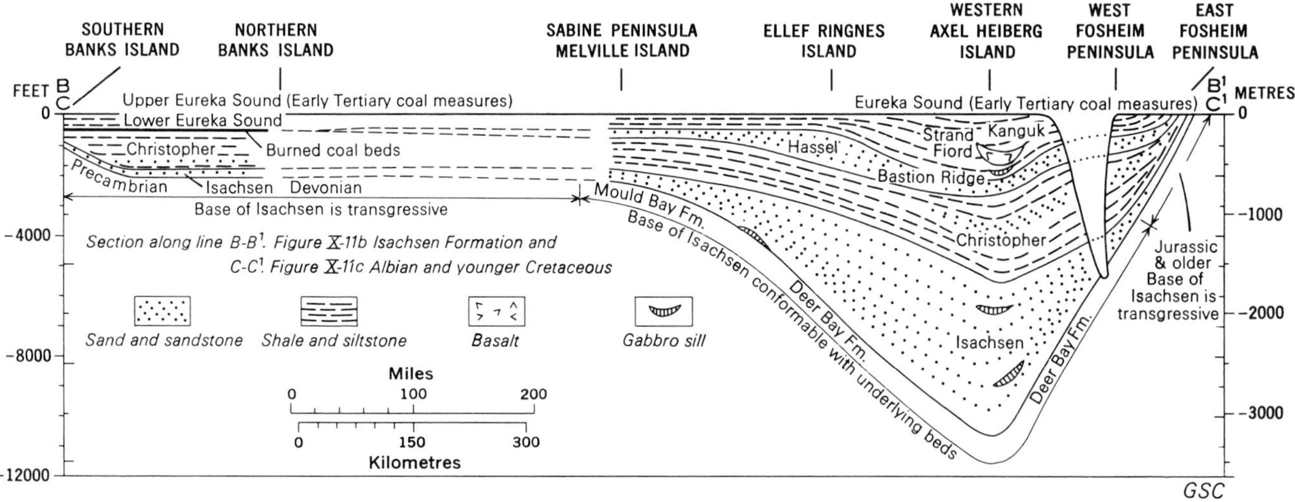

FIGURE X-13. Restored sections, Cretaceous rocks of Arctic Archipelago, along lines B–B′ and C–C′ of Figures X-11b, c (by E. T. Tozer).

mere and Axel Heiberg Islands a prominent member of greenish grey sandstone occurs near the middle. In northern Axel Heiberg Island basalt flows are intercalated. The lower part of the Christopher is commonly unfossiliferous and of uncertain age. *Tropaeum* of Aptian age has been tentatively identified from Mackenzie King Island. Higher beds above the sandstone member of Axel Heiberg and Ellesmere Islands contain the *Cleoniceras* aff. *subbaylei, Beudanticeras affine,* and *Gastroplites* zones of Albian age.

Throughout Sverdrup Basin, on Ellesmere, Axel Heiberg, Ellef Ringnes, and Melville Islands, the Christopher shales are followed by the Hassel Formation, which consists mainly of medium- to fine-grained quartzose sandstone and siltstone. Macrofossils are rare; the marine bivalve *Panopea* has been recorded from Axel Heiberg, *Spirophyton* and worm burrows are also known there. Microplankton tentatively dated as Cenomanian have been described from Graham and Ellef Ringnes Islands. These organisms evidently indicate a marine environment of deposition but much of the Hassel sandstone on Ellesmere Island is highly carbonaceous and has a non-marine appearance. The Hassel Formation probably formed on a delta covered at intervals by marine waters.

On Banks Island, in the western part of the Arctic Lowlands, the Christopher shales are overlain by 25 feet of coal-bearing beds, commonly burned brick-red, followed by about 400 feet of light grey shale and fine-grained sandstone. The latter contains marine microplankton, that are probably Upper Cretaceous and may be equivalent to the Hassel.

Upper Cretaceous

The Kanguk Formation consists of dark grey shale and siltstone with subordinate sandstone and some local thin bentonitic and tuffaceous beds. The Kanguk has been identified only in Sverdrup Basin, although equivalents may occur on Eglinton Island. Normally the Kanguk conformably overlies the Hassel Formation, but on western Axel Heiberg Island the Strand Fiord basalts intervene and a thin shale, the Bastion Ridge Formation, rests on Hassel sandstone. This shale is probably equivalent to basal Kanguk beds of other sections. *Inoceramus* cf. *pictus* of Upper Cenomanian age occurs on Graham Island in beds that probably represent the lower part. *Inocerami* of the *lobatus* species group, dated as Santonian or early Lower Campanian, are common in the upper beds. *Scaphites* species of two zones occur, one of Lower Santonian age and the other of late Lower or early Upper Santonian age. The Kanguk Formation is the youngest marine Mesozoic formation in the Arctic Archipelago.

Cretaceous Volcanic Rocks

Basalt is intercalated with the Cretaceous sediments of western Axel Heiberg Island and northern Ellesmere Island. The oldest are on the west side of Axel Heiberg Island where as many as six flows with columnar jointing may occur within the Isachsen Formation. Their aggregate thickness is not known, but may amount to several hundred feet. A flow about 50 feet thick occurs between the Isachsen and Christopher Formations north of Blaa Mountain, Ellesmere Island. Others intercalated in the Christopher Formation of northwest Axel Heiberg Island are probably more than 2,000 feet thick. The youngest basalts, known as the Strand Fiord Formation, are widely distributed in the vicinity of Strand and Expedition Fiords. They lie between the Bastion Ridge and Kanguk shales and are probably Upper Cretaceous. In the Strand Fiord area the thickness increases from east to west, from 280 feet at the head of Strand Fiord to 600 feet at the tip of Kanguk Peninsula. North of Strand Fiord it is probably greater.

The main area for Cretaceous volcanic activity lay near northwest Axel Heiberg Island. This Cretaceous volcanic activity affecting Sverdrup Basin was evidently an earlier event than the Tertiary, Thulean, volcanicity that affected the North Atlantic area.

Cretaceous (?) Gabbro Sills and Dykes

In the western part of Sverdrup Basin gabbro sills and dykes intrude Carboniferous and Permian rocks and all Mesozoic formations that underlie, or pre-date, the basalts of the Cretaceous Strand Fiord Formation. Within the basin no igneous intrusions are known to cut the Upper Cretaceous Kanguk shales or rocks of Cenozoic age.

The gabbro occurs as individual sills up to 300 feet thick, but most are thinner. Numerous thick sills intrude the Permian rocks of northwest Axel Heiberg Island, Triassic shales, and the lower Heiberg Formation of Eureka Sound area; the Savik and Deer Bay shales of western Axel Heiberg Island; and the Deer Bay of Ellef Ringnes Island. Sills also intrude the Bjorne, Blind Fiord, Awingak, Isachsen, and Bastion Ridge Formations.

Dykes are widespread, occurring as swarms on Cornwall Island and in many parts of Axel Heiberg Island. Near Flat Sound, a dyke intrudes the Blaa Mountain Formation and is bevelled beneath the overlying Cenozoic Eureka Sound beds. They are common on western Ellesmere Island but are scarce farther east. A few occur on the Ringnes Islands, and near Tingmisut Lake of Melville Island, but none is exposed on Prince Patrick, Brock, Borden, and Mackenzie King Islands.

Masses of gabbro are common in some of the anhydrite diapirs that intrude the Sverdrup Basin sequence. Some may be upthrust sills but others may be true ring dykes that have selected the circular anhydrite diapiric intrusion as a conduit.

The stratigraphic evidence suggests that all the gabbro intrusions are not younger than Cretaceous, and it appears probable that they may have been emplaced at about the same time as the extrusion of the Cretaceous basalts of Axel Heiberg Island. Four samples from Ellef Ringnes have provided whole rock K–Ar age determinations ranging from 102 to 110 m.y.

The Cenozoic in the Arctic Archipelago was a time of orogenic activity, non-marine sedimentation and, in limited areas, of volcanic activity. The principal sediments are the early Cenozoic Eureka Sound Formation and the late Cenozoic Beaufort Formation. Eureka Sound beds are found in Sverdrup Basin as outliers upon the folded rocks of the Franklinian Geosyncline and they underlie the western part of the Arctic Lowlands on Banks Island. The principal period of tectonic activity, herein termed the Eurekan Orogeny, involved folding, thrust faulting, and diapiric intrusion of Upper Carboniferous evaporites. The deformation was most intense on Ellesmere and Axel Heiberg Islands. In western Sverdrup Basin the effects of the orogeny were less intense and the Arctic Lowlands were unaffected. An early phase of orogenic activity is recognized locally as occurring before and during the deposition of the Eureka Sound Formation. Most orogenic activity, however, post-dates these beds and precedes the deposition of the Beaufort Formation. Volcanic rocks occur in the Eureka Sound Formation of Bathurst Island and on the east coast of Baffin Island.

The mid-Cenozoic was mainly a period of uplift, followed by peneplanation of the greater part of the archipelago. Parts of the Beaufort Formation on Arctic Coastal Plain probably represent alluvium produced during this interval of denudation. Cenozoic normal faulting occurred in many parts of the archipelago, notably on the Prince Patrick and Boothia Uplifts, and the northwest-trending faults that dislocate the Paleozoic rocks of Baffin Island are probably of this age. Many faults appear to have had a long history of Cenozoic movement. On the Prince Patrick Uplift most of the movement took place between the deposition of the Lower Cretaceous Christopher Formation and the late Cenozoic Beaufort Formation but some movement was later. The very form of the archipelago, with numerous stretches of linear coast, and elevated islands adjacent to the straits and channels, is probably due to late Cenozoic normal faulting, much of which probably took place after the deposition of the Beaufort beds.

Early Cenozoic Non-marine Rocks

The early Cenozoic beds, the Eureka Sound Formation, appear to be entirely non-marine, and locally include considerable conglomerate; they are in part synorogenic. The age and correlation of most of the formation are not precisely known. Plant microfossils have been obtained from many localities; most have been dated as Paleocene or Eocene.

In much of Sverdrup Basin, on Sabine Peninsula, Ellef Ringnes Island, western and southern Axel Heiberg Island, and western Fosheim Peninsula, the Eureka Sound rests with structural conformity upon the Upper Cretaceous Kanguk shales. These rocks consist mainly of sandstone and shale, with numerous coal seams up to 30 feet thick. Conglomerate is rare. About 10,000 feet of beds is present on Fosheim Peninsula and at Strand Fiord.

In northeastern Sverdrup Basin, on eastern Axel Heiberg Island, and in northern Ellesmere Island, the Eureka Sound beds are about 3,000 feet thick and rest unconformably upon rocks ranging in age from early Paleozoic to Lower Cretaceous. In addition to the typical sandstone, shale, and coal beds, these beds include much conglomerate of local derivation. At the head of Mokka Fiord, conglomerate occurs high in the section, above a sequence of coal and sandstone; thirty miles northwest it occurs at the base of the section. In these areas the Eureka Sound outcrops are commonly bounded by faults. The conglomerates occur adjacent to the faults and evidently represent syntectonic fanglomerates as the cobbles are formed from rocks of the upthrown side.

In central Ellesmere Island, the Eureka Sound beds rest disconformably on various Paleozoic formations. The formation is mainly sandstone, shale, and coal, several thousand feet thick. In this area considerable uplift and erosion but no appreciable folding took place during the interval between deposition of the Silurian and Cenozoic strata.

In the Boothia Uplift the Eureka Sound Formation on Bathurst, Cornwallis, western Devon, and Somerset Islands occurs in grabens, unconformably overlying Paleozoic and Precambrian rocks. On Cornwallis Island about 2,500 feet of sand, sandstone, and clay, with coal seams, is present, and on Bathurst Island, unlike the other areas, basalt is interbedded (Kerr and Temple, 1965).

Termination of Uniform Subsidence in Sverdrup Basin

The character of the Eureka Sound Formation shows that the advent of Cenozoic time marked a fundamental change in the pattern of sedimentation and subsidence in Sverdrup Basin. From the Upper Carboniferous to the Upper Cretaceous the basin was more or less continuously an area of subsidence and deposition, filled with sediments derived from lands beyond the basin and not from uplifts within the basin itself. With the deposition of the Eureka Sound Formation the basin ceased to act as a simple downwarp, receiving a concordant sequence of sediments. As already mentioned there are places where the Eureka Sound beds concordantly follow the Upper Cretaceous. From this evidence alone it might be supposed that the Eureka Sound beds simply represent one more deltaic formation, analogous to the Isachsen and Heiberg Formations. However the relations on eastern Axel Heiberg and northern Ellesmere Islands, where the Eureka Sound beds are definitely synorogenic, show that uplifted ridges, being subjected to denudation, were exposed on the site of Sverdrup Basin in early Cenozoic time. The tectonic disturbance indicated by these synorogenic beds marks the end of uniform subsidence within the Sverdrup Basin and the beginning of Eurekan Orogeny.

PLATE X-7

Eurekan folds with diapiric anticlines, western Axel Heiberg Island, south of Strand Fiord. Formations are: A—Carboniferous evaporites, C—Christopher, H—Hassel, B—Bastion Ridge, S—Strand Fiord, K—Kanguk, E—Eureka Sound, diapiric intrusion (X). Ice covered mountains are formed of anticlinally folded Triassic Heiberg Formation and constitute the drainage divide of the island.

Eurekan Orogeny

In mid-Cenozoic time folding and thrust faulting took place throughout much of Sverdrup Basin and the adjacent part of Ellesmere Island. In the axial part of the basin Upper Carboniferous evaporites were intruded as piercement domes and diapirs. The principal Eurekan fold axes, faults, and piercement structures are shown on the tectonic map (Map 1251A). The more intense movements affected much of Ellesmere Island and nearly all of Axel Heiberg Island (Pl. X-7). On Cornwall and the Ringnes Islands there was some Eurekan folding but farther west, in the western Queen Elizabeth Islands, the folds are of low amplitude. Although Eurekan structures are superimposed with concordant strike on older Ellesmerian structures the Eurekan movements were not confined to the area deformed in Paleozoic time, as on much of central Ellesmere Island between Baumann and Canyon Fiords. Eurekan structures on western Ellesmere Island commonly strike northeasterly, parallel to the Ellesmerian structures. Those of Axel Heiberg Island also seem to reflect the strike of older folds, for the northwesterly strike of the major anticlinorium extending from Rens Fiord to the head of Skaare Fiord conforms with the Paleozoic strike imposed on the eugeosynclinal rocks of the Rens Fiord area.

The United States Range and Victoria and Albert Mountains were deformed during the Eurekan Orogeny. Hazen Plateau which lies between these ranges was barely disturbed and apparently formed a rigid block, folded during the Ellesmerian Orogeny but unaffected by the Eurekan deformation.

The Eurekan structures include a variety of folds, thrust faults, and normal faults. In the axial part of the Sverdrup Basin piercement structures, involving the intrusion of Carboniferous evaporitic rocks, are intimately related to the Eurekan structures. The anticlines of southern Axel Heiberg Island south of the belt of piercement structures are mainly box folds, with long, straight axes, flat crests, and steeply inclined limbs. To the north, in west-central Axel Heiberg Island, the folds have short, arcuate, steeply plunging axes. The cores of the anticlines are commonly pierced by Upper Carboniferous evaporites. In this area the mobile layer of evaporites has clearly affected the folding. A belt of relatively intense folding on both sides of Eureka Sound is bordered to the west by the piercement belt. Probably these folds indicate a *décollement* at the Upper Carboniferous evaporites. There are no piercement structures in this belt, probably because competent Upper Carboniferous and Permian limestones immediately overlie the evaporites.

Numerous Eurekan thrust faults, with hanging-walls of Cambrian to Devonian strata, displaced eastwards, occur between Baumann Fiord and Copes Bay, on Ellesmere Island. Many are inclined at relatively low angles at the surface, the fault plane following evaporites in the lower part of the Ordovician Cornwallis Group. Between Bay and Tanquary Fiords many faults affect the upper Paleozoic, Mesozoic, and Cenozoic rocks of the Sverdrup Basin sequence. Most displacements are towards the east, but some, as north of Blaa Mountain, are towards the northwest. On some faults the Upper Carboniferous evaporites (Otto Fiord Formation) form the hanging-wall. The large Whitsunday Bay fault of eastern Axel Heiberg Island, placing Carboniferous rocks adjacent to the Eureka Sound Formation, is also locally soled by these evaporites. This fault is bordered by Eureka Sound fanglomerates and has experienced the early Eurekan movements. Thrust faults, directed to the east, northeast, and west dislocate the upper Paleozoic and Mesozoic rocks between Strand and Bunde Fiords of western Axel Heiberg Island. The Upper Carboniferous evaporitic rocks commonly overlie the thrust plane.

Transcurrent and normal faults occur in the area affected by the Eurekan Orogeny, but their displacements are small.

Piercement bodies of Upper Carboniferous evaporites are characteristic of the axial part of Sverdrup Basin, extending for 400 miles in a northeasterly trending belt from Sabine Peninsula on Melville Island to Otto Fiord, Ellesmere Island. The material forming the piercement structures is part of Otto Fiord Formation, which lies near the base of the Carboniferous section in the axial part of the basin. The piercement bodies seem to be confined to areas where incompetent shales and siltstones of Hare Fiord Formation overlie the evaporites, as described in the part of this chapter dealing with the Carboniferous rocks. Some of the bodies are domes produced by geostatic loading rather than the stresses of the Eurekan Orogeny, but the domes are so intimately related to evaporite-cored diapirs produced during the orogeny that it is appropriate to describe these features together.

The piercement bodies occur in three main structural situations:

1. *In synclinal areas.* These are more or less circular domes, 6 to 7 miles in diameter, confined to the western part of Sverdrup Basin and typified by the domes of Sabine Peninsula, Melville Island, the Isachsen dome of Ellef Ringnes Island (Pl. X-8), and the South Fiord dome of Axel Heiberg Island. The outcropping rock is mainly gypsum and anhydrite with inclusions of Upper Carboniferous limestone and gabbro. Some of the gabbro may represent uplifted sills, but on Sabine Peninsula the igneous rock is in the form of a ring dyke possibly indicating that the dome was in existence, although not necessarily exposed, when the gabbro was intruded, probably in the Cretaceous. Negative gravity anomalies of 10 and 40 milligals above the domes of Ellef Ringnes Island suggest that these bodies are underlain by halite and have risen as a result of geostatic loading of evaporites of low density. The strata adjacent to the domes on Ellef Ringnes and Axel Heiberg Islands are steeply inclined. On Sabine Peninsula the surrounding beds appear to be nearly horizontal. Cretaceous beds become thinner when traced towards the Isachsen dome suggesting that it had formed, and started movement, prior to the Eurekan folding.

2. *In the cores of anticlines.* These bodies are usually narrowly ovoid, pear-shaped or linear, but locally, as on the north side of Mokka Fiord, parts assume circular form. These structures probably owe their origin to tectonic squeezing with subordinate elevation due to density differences. Sedimentary sections on the flanks of these diapiric folds are commonly thick suggesting that the diapirs, unlike the domes, were tectonically inactive during Mesozoic time. Near the diapir east of Cape Levvel small gypsum dykes and sills intrude the Jurassic and Cretaceous shales at a distance up to 3 miles from the main intrusion.

3. *Adjacent to thrust faults.* Numerous piercement bodies occur at or near the surface trace of the Swiss Range and Whitsunday Bay thrust faults of Axel Heiberg Island, and a large diapiric intrusion occurs near the south limit of the thrust fault north of Blaa Mountain, Ellesmere Island. These bodies, like those on the axes of anticlines, probably resulted partly from tectonic squeezing and partly through elevation due to density difference. Immature topography characterizes all the piercement structures. They project above the surrounding landscape suggesting recent uplift or that they may be undergoing uplift. There are, however, some interesting exceptions, notably that on eastern Axel Heiberg Island adjacent to the Whitsunday Bay thrust. For about 15 miles, there is an almost continuous belt of evaporitic rocks which includes three piercement bodies characterized by immature topography, and also an area where the evaporites are bedded and essentially *in situ.* In addition, however, there are evaporites which are apparently intrusive, but bevelled to a level concordant with that of the surrounding country. In this belt, by physiographic criteria, it would appear to be possible to distinguish between active diapiric bodies, characterized by immature topography, and inactive ones that have moved in the past but have not been rejuvenated.

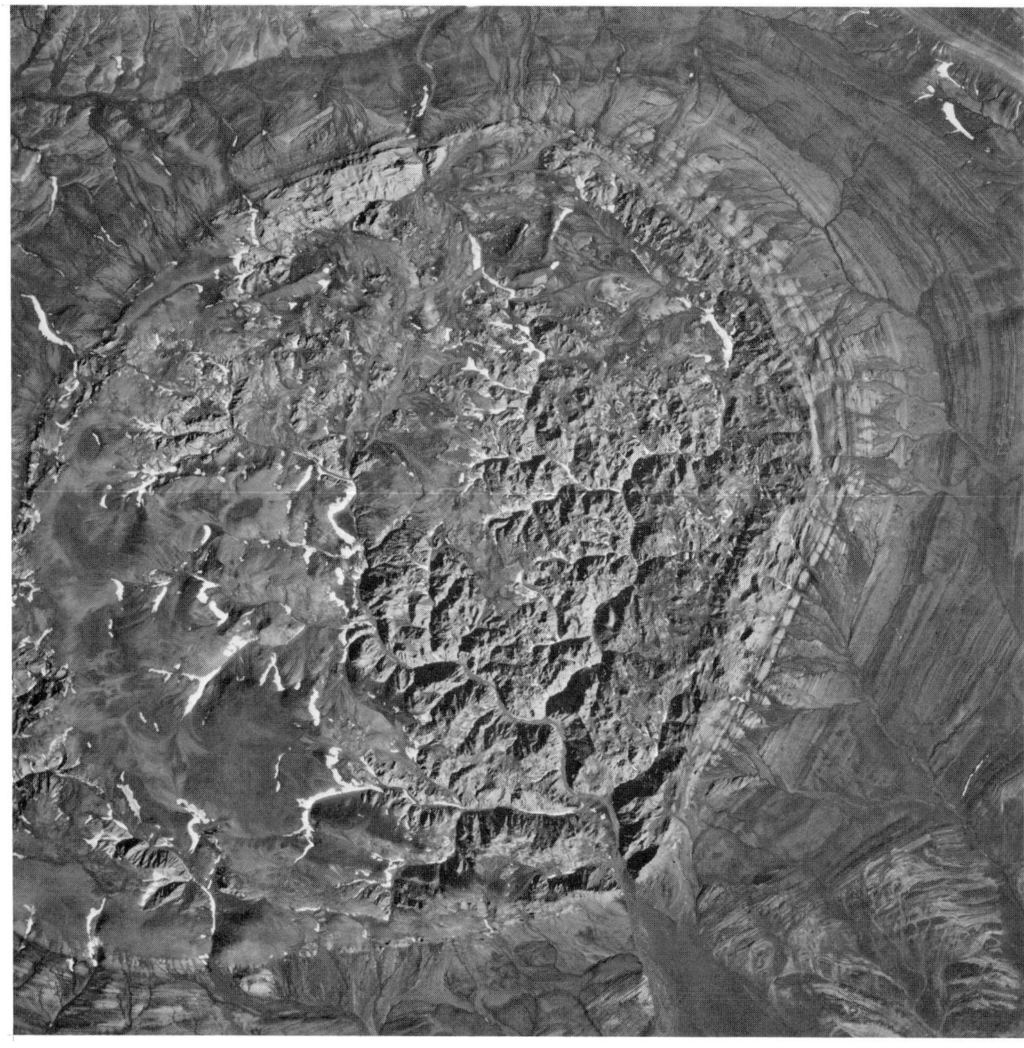

PLATE X-8
Isachsen dome, Ellef Ringnes Island. Core 4 miles in diameter of Upper Carboniferous evaporites, flanked by sharply inclined Cretaceous, Isachsen, and Christopher Formations.

Mid-Cenozoic Normal Faulting

North-trending normal faults characterize Prince Patrick Uplift on Banks and southern Prince Patrick Islands; and Boothia Uplift, on Bathurst, Cornwallis, Devon, and Somerset Islands. Northwesterly trending faults are present throughout much of Baffin Island. The time of fault movement cannot be precisely determined but is probably mid-Cenozoic. Some faults also show evidence for late Cenozoic movement, as noted below.

Late Cenozoic

Wood-bearing alluvial deposits, known as the Beaufort Formation, underlie the Arctic Coastal Plain from Meighen Island to the southwestern tip of Banks Island. In addition, isolated patches of similar deposits occur on hilltops to the east on Prince Patrick, Ellef Ringnes, Banks, and Melville Islands and even on the west side of Ellesmere Island. The Beaufort beds generally rest upon a surface of low relief and overlie unconformably rocks ranging in age from Precambrian to early Cenozoic. On Meighen Island, silts with poorly preserved bivalve shells, probably of marine genera, underlie the Beaufort beds. This occurrence suggests the possibility of other marine deposits beneath the Beaufort on the Arctic Coastal Plain and the Continental Shelf. Towards the east, where the basal beds are visible, the Beaufort is a non-marine, alluvial deposit. On Banks Island it attains a thickness of 400 feet; the total thickness to the north is not known, but exceeds 250 feet. The Beaufort Formation consists of unconsolidated crossbedded sand, gravel, and silt, with woody detritus, wood, and rare peat. The sands are well sorted and quartzose and the gravels contain an abundance of well-rounded resistant rocks derived from distant sources to the east and southeast. Logs of wood more than 10 feet long and up to a foot in diameter are common. The wood is normally unaltered spruce and pine and unlike the carbonized and mineralized wood from the older Cenozoic and Mesozoic formations. As the wood is driftwood, there is no evidence to indicate that it grew where found. Rock samples characteristically contain pollen of spruce, pine, birch, alder, various herbaceous plants, and spores of ferns and mosses. Many samples also contain small amounts of pollen from hemlock and temperate climate hardwoods such as hazel, beech, elm, hornbeam, and oak. Some hardwood pollen grains may be secondary and derived from older Cenozoic strata.

The age of the Beaufort Formation is uncertain. It is probably Pliocene or early Pleistocene but preglacial. The continuity of the formation between islands now separated by straits and channels indicates that the beds were laid down before the archipelago assumed its present form. It seems to represent the thin inland part of a body of sediment (derived from sources to the southeast and east) that extends seaward beyond the present coast. Parts of the formation probably represent detritus produced during denudation of the areas affected by the Eurekan Orogeny.

Structure of the Arctic Coastal Plain and Continental Shelf

The youngest clearly defined structural features in the archipelago are those of the Arctic Coastal Plain. On outcrop the Beaufort beds appear to be horizontal but air photographs reveal that they are inclined (J. G. Fyles). On Prince Patrick Island, east of Discovery Point, the interfluves show chevron patterns that indicate a northwesterly dip at an angle greater than the gentle seaward slope of the plain. On Isachsen Peninsula, Ellef Ringnes Island, a series of low cuestas reveals a northeast dip, away from the Arctic Ocean.

On Prince Patrick Island the plain is traversed by several spectacular lineaments, up to 40 miles long, that represent the surface traces of faults. Northwest of Mould Bay most trend north and are aligned with pre-Beaufort faults. Northwest of Intrepid Inlet they trend northeast. In places these lineaments have virtually no topographic expression, but elsewhere they represent scarps with a relief of 20 to 30 feet. Northwest of Intrepid Inlet the scarps face the Arctic Ocean, suggesting that the northwest sides are downthrown. Although most movement on faults of Prince Patrick Uplift predates deposition of the Beaufort beds, these lineaments indicate later minor movements. Prince Patrick Island currently experiences more seismic activity than neighbouring regions, possibly indicating movement on these faults.

Formation of the Archipelago

Numerous straits and channels indicate a drowned topography, but the physiography of most individual islands shows that they have been uplifted relatively recently. In the areas affected by Eurekan Orogeny the uplift is clearly later than the peneplanation which followed the orogeny, probably the result of late Cenozoic movement on gravity faults.

As previously described, Cenozoic normal faults are widespread in the archipelago. In addition to those recognized on land there are many linear and arcuate stretches of coast, often with seacliffs up to 3,000 feet high, that probably indicate the presence of faults. Many islands seem to have been uplifted, to different degrees, by movement on the faults that border the coasts. Uplift along such faults would account for the different physiographic characters of adjacent islands that are geologically similar, for example, the Ringnes Islands compared with Axel Heiberg Island. These islands are formed of Mesozoic and early Cenozoic rocks that were folded during the Eurekan Orogeny. After the orogeny they experienced planation. The peneplane on Axel Heiberg Island is more elevated than that on the Ringnes Islands. The linear connection between the headlands on the west coast of Axel Heiberg Island indicates the probable position of the faults along which Axel Heiberg Island has been elevated compared with the Ringnes Islands. Some of the uplift on such faults probably took place after deposition of the Beaufort Formation and although a relatively recent event it should not be confused with the later widespread post-Pleistocene uplift. Areas that experienced substantial post-Pleistocene uplift commonly were not appreciably elevated during the earlier period and *vice versa*. The west sides of Axel Heiberg and Melville Islands, for example, show elevated peneplanes but no strandlines at high elevations. Southwest Cornwallis Island, in contrast, shows elevated strandlines but little evidence for the earlier period of uplift. These examples leave little doubt that two periods of uplift, one before the Pleistocene, the other after, have affected the archipelago. The earlier period was probably related to faulting and essentially responsible for the present form of the archipelago; the later one was simply due to isostatic rebound following deglaciation.

ECONOMIC GEOLOGY

With the exception of small amounts of coal for local use the Phanerozoic rocks of the Arctic Archipelago have not, as yet, yielded minerals of economic value. There has been some activity in searching for metallic minerals on the islands, but mostly within the Precambrian terrains dealt with in Chapter IV. From an economic standpoint the principal interest of the arctic islands lies in the petroleum possibilities.

Gypsum and anhydrite. Deposits of gypsum and anhydrite have been found in Cambrian, Ordovician, Silurian, Upper Carboniferous, and Permian formations. The most notable are in the Ordovician and the Upper Carboniferous. Also noteworthy are the evaporites in the Hadrynian, Minto Inlet, Wynniatt, and Kilian Formations of the Shaler Group of Victoria Island.

Iron. Massive magnetite occurs in a gypsum diapir, northwest of the head of Strand Fiord, Axel Heiberg Island.

Sulphur. Native sulphur occurs in association with calcite in a diapir on western Axel Heiberg Island.

Lead and zinc. Lead and zinc sulphides have been found in brecciated dolomite of the Ordovician Cornwallis Formation on Little Cornwallis Island. A small amount of galena has been observed in the Blue Fiord limestone east of Weatherall Bay, Melville Island.

Copper. A few small flecks of native copper have been observed in the volcanic rocks of the Natkusiak Formation, of Hadrynian age, on Victoria Island, and reports from Eskimos suggest that there may be larger occurrences in this formation but this has not been confirmed.

Coal. Coal seams occur in formations of Devonian, Lower Carboniferous, Triassic, Jurassic, Lower Cretaceous, and Cenozoic age. The thickest, up to 30 feet, are in the Cenozoic Eureka Sound Formation. Seams up to 5 feet thick have been reported from the Lower Cretaceous Isachsen Formation. The seams in the older formations are thin, generally less than a few inches thick. A slacking, non-coking sub-bituminous coal, probably of Lower Cretaceous age, has been mined near the settlement of Pond Inlet on northern Baffin Island. Slightly more than 100 tons has been produced annually, mainly for use at the settlement.

Oil and gas. The great volume of Phanerozoic sediment and the presence of numerous structures in the arctic islands have attracted the attention of geologists seeking petroleum. Since 1959 geological parties from several oil companies have visited the islands and in 1961-62 the first exploration well was drilled at Winter Harbour on Melville Island. Since then wells have been drilled on Bathurst and Cornwallis Islands. No commercial production has been found, although a showing of gas was obtained from the Devonian rocks encountered in the Winter Harbour well. Bitumen deposits have been discovered in the Lower Triassic Bjorne Formation of Melville Island (Trettin and Hills, 1966). They are now uneconomic but are a direct indication of petroleum in Sverdrup Basin. Several potential petroleum provinces have been outlined (Douglas, *et al.*, 1963). Porous carbonate rocks, constituting potential reservoirs, occur at many levels in the Paleozoic, notably in the Ordovician, Silurian, Devonian, and Upper Carboniferous. Potential sandstone reservoirs occur in the Devonian, Upper Carboniferous, and Permian and throughout the Mesozoic succession. Marine shales, which may be regarded as potential source rocks, occur at all these levels. Anticlinal structures produced during the Ellesmerian Orogeny are a notable feature of the Parry Islands and Ellesmere Fold Belts. Structures within the northern part of the Boothia Uplift may also provide situations for the accumulation of hydrocarbons. Within the Sverdrup Basin the Eurekan folds and associated piercement domes, composed of upthrust Upper Carboniferous evaporitic rocks, provide possible structural traps for petroleum. Abrupt facies changes occur at many levels in the section, both in Franklinian Miogeosyncline and Sverdrup Basin and may have produced stratigraphic traps.

SELECTED REFERENCES

Blackadar, R. G.

1954: Geological reconnaissance, north coast of Ellesmere Island, Arctic Archipelago, Northwest Territories; *Geol. Surv. Can.*, Paper 53-10.

Blackadar, R. G., and Christie, R. L.

1963: Geological reconnaissance, Boothia Peninsula, and Somerset, King William, and Prince of Wales Islands, District of Franklin; *Geol. Surv. Can.*, Paper 63-19.

Christie, R. L.

1964: Geological reconnaissance of northwestern Ellesmere Island, District of Franklin; *Geol. Surv. Can.*, Mem. 331.

1967: Bache Peninsula, Ellesmere Island, Arctic Archipelago; *Geol. Surv. Can.*, Mem. 347.

Feilden, H. W., and De Rance, C. E.

1878: Geology of the coasts of the Arctic lands visited by the late British Expedition under Captain Sir George Nares, R.N., K.C.B., F.R.S.; *Quart. J. Geol. Soc.*, vol. 34, pp. 556–567.

Fortier, Y. O., Blackadar, R. G., Glenister, B. F., Greiner, H. R., McLaren, D. J., McMillan, N.J., Norris, A. W., Roots, E. F., Souther, J. G., Thorsteinsson, R., and Tozer, E. T.

1963: Geology of the north-central part of the Arctic Archipelago, Northwest Territories (Operation Franklin); *Geol. Surv. Can.*, Mem. 320.

Fricker, P. E.

1963: Geology of the expedition area, western central Axel Heiberg Island, Canadian Arctic Archipelago; Axel Heiberg Island Res. Repts., *McGill Univ.*, Geol. No. 1.

Fricker, P. E., and Trettin, H. P.

1962: Pre-Mississippian succession of northernmost Axel Heiberg Island, District of Franklin; *Geol. Surv. Can.*, Paper 62-18.

Gould, D. B., and De Mille, G.

1964: Piercement structures in the arctic islands; *Bull. Can. Petrol. Geol.*, vol. 12, No. 3, pp. 719–753.

Greiner, H. R.
1963: Southern Goose Fiord, Ellesmere Island; *Geol. Surv. Can.*, Mem. 320, pp. 292–303.

Harker, P., and Thorsteinsson, R.
1960: Permian rocks and faunas of Grinnell Peninsula, Arctic Archipelago; *Geol. Surv. Can.*, Mem. 309.

Heywood, W. W.
1957: Isachsen area, Ellef Ringnes Island, District of Franklin, Northwest Territories; *Geol. Surv. Can.*, Paper 56-8.

Kerr, J. W.
1967: Stratigraphy of Proterozoic and Cambrian rocks, central and eastern Ellesmere Island, District of Franklin; *Geol. Surv. Can.*, Paper 67-27.

Kerr, J. W., and Christie, R. L.
1965: Tectonic history of the Boothia Uplift and Cornwallis Fold Belt; *Bull. Am. Assoc. Petrol. Geol.*, vol. 49, pp. 905–926.

Kerr, J. W., and Temple, R. G.
1965: Stratigraphy and structure of Bathurst Island; *in* Report of activities: Field, 1964, compiled by S. E. Jenness; *Geol. Surv. Can.*, Paper 65-1, pp. 5–8.

Kerr, J. W., and Trettin, H. P.
1962: Mississippian rocks and mid-Palaeozoic earth movements in the Canadian Arctic Archipelago; *J. Alta. Soc. Petrol. Geol.*, vol. 10, No. 5.

King, E. R., Zietz, I., and Alldridge, L. R.
1966: Magnetic data on the structure of central arctic region; *Bull. Geol. Soc. Am.*, vol. 70, pp. 619–646.

Kurtz, V. E., McNair, A. H., and Wales, D. B.
1952: Stratigraphy of the Dundas Harbour area, Devon Island, Arctic Archipelago; *Am. J. Sci.*, vol. 250, pp. 636–655.

Lemon, R. R. H., and Blackadar, R. G.
1963: Admiralty Inlet area, Baffin Island, District of Franklin; *Geol. Surv. Can.*, Mem. 328.

McLaren, D. J.
1963a: Goose Fiord to Bjorne Peninsula, Ellesmere Island; in *Geol. Surv. Can.*, Mem. 320, pp. 310–338.
1963b: Stuart River, Bathurst Island; in *Geol. Surv. Can.*, Mem. 320, pp. 596–620.

Nassichuk, W. W.
1965: Pennsylvanian and Permian rocks in the Parry Islands Group, Canadian Arctic Archipelago; *in* Report of activities: Field, 1964, compiled by S. E. Jenness; *Geol. Surv. Can.*, Paper 65-1, pp. 9–12.

Sweet, Walter C., and Miller, A. K.
1957: Ordovician cephalopods from Cornwallis and Little Cornwallis Islands, District of Franklin, Northwest Territories; *Geol. Surv. Can.*, Bull. 38.

Thorsteinsson, R.
1959: Cornwallis and Little Cornwallis Islands, District of Franklin, Northwest Territories; *Geol. Surv. Can.*, Mem. 294.
1963: Prince Alfred Bay, Devon Island; in *Geol. Surv. Can.*, Mem. 320, pp. 221–232.

Thorsteinsson, R., and Glenister, B. F.
1963: Driftwood Bay, Bathurst Island; in *Geol. Surv. Can.*, Mem. 320, pp. 585–596.

Thorsteinsson, R., and Tozer, E. T.
1960: Summary account of structural history of the Canadian Arctic Archipelago since Precambrian time; *Geol. Surv. Can.*, Paper 60-7.
1962: Banks, Victoria, and Stefansson Islands, District of Franklin, Northwest Territories; *Geol. Surv. Can.*, Mem. 330.

Tozer, E. T.
1960: Summary account of Mesozoic and Tertiary stratigraphy, Canadian Arctic Archipelago; *Geol. Surv. Can.*, Paper 60-5.
1961: Triassic stratigraphy and faunas, Queen Elizabeth Islands, Arctic Archipelago; *Geol. Surv. Can.*, Mem. 316.
1963: Mesozoic and Tertiary stratigraphy, western Ellesmere Island and Axel Heiberg Island, District of Franklin; *Geol. Surv. Can.*, Paper 63-30.

Tozer, E. T., and Thorsteinsson, R.
1964: Western Queen Elizabeth Islands, Arctic Archipelago; *Geol. Surv. Can.*, Mem. 332.

Trettin, H. P.
1963: Caledonian movements in the Canadian Arctic Archipelago; *Bull. Can. Petrol. Geol.*, vol. 11, No. 2, pp. 107–115.
1964: Pre-Mississippian rocks of Nansen Sound area, District of Franklin; *Geol. Surv. Can.*, Paper 64-26.
1965: Lower Palaeozoic sediments of northwestern Baffin Island; *Geol. Surv. Can.*, Paper 64-47.

Trettin, H. P., and Hills, L. V.
1966: Lower Triassic tar sands of northwestern Melville Island, Arctic Archipelago; *Geol. Surv. Can.*, Paper 66-34.

Troelsen, J. C.
1950: Contribution to the geology of northwest Greenland, Ellesmere and Axel Heiberg Islands; *Medd. om Grønland,* vol. 147, No. 7, 85 pp.

XI. Biochronology: Standard of Phanerozoic Time

INTRODUCTION

by D. J. McLaren

Phanerozoic time is represented by rocks that contain abundant fossilized remains of the hard parts of Metazoan animals. It includes all geological periods from Cambrian to Recent and directly succeeds Proterozoic time during which organisms possessing hard parts either did not exist or were very rare. Proterozoic fossils include plant micro-organisms, stromatolitic algae, casts, trails, and imprints, but true body fossils are unknown and appear suddenly in Cambrian rocks.

Biochronology depends on the law of superposition and the continuous evolution of life. It affords a unique method of correlating widely separated events on the earth's crust and of erecting an empirical but remarkably accurate relative time-scale. For example, correlation between continents of events during the Cretaceous Period is effected by means of a faunal zonation based largely on ammonites and tested repeatedly in many parts of the world. Each zone has an average duration of some 1.6 to 1.8 million years, using an estimated duration for the period based on radioactive age determinations. During the Ordovician and Silurian, worldwide graptolite zones had a duration of about 2.5 million years using similar estimates. Within a continent or major region biostratigraphic zonation allows a more accurate temporal subdivision, and zones representing one million years or less are common. An interesting feature of the method is that accuracy does not decrease with time but is roughly constant, depending rather on the group of organisms chosen for such zonation. Thus the percentage error, in terms of absolute age, theoretically decreases with increasing age back to the Cambrian. Biostratigraphic zones based on stromatolites so far proposed for the Proterozoic are broad, each zone corresponding to several hundred million years. Such zonal schemes have not yet been tested in Canada.

All fossils, to a greater or lesser extent, are dependent on facies, and all fossils, similarly, are biochronologically meaningful. Thus trilobites are not found in freshwater sediments, and oysters are unknown in the Paleozoic. Fossils useful biochronologically are those groups in which evolution proceeded rapidly and produced recognizable morphological changes to the skeleton or shell and which were also widespread and found in a variety of rock types. Planktonic or nektonic organisms, such as graptolites, ammonites, or certain Foraminifera, frequently are the most useful, but in some facies such organisms may be rare. Benthonic fossils, such as brachiopods, bryozoans, or pelecypods, may be equally valuable provided facies restrictions are recognized. In many areas, particularly in dealing with Paleozoic rocks, it may be possible to erect a local or regional zonation that is more refined than the standard planktonic zonation used for intercontinental correlation. For example, in western Canada eleven trilobite zones are recognized in Lower Ordovician rocks, and eight brachiopod zones in the Upper Devonian. It appears increasingly likely that zonation by benthonic organisms may prove applicable to intercontinental correlation in many instances.

This chapter deals with the paleontological basis for correlation within the Phanerozoic rocks that are described elsewhere in this volume and which are named on the geotectonic correlation charts. The rock-units are arranged on these charts so that their relative position indicates geological age in terms of a standard succession. The standards shown are worldwide for the Mesozoic and Tertiary, and both North American and European for the Paleozoic. The paleontology of each period is discussed

XI

Biochronology: Standard of Phanerozoic Time

E. W. Bamber, T. E. Bolton, M. J. Copeland, L. M. Cumming, H. Frebold, W. H. Fritz, J. A. Jeletzky, D. C. McGregor, D. J. McLaren, B. S. Norford, A. W. Norris, G. W. Sinclair, E. T. Tozer, and F. J. E. Wagner

Eurypterus lacustris Harlan—an arthropod from the Upper Silurian Bertie Formation of southern Ontario.

briefly and the guide fossils or faunal zonation are shown in the accompanying tables in relation to the standard sequence. Some of the more common or important fossils are figured. The discussion and charts are necessarily brief and highly selective, and do not give a true picture of the complexity and variety of past life. Nor is the treatment of each period necessarily uniform. The phyla and classes of animals and plants found most valuable in each period vary widely as, indeed, does the lithology of the rocks in which they are contained. This, in itself, is a reflection of the complexity of the biochronologic method and its necessary adaptation to local and regional requirements.

The geological time-scale is an empirical artefact that has grown haphazardly, depending on observations spread over nearly 200 years in areas determined by entirely extraneous factors that were largely social and economic. Real stratigraphic boundaries in regions where the hierarchy of time-rock terms was invented have to be searched for elsewhere in sequences of rocks which may represent a stratigraphic continuum or which may be entirely absent. Such correlations are made by fossils. It is not surprising that the correlation of boundaries is not always easy and, strictly in a physical sense, such boundaries may not represent real or easily established events. These comments apply in force to this country in which, over vast areas, rigorous stratigraphic and biochronologic observations date back hardly more than 20 years. It is a remarkable vindication of the methods of biochronology that such accurate time-scales may be erected for most periods, and it is these time-scales that are summarized and discussed here.

CAMBRIAN FAUNAS

by W. H. Fritz

The Cambrian is the oldest geological system containing numerous and diverse megafossils. Strata immediately predating the Cambrian appear to be unfossiliferous only because Precambrian organisms did not have the hard parts necessary for their preservation. Rarely, however, soft-bodied animals such as sea pens and jellyfish did make impressions as in the latest Precambrian strata of Australia (Glaessner, 1962), and so left a brief record of surprisingly advanced forms. Later, in Middle Cambrian time, soft-bodied worms, algae, sponges, holothuroids, jellyfish, and arthropods underwent unusual preservation in what is known as the Burgess Shale of British Columbia (Walcott, 1910–12). Fossils from both localities provide but a glimpse of a large segment of early life that otherwise perished unrecorded.

Although there is still some uncertainty as to the rate and order in which organisms first developed hard parts, there is no doubt that these parts provided an evolutionary advantage. Proof is the abundant skeletal material preserved in Cambrian to Recent strata. As might be expected, the number of fossils diminishes near the base of the Cambrian, and as yet there is no widely accepted agreement as to what faunal or stratigraphic horizon should represent the boundary between the Cambrian and the Precambrian. There has always been, however, a tendency to place the base of the Cambrian at or near

TABLE XI-1 *Ranges of Cambrian trilobite genera in the North American and Atlantic Provinces*

SERIES	LWR. CAMB.		MIDDLE CAMBRIAN					UPPER CAMBRIAN								LWR. ORD.
STAGE								Dresbachian				Franconian			Trempealeauan	
ZONE	*Lower Olenellus*	*Upper Olenellus*	*Plagiura-Poliella*	*Albertella*	*Glossopleura*	*Bathyuriscus Elrathina*	*Bolaspidella*	*Cedaria*	*Crepicephalus*	*Aphelaspis*	*Dunderbergia*	*Elvinia*	*Conaspis*	*Ptychaspis-Prosaukia*	*Saukia*	

NORTH AMERICAN FAUNAL PROVINCE

Nevadia, Nevadella, Olenellus, Wanneria, Paedeumias, Fremontia, Fremontella, Peachella, Pagetides, Bonnia, Onchocephalus, Antagmus, Zacanthopsis, Luxella, Bicella, Austinvillia, Syspacephalus, Wenkchemnia, Stephenaspis, Chancia, Caborcella, Poliella, Fieldaspis, Kochaspis, Schistometopus, Inglefieldia, Plagiura, Pachyaspis, Onchocephalites, Oryctocephalites, Alokistocare, Ptarmiganoides, Albertella, Kochina, Mexicella, Vanuxemella, Spencia, Corynexochides

Athabaskia, Bathyuriscus, Glossopleura, Kistocare, Ehmaniella, Ehmania, Elrathina, Ptychagnostus, Kootenia, Spencella, Ogygopsis, Glyphaspis, Modocia, Zacanthoides, Bolaspidella, Hypagnostus, Asaphiscus, Eldoradia, Olenoides, Pagetia, Lejopyge, Oryctocephalus, Amecephalus, Peronopsis

Kormagnostus, Menomonia, Norwoodia, Densonella, Cedaria, Coosella, Ankoura, Brassicicephalus, Syspacheilus, Bynumia, Arapahoia, Meteoraspis, Tricrepicephalus, Blountia, Kingstonia, Maryvillia, Coosia, Crepicephalus, Glyptagnostus, Raaschella, Aphelaspis, Cheilocephalus, Dytremacephalus

Dunderbergia, Pterocephalia, Iddingsia, Simulolenus, Morosa, Bynumia, Dellea, Camaraspis, Elvinia, Housia, Irvingella, Dokimocephalus, Kindbladia, Comanchia, Bernia, Parabolinoides, Taenicephalus, Kendallina, Maustonia, Wilbernia, Conaspis, Croixana, Ellipsocephaloides, Drumaspis, Ptychaspis, Idahoia, Monocheilus, Briscoia, Prosaukia, Rasettia, Richardsonella, Dikelocephalus, Illaenurus, Eurekia, Stenopilus, Saukia, Pseudagnostus, Idiomesus, Leiocoryphe, Symphysurina, Hystricurus, Pseudohystricurus, Olenaspella

ATLANTIC FAUNAL PROVINCE

Holmia, Kjerulfia, Strenuella, Ellipsocephalus, Weymouthia, Hebediscus, Micmacca, Olenelloides, Nevadia, Serrodiscus, Bonnaria, Calodiscus, Nevadella, Pseudatops, Callavia, Blayacina, Protolenus, Matthewlenus, Elliptocephalus, Schmidtiellus, Ferralsia, Bigotina, Neocobboldia, Protagraulos, Kingaspis, Lusatiops, Strettonia

Catadoxides, Paradoxides, Meneviella, Ctenocephalus, Dawsonia, Holasaphus, Acrocephalops, Condylopyge, Bailiella, Bailiaspis, Parasolenopleura, Agraulos, Peronopsis, Ptychagnostus, Conocoryphe, Eodiscus, Brunswickia, Hypagnostus, Vermontella, Linguagnostus, Centropleura, Agnostus, Dorypyge, Lejopyge, Elyx

Drepanura, Ciceragnostus, Glyptagnostus, Acrocephalites, Olenus, Proceratopyge, Conokephalina, Liostracus, Homagnostus, Irvingella, Parairvingella, Eoasaphus, Pseudagnostus, Protopeltura, Parabolina, Leptoplastus, Parabolinites, Ctenopyge group, Peltura, Sphaerophthalmus, Promegalaspides, Niobella, Nericiaspis, Megalaspis, Niobe, Acerocarina

Euloma, Westergaardia, Pelturina, Acerocare, Jujuyaspis, Boeckaspis, Hysterolenus

ZONE	*Holmia*	*Callavia*	*Protolenus*	*Catadoxides*	*Paradoxides oelandicus*	*P. paradoxissimus*	*P. forchhammeri*	*Agnostus pisiformis*	*Olenus*	*Parabolina*	*Leptoplastus*	*Peltura*	*Acerocare*	

GSC

the first occurrence of the remains of organisms containing hard parts. An important contribution towards resolving the boundary problem will come from additional study of the earliest skeletal-bearing animals such as the archaeocyathids (PL. I, FIG. 11), gastropods (PL. II, FIG. 14), hyolithids (PL. II, FIG. 2), sponges, and trilobites.

Of the various Cambrian fossils, trilobites are by far the most abundant and distinctive, and it is upon this group that the Cambrian biochronological framework is based. This framework for North America has been presented by Lochman-Balk and Wilson (1958), who show the life span or ranges of the trilobite genera and the manner in which their ranges are utilized to subdivide the Cambrian into zones. Each zone bears the name of one or more genera, but the zones are also based in part on additional genera that are considered to be of equal importance. Also, the name-bearing genus may have a range longer or shorter than the time-span of the zone it represents. A range chart generalized from the more extensive compilation by Lochman-Balk and Wilson is shown in Table XI-1.

Actually, not one but two charts are shown in Table XI-1 as the genera represented are from two distinct faunal provinces, the North American and the Atlantic Provinces. Within one province the relative range of various genera is well documented, and the provincial zonation has been used with reasonable success. It is difficult, however, to compare the age of genera or even zones across the provincial boundaries, as only a very small percentage of genera are common to both provinces.

Areally, the two faunal provinces found in North America are unequal. The smaller, the Atlantic Province, is confined to southeastern Newfoundland, eastern New Brunswick, Nova Scotia, and a small part of northeastern United States. Within it, trilobites bear a very close resemblance to those of the Atlantic Province in parts of Great Britain, Sweden, and various countries of Europe. Unique to the Atlantic Province are certain eyeless or nearly blind trilobites like *Bailiaspis* (PL. III, FIG. 16) and *Conocoryphe* (PL. III, FIG. 17) and gargantuan forms such as *Paradoxides* (PL. III, FIG. 18). Many trilobites from the Canadian part of the Atlantic Province have been described by Hutchinson (1962).

The North American Province includes all North America exclusive of the Atlantic Province. This is by far the more important of the two provinces in terms of areal extent and number of fossils collected in Canada, and therefore the paleontology of the North American Province is emphasized here.

The Cambrian fossils of the North American Province are discussed mainly with reference to the zones in which they occur. A broader discussion in terms of stages is not practical, as thus far only three Upper Cambrian stages have been erected. These three, the Dresbachian, Franconian, and Trempealeauan, have type areas in the upper Mississippi Valley where they were thought to represent all Upper Cambrian time. Modification of the three-stage concept is now needed, as a significant unconformity is known to be present at the Dresbachian–Franconian contact. Lochman-Balk and Wilson (1958) have suggested erecting a new stage elsewhere to represent strata and faunas missing in the Cambrian of the upper Mississippi Valley, but no action has yet been taken on their proposal.

Series names are rarely used in the Cambrian, but subdivisions of series magnitude, the Lower, Middle, and Upper Cambrian, have gained wide acceptance. These subdivisions in the North American Province approximately equal the Lower, Middle, and Upper Cambrian of the Atlantic Province. Thus it is the Lower, Middle, and Upper Cambrian and various Cambrian zones which are usually cited as a reference framework in discussing Cambrian fossils of the North American Province, and this procedure is followed here.

In the Lower Cambrian two zones are recognized, the lower and upper *Olenellus* Zones. Both zones characteristically contain olenellids which have large semicircular head shields and crescent-shaped eyes. In the lower *Olenellus* Zone, olenellids such as *Nevadella* (PL. I, FIG. 10) and *Nevadia* have an anteriorly tapered axial region on the head shield that does not reach the raised marginal border. In the upper *Olenellus* Zone, the axial region on olenellid head shields extends farther forward where it widens and has a subglobular shape (see *Olenellus,* PL. I, FIG. 1). Exceptions in the upper *Olenellus* Zone are a few species of *Olenellus* and most species of *Paedeumias* (PL. I, FIG. 2). Small ptychoparioid trilobites, such as *Onchocephalus* (PL. I, FIG. 4), are fairly common in the upper *Olenellus* Zone but are absent or rare in the lower *Olenellus* Zone. *Bonnia* (PL. I, FIGS. 8, 9) is common in the latest part of the upper *Olenellus* Zone.

In addition to trilobites, archaeocyathids (PL. I, FIG. 11) and *Salterella* (PL. I, FIG. 12) are common at some horizons in the Lower Cambrian. More prevalent are hyolithids (PL. II, FIG. 2) and inarticulate brachiopods (PL. II, FIG. 9), both of which range through the Cambrian and into younger systems. Articulate brachiopods (PL. I, FIG. 3) are rare in the Lower Cambrian and do not become common until mid-Upper Cambrian. Ostracods (PL. II, FIG. 13) and gastropods (PL. II, FIG. 14) are known from strata as old as Lower Cambrian, but they are rare, although gastropods increase in number by the late Upper Cambrian.

By Middle Cambrian time the olenellids were extinct and ptychoparioid trilobites with small tails were common. Trilobites belonging to the family Zacanthoididae, such as the genus *Albertella* (PL. II, FIG. 19), are prevalent in the early Middle Cambrian and decrease in numbers in younger strata. Genera that are widespread and prevalent, but restricted in time to the early Middle Cambrian, are *Plagiura* (PL. II, FIGS. 15, 16) in the late part of the *Plagiura–Poliella* Zone, and two genera, *Albertella* and *Glossopleura* (PL. II, FIGS. 4, 5) which are restricted to the zones bearing their names. *Bathyuriscus* (PL. II, FIG.

12) is an example of a genus that is most prevalent in, but overlaps, the zone bearing its name. Still longer ranging genera, such as *Ogygopsis* (PL. II, FIG. 8) and *Oryctocephalus* (PL. II, FIG. 3) are of special interest even though they have little value for dating purposes. These genera are abundant in rocks of a certain lithology, which suggests they may prove to be important paleoenvironmental indicators. Near the close of the Middle Cambrian, in the *Bolaspidella* Zone, ptychoparioid trilobites with convex, smooth central lobes on the head shields and small tails (see *Modocia*, PL. III, FIGS. 19, 20) increase in number. Trilobites belonging to the families Zacanthoididae and Bathyuriscidae are rare and become extinct within the *Bolaspidella* Zone. *Hypagnostus* (PL. III, FIGS. 21, 22) is locally abundant in this zone.

In the earliest Upper Cambrian, trilobites of the *Cedaria* (PL. III, FIG. 24) and *Crepicephalus* (PL. III, FIG. 23) Zones also have ptychoparioid-like heads, but the tails are much larger, being almost equal to the heads in size. These trilobites are accompanied by numerous genera of medium to small size that have low, smooth heads and tails. Also common in the *Cedaria* Zone is the agnostid *Kormagnostus* (PL. III, FIGS. 14, 15).

In the succeeding three Upper Cambrian zones, the *Aphelaspis, Dunderbergia,* and *Elvinia,* numerous genera appear that are characterized by rectangular lobes in the centre of the head shield. The truncated front part of this lobe differs from the rounded front part seen on trilobite head shields in the *Cedaria* and *Crepicephalus* Zones (compare *Aphelaspis,* PL. III, FIGS. 12, 13, and *Dytremacephalus,* PL. III, FIG. 11, with *Cedaria* and *Crepicephalus*). Other trilobites are quite different and distinctive, such as *Irvingella* (PL. III, FIG. 10) which occurs in the *Elvinia* Zone and is one of the best index fossils for worldwide Cambrian correlation.

Near the end of the Cambrian, in the *Conaspis, Ptychaspis–Prosaukia,* and early *Saukia* Zones, there is an increase in the number of large-sized trilobites, many of which have large, fan-shaped tails and rectangular lobes in the middle of the head shield (see *Briscoia,* PL. III, FIGS. 1, 2). In the latest Upper Cambrian, near the end of *Saukia* Zone, the number of large trilobites diminishes. *Eurekia* (PL. III, FIGS. 7, 8) is a distinctive genus in this zone. *Leiocoryphe* (PL. III, FIGS. 5, 6) is locally abundant and is perhaps more typical of the youngest Cambrian genera.

Trilobite genera on either side of the Cambrian–Ordovician boundary are small and diverse in outline, and thus an abrupt change is not apparent. Among the most common that become extinct in latest Cambrian time are *Eurekia, Idiomesus, Illaenurus,* and *Leiocoryphe.* Among the most common that originate in earliest Ordovician time are *Hystricurus* and *Symphysurina.* Slightly younger, larger, and thus more conspicuous Lower Ordovician genera are *Bellefontia, Kainella, Leiostegium,* and *Xenostegium.*

Perhaps the greatest change near the Cambrian–Ordovician boundary is the explosive increase in the number and type of graptolites and conodonts, which are rare and often overlooked in the Upper Cambrian.

Selected References

Glaessner, M. F.
1962: Precambrian fossils; *Biol. Rev.,* vol. 37, No. 4, pp. 467–494.

Grant, R. E.
1965: Faunas and stratigraphy of the Snowy Range Formation (Upper Cambrian) in southwestern Montana and northwestern Wyoming; *Geol. Soc. Am.,* Mem. 96.

Hutchinson, R. D.
1952: The stratigraphy and trilobite faunas of the Cambrian sedimentary rocks of Cape Breton Island, Nova Scotia; *Geol. Surv. Can.,* Mem. 263.
1962: Cambrian stratigraphy and trilobite faunas of southeastern Newfoundland; *Geol. Surv. Can.,* Bull. 88.

Lochman-Balk, C., and Wilson, J. L.
1958: Cambrian biostratigraphy in North America; *J. Paleontol.,* vol. 32, pp. 312–350.

Moore, R. C. (*ed.*)
1959: Treatise on invertebrate paleontology, Part O—Arthropoda 1; *Univ. Kansas Press.*

Palmer, A. R.
1954: The faunas of the Riley Formation in central Texas; *J. Paleontol.,* vol. 28, pp. 709–789.
1965: Trilobites of the Late Cambrian pterocephaliid biomere in the Great Basin, United States; *U.S. Geol. Surv.,* Prof. Paper 493.

Rasetti, F.
1951: Middle Cambrian stratigraphy and faunas of the Canadian Rocky Mountains; *Smithsonian Inst. Misc. Collections,* vol. 116, No. 5.

Walcott, C. D.
1910–12: Cambrian geology and paleontology II; *Smithsonian Inst. Misc. Collections,* vol. 57, Nos. 2, 3, 5, 6, pp. 17–68, 109–228.

PLATE I. Lower and Middle Cambrian Fossils

Figure 1 *Olenellus* sp. Head x2, GSC No. 21348, upper *Olenellus* Zone, Peyto Formation, Chaba River, Alberta.

Figure 2 *Paedeumias* sp. Latex cast of head x2, GSC No. 21349, upper *Olenellus* Zone, Eager Formation, near St. Eugene Mission, B.C.

Figure 3 *Nisusia* sp. Latex cast of brachial and pedicle valves x2, GSC No. 21350, *Bathyuriscus-Elrathina* Zone, Burgess Shale, between Mount Field and Mount Wapta, B.C.

Figure 4 *Onchocephalus* sp. Part of head x5, GSC No. 21351, upper *Olenellus* Zone, unnamed formation near June Lake, District of Mackenzie.

Figure 5 *Fremontia?* sp. Latex cast of exoskeleton x2, GSC No. 21352, Lower Cambrian, Mahto Formation, Munn Peak, Alberta.

Figures 6, 7 *Wanneria* sp. Head x5 with part of area x10 to show reticulate surface pattern, GSC syntype No. 414b, Lower Cambrian, L'Anse au Loup, Labrador.

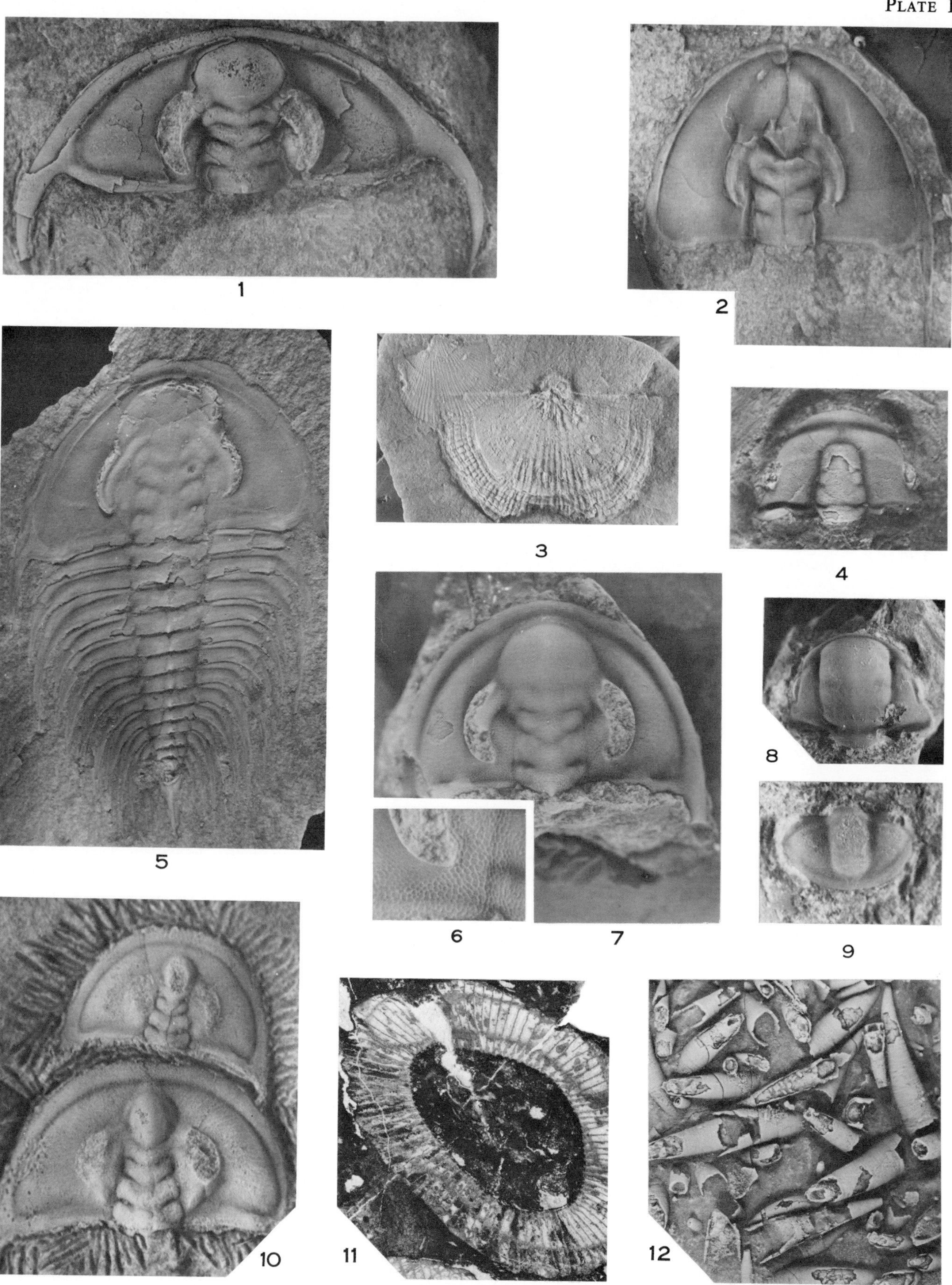
1
2
3
4
5
6
7
8
9
10
11
12

Figures 8, 9 *Bonnia* sp. 8, Part of head x3, GSC No. 21353. 9. Tail x6, GSC No. 21354. Upper *Olenellus* Zone, Peyto Formation, Chaba River, B.C.

Figure 10 *Nevadella* sp. Two heads x2, GSC No. 21355, lower *Olenellus* Zone; formation and locality unknown.

Figure 11 *Coscinocyathus* sp. Transverse slice in thin section x2, GSC No. 13328, Lower Cambrian, Atan Group, near mile post 702, Alaska Highway, Yukon Territory.

Figure 12 *Salterella* sp. Conchs x2, GSC No. 410, Lower Cambrian, Levis Conglomerate, Point Levis, Quebec.

Plate II. Middle Cambrian Fossils

Figure 1 *Elrathina* sp. Exoskeleton x3, GSC No. 21356, *Bathyuriscus-Elrathina* Zone, *Ogygopsis* Shale, Mount Stephen, B.C.

Figure 2 *Hyolithes* sp. Impression of shell x1, GSC No. 21357, *Albertella* Zone, Cathedral Formation, Mount Bosworth, Alberta-British Columbia.

Figure 3 *Oryctocephalus* sp. Exoskeleton x2, GSC No. 21358, *Bathyuriscus-Elrathina* Zone, *Ogygopsis* Shale, Mount Stephen, B.C.

Figures 4, 5 *Glossopleura* sp. 4, Part of head x3, GSC No. 21359. 5, Tail x2, GSC No. 21360. Cathedral Formation, Mount Assiniboine, Alberta, British Columbia.

Figures 6, 7 *Peronopsis* sp. 6, Head x9, GSC No. 21361. 7, Tail x9, GSC No. 21362. *Bathyuriscus-Elrathina* Zone?, formation unknown, Mount Field, B.C.

Figure 8 *Ogygopsis* sp. Exoskeleton, GSC No. 21363, *Bathyuriscus-Elrathina* Zone, *Ogygopsis* Shale, Mount Stephen, B.C.

Figure 9 *Micromitra* sp. Brachial valve x5, GSC No. 21364, *Bathyuriscus-Elrathina* Zone?, formation unknown, Mount Field?, B.C.

Figures 10, 11 *Pagetia* sp. 10, Head x8, GSC No. 21365. 11, Tail x8, GSC No. 21366. *Bathyuriscus-Elrathina* Zone?, formation unknown, Mount Field, B.C.

Figure 12 *Bathyuriscus* sp. Latex cast of exoskeleton x3, GSC No. 21395, *Bathyuriscus-Elrathina* Zone, *Ogygopsis* Shale, Mount Stephen, B.C.

Figure 13 *Bradoria?* sp. Left valve x6, GSC No. 21367, either late *Albertella* or early *Glossopleura* Zone, Gordon Shale, Flathead Range, Alberta.

Figure 14 *"Helcionella"*. Shell x7, GSC No. 21368, *Bolaspidella* Zone, unnamed formation, near June Lake, District of Mackenzie.

Figures 15, 16 *Plagiura* sp. 15, Part of head x2, GSC No. 21369. 16, Latex cast of tail x2, GSC No. 21370. *Plagiura-Poliella* Zone, Mount Whyte Formation, Mount Weed, Alberta.

Figures 17, 18 *Vanuxemella* sp. 17, Part of head x5, GSC No. 21371. 18, Tail x4, GSC No. 21372. *Albertella* Zone, Cathedral Formation, Mount Thompson, Alberta.

Figure 19 *Albertella* sp. Part of head and tail x5, GSC No. 21373, Cathedral Formation, Mount Thompson, Alberta.

Figure 20 *Amecephalus* sp. Latex cast of incomplete exoskeleton x3, GSC No. 21374, *Plagiura-Poliella* or *Albertella* Zone, Mount Assiniboine, Alberta-British Columbia.

Plate III. Middle and Upper Cambrian Fossils

Figures 1, 2 *Briscoia* sp. 1, Part of head x2, GSC No. 21375. 2, Tail x1, GSC No. 21376. *Ptychaspis-Prosaukia* or lower *Saukia* Zone, McKay Formation, 3 miles west of Donald, B.C.

Figures 3, 4 *Ptychaspis* sp. 3, Latex cast of part of head x2, GSC No. 21377. 4, Tail x3, GSC No. 21378. *Ptychaspis-Prosaukia* Zone, Bison Creek Formation, Chaba River, Alberta.

Figures 5, 6 *Leiocoryphe* sp. Head in plan and rear view x5, GSC No. 21379, *Saukia* Zone, Mistaya Formation, Mount Wilson, Alberta.

Figures 7, 8 *Eurekia* sp. 7, Part of head x3, GSC No. 21380. 8, Tail x3, GSC No. 21381. *Saukia* Zone, Mistaya Formation, Mount Wilson, Alberta.

Figure 9 *Drumaspis* sp. Part of head x6, GSC No. 21382, *Ptychaspis-Prosaukia* Zone, Bison Creek Formation, Chaba River, Alberta.

Figure 10 *Irvingella* sp. Part of head x3, GSC No. 21383, *Elvinia* Zone, McKay Formation, Hughes Range, B.C., Alberta.

Figure 11 *Dytremacephalus* sp. Part of head x5, GSC No. 21384, *Aphelaspis* or *Dunderbergia* Zone, Lyell Formation, Chaba River, Alberta.

Figures 12, 13 *Aphelaspis* sp. 12, Part of head x2, GSC No. 21385. 13, Tail x3, GSC No. 21386. *Aphelaspis* Zone, Highway 1, mile post 15, west of Field, B.C.

Figures 14, 15 *Kormagnostus* sp. 14, Head x4, GSC No. 21387. 15, Tail x10, GSC No. 21388. *Cedaria* or *Crepicephalus* Zone, Waterfowl-Sullivan formational contact zone, Mount Brussilof, B.C.

Figure 16 *Bailiaspis?* sp. Head x3, GSC paratype No. 12033, Middle Cambrian, Highland Cove, Trinity Bay, Newfoundland.

Figure 17 *Conocoryphe?* sp. Head x2, GSC No. 12025, Middle Cambrian, Highland Cove, Trinity Bay, Newfoundland.

Figure 18 *Paradoxides* sp. Part of head x2, GSC No. 13069, Middle Cambrian, first small bay east of McLeod Point, Trinity Bay, Newfoundland.

Figures 19, 20 *Modocia* sp. 19, Part of head x4, GSC No. 21389. 20, Tail x6, GSC No. 21390. *Bolaspidella* Zone, Pika Formation, Beauty Creek, Jasper Park, Alberta.

Figures 21, 22 *Hypagnostus* sp. 21, Head x9, GSC No. 21391. 22, Tail x6, GSC No. 21392. *Bolaspidella* Zone, unnamed formation, near June Lake, District of Mackenzie.

Figure 23 *Crepicephalus* sp. Latex cast of part of head and tail x2, GSC No. 28393, *Crepicephalus* Zone, Sullivan? Formation, Ram Range, Alberta.

Figure 24 *Cedaria* sp. Part of head and tail x2, GSC No. 21394, *Cedaria* Zone, Upper Chancellor Formation or lower Ottertail Formation, Wolverine Pass, B.C.

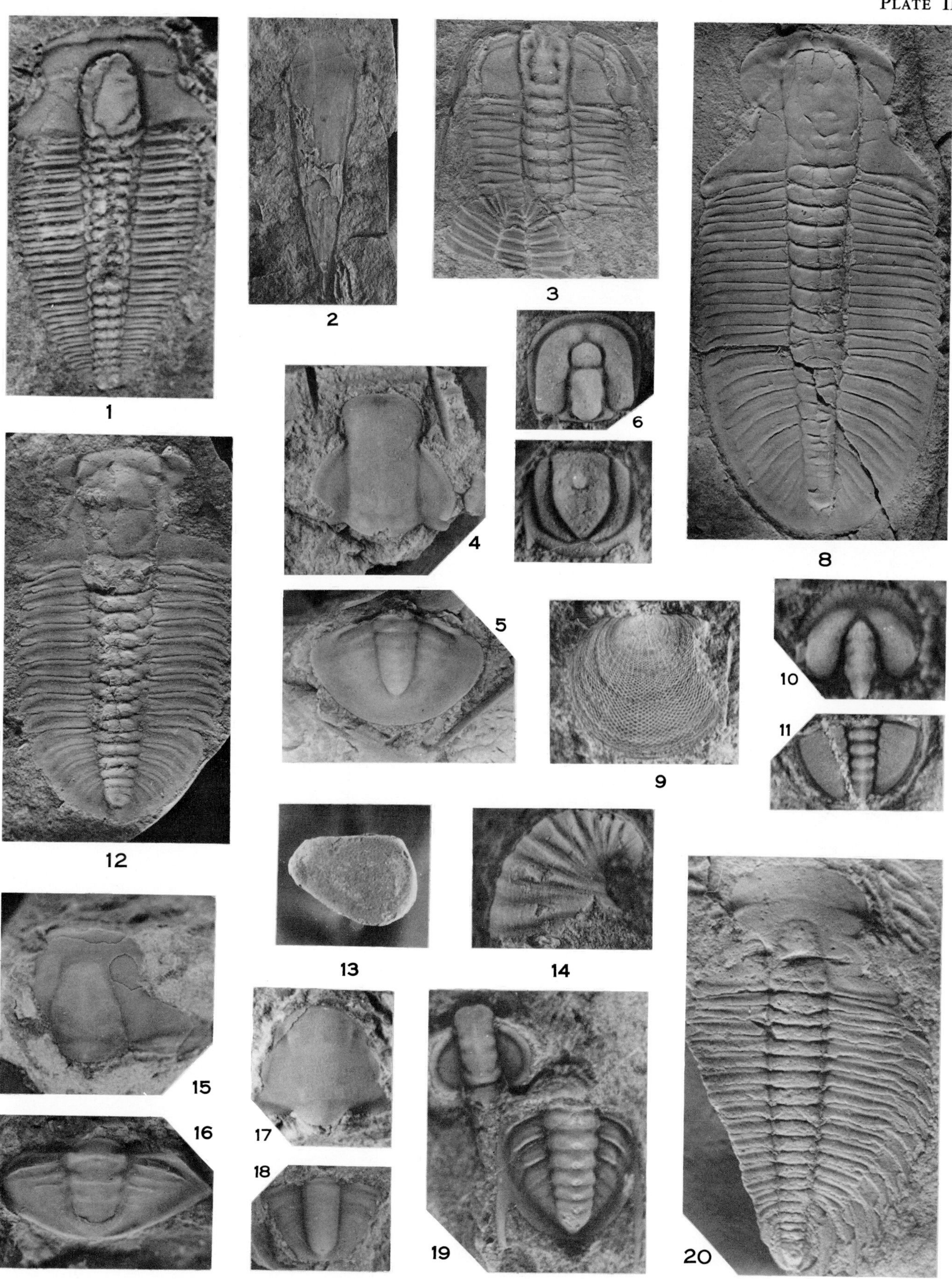
1
2
3
4
5
6
8
9
10
11
12
13
14
15
16
17
18
19
20

Plate III

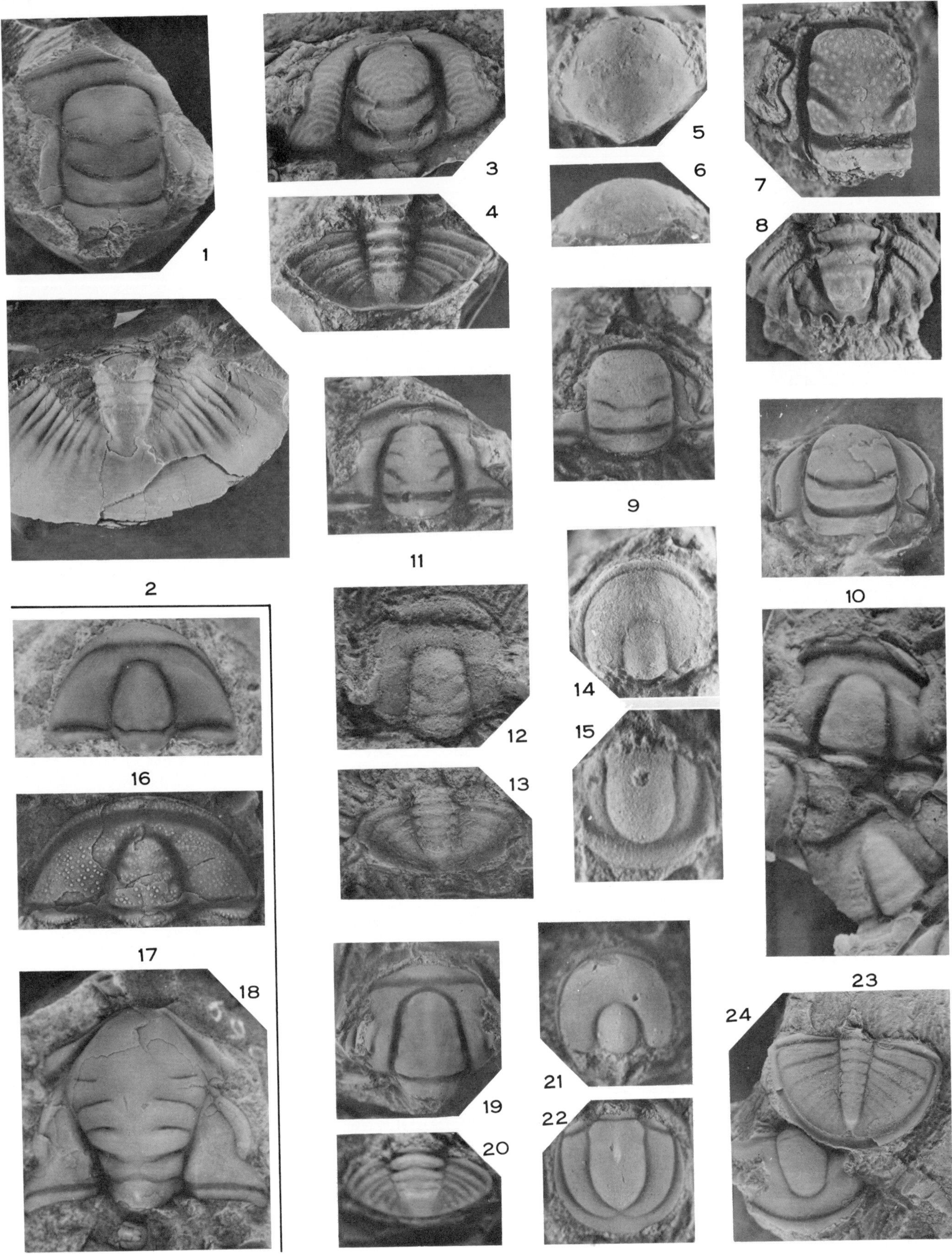

ORDOVICIAN AND SILURIAN FAUNAS

by B. S. Norford, T. E. Bolton, M. J. Copeland,
L. M. Cumming, and G. W. Sinclair

Pelagic Faunas of the Ordovician and Silurian

Worldwide correlation of the Ordovician and Silurian Systems is based on graptolites. Graptolites were pelagic animals; their remains are most abundant and best preserved in rocks deposited in deep water. Rocks of graptolitic facies accumulated seaward of the belts of platform carbonates, sandstones, and siltstones that bordered the North American landmass in early Paleozoic time. Some sequences of graptolitic rocks seem to represent almost continuous deposition throughout the Ordovician and Silurian. Radioactive dating suggests that the duration of the combined Ordovician and Silurian interval was about 100 million years. This interval has been divided into thirty-nine graptolite zones.

The composite sequence of zones shown on Tables XI-2 and XI-3 is based on successions of graptolite faunas in various parts of Canada (Jackson, 1964; Jackson and Lenz, 1962; Thorsteinsson, 1958). The zonal successions are best developed in the Road River, Kechika, and Glenogle units of the Cordillera, and in the Ibbett Bay and Cape Phillips Formations of the arctic islands (Fig. XI-1), all within geosynclines but close to regions of platform sedimentation. Sparse occurrences of graptolites are known from the platform regions and aid in correlation of associated benthonic faunas with the standard graptolite zonation. A few localities in the Rocky Mountains, the northern Yukon, and the arctic islands show interfingering of graptolitic rocks with rocks bearing benthonic faunas.

Bulman (1958) has shown that the sequence of graptolite zones can be grouped into four successive gross faunas that are characterized by generic assemblages, in contrast to the assemblages of species that form the zones. *Anisograptus, Bryograptus, Clinograptus, Dictyonema, Staurograptus,* and *Triograptus* are the dominant genera of the Anisograptid fauna of Tremadoc age. The Arenig Dichograptid fauna consists primarily of the genera *Dichograptus, Didymograptus, Isograptus, Oncograptus, Phyllograptus,* and *Tetragraptus.* The Diplograptid fauna lasted from Llanvirn to early Llandovery and is characterized by a diversity of biserial forms. Common genera include *Amplexograptus, Climacograptus, Cryptograptus, Dicellograptus, Dicranograptus, Didymograptus, Diplograptus, Glossograptus, Glyptograptus, Leptograptus, Nemagraptus,* and *Orthograptus.* In contrast, the Monograptid fauna has one dominant genus, *Monograptus.* Subordinate genera include *Cyrtograptus, Linograptus, Rastrites,* and *Retiolites.* The fauna ranged from early Llandovery to early Devonian time.

Benthonic Faunas of the Ordovician and Silurian

The benthonic faunas of the carbonates and detrital rocks of the platform consisted primarily of corals, echinoderms, brachiopods, molluscs, trilobites, stromatoporoids, bryozoans, and ostracods. Graptolites were extremely rare. Corals were not present in Canadian and Whiterock faunas but were very important in younger Ordovician and Silurian faunas.

Benthonic Ordovician of Eastern Canada

In Ontario and western Quebec the Canadian Series is represented by dolomites with few fossils. The gastropod *Ophileta* is present. A large and varied Canadian fauna does occur in fossiliferous limestones and shales farther east in Quebec (Eastern Townships, Lévis, and the Mingan Islands), and in western Newfoundland. Common and characteristic forms are the brachiopods *Clarkella* and *Finkelnburgia,* the gastropods *Ceratopea* and *Euconia,* the cephalopods *Kirkoceras* and *Piloceras,* and the trilobites *Leiostegium, Pilekia,* and *Shumardia.*

Stages for the interval between the Canadian and Wilderness have recently been revised in the United States and their precise representation in Canada has yet to be established. The Table Head sequence of western Newfoundland is of Whiterock age and contains the trilobites *Ectenonotus, Eorobergia, Galbagnostus, Miracybele,* and *Xystocrania.* The Chazyan formations are considered to be of Marmor age (Cooper, 1956). These rocks are exposed near Ottawa and Montreal, on the Mingan Islands, and in Newfoundland. The first appearance of large numbers of bryozoans, echinoderms, and corals in the geological column is in the Marmor Stage. Common genera are the echinoderms *Blastoidocrinus, Bolboporites,* and *Malocystites,* the corals *Billingsaria* and *Lamottia,* the brachiopods *Mimella* and *Rostricellula,* the gastropod *Scalites,* and the conulariid *Conularina.* Some strata in the Mingan Islands and in Newfoundland that previously have been considered Chazyan may be of post-Marmor age.

Beds of Wilderness age occur throughout southern Ontario and Quebec and are commonly very fossiliferous. The earliest fauna is found in the Gull River Formation of Ontario and includes *Cryptophragmus* and abundant but virtually unstudied molluscs. The fauna of the Lowville Formation and its equivalents is characterized by *Bathyurus extans* and many cephalopod species and is known throughout southern Ontario, and near Montreal and Lake St. John. Later Wilderness faunas are present in the Chaumont and Rockland Formations and their equivalents throughout the Ottawa–St. Lawrence Valley from Lake Timiskaming to Murray Bay, in the Saguenay Valley, and in Newfoundland. These faunas include the echinoderms *Amecystis, Carabocrinus huronensis,* and *Foerstediscus;* the coral *Lambeophyllum;* the brachiopods *Doleroides, Hesperorthis, Opikina,* and *Strophomena filitexta;* the trilobites *Raymondites ingalli* and *Thaleops;* the ostracods *Eoleperditia* and *Pteroleperditia;* and the sponge *Receptaculites.*

The Barneveld is the best known and most fossiliferous of the North American Ordovician stages, containing as it does the formations of the Trenton Group of old usage. Characteristic fossils are the coral *Protaraea vetusta;* the sponges *Brachiospongia* and *Steliella;* the echinoderms *Cleiocrinus, Edrioaster, Glyptocrinus, Lebetodiscus,* and *Pleurocystites;* the brachiopods *Parastrophina, Platystrophia, Rafinesquina trentonensis, Sowerbyella "sericea",* and *Vellamo;* the gastropods *Fusispira, Hormotoma trentonensis,* and *Trochonema;* the cephalopod *Endoceras proteiforme;* the trilobites *Calliops, Ceraurus pleurexanthemus, Cryptolithus tessellatus,* and *Flexicalymene senaria;* and the bryozoans *Arthroclema* and *Prasopora.*

The boundary between the Eden and Maysville Stages is not firmly established in Canada, and lumping of the combined interval may prove to be useful. In eastern Canada, rocks correlated as Eden are mainly shales and argillaceous limestones (e.g., Hillier, Collingwood, and Terrebonne units) with such fossils as the echinoderm *Cheirocrinus;* the brachiopods *Cyclospira, Oxoplecia,* and *Plectatrypa;* the cephalopods *Ephippiorthoceras* and *Probillingsites;* and the trilobites *Pseudogygites, Triarthrus eatoni, T. glaber,* and *T. spinosus.* In contrast the Maysville is mostly represented by sandy beds with abundant pelecypods such as *Byssonychia, Rhytimya,* and *Whitella,* the brachiopods *Leptaena moniquensis* and *Zygospira modesta,* and trilobites (including *Proetus chambliensis*).

The Richmond Stage is known from widely scattered areas of eastern Canada: Manitoulin Island, southern Ontario, Eastern Townships, Lake St. John, Gaspé, and Anticosti Island. Common fossils include the coral

TABLE XI-2 *Ordovician faunal successions*

EUROPEAN STAGES	BENTHONIC ZONES Western & Northern Canada	PELAGIC ZONES	COMMON BENTHONIC FOSSILS Eastern Canada, north and west of Logan's Line	NORTH AMERICAN STAGES
ASHGILL	*Bighornia - Thaerodonta*	*Dicellograptus complanatus ornatus*	*Grewingkia rusticum*, *Catazyga headi*, *Schuchertoceras*, *Billingsites*, *Rhombopora quadrata*, *Beatricea*	RICHMOND
		Orthograptus n. sp. A	*Leptaena moniquensis*, *Cryptolithus bellulus*, *Whitella complanata*, *Isotelus maximus*, *Byssonychia radiata*, *Proetus chambliensis*	MAYSVILLE
CARADOC	Red River fauna	*Orthograptus quadrimucronatus*	*Cyclospira bisulcata*, *Paleschara beani*, *Lambeoceras*, *Pseudogygites*, *Triarthrus spinosus*, *Probillingsites primus*	EDEN
			Platystrophia *Vellamo*, *Prasopora selwyni*, *Onniella whittakeri*, *Ceraurus dentatus*, *Lebetodiscus dicksoni*, *Cryptolithus tessellatus*	BARNEVELD
	Faunas of the Sunblood Formation probably span this interval	*Orthograptus truncatus intermedius* *Climacograptus bicornis*	*Sowerbyella curdsvillensis*, *Hesperorthis tricenaria*, *Receptaculites occidentalis*, *Amecystis laevis*, *Gonioceras*, *Bathyurus extans*, *Doleroides* *Opikina*, *Tetradium cellulosum*, *Raymondites ingalli*	WILDERNESS
		Nemagraptus gracilis	[hatched: faunas poorly known or unknown]	PORTERFIELD
LLANDEILO		*Glyptograptus euglyphus*	[hatched: faunas poorly known or unknown]	ASHBY
			Lamottia, *Scalites*, *Pliomera* *Mimella*, *Blastoidocrinus*, *Sigmacystis*, *Malocystites*, *Rostricellula plena*, *Bolboporites americanus*	MARMOR
LLANVIRN	*Anomalorthis* *Orthidiella*	*Paraglossograptus etheridgei*	*Miracybele* *Xystocrania* *Ampyxoides* *Eoleperditia "bivia"*	WHITEROCK
ARENIG	*Hesperonomia*	*Isograptus caduceus*	*Finkelnburgia*, *Tritoechia*, *Lingula quebecensis*, *Ecculiopteris planidorsalis*, *Ellesmeroceras* *Piloceras*, *Shumardia* *Euconia*, *Ceratopea* *Ophileta*	CANADIAN
	J (*Pseudocybele*) I (*Presbynileus*) H (*Trigonocerca*)	*Didymograptus protobifidus*		
	G_2 (*Protopliomerella*)	*Tetragraptus fruticosus*		
		Tetragraptus approximatus		
TREMADOC	G_1 (*Hintzea*)	*Adelograptus-Clonograptus*		
	F (*Rossaspis*) E (*Tesselacauda*) D (*Leiostegium-Kainella*) C ("*Paraplethopeltis*") B (*Bellefontia-Xenostegium*)			
	A (*Symphysurina-Euloma*)	*Staurograptus* *Dictyonema*		

GSC

[hatched box] *Faunas poorly known or unknown*

Grewingkia; the brachiopods *Catazyga headi* and *Strophomena fluctuosa;* the gastropod *Lophospira beatrice;* and the cephalopods *Apsidoceras, Manitoulinoceras,* and *Schuchertoceras.*

Benthonic Ordovician of Western and Northern Canada

Many fossiliferous rock-units are present in western and arctic Canada but few Ordovician and Silurian fossils have been described. Most of the trilobite zones that have been established for the Canadian Stage of Utah and Nevada can also be recognized in the McKay, Survey Peak, and Outram units of the southern Rocky Mountains of Canada. Some of these zones are also present in the Chushina Formation near Jasper and near Mount Robson, in the Kechika Group of northern British Columbia, in unnamed rocks in the northern Yukon and southwest District of Mackenzie, and probably also in the Mingo River and Nadlo Point Formations of Devon Island.

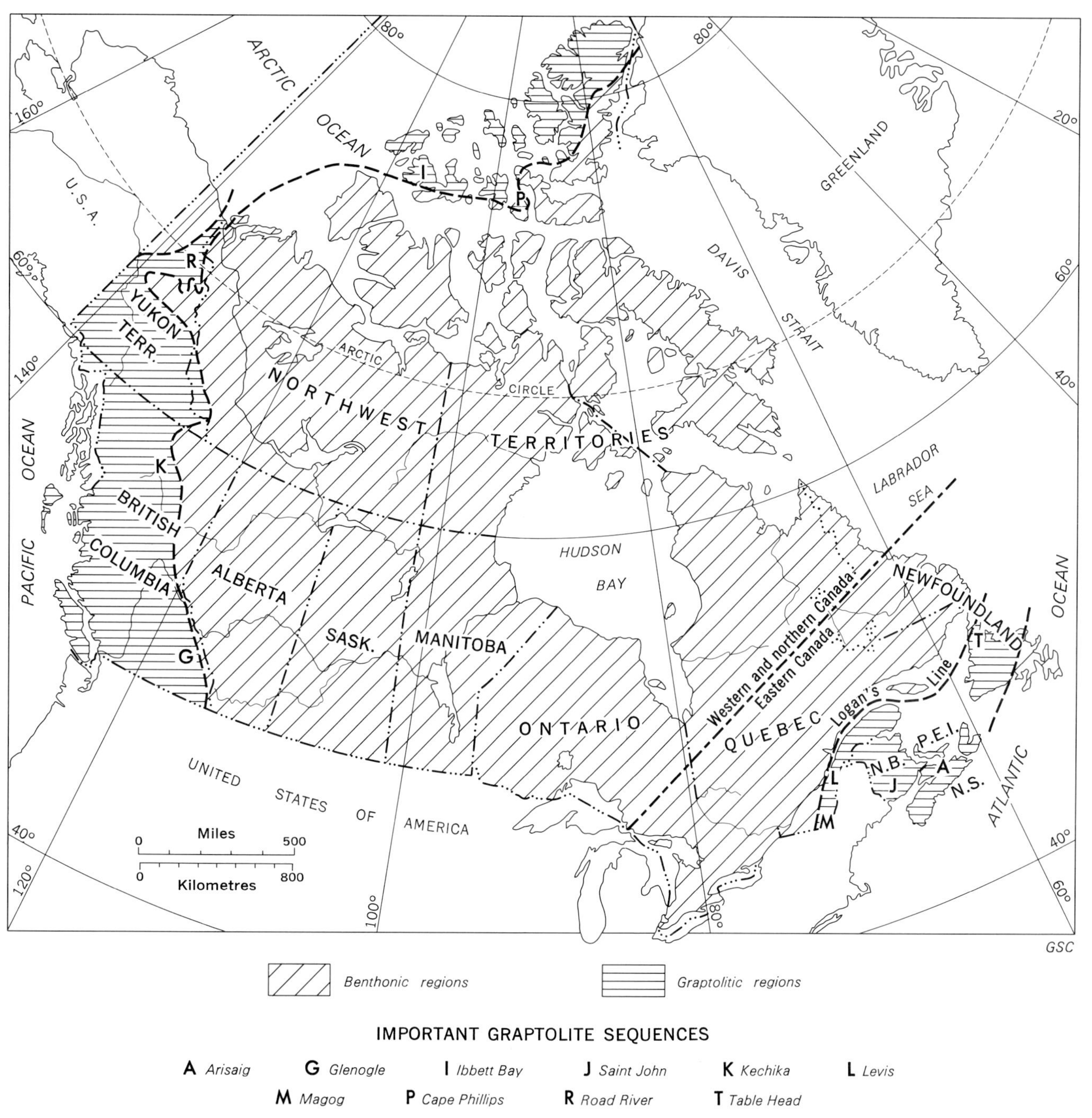

IMPORTANT GRAPTOLITE SEQUENCES

A *Arisaig* G *Glenogle* I *Ibbett Bay* J *Saint John* K *Kechika* L *Levis*
M *Magog* P *Cape Phillips* R *Road River* T *Table Head*

FIGURE XI-1. Distribution of Ordovician and Silurian faunas.

TABLE XI-3 | *Silurian faunal successions*

EUROPEAN STAGES	BENTHONIC ZONES Western & Northern Canada	PELAGIC ZONES	COMMON BENTHONIC FOSSILS Ontario	COMMON BENTHONIC FOSSILS Eastern Canada	NORTH AMERICAN SERIES and STAGES
?DOWNTON?		*Monograptus* n. sp. T		*Kloedenia wilckensiana*	CAYUGAN
LUDLOW		*Monograptus* n. sp. P			
		Monograptus ultimus			
	Atrypella scheii	*Monograptus tumescens minor*	*Schuchertella hydraulica*		
		Monograptus n. sp. O		*Eatonioides, Orthoceras bullatum* var., *Sphaerirhynchia wilsoni*	
		Monograptus n. sp. N	*Leperditia scalaris Eurypterus*		
		Monograptus bohemicus			
		Monograptus nilssoni	*Megalomus canadensis*, *Trimerella grandis*, *Conchidium occidentalis*, *Fletcheria guelphensis*	*Conchidium knighti*, *Salopina lunata*	
WENLOCK		*Monograptus testis* and *Cyrtograptus trilleri*			NIAGARAN: Lockportian
		Cyrtograptus lundgreni	*Cheirurus niagarensis*, *Scutellum acamas*	*Scutellum pompilius*	
		Cyrtograptus perneri			
		Cyrtograptus n. sp. G			
		Cyrtograptus n. sp. F			Tonawandan
		Cyrtograptus n. sp. C			
		Cyrtograptus rigidus	*Caryocrinites ornatus*, *Paraechmina spinosa*		
		Monograptus riccartonensis	*Stephanocrinus angulatus*, *Dicoelosia acutilobus*		
		Cyrtograptus murchisoni		*Costistricklandia brevis, Costistricklandia gaspéensis*	
LLANDOVERY	*Eophacops-Cheirurus*	*Monograptus spiralis*		*Eocoelia sulcata*	
			Costistricklandia canadensis, *Pentameroides*, *Zygobolba*, *Bolbineossia*	*Zygobolba*, *Bolbineossia*, *Ehlersella davidsoni*, *Eocoelia hemisphaerica*	Ontarian
	Pentamerus	*Monograptus turriculatus*			
		Monograptus sedgwicki to *Monograptus convolutus*	*Virgiana decussata*, *Hyattidina congesta*	*Virgiana anticostiensis, Hyattidina congesta* var.	
	Eostropheodonta		*Phaenopora expansa*, *Lingula clintoni*	*Phaenopora superba, Camarotoechia fringilla*	ALEXANDRIAN
		Monograptus millepeda	*Resserella eugeniensis*, *"Coelospira" planoconvexa*	*"Coelospira" planoconvexa*	
		Monograptus gregarius	*Brockocystis tecumseth*		
		Monograptus cyphus			
		Diplograptus modestus			

GSC

Faunas poorly known or unknown (hatched)

The uppermost Canadian *Hesperonomia* and the Whiterock *Orthidiella* and *Anomalorthis* brachiopod assemblage zones are well developed in the Skoki Formation of southwest Alberta. The *Orthidiella* Zone is probably also present in eastern British Columbia at Cecilia Lake and near Peace River. The *Hesperonomia* Zone includes the brachiopods *Diparelasma, Leptella, Syntrophopsis, Taffia,* and *Tritoechia.* Species of *Diparelasma, Orthambonites,* and *Petroria* are found in the *Orthidiella* Zone. Genera in the *Anomalorthis* Zone include *Receptaculites,* the gastropods *Maclurites* and *Palliseria,* and the brachiopod *Syntrophopsis.*

Fossiliferous Marmor to Maysville rocks are rare in western Canada. The most complete sequence seems to be in the southwest District of Mackenzie where the Sunblood Formation contains a succession of well-preserved brachiopod and trilobite faunas. This succession probably spans the entire interval but the faunas are virtually unstudied. Faunules from high in the Kechika Group of northern British Columbia, from the Admiralty and Cornwallis units of the arctic islands and from the Bad Cache Rapids and Red River units of Manitoba probably correlate with faunules in the upper Sunblood. Many faunules in arctic Canada have been referred to "the Arctic Ordovician fauna"; most of these faunules correlate with the fauna of the Red River Formation but some suggest the younger *Bighornia–Thaerodonta* Zone. The Red River fauna includes species of *Receptaculites;* the corals, *Calapoecia, Catenipora, Tollina, Palaeofavosites, Palaeophyllum, Grewingkia,* and *Favistina;* the brachiopods *Rafinesquina,* and *Rhynchotrema;* the gastropods *Fusispira, Hormotoma,* and *Maclurites,* and the cephalopods *Diestoceras, Cyrtogomphoceras, Lambeoceras,* and *Winnipegoceras.*

Richmond faunas are widely distributed in western Canada and can mostly be referred to the *Bighornia–Thaerodonta* assemblage zone that is well developed low in the Beaverfoot Formation of the southern Rockies. Other typical genera are the corals *Catenipora, Favistina, Lobocorallium, Palaeofavosites, Palaeophyllum, Sarcinula,* and *Streptelasma,* and the brachiopods *Dinorthis* and *Rhynchotrema.* Such faunas are present in the lower part of the Sandpile Group of northern British Columbia; in the Chedabucto Lake and lower Mount Kindle Formations of the District of Mackenzie; in unnamed rocks in northeast British Columbia; the Yukon, and the District of Mackenzie; and in the Stony Mountain, Stonewall, and Churchill River units of Manitoba.

Benthonic Silurian of Eastern Canada

In Ontario, the Alexandrian Series consists of the Whirlpool, Power Glen, Manitoulin, Cabot Head, and Grimsby Formations. Characteristic species include the coral *Palaeofavosites asper;* the echinoderm *Brockocystis tecumseth;* the brachiopods *Resserella eugeniensis, "Coelospira" planoconvexa,* and *Lingula clintoni;* the bryozoans *Helopora fragilis* and *Phaenopora expansa;* the trilobite *Liocalymene clintoni;* and the trail *Arthrophycus alleghaniensis.* On Anticosti Island, 15 feet of the Becscie Formation underlies the *Virgiana* beds and may be the eastern representative of the Alexandrian. The fauna includes *"Coelospira" planoconvexa* and *Phaenopora superba.* Alexandrian faunas are present in the Beechhill Formation (with the brachiopod *Eostropheodonta*) and the lower part of the Ross Brook Formation of Arisaig, in Gaspé, and in the Cabano Formation (also with *Eostropheodonta*) and possibly also in the overlying Pointe-aux-Trembles Formation that carries *Eocoelia quebecensis.*

Characteristic fossils of the Ontarian Stage include the brachiopods *Virgiana, Hyattidina, Pentameroides, Camarotoechia winiskensis, Plectatrypa lowi, Costistricklandia canadensis, Eocoelia hemisphaerica,* and *Ehlersella davidsoni*; and the ostracods *Zygobolba* and *Bolbineossia.* Such fossils are found in the Reynales, Dyer Bay, Wingfield, St. Edmund, Wabi, and Thornloe Formations of Ontario; the Becscie, Gun River, and Jupiter Formations of Anticosti Island; part of the Whitehead Formation at Percé; the Awantjish, Burnt Jam Brook, and Clemville Formations of Gaspé; the Quoddy Formation of New Brunswick; the middle member of the Ross Brook Formation of Nova Scotia; and the Pike Arm Formation of Newfoundland.

The brachiopods *Dicoelosia acutilobus, D. biloba, Eocoelia sulcata, Costistricklandia brevis,* and *C. gaspéensis;* the echinoderms *Stephanocrinus angulatus, Caryocrinites ornatus,* and the ostracod *Paraechmina spinosa* are present in faunas of the Tonawandan Stage, found in formations such as the Rochester of southern Ontario; the Val Brillant, La Vieille, and Laforce of Gaspé; the Long Reach of New Brunswick; and in the upper member of the Ross Brook Formation of Nova Scotia.

Benthonic species of the Lockportian Stage include the coral *Fletcheria guelphensis;* the pelecypod *Megalomus canadensis;* the brachiopods *Salopina lunata, Trimerella grandis, Conchidium knighti,* and *C. occidentalis;* and the trilobites *Scutellum acamas, S. pompilius,* and *Cheirurus niagarensis.* Lockportian faunas are found in the Lockport, Amabel, and Guelph Formations of Ontario; in the Sayabec, Gascons, Bouleaux, West Point, Robitaille, Mont Wissick, and Sargent Bay Formations of Quebec; in the Jones Creek and Pembroke Formations of New Brunswick; and in the Kentville Formation and the upper member of the McAdam Formation of Nova Scotia.

Faunas of the Cayugan Series are not widespread and generally consist of few species. Typical forms include the ostracod *Leperditia scalaris,* the brachiopod *Schuchertella hydraulica,* and eurypterids in the Bertie–Akron sequence of Ontario; the brachiopods *Eatonioides* and *Sphaerirhynchia wilsoni* and a variety of the cephalopod *Orthoceras bullatum* in the Moydart Formation, and the ostracod *Kloedenia wilckensiana* in the Stonehouse Formation, both of Nova Scotia.

Benthonic Silurian of Western and Northern Canada

A sequence of Llandovery benthonic zones is present in the Beaverfoot Formation of the southern Rocky Mountains. The *Eostropheodonta* zone contains the brachiopod *Hesperorthis;* the corals *Catenipora, Favosites,* and *Streptelasma;* and the trilobites *Eophacops* and *Encrinurus.* Genera of the *Pentamerus* zone include the corals *Cystihalysites, Favosites,* and *Streptelasma;* and the ostracods *Aparchites, Bythocypris,* and *Tubulibairdia.* The *Eophacops–Cheirurus* zone contains *Encrinurus,* the brachiopods *Glassia* and *Atrypa,* and *Favosites.* Faunas corresponding to the interval *Pentamerus* to *Eophacops–Cheirurus* are widespread in western Canada: Silurian formations of northern British Columbia; much of the Allen Bay Formation of the arctic islands; the *Aulacopleura socialis* beds of the Road River Formation of the northern Yukon; most of the Silurian formations of the Hudson Bay and James Bay Lowlands; the Cedar Lake and East Arm Formations of southern Manitoba. Faunas of the Fisher Branch to Atikameg interval in Manitoba and of the Port Nelson and Severn River limestones of the Hudson Bay Lowland may correlate with the *Eostropheodonta* zone. The Attawapiskat Formation of the Hudson Bay Lowland may be high Llandovery or low Wenlock. Upper

Llandovery and lower Wenlock fish are present in the arctic islands.

Rocks of Wenlock and Ludlow age are missing from most of western Canada, probably as a result of Late Silurian and Early Devonian erosion. Wenlock and Ludlow rocks are found in the Yukon and the Northwest Territories but their benthonic faunas are poorly known. The *Atrypella scheii* zone has been reported from the Read Bay, Douro, Gossage, and Cape Rawson units, and from unnamed rocks near the Alaska–Yukon Boundary. Genera of this zone include the brachiopods *Conchidium* and *Howellella;* the corals *Favosites, Parafavosites, Striatopora,* and *Syringopora;* the trilobites *Encrinurus* (*Frammia*) and *Hemiarges;* the clam *Megalomus,* and eurypterids. Ludlow fish have been found in the Read Bay Formation and Ludlow and Downton fish and graptolites in the Delorme Formation.

Selected References

Bolton, T. E.
1957: Silurian stratigraphy and palaeontology of the Niagara Escarpment in Ontario; *Geol. Surv. Can.,* Mem. 289.
1966: Illustrations of Canadian fossils: Silurian faunas of Ontario; *Geol. Surv. Can.,* Paper 66–50.

Boucot, A. J., Harper, C., Johnson, J. G., and Walmsley, V. G.
1966: Silurian brachiopods and gastropods of southern New Brunswick; *Geol. Surv. Can.,* Bull. 140.

Bulman, O. M. B.
1950: Graptolites from the Dictyonema Shales of Quebec; *Geol. Soc. London, Quart. J.,* vol. 106, pp. 63–99.
1958: The sequence of graptolite faunas; *Palaeontology,* vol. 1, pp. 159–173.

Cooper, G. A.
1956: Chazyan and related brachiopods; *Smithsonian Inst. Misc. Collections,* vol. 127.

Copeland, M. J., and Bolton, T. E.
1960: The Eurypterida of Canada; *Geol. Surv. Can.,* Bull. 60, pp. 13–48.

Foerste, A. F.
1924: Upper Ordovician faunas of Ontario and Quebec; *Geol. Surv. Can.,* Mem. 138.

Hintze, L. F.
1953: Lower Ordovician trilobites from western Utah and eastern Nevada; *Utah Geol. Mineral. Surv.,* Bull. 48.

Jackson, D. E.
1964: Observations on the sequence and correlation of Lower and Middle Ordovician graptolite faunas of North America; *Bull. Geol. Soc. Am.,* vol. 75, pp. 523–534.

Jackson, D. E., and Lenz, A. C.
1962: Zonation of Ordovician and Silurian graptolites of northern Yukon, Canada; *Bull. Am. Assoc. Petrol. Geol.,* vol. 46, pp. 30–45.

McLearn, F. H.
1924: Palaeontology of the Silurian rocks of Arisaig, Nova Scotia; *Geol. Surv. Can.,* Mem. 60.

Nelson, S. J.
1964: Ordovician stratigraphy of northern Hudson Bay Lowland, Manitoba; *Geol. Surv. Can.,* Bull. 108.

Norford, B. S.
1962: Illustrations of Canadian fossils: Cambrian, Ordovician, and Silurian of the Western Cordillera; *Geol. Surv. Can.,* Paper 62-14.

Stearn, C. W.
1956: Stratigraphy and palaeontology of the Interlake Group and Stonewall Formation of southern Manitoba; *Geol. Surv. Can.,* Mem. 281.

Thorsteinsson, R.
1958: Cornwallis and Little Cornwallis Islands, District of Franklin, Northwest Territories; *Geol. Surv. Can.,* Mem. 294.

Whittington, H. B.
1965: Trilobites of the Ordovician Table Head Formation, western Newfoundland; *Bull. Museum Comp. Zool., Harvard Univ.,* vol. 152, No. 4.

Wilson, A. E.
1946: Geology of the Ottawa–St. Lawrence Lowlands, Ontario and Quebec; *Geol. Surv. Can.,* Mem. 241 (also, *Geol. Surv. Can.,* Bulls. 4, 8, 9, 11, 17, 28, 42, 67).

Plate IV. Ordovician Fossils of Eastern Canada

(All figures natural size unless otherwise stated)

Figure 1 *Bathyurus superbus* Raymond. Wilderness; Ontario; 7422a.

Figure 2 *Tetradium clarki* Okulitch. x5.5; Wilderness; Ontario; 7397c.

Figure 3 *Ophileta compacta* (Salter). Canadian; Ontario; 17088.

Figure 4 *Receptaculites occidentalis* Salter. Wilderness; Ontario; 1125p.

Figure 5 *Malocystites murchisoni* Billings. Marmor; Quebec; 1012a.

Figure 6 *Selenoharpes ottawaensis* (Billings). Barneveld; Ontario; 329.

Figure 7 *Hesperorthis tricenaria* (Conrad). Wilderness; Ontario; 1151.

Figure 8 *Lingula cobourgensis* Billings. Eden; Ontario; 1635a.

Figure 9 *Amecystis laevis* (Raymond). Wilderness; Ontario; 7936.

Figure 10 *Onniella whittakeri* (Raymond). x2; Barneveld; Ontario; 3240a.

Figure 11 *Pleurocystites* cf. *P. filitextus* Billings. Barneveld; Ontario; 17696.

Figure 12 *Cupulocrinus jewetti* (Billings). Wilderness; Ontario; 7784z.

Figure 13 *Edrioaster* sp. x2; Barneveld; Ontario; 17087.

Figure 14 *Probillingsites cobourgensis* Flower. Eden; Ontario; 11092.

Figure 15 *Fusispira angusta* Ulrich and Scofield. Barneveld; Quebec; 13247.

Figure 16 *Flexicalymene granulosa* (Foerste). x4; Maysville; Ontario; 18667.

Figure 17 *Catazyga erratica* (Hall). Maysville; Ontario; 18670.

Figure 18 *Cryptolithus bellulus* (Ulrich). Eden; Ontario; 18669.

Figure 19 *Platystrophia clarksvillensis* Foerste. Richmond; Ontario; 18672.

Figure 20 *Glyptorthis insculpta manitoulinensis* Foerste. Richmond; Ontario; 6784.

Figure 21 *Pseudogygites latimarginatus* (Hall). Eden; Ontario; 18666.

Figure 22 *Rafinesquina sardesoni* Salmon. Eden; Ontario; 3256.

Figure 23 *Triarthrus spinosus* Billings. Eden; Ontario; 18668.

Figure 24 *Byssonychia grandis* Ulrich. Richmond; Ontario; 2120.

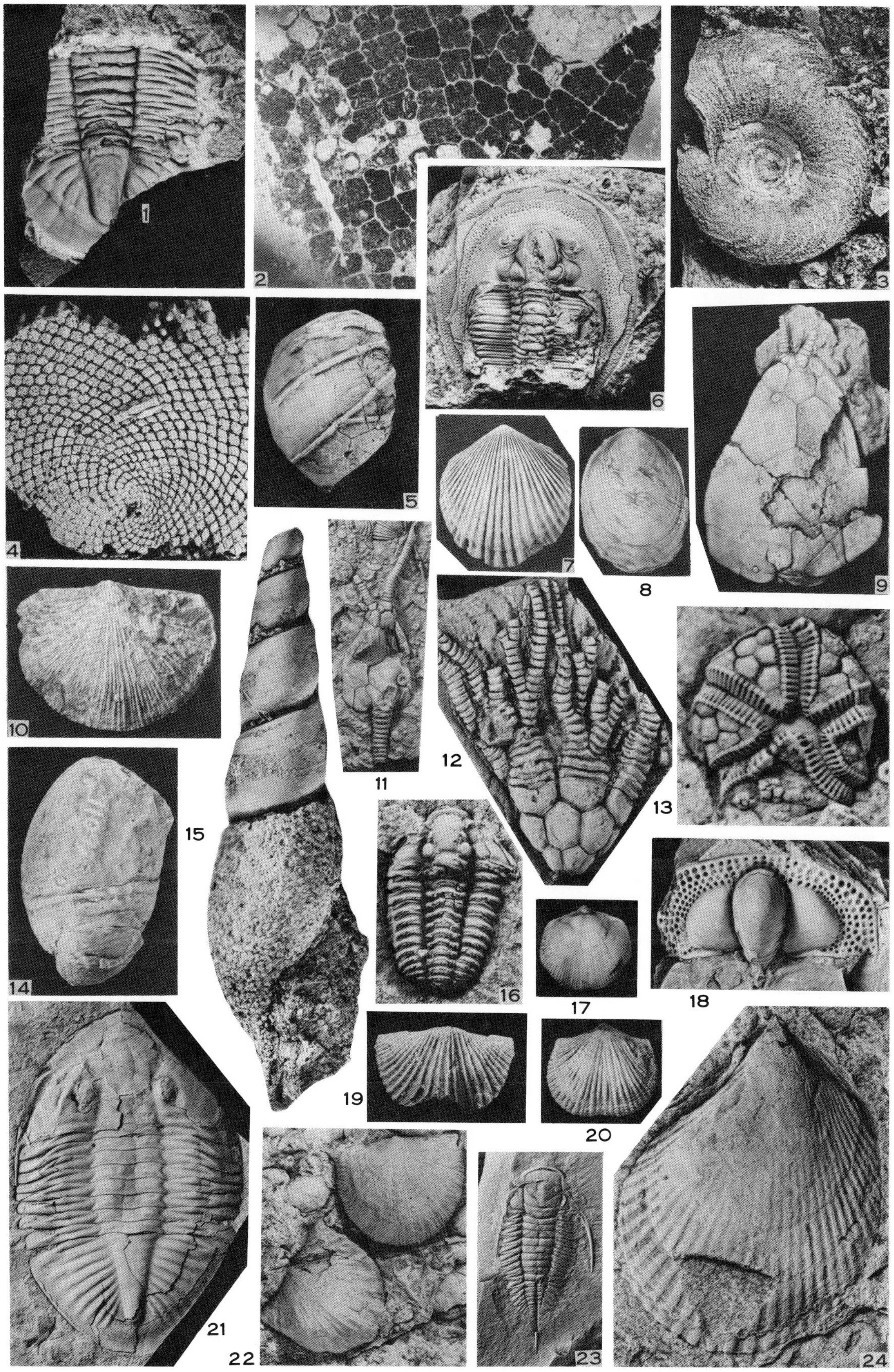
1
2
3
4
5
6
7
8
9
10
11
12
13
14
15
16
17
18
19
20
21
22
23
24

PLATE V. Ordovician Fossils of Western and Northern Canada

(All figures natural size unless otherwise stated)

Figure 1 *Lobocorallium prolongatum* (Wilson). Richmond; Alberta; 16917.

Figure 2 *Dinorthis rockymontana* Wilson. Richmond; Alberta; 16885.

Figures 3, 11 *Bighornia parva* Duncan. Richmond; Wyoming; USNM 127574 (x3) and 124801.

Figures 4, 10 *Dinorthis columbia* Wilson. Richmond; Alberta; 16892.

Figures 5, 8, 18 *Rhynchotrema kananaskia* Wilson. Richmond; British Columbia; 6749.

Figures 6, 7, 9 *Rhynchotrema windermeris* Wilson. Richmond; Alberta; 16895 and 16896.

Figures 12, 13, 14 *Thaerodonta* sp. aff. *T. saxea* (Sardeson). Richmond; Alberta; 16887, 16888, and 16889.

Figures 15, 16 *Calyptaulax* sp. Wilderness; Mackenzie; 16872 and 16873.

Figure 17 *Tollina* sp. Richmond; Mackenzie; 16915.

Figures 19, 20 *Palaeophyllum* sp. Richmond; Mackenzie; 16910 and 16911.

Figures 21, 22 *Leiostegium* sp. x2; Canadian; Mackenzie; 20432 and 20433.

Figure 23 *Oistodus lanceolatus* Pander. x50; Whiterock; Alberta; 20434.

Figure 24 *Catenipora robustus* (Wilson). Richmond; Alberta; 16907.

Figures 25, 26 *Opikina* sp. Wilderness; Mackenzie; 16876 and 16875.

Figures 27, 28 *Maclurites* sp. cf. *M. magnus* Lesueur. Whiterock; Mackenzie; 16883 and 16884.

Figures 29, 30 *Bellefontia* sp. Canadian; British Columbia; 20435 and 20436.

Figures 31, 32 *Kainella billingsi* Walcott. Canadian; British Columbia; USNM 70334 and 70336.

PLATE VI. Ordovician and Silurian Graptolites

(All figures natural size unless otherwise stated)

Figure 1 *Monograptus priodon* (Bronn). x2; Llandovery; Scotland; figure from Bulman (1955).

Figure 2 *Diplograptus* cf. *D. modestus* Lapworth. x5; Llandovery; Iowa; figure from Ross (1964).

Figure 3 *Monograptus turriculatus* (Barrande). x2; Llandovery; Bohemia; figure from Bulman (1955).

Figure 4 *Linograptus* sp. x3; Ludlow; Silesia; figure from Bulman (1955).

Figures 5, 6 *Monograptus bohemicus* (Barrande). x4; Ludlow; Illinois; figures from Ross (1962).

Figure 7 *Climacograptus scharenbergi* Lapworth. x6; Llandeilo-Caradoc; Scotland; figure from Bulman (1955).

Figure 8 *Cyrtograptus murchisoni* Carruthers. x2; Wenlock; Bohemia; figure from Bulman (1955).

Figure 9 *Monograptus convolutus* (Hisinger). x2; Llandovery; Sweden; figure from Bulman (1955).

Figure 10 *Climacograptus bicornis* (Hall). x2; Caradoc; Scotland; figure from Bulman (1955).

Figure 11 *Retiolites* (*Stomatograptus*) *grandis grandis* Suess. x2; Llandovery; Bohemia; figure from Bouček and Münch (1943).

Figure 12 *Didymograptus* sp., pendent species. Llanvirn; Wales; figure from Bulman (1955).

Figure 13 *Dicellograptus morrisi* Hopkinson. x4; Caradoc; Sweden; figure from Bulman (1955).

Figure 14 *Dicranograptus nicholsoni* Hopkinson. x4; Caradoc; Scotland; figure from Bulman (1955).

Figure 15 *Monograptus spiralis spiralis* (Geinitz). Llandovery; Bohemia; figure from Přibyl (1944).

Figure 16 *Phyllograptus angustifolius* Hall. Ventral view, x4; Arenig; Sweden; figure from Bulman (1955).

Figure 17 *Didymograptus spinosus* Ruedemann. x2; Llanvirn; Yukon; figure from Jackson (1964).

Figure 18 *Tetragraptus quadribrachiatus* (Hall). Arenig; Quebec; figure from Bulman (1955).

Figure 19 *Nemagraptus gracilis* (Hall). Caradoc; Scotland; figure from Bulman (1955).

Figure 20 *Phyllograptus typus* Hall. Arenig; Quebec; figure from Bulman (1955).

Figure 21 *Staurograptus dichotomus* Emmons. Tremadoc; New York; figure from Bulman (1955).

Figure 22 *Glyptograptus dentatus* (Brongniart). x4; Arenig; Sweden; figure from Bulman (1955).

Figure 23 *Tetragraptus fruticosus* (Hall). Arenig; Quebec; figure from Bulman (1955).

Figure 24 *Didymograptus extensus* (Hall). Arenig; Quebec; figure from Bulman (1955).

Figure 25 *Isograptus caduceus maximo-divergens* Harris. x2; Arenig; British Columbia; figure from Jackson (1964).

Figure 26 *Bryograptus* sp. Tremadoc; Sweden; figure from Bulman (1955).

Figure 27 *Dictyonema flabelliforme* (Eichwald). Tremadoc; England; figure from Bulman (1955), dashed lines show approximate zones of branching.

Figure 28 *Clonograptus rigidus* (Hall). x½; Arenig; Quebec; figure from Bulman (1955).

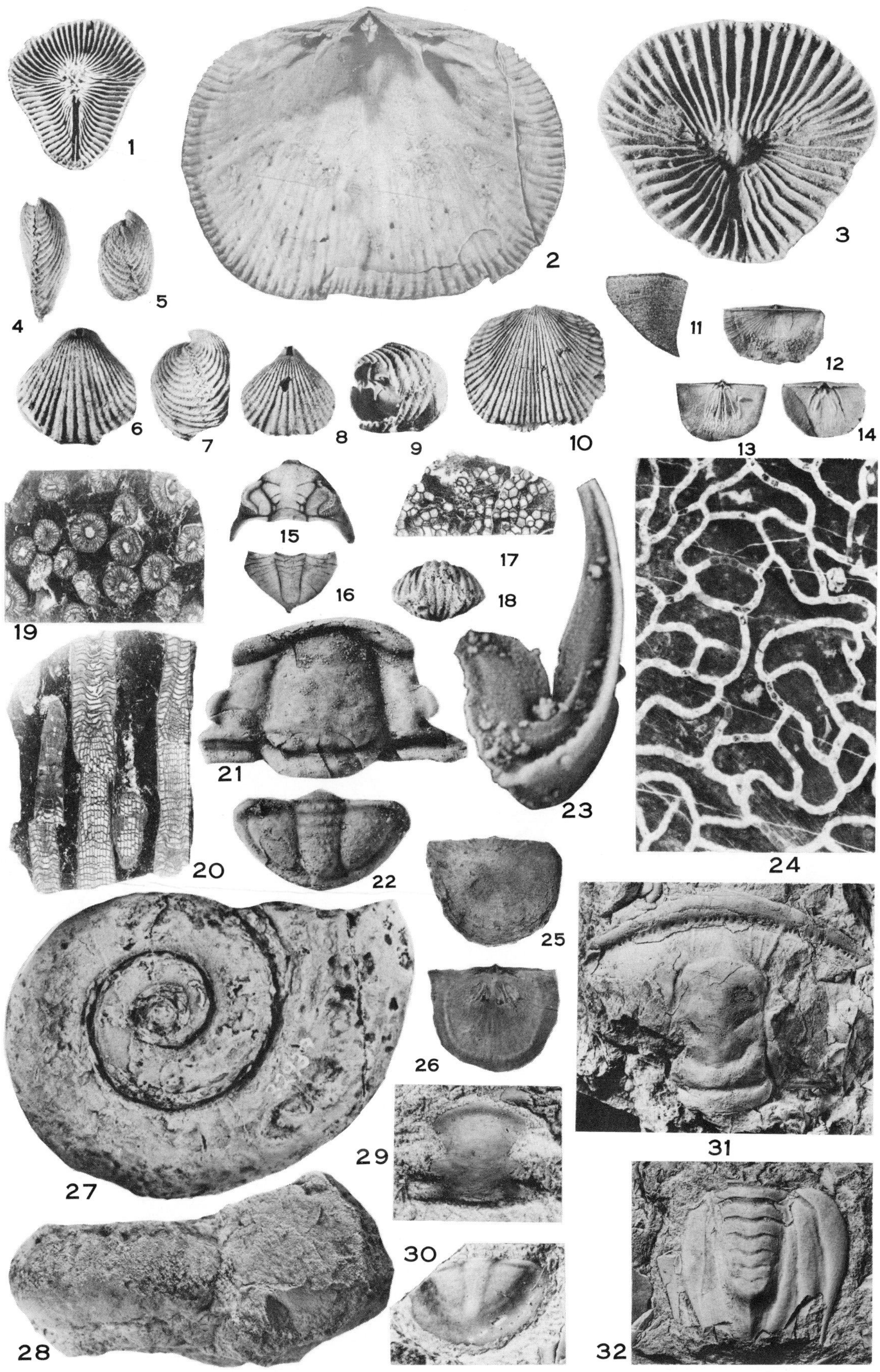
1
2
3
4
5
6
7
8
9
10
11
12
13
14
15
16
17
18
19
20
21
22
23
24
25
26
27
28
29
30
31
32

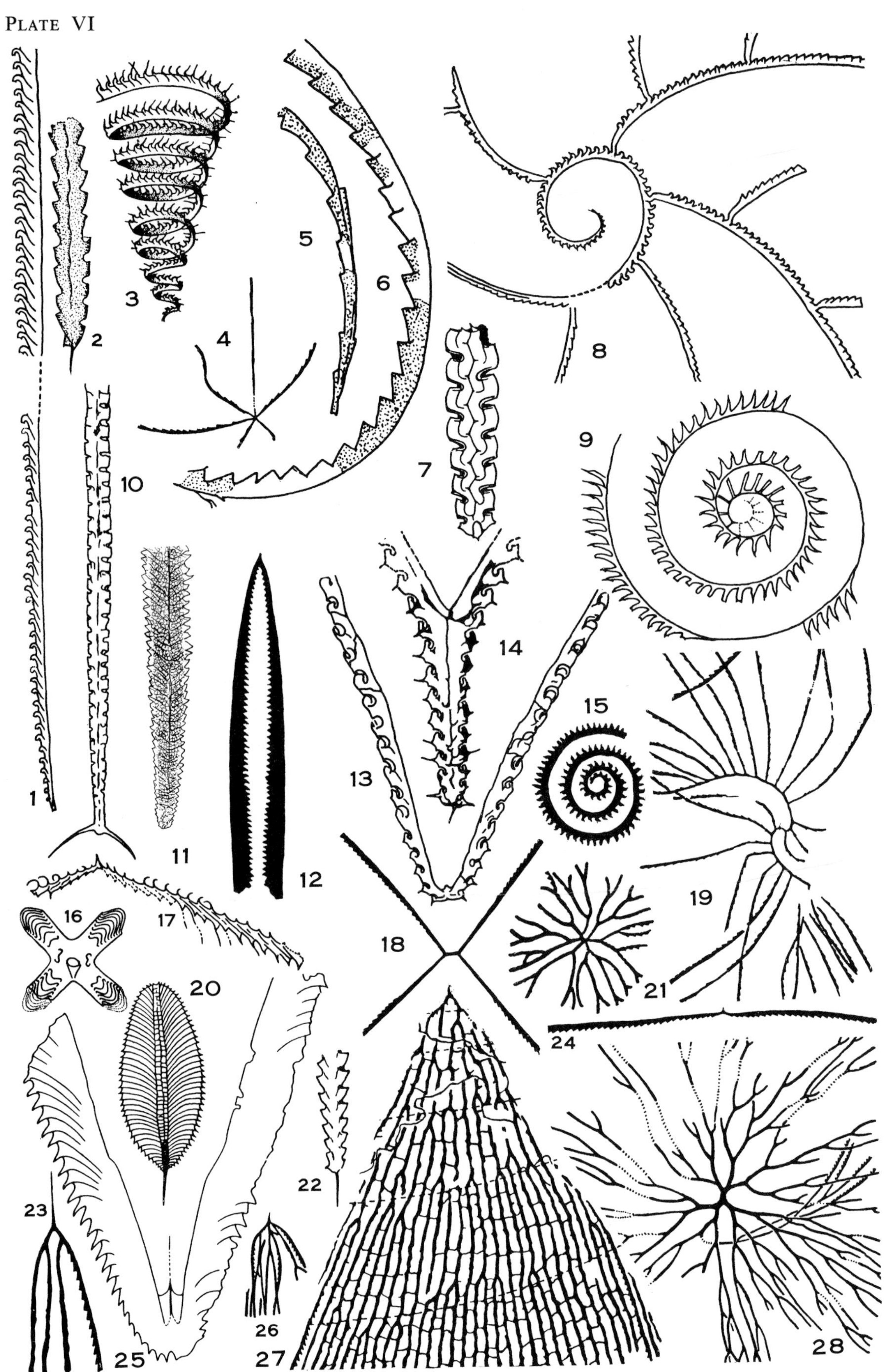
1
2
3
4
5
6
7
8
9
10
11
12
13
14
15
16
17
18
19
20
21
22
23
24
25
26
27
28

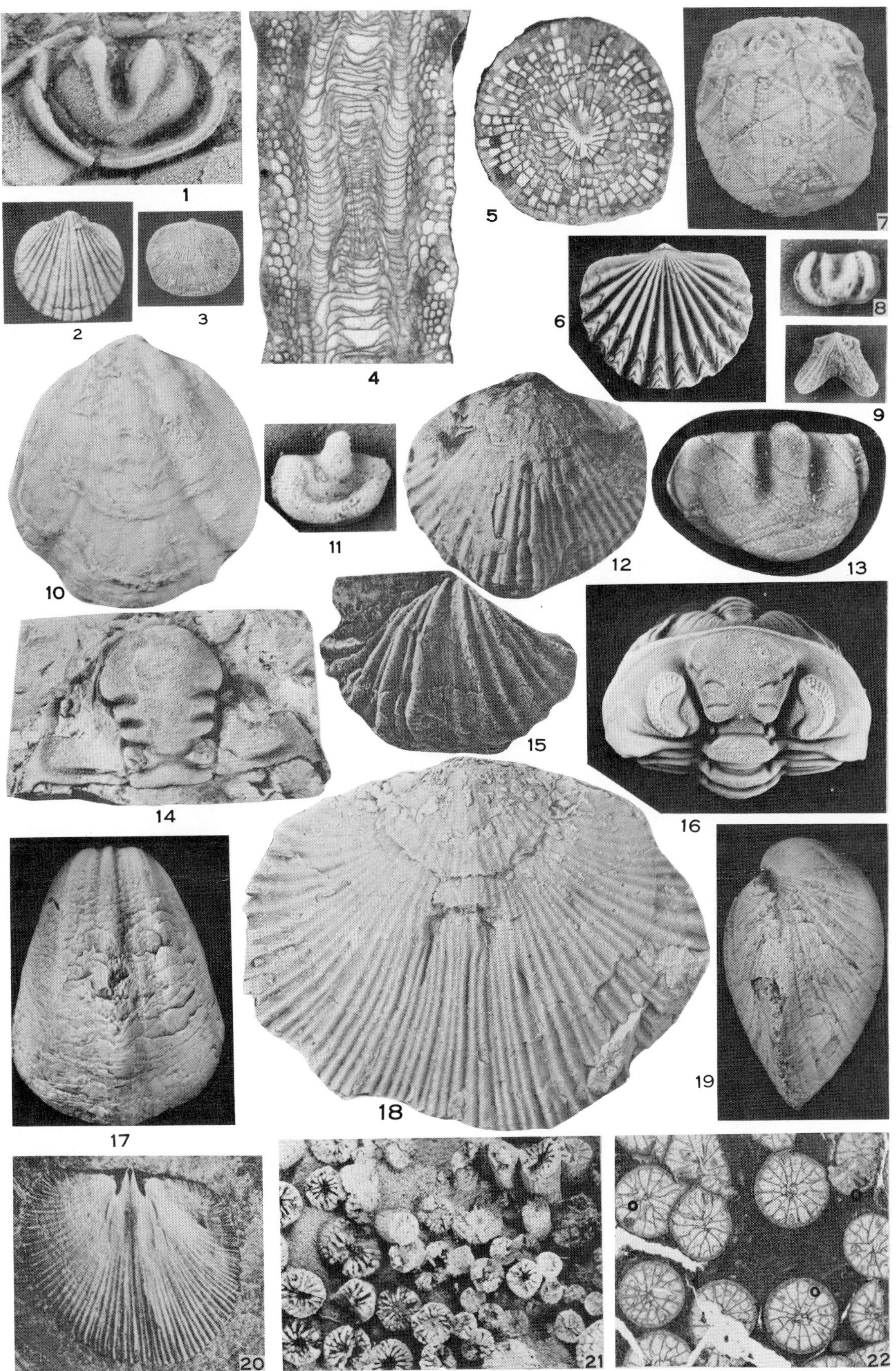
1
2
3
4
5
6
7
8
9
10
11
12
13
14
15
16
17
18
19
20
21
22

Plate VII. Silurian Fossils of Eastern Canada

Figure 1 *Zygobolba decora* (Billings). x16; Niagaran; Quebec; 2547.

Figure 2 *'Coelospira' planoconvexa* (Hall). x1; Alexandrian; Ontario; 17959.

Figure 3 *Mendacella* sp. x1; Alexandrian; Ontario; 17955.

Figures 4, 5 *Entelophyllum pennanti* (Billings). x4; Niagaran; Quebec; 3040m.

Figure 6 *Eocoelia hemispherica* (Sowerby). x3; Niagaran; Quebec; 17090.

Figure 7 *Caryocrinites ornatus* Say. x1; Tonawandan; Ontario; 2656d.

Figure 8 *Dizygopleura symmetrica* (Hall). x15; Tonawandan; Ontario; 15196b.

Figure 9 *Dicoelosia acutilobus* (Ringueberg). x5; Tonawandan; Ontario; 17965.

Figure 10 *Pentameroides* sp. x1; Ontarian; Ontario; 17973.

Figure 11 *Paraechmina spinosa* (Hall). x15; Tonawandan; Ontario; 15192a.

Figure 12 *Costistricklandia gaspéensis* Billings. x1; (after Northrop, 1939); Niagaran; Quebec.

Figure 13 *Kloedenia wilckensiana* (Jones). x15; Downtonian; Nova Scotia; 14514.

Figure 14 *Cheirurus niagarensis* (Hall). x1; Lockportian; Ontario; 17969.

Figure 15 *Janius* sp. x2; (after Boucot, 1963); Niagaran; New Brunswick; 15152.

Figure 16 *Eophacops orestes* (Billings). x3; Niagaran; Quebec; 17091.

Figures 17, 19 *Virgiana barrandei* (Billings). x1; Niagaran; Quebec; 2372, b.

Figure 18 *Costistricklandia canadensis* Billings. x1; Ontarian; Ontario; 17972.

Figure 20 *Salopina lunata* (Sowerby). x2; (after Boucot, *et al.*, 1960); Niagaran; New Brunswick; 14962.

Figure 21 *Palaeophyllum williamsi* Chadwick. x4; Alexandrian; Ontario; 4508.

Figure 22 *Palaeophyllum multicaule* (Hall). x4; Lockportian; Ontario; 17092.

Plate VIII. Silurian Fossils of Western Canada

(All figures natural size unless otherwise stated)

Figures 1, 4 *Conchidium alaskense* Kirk and Amsden. Ludlow; southeast Alaska; USNM 116563 and 116566; figures from Kirk and Amsden (1952).

Figures 2, 3 *Atrypella scheii* (Holtedahl)? Ludlow, southeast Alaska; USNM 116578 and 116573; figures from Kirk and Amsden (1952).

Figures 5, 6 *Eurypterus fischeri* Eichwald. Upper Wenlock or lower Ludlow; Cornwallis Island; 13997 and 14003.

Figures 7, 8 *Atrypa gabrielsi* Norford. Upper Llandovery; British Columbia; 16918a and 16918b.

Figure 9 *Scutellum borealis* (Poulsen). Upper Llandovery; Yukon Territory; 15411.

Figures 10, 13, 17 *Glassia variabilis* Whiteaves. x2; upper Llandovery; British Columbia; 16900.

Figure 11 *Favosites discoideus* (Roemer). Upper Llandovery; British Columbia; 15822.

Figure 12 *Favosites favosus* (Goldfuss). Upper Llandovery; British Columbia; 15850.

Figure 14 *Encrinurus* cf. *E. princeps* Poulsen. Upper Llandovery; Yukon Territory; 16903.

Figure 15 *Halysites occidens* Norford. Upper Llandovery; British Columbia; 14484.

Figure 16 *Dicoelosia* cf. *D. biloba* (Linnaeus). x2; upper Llandovery; British Columbia; 15788.

Figure 18 *Cystihalysites magnitubus* (Buehler). Longitudinal section; upper Llandovery; British Columbia; 15757c.

Figure 19 *Dihogmochilina latimarginata* (Jones). Llandovery; Manitoba; 17089.

Figures 20, 21 *Halysites nitida* Lambe. x4 (longitudinal section) and x1; upper Llandovery; British Columbia; 15825a and 15825.

Figure 22 *Multisolenia tortuosa* Fritz. Longitudinal section x3; Llandovery; Manitoba; 10485.

Figures 23, 25 *Columnaria columbia* Norford. Transverse and longitudinal sections x2; Llandovery; British Columbia; 16524a and 16524b.

Figure 24 *Coenites rectilineatus* (Simpson). Upper Llandovery, British Columbia; 15821.

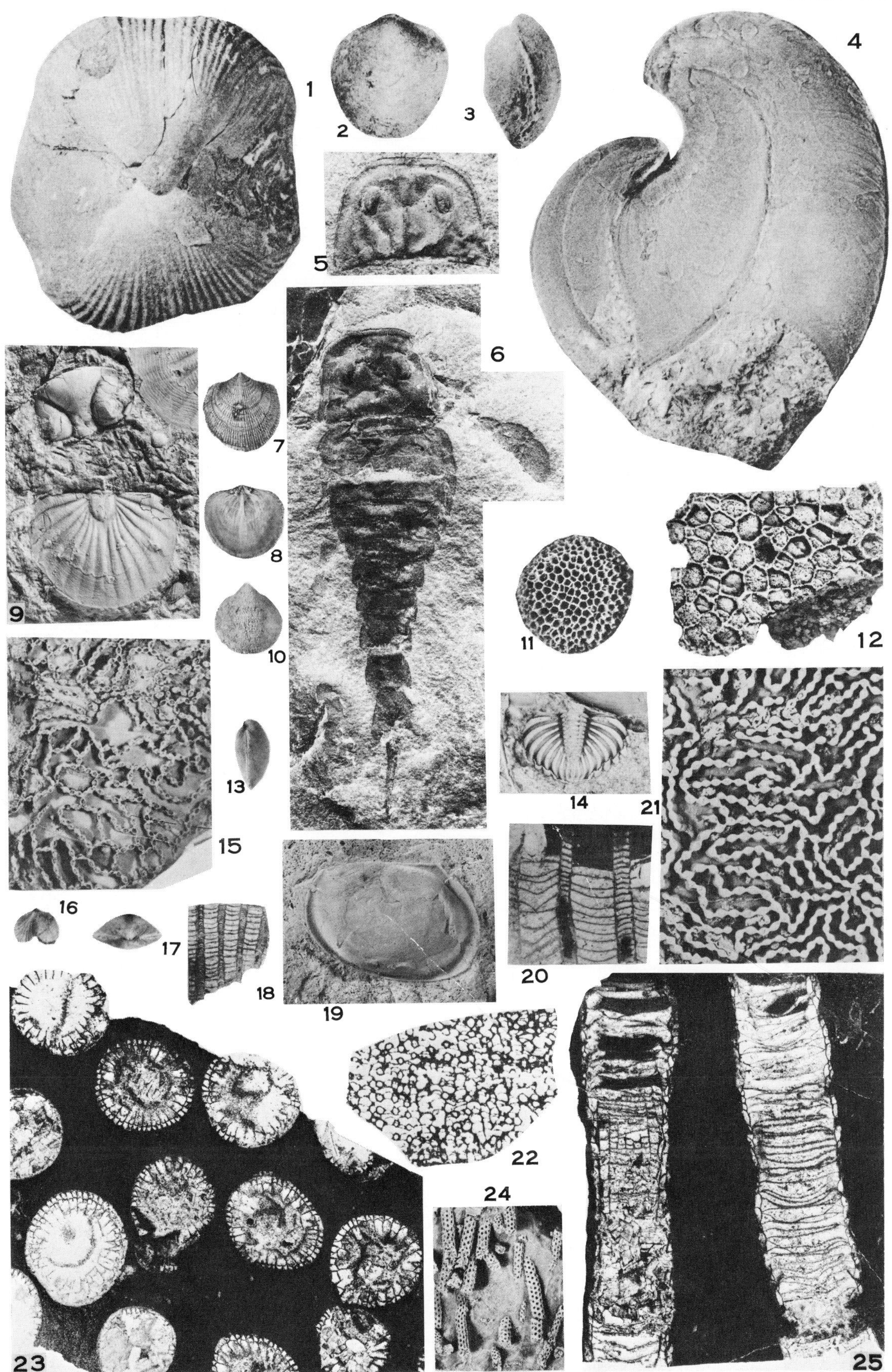
1
2
3
4
5
6
7
8
9
10
11
12
13
14
15
16
17
18
19
20
21
22
23
24
25

DEVONIAN FAUNAS

by D. J. McLaren, A. W. Norris, and L. M. Cumming

In Canada the Devonian was characterized by increasing marine transgression throughout the period. By the Upper Devonian most of the land surface was submerged under shallow seas carrying rich and varied faunas. There is a marked difference between the faunas found in the rocks in western and arctic Canada and those of eastern Canada. Various subprovinces also exist within these two divisions that are dependent largely on rock facies.

Pelagic fossils, especially ammonoids, occur only at widely scattered localities and allow rare correlation with the European standard stages. Conodonts hold out hope of accurate long-range correlation, but their study is still at an early stage. Graptolites from Lower Devonian rocks are now known from northern, western, and eastern Canada, but are largely unstudied. Shelly benthonic faunas, typically corals, brachiopods, and trilobites were widespread in shallow seas with carbonate banks and reefs, especially during the Middle and early Upper Devonian. Zonal schemes have been worked out in some western areas, and in some instances allow intercontinental correlation. In Ontario rocks of similar facies carry very different coral and brachiopod faunas and correlation is not easy with the west or arctic although some overlapping of faunas occurs in Manitoba. Sandstone facies in the Appalachian and parts of arctic Canada again carry different faunas, both marine and non-marine.

Table XI-4 lists some common fossils that are restricted in time and are therefore of value in correlation. They are shown in relation to the standard European stages and to American ammonoid zones, although precise correlation has not always been established. Some typical Devonian fossils are illustrated on PLATES IX to XI.

Western Canada

Lower Devonian

Lower Devonian fossils have been recovered from only a few localities in western Canada, mainly because beds of this age, where present, are generally dolomitized or evaporitic. In the southern plains of Alberta and Saskatchewan only a few ostracods dated as either Lower or Middle Devonian have been found in the lower part of the evaporitic Elk Point Group. From the Delorme Formation on Cathedral Mountain, southern Mackenzie Mountains, brachiopods have been identified by G. A. Cooper (Lenz and Jackson, 1964) including *Gypidula pelagica, Atrypa* aff. *A. reticularis nieczlawiensis, Cyrtina praecedens, Camarotoechia* cf. *C. squamifera,* and others. This fauna is tentatively dated as early Lower Devonian (Gedinnian).

In northern Yukon *Monograptus yukonensis* is present in the upper part of the Road River Formation commonly associated with *M.* cf. *M. praehercynicus* and *Nowakia* cf. *N. acuaria.* The *M. yukonensis* fauna ranges in age from late Siegenian to early Emsian. A shelly fauna including brachiopods and corals occurs at a few places in limestone beds interbedded with the graptolitic shales. A unit of interbedded shale and carbonates unconformably overlying the Road River Formation in the west-central part of Yukon Territory contains a rich shelly fauna characterized by *Dechenellurus* sp. B that is tentatively dated as late Lower Devonian (Emsian) on the basis of trilobites and goniatites.

Middle Devonian

The ostracod *Moelleritia canadensis* occurs in the upper half of a unit of dolomitic carbonates generally otherwise barren of fossils. The unit is roughly equivalent to the lower four fifths of the Bear Rock Formation of the central Mackenzie River area. *M. canadensis* is widely distributed in northern Yukon Territory and occurs also on Victoria Island, District of Franklin. It indicates an Eifelian age.

Distinctive echinoderm ossicles with double and cross-like axial canals occur in a variety of facies in beds immediately above the *Moelleritia canadensis* zone but also overlapping this zone, and below the Hume Formation or equivalent beds. These ossicles occur in the Manetoe Formation and equivalent beds near Virginia Falls, and in the first canyon of South Nahanni River, in the lower part of a limestone in northeastern British Columbia, and elsewhere. They are commonly associated with a wide variety of fossils and are taken to indicate a mid-Eifelian to late Emsian age.

Two widely distributed associations of probable early Givetian age, characterized by *Schuchertella adoceta* and *Carinatina dysmorphostrota,* occur in the lower and upper beds respectively of the Hume Formation of the central Mackenzie region. A form resembling *Carinatina dysmorphostrota* occurs in dolomite beds about the middle of the evaporitic Chinchaga Formation west of Slave River suggesting a correlation with the upper Hume Formation of the central Mackenzie region.

Stringocephalus, the guide fossil for the Givetian, is known from the Burgess Mountain area of Yukon where it occurs throughout a thousand feet of section, and from a number of localities in the central Mackenzie region. In the latter area it occurs mainly in the Kee Scarp Formation, but has been reported also in the uppermost beds of the Hume Formation. Species of *Stringocephalus* occur in the Winnipegosis and Dawson Bay Formations of Manitoba, in the Methy Formation of northeastern Alberta, in the upper two thirds of the Pine Point and in the lower part of the Sulphur Point and Presqu'ile Formations of the Great Slave Lake area, in the McDame Group of northern British Columbia, and elsewhere.

The uncoiled gastropod *Mastigospira* is in places associated with *Stringocephalus* and occurs in the Dawson Bay Formation of Manitoba with other bizarre molluscs, in the Methy (lower part), La Butte and Little Buffalo Formations of northeastern Alberta. *Desquamatia arctica* and closely related forms occur abundantly in the Elm Point Formation of Manitoba, in the lower part of the Methy Formation of Alberta, in the lower part of the Pine Point Formation of the Great Slave Lake area, and in the Hume and Hare Indian Formations of the Mackenzie region.

Characteristic brachiopods of the upper two thirds of the Pine Point Formation include *"Chonetes" aurora, Devonoproductus* sp. E, *Emanuella meristoides, Warrenella* cf. *W. franklini, Warrenella kirki, Leiorhynchus awokanak, Leiorhynchus castanea,* and *Hadrorhynchia sandersoni.* Some of these forms are present also in the Horn River Formation on the northwest side of the Great Slave Lake, in the lower part of the Besa River Formation of northeastern British Columbia, and in the Hare Indian Formation of central Mackenzie region. *Leiorhynchus castanea* generally occurs in the basal beds of the Hare Indian Formation, but at some localities, as at Carcajou Ridge, it may range as high as middle Kee Scarp.

Post-*Stringocephalus* Middle Devonian megafaunas are with few exceptions not abundant in western Canada.

TABLE XI-4 *Distribution and succession of Devonian faunas*

SERIES	EUROPEAN STAGES	NORTH AMERICAN AMMONOID ZONES (House, 1962, p. 265)	YUKON TERRITORY AND CENTRAL MACKENZIE BASIN	ROCKY MOUNTAINS AND PLAINS	ARCTIC ISLANDS	ONTARIO	APPALACHIAN MOUNTAINS (Invertebrates)	APPALACHIAN MOUNTAINS (Vertebrates and plants)
UPPER DEVONIAN	FAMENNIAN	? *Cyrtoclymenia strigata* ? *Falciclymenia bowsheri* *Platyclymenia americana* *Sporadoceras milleri (?)* *Sporadoceras pompeckji* *Cheiloceras amblylobum*	*Basilicorhynchus* *Cyrtospirifer*	*Gastrodetoechia utahenis* *Evanescirostrum seversoni* *Eoparaphorhynchus walcotti*	*Acanthatia* *Basilicorhynchus* and *Cyrtospirifer*			
	FRASNIAN	*Manticoceras cataphractum* *Manticoceras rhynchostoma* *Probeloceras lutheri* *Manticoceras styliophilum* *Ponticeras perlatum* *Pharciceras amplexum*	*Theodossia scopulorum* *Calvinaria albertensis* *Ponticeras*	*Theodossia scopulorum* *Adolphia* *Calvinaria albertensis* *Calvinaria insculpta* *Calvinaria athabascensis* *Allanaria allani* *Ladogioides kakwaensis*	*Cyrtospirifer* *Eleutherokomma* *Allanaria* *Devonoproductus*	Conodonts, and *Tasmanites huronensis*		*Archaeopteris gaspensis*, and *Bothriolepis canadensis*
MIDDLE DEVONIAN	GIVETIAN	*Wedekindella brilonense* or *Tornoceras uniangulare* *Sobolewia virginiana (?)* *Cabrieroceras plebeiforme*	*Emanuella* sp. F *Stringocephalus* *Leiorhynchus castanea* *Carinatina dysmorphostrota*	*Eleutherokomma implana* *Emanuella* sp. F *Stringocephalus* *Leiorhynchus castanea* *Carinatina dysmorphostrota*	*"Camarotoechia princeps"* *Emanuella* *Leiorhynchus castanea*	*Spinocyrtia carinata* *Leiorhynchus laura,* *Mucrospirifer thetfordensis* *Fimbrispirifer divaricatus,* *Gallipleura nobilis* *Mucrospirifer arkonensis,* *Leiorhynchus kelloggi*		Spores in Gaspé and Cobequid Mountains areas.
	EIFELIAN	*Foordites buttsi*	*Schuchertella nevadensis* Echinoderm ossicles with double and cross-like axial canals *Moelleritia canadensis*	Echinoderm ossicles with double and cross-like axial canals	*Cortezorthis,* *"Reticularia curvata"* and *Indospirifer*	*Martiniopsis maia* *Rhipidomella vanuxemi* *Paraspirifer acuminatus* *Prosserella lucasi*		
LOWER DEVONIAN	EMSIAN		*Dechenellurus* sp. B ?		*Cortezorthis* and *Dalejina*	*Amphigenia* cf. *A. curta* *Aemulophyllum exiguum*	*Amphigenia* *Etymothyris-Eodevonaria*	*Prototaxites,* and *Drepanophycus spinaeformis*
	SIEGENIAN		*Monograptus yukonensis* ?		*Monograptus hercynicus* and *M.* n. sp. A	*Costispirifer arenosus* *Hipparionyx proximus*	*Rensselaeria* *Costispirifer arenosus,* *Murchisonia,* and *Meristella* *Globithyris*	
	GEDINNIAN			*Gypidula* cf. *pelagica*	*Monograptus uniformis* and *M. angusitidens*		*Tubulibairdia,* and *Zygobeyrichia Podolella,* and *Howellella*	*Traquairaspis*

GSC

Atrypa cf. *A. independensis, Emanuella* sp. C, and *Emanuella* sp. F are the main forms other than stromatoporoids present in the Slave Point Formation of the Great Slave Lake area, northeastern Alberta, and the Rocky Mountains of northeastern British Columbia. A unique coral and brachiopod fauna of late Givetian age occurs in the Horn Plateau Formation, a local reef development northwest of Great Slave Lake. Characteristic brachiopods include *Pholidostrophia?* sp., *Longispina whittakeri, Hypothyridina cameroni, Atrypa nasuta, Spinatrypa hornensis, Eleutherokomma implana,* and *Trematospira* sp. Important corals in this fauna include *Cylindrophyllum gruensis, Heliophyllum borealis,* and *Sociophyllum redactum.* Two of the above brachiopods, *Hypothyridina cameroni* and *Atrypa nasuta,* occur in beds elsewhere closely associated with *Stringocephalus* sp.

Upper Devonian

The Frasnian rocks of western Canada may be divided, on the basis of brachiopods, into a series of zones that are remarkably widespread and consistent. The lowest beds of the Waterways Formation contain a fauna markedly different from that of the underlying Middle Devonian, including productellids, *Ladogioides pax, Leiorhynchus russelli, Cyrtina billingsi,* and *Atrypa.* A similar fauna marks the base of transgressive Upper Devonian beds at scattered points in the Alberta Rocky Mountains. Succeeding faunas include the coral *Tabulophyllum athabascense* and the brachiopod genera *Devonoproductus, Allanaria,* and *Eleutherokomma.*

The middle Frasnian is marked by the incoming of abundant rugose corals, *Cyrtospirifer,* and, after a brief overlap, by the disappearance of *Eleutherokomma.* In the argillaceous sequence of the Hay River region and Alberta Rockies, the rhynchonellid zones, in ascending order, *Calvinaria athabascensis, C. insculpta,* and *C. albertensis* are the temporal equivalents of reef and massive carbonate bank developments with stromatoporoids, tabulate, and rugose corals, including species of *Hexagonaria, Phillipsastraea,* and *Thamnophyllum.* The latest Frasnian carbonates contain different species of corals and the brachiopod genera *Hypothyridina* and *Theodossia.*

Regression and erosion occurred at the end of the Frasnian which is marked by the disappearance of stropheodontids, pentamerids, atrypids, and a considerable reduction of stromatoporoids. The lower and middle Famennian beds are typified by distinctive productellids, rhynchonellids, and *Cyrtospirifer* species. Typical rhynchonellids, in ascending order, include *Eoparaphorhynchus walcotti, Evanescirostrum seversoni,* and *Gastrodetoechia utahensis.* No late Famennian shelly faunas are known.

Arctic Islands

Many Lower Devonian rocks in the arctic islands have previously been considered Silurian on the basis of graptolites. Revision of the correlation between graptolitic and shelly fauna sequences in Europe suggests that several Devonian graptolite zones are present in the islands. On Bathurst Island, the upper part of the Cape Phillips Formation contains *Monograptus ultimus* succeeded by *M. uniformis* generally accepted as marking the base of the Gedinnian. The overlying Bathurst Island Formation contains *M. hercynicus* and a characteristic new species of *Monograptus* now believed to be of Siegenian age.

Lower Devonian shelly faunas which commonly overlie the graptolitic rocks are not widespread, and occur in highly variable successions not easy to correlate in detail between islands. On Bathurst Island, the Stuart Bay Formation contains brachiopods that suggest a Siegenian to Emsian age. Other faunas elsewhere have not yet been adequately studied. A large and varied fish fauna occurs in Lower Devonian rocks on Somerset and Prince of Wales Islands.

The Middle Devonian rocks are richly fossiliferous and the Blue Fiord Formation predominantly of Eifelian age contains abundant rugose corals, the brachiopods *Cortezorthis, "Reticularia* cf. *R. curvata", Indospirifer,* and a large variety of trilobites in which dechenellids predominate. In some districts the Blue Fiord may extend downwards into the Emsian Stage. The succeeding Bird Fiord Formation, of Givetian age, has a relatively restricted fauna; corals are rare but may be abundant locally; brachiopods include *"Camarotoechia princeps", Emanuella,* and abundant *Atrypa;* trilobites are present in large numbers. Brackish-water shales and sandstones upwards contain rich pelecypod–gastropod faunas with few brachiopods and fewer trilobites. On Melville Island, in a shale–sandstone sequence, the common Mackenzie Valley Givetian brachiopod *Leiorhynchus castanea* is found. The absence of the Givetian genus *Stringocephalus,* presumably due to lack of carbonate rocks, is noteworthy.

The Upper Devonian rocks of the eastern arctic islands are predominantly non-marine clastics with plant fossils, spores, and fish fragments. Scattered localities on Banks, Melville, and Prince Patrick Islands have yielded marine faunas including basal Frasnian rocks with *Eleutherokomma, Allanaria,* and *Spinatrypa,* succeeded by beds with *Cyrtospirifer.* Coral reefs developed in the early middle Frasnian on northeastern Banks Island. A widespread brachiopod fauna occurs in the early Famennian of Melville and Bathurst Islands and includes *Acanthatia, Basilicorhynchus,* and *Ptychomaletoechia.*

Eastern Canada

Ontario

The Lower Devonian Oriskany Sandstone, with the brachiopods *Costispirifer arenosus* and *Hipparionyx,* occurs sporadically in Niagara Peninsula. It is succeeded by a thin unit below the Onondaga, probably of Lower Devonian age, with the corals *Acrophyllum oneidense, Aemulophyllum exiguum,* and *"Cystiphyllum",* and the brachiopods *Amphigenia* cf. *A. curta, Centronella,* and *Eodevonaria.*

The overlying beds from Niagara to the Woodstock area, equivalent to the Onondaga of New York, include the Detroit River Group, with the brachiopods *Prosserella lucasi* and *Paraspirifer acuminatus.* Corals, abundant throughout this interval, include *Acinophyllum, Bethanyphyllum, Blothrophyllum, Cystiphylloides, Eridophyllum, Siphonophrentis,* and *Synaptophyllum.*

The Delaware Limestone follows disconformably and contains the brachiopods *"Martiniopsis" maia* and *Rhipidonella vanuxemi,* and the pelecypod *Paracyclas proava.* The succeeding calcareous shales of the Hamilton Group are rich in solitary corals and brachiopods, including *Heliophyllum, Cystiphylloides, Mucrospirifer, Fimbrispirifer divaricatus, Leiorhynchus laura,* and *Spinocyrtia carinata,* and the trilobites *Greenops* and *Phacops.* The Kettle Point Shale rests with disconformity on the underlying beds and represents much of Upper Devonian time. Concretions within the shale contain plant spores, radiolarians, conodonts, and fish bones.

At a few places in the Hudson Bay Lowland, clastic deposits of the Sextant Formation immediately overlie Precambrian rocks and contain plant remains, including *Drepanophycus spinaeformis* Geoppert, dated as Lower Devonian. The overlying Abitibi River Formation, mainly limestone, contains numerous corals, stromatoporoids, bryozoans, brachiopods, pelecypods, cephalopods, and trilobites of Lower and Middle Devonian ages. The Williams Island Formation consisting of limestones, shales, sandstones, and gypsum contains Hamilton fossils in the lower part and *Hypothyridina* sp. in the uppermost bed suggesting correlation with the Tully of New York. Dark shales of the Long Rapids Formation are the youngest Devonian rocks in the Hudson Bay Lowland containing plant spores similar to those in the Kettle Point Formation of southwestern Ontario.

Appalachian Mountains

Lower Devonian fossils are widely distributed in Newfoundland, Nova Scotia, New Brunswick, and Quebec, and several distinct facies occur.

A Gedinnian marine faunule characterized by the brachiopods *Howellella* and *Podolella* occurs in the Nictaux–Torbrook region of Nova Scotia. This non-limestone facies is associated with quartzites and sedimentary iron-formation and is similar to the European Rhenish facies. An Old Red Sandstone facies, terrestrial in origin and containing *Traquairaspis* occurs in the Arisaig region, 175 miles to the east.

In central Gaspé Peninsula of Quebec, a marine marginal-basin facies characterized by the zonal brachiopods *Meristella, Rensselaeria, Etymothyris,* and *Amphigenia* represents a typical benthonic Appalachian limestone facies of Siegenian and Emsian ages. This abundant fauna occurs in the Gaspé Limestone and lower calcareous part of the overlying Gaspé Sandstone. Ostracods (e.g., *Tubulibairdia* and *Zygobeyrichia*) and corals characterize the limy marine Dalhousie shale of New Brunswick.

Also in Gaspé, a transitional facies, characterized by *Globithyris* and *Rhenorensselaeria,* is laterally associated with a plant-eurypterid-fish-bearing sandstone with *Psilophyton, Drepanophycus,* and *Prototaxites.* The change in Lower Devonian sedimentation from limestone to sandstone deposition in Gaspé reflects the Acadian Orogeny the main uplift lying south of the subsiding marginal-basin in Gaspé. Because of widespread uplift of the eastern Appalachians during orogeny, marine faunas of Middle and Upper Devonian ages are unknown in the Canadian Appalachians. Middle Devonian plant material is probably present in the upper part of the Gaspé Sandstone and in other terrestrial deposits in Cobequid Mountains. Upper Devonian deposits with *Bothriolepis* and *Archaeopteris* are best known at Escuminac, Quebec. Similar post-orogenic sandstones and shales of terrestrial origin occur at Terranceville, Newfoundland, and in Charlotte county, New Brunswick.

Selected References

Copeland, M. J.

1962: Some leperditiid ostracods from northern Canada; *Geol. Surv. Can.,* Bull. 91, pp. 1–8, pl. 1, figs. 1, 2.

1962: Ostracoda from the Lower Devonian Dalhousie beds, northern New Brunswick; *Geol. Surv. Can.,* Bull. 91, pp. 18–49.

Crickmay, C. H.

1952: Discrimination of the late Upper Devonian; *J. Paleontol.,* vol. 26, No. 4, pp. 585–609, pls. 70–78.

1960a: The older Devonian faunas of the Northwest Territories; published by author, Imperial Oil Ltd., Calgary, Alberta, 21 pp.

1960b: Studies of western Canada Stringocephalinae; *J. Paleontol.,* vol. 34, No. 5, pp. 874–890.

1963: Significant new Devonian brachiopods from western Canada; Imperial Oil Ltd., Calgary, Alberta.

Fagerstrom, J. A.

1961: The fauna of the Middle Devonian Formosa Reef limestone of southwestern Ontario; *J. Paleontol.,* vol. 35, pp. 1–48, 14 pls.

House, M. R., and Pedder, A. E. H.

1963: Devonian goniatites and stratigraphical correlations in western Canada; *Palaeontology,* vol. 6, pt. 3, pp. 491–539, pls. 70–77.

Jackson, D. E., and Lenz, A. C.

1963: A new species of *Monograptus* from the Road River Formation, Yukon; *Palaeontology,* vol. 6, pt. 4, pp. 751–753.

Kerr, J. W., McGregor, D. C., and McLaren, D. J.

1965: An unconformity between Middle and Upper Devonian rocks on Bathurst Island, with comments on Upper Devonian faunas and microfloras of the Parry Islands; *Bull. Can. Petrol. Geol.,* vol. 13, No. 3, pp. 409–431, 2 figs., 4 pls.

Klovan, J. E.

1966: Upper Devonian stromatoporoids from the Redwater Reef Complex, Alberta; *Geol. Surv. Can.,* Bull. 133.

Lenz, A. C.

1961: Devonian rugose corals of the lower Mackenzie Valley, Northwest Territories; *in* Raasch, G. O. (editor), Geology of the Arctic, vol. 1, *Alberta*

Soc. Petrol. Geol., and Univ. Toronto Press, pp. 481–495.

Lenz, A. C., and Jackson, D. E.
1964: New occurrences of graptolites from south Nahanni region, Northwest Territories and Yukon; *Bull. Can. Petrol. Geol.*, vol. 12, No. 4, pp. 892–900.

Loewe, S.
1913: Die devonischen Korrallen von Ellesmereland. Report of the Second Norwegian Arctic Expedition in the *Fram*, 1898–1902; *Vidensk.-Selsk. i Kristiania*, vol. 4, No. 30, pp. 1–23, 1 pl.

McCammon, H.
1960: Fauna of the Manitoba Group in Manitoba; *Manitoba Dept. Mines Nat. Resources*, Mines Br., Publ. 59-6.

McLaren, D. J.
1954: Upper Devonian rhynchonellid zones in the Canadian Rocky Mountains; Western Canada Sedimentary Basin, Symp., *Am. Assoc. Petrol. Geol.*, pp. 159–181.
1962: Middle and early Upper Devonian rhynchonelloid brachiopods from western Canada; *Geol. Surv. Can.*, Bull. 86.

McLaren, D. J., and Norris, A. W.
1964: Fauna of the Devonian Horn Plateau Formation, District of Mackenzie; *Geol. Surv. Can.*, Bull. 114,

McLaren, D. J., Norris, A. W., and McGregor, D.C.
1962: Illustrations of Canadian fossils, Devonian of western Canada; *Geol. Surv. Can.*, Paper 62-4.

Meek, F. B.
1867: Remarks on the geology of the valley of the Mackenzie River, with figures and descriptions of fossils from that region, in the Museum of the Smithsonian Institution, —chiefly collected by the late Robert Kennicott, Esq.; *Chicago Acad. Sci.*, vol 1, pt. 1, art. 3, pp. 61–113, pls. 11–15.

Meyer, O. E.
1913: Die devonischen brachiopoden von Ellesmereland. Report of the Second Norwegian Arctic Expedition in the *Fram*, 1898–1902; *Vidensk.-Selsk. i Kristiania*, vol. 4, No. 29, pp. 1–43, 8 pls.

Ormiston, A. R.
1967: Lower and Middle Devonian trilobites of the Canadian Arctic islands; *Geol. Surv. Can.*, Bull. 153.

Sartenaer, P.
1961: Late Upper Devonian (Famennian) rhynchonelloid brachiopods; *Inst. Roy. Sci. Nat. Belg.*, Bull., vol. 37, No. 24, pp. 1–10, 2 pls.
1965: Trois nouveaux genres de brachiopodes rhynchonellides du Famennien; *Inst. Roy. Sci. Nat. Belg.*, Bull., vol. 41, No. 3, pp. 1–12, 2 pls.
1969: Late Upper Devonian (Famennian) rhynchonellid brachiopods from western Canada; *Geol. Surv. Can.*, Bull. 169.

Smith, S.
1945: Upper Devonian corals of the Mackenzie River region, Canada; *Geol. Soc. Am.*, Spec. Paper No. 59.

Stearn, C. W.
1966: Upper Devonian stromatoporoids from southern Northwest Territories and northern Alberta; *Geol. Surv. Can.*, Bull. 133.

Warren, P. S.
1944: Index brachiopods of the Mackenzie River Devonian; *Trans. Roy. Soc. Can.*, sec. 4, ser. 3, vol. 38, pp. 105–135, 3 pls.

Warren, P. S., and Stelck, C. R.
1956: Devonian faunas of western Canada; *Geol. Assoc. Can.*, Spec. Paper No. 1

Whiteaves, J. F.
1891: Description of some new or previously unrecorded species of fossils from the Devonian rocks of Manitoba; *Trans. Roy. Soc. Can.*, sec. 4, ser. 3, vol. 8, pp. 93–110, pls. 4–10.
1891: Fossils of the Devonian rocks of the Mackenzie River basin; *Geol. Surv. Can.*, Contrib. Can. Palaeontology, vol. 1, pt. 3, pp. 197–253, pls. 27–32.
1892: The fossils of the Devonian rocks of the islands, shores or immediate vicinity of Lakes Manitoba and Winnipegosis; *Geol. Surv. Can.*, Contrib. Can. Palaeontology, vol. 1, pt. 4, pp. 255–359, pls. 33–47.

PLATE IX. Devonian Fossils, Yukon Territory and Northern Interior Plains

Figures 1, 2 *Monograptus yukonensis* Jackson and Lenz. x3; upper Road River Formation; Siegenian; Yukon Territory (from Jackson and Lenz, 1963).

Figure 3 *Moelleritia canadensis* Copeland. Eifelian; Yukon Territory; 20690.

Figures 4, 5 *Gasterocoma? bicaula* Johnson and Lane. x10; Eifelian; Yukon Territory; 20691,a.

Figures 6, 7 *Carinatina dysmorphostrota* Crickmay. Upper Hume Formation; Givetian; Yukon Territory; 16695.

Figure 8 *Spinatrypa coriacea* Crickmay. Upper Hume Formation; Givetian; District of Mackenzie; 16694.

Figures 9, 10 *Desquamatia arctica* (Warren). Upper Hume Formation; Givetian; District of Mackenzie; 16691.

Figures 11, 12 *Mesophyllum (Digonophyllum) rectum* (Meek). x2; upper Hume Formation; Givetian; District of Mackenzie; 16529.

Figures 13, 14 *Utaratuia laevigata* Crickmay. x2; Nahanni Formation; Givetian; District of Mackenzie; 16541.

Figures 15, 16 *Grypophyllum* cf. *G. wedekindi* Middleton. x2; Kee Scarp Formation; Givetian; District of Mackenzie; 16532.

Figures 17, 18 *Sociophyllum glomerulatum* (Crickmay). Middle Devonian Limestone Unit; Givetian; Yukon Territory; 16551.

Figures 19, 20 *Xystriphyllum hyperbolicum* Crickmay. x2; McDame Group; Givetian; British Columbia; 16539.

Figures 21, 22, 23 *Leiorhynchus castanea* (Meek). Upper Hume Formation; Givetian; District of Mackenzie; 15361.

Figures 24, 25 *Hadrorhynchia sandersoni* (Warren). Kee Scarp Formation; Givetian; District of Mackenzie; 15331.

Figure 26 *Stringocephalus* sp. Kee Scarp Formation; Givetian; District of Mackenzie, 20683.

Figure 27 *Cyrtospirifer thalattodoxa* Crickmay. Hay River Formation; Frasnian; District of Mackenzie; 16563.

Figures 28, 29 *Basilicorhynchus basilicus* (Crickmay). Famennian; District of Mackenzie; Crickmay holotype, 1952.

(Plates IX–XI—all figures natural size unless otherwise stated)

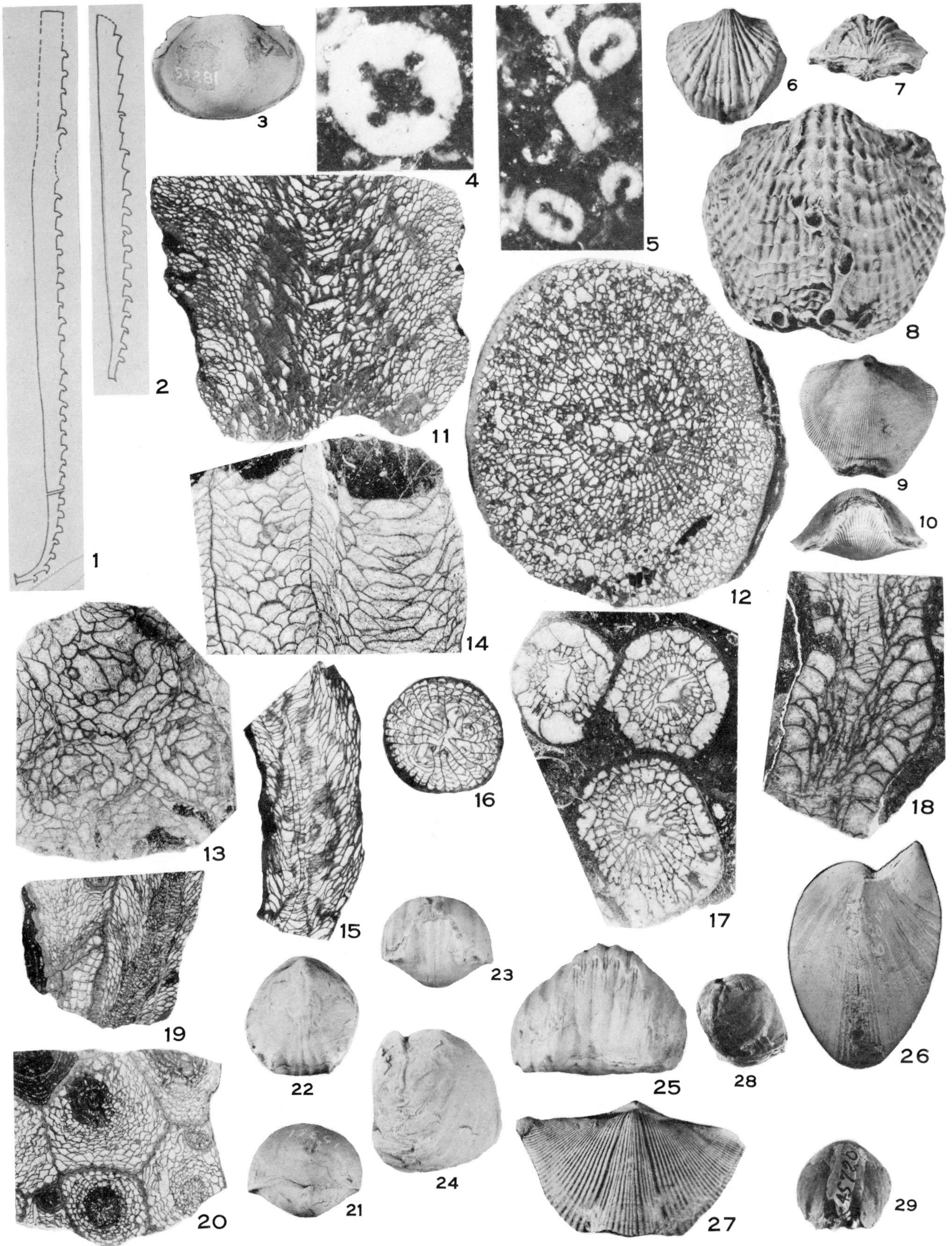
1
2
3
4
5
6
7
8
9
10
11
12
13
14
15
16
17
18
19
20
21
22
23
24
25
26
27
28
29

Plate X. Devonian Fossils, Rocky Mountains, Southern Interior Plains, and Ontario

ROCKY MOUNTAINS AND INTERIOR PLAINS

Figures 1, 2 *Gypidula pelagica* (Barrande); Delorme Formation; Lower Devonian; Cathedral Mountain, District of Mackenzie; 16688.

Figure 3 *Atrypa* cf. *A. reticularis nieczlawiensis* Kozlowski; same horizon and locality as above; 16689.

Figures 4, 5, 6 *Emanuella meristoides* (Meek); Pine Point Formation; Givetian; Great Slave Lake, District of Mackenzie; 16701.

Figures 7, 8 *Dendrostella trigemme* (Quenstedt); Nahanni Formation; Givetian; Nahanni Range, District of Mackenzie; GSC loc. 32125.

Figure 9 *Mastigospira alata* (Whiteaves); Dawson Bay Formation; Givetian; Lake Winnipegosis, Manitoba; 4099a.

Figure 10 *Emanuella* sp. F; x2; Sulphur Point Formation; Givetian; Great Slave Lake, District of Mackenzie; 16707.

Figures 11, 12 *Eleutherokomma implana* Norris; Horn Plateau Formation; Givetian; Horn Plateau, District of Mackenzie; 16106.

Figures 13, 14 *Ladogioides kakwaensis* (McLaren); Flume Formation; Frasnian; British Columbia; 13819.

Figures 15, 16 *Calvinaria variabilis athabascensis* (Kindle); Maligne Formation; Frasnian; Jasper National Park; 11232.

Figure 17 *Polygnathus asymmetrica ovalis* Ziegler and Klapper; x45; Moberly? Member of Waterways Formation; Frasnian; Alberta; 20693.

Figures 18, 19 *Allanaria allani* (Warren); Moberly Member of Waterways Formation; Frasnian; Alberta; 16714.

Figure 20 *Eleutherokomma* cf. *E. hamiltoni* Crickmay; Moberly Member of Waterways Formation; Frasnian; Alberta; 16715.

Figure 21 *Ancyrodella gigas* Youngquist; x45; Moberly Member of Waterways Formation; Frasnian; Alberta; 20694.

Figures 22, 23, 24 *Calvinaria variabilis insculpta* (McLaren); Cairn Formation; Frasnian; Alberta; 14939.

Figures 25, 26 *Calvinaria albertensis albertensis* (Warren); Mount Hawk Formation; Frasnian; Alberta; 11237.

Figures 27, 28 *Indospirifer orestes* (Hall and Whitfield); Mount Hawk Formation; Frasnian; Alberta; 13811.

Figures 29, 30 *Pterorrhiza proteus* (Smith); Hay River Formation; Frasnian; District of Mackenzie; 16540.

Figures 31, 32, 33 *Theodossia scopulorum* (Crickmay); Kakisa Formation; Frasnian; District of Mackenzie; 16562.

Figures 34, 35 *Tabulophyllum mcconnelli* (Whiteaves); Hay River Formation; Frasnian; District of Mackenzie; 16531.

Figures 36, 37 *Evanescirostrum seversoni* (McLaren); Palliser Formation; Famennian; Alberta; 10016.

ONTARIO

Figures 38, 39, 40 *Rensselaeria ovalis* Hall; Oriskany Formation; Lower Devonian; Ontario; 3366.

Figures 41, 42 *"Martinia" maia* (Billings); Onondaga Formation; Eifelian; Ontario; 3496b.

Figures 43, 44 *Aemulophyllum exiguum* (Billings); Bois Blanc Formation; Lower Devonian; Ontario; 3424.

Figures 45, 46, 47 *Leiorhynchus laura* (Billings); Hamilton Group; Givetian; Ontario; 3705h.

Figures 48, 49 *Macrospirifer thedfordensis* (Shimer and Grabau); Hamilton Group, Givetian; Ontario; 20689.

Plate XI. Devonian Fossils, Arctic Islands and Appalachian Mountains

ARCTIC ISLANDS

Figure 1 *Spyroceras thoas* (Hall); x2; Eids Formation; Emsian or Eifelian; Ellesmere Island, GSC loc. 57730.

Figures 2, 3 *Indospirifer* sp.; Blue Fiord Formation; Eifelian; Ellesmere Island; 20688.

Figures 4, 5 *"Reticularia"* ex gr. *curvata* (Schlotheim); Blue Fiord Formation; Eifelian; Ellesmere Island; 20686.

Figures 6, 7 "*Eatonia medialis* var." Meyer 1913; Blue Fiord Formation; Eifelian; Ellesmere Island; 20687.

Figures 8, 9, 10 *Cupularostrum?* sp; Bird Fiord Formation; Givetian; Bathurst Island; 20685.

Figures 11, 12 *Gypidula recurrens* (Meyer); Blue Fiord Formation; Eifelian; Ellesmere Island; 20684.

APPALACHIAN MOUNTAINS

Figure 13 *Octonaria foordi* Copeland; x30; upper Dalhousie beds; Gedinnian; New Brunswick; 14525.

Figure 14 *Octonaria* cf. *O. typicus* (Bassler); x30; upper Dalhousie beds; Gedinnian; New Brunswick; 14524.

Figure 15 *Zygobeyrichia dalhousiensis* Copeland; x15; upper Dalhousie beds; Gedinnian; New Brunswick; 14536.

Figure 16 "*Amphissites* (?)" *concentricus* (Ulrich and Bassler); x15; lower Dalhousie beds; Gedinnian; New Brunswick; 14530d.

Figure 17 *Dizygopleura chaleurensis* Copeland; x15; upper Dalhousie beds; Gedinnian; New Brunswick; 14531c.

Figure 18 *Kloedenia retifera* Ulrich and Bassler; x15; upper Dalhousie beds; Gedinnian; 14540f.

Figure 19 *Mesomphalus magnificus* Copeland; x15; upper Dalhousie beds; Gedinnian; New Brunswick; 14537k.

Figure 20 *Billingsastraea affinis* (Billings); Grande Grève Formation; Siegenian; Gaspé Bay, Quebec; 3270.

Figures 21, 22 *"Spirifer" arenosus* var. *unicus* Hall; Grande Grève Formation; Siegenian; Gaspé Bay; 3301.

Figure 23 *Strophonella planulata* (Hall); Gaspé Limestone Group; Gedinnian; Quebec; 3210.

Figure 24 *Rensselaeria ovoides* var. *gaspensis* Clarke and *Spirifer gaspensis* Billings; internal casts; Gaspé Sandstone Group; Siegenian; Gaspé Bay; 3307.

Figure 25 *Proetus phocion* Billings; Grande Grève Formation; Siegenian; Gaspé Bay; 3337.

Figures 26, 27, 28 *"Spirifer" cyclopterus* Hall; Grande Grève Formation; Siegenian; Quebec; 3303.

Figure 29 *Leptostrophia magnifica* var. *tullia* (Billings); Mount Joli Formation; Gedinnian; Quebec; 3285.

Figure 30 *Proschizophoria* sp.; Torbrook Formation; Gedinnian; Nova Scotia; 14761b.

Figure 31 *Etymothyris gaspensis* Boucot; York River Formation; Siegenian; Gaspé; 20692.

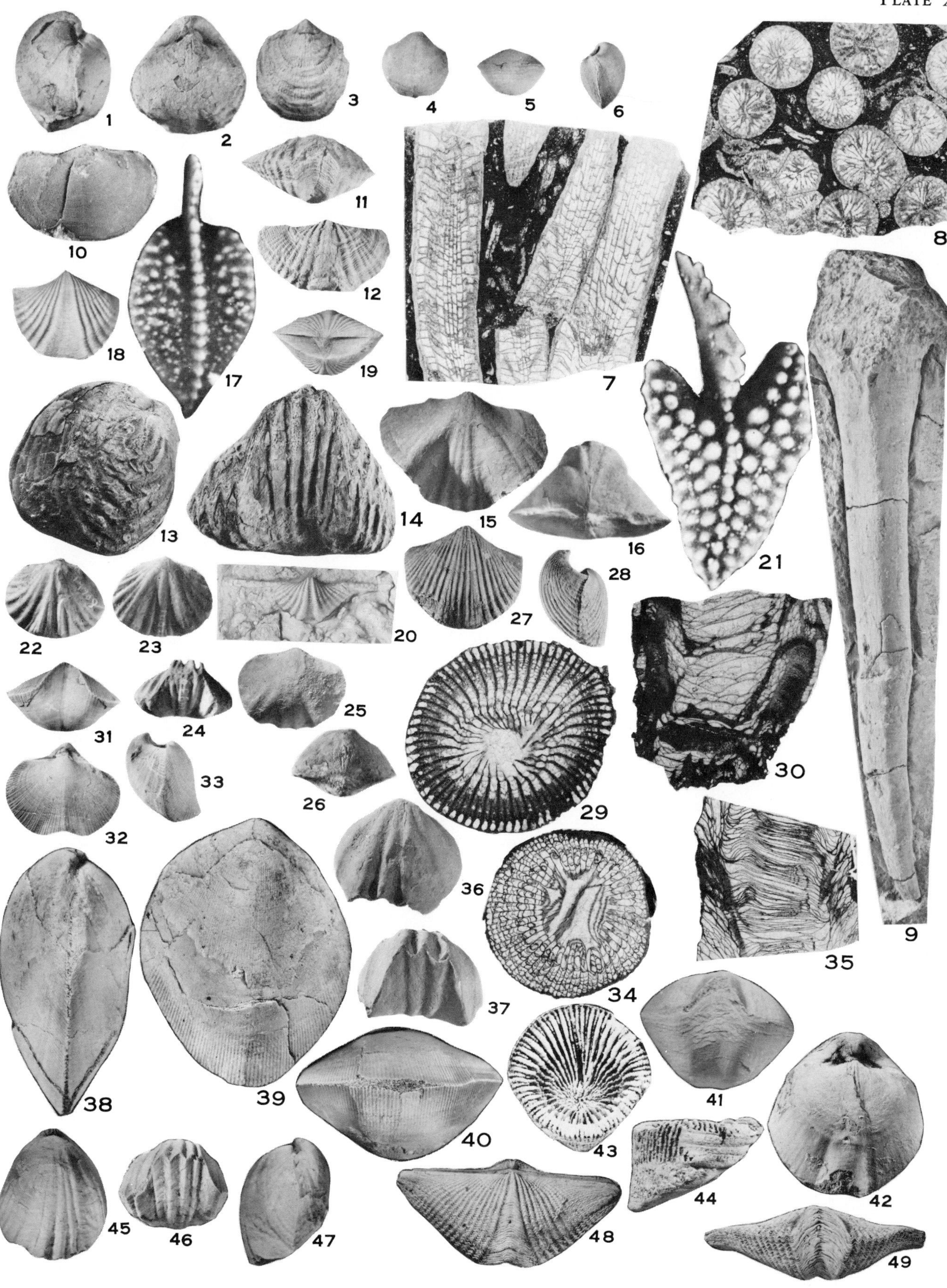
1
2
3
4
5
6
7
8
9
10
11
12
13
14
15
16
17
18
19
20
21
22
23
24
25
26
27
28
29
30
31
32
33
34
35
36
37
38
39
40
41
42
43
44
45
46
47
48
49

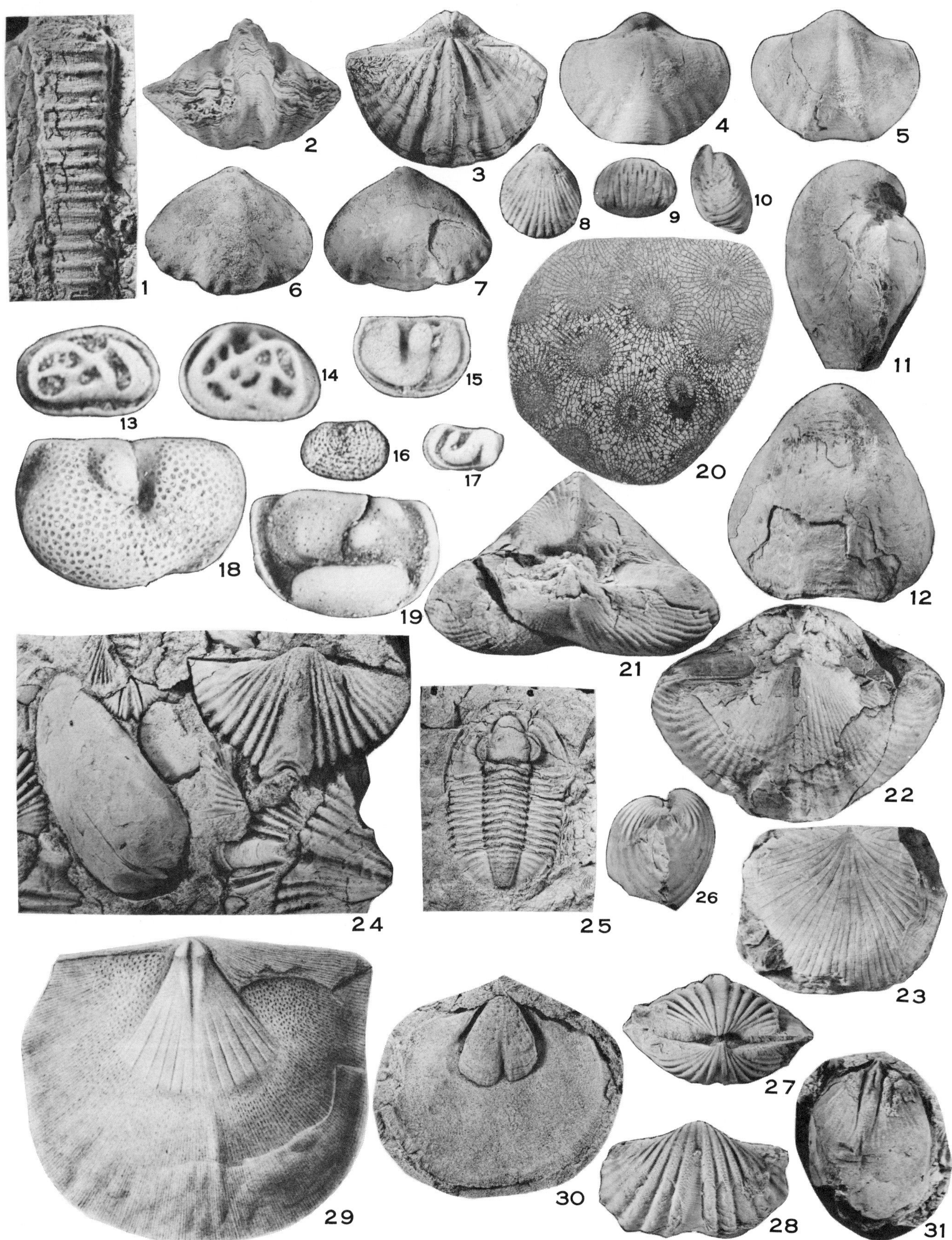
1
2
3
4
5
6
7
8
9
10
11
12
13
14
15
16
17
18
19
20
21
22
23
24
25
26
27
28
29
30
31

CARBONIFEROUS AND PERMIAN FAUNAS

by E. W. Bamber and M. J. Copeland

Most major groups of marine invertebrate fossils are present in Carboniferous and Permian rocks. The characteristic fossils of these systems are productoid and spiriferid brachiopods, fenestrate bryozoans, rugose corals, and foraminifers.

Western and Northern Canada

Mississippian

The main emphasis for dating Mississippian rocks in Canada has been on brachiopods, corals, rare ammonoids, and more recently on foraminifers and ostracods. The remainder of the fauna is too rare or too poorly known to be stratigraphically useful. The ammonoids, which are useful for intercontinental correlation, occur mainly in the black shale facies. It is therefore difficult to integrate the dates afforded by ammonoids with those from other faunas that occur mainly in calcareous rocks.

Several zonal schemes have been proposed for the eastern Cordillera, based mainly on brachiopods, corals, and foraminifers (Nelson, 1961; McKay and Green, 1963). Only the macrofauna is discussed here. The most complete faunal sequence is found in the Rocky Mountains from the Banff area south to the United States border. These macrofossils have closer affinities with those from the Mississippi Valley region and the western United States and northern Mexico, than with the European Lower Carboniferous fauna. Their age is therefore given in terms of the standard Mississippi Valley sequence. Several species are very widespread and useful for correlation within North America. Table XI-5 gives the ranges of some of the most useful macrofossils in the Mississippian of western and northern Canada, but is not intended as a formal sequence of zones.

Lower Mississippian fossils are widespread in the eastern Cordillera and in subsurface from the United States border north to the southwestern District of Mackenzie, and are locally present in north–central British Columbia.

Rocks of Kinderhookian age contain mainly brachiopods, such as the distinctive *"Platyrachella" rutherfordi* (Warren) and the split ribbed *Spirifer esplanadensis* Brown and *Spirifer missouriensis* Swallow. The last mentioned brachiopod, and several brachiopod species associated with it, also occur in the Kinderhookian of the Mississippian Valley. The oldest lithostrotionid coral in Canada—*Lithostrotionella microstylum* (White)—appears approximately at the Kinderhook–Osage boundary. This species is a useful guide fossil, since it is widespread in the Mississippi Valley region and United States Cordillera at a stratigraphic position similar to that in western Canada.

Among the most common fossils in the lower Osagian rocks in the Rocky Mountains are the spiriferid brachiopods such as *Spirifer* cf. *rowleyi* Weller and *Spirifer minnewankensis* Shimer. The latter species, however, includes a rather heterogeneous group of brachiopods and has been identified from rocks as young as late Osagian. Both species may range into the upper Kinderhookian. The stratigraphically lowest phaceloid lithostrotionid coral, *Lithostrotion (S.) mutabile* (Kelly), is present but rare in the lower to middle Osagian. The early Osagian spiriferids are succeeded by *Spirifer banffensis* Warren, *S. rundlensis* Warren, and several other brachiopods, but this fauna is rare, and rocks of middle to late Osagian age are generally unfossiliferous in western Canada. The phaceloid coral *L. (S.) sinuosum* (Kelly), ranges from late Osagian to early Meramecian age. Very few fossils, other than this species are present at this level. The horn coral *Vesiculophyllum* ranges through rocks of latest Kinderhookian to early Meramecian age. It is one of the most abundant corals.

Early Meramecian macrofossils are not abundant in western Canada and little work has been done on them. It is therefore difficult to define the boundary between the Lower and Upper Mississippian. Rocks that are probably of early Meramecian age typically contain unnamed horn corals, the two colonial corals *Lithostrotion (S.) oculinum* and *L. (S.) sinuosum,* and rare horn corals of the genus *Ekvasophyllum. L. (S.) oculinum* is a widespread species that has been found in the Cordillera and in subsurface from Arizona to northern British Columbia. It appears to be restricted to lower Meramecian rocks. The middle and upper Meramecian are marked by an abundant and diversified coral fauna, dominated by species of *Lithostrotionella, Lithostrotion (Siphonodendron)*, and *Ekvasophyllum.* Several productoid and other brachiopods are also present. Above the main coral-bearing interval is a distinctive fauna including the horn coral *Faberophyllum* with abundant *?Gigantoproductus* and other brachiopods. This fauna is widespread in the southern Rocky Mountains but appears to be absent north of the Banff area. The brachiopod *Spirifer* cf. *pellaensis* Weller begins high in the Meramecian and ranges up through the Chesteran. *Lithostrotion (S.) genevievensis* Easton provides a useful key for correlation, since it occurs in the Rocky Mountains, in the northern Yukon (British Mountains), and is found in the St. Genevieve Limestone of the Mississippi Valley region (uppermost Meramecian). It has a considerable stratigraphic range in Canada, and may range from the uppermost Meramecian into the Chesteran.

Chesteran rocks in western Canada contain a varied brachiopod fauna and relatively few corals. *Spirifer leidyi* Norwood and Pratten is characteristic and abundant within the uppermost Meramecian and throughout the Chesteran of the Rocky Mountains and occurs in Ches-

TABLE XI-5 | *Distribution and range of Carboniferous and Permian invertebrate fossils*

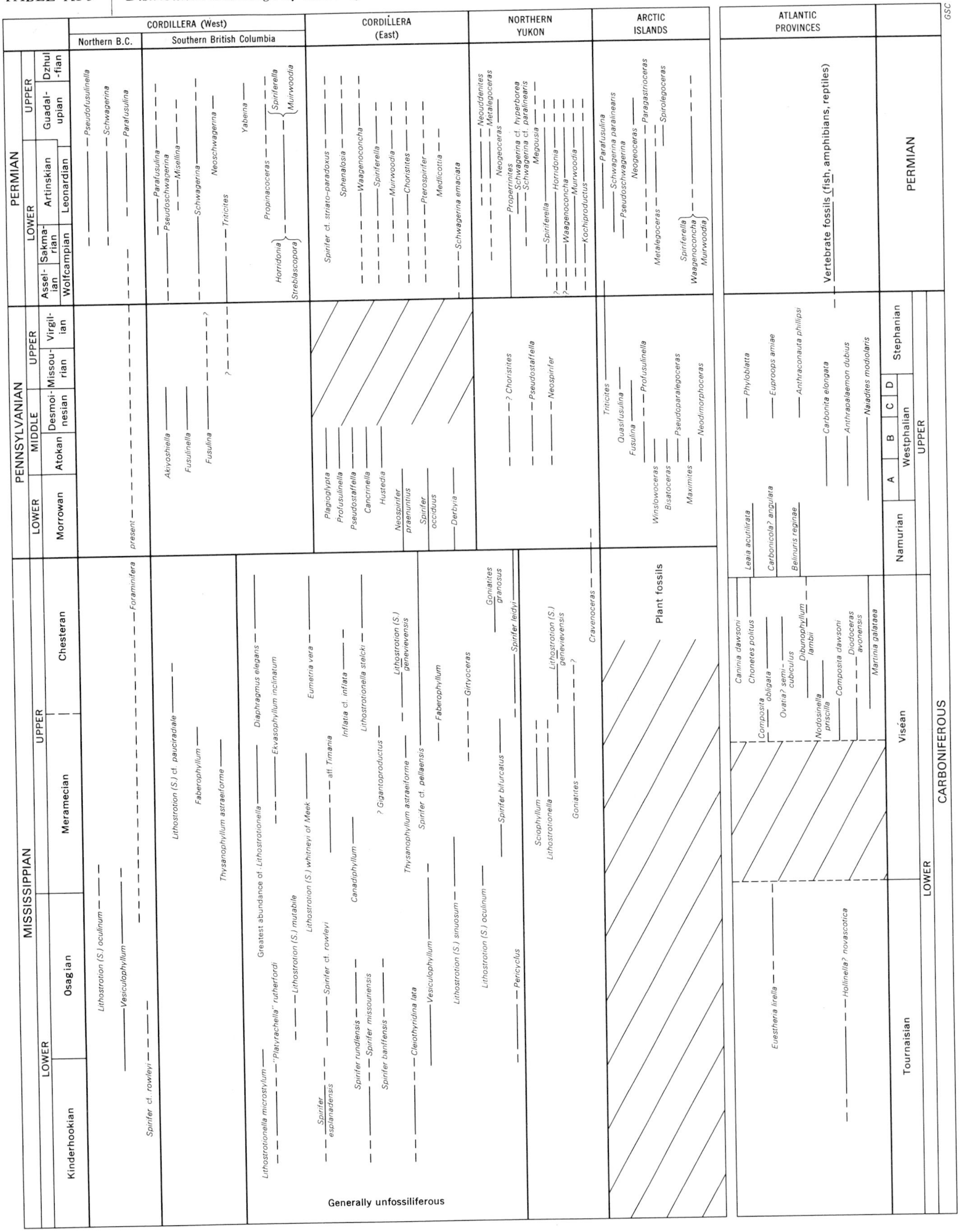

GSC

Time scale: CARBONIFEROUS — MISSISSIPPIAN (LOWER: Kinderhookian, Osagian; UPPER: Meramecian, Chesteran); PENNSYLVANIAN (LOWER: Morrowan; MIDDLE: Atokan, Desmoinesian; UPPER: Missourian, Virgilian); PERMIAN (LOWER: Asselian, Sakmarian, Artinskian / Wolfcampian, Leonardian; UPPER: Guadalupian, Dzhulfian)

Atlantic Provinces scale: CARBONIFEROUS — LOWER: Tournaisian, Viséan; UPPER: Namurian, Westphalian (A, B, C, D), Stephanian; PERMIAN

CORDILLERA (West)

Northern B.C.

- Mississippian: Lithostrotion (S.) oculinum; Vesiculophyllum; Spirifer cf. rowleyi; Foraminifera
- Pennsylvanian: present
- Permian: Pseudofusulinella; Schwagerina; Parafusulina

Southern British Columbia

- Mississippian: Lithostrotion (S.) cf. pauciradiale; Faberophyllum; Thysanophyllum astraeiforme
- Lithostrotionella microstylum; "Platyrachella" rutherfordi; Greatest abundance of Lithostrotionella; Diaphragmus elegans; Ekvasophyllum inclinatum; Lithostrotion (S.) mutabile; Lithostrotion (S.) whitneyi of Meek; Eumetria vera; Spirifer esplanadensis; Spirifer cf. rowleyi; aff. Timania; Inflatia cf. inflata; Lithostrotionella stelcki; Spirifer rundlensis; Spirifer missouriensis; Spirifer banffensis; Canadiphyllum; ? Gigantoproductus; Lithostrotion (S.) genevievensis; Cleiothyridina lata; Vesiculophyllum; Thysanophyllum astraeiforme; Spirifer cf. pellaensis; Faberophyllum; Lithostrotion (S.) sinuosum; Girtyoceras; Lithostrotion (S.) oculinum; Spirifer bifurcatus; Goniatites granosus; Pericyclus; Spirifer leidyi
- Pennsylvanian: Akiyoshiella; Fusulinella; Fusulina; Triticites
- Permian: Parafusulina; Pseudoschwagerina; Misellina; Schwagerina; Neoschwagerina; Yabeina; Triticites; Propinacoceras; Spiriferella; Muirwoodia; Horridonia; Streblascopora

Generally unfossiliferous

CORDILLERA (East)

- Pennsylvanian: Plagioglypta; Profusulinella; Pseudostaffella; Cancrinella; Hustedia; Neospirifer praenuntius; Spirifer occiduus; Derbyia
- Permian: Spirifer cf. striato-paradoxus; Sphenalosia; Waagenoconcha; Spiriferella; Muirwoodia; Choristites; Pterospirifer; Medlicottia; Schwagerina emaciata

NORTHERN YUKON

- Mississippian: Sciophyllum; Lithostrotionella; Lithostrotion (S.) genevievensis; Goniatites; Cravenoceras
- Pennsylvanian: ? Choristites; Pseudostaffella; Neospirifer
- Permian: Neouddenites; Metalegoceras; Neogeoceras; Properrinites; Schwagerina cf. hyperborea; Schwagerina cf. paralinearis; Megousia; Spiriferella; Horridonia; Waagenoconcha; Muirwoodia; Kochiproductus

ARCTIC ISLANDS

- Mississippian: Plant fossils
- Pennsylvanian: Triticites; Quasifusulina; Fusulina; Profusulinella; Winslowoceras; Bisatoceras; Pseudoparalegoceras; Maximites; Neodimorphoceras
- Permian: Parafusulina; Schwagerina paralinearis; Pseudoschwagerina; Neogeoceras; Paragastrioceras; Spirolegoceras; Metalegoceras; Spiriferella; Waagenoconcha; Muirwoodia

ATLANTIC PROVINCES

- Tournaisian: Euestheria lirella; Hollinella? novascotica
- Viséan: Caninia dawsoni; Chonetes politus; Composita obligata; Ovatia? semicubiculus; Dibunophyllum lambii; Nodosinella priscilla; Composita dawsoni; Diodoceras avonensis; Martinia galataea
- Namurian: Leaia acutilirata; Carbonicola? angulata; Belinurus reginae
- Westphalian: Phyloblatta; Euproops amiae; Anthraconauta phillipsi; Carbonita elongata; Anthrapalaemon dubius; Naiadites modiolaris
- Stephanian–Permian: Vertebrate fossils (fish, amphibians, reptiles)

teran rock of the Mississippi Valley region. Lower Chesteran rocks contain *Inflatia* cf. *inflata* McChesney, along with the genera *Girtyella, Dielasma, Rhipidomella, Orthotetes,* and others. The middle to upper Chesteran is characterized by several brachiopods including *Diaphragmus elegans* Norwood and Pratten, *Eumetria vera* (Hall) and *Punctospirifer transversa* (McChesney), which are found in the Chesteran of the United States. The highest rocks assigned to the Chesteran in western Canada contain very little other than spiriferid brachiopods, and their exact age within the Chesteran is not known. There may be a hiatus between these and the overlying Morrowan rocks, but the faunal evidence is not conclusive.

Upper Mississippian fossils are abundant in the eastern Cordillera as far north as the South Nahanni River valley, and also occur in the northern Yukon and north–central British Columbia (Mamet and Gabrielse, 1969), but Meramecian and Chesteran colonial and horn corals occur in the Milford Group in the Lardeau map-area west of the Rocky Mountain Trench, southern British Columbia. In parts of Alberta and northeastern British Columbia, Chesteran and uppermost Meramecian fossils are absent because of erosion. In the mountains from Peace River north to the southeastern Yukon, the westernmost Mississippian rocks of the Besa River Formation are mainly black shale which contains only rare ammonoids, nautiloids, and pelecypods. These ammonoids are locally present in northern Yukon and include *Goniatites* and *Cravenoceras* which indicate correlation with the Viséan of Europe. They have not been found in association with the abundant coral–brachiopod fauna to the east in British Columbia.

In the arctic islands, Chesteran plants are the only Mississippian fossils that have been reported.

Pennsylvanian

Little is known of Pennsylvanian fossils in western and northern Canada. The most reliable Pennsylvanian age determinations are based on ammonoids and fusulinid foraminifers, although several other phyla are present.

Lower Pennsylvanian (Morrowan) fossils occur in the Rocky Mountains from the Jasper area south to the United States border. They include mainly brachiopods, such as *Neospirifer praenuntius* Easton, *Spirifer occiduus* Sadlick, and *Antiquatonia*? cf. *hermosana* Girty. The last species is restricted to a narrow interval low in the sequence. Morrowan ammonoids with brachiopods and corals occur at Barrow Dome, Melville Island.

Middle Pennsylvanian rocks are fairly widespread in northern and western Canada. They contain the first well-developed fusulinids, rare ammonoids, and numerous brachiopods, corals, bryozoans, and other phyla. The fauna is largely undescribed, and the main work that has been done deals with the fusulinids and ammonoids. Middle Pennsylvanian fusulinids are most abundant in the arctic islands where several genera occur, including *Profusulinella* and *Fusulinella,* which are worldwide zone fossils for rocks of this age. Definite Middle Pennsylvanian fossils are known in the northern Yukon from only one locality in the Ogilvie Mountains, where *Pseudostaffella* occurs. Desmoinesian fusulinids including *Fusulina, Fusulinella,* and others occur locally in south–central British Columbia. In the Rocky Mountains of southern Alberta and British Columbia there are Middle Pennsylvanian brachiopods, scaphopods, pelecypods, bryozoans, and fusulinids. This fauna and the underlying Morrowan fauna appear to be closely related to those in the western and central United States.

Fossils of definite Late Pennsylvanian age have not been found in western Canada. Their absence is caused, in some areas at least, by an erosional break beneath the overlying Permian beds, and may indicate a very widespread hiatus in the faunal succession. In the arctic islands, Upper Pennsylvanian rocks are dated by several fusulinid genera, including *Triticites* and *Quasifusulina.*

Permian

Permian rocks of northern and western Canada have been dated mainly by fusulinid foraminifers, ammonoids and brachiopods, but corals, bryozoans, and other phyla are locally abundant.

Fossils of Wolfcampian age occur in much of the eastern Cordillera, in western and central British Columbia, and in the arctic. Only the fusulinids have been studied. The remainder of the fauna is undescribed. In northeastern British Columbia and the southwestern District of Mackenzie there is a Lower Permian fauna consisting mainly of brachiopods, which is probably Wolfcampian, but may be Leonardian. This fauna includes *Spiriferella, Pterospirifer, Choristites, Waagenoconcha,* and other brachiopods. A similar fauna occurs below the Wolfcampian fusulinid *Schwagerina* cf. *paralinearis* Thorsteinsson in the Ogilvie Mountains of northern Yukon.

Wolfcampian faunas are succeeded by a widespread boreal fauna that has been found in the arctic islands, northern Yukon, central and western British Columbia, and in the Rocky Mountains as far south as Crowsnest Pass, British Columbia. This assemblage consists largely of brachiopods with some corals and other groups. It has been dated in several places by associated fusulinids and ammonoids as mainly Leonardian to early Guadalupian. The upper age limit of the fauna is in doubt in the arctic, however, as several of the genera that it includes range upward into rocks containing no fusulinids. Elements of the boreal fauna occur as far south as Oregon, U.S.A., but it is found mainly in a circumpolar belt including the arctic areas of North America, Europe, and Asia. The northern fauna has little in common with that from the standard sequence of southwestern United States and its age assignment, in terms of this sequence, is in doubt.

The youngest Permian fauna of central British Columbia is distinct from other Permian assemblages in Canada. It contains fusulinids such as *Yabeina* and other neoschwagerinids, which appear to overlie the boreal fauna.

ıest in the sequence and is thought to be ,rmian form in North America. These .ds have also been found in the Mediter- southern and eastern Asia, and the north- ,iited States. Their absence from the arctic ıwestern United States faunas has led to un- cc. y regarding age relationships between the youngest Permıan of these regions and that of central British Columbia.

Atlantic Provinces

Carboniferous rocks of the Atlantic Provinces are divided into six units, in ascending order, the Horton, Windsor, Canso, Riversdale, Cumberland, and Pictou Groups. Their fauna closely resembles that of the standard European sequence. European age terminology is, therefore, applied to these rocks.

Lower Carboniferous

The Horton Group contains abundant plants and a non-marine fauna of Tournaisian age characterized by arthropods (*Hollinella*?, *Euestheria, Eoleaia*) and fish. These rocks are unconformably overlain by Viséan strata of the Windsor Group which contain marine fossils. The Windsor has been subdivided by Bell (1929) into five subzones as follows:

Upper Windsor. Zone of *Martinia galataea*
- Subzone E. *Caninia dawsoni, Chonetes politus*
- Subzone D. *Ovatia? semicubiculus*
- Subzone C. *Dibunophyllum lambii* and *Nodosinella priscilla*

Lower Windsor. Zone of *Composita dawsoni*
- Subzone B. *Diodoceras avonensis*
- Subzone A. Sparse fauna

Upper Carboniferous

The Canso Group contains a Namurian flora and a distinctive local assemblage of non-marine and brackish-water arthropods (*Leaia, Euestheria, Belinurus, Dithyrocaris, Beyrichiopsis*) and pelecypods (*Anthracomya, Carbonicola*).

The overlying fauna of the Riversdale and Cumberland Groups ranges through Westphalian A and B. Distinctive elements of this fauna include the arthropods *Anthrapalaemon, Carbonita, Xylobius,* the gastropod *Pupa,* and the pelecypods *Anthracomya* and *Naiadites.*

The uppermost Carboniferous unit, the Pictou Group, contains abundant insects (Blattoidea), other arthropods (*Carbonita, Euproops*) and pelecypods (*Anthraconauta*). This fauna is characteristic of Westphalian C and D rocks both in Europe and Nova Scotia.

Permian

Permian vertebrates (Langston, 1963) and a limited flora occur on Prince Edward Island. All were deposited in a non-marine environment and are considered to be early Permian.

Selected References

Bell, W. A.
1929: Horton-Windsor district, Nova Scotia; *Geol. Surv. Can.*, Mem. 155.

Brown, R. A. C.
1952: Carboniferous stratigraphy and palaeontology in the Mount Greenock area, Alberta; *Geol. Surv. Can.*, Mem. 264.

Copeland, M. J.
1957: The arthropod fauna of the Upper Carboniferous rocks of the Maritime Provinces; *Geol. Surv. Can.*, Mem. 286.
1957: The Carboniferous genera *Palaeocaris* and *Euproöps* in the Canadian Maritime Provinces; *J. Paleontol.*, vol. 31, No. 3, pp. 595–599.

Harker, P., and Raasch, G. O.
1958: Megafaunal zones in the Alberta Mississippian and Permian; *in* Jurassic and Carboniferous of western Canada, *Am. Assoc. Petrol. Geol.*, pp. 216–231.

Harker, P., and Thorsteinsson, R.
1960: Permian rocks and faunas of Grinnell Peninsula, Arctic Archipelago; *Geol. Surv. Can.*, Mem. 309.

Langston, W., Jr.
1963: Fossil vertebrates and the late Palaeozoic red beds of Prince Edward Island; *Natl. Museum Can.*, Bull. 187.

Lewis, H. P.
1935: The Lower Carboniferous corals of Nova Scotia; *Ann. Mag. Nat. Hist.*, ser. 10, vol. 16, pp. 118–142.

Mamet, B. L., and Gabrielse, H.
1969: Foraminiferal zonation and stratigraphy of the type section of the Nizi Formation (Carboniferous System, Chesteran Stage), British Columbia; *Geol. Surv. Can.*, Paper 69-16.

McCugan, A., Roessingh, H. K., and Danner, W. R.
1964: Permian, *in* Geological history of western Canada; *Alta. Soc. Petrol. Geol.*, pp. 103–112.

McKay, W., and Green, R.
1963: Mississippian Foraminifera of the southern Canadian Rocky Mountains, Alberta; *Res. Council Alta.*, Bull. 10.

Nassichuk, W. W., Furnish, W. M., and Glenister, B. F.
1965: The Permian ammonoids of arctic Canada; *Geol. Surv. Can.*, Bull. 131.

Nelson, S. J.
1960: Mississippian lithostrotionid zones of the southern Canadian Rocky Mountains; *J. Paleontol.*, vol. 34, No. 1, pp. 107–126.
1960: Permo-Carboniferous of the northern Yukon Territory; *J. Alta. Soc. Petrol. Geol.*, vol. 9, No. 1, pp. 1–9.
1961: Mississippian faunas of western Canada; *Geol. Assoc. Can.*, Spec. Paper No. 2.

Sellers, D. H. A., and Furnish, W. M.
1960: Mississippian ammonoids from northwestern Canada; *J. Paleontol.*, vol. 34, No. 6, pp. 1124–1128.

Shimer, H. W.
1926: Upper Palaeozoic faunas of the Lake Minnewanka section, near Banff, Alberta; *Geol. Surv. Can.*, Museum Bull. 42, pp. 1–84.

Sutherland, P. K.
1958: Carboniferous stratigraphy and rugose coral faunas of northeastern British Columbia; *Geol. Surv. Can.*, Mem. 295.

Warren, P. S.
1927: Banff area, Alberta; *Geol. Surv. Can.*, Mem. 153.

Yole, R. W.
1963: An Early Permian fauna from Vancouver Island, British Columbia; *Bull. Can. Petrol. Geol.*, vol. 11, No. 2, pp. 138–149.

PLATE XII. Mississippian Fossils of Western Canada

(All figures natural size unless otherwise stated)

Figure 1 *Cleiothyridina lata* Shimer. Kinderhookian, Alberta; 21735.

Figure 2 *Spirifer missouriensis* Swallow. Kinderhookian, Alberta; 21736.

Figure 3 *Rhynchotetra usheri* Brown. Kinderhookian, Alberta; 21737.

Figure 4 *Cleiothyridina* cf. *obmaxima* (McChesney). Kinderhookian, Alberta; 21738.

Figure 5 "*Platyrachella*" *rutherfordi* (Warren). Kinderhookian, Alberta; 21739.

Figure 6 *Marginatia jasperensis* (Warren). Kinderhookian, Alberta; 10081.

Figure 7 *Spirifer esplanadensis* Brown. Kinderhookian, Alberta; 21741.

Figure 8 *Lithostrotionella microstylum* (White). x2, late Kinderhookian to early Osagian, Alberta; 16840.

Figure 9 *Spirifer minnewankensis* Shimer. Kinderhookian to early Osagian, Alberta; 21742.

Figure 10 *Spirifer* cf. *rowleyi* Weller. Osagian, Alberta; 21743.

Figure 11 *Lithostrotionella micra* Kelly. x2, Osagian, Alberta; 9648.

Figure 12 *Spirifer rundlensis* Warren. Osagian, Alberta; 8921.

Figure 13 *Vesiculophyllum* sp. Osagian, Mackenzie; 10570.

Figure 14 *Lithostrotion* (*Siphonodendron*) *oculinum* Sando. x2, Meramecian, subsurface, British Columbia; 21744.

Figure 15 *L.* (*S.*) *sinuosum* (Kelly). x2, late Osagian–Meramecian, Alberta; 16843.

Figure 16 *Spirifer bifurcatus* Hall. Meramecian, Alberta; 21745.

Figure 17 *Ekvasophyllum inclinatum* Parks. x2, Meramecian, Alberta; 21746.

Figure 18 *Lithostrotionella pennsylvanica* (Shimer). x2, Meramecian, Alberta; 16829.

PLATE XIII. Mississippian and Pennsylvanian Fossils of Western Canada

(All figures natural size unless otherwise stated)

Figure 1 *Lithostrotion* (*Siphonodendron*) *whitneyi* of Meek. x2, Meramecian, Alberta; 16832.

Figure 2 *Thysanophyllum astraeiforme* (Warren). x2, Meramecian, Alberta; 8911.

Figure 3 *Goniatites crenistria* Phillips. x2½, Viséan, northern Yukon, from Sellers and Furnish, 1960, Pl. 141, fig. 4.

Figure 4 *Spirifer* cf. *pellaensis* Weller. Meramecian, Alberta; 21747.

Figure 5 *Faberophyllum* sp. x2, Meramecian, Alberta; 21748.

Figure 6 ?*Gigantoproductus* sp. Meramecian, Alberta; 21749.

Figure 7 *Lithostrotion* (*Siphonodendron*) cf. *pauciradiale* (McCoy). x2, Chesteran, Alberta; 21750.

Figure 8 *L.* (*S.*) *genevievensis* Easton. x2, Chesteran, Alberta; 16844.

Figure 9 *Spirifer leidyi* Norwood and Pratten. Chesteran, Alberta; 21751.

Figure 10 *Punctospirifer transversa* (McChesney). Chesteran, Alberta; 21752.

Figure 11 *Neospirifer* cf. *triplicatus* (Hall). Morrowan, Alberta; 21753.

Figure 12 *Spirifer occiduus* Sadlick. Morrowan, Alberta; 21754.

Figure 13 *Rhynchopora* cf. *magnicosta* Mather. Morrowan, Alberta; 21755.

Figure 14 ?*Reticulariina* sp. Morrowan, Alberta; 21756.

Figure 15 *Antiquatonia*? cf. *hermosana* (Girty). Morrowan, Alberta; 21757.

Figure 16 *Neospirifer praenuntius* Easton. Morrowan, Alberta; 21758.

Figure 17 *Plagioglypta* sp. Atokan, Alberta; 21759.

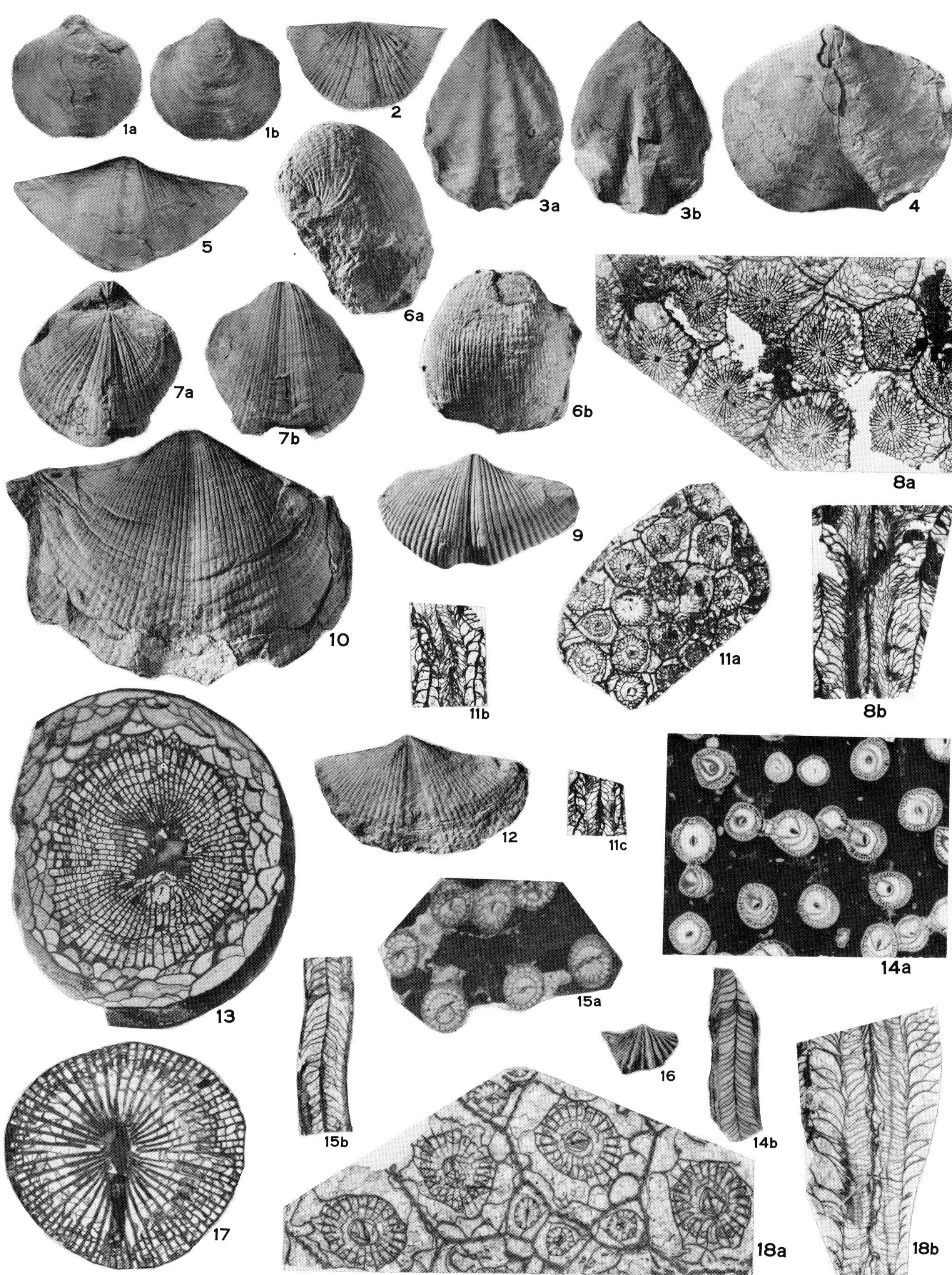
1a
1b
2
3a
3b
4
5
6a
6b
7a
7b
8a
8b
9
10
11a
11b
11c
12
13
14a
14b
15a
15b
16
17
18a
18b

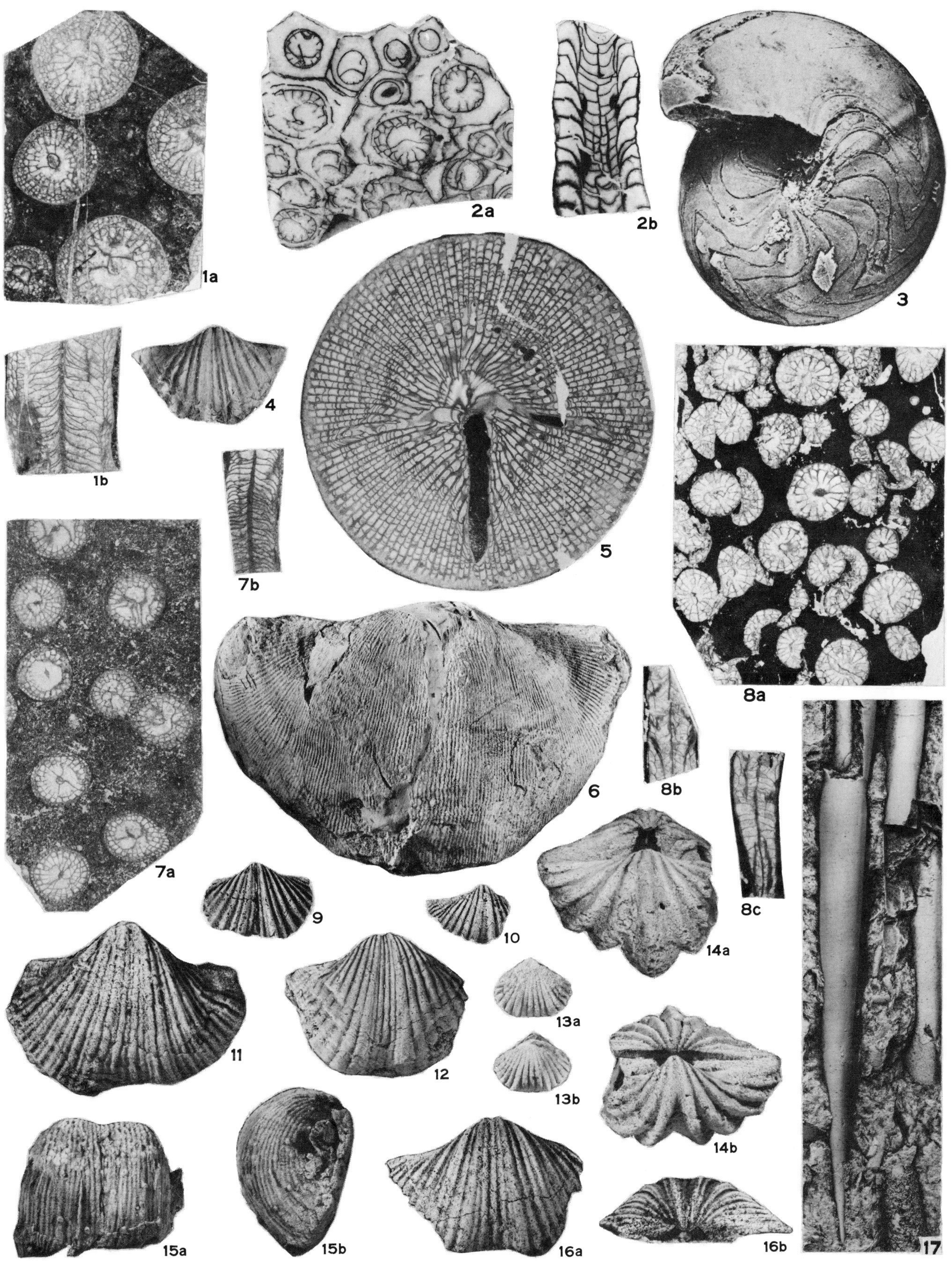
1a
1b
2a
2b
3
4
5
6
7a
7b
8a
8b
8c
9
10
11
12
13a
13b
14a
14b
15a
15b
16a
16b
17

Plate XIV. Permian Fossils of Western and Northern Canada

(All figures natural size unless otherwise stated)

Figure 1 *Parafusulina belcheri* Thorsteinsson. x5, Leonardian, Grinnell Peninsula; 13977.

Figure 2 *Neospirifer* sp. Early Permian, northern Yukon; 21760.

Figure 3 *Antiquatonia* cf. *neoninflatus* Licharew. Leonardian, Grinnell Peninsula; 13527.

Figure 4 *Waagenoconcha* sp. Early Permian, northern Yukon; 21761.

Figure 5 *Horridonia* sp. Early Permian, northern Yukon; 21762.

Figure 6 *Pterospirifer* cf. *alatus* (Schlotheim). Leonardian, Grinnell Peninsula; 13752.

Figure 7 *Daubichites fortieri* (Harker). Leonardian, Grinnell Peninsula; 13773.

Figure 8 *Streptorhynchus kempei* Andersson. Leonardian or Guadalupian, Grinnell Peninsula; 13517.

Figure 9 *Spirifer striato-paradoxus* Toula. Leonardian or Guadalupian, Grinnell Peninsula; 13748.

Figure 10 "*Stenoscisma*" *pliçatum* (Kutorga). Leonardian or Guadalupian, Grinnell Peninsula; 13737.

Figure 11 *Spiriferella* sp. Wolfcampian or Leonardian, northern Yukon; 21763.

Figure 12 *Muirwoodia* sp. Wolfcampian or Leonardian, northern Yukon; 21764.

Figure 13 *Megousia* sp. Guadalupian, northern Yukon; 21765.

Figure 14 *Megousia* sp. Guadalupian, northern Yukon; 21766.

Figure 15 *Caninophyllum belcheri* (Harker). Leonardian, Grinnell Peninsula; 13503a.

Figure 16 *Kochiproductus freboldi* (Stepanow). Leonardian or Guadalupian, Grinnell Peninsula; 13534.

Plate XV. Carboniferous Fossils of Eastern Canada

Figure 1 *Composita dawsoni* (Hall and Clarke). x1, Viséan, Hants co., N.S.; 7501a.

Figure 2 *Diodoceras avonensis* (Dawson). x1, Viséan, Hants co., N.S.; 4373.

Figure 3 *Conularia planicostata* Dawson. x1, Viséan, Irish Cove, N.S.; 21767.

Figure 4 *Aviculopecten lyelli* Dawson. x1, Viséan, Hants co., N.S.; 7553.

Figure 5 *Dibunophyllum lambii* Bell. x2, Viséan, Hants co., N.S.; 13589g.

Figure 6 *Cypridina acadica* Bell. x4, Viséan, Hants co., N.S.; 7742.

Figure 7 *Koninckophyllum* sp. x2, Viséan, Hants co., N.S., from Lewis, 1935, Pl. VII, fig. 2a, b.

Figure 8 *Spirifer adonis* Bell. x1, Viséan, Nova Scotia, holotype, Peabody Museum, Yale University.

Figure 9 *Ovatia lyelli* (de Verneuil). x1, Viséan, Hants co., N.S.; 7952.

Figure 10 *Martinia galataea* Bell. x1, Viséan, Hants co., N.S.; 7523.

Figure 11 *Schellwienella kennetcookensis* Bell. x1, Viséan, Hants co., N.S.; 7654.

Figure 12 *Diaphragmus avonensis* (Bell). x1, Viséan, Hants co., N.S.; 7953.

Figure 13 *Amplexizaphrentis enniskilleni* var. *minas* (Dawson). x2, Nova Scotia, from Lewis, 1935, Pl. V, fig. 1a.

Figure 14 *Spirifer nox* Bell. x1, Viséan, Hants co., N.S.; 7532.

Figure 15 *Euproops thompsoni* Raymond. x2½, Viséan, Cumberland co., N.S., from Copeland, 1957, Pl. 67, fig. 9.

Figure 16 *Beyrichiopsis lophota* Copeland. x30, Namurian, Cape Breton co., N.S.; 10387.

Figure 17 *Leaia baentschiana* (Beyrich). x2, Namurian, Richmond co., N.S.; 12793.

Figure 18 *Belinurus grandaevus* Jones and Woodward. x3, Namurian, Cumberland co., N.S.; 12804b.

Figure 19 *Leaia acutilirata* Copeland. x5½, Namurian, Pictou co., N.S.; 10396.

Figure 20 *Asmussia tenella* (Bronn). x6½, Westphalian, Pictou co., N.S.; 12853.

Figure 21 *Anthrapalaemon dubius* (Milne-Edwards). x1½, Westphalian, Cumberland co., N.S.; 12821.

Figure 22 *Carbonita agnes* (Jones). x30, Westphalian, Inverness co., N.S.; 12841.

Figure 23 *Hilboldtina evelinae* (Jones). x30, Westphalian, Cumberland co., N.S.; 12832.

Figure 24 *Gutschickia bretonensis* Copeland. x30, Westphalian, Inverness co., N.S.; 12836b.

Figure 25 *Phylloblatta*? sp. x1½, Westphalian, Pictou co., N.S.; 12847e.

Figure 26 *Archimylacris morienensis* Copeland. x2½, Westphalian, Cape Breton co., N.S.; 10394.

Figure 27 *Euproops amiae* Woodward. x2, Westphalian, Cape Breton co., N.S.; 12808e.

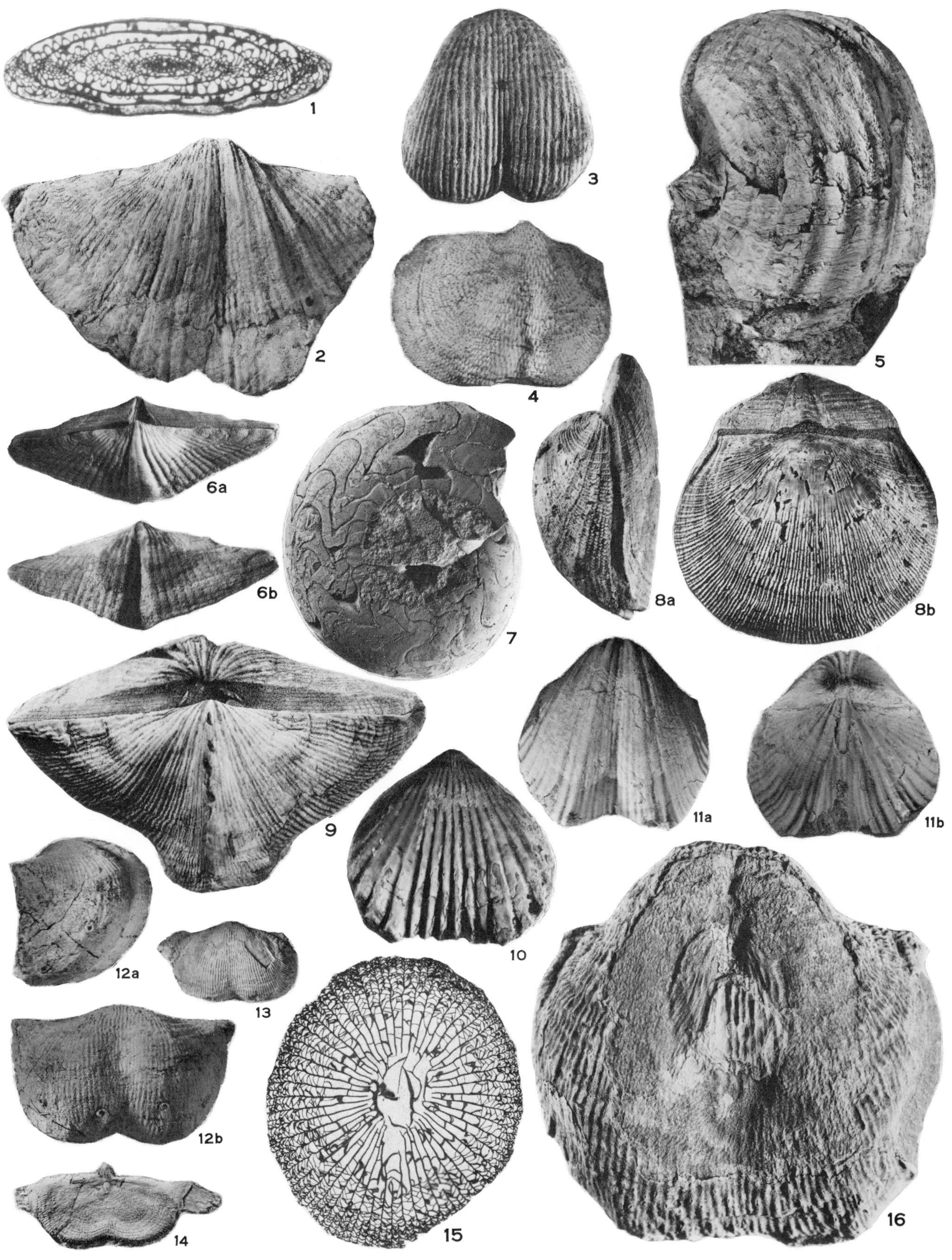
1
2
3
4
5
6a
6b
7
8a
8b
9
10
11a
11b
12a
12b
13
14
15
16

1a
1b
2
3
4
5
6
7a
7b
8a
8b
9
10a
10b
11
12a
12b
13
14a
14b
15
16a
16b
17
18
19
20
21
22
23
24
25
26
27

MARINE TRIASSIC FAUNAS

by E. T. Tozer

Triassic rocks containing marine faunas occur in the arctic islands and in western Canada. In the west exposures are confined to the Cordillera but the rocks also extend beneath the plains of northern Alberta and northeastern British Columbia. The following groups of marine organisms are known from the Triassic rocks of Canada: sponges, scleractinian corals; hydrozoans; crinoids (columnals only); echinoids; ophiuroids; bryozoans, terebratulid, rhynchonellid and spiriferid brachiopods; a great variety of bivalve molluscs; gastropods; ammonoids, nautiloids; belemnoids; ganoid fish and ichthyosaurs. The ammonoids and bivalves have proved most useful for dating rocks and have received most study. Corals, a bryozoan, brachiopods, nautiloids, and fish have received some attention, but many of the Triassic fossils have not yet been studied in any detail.

In discussing the distribution of Triassic faunas in Canada, it is convenient to distinguish four main regions: the arctic islands, and the eastern, western, and northern parts of the Cordillera. The arctic islands region refers to the Triassic deposits of Sverdrup Basin. The eastern Cordillera region includes the formations of the Foothills and Eastern Ranges of the Rocky Mountains in northeastern British Columbia and western Alberta. The western Cordillera region comprises the parts of British Columbia and southern Yukon that lie west and south of Rocky Mountain and Tintina Trenches. The northern Cordillera region, which, strictly speaking, represents the northern part of the eastern Cordillera, includes the parts of Yukon and the Northwest Territories that lie northeast of Tintina Trench.

Boundaries of the Triassic System

Virtually the whole of Triassic time is represented by marine deposits in Canada, although a complete faunal sequence is not known in any one region. The oldest faunas, known only from the arctic islands, are correlated with the *Otoceras* beds of the Himalayas, which are generally taken to define the base of the Triassic System. The *Otoceras* beds of Canada rest disconformably upon Permian rocks. As previously noted, these Permian rocks do not represent the youngest part of that system. In Canada, as in most and probably all parts of the world, there was a break in marine sedimentation between the Permian and the Triassic.

In most parts of Canada latest Triassic time is unrepresented by marine rocks. Upper Norian marine rocks occur in all regions but marine Rhaetian beds have been recognized only at Tyaughton Creek, British Columbia, in the western Cordillera. Hettangian, lowermost Jurassic, rocks are also present at this locality, and there is apparently no detectable stratigraphic break between the Triassic and Jurassic rocks. In the arctic islands there are non-marine beds, the upper part of Heiberg Formation, lying between marine upper Norian and Sinemurian beds. These non-marine strata may include beds of Rhaetian age.

The boundaries of the Triassic are thus marked by evidence of widespread marine regression. At the base of the Triassic the interval of regression lies mainly, or entirely, within the Permian. At the top, however, the regressive interval commonly spans both latest Triassic and earliest Jurassic time, but in one place at least this gap is bridged by marine sediments.

Faunal Facies

For present purposes two types of faunas may be distinguished among the assemblages known in Canada.

First there are the faunas in which the dominant fossils are cephalopods, mainly ammonoids, and thin-shelled bivalves, such as *Claraia, Posidonia, Daonella, Halobia,* and *Monotis*. The exact environment in which these animals lived is unknown, but it is certain that they do not represent a normal shallow-water benthonic assemblage. They probably did not live on the sea floor and are accordingly referred to as the pelagic faunas.

The second marine faunal facies is clearly benthonic and includes sponges, corals, echinoderms, bivalves, and brachiopods. The bivalve faunas include trigoniids and other dimyarian groups, ostreids, limids, pernids, pectinids, etc., commonly in rich variety. These bivalve faunas are quite unlike the monotonous suite of Pectinacea *(Claraia,* etc.) that characterizes the pelagic facies. Ammonoids and pelagic bivalves are occasionally associated with the benthonic forms, but they are generally rare. At some levels ammonoids are relatively abundant in both the benthonic and pelagic assemblages. *Nathorstites* (upper Ladinian) is one example; this genus is commonly found with brachiopods and ostreid bivalves, but it nevertheless achieves its greatest abundance in the pelagic facies. In the upper Norian *Rhabdoceras* occurs in both benthonic and pelagic assemblages.

Faunal Provinces

The pelagic faunas of the Triassic include many cosmopolitan genera and even species. Consequently correlation of rocks that contain pelagic faunas is usually a fairly easy matter. The pelagic faunas of low latitudes, as in British Columbia, appear to show greater taxonomic diversity than contemporary assemblages in the arctic islands. For example, only three ammonoid genera are known in the upper Ladinian of arctic islands whereas in northeastern British Columbia about a dozen genera occur in each of the three zones of the upper Ladinian. These differences are not obviously related to conditions of sedimentation and more likely indicate a taxonomic diversity gradient related to variations in the temperature of the Triassic seas. The apparent decrease in diversity towards the north suggests that the Triassic seas that covered the site of the arctic islands were cooler than those of the Cordillera. Comparable differences between the faunas of the eastern Cordillera and the arctic islands occur in the Dienerian, Spathian, Anisian, Karnian, and Norian. Despite these apparent gradients there are, at all levels, a few cosmopolites that satisfy the needs of correlation. The pelagic faunas provide no evidence that isolated zoogeographic provinces existed in Triassic time.

The benthonic faunas of the western Cordillera region are in some respects unlike those of the other regions and seem to form a distinct zoogeographic province. These

TABLE XI-6 *Range and distribution of Triassic pelagic faunas. (Numbers refer to occurrence in the appropriate region.)*

SERIES	LOWER TRIASSIC										MIDDLE TRIASSIC									UPPER TRIASSIC											
STAGE	Griesbachian				Dienerian		Smithian		Spathian		Anisian				Ladinian					Karnian					Norian						
SUBSTAGE	Lower		Upper								Lwr	Mid	Upper		Lower		Upper			Lower		Upper			Lower		Middle		Upper		
ZONE	*Concavum*	*Boreale*	*Commune*	*Strigatus*	*Candidus*	*Sverdrupi*	*Romunderi*	*Tardus*	*Pilaticus*	*Subrobustus*	*Caurus*	*Varium*	*Deleeni*	*Chischa*	*Subasperum*	*Poseidon*	*Meginae*	*Maclearni*	*Sutherlandi*	*Obesum*	*Nanseni*	*Dilleri*	*Welleri*	*Macrolobatus*	*Kerri*	*Dawsoni*	*Magnus*	*Rutherfordi*	*Columbianus*	*Suessi*	*Marshi*
OCCURRENCE: 1 ARCTIC ISLANDS	×	×	×	×	×	×	×	×	×	×	×	×	×	?	×			×		?	×		×						×	×	
OCCURRENCE: CORDILLERA 2 EAST			×		×	×	×	×		×	×	×	×	×	×	×	×	×	×	×	×	×	×	×	×	×	×	×	×	×	
OCCURRENCE: CORDILLERA 3 WEST															×					×	?	×	×		×		×		×	×	×
OCCURRENCE: CORDILLERA 4 NORTH							×								×								×						×	×	

1 — *Otoceras concavum*
1 — *Otoceras boreale*
1 — *Metophiceras nielseni*
1 — *Ophiceras* spp.
1 — *Ophiceras commune*
1 — *Ophiceras decipiens*
1 — *Pachyproptychites strigatus*
1,2 — *Claraia stachei*
1,2 — *Proptychites candidus*
1,2 — *Prionolobus lilangense*
1,2 — *Paranorites sverdrupi*
1 — *Paranorites heibergensis*
1,2 — *Euflemingites* spp.
1,2 — *Juvenites* spp.
1,2,1 — *Arctoceras* spp.
1,2 — *Posidonia mimer*
2 — *Anasibirites* sp.
1,2 — *Wasatchites* spp.
1,2 — *Xenoceltites subevolutus*
1,2 — "*Pseudomonotis*" *occidentalis*
1 — *Olenikites pilaticus*
1 — *Columbites* sp.
2 — *Isculitoides minor*
1,2 — *Popovites* spp.
2 — *Metadagnoceras pulcher*
1,2 — *Keyserlingites subrobustus*
1 — *Olenikites canadensis*
1,2 — *Svalbardiceras* spp.
2 — *Procarnites modestus*
1,2 — *Posidonia aranea*
1,2 — *Lenotropites caurus*
1,2 — *Pearylandites* spp.
2 — *Arctohungarites bufonis*
2 — *Acrochordiceras americanum*
1,2 — *Parapopanoceras* spp.
1,2 — *Anagymnotoceras varium*
2 — *Epiczekanowskites hayesi*
2 — *Longobardites larvalis*
2 — *Longobardites nevadanus*
Daonella spp.
1,2 — *Daonella americana*
2 — *Daonella moussoni*
1 — *Daonella frami*
1,2,3,4 — *Daonella* cf. *degeeri*
2 — *Daonella nitanae*
2 — *Daonella elegans*
2 — *Gymnotoceras* s.s. spp.
2 — *Gymnotoceras deleeni*
2 — *Gymnotoceras chischa*
2 — *Celtites gabbi*
1,2 — *Protrachyceras* spp.
1,2 — *Protrachyceras* cf. *meeki*
2 — *Protrachyceras sikanianum*
2 — *Ptychites* s.l. spp.
1 — *Ptychites nanuk*
2 — *Progonoceratites poseidon*
1,2 — *Nathorstites* s.s. spp.
2 — *Nathorstites mcconnelli*
2 — *Meginoceras meginae*
2 — *Silenticeras hatae*
2 — *Maclearnoceras maclearni*
2 — *Liardites whiteavesi*
2 — *Anolcites* cf. *doleriticum*
2 — *Paratrachyceras sutherlandi*
2 — *Asklepioceras glaciense*
2 — *Daxatina canadense*
1,2 — *Lobites* s.s. spp.
2 — *Megaphyllites selwyni*

Halobia spp.
2 — *Halobia* cf. *rugosa*
1,2 — *Halobia zitteli* s.l.
2 — *Halobia ornatissima*
2 — *Halobia superba*
2,3 — *Halobia alaskana*
2,3 — *Halobia* cf. *fallax*
1,2,3 — *Monotis scutiformis* s. l.
2,3 — *Monotis subcircularis*
2,3,4 — *Monotis ochotica*
2,3 — *Trachyceras* s.s. spp.
2 — *Coroceras* cf. *nasutus*
1,2 — *Sirenites nanseni*
1,2,3 — *Sirenites senticosus*
2,3 — *Tropites dilleri*
2,3 — *Spirogmoceras shastense*
3 — *Trachysagenites* spp.
2,3 — *Discotropites* spp.
1,2,3 — *Tropites* spp.
2,3 — *Tropites* aff. *welleri*
2,3,4 — *Juvavites* cf. *knowltoni*
2,3 — *Homerites semiglobosus*
1,2 — *Arctosirenites canadensis*
1,2 — *Jovites* spp.
2 — *Anatropites* sp.
2 — *Gonionotites gethingi*
2,3 — *Mojsisovicsites kerri*
2 — *Guembelites clavatus*
2 — *Guembelites jandianus*
2 — *Sirenites nabeschi*
2 — *Dimorphites pardonetiensis*
2 — *Malayites dawsoni*
2 — *Waldthausenites* spp.
1,2 — *Proclydonautilus natosini*
2 — *Juvavites magnus*
2,3 — *Indojuvavites* cf. *angulatus*
2 — *Pterotoceras caurinum*
2 — *Cyrtopleurites* spp.
2 — *Drepanites rutherfordi*
2 — *Didymites* sp.
2 — *Pseudosirenites* spp.
2 — *Alloclionites* spp.
2,3,4 — *Steinmannites* spp.
1,2,3 — *Himavatites* spp.
2,3 — *Distichites* spp.
2,3 — *Parajuvavites* spp.
2,3 — *Episculites* spp.
2,3 — *Sagenites* spp.
2,3 — *Halorites americanus*
2,3 — *Rhabdoceras suessi*
Paracochloceras suessi — 3
3 — *Metasibirites* sp.
2,3 — *Placites* spp.
Choristoceras suttonensis — 3
Choristoceras marshi — 3
Arcestes sp. — 3

GSC

faunas are all Upper Triassic. They include the only Triassic coral faunas known in Canada. Also present are megalodont bivalves, and a rich, but as yet poorly known, fauna of brachiopods and gastropods. The coral faunas occur at several levels in the Karnian and Norian and attain a latitude of 61°N in southern Yukon. There can be no doubt that these faunas testify to warm water conditions. At several levels, notably in the Dilleri and Welleri Zones of the Karnian, and in the Columbianus and Suessi Zones of the Norian, pelagic faunas, identical with those of the eastern Cordillera region are also present in the western Cordillera. Whatever the factor or feature that restrained Triassic corals from reaching the eastern and northern parts of the Cordillera, and also the arctic islands, it did not constitute a comparable barrier to the pelagic faunas.

As already mentioned, the evidence from the pelagic faunas suggests that the Triassic deposits of the eastern Cordillera region were deposited in warmer waters than those of the arctic islands. This presents no problems; the arctic islands are at a higher latitude than the eastern Cordillera today, and according to the paleomagnetic data this was also true in Triassic time. The Triassic rocks of the western Cordillera were evidently deposited in even warmer water than those of the eastern Cordillera. This is dramatically shown by the presence in southern Yukon of thick bioclastic formations containing coral faunas that range in age from Karnian to upper Norian. No comparable rocks occur in the contemporary deposits of the eastern Cordillera which are today at a lower latitude. The close similarities between the pelagic faunas of the eastern and western parts of the Cordillera, and the extraordinarily rich representation of cosmopolitan pelagic faunas in the eastern Cordillera show, without any doubt, that the eastern Cordillera was not isolated at any time between the Griesbachian and the upper Norian from the routes of migration open to the pelagic faunas. There is, therefore, no faunal evidence to support the placing of a land barrier between the sites of Triassic deposition now preserved in the eastern and western parts of the Cordillera. The unrivalled sequence of Norian ammonoid faunas preserved in the Pardonet Formation of Peace River show close relationships to the faunas of the Alps, Timor, and the Himalayas. There is no evidence that these faunas penetrated to the Peace River area via the arctic; nor did they come from the south or east. The Peace River area must have had free access to the Circumpacific and Tethyan seaways of Upper Triassic time.

Possibly the faunal peculiarities of the western Cordillera may be explained by post-Triassic tectonic events. There is evidence from various parts of the Cordillera that post-Triassic, right lateral transcurrent movement, of the order of 250 miles, has affected segments of the Cordillera. The Tintina Trench, according to Roddick, may define one such segment of the Cordillera. Structural interpretations of this nature introduce the possibility that the warm-water Triassic deposits of the western Cordillera were originally deposited south of the latitude of the contemporary rocks in the eastern Cordillera. Their present juxtaposition at comparable latitudes would thus be the result of movement of the western rocks to the north, in post-Triassic time. This, rather than an ecological barrier on the site of the Rocky Mountain and Tintina Trenches, seems a more satisfactory explanation for the observed anomalies of faunal distribution.

The Sequence of Triassic Faunas

The Triassic rocks of Canada provide a fairly continuous sequence of strata containing pelagic faunas. In these rocks the ranges of the faunas can be empirically determined, and a succession of zones forming a time-scale can be established. With the benthonic faunas this is not so. There are no continuous sequences with benthonic assemblages that cover more than two stages at most. The ranges of the various benthonic faunas are thus not well known. The record provided by the pelagic faunas permits something that approaches continuous observation, throughout Triassic time. In contrast, the record for the benthonic groups represents little more than an occasional glimpse of the life of the time.

In the pelagic succession thirty-one ammonoid zones have been recognized in Canada and these zones are grouped into eight stages (Table XI-6). The four Lower Triassic stages are defined in arctic Canada; those of the Middle and Upper Triassic were defined in Alpine Europe. The range in time and geographic distribution of the principal pelagic guide fossils are also shown. The faunal sequence in the arctic islands and the eastern Cordillera region is far more complete than in the western and northern parts of the Cordillera. The incompleteness of the sequence in the northern part partly reflects lack of knowledge. In the western Cordillera the absence of Lower Triassic faunas and the rarity of Middle Triassic is probably real for, as shown in Chapter VIII, widespread volcanic and orogenic activity occurred which may account for the rarity of faunas for this interval.

The record of benthonic faunas is very fragmentary. A few, however, deserve mention because they are locally useful for stratigraphic purposes. Dienerian rocks of the arctic islands, in the shallow-water facies, locally contain *Myalina* coquina. *Arcticopora christiei* from Ellesmere Island, which is one of the very few trepostome bryozoans known younger than Paleozoic, is probably Dienerian. The Anisian is not well represented by benthonic faunas, but *Spiriferina stracheyi* has been described from the eastern Cordillera.

In Ladinian time, benthonic faunas became fairly abundant in eastern Cordillera region and arctic islands. Spiriferid brachiopods and bivalves are most abundant in rocks of calcareous sandstone and siltstone facies, such as the "Grey Beds" of the eastern Cordillera, and the Schei Point Formation of arctic islands. The Ladinian and Karnian benthonic faunas are not obviously dissimilar and usually include one or two species of spiriferinid and terebratuloid brachiopods, and up to a dozen species of bivalves, including representatives of *Meleagrinella, Oxytoma, Gervillia, Hoernesia, Entolium, Pecten, Ostrea, Lopha, Gryphaea, Plagiostoma, Mysidioptera, Mytilus, Modiola, Myophoria, Cardinia,* and *Pleuromya.*

A Karnian, probably upper Karnian, assemblage characterized by *Mysidioptera poyana* is fairly widely distributed in the eastern Cordillera region and may also occur in the southern Yukon. Another notable local fauna, probably also upper Karnian, characterized by *Gryphaea* cf. *arcuatiformis, Plicatula,* and other bivalves, is widespread in the upper Schei Point beds that rim the Sverdrup Basin.

The lower Norian in the eastern Cordillera is known mainly from pelagic faunas, but species of *Pleuromya* and *Gryphaea chakii* are locally present in lower Norian beds. The *Meleagrinella antiqua* fauna which occurs in the lower part of the Heiberg Formation of arctic islands is probably lower or middle Norian, but somewhat similar assemblages are also known from the underlying beds in the Blaa Mountain Formation that are definitely Karnian. *Oxytoma kiparisovae* is a member of this fauna and specimens of *Halobia* are also known. Typical dimyarian bivalves do not occur and it is possible that this assemblage represents some sort of pelagic fauna; at any rate, it is not a typical benthonic assemblage. Large megalodont bivalves (*Megalodon canadensis*) occur in coralline limestone immediately below *Monotis subcircularis* at Tyaughton Creek in the western Cordillera. These fossils are probably middle or upper Norian.

The richest Triassic benthonic fauna known in Canada is that of the Norian of the western Cordillera, where it occurs in the Lewes River Group of Yukon, the Tyaughton Group of southern British Columbia, the Sutton and Bonanza Groups of Vancouver Island, and in other unnamed formations. This fauna includes corals, sponges, echinoids, brachiopods, bivalves and gastropods, and cephalopods. Widely distributed species are *Spondylospira lewesensis, Pecten tyaughtonae, "Pecten" yukonense,* at least nine species of Trigoniidae (*"Myophoria" suttonensis, "Myophoria" cairnesi, "Trigonia" textilis,* etc.) *Cassianella lingulata, Plicatula perimbricata.* Also present are representatives of *Plagiostoma, Rhaetavicula, "Astarte", Modiolus,* etc. More than thirty species of bivalves are certainly present. Ammonoids, including *Rhabdoceras* and *Paracochloceras* occur at some localities associated with many of the benthonic fossils, and their presence shows that most of the occurrences of this fauna are upper Norian. It should be noted, however, that at least some species (e.g., *"Myophoria" suttonensis*) range up into the Marshi Zone, of Rhaetian age.

Selected References

Logan, A.
1967: Middle and Upper Triassic spiriferinid brachiopods from the Canadian Arctic Archipelago; *Geol. Surv. Can.,* Bull. 155. (Includes most references to papers of Triassic brachiopods from the eastern Cordillera.)

McLearn, F. H.
1960: Ammonoid faunas of the Upper Triassic Pardonet Formation, Peace River Foothills, British Columbia; *Geol. Surv. Can.,* Mem. 311.

Tozer, E. T.
1967: A standard for Triassic time; *Geol. Surv. Can.,* Bull. 156. (Includes references to all previously published reports that deal with pelagic faunas, and many references to papers on benthonic faunas.)

Plate XVI. Lower Triassic Ammonoids and Bivalves

Figures 1a, b *Otoceras boreale* Spath. Lower Griesbachian, Blind Fiord Formation, Ellesmere Island; 14015.

Figures 2a, b *Ophiceras commune* Spath. Upper Griesbachian, Blind Fiord Formation, Axel Heiberg Island; 14030.

Figures 3a, b *Pachyproptychites strigatus* (Tozer). Upper Griesbachian, Blind Fiord Formation, Axel Heiberg Island; 14035.

Figure 4 *Claraia clarai* (Emmrich). Griesbachian, Sulphur Mountain Formation, Alberta; 14196.

Figure 5 *Claraia stachei* Bittner. Griesbachian, Grayling Formation, northeastern British Columbia; 14228.

Figures 6a, b *Prionolobus lilangense* (Krafft). Dienerian, Toad Formation, northeastern British Columbia; 21768.

Figures 7a, b *Paranorites sverdrupi* Tozer. Dienerian, Blind Fiord Formation, Ellesmere Island; 14277.

Figures 8a, b *Arctoceras blomstrandi* (Lindstrom). Smithian, Blind Fiord Formation, Ellesmere Island; 14067.

Figure 9 *Posidonia mimer* Oeberg. Smithian, Blind Fiord Formation, Ellesmere Island; 14201.

Figures 10a, b *Prosphingites spathi* Frebold. Smithian, Blind Fiord Formation, Ellesmere Island; 14085.

Figures 11a, b *Juvenites needhami* Tozer. Smithian, Toad Formation, northeastern British Columbia; 14290.

Figures 12a, b *Anakashmirites borealis* Tozer. Smithian, Blind Fiord Formation, Ellesmere Island; 14073.

Figures 13a, b *Euflemingites romunderi* Tozer. Smithian, Blind Fiord Formation, Ellesmere Island; 14050.

Figures 14a, b *Wasatchites tardus* (McLearn). Smithian, Toad Formation, northeastern British Columbia; 9470.

Figures 15a, b *Xenoceltites subevolutus* Spath. Smithian, Toad Formation, northeastern British Columbia; 14303.

Figure 16 *"Pseudomonotis" occidentalis kindlei* McLearn. Smithian, Toad Formation, northeastern British Columbia; 9478, 9598.

Figure 17 *"Pseudomonotis" occidentalis* Whiteaves. Smithian, Toad Formation, northeastern British Columbia; 4728.

Figures 18 *Posidonia aranea* Tozer. Spathian, Toad Formation, northeastern British Columbia; 14230.

Figures 19a, b *Olenikites canadensis* Tozer. Spathian, Blaa Mountain Formation, Ellesmere Island; 14094.

(Plates XVI, XVII, and XVIII—all figures are natural size unless otherwise stated)

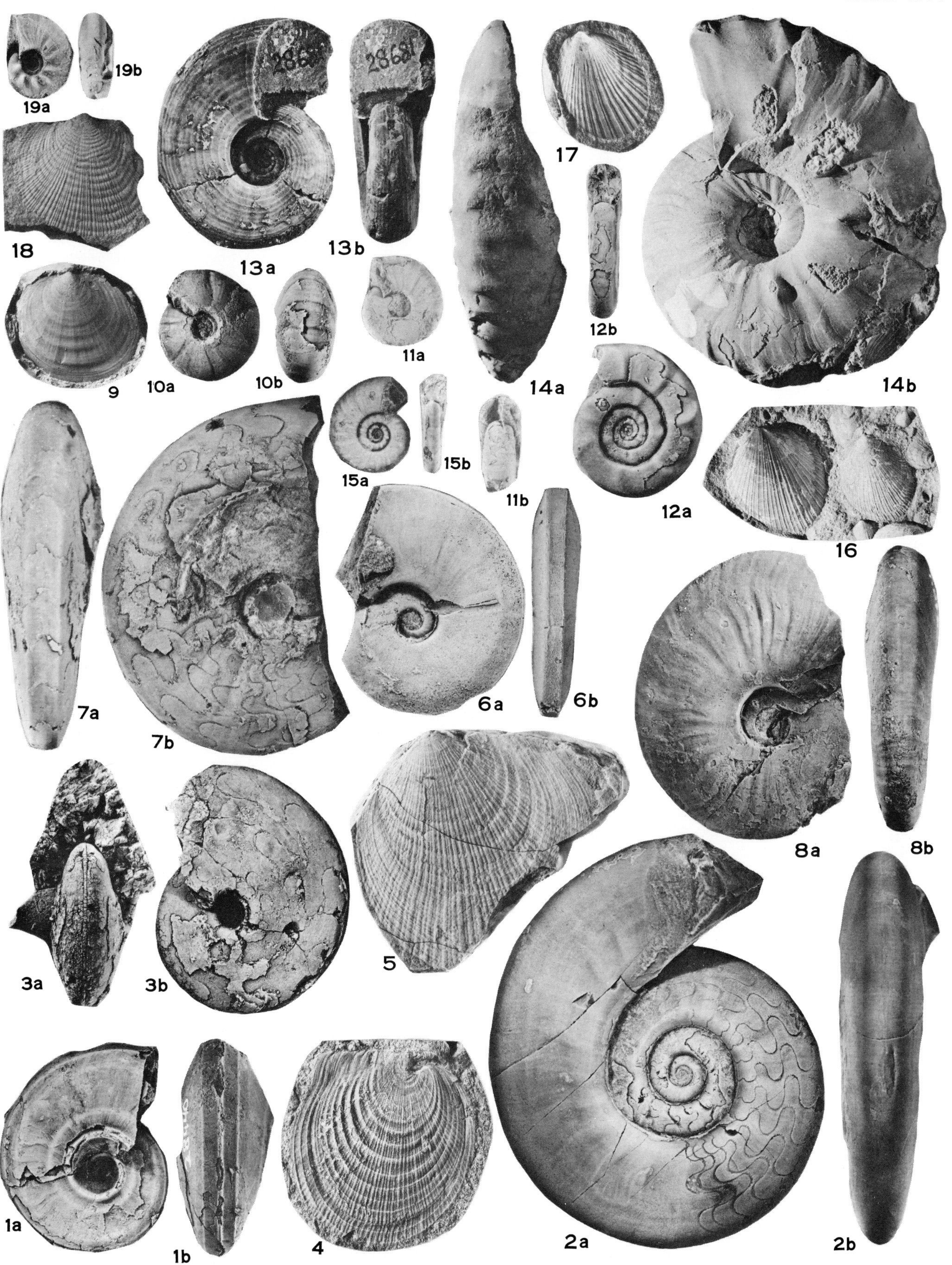
19a
19b
18
13a
13b
17
14a
14b
12b
9
10a
10b
11a
15a
15b
11b
12a
16
7a
7b
6a
6b
8a
8b
3a
3b
5
1a
1b
4
2a
2b

Plate XVII. Middle Triassic Ammonoids and Bivalves

Figures 1a, b *Lenotropites caurus* (McLearn), Lower Anisian, Toad Formation, northeastern British Columbia; 9585.

Figures 2a-c *Ptychites* cf. *trochlaeformis* (Lindström). Upper Anisian, Schei Point Formation, Exmouth Island; 14186, 14187.

Figures 3a, b *Anagymnotoceras helle* (McLearn). Middle Anisian, Toad Formation, northeastern British Columbia; 9592.

Figures 4a, b *Parapopanoceras selwyni* McLearn. Middle Anisian, Toad Formation, northeastern British Columbia; 9580, 9579.

Figures 5a, b *Longobardites nevadanus* Hyatt and Smith. Anisian, Toad Formation, northeastern British Columbia; 6450.

Figures 6a, b *Gymnotoceras deleeni* McLearn. Upper Anisian, Toad Formation, northeastern British Columbia; 21707.

Figure 7 *Daonella frami* Kittl. Lower Ladinian, Blaa Mountain Formation, Ellesmere Island; 14205.

Figures 8a, b 9a, b *Progonoceratites poseidon* Tozer. Lower Ladinian, Liard Formation, northeastern British Columbia; 18887, 18888.

Figures 10a, b *Protrachyceras sikanianum* McLearn. Upper Ladinian, Liard Formation, northeastern British Columbia; 9044.

Figures 11a, b *Meginoceras meginae* McLearn. Upper Ladinian, Liard Formation, northeastern British Columbia; 8811, 9042.

Figures 12a, b *Lobites pacianus* McLearn. Upper Ladinian, Liard Formation, northeastern British Columbia; 9525, 8789.

Figure 13 *Daonella nitanae* McLearn. Upper Ladinian, Liard Formation, northeastern British Columbia; 8773.

Figures 14a, b *Spiriferina abichi* Oppel. Ladinian, Liard Formation, northeastern British Columbia; 4733.

Figures 15a-c *"Terebratula" liardensis* Whiteaves. Ladinian, Liard Formation, northeastern British Columbia; 4734.

Figures 16a, b *Maclearnoceras maclearni* Tozer. Upper Ladinian, Liard Formation, northeastern British Columbia; 14296, 14298.

Figure 17 *Hoernesia woyoniana* McLearn. Upper Ladinian, "Grey Beds", northeastern British Columbia; 8768.

Figure 18 *Modiolus ahsisi* McLearn. Upper Ladinian, "Grey Beds", northeastern British Columbia; 8767.

Figure 19 *Daonella elegans* McLearn. Upper Ladinian, Liard Formation, northeastern British Columbia; 9537.

Figures 20a, b *Nathorstites mcconnelli* (Whiteaves). Upper Ladinian, Liard Formation, northeastern British Columbia; 21769.

Figures 21a, b *Daxatina canadensis* (Whiteaves). Upper Ladinian, Liard Formation, northeastern British Columbia; 4718.

Figures 22a, b *Paratrachyceras sutherlandi* McLearn. Upper Ladinian, Liard Formation, northeastern British Columbia; 18903.

Plate XVIII. Upper Triassic Ammonoids, Bivalves, and Corals

Figures 1a, b *Sirenites nanseni* Tozer. Lower Karnian, Blaa Mountain Formation, Ellesmere Island; 14158.

Figure 2 *Mysidioptera poyana* (McLearn). Karnian, "Grey Beds", northeastern British Columbia; 8772.

Figure 3 *Halobia zitteli* Lindstrom. Karnian, Schei Point Formation, Ellesmere Island; 14208.

Figures 4a, b *Discotropites* sp. Upper Karnian, Pardonet Formation, northeastern British Columbia; 14239.

Figures 5a, b *Tropites johnsoni* Smith. Upper Karnian, northwestern British Columbia; 14243.

Figures 6a, b *Homerites semiglobosus* (Hauer). Upper Karnian, Pardonet Formation, northeastern British Columbia; 14235.

Figures 7a, b *Juvavites* cf. *knowltoni* Smith. Upper Karnian, Pardonet Formation, northeastern British Columbia; 14244.

Figures 8a, b *Mojsisovicsites kerri* (McLearn). Lower Norian, Pardonet Formation, northeastern British Columbia; 9048, 18911.

Figures 9a, b *Malayites dawsoni* McLearn. Lower Norian, Pardonet Formation, northeastern British Columbia; 8836, 12604.

Figures 10a, b *Himavatites columbianus* McLearn. Middle Norian, Pardonet Formation, northeastern British Columbia; 9265.

Figure 11 *Meleagrinella antiqua* Tozer. Probably Lower Norian, Heiberg Formation, Axel Heiberg Island; 14212.

Figure 12 *Gryphaea chakii* McLearn. Norian, Pardonet Formation, northeastern British Columbia; 8770.

Figure 13 *Elysastraea profunda* (Reuss). x1.5, Upper Norian, Sutton Formation, Vancouver Island; 7807.

Figure 14 *Thecosmilia dawsoni* (Clapp and Shimer). x1.5, Upper Norian, Sutton Formation, Vancouver Island; 7806.

Figures 15a-c *Spondylospira lewesensis* (Lees). Upper Norian, Lewes River Group, Yukon; 14259, 14260, 14261.

Figures 16a, b *"Myophoria" suttonensis* Clapp and Shimer. Upper Norian, Sutton Formation, Vancouver Island; 14256.

Figure 17 *Paracochloceras suessi* Mojsisovics. x2, Upper Norian, Bonanza Group, Vancouver Island; 17016.

Figures 18a, b *Rhabdoceras suessi* Hauer. Upper Norian, Lewes River Group, Yukon; 14265, 14264.

Figures 19a, b *Cassianella lingulata* Gabb. Upper Norian, Bonanza Group, Vancouver Island; 14249.

Figure 20 *Monotis subcircularis* Gabb. Upper Norian, southwestern Yukon; 14265.

Figures 21a-c *Choristoceras marshi,* Hauer. Rhaetian, Tyaughton Group, southern British Columbia; 18912, 18913.

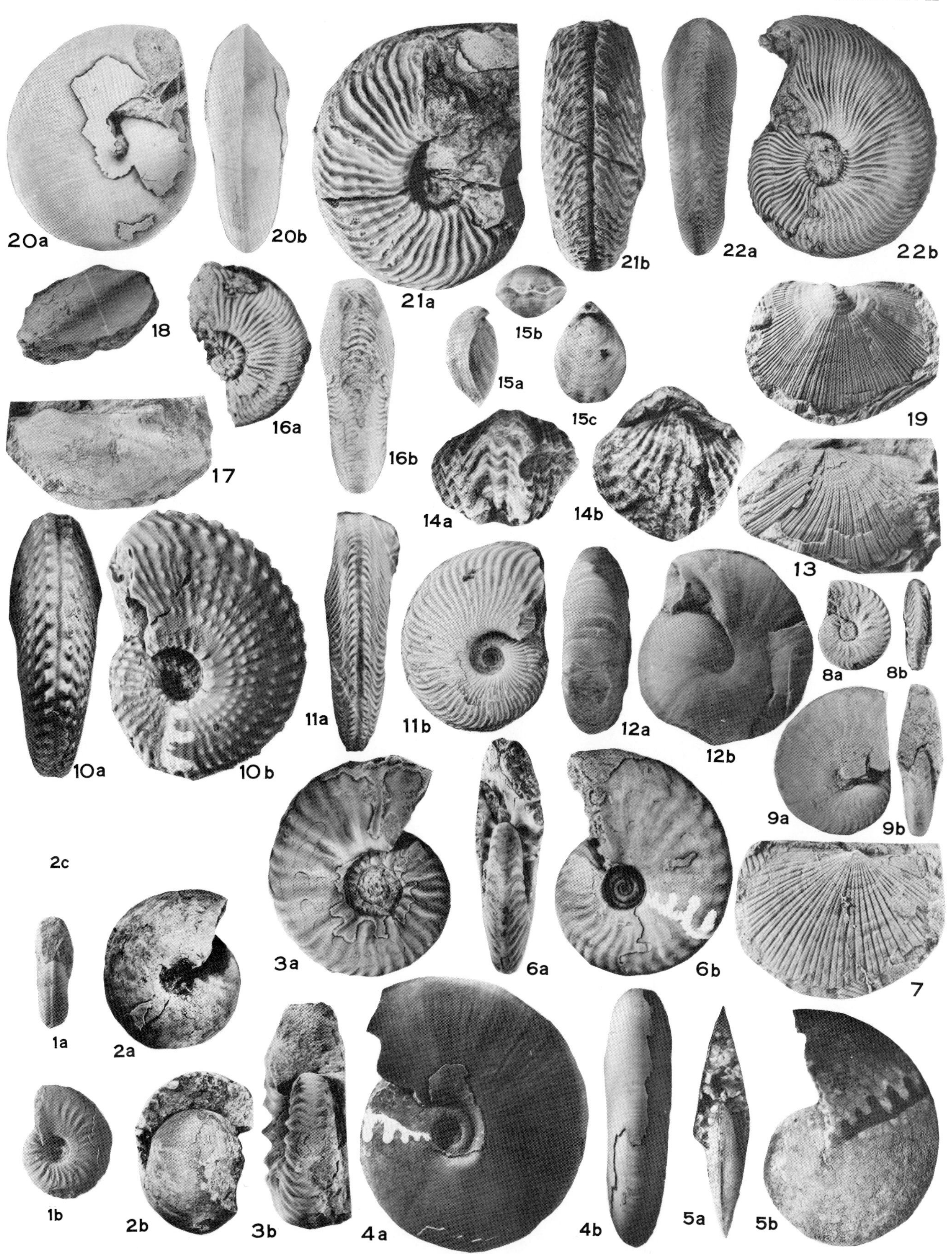

20a
20b
21a
21b
22a
22b
18
16a
16b
15a
15b
15c
19
17
14a
14b
13
10a
10b
11a
11b
12a
12b
8a
8b
9a
9b
2c
3a
6a
6b
7
1a
2a
1b
2b
3b
4a
4b
5a
5b

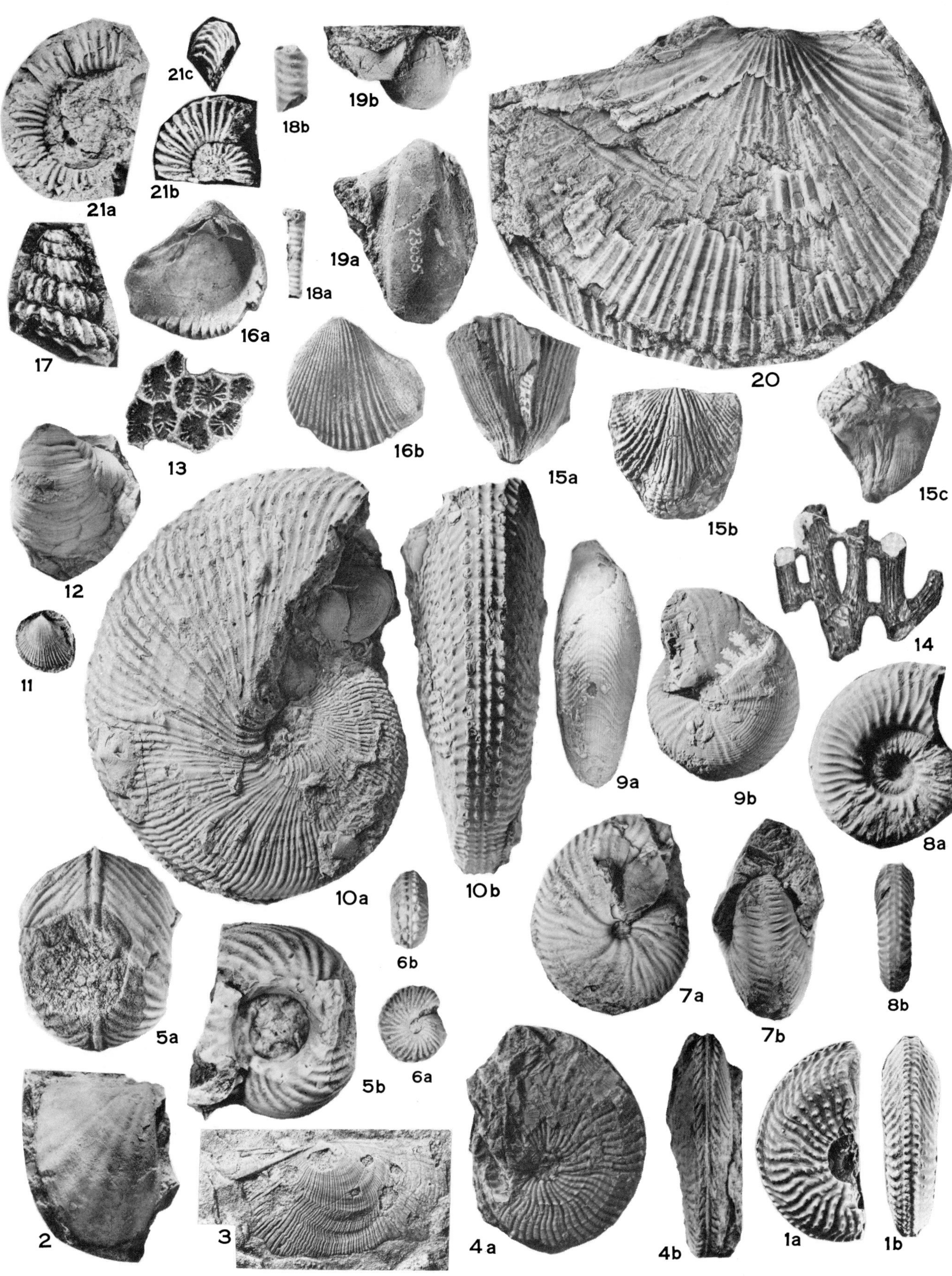
21a
21b
21c
18b
19b
19a
18a
17
16a
16b
20
13
15a
15b
15c
12
14
11
10a
10b
9a
9b
8a
8b
5a
6b
7a
7b
5b
6a
2
3
4a
4b
1a
1b

MARINE JURASSIC FAUNAS

by Hans Frebold

Distribution and General Features

Faunas of Jurassic age are present in arctic and western Canada, which regions represent two distinctive zoogeographical provinces (Table XI-7). The arctic area includes the northern part of the Canadian arctic islands, northwestern parts of the Northwest Territories, and northern and central Yukon. The western area includes the subsurface of the southern part of the Prairie Provinces, Manitoba, Saskatchewan, and eastern Alberta, the Rocky Mountains and Foothills, various parts of central and western British Columbia, including Vancouver Island and the Queen Charlotte Islands.

The subdivision of the Jurassic into zones and stages is based on ammonites, and in the Upper Jurassic also on representatives of the pelecypod genus *Buchia.* The ammonites also establish the zoogeographical provinces. Of other invertebrates belemnites, pelecypods, gastropods, corals, a few brachiopods, echinoderms, arthropods, and microfaunas occur. There are a few marine vertebrate remains. Of the invertebrate macrofossils, pelecypods and gastropods have also provided valuable guide fossils. Microfaunas have particular importance in the subsurface where macrofossils are rarely available.

A great number of faunal gaps, often coincidental with absence of sediments, are characteristic of the Jurassic in Canada. This is evident when comparing the Jurassic faunas of western Canada with those of northwestern Europe or other parts of the world. A considerable number of the ammonites characteristic of certain zones are missing, sometimes amounting to the greater part of a stage.

Zoogeography

Lower Jurassic ammonite faunas in Canada do not show any zoogeographical differences. Their character is not basically different from that of those of other parts of the world, and most show close affinities, even at the specific level, to the Lower Jurassic ammonites of northwestern Europe. As far as the Hettangian ammonites of British Columbia are concerned, similarities to the northeastern Alps exist mainly on generic level. Thus, the well-known cosmopolitan character of the Lower Jurassic ammonite faunas is also clearly evident in both western and arctic Canada. Lower Jurassic pelecypods seem to be evenly distributed in these areas, and even show a considerable independence of facies. Corals are, however, restricted to southwestern British Columbia, where they are found in rocks closely associated with volcanic and greywacke sequences.

The same zoogeographical conditions exist in the lower Bajocian, earliest Middle Jurassic. In the middle Bajocian, the Bathonian, lower and middle Callovian — that is throughout most of the Middle Jurassic, as the presence of upper Callovian is not recognized in Canada —clear zoogeographical differences in the ammonite faunas are apparent, particularly between arctic and western Canada. The arctic province is characterized, in ascending order, by the genera *Arkelloceras* (probably middle Bajocian), *Cranocephalites* (upper Bajocian and lower Bathonian), *Arctocephalites* (mainly middle Bathonian), *Arcticoceras* (upper Bathonian), and various arctic species of the genus *Cadoceras* (upper Bathonian and lower Callovian). With few exceptions these faunas are more or less completely represented in East Greenland, Spitsbergen, Frans Josef Land, Novaya Zemlya, and northern Siberia but are still unknown in western Canada. In the western province, the middle Bajocian is characterized uniformly by such genera as *Stephanoceras, Stemmatoceras, Teloceras, Chondroceras,* and others, which are all absent in the arctic province. No typical arctic Bathonian ammonites were found in the western province. The lower Callovian ammonite genera of western Canada as *Paracephalites, Warrenoceras, Paracadoceras, Lilloettia, Imlayoceras,* and *Kepplerites* are absent in arctic Canada, but also within the western province some differences in the lower Callovian ammonite fauna seem to exist. The genera *Paracephalites, Warrenoceras,* and *Imlayoceras* of the Fernie Group of the Rocky Mountains and Foothills have hitherto not been found in any area of British Columbia whereas *Lilloettia* and *Paracadoceras* found in British Columbia do not appear in the Fernie Group. On the other hand, close faunal and stratigraphic relationships exist between the Callovian ammonite faunas of the Fernie Group and those of the United States western Interior. A fairly rich *Cadoceras* fauna different from that of other parts of western Canada and arctic Canada is present on Vancouver Island.

Beginning with the lower Oxfordian of the Upper Jurassic, the differences between the arctic and western faunal provinces of Canada are no longer recognizable, at least on the basis of present knowledge. The ammonite genera *Cardioceras* and *Amoeboceras* of the lower and upper Oxfordian and lower Kimmeridgian respectively are uniformly distributed in both arctic and western Canada and the same applies to the upper Oxfordian–lower Kimmeridgian pelecypod guide species *Buchia concentrica.* Also in younger Upper Jurassic beds the various *Buchia* species appear widely distributed in both northern and western Canada. However, as ammonites of these beds are extremely rare, it cannot yet be stated with confidence that no different faunal provinces existed in Canada during the late Upper Jurassic.

With the exception of the corals that seem to be restricted to regions of British Columbia, no other groups

TABLE XI-7 *Distribution and succession of Jurassic guide fossils*

EPOCH	STAGES	ARCTIC ISLANDS	RICHARDSON AND BRITISH MOUNTAINS	CENTRAL YUKON TERRITORY	SOUTHERN YUKON TERRITORY	QUEEN CHARLOTTE ISLANDS	VANCOUVER ISLAND	WESTERN AND INTERIOR PARTS OF BRITISH COLUMBIA	ROCKY MOUNTAINS	SOUTHERN PLAINS
UPPER JURASSIC	Tithonian: Purbeckian s. st. (Aquilonian, upper Volgian)	Buchia fischeriana / Buchia piochii	Buchia fischeriana / Buchia piochii		Buchia fischeriana		Buchia cf. blanfordiana	B. terebratuloides / B. fischeriana / Buchia cf. blanfordiana	Buchia cf. fischeriana / Titanites occidentalis, Buchia piochii	
	Tithonian: Portlandian or lower Volgian	Dorsoplanites (Stratigraphic position doubtful)								
	Tithonian: Upper Kimmeridgian	Buchia mosquensis Buchia spp.	Buchia mosquensis Buchia spp.	Not known			Buchia mosquensis	Buchia mosquensis	Buchia mosquensis	
	Middle Kimmeridgian					Absent				Present
	Lower Kimmeridgian Upper Oxfordian	Amoeboceras sp., Buchia concentrica	Amoeboceras sp., Buchia concentrica				Buchia concentrica	Amoeboceras spp., Buchia concentrica	Amoeboceras spp., Buchia concentrica	
	Lower Oxfordian	Cardioceras aff. mirum	Cardioceras spp.	Cardioceras spp.	Absent		Cardioceras spp.	Cardioceras spp.	Cardioceras spp., Goliathiceras cf. crassum	
MIDDLE JURASSIC	Upper Callovian	Not Known	Not Known	Not Known			Not Known	Not Known	Not Known	Not Known
	Middle Callovian	Not Known	Not Known	Not Known		Not Known	Cadoceras spp.	Lilloettia lilloettensis Stenocadoceras spp. Pseudocadoceras spp.	Not Known	Not Known
	Lower Callovian	Cadoceras septentrionale / Cadoceras bodylevskyi / Kepplerites not known / Cadoceras spp.	Cadoceras septentrionale / / Kepplerites not known / Cadoceras spp.	Cadoceras? sp.		Kepplerites spp.		Kepplerites spp. Cadoceras sp., Paracadoceras sp. etc.	Imlayoceras miettense / Kepplerites mclearni / Kepplerites aff. K. tychonis / Warrenoceras henryi / Paracephalites glabrescens P. hashimotoi	K. mclearni
	Bathonian	/ Arcticoceras ishmae / Arctocephalites spp. / Cranoc. vulgaris	Cadoceras spp. / Arcticoceras kochi / Cadoceras crassum? / Arctocephalites elegans / Not Known	Arctocephalites? sp.		Not Known	Not Known	Not Known	Not Known	
	Upper Bajocian	Not Known	Cranocephalites borealis							
	Middle Bajocian	Arkelloceras spp. Inoceramus lucifer	Arkelloceras elegans, Inoceramus lucifer		Possibly present in part	Stephanoceras spp. Chondroceras spp.		Stephanoceras spp., Chondroceras spp.	Stephanoceras spp., Stemmatoceras spp., Teloceras spp., Chondroceras spp.	Present
	Lower Bajocian	Leioceras opalinum, Pseudolioceras m'clintocki O. jacksoni	Erycites cf. howelli and Pseudolioceras sp.			Not Known		Tmetoceras regleyi	Not Known	
LOWER JURASSIC	Toarcian	Pseudolioceras compactile, Catacoeloceras spinatum / Dactylioceras commune Harpoceras cf. exaratum	Pseudolioceras sp. / Dactylioceras commune Harpoceras sp.		Grammoceras aff. G. fallaciosum / ?	Harpoceras spp. Dactylioceras spp.	Harpoceras spp.	Grammoceras Phymatoceras sp. / Dactylioceras spp., Harpoceras cf. exaratum	Grammoceras boreale Phymatoceras sp. / Dactylioceras sp., Harpoceras cf. exaratum	
	Pliensbachian	Not Known	Not Known / Amaltheus stokesi / Not Known	Not Known	Not Known / Amaltheus stokesi, Arieticeras spp., Leptaleoceras sp. / Prodactylioceras sp.	Not Known / Possibly present / Fanninoceras spp. Tropidoceras	Fanninoceras Acanthopleuroceras	? / Amaltheus stokesi, Arieticeras spp., L. pseudoradians / Becheiceras cf. bechei / Platypleuroceras sp.	Pleuroceras ? / Amaltheus spp. Amaltheus stokesi / Phricodoceras sp.	Absent
	Sinemurian	Echioceras s.l. / Gleviceras sp. / / Arietites s.l.	Echioceras s.l. / Arctoasteroceras jeletzkyi, Oxynoticeras oxynotum, Gleviceras sp. / / Arietites s.l.		Probably absent / Arnioceras sp. Paracoroniceras cf. gmündense	Echioceras / Asteroceras ? / Arniotites spp.	Echioceras / Asteroceras sp. / Arniotites spp.	Echioceras sp. / / Asteroceras sp. / Arniotites spp. Coroniceras	Eoderoceras sp. / / Arietites spp. Arnioceras spp.	
	Hettangian	Not Known	Not Known		Not Known / Psiloceras cf. erugatus	Not Known	Not Known	Psil. (Curv.) columbiae Psiloceras canadense Psil. aff. planorbis	Not Known	

GSC

seem to be dependent on facies. This may be due partly to the fact that such groups have not yet been studied to the same extent as the ammonites.

Succession of Faunas

The succession of ammonites and buchias is shown in Table XI-7; the latter is based on studies mainly by J. A. Jeletzky. The succession of ammonites in the Lower Jurassic and the lower Bajocian established in various areas of Canada is in agreement with standard sequences in northwestern Europe, and the Hettangian is similar to a certain degree to that of the northeastern Alps. Wherever in Canada a more continuing section could be studied it follows the European pattern and that of other parts of the world, and accordingly the same succession of ammonite zones as in Europe can be applied to the Lower Jurassic of Canada. However, the local or regional incompleteness of the Canadian Lower Jurassic zonal sequence has to be emphasized. The absence of the Hettangian faunas so richly represented in parts of British Columbia in other areas of western and northern Canada is caused by non-deposition of beds of this age. Lower and upper Pliensbachian have now been found in western Canada and are considered to be primarily absent in other areas.

The succession of ammonite faunas and ammonite zones of the Canadian arctic in the upper Bajocian, Bathonian, and Callovian (Table XI-7) is almost the same as the succession in East Greenland established by Callomon (1959). In the middle Bajocian of western Canada, ammonite faunas follow again the northwest European pattern whereas the succession of ammonite faunas in the uppermost Bathonian and the lower Callovian of the Fernie Group in the Rocky Mountains and Foothills is almost completely the same as in the western Interior of the United States. The absence of upper Callovian ammonites in western Canada and the western Interior indicates a considerable gap in the sequence. In the Oxfordian and lower Kimmeridgian, the succession of ammonite fauna is the same as known from other parts of the world, but in the younger Upper Jurassic stages, ammonites are very rare and, if present, poorly preserved. Consequently, the subdivision of the beds concerned is based mainly on various *Buchia* species that show a zonal arrangement similar to that of other regions.

Selected References

Comprehensive lists of references, including publications by S. S. Buckman, C. H. Crickmay, H. Frebold, F. H. McLearn, P. S. Warren, and J. F. Whiteaves are given in:

Frebold, Hans
1964: Illustrations of Canadian fossils. Jurassic of western and arctic Canada; *Geol. Surv. Can.*, Paper 63–4.

Frebold, H., and Tipper, H. W.
1970: Status of the Jurassic in the Canadian Cordillera of British Columbia, Alberta, and southern Yukon; *Can. J. Earth Sci.*, vol. 7, pp. 1–22.

Other publications are:

Callomon, J. H.
1959: The ammonite zones of the Middle Jurassic beds of East Greenland; *Geol. Mag.*, vol. 96, No. 6.

Copeland, M. J.
1960: *Erymastacus bordenensis* a new Mesozoic decapod from the Canadian arctic; *Geol. Surv. Can.*, Bull. 60.

Jeletzky, J. A.
1964: Illustrations of Canadian fossils. Lower Cretaceous marine index fossils of the sedimentary Basins of western and arctic Canada; *Geol. Surv. Can.*, Paper 64-11.
1965: Late Upper Jurassic and early Lower Cretaceous fossil zones of the Canadian Western Cordillera, British Columbia; *Geol. Surv. Can.*, Bull. 103.

Plate XIX. Lower Jurassic Ammonites

Figure 1 *Eolytoceras tasekoi* Frebold. Hettangian; Taseko Lakes, British Columbia; 20059.

Figure 2 *Psiloceras* ex aff. *planorbis* (Sowerby). Hettangian; Taseko Lakes, British Columbia; 20053.

Figures 3a, b *Psiloceras canadense* Frebold. Hettangian; Taseko Lakes, British Columbia; 62504.

Figure 4 *Discamphiceras? tipperi* Frebold. Hettangian; Taseko Lakes, British Columbia; 19926.

Figure 5 *Psiloceras* (*Curviceras*) *columbiae* Frebold. Hettangian; Taseko Lakes, British Columbia; 19921.

Figure 6 *Psiloceras* (*Curviceras*) *columbiae* Frebold. Hettangian; Taseko Lakes, British Columbia.

Figure 7 *Charmasseiceras marmoreum* (Oppel). Hettangian; Taseko Lakes, British Columbia; 20056.

Figures 8a, b *Charmasseiceras marmoreum* (Oppel). Hettangian; Taseko Lakes, British Columbia; 20052.

(Plates XIX–XXII—all figures natural size)

Figure 9 *Paracaloceras multicostatum* Frebold. Hettangian; Taseko Lakes, British Columbia; 19939.

Figure 10 *Paracoroniceras* cf. *gmündense* (Oppel). Laberge Group, Sinemurian; Atlin, British Columbia; 15969.

Figure 11 *Oxynoticeras oxynotum* (Quenstedt). Upper Sinemurian; Aklavik Range, N.W.T.; 14631.

Figure 12 *Arctoasteroceras jeletzkyi* Frebold. Upper Sinemurian; Aklavik Range, N.W.T.; 14623.

Figure 13 *Amaltheus stokesi* (Sowerby). Upper Pliensbachian; southern Yukon; 15974.

Figure 14 *Arieticeras* cf. *A. algovianum* (Oppel). Upper Pliensbachian; Telegraph Creek, British Columbia; 15989.

Figure 15 *Fanninoceras kunae* var. *latum* McLearn. Maude Formation, Pliensbachian: Queen Charlotte Islands; 9058.

Figure 16 *Fanninoceras fannini* McLearn. Maude Formation, Pliensbachian; Queen Charlotte Islands; 6493.

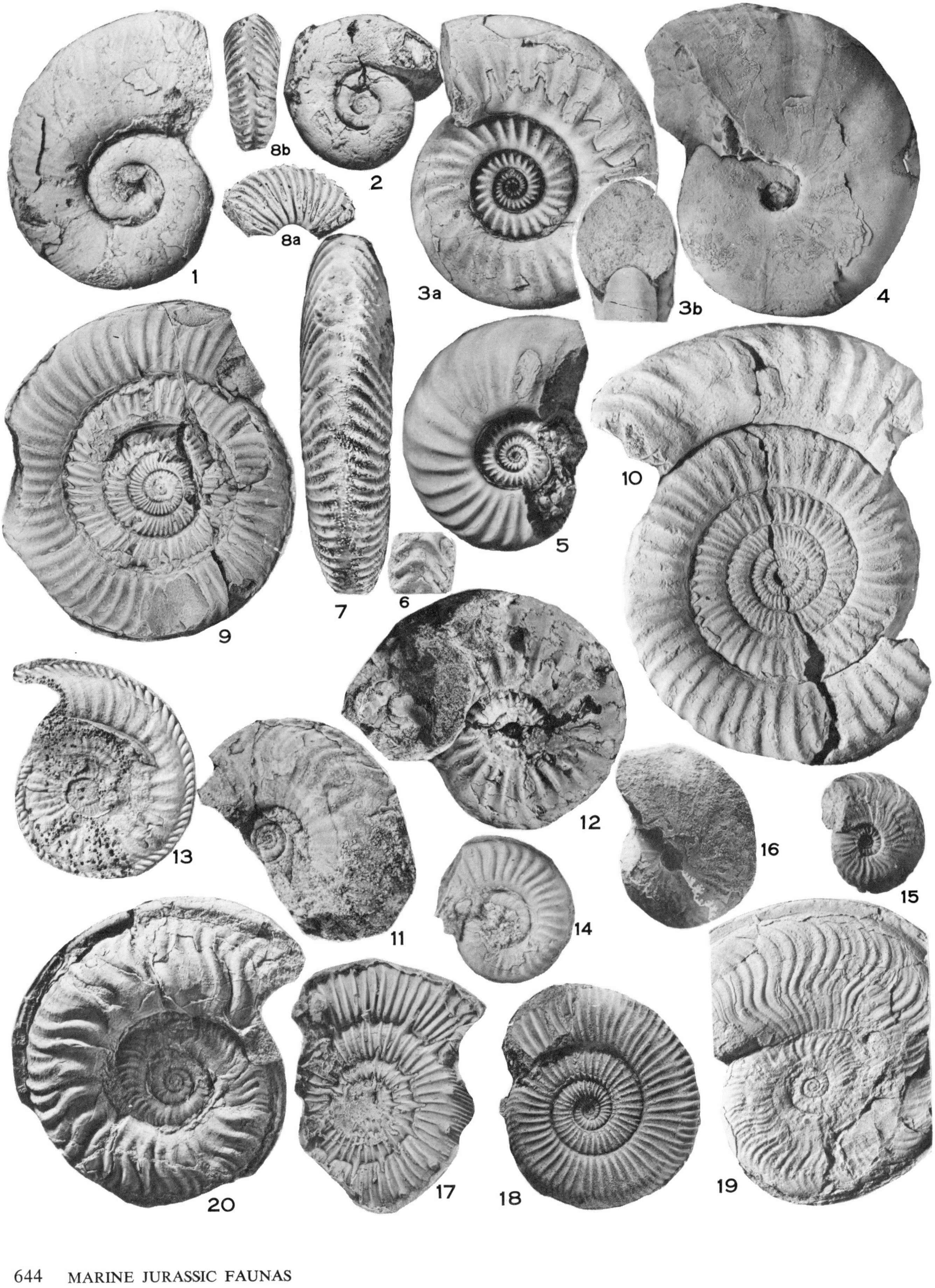

1 8b 2 3a 3b 4 8a 9 7 5 6 10 12 13 11 16 15 14 20 17 18 19

1
2
3
4
5
6
7
8
9
10
11
12
13
14

Figure 17 *Catacoeloceras spinatum* (Frebold). Wilkie Point Formation, Toarcian; Prince Patrick Island; 13361.

Figure 18 *Dactylioceras commune* (Sowerby). Wilkie Point Formation, Toarcian; Prince Patrick Island; 13355.

Figure 19 *Harpoceras* cf. *H. exaratum* (Young and Bird). Toarcian; Tulsequah, British Columbia; 16003.

Figure 20 *Grammoceras boreale* (Whiteaves). Laberge Group, Toarcian; southern Yukon; 9703.

PLATE XX. Middle Jurassic Ammonites and Pelecypods

Figure 1 *Stephanoceras yakounense* McLearn. Yakoun Formation, middle Bajocian; Queen Charlotte Islands; 9057.

Figure 2 *Normannites canadensis* McLearn. Yakoun Formation, middle Bajocian; Queen Charlotte Islands; 9019.

Figure 3 *Zemistephanus funteri* McLearn. Yakoun Formation, middle Bajocian; Queen Charlotte Islands; 9007.

Figure 4 *Chondroceras allani* (McLearn). Middle Bajocian; Tulsequah, British Columbia; 16024.

Figure 5 *Warrenoceras rierdonense* (Imlay). Fernie Group, lower Callovian; Alberta; 14693.

Figure 6 *Kosmoceras* (*Gulielmiceras*) *knechteli* Imlay. Lower Callovian; Esterhazy Shaft, Saskatchewan; 14696.

Figure 7 *Torricellites? spinosum* Frebold. Fernie Group, lower Callovian; Alberta; 14710.

Figure 8 *Kepplerites newcombii* (Whiteaves). Yakoun Formation, lower Callovian; Queen Charlotte Islands; 5990.

Figure 9 *Cobbanites* sp. indet. aff. *engleri* Frebold. Fernie Group, lower Callovian; Alberta; 12908.

Figure 10 *Kepplerites mcevoyi* (McLearn). Fernie Group, lower Callovian; Alberta; 5018.

Figure 11 *Paracephalites glabrescens* Buckman. Fernie Group, upper Bathonian or lower Callovian; Alberta; 14705.

Figure 12 *Imlayoceras miettense* Frebold. Fernie Group, lower Callovian; Alberta; 14707.

Figure 13 *Lima albertensis* McLearn. Fernie Group, upper Bathonian or lower Callovian; Alberta; 6075.

Figure 14 *Corbula munda* McLearn. Enlarged x3, Fernie Group, upper Bathonian or lower Callovian; Alberta; 6092.

PLATE XXI. Middle Jurassic Ammonites and Pelecypods

Figure 1 *Pseudolioceras m'clintocki* (Haughton). Wilkie Point Formation, lower Bajocian; Mackenzie King Island; 14658.

Figure 2 *Leioceras opalinum* (Reinecke). Wilkie Point Formation, lower Bajocian; Prince Patrick Island; 13379.

Figure 3 *Oxytoma jacksoni* (Pompeckj). Wilkie Point Formation; lower Bajocian; Prince Patrick Island; 13390.

Figures 4a-c *Arkelloceras tozeri* Frebold. Wilkie Point Formation, probably middle Bajocian; Prince Patrick Island; 13404.

Figure 5 *Cranocephalites borealis* (Spath). Bug Creek Formation, upper Bajocian; Aklavik Range, N.W.T.; 15103.

Figure 6 *Cranocephalites vulgaris* Spath. Wilkie Point Formation, lower Bathonian; Prince Patrick Island; 13398.

Figure 7 *Arctocephalites elegans* Spath. Bathonian; Richardson Mountains; 15108.

Figure 8 *Arcticoceras kochi* Spath. Bathonian; Porcupine River, Yukon; 15117.

Figure 9 *Arcticoceras ishmae* (Keyserling). Wilkie Point Formation, Bathonian; Prince Patrick Island; 15120.

Figure 10 *Cadoceras septentrionale* Frebold. Savik Formation, Callovian; Axel Heiberg Island; 17657.

Figure 11 *Cadoceras* cf. *falsum* Voronets. Savik Formation, Callovian; Axel Heiberg Island; 17659.

Figure 12 *Cadoceras canadense* Frebold. Callovian; Aklavik Range, N.W.T.; 17664.

PLATE XXII. Upper and Middle Jurassic Ammonites and Pelecypods

Figure 1 *Titanites occidentalis* Frebold. Lower Kootenay Sandstone, Portlandian; Fernie, British Columbia.

Figure 2 *Buchia* cf. *blanfordiana* (Stoliczka). Uppermost Portlandian?; Vancouver Island; 16584.

Figures 3a, b *Buchia fischeri* (d'Orbigny). Aquilonian; Aklavik Range, N.W.T.; 17991.

Figure 4 *Buchia piochii* (Gabb) var. *mniovnikensis* (Pavlow). Mould Bay Formation, upper Portlandian; Prince Patrick Island; 17120.

Figure 5 *Buchia mosquensis* (von Buch) sensu lato. Middle Kimmeridgian to lower Portlandian; Dave Lord Ridge, Yukon; 17990.

Figure 6 *Buchia mosquensis* (von Buch) sensu lato. Middle Kimmeridgian to lower Portlandian; Richardson Mountains, Yukon; 17989.

Figures 7a, b *Buchia concentrica* (Sowerby) var. *erringtoni* (Gabb). Tyaughton Lake, British Columbia; 17012.

Figure 8 *Pleuromya postculminata* McLearn. Fernie Group, upper Bathonian or lower Callovian; Alberta; 6089.

Figure 9 *Oxytoma blairmorensis* McLearn. Fernie Group, lower Callovian; Alberta; 6050.

Figure 10 *Sonninia gracilis* (Whiteaves). Fernie Group, middle Bajocian; Alberta; 4809.

Figure 11 *Inoceramus lucifer* Eichwald. Wilkie Point Formation, probably middle Bajocian; Prince Patrick Island; 13417.

Figure 12 *Cardioceras canadense* Whiteaves. Fernie Group, Oxfordian; British Columbia; 7437.

Figure 13 *Cardioceras* (*Scarburgiceras*) *alphacordatum* Spath. Fernie Group, Oxfordian; Alberta; 13892.

Figure 14 *Amoeboceras* sp. indet. Mould Bay Formation; upper Oxfordian or lower Kimmeridgian; Mackenzie King Island; 15131.

1
3
2
4c
4b
5
6
4a
9
7
11
10
8
12

1
2
3b
4
5
26987
3a
6
7a
8
7b
10
9
13
11
12
14

CRETACEOUS MACROFAUNAS

by J. A. Jeletzky

Considerable parts of the Cretaceous System are present throughout much of western and arctic Canada, the faunal successions of which are shown in Table XI-8. None of these faunal successions, however, is complete, and the missing standard zones and stages vary greatly from one region to another.

Only a few groups of macrofossils are practically useful for subdivision of the Canadian Cretaceous rocks. As in some other systems, ammonites are by far the most useful index fossils but are rather unevenly distributed. They may be extremely rare or absent in the Neocomian (Berriasian to Aptian) part of the system, and there less reliable index fossils such as species of *Inoceramus* and *Buchia* (also known as *Aucella*) have to be used. These two pelecypod genera occur in abundance and variety in most marine facies. The remaining pelecypods, including the Trigoniidae, appear to be far too long-ranging or facies-bound to be useful. Although valuable for intercontinental correlation, crinoids and belemnites are too rare and restricted in occurrence for regional or interregional zonal indices. The sponges, echinoderms, corals, brachiopods, gastropods, and crustaceans are very rare and little understood.

In non-marine rocks, reptiles, especially dinosaurs, have been found to be the best index fossils available, but they are rather unevenly distributed and generally rare. More common, but often less reliable, are non-marine mollusca, plants, and ostracoda.

Boundaries and Major Divisions

The lower boundary of the system is drawn at the base of the Berriasian stage which includes the *Berriasella grandis* zone. The upper boundary is placed at the top of the Maestrichtian stage where ammonites, belemnites, inocerami, dinosaurs, and other Mesozoic index fossils apparently disappear completely (Jeletzky, 1962; Jeletzky and Clemens, 1965). The two-fold subdivision of the Cretaceous System is followed. The boundary between the Lower and Upper Cretaceous is drawn between the Albian and Cenomanian stages as defined by Muller and Schenck (1943), Cobban and Reeside (1952, p. 104), and Jeletzky (1968). In the western Interior region this boundary is placed tentatively between *Neogastroplites mclearni* and *N. septimus* zones.

A close similarity of all boreal marine faunas of Canada with those of northern Eurasia permits general use of the international standard stages based on West European fossil zones and type localities. Furthermore, it is easy to use these stages in the non-marine sequences because of widespread intertonguing with marine rocks. A separate stage scale has recently been proposed by Russell (1964) for the non-marine Cretaceous of the western Interior region. These stages are used as regional zones.

The international standard stages can also be used in the North Pacific faunal realm. However, the North Pacific faunas of Canada have to be correlated with the mixed faunas of South America, India, and Madagascar before they can be correlated with the international standard stages and zones (Popenoe, *et al.*, 1960) and regional zones of other parts of Canada.

Marine Faunal Realms

On the whole, the Cretaceous was a time of a progressively increasing differentiation of marine paleozoogeographical provinces or faunal realms. This differentiation was caused by a gradual but major redistribution of land and sea areas in western and arctic Canada during the Lower Cretaceous, followed in the late Upper Cretaceous by a gradual retreat of the seas beyond the present shoreline, completed apparently before the end of the Maestrichtian.

Two principal faunal realms existed throughout Cretaceous time. The North Pacific realm was dominated by marine faunas closely related to those of the Indo-Pacific region, Tethyan, and Andean Geosynclines (Jeletzky, 1965). Its faunas are, however, peculiar in that a number of endemic taxa are present, e.g., *Homolsomites, Shasticrioceras, Shastoceras, Buchia tolmatschowi, Buchia pacifica,* as well as others diagnostic of the Pacific slope of Siberia, Japan, Alaska, and California–Oregon region, e.g., *Inoceramus* ex gr. *naumanni–orientalis–schmidti, Inoceramus colonicus,* and yet others diagnostic of the boreal realm, e.g., *Tollia, Subcraspedites, Simbirskites, Hoplocrioceras, Tropaeum,* and a number of *Buchia* species. The North Pacific realm was restricted to the western Cordilleran region and to the Peace River region during Berriasian to Barremian time. Thereafter it was restricted to the western Cordillera region alone.

The Boreal faunal realm characterized by marine faunas almost identical to those of northern Eurasia was restricted to the Arctic Archipelago and parts of the mainland in northern Yukon during Berriasian to Aptian time. In Albian and Upper Cretaceous time it also included most of the Interior Plains and eastern Cordillera region. On the basis of the generally minor differences between the Albian and Upper Cretaceous marine faunas of the western Interior region and those of arctic Canada, two groups of marine basins may be distinguished in this realm.

SERIES	STAGES	N. PACIFIC FAUNAL REALM–W. CORDILLERAN BASINS			BOREAL FAUNAL REALM – ARCTIC BASINS		
		BRITISH COLUMBIA			YUKON TERRITORY		
		QUEEN CHARLOTTE ISLANDS	VANCOUVER ISLAND AND GULF ISLANDS	WESTERN MAINLAND	PORCUPINE PLATEAU	RICHARDSON MOUNTAINS PEEL PLATEAU	WESTERN AND NORTHERN ARCTIC ARCHIPELAGO
UPPER CRETACEOUS	MAESTRICHTIAN	Unknown	Unknown non-marine faunas ? — ? *Pachydiscus suciaensis* *Pseudophyllites indra*	Unknown non-marine faunas	Unknown non-marine faunas	Unknown	Unknown non-marine faunas
	CAMPANIAN		*Hoplitoplacenticeras vancouverense* *Inoceramus schmidti* ? *I. orientalis* / *Bostrychoceras elongatum*	*Inoceramus* cf. *schmidti*	? — ? — ?		*Inoceramus* ex gr. *lobatus*:
	SANTONIAN		? *Diplomoceras ? subcompressum* *I. naumanni* ? *I.* cf. *japonicus* ?		*Inoceramus* cf. *steenstrupi* ? ? — ?		*S. (Clioscaphites)* cf. *montanensis* *Scaphites* cf. *depressus*
	CONIACIAN			Unknown non-marine faunas	Unknown	*Scaphites* cf. *preventricosus*	Unknown non-marine faunas
	TURONIAN	*Inoceramus* cf. *labiatus*	Absent		*Inoceramus lamarcki* s. lato Unknown	Unknown *Scaphites* cf. *delicatulus* *Inoceramus* cf. *labiatus*	
	CENOMANIAN	*Turrilites (Euturrilites)* sp. indet.			*Inoceramus* cf. *dunveganensis*	*Inoceramus crippsi* s. lato *Inoceramus* cf. *dunveganesis*	*Inoceramus* cf. *pictus*
LOWER CRETACEOUS	ALBIAN	*Mortoniceras (Deiradoceras)* spp., *Desmoceras (Pseudo-ughligella) dawsoni* *Cleoniceras (Grycia?) perezianum, Desmoceras (Pseudoughligella)* cf. *alamoense* *Brewericeras hulenense* *Douvilleiceras spiniferum* *Brewericeras lecontei* subsp. *whiteavesi*	Unknown non-marine faunas ?	*Mortoniceras* (s. lato) sp. indet. *Cleoniceras (Grycia?) perezianum, Desmoceras (Pseudoughligella)* cf. *alamoense* ? *Brewericeras hulenense* *Douvilleiceras* cf. *spiniferum* ? *Brewericeras lecontei* s. lato	Unknown *Beudanticeras affine*: *Arcthoplites* cf. *belli* *Sonneratia* (s. lato) ? sp. A	Unknown *Posidonia?* cf. *nahwisi*, *Neogastroplites ?* sp. indet. ? Unknown ? *Gastroplites?* spp. indet ? ? *Beudanticeras affine*: *Arcthoplites* cf. *talkeetnanum* *Arcthoplites* cf. *belli* Probably present *Sonneratia* (s. lato) ? sp. A	Unknown non-marine faunas ? ? ? *Gastroplites?* n. sp. aff. *liardense* ? ? *Gastroplites* aff. *canadensis* "*Gastroplites*" n. sp. A ? ? ? *Beudanticeras affine*: *Arcthoplites belli* *Cleoniceras* aff. *subbaylei*
	APTIAN	Unknown		*Acanthohoplites* cf *reesidei* ? ? ? *Aconeceras* ex gr. *nisus*	Absent ? ? ? *Aucellina* ex gr. *aptiensis-caucasica*	Absent ? *Aucellina* ex gr. *aptiensis-caucasica*: *Tropaeum australe*, *Tropaeum* n. sp. aff. *arcticum* ? ? ? ?*Tropaeum* ? cf. *hillsi* ? ? ? ? Unknown	Absent ? ? ? *Inoceramus* cf. *labiatiformis* *Tropaeum ?* sp. ? ? ?
	BARREMIAN	*Heteroceras (Heteroceras)* sp. *Shasticrioceras* cf. *pontiente*	? ? *Heteroceras* cf. *helicoceroides*, *Phyllopachyceras infundibulum* *Argonauticeras* cf. *argonautarum* *Eulytoceras* cf. *inequalicostatum*	? ? ? *Quoiecchia* ex gr. *aliciae*: *Costidiscus* cf. *striatosulcatus*, *Ancyloceras* cf. *durrelli* *Shasticrioceras* cf. *hesperium*, *Hoplocrioceras* ex gr. *laeviusculum*, *Acrioceras* ex gr. *starrkingi*	? ? Unknown	*Acroteuthis?* cf. *A. mitchelli* and *A. kernensis* *Hoplocrioceras* n. sp. aff. *laeviusculum*, *Acrioceras* aff. *starkingi* ? *Crioceratites emerici* *Crioceratites* cf. *latum*, *Oxyteuthis* cf. *jasikowi*	Unknown non-marine faunas
	HAUTERIVIAN	*Inoceramus colonicus*	*Shasticrioceras* sp. *Simbirskites* cf. *broadi* *Holisites lucasi* *Homolsomites oregonensis*	*Inoceramus colonicus*: *Craspedodiscus* cf. *discofalcatus* *Holisites lucasi* *Speetoniceras agnessense* ? *Homolsomites oregonensis*	*Simbirskites (Simbirskites)* ex gr *progredicus* Unknown	*Acroteuthis* ex aff. *conoides*: *Craspedodiscus* cf. *discofalcatus* *Simbirskites* cf. *kleini* *Acroteuthis* cf. *conoides* Unknown	? ? ? ?
	VALANGINIAN	*Buchia crassicollis* Absent	*Buchia crassicollis* Unknown *Buchia pacifica* *Buchia tolmatschowi*	*Buchia crassicollis* *Buchia inflata* and var. *crassa* *Buchia pacifica* *Buchia tolmatschowi* s. lato	*Buchia inflata*, s. lato *Buchia* n. sp. aff. *inflata* *Buchia keyserlingi* f. typ.	*Buchia* n. sp. aff. *inflata*, *Buchia bulloides* *Buchia* aff. *keyserlingi*	*Buchia inflata* / *Buchia keyserlingi*: *Homolsomites* aff. *quatsinoensis* *Euryptychites stubbendorfi* ? ? ? *Thorsteinssonoceras ellesmerensis* *Temnoptychites novosemelicus*
	BERRIASIAN		*Buchia uncitoides* s. lato *Buchia okensis*	*Buchia uncitoides* s. lato *Berriasella* aff. *gallica* *Buchia okensis*	*B. volgensis* *B. uncitoides* *S.* cf. *payeri* *Buchia okensis* Unknown	*Buchia volgensis* *Buchia okensis* Unknown	Unknown ? ? ? *Buchia okensis*, *S.* aff. *suprasubdites*
JUR.			Hiatus	*Buchia terebratuloides* var. *subinflata*	*Buchia* cf. *unschensis*	*Buchia* cf. *unschensis*	? ? ? *Subcraspedites* n. sp. *Buchia* ex gr. *uncitoides* ? ? ?

Series	Stages	BOREAL FAUNAL REALM—WESTERN INTERIOR BASINS: NORTHWEST-TERRITORIES: ANDERSON PLAIN Including Peel and Arctic Red R. areas	NORTHWEST-TERRITORIES: MACKENZIE AND LIARD RIVERS	NE. BRITISH COLUMBIA: PEACE RIVER LOWLAND, ROCKY MOUNTAIN FOOTHILLS	ALBERTA: ROCKY MOUNTAIN FOOTHILLS, ALBERTA PLAIN	SASK. AND MAN.: SASKATCHEWAN AND MANITOBA PLAINS
UPPER CRETACEOUS	MAESTRICHTIAN	Unknown	Unknown	Unknown	*Tyrannosaurus, Ankylosaurus, Triceratops, Thescelosaurus, Leptoceratops, Unio stantoni and Viviparus prudentius willovensis* *Albertosaurus, Edmontosaurus, Hypacrosaurus, Anchiceratops, Saurolophus, Unio stantoni, Viviparus westoni, Lioplacodes sanctamariensis* and *Polygyra parvula*	Unknown *Baculites grandis, Discoscaphites* ex gr. *roanensis* *Hoploscaphites plenus, Baculites baculus, Inoceramus fibrosus*
	CAMPANIAN	?—?—?	?—?—?	?—?—? *Baculites* cf. *obtusus* ?—?—? *Hoploscaphites hippocrepis*	*Hoploscaphites nodosus* *Gorgosaurus, Corythosaurus, Lambeosaurus, Kritosaurus, Viviparus conradi*; *Baculites obtusus* and var. *mclearni* *Brachyceratops, Viviparus conradi*	*Baculites compressus* s. lato: *Hoploscaphites brevis, H. quadrangularis*; *Hoploscaphites nodosus* *Hoploscaphites gilli* *Hoploscaphites hippocrepis, Haresiceras natronense*
	SANTONIAN	*Inoceramus* ex gr. *lobatus* ?—?—?	*Inoceramus* ex gr. *lobatus* *Scaphites* cf. *saxitonianus* ?—?—?	?—?—? *Inoceramus* ex gr. *lobatus*: *Scaphites (Desmoscaphites)* spp. *S. (Clioscaphites) montanensis* *S. (Clioscaphites) vermiformis*; *I. cordiformis* *Scaphites depressus*	*Scaphites (Desmoscaphites)* spp. *S. (Clioscaphites) choteauensis* *S. (Clioscaphites) montanensis* *S. (Scaphites) vermiformis*; *I. cordiformis* *Scaphites depressus*	*Inoceramus* ex gr. *lobatus*: *S. (Clioscaphites) montanensis* *S. (Clioscaphites) vermiformis* *Scaphites depressus*
	CONIACIAN	Absent	Absent ?	*Inoceramus involutus* (= *I. umbonatus*) *Scaphites ventricosus* s. str. *S. preventricosus* and *I. deformis*	*Inoceramus involutus* (= *I. umbonatus*) *Scaphites ventricosus* s. str. *S. preventricosus* and *I. deformis*	*Scaphites ventricosus* s. str. *S. preventricosus* and *Actinocamax* n. sp.
	TURONIAN		*Watinoceras reesidei, Scaphites delicatulus, I. labiatus*	*I. lamarcki, Prionocyclus* s. lato: *P.* aff. *wyomingensis*; *Scaphites warreni*; *P. (Collignoniceras) hyatti*; *P. (Collignoniceras) woollgari* s. lato *Watinoceras, I. labiatus*: *Watinoceras reesidei*; *Baculites* cf. *gracile*	*I. lamarcki, Prionocyclus* s. lato; *Ostrea lugubris*: *P. wyomingensis*; *Scaphites warreni*; *P. (Collignoniceras) woollgari* s. lato *Watinoceras, I. labiatus*: *Watinoceras reesidei*; *Baculites* cf. *gracile*	Unknown *Prionocyclus (C.) hyatti* *Actinocamax manitobensis* s. lato, *"Metoicoceras"* sp. *Inoceramus labiatus*
	CENOMANIAN		Probably present in part at least	*Inoceramus* aff. *I. fragilis* *Dunveganoceras* zone: *D. hagei*; *D.* cf. *parvum*; *D. albertense*; *D.* cf. *conditum* *Unio dowlingi*: *I. dunveganensis*; *I. rutherfordi*; *Acanthoceras athabascense* ?—?—? *N. septimus, Irenicoceras bahani* ?—?—? *Neogastroplites* zone: *Neogastroplites mclearni*	Unknown *Dunveganoceras* spp. *Inoceramus corpulentus* Unknown *N. mclearni*; Absent	*Inoceramus* cf. *dunveganensis* *Inoceramus* cf. *mcconnelli*
LOWER CRETACEOUS	ALBIAN	?—?—? *Beudanticeras affine* *Beudanticeras glabrum* *Colvillia crassicostata* *Sonneratia* (s. lato) ? sp. A Absent	*Neogastroplites cornutus* *Gastroplites ? liardense* *Gastroplites* spp. *Beudanticeras affine*: *Arcthoplites mcconnelli*; *Arcthoplites irenense*; *Arcthoplites belli*; *"Lemuroceras* cf. *indicum"*; *Cleoniceras* cf. *subbaylei*; *Sonneratia* cf. *kitchini*	*Neogastroplites americanus* *Posidonia ? nahwisi*: *Neogastroplites cornutus*; *Neogastroplites selwyni* ?—?—? *Gastroplites*: *Gastroplites ? liardense*; *Gastroplites* cf. *cantianus*; *Gastroplites canadensis*, etc. *Beudanticeras affine*: *Arcthoplites mcconnelli*; *Arcthoplites irenense*; *Arcthoplites belli*; *"Lemuroceras* cf. *indicum"*; *Astarte natosini* *Protoelliptio biornatus, Viviparus murrayensis, Lioplacodes bituminis* ?	*Eupera onestae* *Protoelliptio douglassi* *Protoelliptio hamili*	Unknown non-marine faunas ?
	APTIAN	?—?—? *Aucellina* ex gr. *aptiensis* *Tropaeum* sp. ? ?—?—?	Absent	Unknown non-marine faunas?	*Tritigonia natosini* ?—?—?	
	BARREMIAN	Absent			Absent	
	HAUTERIVIAN					
	VALANGINIAN			*Buchia* n. sp. aff. *inflata*: *Homolsomites* cf. and aff. *quatsinoensis*; *Homolsomites* cf. *giganteus* ?—?—? *Polyptychites* cf. *keyserlingi* ? *Tollia* cf. *tolli*		
	BERRIASIAN			*Buchia* cf. *uncitoides* *Buchia okensis* Unknown		
JUR.		Unknown	Absent	*Buchia* cf. *fischeriana, B. piochii*	Unknown	Unknown

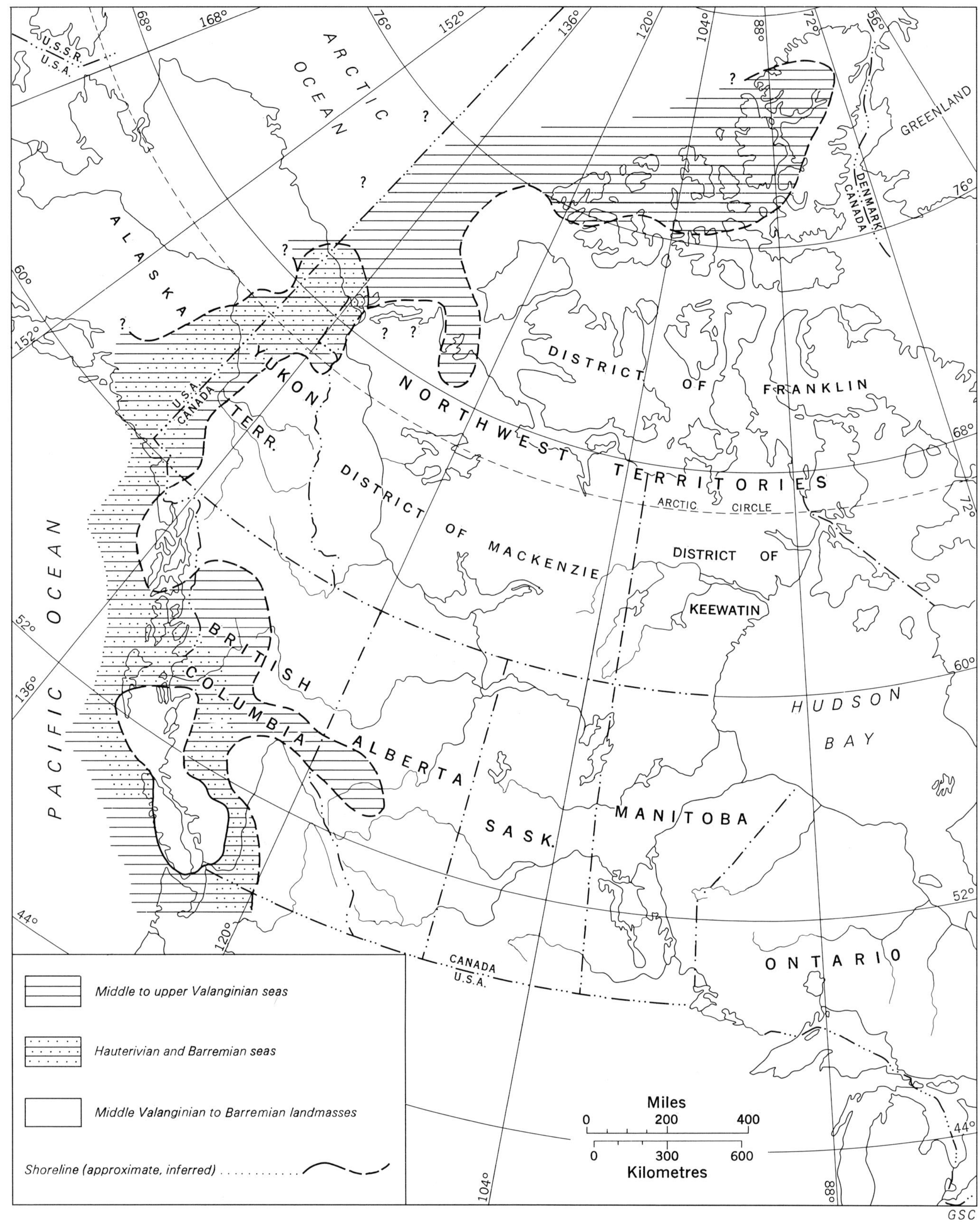

FIGURE XI-2. Inferred maximum extent of Lower Cretaceous (Berriasian to Barremian) seas in western and arctic Canada.

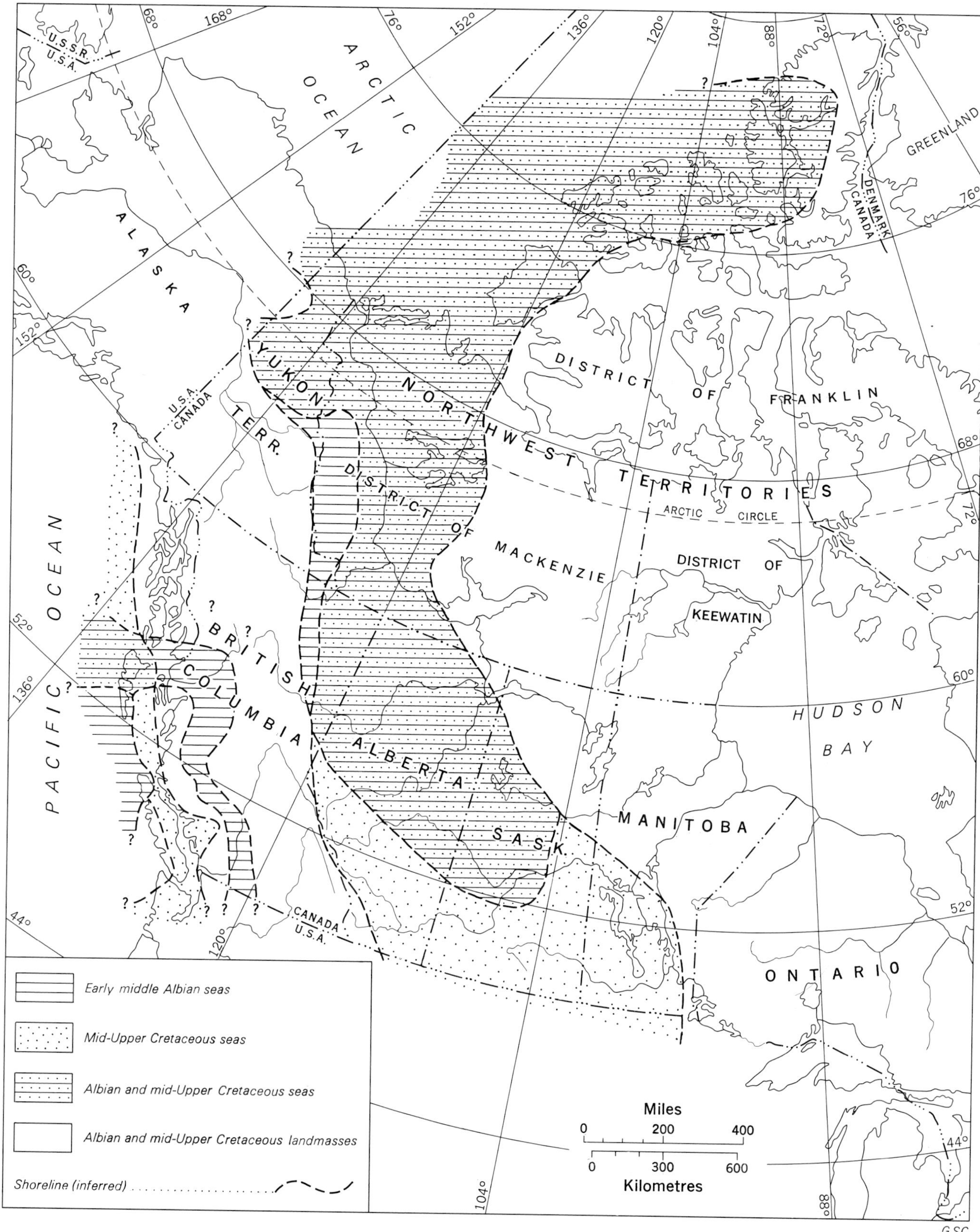

FIGURE XI-3. Inferred maximum extent of Early middle Albian and mid-Upper Cretaceous seas in western and arctic Canada.

A characteristic feature of most boreal Cretaceous faunas in Canada is their lack of diversity; they are, as a rule, dominated by only a few, or even a single, molluscan species occurring in great abundance. This extreme faunal depauperation was probably caused by a relative coldness of water and abundance of silt and clay particles compared to more southerly regions of North America and to the North Pacific realm.

The marine faunas of the North Pacific realm contain a great variety of ammonite, pelecypod, and gastropod species and genera. This is especially true of the mid- to late Upper Cretaceous faunas of the Nanaimo Group (Usher, 1952; Whiteaves, 1876-1903) on Vancouver Island.

Even the earliest Cretaceous, Berriasian, marine faunas of the western Cordillera and Peace River regions differ markedly from their arctic counterparts in the presence of Tethyan ammonites such as *Berriasella, Spiticeras, Neocomites,* and marked endemism of *Buchia* species (Jeletzky, 1964, 1965). However, these endemisms are strongly tempered by the presence of a number of species and genera common to the boreal and North Pacific realms which permit reasonably accurate zonal correlations of their Berriasian faunas. The same conditions persisted through Valanginian, Hauterivian, and Barremian times.

The relatively easy exchange of the Berriasian to Barremian marine faunas between the western Cordillera, Peace River, and arctic regions of Canada was facilitated by the existence of at least two apparently more or less narrow seaways as shown in Figure XI-2. Dawson Strait apparently extended from the Kluane Lake–St. Elias area into the Dawson City area, and thence into the northern Yukon and northern Richardson Mountains. Vanderhoof Strait extended from the headwaters of Skeena River into the Carbon Creek area connecting Bowser and Peace River Basins (Fig. XI-2). The inferred maximum extent and general configuration of the Berriasian to Valanginian seas of western and arctic Canada is exemplified by those of the mid- to late Valanginian time; Berriasian and Lower Valanginian seas were similarly distributed but somewhat less widespread. A strong regression resulted in an apparently complete withdrawal of the Hauterivian seas from the Peace River region and their restriction to the depositional troughs in western Cordillera, northern Yukon, and northern Richardson Mountains. The Barremian seas were apparently as extensive as the Hauterivian seas, except that they also penetrated at times into the Peace River region via Vanderhoof Strait (Jeletzky and Tipper, 1968).

In the western Cordillera, Aptian seas were even more restricted than those of Hauterivian–Barremian time. So far as known, they were limited by strong early Aptian uplifts of Vanderhoof and Dawson Straits. However, in northern Yukon and Richardson Mountains Aptian seas were almost as widespread as the Barremian. They probably extended along the Arctic coast to connect directly with the Aptian seas of the European arctic. This radically new configuration of Aptian land and seas (Warren and Stelck, 1961) was similar to that of early middle Albian time (Fig. XI-3), except that the arctic Aptian seas apparently did not extend south beyond Dawson City area, southern Richardson Mountains and a narrow belt of the Arctic coast between the Mackenzie Delta and Darnley Bay area. The complete isolation of the Aptian western Cordilleran marine basins from those of the arctic and western Interior regions persisted throughout Albian and Upper Cretaceous time and is reflected by almost total dissimilarity of the faunas. Except for the extremely rare occurrence of *Arcthoplites* ex gr. *belli* in the *Brewericeras hulenense* fauna of Queen Charlotte Islands (Jones, Murphy, and Packard, 1965; McLearn, *in press)* and the occurrence of *Inoceramus* cf. *labiatus* in the Honna and Skidegate Formations of the same area, the North Pacific and Boreal realms of Canada lack any common species following the Barremian whereas the western Cordilleran basins have a great many species in common with Japan, India, Pacific coast of Siberia, California, etc.

The western Interior boreal basins were connected with the Gulf of Mexico Tethyan seas as early as the middle Albian (Warren and Stelck, 1961). This connection persisted thereafter at least until late Santonian–early Campanian time and possibly into Maestrichtian time. The rather restricted Pacific Upper Cretaceous transgression probably began in Santonian time, except in Queen Charlotte Islands but the western Interior Upper Cretaceous transgression apparently reached its maximum already in lower Turonian (*Inoceramus labiatus*) time.

Selected References

Most of the older references have been omitted. They can be found in bibliographies attached to the reports of McLearn and Kindle (1950) or of the writer.

Cobban, W. A., and Reeside, J. B., Jr.

1952: Correlation of the Cretaceous formations of the western Interior of the United States; *Bull. Geol. Soc. Am.*, vol. 63, pp. 1011–1044, 2 figs., 1 pl.

Jeletzky, J. A.

1962: The allegedly Danian dinosaur-bearing rocks of the globe and the problem of the Mesozoic–Cenozoic Boundary; *J. Paleontol.*, vol. 36, No. 5, pp. 1005–1018, 2 figs., 1 pl.

1964: Illustrations of Canadian fossils. Lower Cretaceous marine index fossils of the sedimentary basins of western and arctic Canada; *Geol. Surv. Can.*, Paper 64-11, 100 pp., 36 pls., 1 table.

1965: Late Upper Jurassic and early Lower Cretaceous fossil zones of the Canadian Western Cordillera, British Columbia; *Geol. Surv. Can.*, Bull. 103, 70 pp., 22 pls., 3 figs.

1968: Macrofossil zones of the marine Cretaceous rocks of the Canadian western Interior and their correlation with the European and the United States western interior zones and stages; *Geol. Surv. Can.*, Paper 67–72.

Jeletzky, J. A., and Clemens, W. A.

1965: Comments on Cretaceous Eutheria, Lance *Scaphites*, and *Inoceramus?* ex gr. *tegulatus; J. Paleontol.*, vol. 39, No. 5, pp. 952–959.

Jeletzky, J. A., and Tipper, H. W.
1968: Upper Jurassic and Cretaceous rocks of Taseko Lakes map-area and their bearing on the geological history of southwestern British Columbia; *Geol. Surv. Can.*, Paper 67-54.

Jones, D. L., Murphy, M. A., and Packard, E. L.
1965: The Lower Cretaceous (Albian) ammonite genera *Leconteites* and *Brewericeras; U.S. Geol. Surv.*, Prof. Paper 503-F, pp. F1-F21, 11 pls., 17 figs.

McLearn, F. H.
In press: Ammonoids of the Lower Cretaceous Sandstone Member of the Haida Formation, Skidegate Inlet, Queen Charlotte Islands; *Geol. Surv. Can.*, Bull. 188.

McLearn, F. H., and Kindle, E. D.
1950: Geology of northeastern British Columbia; *Geol. Surv. Can.*, Mem. 259, 236 pp., 8 pls., 1 map, 16 figs., 6 tables.

Muller, S. W., and Schenck, H. G.
1943: Standard of Cretaceous System; *Bull. Am. Assoc. Petrol. Geol.*, vol. 27, No. 3, pp. 262–278, 7 figs.

Popenoe, W. P., Imlay, R. W., and Murphy, M. A.
1960: Correlation of the Cretaceous formations of the Pacific Coast (United States and northwestern Mexico); *Bull. Geol. Soc. Am.*, vol. 71, pp. 1491–1540, 5 figs., 1 pl.

Russell, L. S.
1964: Cretaceous non-marine faunas of northwestern North America; *Roy. Ont. Museum, Univ. Toronto*, Contrib. 61, 24 pp.

Usher, J. L.
1952: Ammonite faunas of the Upper Cretaceous rocks of Vancouver Island, British Columbia; *Geol. Surv. Can.*, Bull. 21, 182 pp., 31 pls., 4 figs., 3 tables.

Warren, P. S., and Stelck, C. R.
1961: Pacific floodings of the Canadian Rocky Mountain area. *Proc. Pacific Sci. Congr. Pacific Sci. Assoc. 8th*, vol. 12, Geol. and Geophys., pp. 50–57, 8 maps (on 4 pls.).
In press: Significance of the Cretaceous fossil succession of western Canada *in* Cretaceous Symposium *Intern. Geol. Congr. 20th*, Mexico City, vol. III.

Whiteaves, J. F.
1876-1903: On invertebrate fossils of the coal-bearing deposits of the Queen Charlotte, Vancouver, and Gulf Islands; *Geol. Surv. Can.*, Mesozoic Fossils, vol. 1, pts. 1-5, 415 pp., 51 pls., 27 text-figs.

Plate XXIII. Early Lower Cretaceous (Berriasian and Valanginian) Fossils, North Pacific and Boreal Realms

Figures 1a-1b *Acroteuthis subquadratus* (Roemer). Upper Valanginian; Northwest Territories; 17253.

Figures 2a-2c *Buchia inflata* (Toula) var. *crassa* (Pavlow). Mid-Valanginian; British Columbia; 17333.

Figures 3a-3d *Buchia tolmatschowi* (Sokolov) f. typ. Lower Valanginian; British Columbia; 16623.

Figures 4a-4c *Buchia crassicollis* (Keyserling) f. typ. Upper Valanginian; British Columbia; 16659.

Figures 5a-5b *Buchia volgensis* (Lahusen) s. str. Upper Berriasian; Northwest Territories; 16601.

Figures 6a-6c *Neocomites (Neocomites?)* aff. *indomontanus* Uhlig. Middle Valanginian; British Columbia; 17223.

Figures 7a-7b *Spiticeras (Spiticeras)* sp. indet. Juven., upper Berriasian; British Columbia; 16608.

Figures 8a-8b *Tollia (Tollia) paucicostata* (Donovan) var. Lower Valanginian; British Columbia; 16626.

Figures 9a-9c *Buchia uncitoides* (Pavlow) var. *acutistriata* (Crickmay). Upper Berriasian; British Columbia; 16603.

Figures 10a-10b *Tollia* (*Subcraspedites*) aff. *analogus* (Bogoslovsky). Upper Berriasian; Yukon; 17138.

Figures 11a-11c *Buchia keyserlingi* (Lahusen) f. typ. Lower Valanginian; Northwest Territories; 17163.

Figures 12a-12b *Tollia* (*Tollia*) *tolli* (Pavlow) var. *latelobata* Pavlow. Lower Valanginian; Northwest Territories; 17167.

Figures 13a-13c *Buchia okensis* (Pavlow). Lower Berriasian; Northwest Territories; 17122.

Figures 14a-14b *Berriasella* aff. *gallica* Mazenot. Lower Berriasian; British Columbia; 21835.

Plate XXIV. Mid-Lower Cretaceous (Hauterivian and Barremian) Fossils, North Pacific Realm

Figures 1a-1c *Speetoniceras agnessense* Imlay. x1, lower Hauterivian; British Columbia; 21821.

Figures 2a-2d *Inoceramus colonicus* Anderson. x1, Hauterivian and lower Barremian; British Columbia; 21822.

Figures 3a-3b *Costidiscus* cf. *striatisulcatus* (d'Orbigny). x1, upper Barremian; British Columbia; 21823.

Figures 4a-4b *Crioceratites (Hemihoplites)* n. sp. ex aff. *C.* (*H.*) *soulieri* (Matheron). x1, Barremian; British Columbia; 21824.

Figures 5a-5b *Heteroceras (Heteroceras)* cf. *heliceroides* (Karsten). x1, upper Barremian; British Columbia; 21825.

Figures 6a-6c *Homolsomites oregonensis* (Anderson). x1, lower Hauterivian; British Columbia; 21826.

Figure 7 *Eulytoceras* n. sp. ex aff. *E. inaequalicostatus* (d'Orbigny). x1, Barremian; British Columbia; 21827.

Figures 8a-8b *Phyllopachyceras infundibulum* (d'Orbigny). x1, Barremian; British Columbia; 21828.

Figures 9a-9c *Shasticrioceras* aff. *hesperium* Anderson. x1, Barremian; British Columbia; 21829.

Figures 10a-10c *Heteroceras* (*Heteroceras*) cf. *heliceroides* (Karsten). x1, upper Barremian; British Columbia; 21830.

Figures 11a-11b *Simbirskites* (*Hollisites*) *lucasi* Imlay. x1, lower Hauterivian; British Columbia; 21831.

(Plates XXIII–XXVIII — all figures are natural size unless otherwise stated)

1a
1b
2a
2b
3a
3b
3c
3d
4a
4b
4c
5a
5b
6a
6b
6c
7b
8a
8b
9a
9b
9c
10a
10b
11a
11b
11c
12a
12b
13a
13b
13c
14a
14b

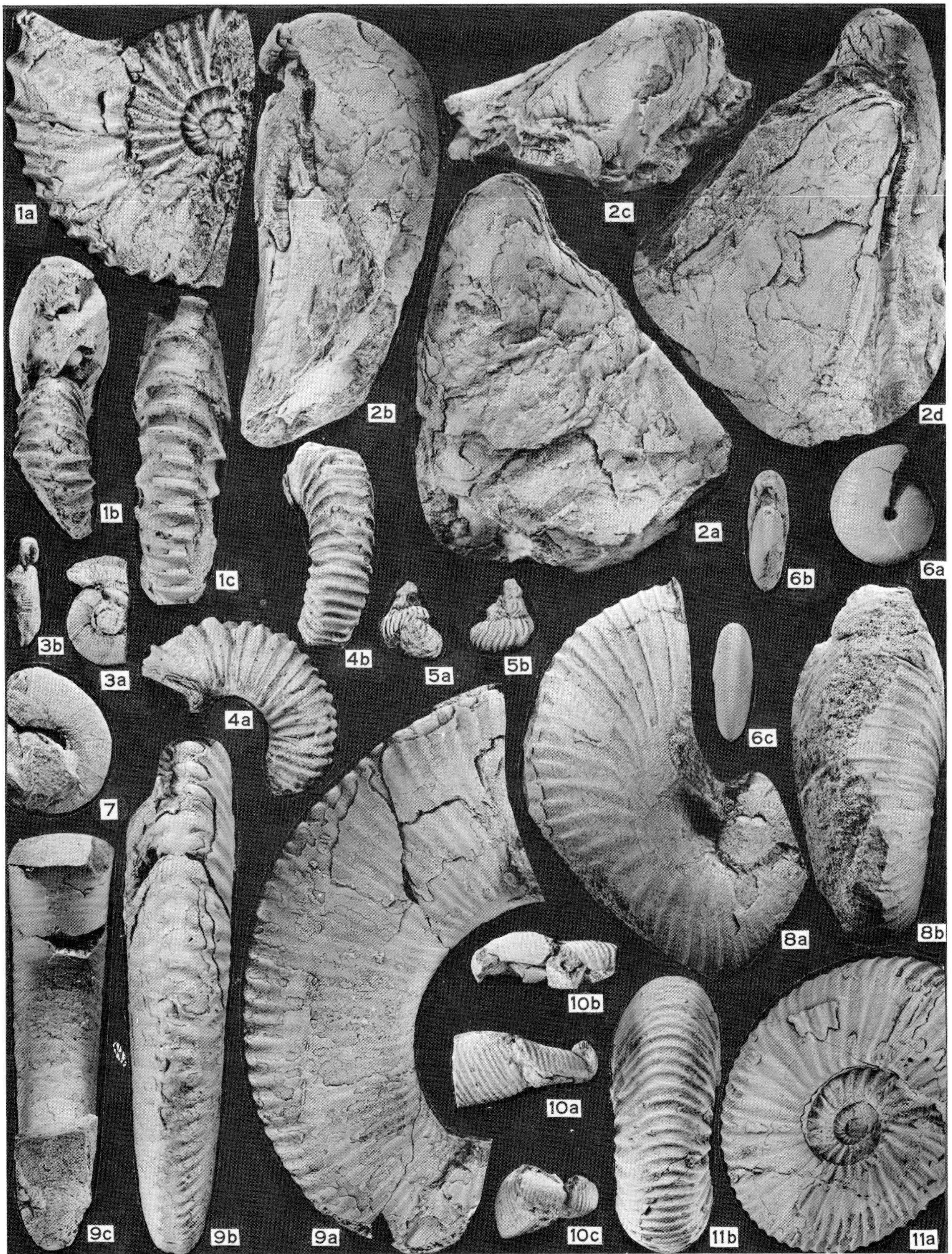
1a
1b
1c
2a
2b
2c
2d
3a
3b
4a
4b
5a
5b
6a
6b
6c
7
8a
8b
9a
9b
9c
10a
10b
10c
11a
11b

Plate XXV. Mid- to Late Lower Cretaceous (Barremian to Albian) Fossils, North Pacific to Boreal Realms

Figures 1a-1b *Douvilleiceras spiniferum* (Whiteaves). Early middle Albian; British Columbia; 21240.

Figures 2a-2b *Cleoniceras (Grycia?) perezianum* (Whiteaves). Middle Albian; British Columbia; 21233.

Figures 3a-3c *Gabbioceras?* ex gr. *wintunium* Anderson. Lower Aptian or upper Barremian; British Columbia; 21818.

Figures 4a-4c *Douvilleiceras spiniferum* (Whiteaves). Early middle Albian; British Columbia; 5993.

Figures 5a-5b *Ancyloceras (Dissimilites)* n. sp. ex aff. *A. (D.) dissimile* (d'Orbigny). Barremian; British Columbia; 21819.

Figure 6 *Argonauticeras* aff. *argonautarum* Anderson. Lower Aptian or upper Barremian; British Columbia; 21820.

Figures 7a-7b *Brewericeras hulenense* (Anderson). Early middle Albian; British Columbia; 4984.

Figures 8a-8b *Aucellina gryphaeoides* (J. deC. Sowerby). Albian; British Columbia; 17396.

Figures 9a-9b *Arcthoplites belli* (McLearn). Early middle Albian; British Columbia; 17407.

Figures 10a-10b *Gastroplites canadensis* (Whiteaves). Late middle Albian; British Columbia; 7430.

Figures 11a-11b *Aucellina aptiensis* (d'Orbigny) Pompeckj, 1901, var. *nassibianzi* Sokolov, 1908. Aptian; Mackenzie District, N.W.T.; 17319.

Figures 12a-12b *Tropaeum* n. sp. aff. *arcticum* (Stolley). Early upper Aptian; Mackenzie District, N.W.T. (?); 17322.

Figures 13a-13b *Beudanticeras affine* (Whiteaves). Lower and early middle Albian; Alberta; 17400.

Figures 14a-14b *Neogastroplites maclearni* Reeside and Cobban. Late upper Albian; Alberta; 13658.

Figure 15 *Posidonia? nahwisi* (McLearn) var. *goodrichensis* (McLearn). Early upper Albian; British Columbia; 8943.

Plate XXVI. Upper Cretaceous (Turonian to Lower Campanian) Fossils, Boreal Realm

Figures 1a-1c *Inoceramus lamarcki* Parkinson. Upper Turonian; Alberta; 21836.

Figures 2a-2b *Scaphites depressus* Reeside. Basal Santonian; Alberta; 21837.

Figure 3 *Prionocyclus (Prionocyclus) wyomingensis* Meek var. *robusta* Haas. Late upper Turonian; Alberta; 21838.

Figures 4a-4b *Watinoceras* cf. *coloradoense* (Henderson). Lower Turonian; British Columbia; 21839.

Figures 5a-5b *Haresiceras natronense* Reeside. Early lower Campanian; Manitoba; 21840.

Figure 6 *Inoceramus labiatus* (Schlotheim). Lower Turonian; Alberta; 21841.

Figures 7a-7b *Scaphites carlilensis* Morrow. Mid-upper Turonian; Manitoba; 21842.

Figures 8a-8b *Prionocyclus (Prionocyclus) wyomingensis* Meek var. *elegans* Haas. Late upper Turonian; Alberta; 21843.

Figures 9a-9b *Prionocyclus (Collignoniceras) woolgari* (Mantell). Early upper Turonian; British Columbia; 21844.

Figure 10 *Desmoscaphites* aff. *bassleri* Reeside. Uppermost Santonian; Alberta; 21845.

Plate XXVII. Upper Cretaceous (Cenomanian to Maestrichtian) Fossils, Boreal Realm

Figures 1a-1b *Ponteixites robustus* Warren. Uppermost Campanian or ? basal Maestrichtian; Saskatchewan; 21846.

Figures 2a-2b *Inoceramus coulthardi* McLearn. Basal Santonian; British Columbia; 6104.

Figure 3 *Inoceramus patootensis* de Loriol. Upper Santonian to early lower Campanian; Alberta; 21847.

Figures 4a-4b *Baculites compressus eliasi* Cobban. Uppermost Campanian; Saskatchewan; 21848.

Figure 5 *Inoceramus corpulentus* McLearn. Upper Cenomanian; British Columbia; 6109.

Figure 6 *Scaphites hippocrepis* deKay. Early lower Campanian; Saskatchewan; 21849.

Figures 7a-7b *Scaphites nodosus* Owen. Mid-upper Campanian; Saskatchewan; 5369.

Figure 8 *Inoceramus steenstrupi* de Loriol. x½, early lower Campanian and ?upper Santonian; Northwest Territories; 21851.

Figures 9a-9b *Scaphites brevis* Meek. Uppermost Campanian or ?basal Maestrichtian; Saskatchewan; 21852.

Figures 10a-10b *Scaphites (Discoscaphites)* ex gr. *roanensis* Stephenson. Lower? Maestrichtian; Saskatchewan; 21853.

Plate XXVIII. Mid- to Late Upper Cretaceous (Santonian to Campanian) Fossils, North Pacific Realm

Figures 1a-1b *Inoceramus schmidti* Michael s. str. Early upper Campanian?; British Columbia; 5832.

Figures 2a-2b *Inoceramus naumanni* Yokoyama s. str. Upper Santonian?; British Columbia; 21832.

Figures 3a-3b *Epigoniceras epigonum* (Kossmat). Upper Santonian to early lower Campanian; British Columbia; 10015.

Figures 4a-4b *Neophylloceras ramosum* (Meek). Latest upper Campanian?; British Columbia; 5811.

Figures 5a-5c *Inoceramus elegans* Sokolov. Early upper Campanian?; British Columbia; 21833.

Figure 6 *Nostoceras hornbyense* (Whiteaves). Latest upper Campanian?; British Columbia; 10069.

Figure 7 *Bostrychoceras elongatum* (Whiteaves). x½, upper Santonian to early lower Campanian; British Columbia; 10062.

Figure 8 *"Hamites" obstrictus* Jimbo. Latest upper Campanian?; British Columbia; 5958.

Figures 9a-9c *Inoceramus* cf. *sachalinensis* Sokolov. Early upper Campanian?; British Columbia; 21834.

Figures 10a-10b *Schluteria selwyniana* (Whiteaves). Upper Santonian to early lower Campanian; Washington, U.S.A.; 5803b.

Figures 11a-11b *Ptychoceras vancouverense* Whiteaves. Upper Santonian to early lower Campanian; British Columbia; 5798.

Figures 12a-12b *Pachydiscus suciaensis* (Meek). Latest upper Campanian?; British Columbia; 10035.

1a
1b
2a
2b
3a
3b
3c
4a
4b
4c
5a
5b
6
7a
7b
8a
8b
9a
9b
10a
10b
11a
11b
12a
12a
13a
13b
14a
14b
15

1a
1b
1c
2a
2b
3
4a
4b
5a
5b
6
7a
7b
8a
8b
9a
9b
10

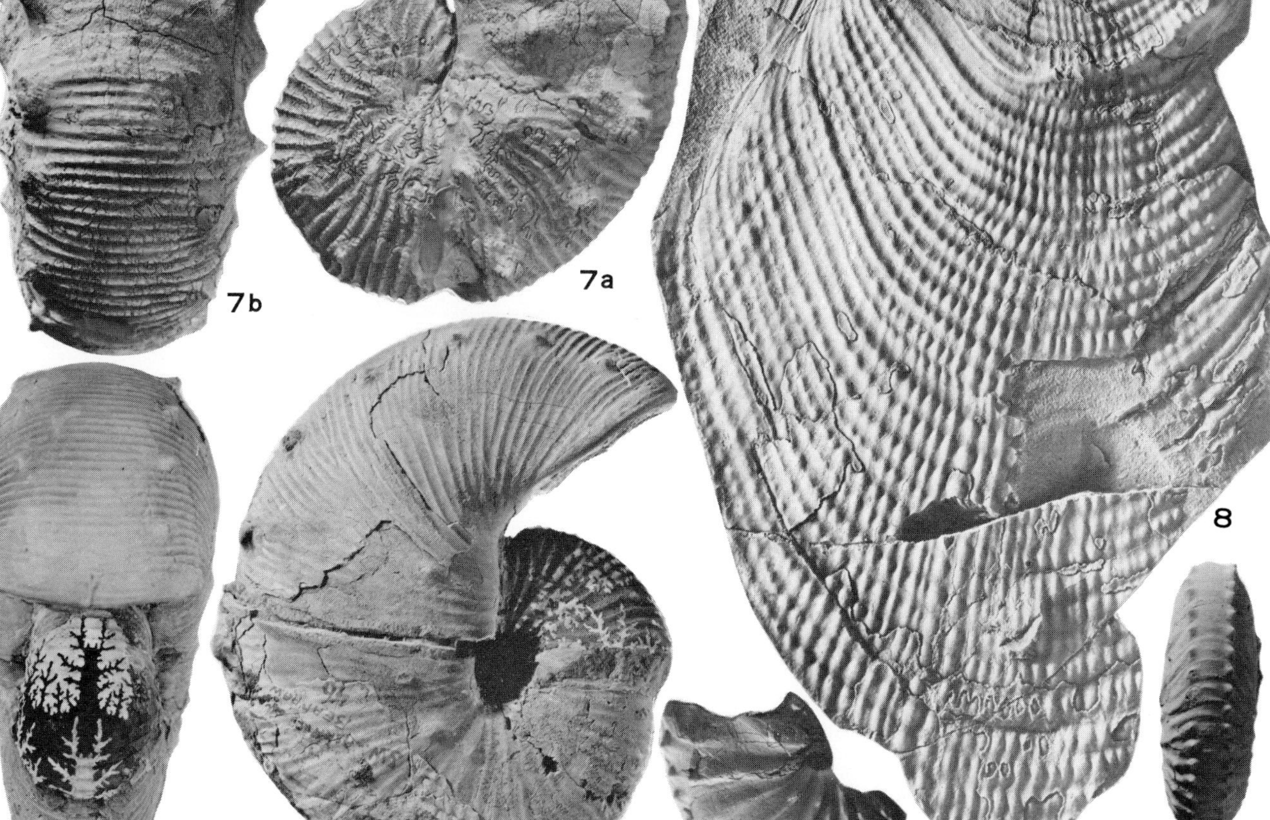
1a
2a
2b
3
4a
4b
5
1b
6
7b
7a
8
9b
9a
10a
10b

1b
2b
2a
3a
4a
6
1a
5a
4b
3b
10b
5b
5c
9b
9c
7
9a
10a
8
11a
11b
12b
12a

PALEOBOTANY

by D. C. McGregor

Until about fifteen years ago the attention of paleobotanists in Canada was directed almost exclusively towards megascopic remains. More recently, however, palynologists have disclosed a great variety of microfossils, including spores, pollen, acritarchs, dinoflagellates, diatoms, and other algal, fungal and cuticular fragments in Canadian rocks, and paleobotanical research in this country is now directed towards both megafossils and microfossils. A brief résumé of the development and present status of paleobotanical studies in Canada is given here.

One of the more recent emphases in Canadian paleobotany involves the organic microplankton (acritarchs and dinoflagellates). Acritarchs (PL. XXXI, FIGS. 40, 44), apparently all marine but of unknown biological affinities, have been discovered in rocks representing all the geological systems from Cambrian to Tertiary. Dinoflagellates (PL. XXXI, FIG. 45), both marine and non-marine, have a shorter geological range in Canada, from Permian to Recent. Although the study of Canadian acritarchs and dinoflagellates is still in its infancy, these fossils have considerable promise for local stratigraphic zonation and long-distance correlation.

The remains of terrestrial plants, in the form of petrified, carbonized or mummified megascopic fragments, and highly varied assortment of spores and pollen are known in rocks ranging in age from Devonian to Pleistocene. They are most abundant in Devonian and Carboniferous rocks of the Gaspé Peninsula and the Maritime Provinces, Devonian rocks of the arctic, and Middle Jurassic through Tertiary rocks of western Canada and the Sverdrup Basin. Table XI-9 summarizes the known occurrences of taxonomically identifiable trilete spores, pollen, and terrestrial megaplants in Canada.

The Lower Devonian *Psilophyton–Drepanophycus–Prototaxites* flora of Gaspé (PL. XXIX, FIG. 1) was the first to be described, by Sir William Dawson in several papers between 1856 and 1882; it is now known throughout the world as a classic example of one of the earliest known land floras. In addition to megascopic remains, trilete spores are abundant in the Gaspé Sandstone (PL. XXXI, FIGS. 1–4). Both the megafossils and the microfossils in these beds have definite interregional and intercontinental affinities. Similar floras occur in the Sextant Formation of the Hudson Bay Lowland, the Old Red Sandstone of Scotland, and Lower Devonian rocks of Germany, Belgium, Spain, and eastern Siberia.

Upper Devonian plant remains have been discovered in several parts of Canada. Well-preserved specimens of the gymnosperm *Archaeopteris* (PL. XXIX, FIG. 2), associated with Frasnian fish, occur in the Escuminac Formation of northern New Brunswick. *Archaeopteris* has been found only in the Upper Devonian, and is of worldwide distribution in both northern and southern hemispheres. Occurring with it but not produced by it are large spores with distinctive bifurcate appendages, similar to the specimen illustrated on PLATE XXXI, FIGURE 7. These spores also have a worldwide distribution, but a somewhat longer stratigraphic range than *Archaeopteris*—from Emsian to latest Famennian in Canada. Rare single specimens of this type of spore have been reported from Lower Carboniferous rocks outside of Canada, but they are abundant only in the Devonian.

Archaeopteris and the "anchor-spined" spores occur together in the Griper Bay Formation of the Arctic Archipelago (PL. XXXI, FIG. 7) and in the Imperial Formation of the Mackenzie Basin. Other spores occur in great abundance and variety in these beds, as well as in other marine and non-marine Givetian to Famennian rocks of Canada (PL. XXXI, FIGS. 5, 6, 8). Several successive spore assemblage zones are recognized in Middle and Upper Devonian rocks of southeastern, western, and arctic Canada, many species of which have worldwide distribution, for example *Archaeoperisaccus* spp. and *Hymenozonotriletes lepidophytus* Kedo (PL. XXXI, FIGS. 5, 6).

The Carboniferous floras of New Brunswick and Nova Scotia are well known as a result of the work of W. A. Bell. Plant megafossil zones have been established by Bell in the Horton Group (Tournaisian), Windsor Group (Viséan), Canso Group (late Viséan and early Namurian), Riversdale Group (late Namurian–early Westphalian), Cumberland Group (Westphalian B), and Pictou Group (*Lonchopteris* and *Linopteris obliqua* zones, Westphalian C, and the *Ptychocarpus unitus* zone, Westphalian D). Representative plant fossils from the Carboniferous of the Maritimes are illustrated on PLATE XXIX, FIGURES 3–10.

Spore assemblage zones have also been recognized in the Carboniferous rocks of the Maritimes. It is now possible to correlate using spores, not only from shales bearing megaplant fossils but also from other intervals including the coals themselves, where megafossils are not identifiable.

Inter-regional studies of Lower Carboniferous spores in Canada have resulted in the recognition of two distinct and apparently synchronous Viséan assemblages, one in the Windsor Group of the Maritimes and the other in the Golata and Mattson Formations of western Canada, and the Emma Fiord Formation of the arctic islands. The latter assemblage includes the spores shown on PLATE XXXI, FIGURES 9 and 10 and has a remarkable similarity in species to those of the Viséan of the western U.S.S.R. and Spitsbergen.

As information is accumulated on stratigraphic range, distribution, and facies sensitivity of Carboniferous spores and pollen, certain individual taxa are assuming biostrati-

TABLE XI-9 *Known occurrences (1966) of taxonomically identifiable plant fossils in Canada*

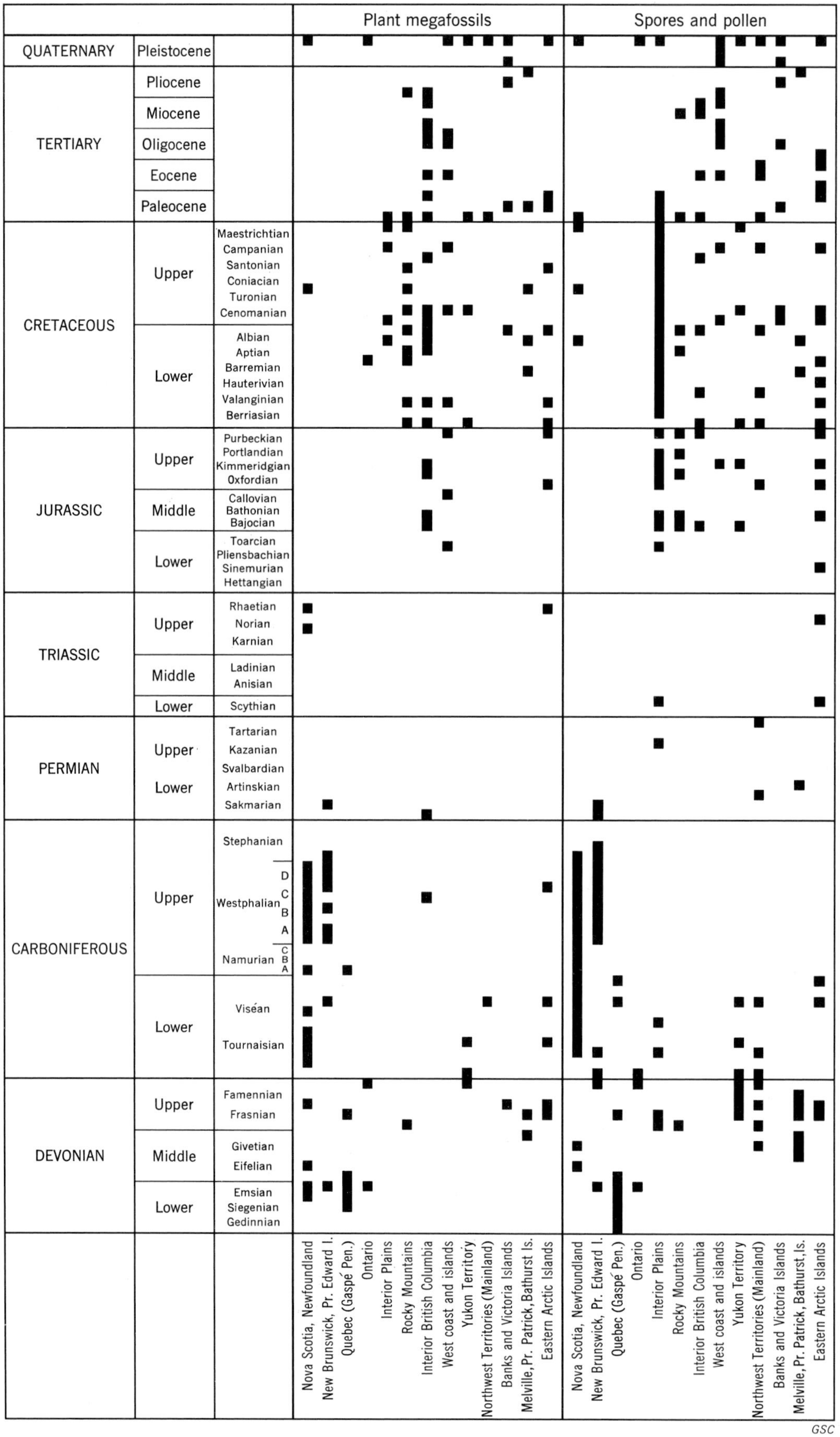

Period	Epoch	Stages	Plant megafossils: Nova Scotia, Newfoundland	New Brunswick, Pr. Edward I.	Quebec (Gaspé Pen.)	Ontario	Interior Plains	Rocky Mountains	Interior British Columbia	West coast and islands	Yukon Territory	Northwest Territories (Mainland)	Banks and Victoria Islands	Melville, Pr. Patrick, Bathurst Is.	Eastern Arctic Islands	Spores and pollen: Nova Scotia, Newfoundland	New Brunswick, Pr. Edward I.	Quebec (Gaspé Pen.)	Ontario	Interior Plains	Rocky Mountains	Interior British Columbia	West coast and islands	Yukon Territory	Northwest Territories (Mainland)	Banks and Victoria Islands	Melville, Pr. Patrick, Bathurst, Is.	Eastern Arctic Islands
QUATERNARY	Pleistocene		■			■				■	■	■	■		■	■			■	■			■	■	■	■		■
TERTIARY	Pliocene							■	■				■	■									■			■	■	
	Miocene								■												■	■	■					
	Oligocene								■	■													■			■		
	Eocene								■	■												■	■		■			■
	Paleocene						■	■	■		■	■	■	■	■	■				■	■	■			■	■		■
CRETACEOUS	Upper	Maestrichtian, Campanian, Santonian, Coniacian, Turonian, Cenomanian	■				■	■	■	■	■			■	■	■				■		■	■	■	■	■		■
	Lower	Albian, Aptian, Barremian, Hauterivian, Valanginian, Berriasian				■	■	■	■	■	■		■	■	■	■				■	■	■		■	■		■	■
JURASSIC	Upper	Purbeckian, Portlandian, Kimmeridgian, Oxfordian							■	■					■					■	■	■	■	■	■			■
	Middle	Callovian, Bathonian, Bajocian							■	■										■	■	■		■				■
	Lower	Toarcian, Pliensbachian, Sinemurian, Hettangian								■										■								■
TRIASSIC	Upper	Rhaetian, Norian, Karnian	■												■													■
	Middle	Ladinian, Anisian																										
	Lower	Scythian																		■								■
PERMIAN	Upper	Tartarian, Kazanian																		■					■			
	Lower	Svalbardian, Artinskian, Sakmarian		■					■								■								■		■	
CARBONIFEROUS	Upper	Stephanian, Westphalian (D, C, B, A), Namurian (C, B, A)	■	■	■				■						■	■	■											
	Lower	Viséan, Tournaisian	■	■							■	■			■	■	■	■		■				■	■			■
DEVONIAN	Upper	Famennian, Frasnian	■		■	■		■			■		■	■	■		■	■	■	■	■			■	■		■	■
	Middle	Givetian, Eifelian	■											■		■									■		■	
	Lower	Emsian, Siegenian, Gedinnian	■	■	■	■											■	■	■									

GSC

graphic significance. For example, *Lophozonotriletes rarituberculatus* (PL. XXXI, FIG. 14) is characteristic of Lower Carboniferous (Tournaisian) assemblages in various parts of the world. In the Upper Carboniferous, species of *Vestispora* and *Torispora* (PL. XXXI, FIGS. 11 and 16) and several other genera are important biostratigraphic markers because of their restricted time range and wide geographic distribution.

There are relatively few Permian or Triassic fossil plants in Canada. The Permian megafossils that occur on Prince Edward Island are too poorly preserved to be of value for correlation or dating purposes. Spores and pollen, on the other hand, do occur in several areas. For example, Lower Permian spores and pollen (PL. XXXI, FIGS. 13, 15, and 27) including *Nuskoisporites, Vittatina* and disaccate Striatiti, have been recovered from Prince Edward Island, from the upper beds of the Mattson Formation of Liard Plateau, and from the Sabine Bay Formation of Melville Island. Upper Permian spores and pollen, including *Vittatina* (PL. XXXI, FIG. 20), occur in the subsurface of the Interior Plains and the Yukon Territory.

Late Triassic megafossil plants, apparently similar to those that occur in Rhaetic to Liassic strata of Eastern Greenland, have been discovered in the upper part of the Heiberg Formation in the Queen Elizabeth Islands. The upper Heiberg also contains well-preserved spores and pollen (PL. XXXI, FIGS. 18, 19, 21, and 24), some of which are identical to species in Rhaetic to Liassic rocks of Europe. Lower and Upper Triassic plant remains occur in certain other areas of Canada as well (Table XI-9), but their botanical affinities and stratigraphic implications are not yet known.

The principal areas of occurrence of Jurassic terrestrial plants are parts of British Columbia, the southern Interior Plains, and the Queen Elizabeth Islands. One of the most significant areas, both botanically and stratigraphically, is the west coast of Vancouver Island and the Queen Charlotte Islands. The fossils on Vancouver Island, comprising petrifactions, carbonized compressions of megaplants (PL. XXX, FIG. 1), and corroded spores occur in beds dated as Toarcian by marine faunas. This flora existed around the fringes of the Pacific from Mexico to southeast Asia. A slightly younger, probably Callovian, flora of undetermined affinities has also been found on Vancouver Island and the Queen Charlotte Islands. Lower, Middle, and Upper Jurassic plant megafossils and microfossils, usually highly carbonized, occur in various parts of the western mainland. Well-preserved spores and pollen have been obtained from Sinemurian and Callovian to Kimmeridgian strata of the Queen Elizabeth Islands (PL. XXXI, FIGS. 17, 22, 23, and 25), and megaplants have been reported but not collected.

Cretaceous sedimentary deposits are widespread in Canada, and have received probably more attention by paleobotanists than those of any other age. They are of special significance both geologically and botanically, for they are an important source of coal, oil, and gas, and contain floras in which angiospermous plants first make their appearance.

Both Lower and Upper Cretaceous megafossil plants of western Canada (PL. XXX, FIGS. 2–9, 12, 15) have been studied extensively by W. A. Bell, and in recent years palynological investigations encompassing most of the Lower and Upper Cretaceous of western Canada have been undertaken. Much of the palynological data is still unpublished, but sufficient information is now available to establish both local and long-distance age correlations based on miospore assemblages. In some instances, individual miospore taxa may be significant zone fossils, provided various factors affecting their occurrence such as lithological variation, diagenetic compaction, and paleoclimatic effects, are properly understood. For example, species of *Plicatella, Appendicisporites, Aquilapollenites* (PL. XXXI, FIG. 39), *Wodehouseia* (PL. XXXI, FIG. 33), and *Proteacidites* (PL. XXXI, FIG. 34) appear to have similar stratigraphic ranges in the Cretaceous of North America, Europe, U.S.S.R., and Australia. In the Arctic Archipelago, the Cretaceous Isachsen, Christopher, Hassel, and Kanguk Formations contain plant remains, the spores and pollen of which are currently under study.

Thick sequences of plant-bearing Tertiary sediments occur in western Canada and the arctic islands. The earliest studies in western Canada were of fossil leaves, fruits, and seeds by J. W. Dawson, D. P. Penhallow, E. W. Berry, and more recently by W. A. Bell. They revealed the presence of Paleocene, Middle Eocene, and Miocene–Pliocene floras in several small intermontane sedimentary basins of British Columbia and Yukon, and in widespread non-marine formations of the Interior Plains. Systematic studies of spores and pollen from the plains are in progress. In British Columbia, Rouse and Mathews have related the megafloral and microfloral content of several deposits to the radiogenic ages of associated ash beds.

Accounts of Tertiary megafossil plants of the Canadian arctic were written by Heer and Nathorst several decades ago, but need extensive revision. However, even though many specimens may be incorrectly identified, the early to middle Tertiary floras of the arctic strongly suggest a temperate climate, the paleogeographical and paleoecological implications of which have not been thoroughly investigated. In the Pleistocene epoch, interglacial and interstadial intervals have been delimited in Canada by paleobotanical studies. The development of muskeg and its relationship to forest growth on peat have also been studied using paleobotanical methods. In contrast to paleobotanical studies of pre-Pleistocene deposits, the evolutionary changes and extinction of species have a more limited use in the Pleistocene and the emphasis is placed primarily on climatic changes and species composition of the vegetation.

Selected References

Baker, F. C.
1920: The life of the Pleistocene or Glacial period as recorded in the deposits laid down by the great ice sheets; *Univ. Illinois Bull.*, vol. 17, No. 41.

Bell, W. A.
1956: Lower Cretaceous floras of western Canada; *Geol. Surv. Can.*, Mem. 285.
1962: Flora of Pennsylvanian Pictou Group of New Brunswick; *Geol. Surv. Can.*, Bull. 87.

Berry, E. W.
1926: Tertiary floras from British Columbia; *Can. Natl. Museum*, Bull. 42, pp. 91–116.

Dawson, J. W.
1859: On fossil plants from the Devonian rocks of Canada; *Quart. J. Soc. London*, vol. 15, pp. 477–488.

Evitt, W. R.
1963: A discussion and proposals concerning fossil dinoflagellates, hystrichospheres, and acritarchs, I, II; *Proc. Natl. Acad. Sci.*, vol. 49, Nos. 2, 3, pp. 158–164, 298–302.

Hacquebard, P. A., Barss, M. S., and Donaldson, J. R.
1960: Distribution and stratigraphic significance of small spore genera in the Upper Carboniferous of the Maritime Provinces of Canada; *Congr. Avanç. Etudes Stratigraph. Geol. Carbonifèra, Compt. Rendè. 4me*, vol. 1, pp. 237–245.

McGregor, D. C.
1965: Illustrations of Canadian fossils: Triassic, Jurassic, and Lower Cretaceous spores and pollen of arctic Canada; *Geol. Surv. Can.*, Paper 64-55.

Penhallow, D. P.
1902: Notes on Cretaceous and Tertiary plants of Canada; *Trans. Roy. Soc. Can.*, 1901, 2nd ser., vol. 8, sec. IV, pp. 31–91.

Rouse, G. E., and Mathews, W. H.
1961: Radioactive dating of Tertiary plant-bearing deposits; *Science*, vol. 133, pp. 1079–1080.

Terasmae, J.
1960: Contributions to Canadian Palynology 2; *Geol. Surv. Can.*, Bull. 56. (Includes extensive bibliography.)

Plate XXIX. Devonian and Carboniferous Plants

(All figures natural size unless otherwise stated)

Figure 1 *Psilophyton princeps* var. *ornatum* Dawson. Lower Devonian; Gaspé Peninsula; 13048.

Figure 2 *Archaeopteris jacksoni* Dawson. Frasnian; Gaspé Peninsula; 13050.

Figure 3 *Aneimites acadica* Dawson. Tournaisian; Nova Scotia; 720.

Figure 4 *Lepidodendropsis corrugata* (Dawson) Bell. Tournaisian; Nova Scotia; 15098.

Figure 5 *Calamites suckowi* Brongniart. Westphalian B; Nova Scotia; 14920.

Figure 6 *Alethopteris serli* (Brongniart) Goeppert. Early Westphalian D; Nova Scotia; 14996.

Figure 7 *Linopteris obliqua* (Bunbury) Zeiller. x2, early Westphalian C; Nova Scotia; 14945.

Figure 8 *Lepidodendron aculeatum* Sternberg. Westphalian B; Nova Scotia; 14937.

Figure 9 *Ptychocarpus unitus* (Brongniart) Zeiller. x2, early Westphalian D; Nova Scotia; 1370.

Figure 10 *Asterophyllites equisetiformis* (Schlotheim) Brongniart. Early Westphalian D; Nova Scotia; 3003.

Plate XXX. Mesozoic and Cenozoic Plants

(All figures natural size)

Figure 1 ?*Dictyophyllum* sp. Lower Jurassic; Vancouver Island; 15099.

Figure 2 *Cladophlebis virginiensis* Fontaine forma *martiniana* Dawson. Neocomian-Barremian; British Columbia; 13446.

Figure 3 *Athrotaxites berryi* Bell. Aptian or early Albian; Alberta; 13462.

Figure 4 *Cladophlebis yukonensis* Bell. Neocomian-Barremian; Alberta; 13440.

Figure 5 *Nilssonia californica* Fontaine. Aptian or early Albian; Alberta; 13510.

Figure 6 *Araliaephyllum westoni* (Dawson) Bell. Albian; Alberta; 13541.

Figure 7 *Sagenopteris williamsii* (Newberry) Bell. Aptian or early Albian; Alberta; 13474.

Figure 8 Cone, *Sequoia* sp. Santonian-Campanian; Alberta; 5092.

Figure 9 Seed, *Carpites* sp. Santonian-Campanian; Alberta; 5098.

Figure 10 *Metasequoia occidentalis* (Newberry) Chaney. Paleocene; Alberta; 5991.

Figure 11 *Ilex? mammillata* Bell. Santonian-Campanian; Alberta; 1249.

Figure 12 *Artocarpus* sp. Maestrichtian; Alberta; 14856.

Figure 13 Cone, *Larix laricina* (DuRoi) K. Koch. Pleistocene; Mackenzie River Delta; 3586.

Figure 14 *Viburnum asperum* Newberry. Paleocene; Alberta; 14838.

Figure 15 *Pseudoprotophyllum boreale* (Dawson) Hollick. Cenomanian; Alberta; 5398.

Figure 16 *Osmunda macrophylla* Penhallow. Paleocene; Alberta; 6163.

Figure 17 Cone of *Pinus contorta* Dougl. Pleistocene (late-glacial); Vancouver Island; 3556.

Figure 18 *Dryas drummondii* Richards. Pleistocene (late-glacial); Vancouver Island; 3573.

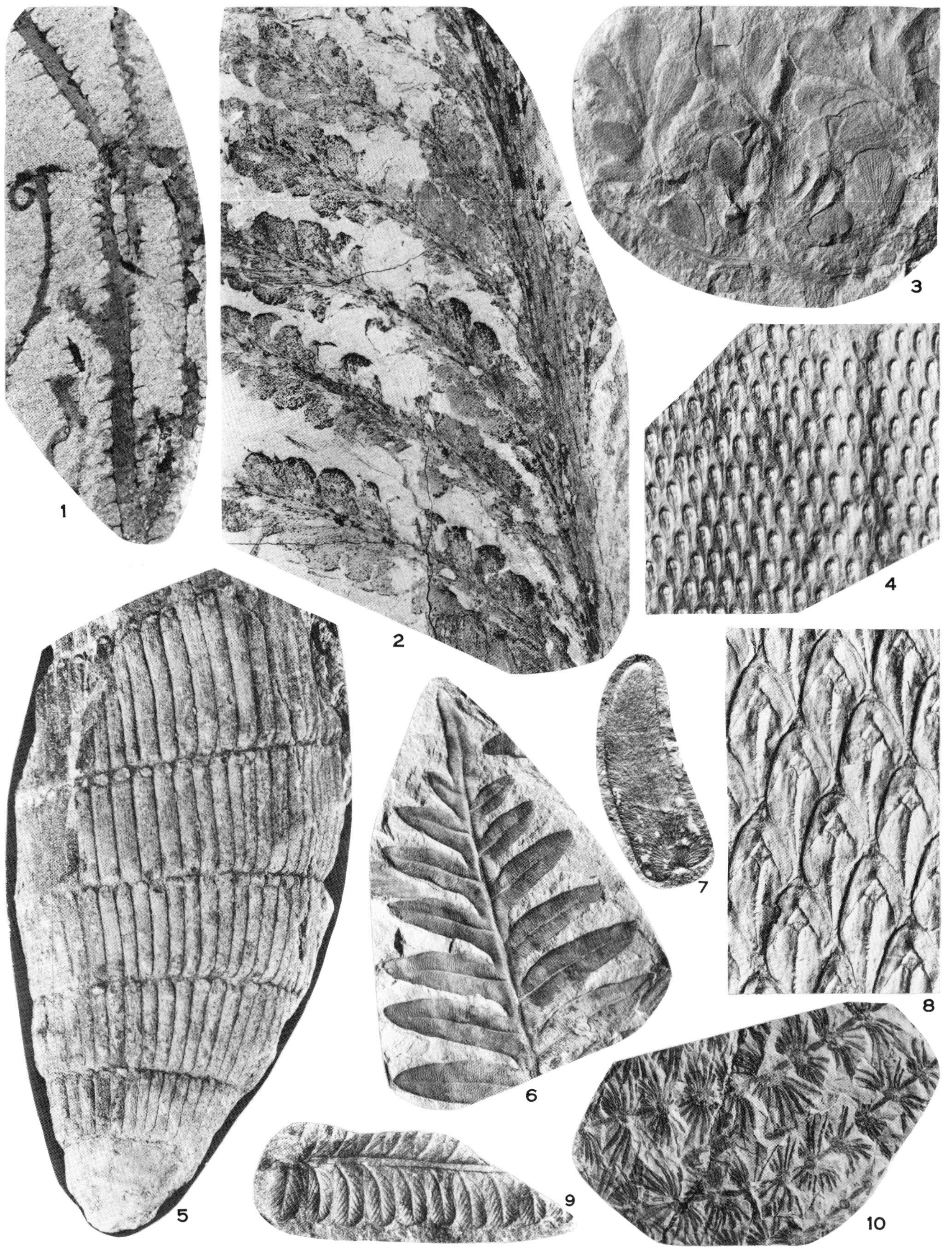
1
2
3
4
5
6
7
8
9
10

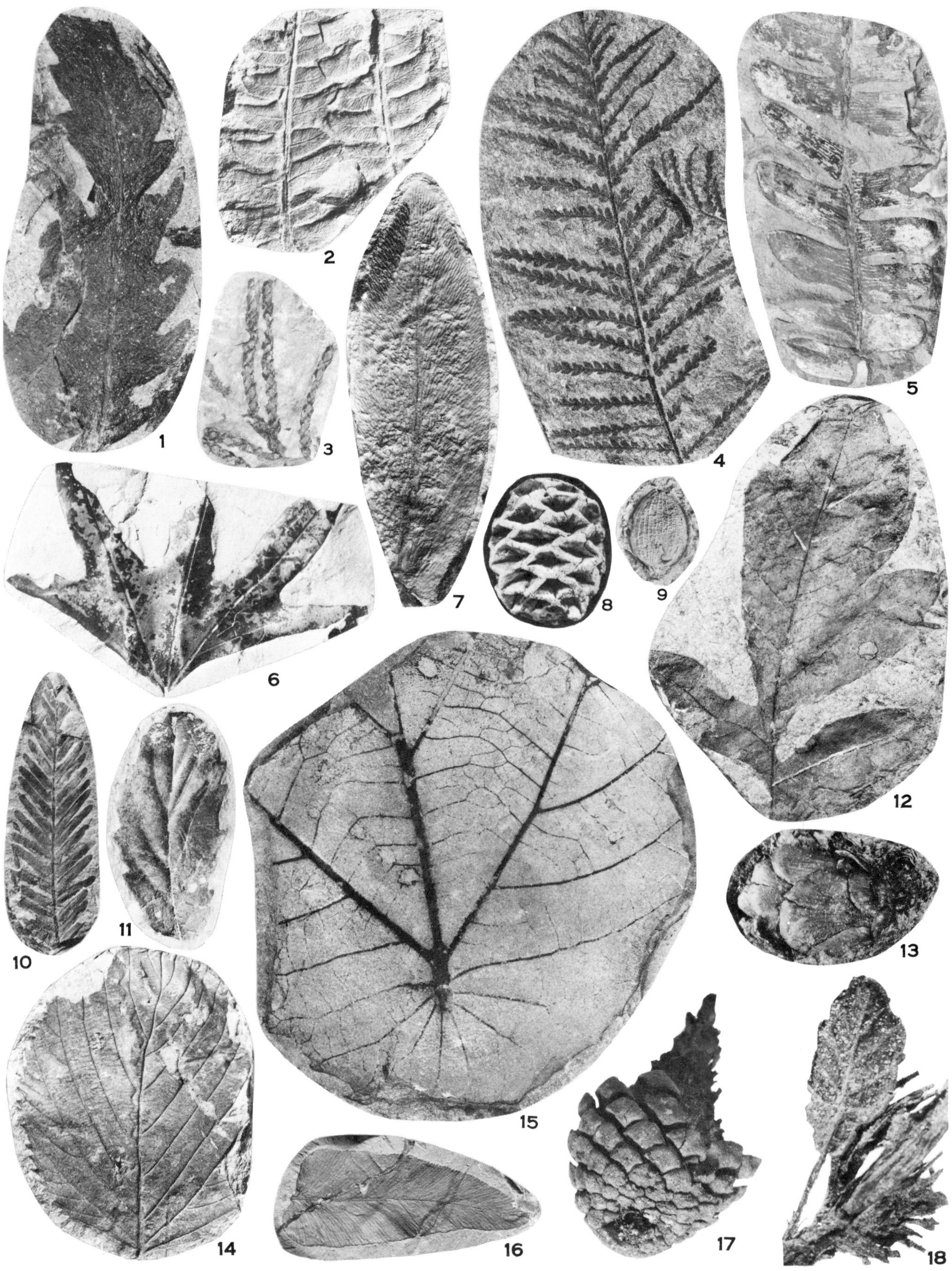
1
2
3
4
5
6
7
8
9
10
11
12
13
14
15
16
17
18

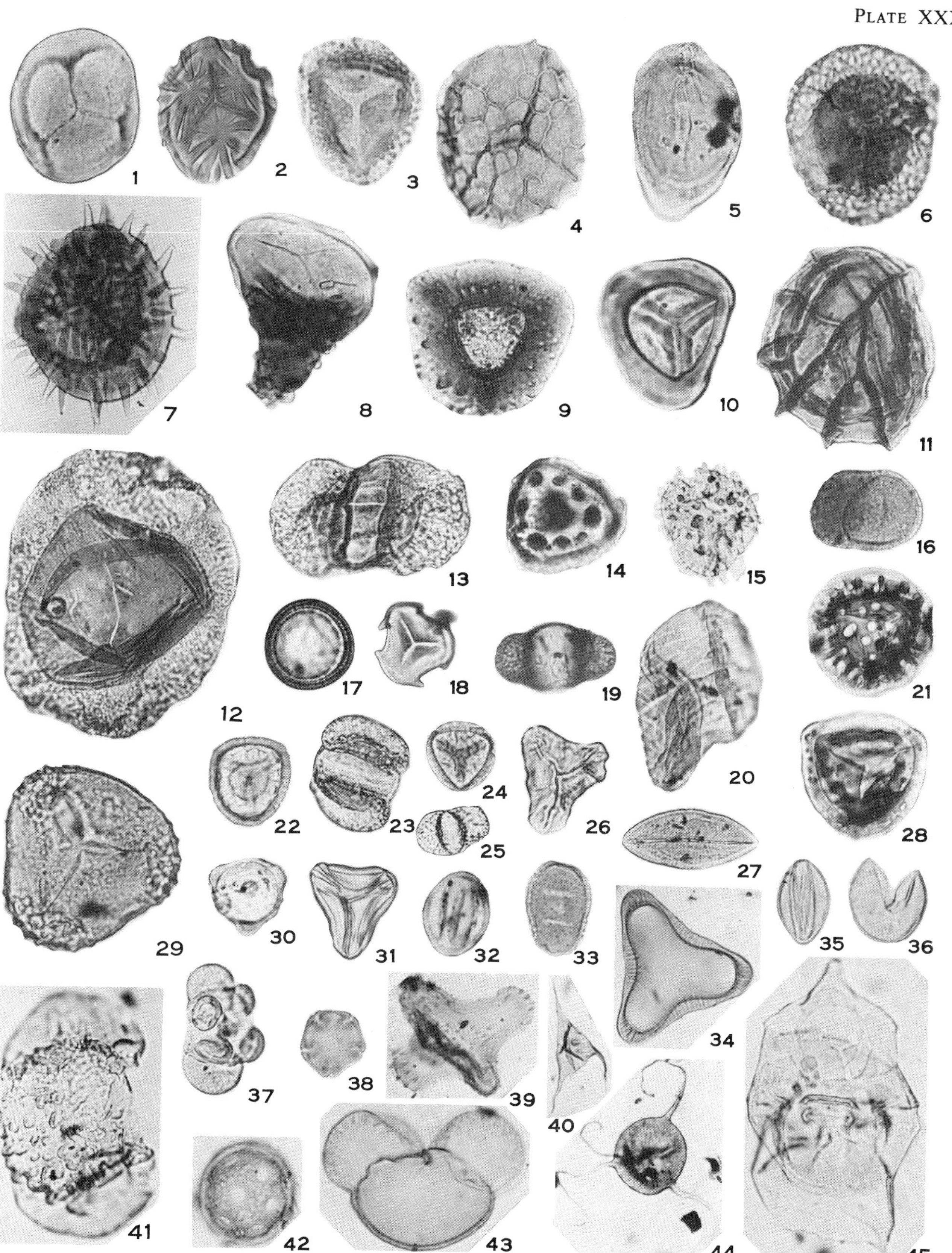
1
2
3
4
5
6
7
8
9
10
11
12
13
14
15
16
17
18
19
20
21
22
23
24
25
26
27
28
29
30
31
32
33
34
35
36
37
38
39
40
41
42
43
44
45

Plate XXXI. Palynomorphs

(Fig. 7 x250; others x500)

Figure 1 *Retusotriletes* sp. Lower Devonian; Gaspé Peninsula, GSC loc. 6583; 15064.

Figure 2 *Emphanisporites* sp. Lower Devonian; Gaspé Peninsula, GSC loc. 7094; 15065.

Figure 3 Unidentified spore. Lower Devonian; Gaspé Peninsula, GSC loc. 6583; 15066.

Figure 4 *Reticulatisporites ?emsiensis* Allen. Lower Devonian; Gaspé Peninsula, GSC loc. 6583; 15067.

Figure 5 *Archaeoperisaccus* sp. Middle Frasnian; Great Slave Lake, N.W.T., GSC loc. 30425; 15068.

Figure 6 *Hymenozonotriletes lepidophytus* Kedo. Late Famennian; southern Ontario, GSC loc. 7057; 15069.

Figure 7 *Hystricosporites* sp. Frasnian; Prince Patrick Island, GSC loc. 7026; 15070.

Figure 8 *Lophozonotriletes cristifer* (Luber) Kedo. Late Frasnian or early Famennian; Bathurst Island, GSC loc. 59041; 13625.

Figure 9 *Densosporites spitsbergensis* Playford. Viséan; South Nahanni River, N.W.T., GSC loc. 5004; 15071.

Figure 10 *Murospora aurita* (Waltz) Playford. Viséan; South Nahanni River, N.W.T., GSC loc. 5004; 15072.

Figure 11 *Vestispora costata* (Balme) Bhardwaj. Early Westphalian C; New Brunswick, GSC loc. 7570; 15073.

Figure 12 *Potonieisporites* sp. Lower Permian; Prince Edward Island, GSC loc. 7571; 15074.

Figure 13 *Protohaploxypinus* sp. Lower Permian; Prince Edward Island, GSC loc. 7571; 15075.

Figure 14 *Lophozonotriletes rarituberculatus* (Luber) Kedo. Tournaisian; Nova Scotia, GSC loc. 2531; 15076.

Figure 15 *Neoraistrickia* sp. Mid-Permian; Melville Island, GSC loc. 5221; 15077.

Figure 16 *Torispora securis* Balme. Westphalian C; Nova Scotia, GSC loc. 7574; 15078.

Figure 17 *Classopollis classoides* Pflug emend. Pocock and Jansonius. Lower Jurassic; Ellesmere Island, GSC loc. 6660; 13769.

Figure 18 *Triancoraesporites communis* Schulz. Norian or Rhaetian; Ellesmere Island, GSC loc. 4905; 13691.

Figure 19 *Klausipollenites vestitus* Jansonius. Norian or Rhaetian; Ellesmere Island, GSC loc. 4905; 13722.

Figure 20 *Vittatina* sp. Upper Permian; Peel River area, N.W.T., GSC loc. 5279; 15079.

Figure 21 *Limbosporites lundbladii* Nilsson. Norian or Rhaetian; Ellesmere Island, GSC loc. 4905; 13689.

Figure 22 *?Taurocusporites* sp. Lower Jurassic; Ellesmere Island, GSC loc. 6660; 13763.

Figure 23 *?Pinuspollenites vancampoi* Danzé-Corsin and Laveine. Lower Jurassic; Ellesmere Island, GSC loc. 6660; 13781.

Figure 24 *Camarozonosporites rudis* (Leschik) Klaus. Norian or Rhaetian; Ellesmere Island, GSC loc. 4905; 13682.

Figure 25 *Vitreisporites pallidus* (Reissinger) Nilsson. Lower Jurassic; Ellesmere Island, GSC loc. 6660; 13775.

Figure 26 *?Leiotriletes lineatus* Bolkhovitina. Lower Cretaceous; Alberta, GSC loc. 5925; 15084.

Figure 27 *Cycadopites* sp. Mid-Permian; Melville Island, GSC loc. 5221; 15080.

Figure 28 *Contignisporites ?cooksonii* (Balme) Dettmann. Lower Cretaceous; Richardson Mountains, GSC loc. 26909; 13835.

Figure 29 *Trilobosporites* sp. Lower Cretaceous; Alberta, GSC loc. 5925; 15081.

Figure 30 *Leiotriletes venustus* Bolkhovitina. Upper Cretaceous; Saskatchewan, GSC loc. 6658; 15082.

Figure 31 *Gleicheniidites senonicus* Ross. Lower Cretaceous; Alberta, GSC loc. 5925; 15083.

Figure 32 *Eucommiidites troedssonii* Erdtman. Lower Cretaceous; Nova Scotia, GSC loc. 6327; 13215.

Figure 33 *Wodehouseia* sp. Late Upper Cretaceous; Devon Island, GSC loc. 4723; 15085.

Figure 34 *?Proteacidites* sp. Late Upper Cretaceous; Devon Island, GSC loc. 4723; 15086.

Figure 35 Unidentified angiosperm pollen. Early Miocene; Vancouver Island, GSC loc. 7572; 15087.

Figure 36 Pollen of Taxodiaceae. Early Miocene; Vancouver Island, GSC loc. 7572; 15088.

Figure 37 Unidentified gymnosperm pollen. Upper Cretaceous; Saskatchewan, GSC loc. 6658; 15089.

Figure 38 Unidentified angiosperm pollen. Late Upper Cretaceous; Devon Island, GSC loc. 4723; 15090.

Figure 39 *Aquilapollenites amplus* Stanley. Late Upper Cretaceous; Devon Island, GSC loc. 4723; 15091.

Figure 40 *Veryhachium* sp. Late Famennian; southern Ontario, GSC loc. 7057; 15092.

Figure 41 *Rugubivesiculites* sp. Upper Cretaceous; Saskatchewan, GSC loc. 6658; 15093.

Figure 42 Pollen of Caryophyllaceae. Pleistocene; Cape Breton Island, GSC loc. 7575; 15094.

Figure 43 *Pinus* sp. Pleistocene; Cape Breton Island, GSC loc. 7575; 15095.

Figure 44 *Baltisphaeridium* sp. Late Famennian; southern Ontario, GSC loc. 7057; 15096.

Figure 45 *Deflandrea* sp. Upper Cretaceous; Ellef Ringnes Island, GSC loc. 7573; 15097.

MARINE PLEISTOCENE FAUNAS

by F. J. E. Wagner

Unlike other periods, the part of the Pleistocene from which fossils have been obtained was not of sufficient duration for evolutionary changes to have taken place. Therefore, the faunal assemblages are of little value stratigraphically. They do, however, show regional differences, as between Atlantic and Pacific, and they are also useful as indicators of water depths and water temperatures in late Pleistocene time.

The areal aspects of the faunas, as shown by the most common species, are set forth in the explanations accompanying PLATES XXXII and XXXIII. Arctic areas were apparently populated mainly through migration of species from the North Atlantic and have few species in common with western Canada. The cosmopolitan species indicate boreal or subarctic water temperatures, rather than high-arctic temperatures. Of the other species illustrated, *Natica clausa, Neptunea lyrata, Nuculana fossa, Nuculana minuta, Portlandia arctica, Astarte borealis, Astarte montagui striata,* and *Mya pseudoarenaria* are particularly typical of boreal temperatures, and *Buccinum cyaneum, Neptunea despecta tornata, Chlamys hindsi, Saxidomus giganteus, Mya arenaria,* and *Balanus hameri* are found in cool temperate waters. In western Canada, faunal assemblages indicate an amelioration of the hydroclimate between about 12,000 to 14,000 years ago and the present. A similar warming trend is shown by the faunas of eastern Canada, but covering the shorter time span of the Champlain Sea (approximately 11,500 years B.P. to between 8,000 and 9,000 years B.P.) Fossil assemblages from the region of Boothia Peninsula to eastern Back River area in the arctic mainland suggest a shallowing of the water from a possible maximum depth of 200 feet for deposits about 23,300 years old that now lie 640 feet above present sea level to a possible minimum depth of 15 to 20 feet for deposits now 70 feet above sea level and about 3,690 years old. Similar changes in depth, that is deeper at first and then becoming shallower, have also been noted for eastern Canada.

Selected References

Bolton, T. E., and Lee, P. K.
1960: Post-glacial marine overlap of Anticosti Island; *Proc. Geol. Assoc. Can.,* vol. 12, pp. 67–78.

Dawson, Sir J. W.
1893: The Canadian ice age; Montreal, William V. Dawson.

Grant, U. S., IV, and Gale, H. R.
1931: Catalogue of the marine Pliocene and Pleistocene Mollusca of California; *Mem. San. Diego Soc. Nat. Hist.,* vol. 1.

Richards, H. G.
1962: Studies on the marine Pleistocene; *Trans. Am. Phil. Soc.,* n. ser., vol. 52, pt. 3, 141 pp., 21 pls.

Wagner, F. J. E.
1959: Palaeoecology of the marine Pleistocene faunas of southwestern British Columbia; *Geol. Surv. Can.,* Bull. 52.

Plate XXXII. Marine Pleistocene Fossils

(All figures natural size unless otherwise stated)

COSMOPOLITAN[1]

Figure 1 *Serripes groenlandicus* (Bruguière). Grande Rivière du Chêne, Quebec; 20156.

Figures 2, 3 *Hiatella arctica* (Linné). Chevalier, Quebec; 20164.

Figure 4 *Balanus crenatus* Bruguière. Atlantic Coast (Recent); 20191.

Figure 5 *Macoma calcarea* (Gmelin). Richelieu River, Quebec; 20158.

Figure 6 *Mytilus edulis* Linné. St. Joseph du Lac, Quebec; 20149.

Figure 8 *Mya truncata* Linné. Grande Rivière du Chêne, Quebec; 20161.

Figures 11, 12 *Hemithiris psittacea* (Gmelin). St. Nicholas, Quebec; 20131.

EASTERN CANADA

Figure 7 *Lepeta caeca* Müller. St. Nicholas, Quebec; 20132.

Figure 9 *Mya arenaria* Linné. St. Remi, Quebec; 20160.

Figure 10 *Balanus hameri* (Ascanius). St. Philomène, Quebec; 20192. (*See also* Pl. XXXIII, fig. 6).

Figure 25 *Tethya logani* Dawson. Montreal, Quebec; 20130. (x2)

Figure 31 *Neptunea despecta tornata* (Gould). Grande Rivière du Chêne, Quebec; 20140.

1 All areas of marine submergence in eastern Canada (Champlain Sea submergence in Ontario and Quebec plus the Atlantic Provinces), Tyrrell Sea submergence (ancestral Hudson Bay), Arctic regions and western Canada (coastal British Columbia).

EASTERN CANADA AND ARCTIC CANADA

Figure 13 *Buccinum tenue* Gray. Ste. Geneviève, Quebec; 20138.

Figure 14 *Buccinum cyaneum* Bruguière. St. Janvier de Joly, Quebec; 20137.

Figure 15 *Trichotropis borealis* Broderip and Sowerby. Montreal, Quebec; 20134. (x2)

Figure 16 *Balanus balanus* (Linné). Atlantic Coast (Recent); 20190.

Figure 19 *Cylichna alba* Brown. Montreal, Quebec; 20143. (x2)

Figure 20 *Tachyrhynchus erosum* (Couthouy). St. Nicholas, Quebec; 20133.

EASTERN CANADA, ARCTIC CANADA, AND TYRRELL SEA

Figure 17 *Protelphidium orbiculare* (Brady). Montreal, Quebec; 20126. (x55)

Figure 18 *Islandiella teretis* (Tappan). Alexandria, Ontario; 20112. (x45)

Figures 21, 22 *Portlandia arctica* (Gray). Ste. Geneviève, Quebec; 20148.

Figures 23, 24 *Nuculana pernula* (Müller). Ste. Geneviève, Quebec; 20145.

Figure 26 *Mya pseudoarenaria* Schlesch. St. Janvier de Joly, Quebec; 20163a.

Figures 27, 28 *Macoma balthica* (Linné). St. Joseph du Lac, Quebec; 20157.

Figures 29, 30 *Astarte montagui striata* (Leach). St. Janvier de Joly, Quebec; 20151.

Plate XXXIII. Marine Pleistocene Fossils

(All figures natural size unless otherwise stated)

EASTERN CANADA, ARCTIC CANADA, AND WESTERN CANADA

Figure 4 *Natica clausa* Broderip and Sowerby. Ste. Geneviève, Quebec; 20135.

Figure 5 *Natica pallida* Broderip and Sowerby. Ste. Geneviève, Quebec; 20136.

ARCTIC CANADA AND TYRRELL SEA

Figures 11, 12 *Astarte borealis* Schumacher. Bathurst Island, Northwest Territories; 20997.

ARCTIC CANADA AND WESTERN CANADA

Figure 13 *Neptunea lyrata* (Gmelin). Vancouver Island, British Columbia; 20998.

Figure 15 *Nuculana minuta* (Fabricius). Whatcom co., Washington, U.S.A.; 20999. (x2)

WESTERN CANADA

Figure 1 *Saxidomus giganteus* (Deshayes). Point Roberts, British Columbia; 21005.

Figures 2, 3 *Macoma incongrua* (Martens). Surrey municipality, British Columbia; 21006.

Figures 7, 8 *Protothaca staminea* (Conrad). Redondo Beach, California, U.S.A.; 21004.

Figures 9, 10 *Chlamys hindsi* (Carpenter). Point Roberts, British Columbia; 21002.

Figure 14 *Trichotropis cancellata* Hinds. Surrey municipality, British Columbia; 21000. (x2)

Figure 16 *Nuculana fossa* (Baird). Vancouver Island, British Columbia; 21001.

Figure 17 *Clinocardium nuttalli* (Conrad). Point Roberts, British Columbia; 21003.

Figure 6 *Balanus hameri* (Ascanius). Eastern Canada (*see* Pl. XXXII, fig. 10).

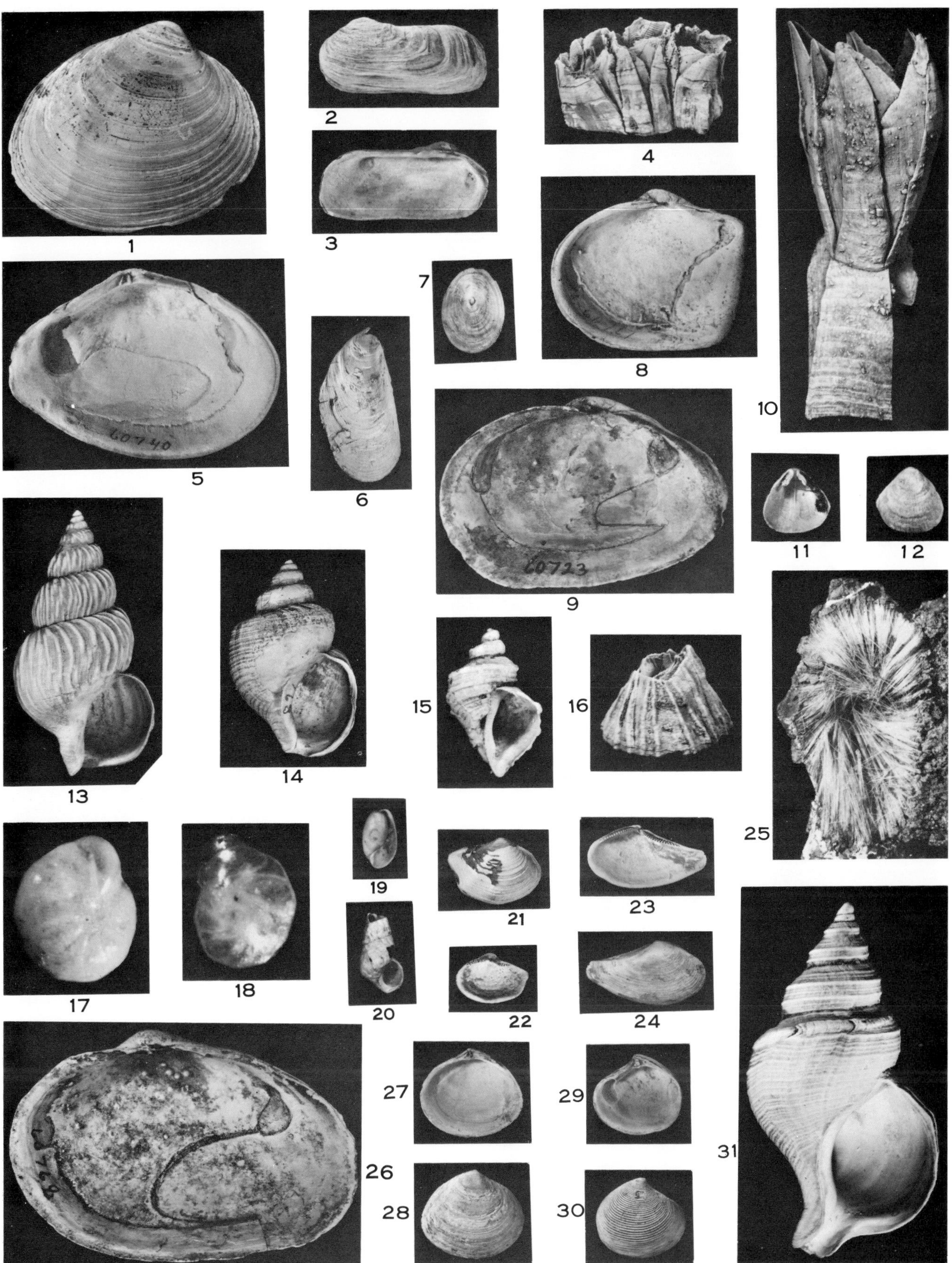
1
2
3
4
5
6
7
8
9
10
11
12
13
14
15
16
17
18
19
20
21
22
23
24
25
26
27
28
29
30
31

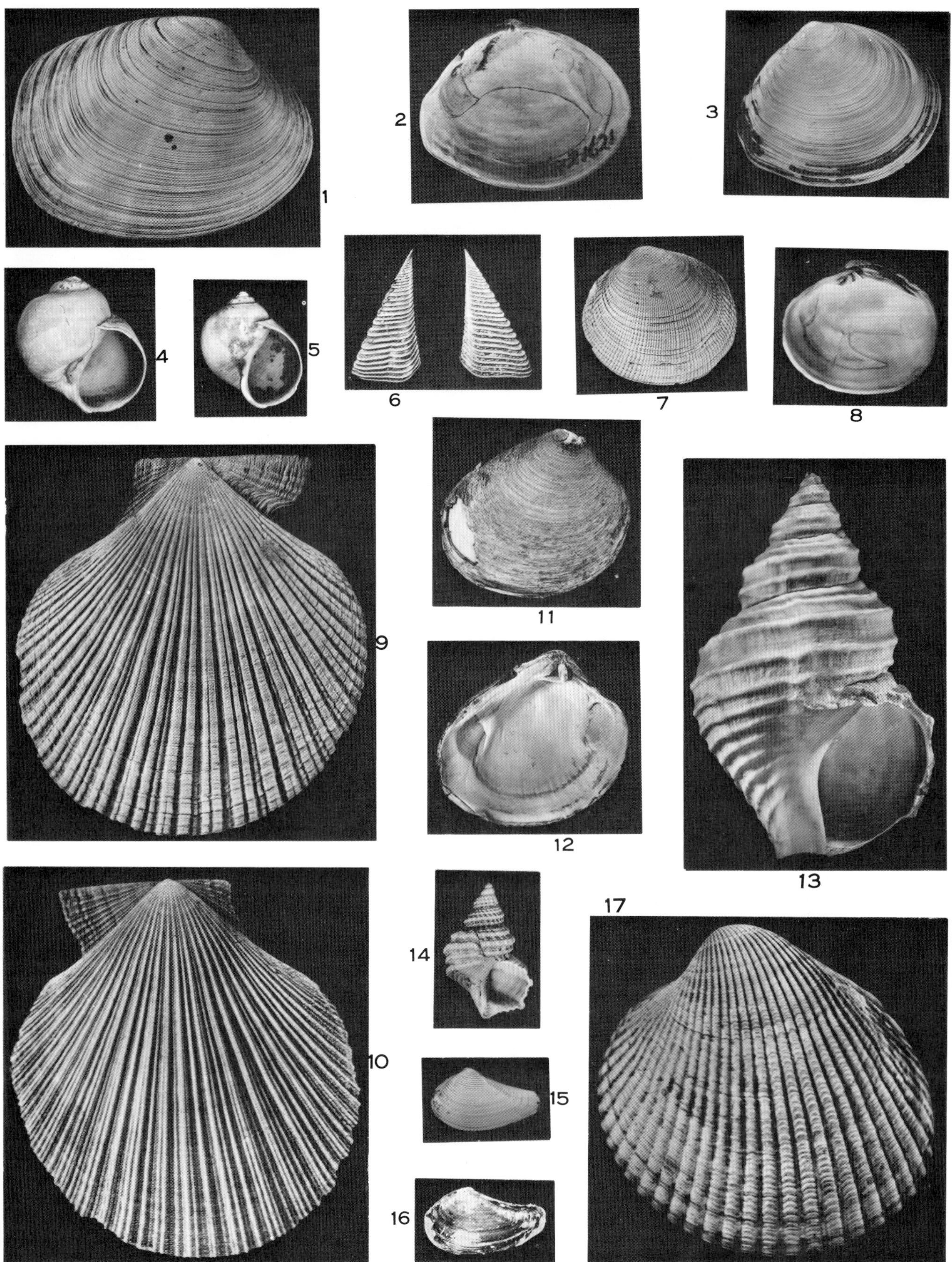
1
2
3
4
5
6
7
8
9
11
12
13
10
14
15
16
17

XII. Quaternary Geology of Canada

INTRODUCTION

The term Quaternary refers to about the last million years of the earth's history and is set apart from the Tertiary period by reason of the climatic changes that gave rise to successive glaciations of vast regions, and to a general lowering of snowlines throughout the world. Some recent oceanographical and paleontological data suggest that the climatic changes actually may have begun as early as 3 million years ago.

The geology of the glacial and non-glacial deposits that mantle the bedrock and various aspects of the landscape that are attributable to Quaternary events are discussed in this chapter. The term Quaternary in the writer's opinion, may be interchanged with Pleistocene as applied to Canada. This term is frequently used in Canada as it more readily conveys the glacial and climatic connotations, and accordingly is generally used here. The Pleistocene also includes the present, very short, non-glacial interval which is commonly termed Recent. In Canada, Recent may be regarded as comprising the last 7,000 years—the period following dissipation of the major part of the last mainland ice sheet.

At present, about 10 per cent of the earth's land surface is covered by glacier ice whereas during former glaciations as much as 30 per cent was under ice and permanent snowfields. About 97 per cent of Canada has been glaciated, and hence this country contains more glaciated terrain than any other; at present about one per cent remains under glacial cover—in the Queen Elizabeth Islands, Baffin Island, and in the mountains of western Canada. An area of about 70,000 square miles in the western Yukon, in the shadow of the coastal mountains, escaped glaciation altogether. Two elongate areas along the mountain front west of Mackenzie River in Northwest Territories, comprising about 4,000 square miles, are also thought to be partly unglaciated, but have been little studied. A small area in the Foothills of southwestern Alberta stood higher than the adjacent interior ice sheet, but harboured elongate valley glaciers from the mountain ice on its western side. Parts of the southern Interior Plains close to the International Boundary and near the southern terminus of the interior ice sheet apparently stood higher than the surrounding glaciers and escaped glaciation.

The organic remains preserved in the surficial deposits are mainly those of modern species. Study of their stratigraphic position and geographic location relative to their present distribution reveals information on former migration of plants and animals. Extinction and evolution of species occurred in the Quaternary, but not to the same degree as in earlier periods.

Man made his appearance during the Quaternary and his development has been controlled to a large degree by the climatic conditions so characteristic of the period. It is generally believed that it was the lowering of sea level, consequent upon the amount of water incorporated in continental ice, that allowed Asiatic tribes to migrate to

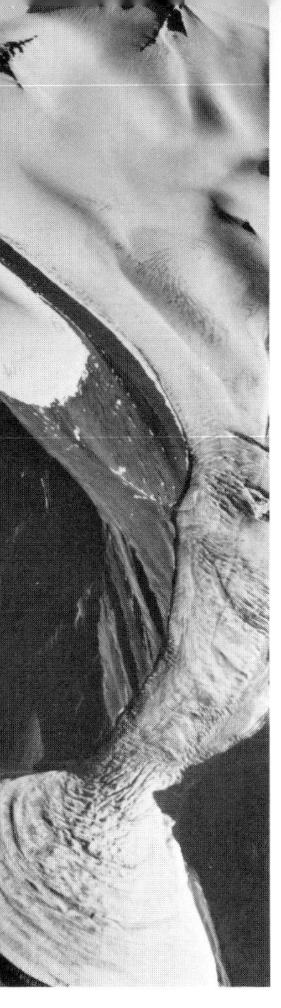

XII Quaternary Geology of Canada

V.K. Prest

Viking Ice Cap and glaciers, Ellesmere Island, Northwest Territories.

North America, mainly by land, via the Bering Sea land-bridge (north of Aleutian Islands chain). Later, as the glaciers waned, these people left the unglaciated *refugia* in Alaska and Yukon Territory, migrating eastward along the arctic coast and southward into the interior of the continent. Some of these people—the early North American Indians—camped along glacial lakes and spillways that have long since disappeared.

The Quaternary includes four major glaciations each of which occupied a period of about 100,000 years. From oldest to youngest these are known as Nebraskan, Kansan, Illinoian, and Wisconsin. They were separated by longer-term, interglacial intervals—the Aftonian, Yarmouth, and Sangamon—when climates were as warm or warmer than now and when the continent must have been largely ice free. Under such conditions a rich and varied flora and fauna must have occupied most parts of Canada. Few deposits, however, can be assigned with certainty to these interglacial intervals though all are probably represented in some known occurrences. Interglacial sediments buried by glacial drift have been reported from the Maritimes, Great Lakes, Interior Plains, Cordillera, and Arctic; all the intervals must be represented in the stratigraphy of Porcupine Plain in northern Yukon Territory, though this has as yet been little studied.

Each of the four major glaciations was interrupted by relatively short-term non-glacial intervals or interstades. These were times when the climate ameliorated and the glaciers receded extensively from peripheral zones but presumably continued to occupy part of the mainland. Plants and animals tolerant of a cool climate migrated into the newly deglaciated areas, only to have their progeny displaced by the re-advancing glaciers at a later date. In Canada such interstades have been recognized only within the Wisconsin Glaciation. The best known occurrences are in Lake Erie region of Ontario and around Strait of Georgia, British Columbia.

There is no generally accepted classification scheme for Wisconsin age sediments, but they may be subdivided on the basis of glacial and non-glacial deposits. By means of radiocarbon (C^{14}) dates of organic materials contained in some deposits, reliable correlation between scattered sites dating back to about 45,000 years have been made, but the detailed geological and biological studies necessary to support the age determinations are usually lacking. Reliable age-datings are generally restricted to the last 25,000 or 30,000 years B.P.[1]. Investigations in the Lake Erie region indicate a mid-Wisconsin interstade occupying a period of about 20,000 years. This has enabled subdivision of the Wisconsin Glaciation into two main stages—early and late. The latter is commonly termed the 'Classical' Wisconsin. Fluctuations of the ice fronts during the mid-Wisconsin interstade complicate the stratigraphic record. This interstade was brought to a close by a major ice-frontal advance

[1] B.P., "Before Present", refers to the year 1950. This is to be understood in connection with all datings that follow, though it will not always be repeated.

during which the glaciers returned to the vicinity of the limit reached during the earlier Wisconsin Glaciation. The late or Classical Wisconsin climax occurred about 20,000 years ago, and as mentioned earlier most ice had disappeared from the mainland by 7,000 years B.P. The time transgressive stratigraphic relationships recognized

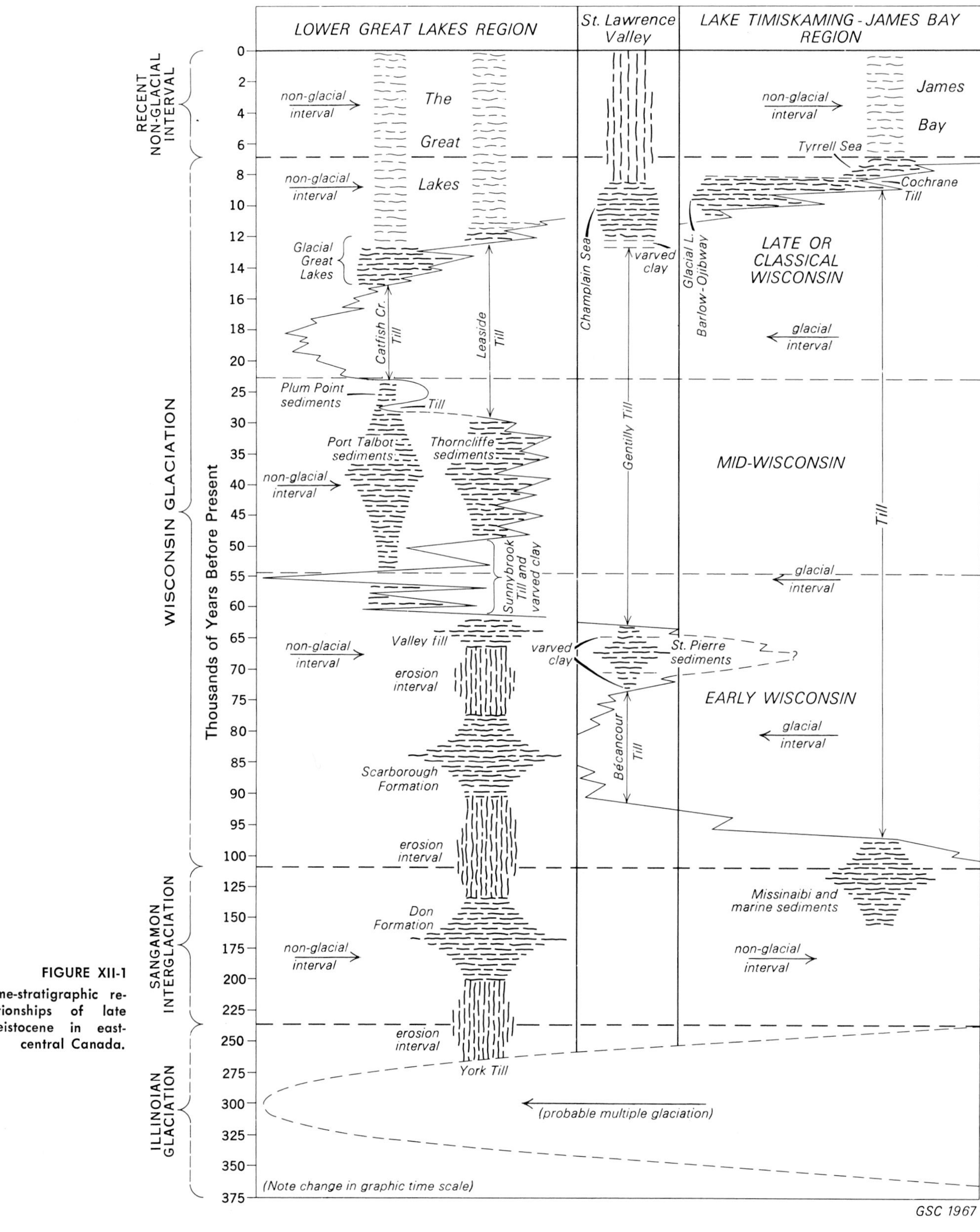

FIGURE XII-1 Time-stratigraphic relationships of late Pleistocene in east-central Canada.

in east-central Canada during the late Quaternary are illustrated diagrammatically in Figure XII-1; similar relationships are no doubt applicable to the whole of the Quaternary and to all parts of Canada.

Because there are uncertainties regarding Wisconsin events and their implications in different parts of Canada, and because many samples submitted for radiocarbon analyses have been given "greater than" datings, it is not yet possible to discuss interglacial deposits separately from Wisconsin, or other interstadial deposits. Furthermore, because of the general lack of paleontological or other data sufficiently accurate to identify specific interglacial deposits, the associated till sheets cannot be identified. Thus all deposits that predate the climax of the late, main, or Classical Wisconsin are discussed together, followed by an account of the last glaciation, and of deglaciation. In some parts of the Arctic and the Cordillera, glacial conditions have prevailed to the present and are manifested in the form of ice caps and mountain glaciers; for convenience, fluctuations of these ice masses are discussed along with Wisconsin deglacial events though strictly speaking they are post-Wisconsin.

THE OLDER GLACIAL AND NON-GLACIAL RECORD

This section deals with the Canadian record of the Quaternary prior to the climax of the Classical Wisconsin Glaciation; it includes glacial, interglacial, and interstadial deposits and the events that caused them or otherwise modified the landscape. Locally the deposits may be preglacial and represent events occurring in the earliest Quaternary.

Organic remains form a small but vitally important part of the sedimentary record, and are given considerable attention here. As a result of recognition of the environment and age of the non-glacial sediments the glacial sediments above or below them may be tentatively assigned to a particular glaciation. The deposits themselves and pertinent aspects of the physiography are treated on a regional rather than temporal basis.

Appalachian Region

The physiography of the Appalachian Region reflects some aspects of the older glacial and non-glacial intervals but these are, in general, effectively masked by the more obvious fresh landforms and deposits of the last glaciation. Numerous estuaries represent the drowned parts of former river systems that may have been operative during times of lower sea level in Quaternary time. R. H. MacNeill (Acadia Univ.) believes many of the streams in Nova Scotia are re-excavated preglacial channels, and also that some till-mantled coastal terraces were probably cut during preglacial times. A grey sandstone regolith is found in parts of eastern New Brunswick both at the surface and beneath a mantle of red, sandy till. It is formed of soft Pennsylvanian sandstone and siltstone, up to 25 feet thick, and argues against extensive modification of much of the topography at this time. The highlands of New Brunswick show surprisingly little evidence of glaciation; erratics appear to be absent over large areas and the bedrock is soft and deeply weathered.

Interglacial and interstadial deposits together with associated glacial deposits that predate the Classical Wisconsin have been recognized on Cape Breton Island, and one deposit is known on the Nova Scotia mainland; none has been recognized in Newfoundland, Prince Edward Island, New Brunswick, or the Gaspé.

Buried Organic Deposits (Fig. XII-2)

Bay St. Lawrence. Unconsolidated materials on the northeastern end of Cape Breton Island form a seacliff up to 150 feet high and comprise stratified sediments, with some organic materials, between stony till-like layers. Towards the southwest, bevelled bedrock is exposed beneath the drift. Up to 20 feet of hard-packed sand-gravel 'till' occurs at the base of the drift section. This is overlain by as much as 4 feet of interbedded fine gravel and silt, or by a boulder layer believed to be a washed-surface of the till. The stratified unit and boulder layer is overlain by a dense organic layer, a few inches to a foot thick, followed by 2 feet of stratified silt and as much as 30 feet of interbedded sand and gravel grading upward into cobble gravel. The silt beneath the organic layer was

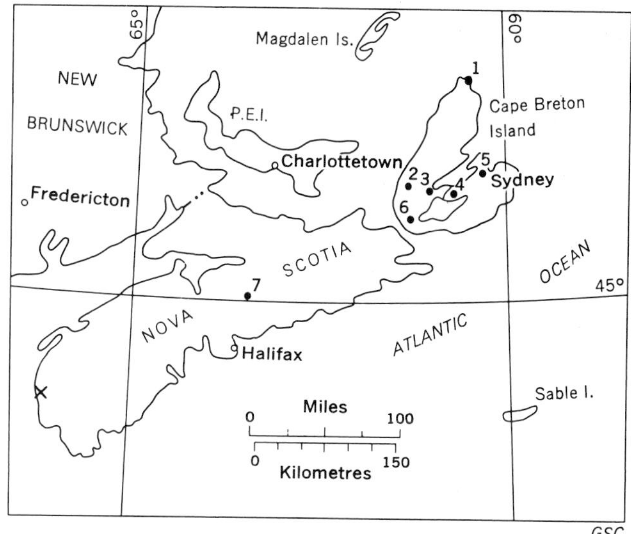

1. Bay St. Lawrence 2. Hillsborough 3. Whycocomagh 4. Benacadie 5. Leitches Creek 6. Inhabitants River 7. Milford
× Old' shell site: shells in till, Cape St. Mary

FIGURE XII-2. Location of buried organic deposits in Nova Scotia.

found to contain spores derived solely from Mississippian rocks. The organic bed represents a detrital sediment and contains pollen of alder, birch, black and white spruce, jack pine, balsam fir; a trace of juniper, willow, blue beech and walnut; and a variety of shrubs, herbs, grasses, ferns, mosses, and fungi (Mott and Prest, 1967). A piece of wood identified as tamarack has yielded a radiocarbon dating of >38,300 years (GSC-283)[1]. The immediately overlying silt beds contain similar pollen and spores but higher strata are barren. Nearby, E. H. Muller noted a lens of tan, silty clay, 12 feet thick at its maximum and 200 feet long. Overlying this lens and the cobble gravel (reported above) is a sandy boulder till some 30 to 90 feet thick, which becomes increasingly coarser upward; boulders as much as 8 by 5 feet occur near the surface.

In the clay lens are fragments of *Megayoldia thracaeformis*, a marine mollusc inhabiting waters colder than those surrounding Cape Breton today. The clay also contains pollen of alder and birch indicative of a cool climate but with pine, some oak, and a trace of basswood; otherwise the assemblage is similar to that of the detrital organic layer. Dinoflagellate cysts of Quaternary age and spores from the nearby Mississippian rocks are also present. The fossil record and radiocarbon date on the buried organic materials clearly indicate a pre-Classical Wisconsin cool period; this may be very early Wisconsin or perhaps late Sangamon.

Hillsborough. In southwestern Cape Breton Island between Mabou and Hillsborough from 8 to 12 feet of dull red, compact, clayey till overlies some 5 feet of stratified silty to clayey sediments that contain streaks and thin lenticular beds of carbonaceous material, and a basal layer of peat, silt, and wood a few inches to two or more feet thick. The organic layer rests on up to 18 inches of silt which in turn rests on an uneven ortstein layer developed on the surface of a highly oxidized sand and gravel more than 11 feet thick. The base of the exposed section at road level is about 10 feet above the level of the river and the sea.

The silty sediments and the peat bed (Mott and Prest, 1967) contain five pollen zones with a different assemblage predominating in each. The whole assemblage indicates a forest cover similar to that of the Boreal Forest Region rather than that of Cape Breton today. Wood from the base of the peat layer is dated at >51,000 years (GSC-370). An early Wisconsin or other interstadial interval is indicated but correlation with the Bay St. Lawrence site is not justifiable.

Whycocomagh. Buried organic beds in a highway-cut in the village of Whycocomagh, Cape Breton Island, were re-examined by the writer following an anomalous radiocarbon dating obtained on wood from this site. Gravelly till-like material 10 feet thick overlies 5 feet of stratified sediments ranging from fine gravel to silt and including a few inches of silty peat with scattered wood. The organic layers rest on 15 inches of partially oxidized clay and silt overlying 10 to 16 feet or more of stony, clay till that rests on an irregular bedrock surface. The stratified sediments extend for more than 50 feet, pinching out to the west as both bedrock and till mantle rise towards the surface. Pollen in the organic layer (Mott and Prest, 1967) is characterized by an assemblage dominated by alder, birch, spruce, and pine, and similar to part of the Hillsborough pollen diagram. Wood from the organic layer has an age of >44,000 years (GSC-290). The sites are only 15 miles apart at opposite ends of a throughgoing valley with a low drainage-divide; both sites lie close to sea level. They are believed correlative.

Benacadie. Intertill stratified sediments occur in a shore-cliff south of Benacadie at the entrance to East Bay, Bras d'Or Lake. Some 50 feet of reddish, stony, clay till overlies 5 feet of well-bedded clayey silts and a lower 20 feet of sand-gravel till. The clay-silt beds have a high percentage of pollen of pine (probably jack pine) and sedge, with lesser amounts of birch, alder, and grass (Mott and Prest, 1967). The assemblage has more affinities with the Bay St. Lawrence pollen diagrams than with those of the nearer Whycocomagh and Hillsborough sites. Another occurrence of intertill stratified sediments was found by Terasmae and Mott near Derby Point 4 miles northwest of Benacadie. Beneath the level of the shore road, 2 feet of reddish, clayey till overlies a few feet of silty clay, sand with plant detritus, and sandy gravel that rest on about 10 feet of slumped till down to sea level. The intertill silty clay did not carry pollen.

Leitches Creek. Part of a drill-log and some samples from a borehole at Leitches Creek, west of Sydney, that penetrated some 190 feet of overburden, indicate the presence of two layers of organic-bearing sediments each underlain and overlain by till. Preliminary pollen studies suggest that the lower organic layer is of interglacial age and that the upper layer correlates with the Hillsborough interstadial interval.

Inhabitants River. Buried organic deposits were reported in 1868 by J. W. Dawson from Inhabitants River, Cape Breton Island. A hard, peaty bed with roots and branches of coniferous trees rests on grey clays and underlies about 20 feet of till. The site has not been relocated.

Milford. A unique deposit of buried organic material found as overburden was removed at the gypsum quarry 2½ miles south of Milford Station, Nova Scotia. Beech nut *(Fagus* sp.), hickory nut *(Carya* sp., cf. *C. aquatica)*, bayberry seed *(Myrica pennsylvanica)*, and a beaver-cut stick were collected from a sinkhole in the gypsum. The

[1] These letters refer to the radiocarbon laboratory responsible for the age dating and the number is the sample reference number. GSC, Geological Survey of Canada; Gx, Geochron. Laboratories; Gro and GrN, Groningen, Netherlands; I, Isotopes Inc.; L, Lamont Geological Observatory; S, University of Saskatchewan; Y, Yale University; W, U.S. Geological Survey.

PLATE XII-1
Karst topography on gypsum at site of interglacial deposits, Milford, Nova Scotia. The sinkholes contained a mixture of glacial and non-glacial sediments including organic materials dated at >38,000 years B.P. The gypsum surface is ice scoured and overlain by a complex of tills and fossiliferous sediments visible in bluff in background.

wood was dated at >33,800 years (GSC-33). The following notes on the quarry site and its environs are based on observations by W. Take (Nova Scotia Museum).

The surface of the gypsum displays a karst topography (Pl. XII-1). In the base of depressions there is usually a mixture of slumped till and glaciofluvial materials, overlain by unfossiliferous brown to grey clay and sphagnum peat containing gastropods and patches of slumped till. Overlying the peat unit is highly fossiliferous grey clay and sandy clay. The thin basal part of the clay is characterized by abundant macrofossils of white pine and rare hemlock; the latter increases upward and is evenly distributed. Logs, beaver-sharpened sticks, cones, insects, mollusca, amphibian and mammalian remains were collected from the stratified clays. An erosional unconformity separates the clay from plant-bearing sands—mainly spruce, fir, and rare white pine cones.

The sinkhole deposits and the glacially scoured surface of the bedrock are evenly truncated and overlain by a compact, grey, gypsiferous till. In places this till carries woody detritus; in two places it has a boulder pavement developed on it. The till is generally overlain by sediments grading from unfossiliferous grey clay through fossil-bearing silty clay, into highly fossiliferous grey sand with abundant twigs of coniferous trees as well as cones of spruce and rarely of fir. Overlying these sediments are two very similar tills, separated in valley bottoms by orange-brown gravelly sands. The basal part of each till, and especially of the lower one, is gypsiferous. The tills change from grey near the base to grey-brown at the top. In upland sections the combined till is a uniform brown colour, does not contain gypsum but is deeply oxidized. At one locality it has a well-developed soil-profile.

Lying on a grey-brown till about 35 feet above sea level in some valleys is an orange-brown to red-brown laminated clay with vertical rootlets in its upper part suggestive of a marsh environment. At somewhat higher elevations, a black clay carries mollusc remains, white pine cones, hemlock bark and cones, and red oak acorns. A distinctive red-brown clay till overlies the stratified sediments in low areas, and the grey-brown tills on higher ground. This is followed by a complex of red clays, red till, minor glaciofluvial sand and gravel, and a thin sand-gravel till unit, the last strictly confined to the valleys. Glaciofluvial sand and gravel, and stratified clay and silty clay, both with the modern soil profile or a cultivated surface, complete the sequence of deposits.

Take considers the Milford deposits to represent parts of the Kansan, Illinoian, and Wisconsin Glaciations, as well as the Yarmouth and Sangamon interglacial intervals. Certainly interglacial as well as interstadial fossil assemblages are indicated, but the implications of the karst topography have precluded definite correlations.

St. Lawrence Lowlands

Major features of the physiography of the St. Lawrence Lowlands, such as Niagara Escarpment and the bordering highlands of the Canadian Shield and Appalachian Region, predate the Quaternary and, except for local over-deepening of valleys and some glacial scour, were little changed by glaciation. The great morainal belts in southwestern Ontario bear testimony to the direct effects of glaciation. Drift thickness in the Oak Ridges interlobate moraine reaches over 1,000 feet, and there is some evidence of a buried drainage system north of Lake Ontario beneath what is now a major ridge overlooking the lake. The St. Lawrence and Ottawa River valleys are filled by 100 to 200 feet of marine sediments, and in an area of high bedrock knobs north of Oka-sur-le-Lac a channel containing about 400 feet of drift rests on rotted bedrock some 175 feet below present sea level. Thus the flat valley bottoms bear little resemblance to the more mature drainage systems of interglacial and preglacial times.

In the St. Lawrence Lowlands the only undoubted interglacial deposits are those of the Toronto area where the Don Formation is assigned to the Sangamon interglacial interval, and the basal York Till is thought to represent an Illinoian glaciation (Karrow, 1967). Near Trois-Rivières, Quebec, and Toronto and London, Ontario, numerous occurrences of buried organic materials appear to represent non-glacial intervals within the span of the Wisconsin glacial period.

Buried Organic Deposits (Fig. XII-3)

Trois-Rivières. The Quebec part of the St. Lawrence Lowlands near Trois-Rivières has been studied in some detail by Gadd (1960, *in press*). The St. Lawrence Valley drainage system appears to have been blocked in very early Wisconsin time, giving rise to a glacial lake and deposition of reddish varved clays (Table XII-1). These clays were later overridden by the glacier and the Bécancour Till, a brick-red, somewhat sandy, clay till, was deposited. This till is known over a wide area south of the St. Lawrence, but the southern limit reached by the glacier is unknown. The till derives its rich red colour from the Ordovician, Queenston, red shales. Most stones in the till, however, are Precambrian types and hence the glacier that deposited the till came from the Canadian Shield, presumably from the Laurentian Highlands. However, neither the red till nor a correlative grey till has been recognized north of St. Lawrence River.

The type section of the St. Pierre sediments is near St. Pierre les Becquets, Quebec (Gadd, 1960). The name 'St. Pierre' is given to the intertill sediments and to the interval during which they were deposited. The sediments overlie the red Bécancour Till and consist of sand and silty sand with lenticular and discontinuous beds of highly compressed peat and some disseminated organic matter. The sand unit has a maximum thickness of 25 feet, but at the type section is only 13 feet thick and includes three layers of peat. The upper and thickest peat bed where observed along a ravine near St. Pierre les Becquets was 1.75 feet thick and was traced for over 200 yards. Each peat layer begins with a gyttja and grades upward through *Carex* peat into *Sphagnum* peat with abundant tree and other plant remains, the whole suggestive of periodic flooding of the lowlands.

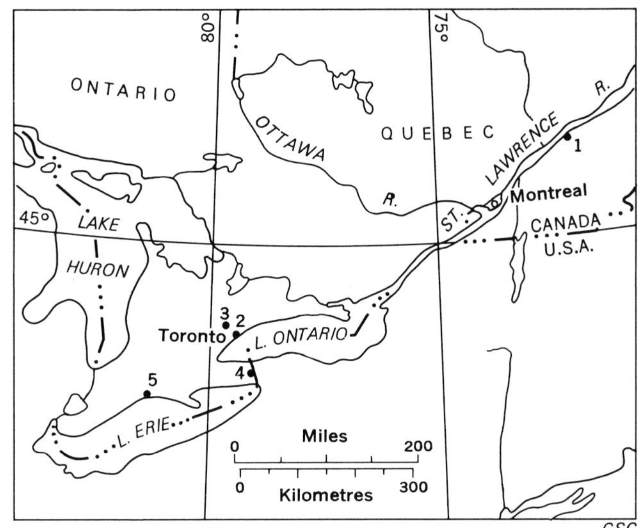

1. Trois Rivières area
2. Toronto
3. Woodbridge
4. Niagara Falls
5. Port Talbot

FIGURE XII-3. Location of buried organic deposits in St. Lawrence Lowlands.

The St. Pierre sediments occur for about 50 miles along the south side of St. Lawrence River from Pierreville to Deschaillons and inland for about 20 miles to Ste. Brigitte (Pl. XII-2). They have also been found on the north side of the river, at Les Veilles Forges, about 6 miles northwest of Trois-Rivières (Gadd and Karrow, 1960). According to P. F. Karrow, it is very likely that the organic-bearing sediments reported by A. P. Coleman at Donnacona 50 miles to the east are the equivalent of the St. Pierre sediments. Some peaty sediments of uncertain stratigraphic position and non-organic sediments between

PLATE XII-2

Section of postglacial sediments, Gentilly Till, and St. Pierre sediments on Bécancour River, north of Aston Junction, Quebec. Sediments are probably underlain by red Bécancour till exposed downstream. (A) St. Pierre sand and pebbly sand >60 feet, (B) Gentilly Till 15 feet, (C) Champlain Sea clay 24 feet, (D) alluvial sand 6 feet.

two tills elsewhere in the region suggest that the St. Pierre sediments are even more widespread. The whole appears to represent an old fluvial system that is slowly being exposed by the St. Lawrence River and its tributaries.

Palynological studies of St. Pierre sediments reveal that spruce, pine, birch, and alder are the main tree types present, and that oak, beech, maple, elm, ash, and hickory together form only 2 to 5 per cent of the tree pollen in the middle and warmest part of the sequence. Hemlock is noticeably absent. The pollen spectrum is similar to that of the early postglacial assemblages in the St. Lawrence Lowlands, except for the absence of hemlock, and it is similar to that of the boreal forest today (Terasmae, 1958, p. 20). Beetle wings are fairly common in the peat beds and a few ostracods have been noted. Terasmae concludes that the climate remained fairly constant throughout most of the St. Pierre interval with sub-arctic conditions prevailing near the bottom and top, and that a relatively short span of time is involved.

Samples from Pierreville and St. Pierre were dated at Groningen by an isotopic enrichment method at 67,000 ± 2,000 years and 64,000 ± 1,000 years, and a sample from Donnacona by conventional techniques at >44,470 years (Y-463). Thus, St. Pierre sediments are inferred to represent an early Wisconsin non-glacial interval. The St. Pierre sediments are overlain by the Lake Deschaillons varved clay, 70 feet thick, deposited in a proglacial lake; these in turn are overlain by Gentilly Till deposited by the advancing ice sheet. This ice cover persisted throughout the greater part of Wisconsin time until final recession of the ice sheet and incursion of the sea into St. Lawrence

TABLE XII-1 *Composite section of Pleistocene deposits, St. Lawrence Lowlands (by N. R. Gadd)*

	(Max. known thickness, feet)
Bog deposits	20
Low terrace sands, el. ca. 100′	10
High terrace sands, el. ca. 300′	10
Champlain Sea sand	25
St. Narcisse Till	15+
Champlain Sea clay	100
Gentilly Till	15
Lake Deschaillons varved clay	70
St. Pierre sediments	25
Red-banded varved clay	5
Bécancour Till	55
Red varved clay	5
Bedrock (Queenston red shale)	—

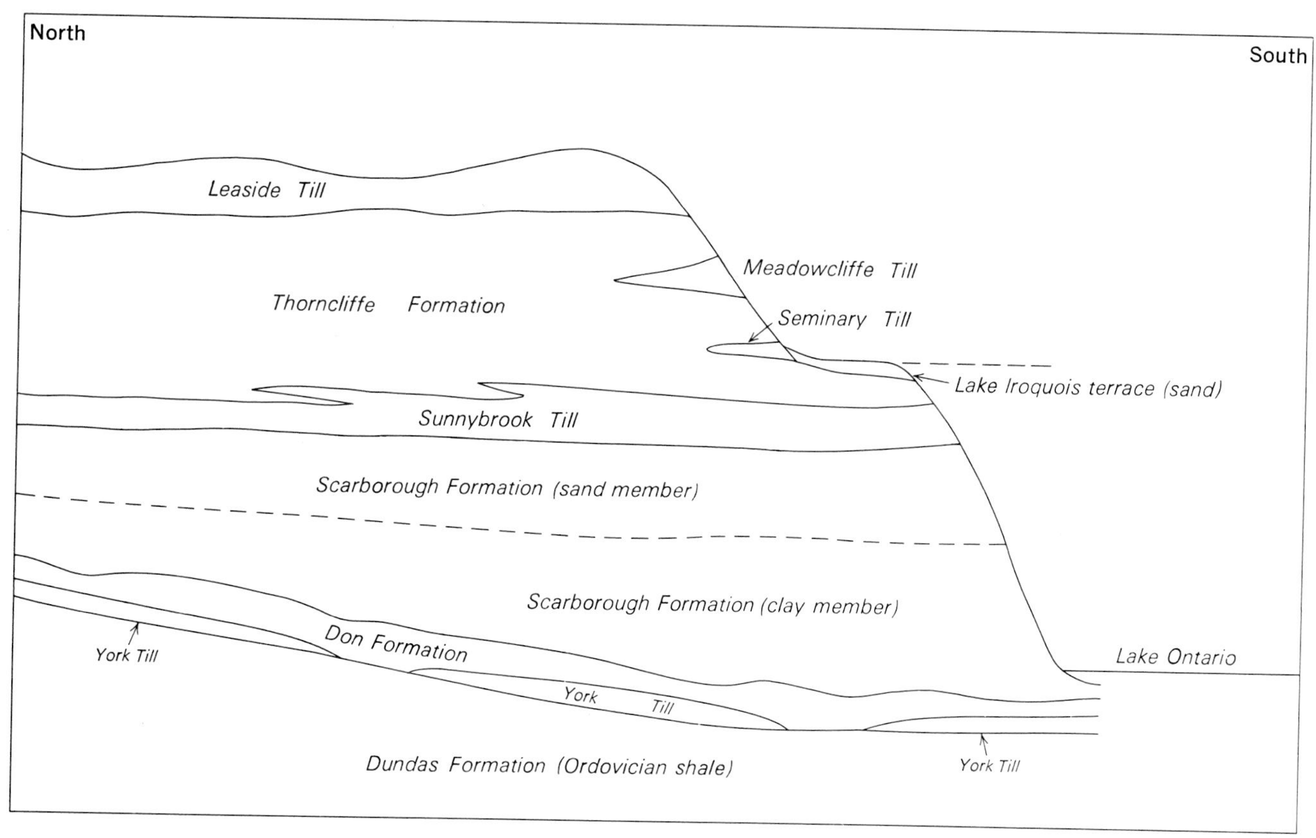

FIGURE XII-4. Schematic diagram showing stratigraphic relationships of Pleistocene deposits at Scarborough Bluffs, Toronto, Ontario (after Karrow, 1964).

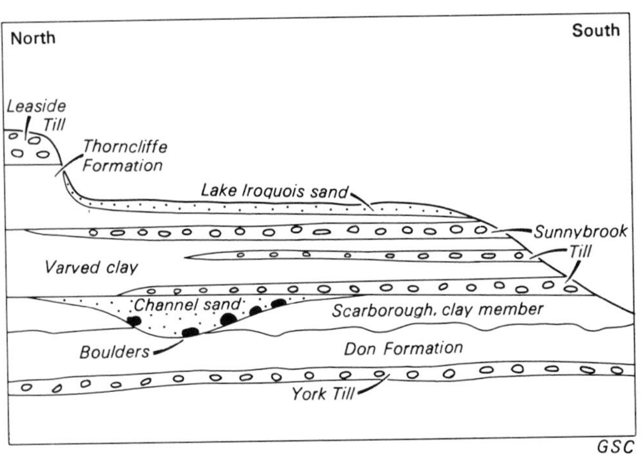

FIGURE XII-5. Schematic diagram showing stratigraphic relationships of Pleistocene deposits in Don Valley brickyard, Toronto, Ontario (after Karrow, 1964).

Lowlands almost 12,000 years ago. Subsequently, differential uplift of the land caused regression of the sea, and the present drainage system was established.

Toronto. The most famous buried, non-glacial Pleistocene deposits in Canada are those of the Toronto area. They have been known for over a century and have been under more or less continual observation in the Don Valley brickyard operations since 1889. Recent studies have done much to clarify the chronology recorded by the complex deposits. The non-glacial organic-bearing beds have been encountered in the extensive subway excavations and other construction projects of the last decade. The sequence of non-glacial deposits in the region is shown schematically in Figures XII-4 and 5.

In the Don Valley brickyard the basal York Till is one to four feet thick and rests on Ordovician strata. It is overlain by fossil-bearing stratified sediments of the Don Formation (Karrow, 1964, 1967). An appreciable hiatus occurred between the deposition of the York Till and the Don Formation as the basal parts of the latter contain pollen of a warm flora (Terasmae, 1960, p. 33).

The Don Formation consists of up to 25 feet of generally well stratified clay and sand displaying some crossbeds and cut-and-fill structures, and containing scattered remains of a wide variety of plants and animals. Noteworthy among the plants, in that they do not range so far north today, are southern white cedar, blue ash, osage orange, iron oak, chestnut oak, and black locust. In all, some 44 taxa of plants have been identified from macroscopic remains. Most of these have been recognized also as pollen, plus an additional 28 taxa, including pollen of sweet gum, that are not found in the Toronto area today (Terasmae, 1960). Terasmae also identified some 20 species of diatoms, and noted the presence of freshwater sponge spicules from the middle part of the Don Formation, which indicate lake, stream, and bog habitats. Animal remains recovered include the shells of some 40 species of pelecypods and gastropods (including a few land snails), part of a catfish, and bones of groundhog, deer, bison, bear, and giant beaver. Terasmae states: "An ecological-climatological interpretation of all evidence supplied by the fossils from the Don beds suggests that the annual mean temperature at the time of their deposition reached a maximum probably 5°F warmer than the present." In recent years investigations by Karrow and others have shown that wood is not common and leaves and vertebrate remains are very rare.

The Don Formation occurs some 60 feet above the level of Lake Ontario (el. 246 feet) in the brickyard but its upper surface is below lake level at Scarborough Bluffs. The lower part was deposited at the mouth of a river as it entered a lake in the Ontario basin. Lowering of the lake level is recorded by the character of the diatom assemblage in the middle part of the beds and by the sandy nature of the upper part of the formation. The upper sandy beds furthermore had been leached and weathered (Terasmae, 1960; Karrow, 1964) prior to the deposition of the overlying cool-climate Scarborough Formation. In the Don Valley brickyard the Don Formation is locally separated from the overlying Scarborough Formation by a layer of hard, compact, non-calcareous sand with some pebbles and cobbles. The formational contact was also encountered in borings at Scarborough Bluffs 15 feet below lake level. The Don Formation clearly represents part of an interglacial interval. It is generally assigned to the Sangamon but exact dispositon must await further work.

The Scarborough Formation (Karrow, 1964) is best known from the exposures on Scarborough Bluffs where it comprises a lower clayey-silt unit about 100 feet thick and an upper sandy unit about 50 feet thick, but it is also present in the Don Valley brickyard. There, the Scarborough clay unit is less than 25 feet thick and seemingly devoid of fossils although a few plant detrital seams have been noted between the thin clay layers. This deposit is very finely bedded and is regarded as a deep water deposit. The clay unit at Scarborough Bluffs includes peaty layers in places half an inch or more thick. These have yielded many small fossils including diatoms, and the leaves, seeds or spores of some 15 plants and, notably, the wing covers and other chitinous parts of some 72 species of beetle (Coleman, 1933). The beetles are reported as mostly extinct species but a re-study of the beetle content of the Scarborough plant detrital layers is needed. Terasmae has identified 41 plants from the clay unit, which indicates a boreal forest cover. The overlying sandy unit also contains plant detrital layers, sparse ostracods, and molluscs. Terasmae reports a pollen assemblage of boreal forest species similar to those found in the lower clay unit. He concludes that the climate during Scarborough times was perhaps 10°F cooler than now. The sands were deposited by southeast-flowing waters and presumably represent a delta formed in a lake (Lake Scarborough) that stood some 200 feet higher than the present lake. A piece of wood from near the top of the Scarborough Formation at Scarborough was dated at >52,000 years (Gro-2555), hence the precise age of the beds remains unknown.

The writer considers the Scarborough beds to be older than the St. Pierre sediments. Lake Scarborough formed after a lengthy erosional interval during which the Don beds were scoured and weathered. Lake Scarborough may be attributed to plugging of the drainage system by an advancing glacier, and the biotic record seems to support this view. The St. Pierre sediments represent an old river system with associated flood plain deposits, which required a through-flowing St. Lawrence Valley drainage system. Thus the Scarborough Formation has to be either younger or older than the St. Pierre sediments, and based on other evidence noted below it is considered to be older.

Organic matter is also present in post-Scarborough deposits. During and following the lowering of the Scarborough lake, deep valleys were cut into the Scarborough Formation, and in places into the Don Formation. Rising lake levels again brought about deposition of sandy sediments within these valleys. Boulders and cobbles, and occasional balls of till occur in the bottom of a channel in the Don Valley brickyard, which may indicate a significant time gap. The organic materials found in these sediments have been in part re-deposited from the older beds but some are indigenous to this stage of sedimentation. Of special interest is the first occurrence noted in Canada of the distinctive gastropod *Hendersonia occulta.* Coleman (1933) records water-worn "vertebrae of bison, part of a lower jaw of a bear, and a horn of an extinct deer, *Cervalces borealis,*" and bits of ivory from mammoth or mastodon; these are from the Christie Street sand pits which P. F. Karrow correlates with the above-mentioned valley-fillings.

Subsequent to a mid-Wisconsin glacial invasion into the Lake Ontario basin and deposition of the Sunnybrook Till and varved clays, another period of non-glacial sedimentation occurred. The sediments formed at this time contain sparse plant remains and comprise the Thorncliffe Formation (Karrow, 1964), which consists of stratified clay, silt, and sand believed to have been deposited in both lakes and streams. Near Lake Ontario two wedges of till interfinger with the Thorncliffe Formation as a result of short-term expansions of the westward-moving ice. Both the sparse plant fragments and the till lenses (Seminary and Meadowcliffe Tills) indicate a rather cold climate. Jack pine and spruce were the dominant tree types with minor tamarack, oak, and birch; non-arboreal pollen was rather abundant. A small sample of plant material from the Thorncliffe beds has been dated at 38,900±1,300 years (GSC-271). Glaciation, foreshadowed by the interfingering tills, then engulfed the region during the classical Wisconsin with deposition of the Leaside Till. Vegetal and animal life did not return until late glacial and early postglacial times.

Markham and Woodbridge. A few miles north of Toronto old organic materials have been observed beneath till. At Markham, a peat ball found in a gravel pit and dated at >34,000 years (W-194) is thought to have been derived from Thorncliffe beds or the Scarborough Formation. At Woodbridge, five discrete tills and a few feet of bedded silt, the whole comprising up to 35 feet, rest on some 25 feet of clayey silt with streaks and lenses of

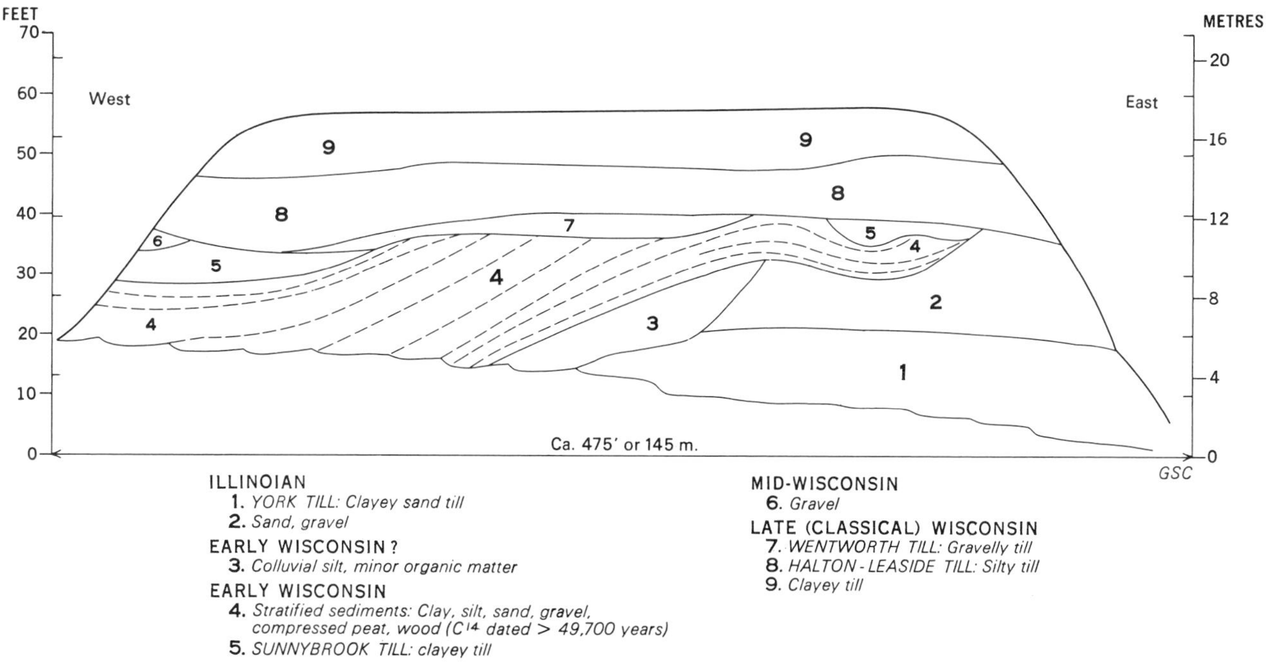

FIGURE XII-6. Wisconsin and Illinoian drift in railway-cut, Woodbridge, Ontario (after Karrow, 1965).

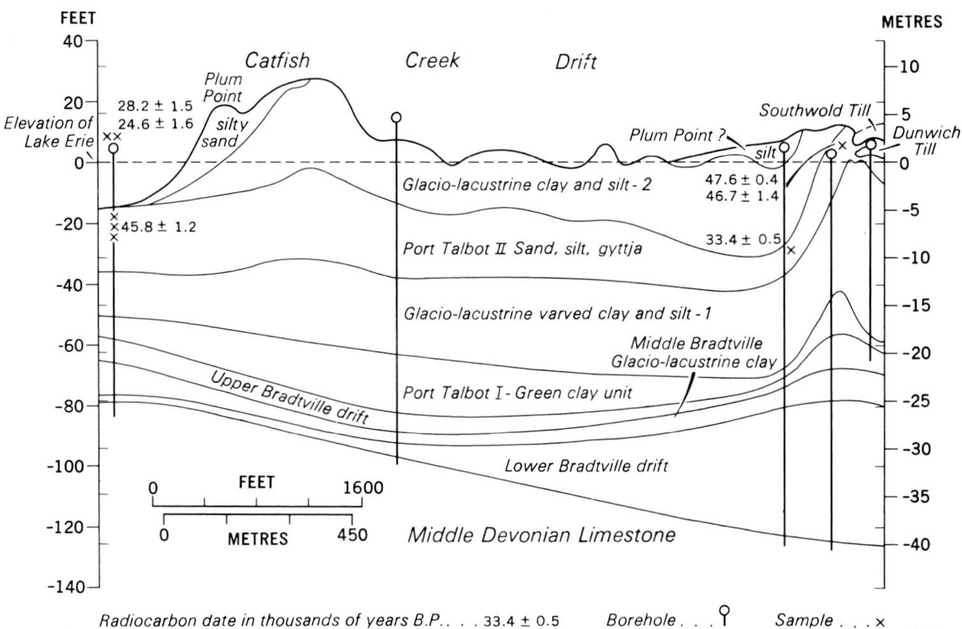

FIGURE XII-7
Generalized profile through Pleistocene deposits near Port Talbot, Ontario (after Dreimanis, et al., 1966).

peat and wood (Fig. XII-6). Another 14 feet of sand and gravel and 9 feet of till of Illinoian age are exposed at the base of the cut (Karrow, 1965). Some peat balls have been seen in the clayey till that overlies the peaty sediments. Palynological studies reveal that a northern boreal forest grew in the area at that time, with jack pine, black and white spruce, and birch the main tree types. This assemblage and a radiocarbon dating of >49,700 years (GSC-203) suggest a correlation with the Scarborough Formation, though a post-Scarborough age is also possible.

Niagara Falls. Silt in the buried St. David's channel near Niagara Falls has yielded a spore and pollen assemblage that is indicative of the northern boreal forest zone. Pollen studies by Terasmae substantiate the early report of fragments of spruce wood, from a boring over the channel, at a depth of 186 feet. Correlation of these silt deposits with other non-glacial beds in Ontario is not yet conclusive, but they may well be mid-Wisconsin.

Port Talbot. Buried organic deposits indicative of non-glacial conditions were reported by A. Dreimanis in 1951 from the Lake Erie shore south of London. As investigations progressed both along the shore and by drilling a complex sequence of deposits was indicated (Fig. XII-7). Radiocarbon datings on organic materials appeared to fall into main groupings, namely, about 48,000 to 44,000 years B.P. and about 28,000 to 23,000 years B.P. The indicated non-glacial intervals were thought to be separated by a glacial period represented by a till sheet (Southwold) found overlying the 'older' sediments in several places. The two intervals were named Port Talbot and Plum Point by Dreimanis (1957, 1958).

The main organic-bearing deposit at Port Talbot is exposed at the base of a 100-foot bluff overlooking Lake Erie. Contorted beds of silt, clay, calcareous gyttja, and scattered peat balls are overlain by glaciolacustrine clay and silt, organic-bearing silt and silty sand of Plum Point unit, and an uppermost drift complex of the main or Classical Wisconsin Glaciation. The gyttja contains larch, spruce, and water plants (*Potamogeton, Menyanthes,* and *Najas*) (Dreimanis, *et al.,* 1966). Part of a mastodon tusk was found in a clayey bouldery gravel some 600 feet east of the gyttja site at the same stratigraphic horizon. Some 17 species of ostracods have been recorded from the clayey silts both above and below the gyttja horizon. Mollusc shells from both the silts and the gyttja appear to have been crushed by the glacial action that contorted the beds but three genera have been recognized. The pollen assemblage from the gyttja horizon indicates that pine (mostly jack pine), spruce, larch, and birch were the dominant trees in the region. The base of the gyttja includes also large pollen grains of either white or red pine. The organic record indicates that the climate was cooler than that at present along the Lake Erie shore.

In boreholes at Port Talbot, beneath stratified sediments dating 47,700±1,200 years (GSC-217), up to about 30 feet of brownish buff varved silt and clay with a sparse pollen content overlies a few feet of greenish clay and silt with abundant pollen of jack pine, spruce, oak, and non-arboreal pollen. Mineralogical characteristics of the green clay and silt suggest a gap in the record after deposition of the basal, reddish (Bradtville) till, which rests on bedrock some 130 feet below surface of Lake Erie. Thus the Port Talbot non-glacial interval may extend back 50,000 years B.P. The lower Bradtville Till has been subdivided into three units of very similar lithology with the lower two separated by a glaciolacustrine clay. The initial advance of Wisconsin ice into Erie basin, from the east, appears to have removed all evidence of interglacial or older glacial deposits in Port Talbot area. The initial advance was followed by a retreat stage during which a glacial lake occupied the basin. Two later encroachments of the ice formed the middle and upper Bradtville Till sheets. The time occupied by these early Wisconsin events is unknown but possibly 5,000 to 10,000 years.

Recent radiocarbon dates of 33,400±500 and 38,000±1,500 (GrN-4238, 4272) indicate that the time gap between the Port Talbot and Plum Point non-glacial intervals was short. It now appears that one long-continued interval, a mid-Wisconsin interstade, may be represented by the intertill stratified sediments and their contained organic matter. Southwold Till, formerly considered to intervene, is now correlated with the younger Catfish Creek Till which overlies the Plum Point sediments (Dreimanis, *et al.,* 1966). Thus, non-glacial conditions may have prevailed in the Port Talbot area from about 50,000 years to about 24,000 years ago. The ice front was, however, not too far away during this long period of sedimentation; the eastern end of Erie basin was blocked by ice on two occasions during which glacial lake clays were deposited and also ice of northern derivation was nearby when the Dunwich Till was deposited at some time during the Port Talbot interval.

Hudson Bay Lowland

The history of Pleistocene events in Hudson Bay Lowland has been dealt with by Lee (1968a). Important deposits bearing on the early Pleistocene record have recently been obtained by Craig and McDonald (1968).

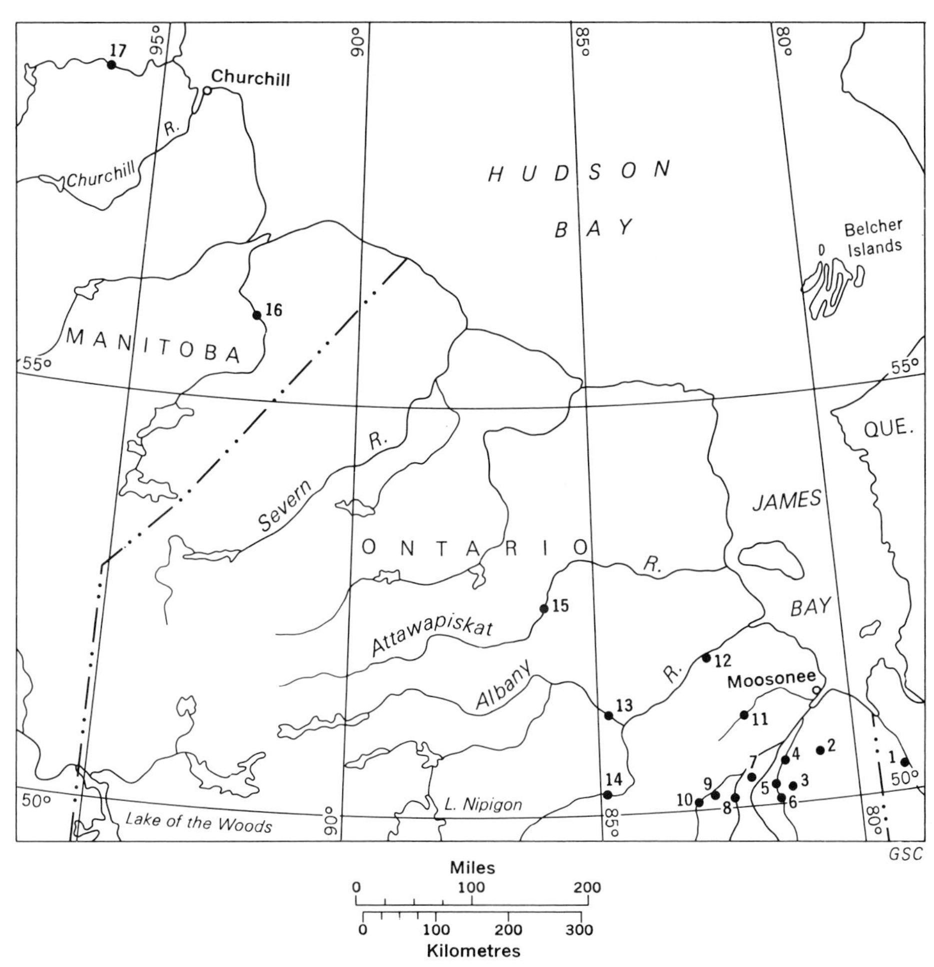

FIGURE XII-8
Location of buried organic deposits in Hudson Bay Lowland.

1. Harricanaw River
2. Nettogami River
3. Little Abitibi River
4. 5. 6. Abitibi River
7. Campbell Lake
8. 9. 10. Missinaibi and Opasatika River
11. Kwataboahegan River
12. 13. Albany River
14. Kenogami River
15. Attawapiskat River
16. Gods River
17. Seal River

Buried Organic Deposits (Fig. XII-8)

In the Hudson Bay Lowland there are numerous records of organic deposits lying below or between glacial tills. The published records are confusing in that the term lignite has been applied not only to Lower Cretaceous lignite deposits but also to Quaternary compressed peat and to sands, of both glacial and non-glacial affinities, containing detrital lignite. Eliminating the occurrences that are probably Cretaceous and the sands with detrital lignite grains of Quaternary age, a great many occurrences remain which, in the writer's opinion, record Quaternary non-glacial intervals in the Lowland. The occurrences are commonly cited as of interglacial age and indeed their wide distribution lends credence to this concept, but with present knowledge of Wisconsin interstades, a younger setting must be kept in mind where there is no strong evidence to the contrary. The more important sites exclusive of new ones found by Craig and McDonald are described below from east to west:

Harricanaw River. Two miles below Seven Mile Island, rhythmically bedded silt and sand with some thin vegetal layers underlie a marine clay beneath river sand and gravel. The vegetal layers were dated at >42,000 years (Y-1165).

Nettogami River. On the Nettogami River the lignite reported by Bell (1904) is most probably Pleistocene compressed peat. He refers (p. 161) to thick beds of black clay-shale with a great many very thin seams of a rather peaty lignite and to boulder clay containing striated pebbles both above and below the organic beds.

Little Abitibi River. Sections along the lower part of Little Abitibi River and along the adjacent Abitibi River reveal dark grey, compact and jointed silty clay beneath till and Tyrrell Sea deposits. Thin peaty laminae yielded pollen of black spruce, jack pine, and birch, together with varied non-arboreal pollen and spores of ferns and mosses. Farther up Little Abitibi River, silty and carbonaceous beds in the lower part of a 70-foot section of sand yielded much the same pollen assemblage. Wood from the lower part of the sand unit gave an age of >43,600 years (GSC-435). These deposits probably correlate with the Missinaibi beds on the Missinaibi River.

Abitibi River. The occurrence of buried Pleistocene organic deposits in the Moose River basin, including sites along Abitibi River (Bell, 1904; Wilson, 1906), may appear doubtful because of the Lower Cretaceous lignite found along Abitibi, Mattagami, and Missinaibi Rivers. Study of borehole data and excavations at Otter Rapids, however, revealed plant detritus in intertill sediments and indicated correlation with Pleistocene beds along Missinaibi River (Terasmae and Hughes, 1960). Furthermore at the Onakawana lignite workings, close to the river sections observed by Bell and Wilson, buried organic deposits of Pleistocene age were encountered in a shaft and in some 116 exploratory drillholes (Martison, 1953). Two till sheets separated by interglacial or interstadial sand, gravel, and clay are clearly present.

On Abitibi River 8 miles below Otter Rapids the writer has observed contorted beds of compact, dark grey, stony clay, containing broken or fractured marine shells, beneath younger drift. Eleven species of foraminifers, three of ostracods, and two of pelecypods were identified along with indeterminate species of forams, a pelecypod, and sponge spines, and spicules. Most of the species live in Hudson Bay at present. The stony marine clay overlies an oxidized quartzose sand, with a bed of differentially rotted igneous boulders. The marine deposits and the oxidized sand are considered to represent an interglacial interval. They are overlain by a Wisconsin clayey till and Tyrrell Sea deposits. Half a mile downstream the till rests on several feet of gravel containing limestone and igneous rocks; although the gravel appears to overlie the interglacial stony clay it is presumed to be much younger. Coleman (1941) also reported peaty clay and marine shells from interglacial sediments along Abitibi River, as well as shells from crumpled clay beds beneath till at Moose Factory.

Campbell Lake. A drillhole at Campbell Lake (Wawa Lakes) intersected 725 feet of drift resting on Paleozoic rocks (Hogg, *et al.*, 1953). J. Satterly reports that microfauna were recovered from samples taken at intervals between 262 and 645 feet—a section that includes two tills and two or three stratified clayey units. The fauna are of Pleistocene age and, as they were largely marine foraminifers, it is probable that the beds are interglacial. The great depth of overburden, in a section that includes both tills and marine beds, appears to indicate the presence of both preglacial and interglacial valleys of the Mattagami River. Microfauna identified in research laboratories, Shell Oil Co., are as follows:

Nonion grateloupi (d'Orbigny)
Elphidium gunteri (Cole)
Cibicides concentricus (Cushman)
Quinqueloculina lamarckiana (d'Orbigny)
Quinqueloculina seminulum (Linnaeus)
Discorbis sp.
Elphidium discoidale (d'Orbigny)
Siphonina cf. *pulchra* Cushman
echinoid spines
fragments gastropods and pelecypods
unidentified ostracod and plant spores
Cibicides pseudoungeriana (Cushman)
Globigerina bulloides d'Orbigny
Discorbis orbicularis (Terquem)

Missinaibi and Opasatika Rivers. Along Missinaibi River, above its junction with Opasatika River, lignite visible at low water was first noted by Bell (1879, p. 4C). Some of the lignite is undoubtedly the equivalent of the lignite of the Lower Cretaceous Mattagami Formation, but Bell's description suggests that at least some of the occurrences are Pleistocene intertill compressed peat and wood. A section 9 miles above the mouth of Opasatika River is as follows:

Feet	
0 - 10	Hard, drab clay with striated pebbles and small boulders, and holding rather large valves of *Saxicava rugosa, Macoma calcarea,* and *Mya truncata.*
10 - 15	Hard, lead-coloured clay with yellow seams and spots, and red, grey, drab, and buff layers.
15 - 21	Lignite, made up of laminae of moss and sticks.
21 - 22	Clay with spots of lignite.
22 - 62	Unstratified drift full of small pebbles.
62 - 65	Yellowish stratified sand and gravel.

Three miles farther up the river Bell records:

0 - 45	Blue clay with pebbles, some striated.
45 - 47½	Lignite, made up principally of sticks and rushes.
47 - 127	Yellow weathering grey clay with pebbles, some striated.

Important observations were made also by J. M. Bell (1904) and J. Keele (1921), but the occurrence of both Cretaceous and Pleistocene deposits remained unproven until the area was restudied and pollen analyses were made by R. Auer (McLearn, 1927).

Terasmae and Hughes (1960) recognize five main Pleistocene units: (1) a lower drift; (2) a middle drift consisting of till and glaciofluvial sand and gravel; (3) layers of peat, organic silt, and clay, termed the Missinaibi beds; (4) an upper drift consisting mainly of till; and (5) marine clay, sand, and silt. Locally this sequence is eroded and overlain by the fluviatile deposits of the terraces along the rivers. Wood from Missinaibi beds gave a radiocarbon age of >53,000 years (Gro-1435). Palynological studies by Terasmae (1958) indicate a climate similar to the present or slightly cooler and possible correlation with the St. Pierre beds of St. Lawrence Lowlands. The inferred climate is unlike that represented by the Toronto Don beds, even allowing for the difference in latitude between the two areas, and hence the Missinaibi beds, if not representative of a late part of the Sangamon Interglaciation, must have been deposited during an early part of the Wisconsin glacial interval.

Kwataboahegan River. Wilson (1906) found solid peaty material in the bed of this river some 65 miles above its mouth:

> The mass where examined was six feet thick and it can be traced along the river for 430 feet. It is a dark brown colour and breaks off into lumps two to three feet thick. It burned slowly in the camp fire but left a large quantity of ash. Thin layers of the same material are exposed in the bank intercalated with the clay for several miles up the river.

A section, 60 miles above the mouth, is described by J. M. Bell (1904, p. 168) as follows:

> The seam, which has a maximum width of two feet six inches, outcrops almost continuously along the edge of the river for 450 feet in a bank 40 feet high. Though compact and hard it is never pure and is for the most part mixed with clay. Above it lies about 25 feet of hard, blue clay surmounted by six feet of shell-bearing post-glacial material. Below the seam is a hard stony clay containing many shells. This is of great scientific interest as it is the only point in the Moose Basin where interglacial shells are known to occur. The lignite itself is both arenaceous and argillaceous. It consists of thin layers of indurated moss with partings of clay and sand. It burned with considerable difficulty in the camp fire leaving a large residuum of clay and sand.

Though Martison (1953) did not examine the Kwataboahegan organic deposits, he considered them of Pleistocene age, and noted that high ash content is not characteristic of the Cretaceous lignites at Onakawana.

Albany River. Here till overlies a few feet of blue and brown clay (reported as leached) with two 2-inch beds of 'lignite.' Williams (1921) reported one bed to be "composed mostly of moss" and the other as "containing compressed roots." Nearby in a 90-foot section on the north bank of the river the till cover is 50 feet thick and rests on similar clay though no 'lignite' was observed. The Pleistocene age of these materials was corroborated by Terasmae and Hughes (1960). They conclude that the spore and pollen assemblages are entirely unlike those of the lignite of the Cretaceous Mattagami Formation, known on Mattagami, Abitibi, Missinaibi, and Opasatika Rivers.

Farther down Albany River 10 feet of stratified sand rests on 20 feet of pebble clay, presumably till, that in turn rests on 20 feet of thin-bedded clay, peat and moss, and 2 feet varved clay and pebble clay beneath which are 8 feet of pebble clay possibly a till. The bedded clay, peat, and moss sequence was considered by Martison to be interglacial.

Kenogami River, a tributary of Albany River, intersects a preglacial river channel cut into Silurian limestone. R. Bell (1887, p. 38) reported a basal till overlain by a 6- to 8-foot bed of soft lignite, containing many flattened stems of small trees and succeeded by 30 to 40 feet of rudely stratified red and grey drift with rounded boulders and many pebbles. This is most probably interglacial.

Attawapiskat River. Well-stratified clay with silt and sand laminae and sparse plant fragments occurs beneath 6 to 10 feet of sand and gravel and 12 to 15 feet of clayey till. The plant fragments are dated at >35,800 years (GSC-83). It is likely that the organic-bearing sediments are related to the Missinaibi beds.

Gods River. On Gods River, formerly called the Shamattawa, Tyrrell (1913) reports that intertill sand and gravel and the basal part of the overlying till contain moss and wood, partly altered to lignite. He recognized two tills over a wide area, in places separated by a striated boulder pavement. He noted the intertill sand and gravel also along Hayes River but could find no organic remains.

Seal River. A buried non-glacial deposit carrying organic materials was reported by Taylor (1961). This occurrence is on the Precambrian Shield, 85 miles west of the Paleo-

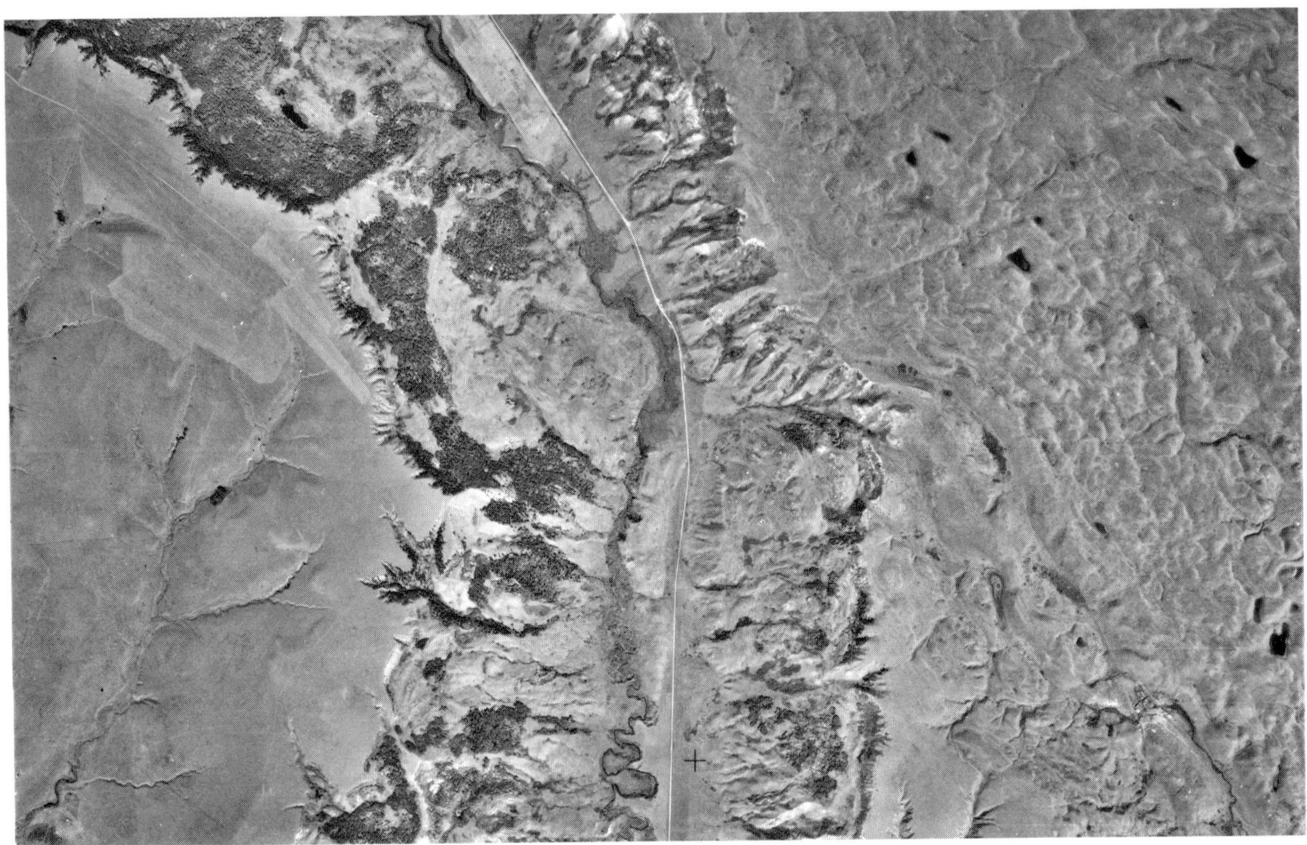

PLATE XII-3. Deep meltwater channel between unglaciated Cypress Hills and Wisconsin end moraine complex, southwestern Saskatchewan. Vertical airphoto of meltwater channel, about 700 feet deep, now occupied by Adams Creek. Road leads north to Maple Creek, Saskatchewan. Scale 1 inch to 3,000 feet.

zoic rocks, very close to the limit reached by the Tyrrell Sea. Beneath sandy till typical of Shield areas, is a fluviatile bouldery gravel with a matrix of goethite. Two 6-inch layers in the gravel contain casts and impressions of leaves and twigs partly replaced by, and set in a matrix of, goethite. The plant-bearing layers represent the replacement of a woody peat composed of moss, sedge, grass, and shrubs including herbaceous plants such as leatherleaf, dwarf lamel, and bear-berry. The plant assemblage is similar to that of the area today, and is believed to have been deposited during an interglacial interval.

Interior Plains

Early Pleistocene Events

Pediment surfaces. In late Tertiary the climate of the Interior Plains is inferred to have been arid to semiarid, and a series of pediplains was developed along the mountain front and around smaller uplands to the east (Gravenor and Bayrock, 1961; Parizek, 1964; Barton, *et al.*, 1965). With the change to a cooler and moister climate at the close of the Tertiary and in earliest Quaternary extensive valley erosion, locally accompanied by alluviation, left the present uplands as remnants of the pediplain system. Some of these uplands that escaped glacial modification are Cypress Hills (Pl XII-3) and Wood Mountain near the International Boundary. Other uplands such as Missouri Coteau in southern Saskatchewan and Hand Hills in east-central Alberta have been extensively modified. There is some disagreement as to the degree of the effects of glaciation on the gross topography of the Plains. Contour maps of the bedrock surface give a general picture of the preglacial topography but as much as 1,000 feet of drift is known in some valleys in Saskatchewan, indicating that considerable modification of the topography has taken place.

Drainage systems. At the end of the Tertiary period a mature, dendritic drainage system existed on the Interior Plains (Fig. XII-9). A good account of early work on buried valleys dating back to that of Dawson in 1885 is given by Stalker (1961). He reports also that the glaciers responsible for the numerous till sheets recognized on the southern plains had the over-all effect of forcing rivers to follow more southerly courses. In a general way the major elements of the present-day drainage reflect the trend of the old valleys, but there are many divergences as a result of disruption and modification of the preglacial rivers. For instance, near the town of Peace River Hen-

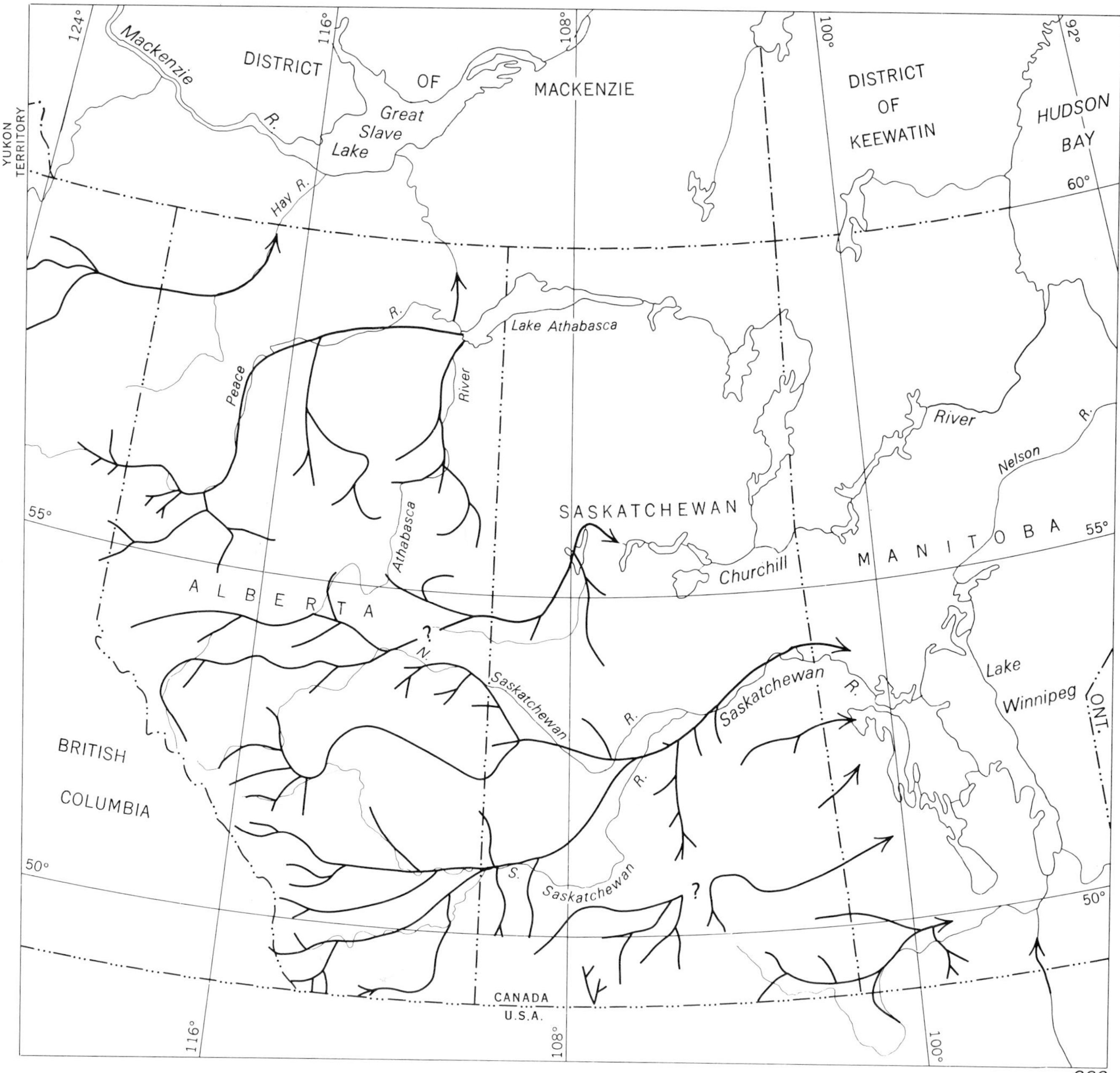

FIGURE XII-9. Inferred preglacial drainage systems of the Interior Plains (modified from available sources).

derson (1959a) records 800 feet of drift in a preglacial channel 3 miles southeast of the present river, and also shows that the preglacial Smoky River joined Peace River some 20 miles southwest of the present junction. In central Alberta the preglacial Red Deer River followed a markedly different course from that of the present, north of Red Deer; this preglacial channel is now occupied in places by Battle River. Similarly the preglacial South Saskatchewan River system in both Alberta and Saskatchewan was quite different from that of the present (Stalker, 1961; Christiansen, 1967). The preglacial Milk River in southern Alberta was probably a tributary of the South Saskatchewan rather than Missouri River, and farther east this latter river may have flowed across southeastern Saskatchewan into Manitoba and thence presumably northward to Hudson Bay rather than joining the Mississippi as at present (Meneley, 1957). The course of the preglacial Qu'Appelle River in south-central Saskatchewan is in doubt (Kupsch, 1964).

On the basis of shape and contained sediments Stalker has identified both preglacial and interglacial valleys in southern Alberta. He has noted a very dark grey till in the lower parts of all preglacial valleys. In the bottom of their channels the preglacial valleys are characterized by the presence of the Saskatchewan gravels, free of stones derived from the Canadian Shield. Gravel is uncommon in the interglacial valleys, and where present contains some Canadian Shield stones, although they may be very rare. The preglacial valleys in southern Saskatchewan are generally 4 to 10 miles wide and have gently sloping sides, whereas interglacial valleys are a mile to 2 miles wide with steeply sloping walls (Christiansen, 1967). Christiansen records that the preglacial valleys are filled with 50 to 1,000 feet of drift. They may be apparent at the surface where the drift is thin, but are completely obscured where it is thick.

Saskatchewan gravels. The occurrence of preglacial Saskatchewan gravels on the Interior Plains is of great interest and their age has long been controversial (Westgate, 1965). These buried gravels are recognized in Alberta, Saskatchewan, and Manitoba, occurring as alluvial terraces and benches below the Tertiary (Miocene–Pliocene) pediment surfaces and as lower-level channels or valley fills. They are very extensive beneath the drift mantle whether this be a few feet or more than 1,000 feet thick; generally they are a few feet to a few tens of feet thick, varying laterally from sand to sand mixed with coarse gravel. Henderson (1959a), however, reports more than 100 feet of gravel in Peace River area. Westgate found that 98 per cent of the gravel-sized material in southeastern Alberta is made up of quartzite, argillite, and chert, the remainder being arkose, limestone, a green porphyry, and local bedrock. Their source is the Cordilleran Region to the west, also earlier deposited Cordilleran gravels that capped the pediment surfaces of the Interior Plains. Over most of the Plains they rest unconformably on Cretaceous rocks. Frost-action structures have been observed beneath Saskatchewan gravels by J. A. Westgate in southern Alberta, and by Westgate and Bayrock (1964) in central Alberta. In places the gravels are undisturbed by the frost structures. A periglacial environment prevailed during deposition of at least the early part of the unit. Westgate notes the occurrence of bones of a woolly mammoth *Mammuthus primigenius,* and of a horse (*Equus* sp.) somewhat smaller than the present-day horse. He considers that the bulk of the Saskatchewan gravels probably range in age from early to late Pleistocene. Stalker, however, considers them to be early Pleistocene.

Proglacial deposits. Fine-grained sediments including varved sediments have been noted resting on Saskatchewan gravels in major preglacial valleys and directly on bedrock in their tributaries. Thicknesses up to 150 feet have been recorded. They have formerly been included with the Saskatchewan gravels as there is no evidence of a prolonged break in sedimentation prior to their deposition. Westgate (1965), however, treats them as a separate stratigraphic unit—the Wolf Island sediments. They were deposited in cold, quiet, proglacial lakes rather than in swift-flowing

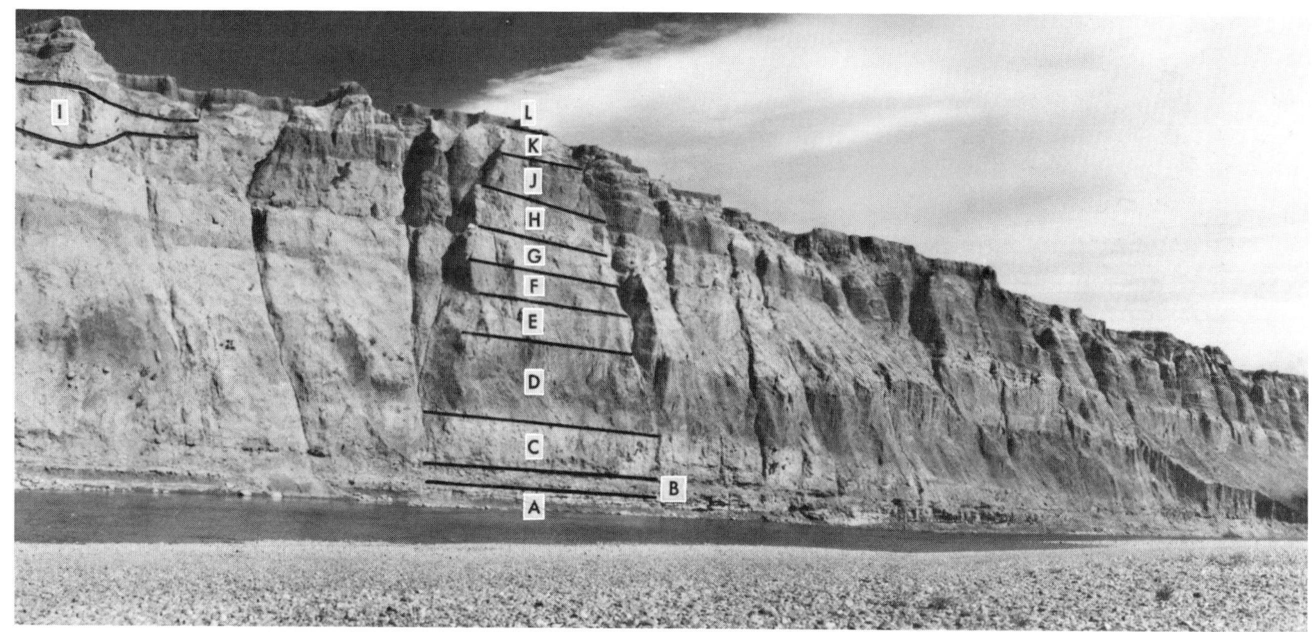

PLATE XII-4. Section of non-glacial and glacial sediments on Oldman River at Brocket, Alberta.

L. Sandy loam; modern soil.
K. Sand; lake and outwash.
J. Varved clay, silt and fine sand; glacial lake.
I. Till (Buffalo Lake); Laurentide.
H. Sand, silt, clay; lacustrine or alluvial; possibly mid-Wisconsin.
G. Till (unnamed), medium light brown; Laurentide?
F. Till (Brocket), dark brown; Laurentide.
E. Till (Maunsell), light bluish grey; Laurentide.
D. Till (Labuma), dark brown to black; Laurentide.
C. Till (Albertan), light grey; Cordilleran.
B. Gravel (no Canadian Shield stones); mostly outwash.
A. Bedrock (Willow Creek Formation); Paleocene.

streams, and appear to reflect a blockage of the northeast-flowing rivers by encroachment of Laurentide ice.

Early glaciations. Very little is known as to the course or extent of pre-Classical Wisconsin glaciers. The generally flat character of the Plains limits observations of Pleistocene stratigraphy to the relatively few sections along entrenched rivers. In Saskatchewan great use has been made of drilling rigs and side-hole samplers to establish the stratigraphy; this practice gives great promise of the establishment of a firm chronology in a region that might otherwise remain an enigma. In many places multiple till sheets, with and without intervening stratified sediments, have been recognized (Pl. XII-4). There is as yet little agreement as to the precise ages of the tills or sediments. Opinions vary from those who believe that all stages of the Pleistocene are represented to those believing in only a Wisconsin glaciation. Some writers place the limit of the Classical Wisconsin drift south of the 49th parallel while others contend that it lies well north of Cypress Hills. Only recently have radiocarbon datings proved the existence of Pleistocene age organic-bearing sediments that predate the Classical Wisconsin. Extensive oxidized zones are recognized in some thick till sections; these appear to represent periods of near-surface exposure during both interglacial and intraglacial times.

In the vicinity of Del Bonita Hills and Cypress Hills an old drift topography occurs at higher altitudes than the surrounding more youthful hummocky terrain. Westgate (1965) terms the higher and older drift the Elkwater

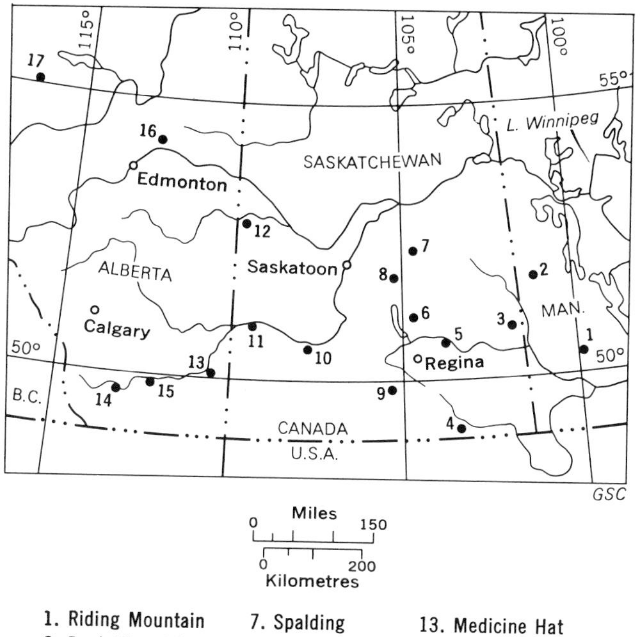

1. Riding Mountain
2. Duck Mountain
3. Churchbridge
4. Outram
5. Fort Qu'Appelle
6. Gregherd
7. Spalding
8. Lanigan
9. Spring Valley
10. Swift Current
11. Prelate Ferry
12. Marsden
13. Medicine Hat
14. Lethbridge area
15. Taber
16. Smoky Lake
17. Goose River

FIGURE XII-10. Location of buried organic deposits in Interior Plains.

drift and considers it correlative with the most extensive and southernmost drift sheet in Montana. He recognizes five Laurentide drift sheets in the Foremost–Cypress Hills area of southeastern Alberta and attributes end moraines to each. The ice sheets generally advanced southeast but with some variations due to lobing in the marginal zones. He considers the oldest drift sheet to be post-Sangamon. Stalker (1963), however, believes that most, if not all, the pre-Wisconsin glacial periods are represented by tills in southern Alberta.

Buried Organic Deposits (Fig. XII-10)

Organic materials in stratified deposits beneath one or more till sheets are known from many places on the Interior Plains.

Riding Mountain. Buried organic materials were found in a highway-cut on the north side of Minnedosa River valley (Klassen, *et al.,* 1967). Three till units are separated by silt and sand layers, the whole comprising 61 feet (Pl. XII-5). This complex overlies a 5-foot silt layer that contains plant remains and rodent bones. The silt unit rests on a foot of limonite-stained gravel with small limestone pebbles weathered to a powder. Beneath is 16 feet of dark grey, shale-rich till, the surface of which also appears to be weathered in places. The sediments are almost devoid of pollen, presumably due to oxidation. Bone fragments are of arctic ground squirrel *(Citellus undulatus)* and a large vole (*Microtus* sp.). Plant fragments gave an age of >31,300 years (GSC-297). Several boreholes on the south side of Riding Mountain encountered stratified sediments beneath two tills and overlying a third. Wood chips from a hole near Inglis, farther northwest, were encountered in clay at a depth of 196 to 212 feet and were dated at >30,000 years (GSC-218). Bedded silts 75 feet thick occur beneath the clay unit and rest directly on shale bedrock. It may be that the Riding Mountain buried deposits are interglacial.

Duck Mountain. In 1964 R. W. Klassen re-examined the locale of interglacial sediments reported by Tyrrell (1892, p. 116). The section on Rolling (Roaring) River was heavily slumped but the Heart Hill section was clear. Two or more tills totalling 54 feet overlie 8.5 feet of silty beds containing small pelecypods, gastropods, ostracods, plant fragments, and seeds. The silt beds overlie 10 feet sand and gravel, and 15 feet sand; the lower 58 feet down to river level was heavily slumped. The upper 1.5 feet of organic-bearing silt is brown rather than grey, suggestive of a weathered zone. The contact with the overlying till is gradational over some 6 inches. The basal inch or two of the silt unit is a clayey sand, cemented with limonite. It contains pelecypods and much carbonaceous material including plant fragments. Some of the latter gave a radiocarbon dating of >38,000 years (GSC-284).

The silt unit was sampled at 2½-inch intervals and examined for both shells and pollen. Seven species of

PLATE XII-5

Section of glacial and interglacial deposits on Minnedosa River, north of Minnedosa, Manitoba. A, till; B, silt with bones (collection site); C, till; D, silt, sand, gravel; E, till; F, sand and gravel; G, till.

pelecypods, three gastropods, and ten ostracods have been identified. The ostracods and the pollen indicate a moist climate about as warm as the present, which supports the interglacial interpretation of Tyrrell. The fossil assemblage also indicates a cool–warm–cool sequence; this sequence was terminated by glaciation and deposition of till.

Churchbridge. Tyrrell (1892, p. 142E) recorded the log of a well at Churchbridge that appears to indicate some 32 feet of drift, mainly till, overlying more than 235 feet of clayey and sandy sediments. A piece of wood was found at a depth of 200 feet and identified as a species of larch, *Larix churchbridgensis.* Elsewhere in the area as much as 165 feet of till is reported overlying sand or gravel.

Outram. Christiansen and Parizek (1961) report wood chips from probable lacustrine sediments at a depth of 170 feet from a test-hole in southeastern Saskatchewan. The section from the top down is, light, olive-brown calcareous till, 10 feet; grey, calcareous till with two clayey beds, 92 feet; stratified, oxidized and leached sand rich in organic matter, 8 feet; grey, calcareous till, 20 feet; grey, interbedded sand, silt and clay (from which wood chips were obtained at depth 170 feet), 71 feet; grey, calcareous till, 15 feet; stratified sediments, 144 feet; light brownish grey, calcareous till, 8 feet; gravel, 3 feet; pale yellow, kaolinitic, calcareous till, 4 feet; sand, 2 feet; and light brownish grey, calcareous till, 1 foot +. The wood chips were dated at 27,750 ± 1,200 years (S-96), which suggests correlation with the Prelate Ferry interval.

Fort Qu'Appelle. Fossiliferous sediments beneath 200 feet of drift were reported by Christiansen (1960). He reports that upstream from Fort Qu'Appelle a till overlies 10 to 25 feet sand and 20 to 40 feet of exposed gravel; down the valley towards Lebret, terraced valley-fill is at least 120 feet thick. Vertebrate fossils in the sediments, including bones and teeth of bison, mammoth, horse, wolf, and bear, are tentatively assigned to the Sangamon by L. S. Russell. Christiansen thinks that there is an older drift beneath these sediments.

Gregherd. Wood chips from sand beneath till, in a well at a depth of 300 feet, were dated at >30,000 years (S-111). The overlying till is considered late Wisconsin but the age of the non-glacial sediments is unknown.

Spalding. A boring has yielded wood chips from the lowest of three tills at a depth of 221 feet. The wood was dated at >34,000 years (S-127). It probably represents an interglacial deposit.

Lanigan. Wood from a depth of 540 feet in a drift-filled valley and only 20 feet above bedrock was encountered during sinking of a mine shaft. It was dated at >42,000 years (GSC-632), and is believed to be of Pleistocene age.

Spring Valley. Layers and lenses of peat associated with silty-clay beds occur beneath a till mantle in the hummocky ice-thrust moraine of the Dirt Hills. The peat was dated >38,000 years (GSC-790) and pollen indicates Pleistocene age.

Swift Current Creek. Wickenden (1931) reported a multiple till section, with intervening sediments and organic matter, in Swift Current Creek valley near its junction with South Saskatchewan River. From the surface downward are thin lacustrine clays; 20 to 70 feet of till; 35 feet white sand and gravel with some poorly preserved plant material; 3 to 45 feet dark grey till; and up to 225 feet sand and gravel with some poorly preserved peat and plant detritus. The last sediments rest either directly on bedrock or on a brown to yellowish till that locally displays a weathered zone, 8 feet thick, with poorly preserved plant materials and rootlets. On the basis of the great thickness of the lower gravels, the presence of plant materials, and the weathered zone on the basal till, Wickenden regarded the lower gravels as deposited during a long, moist interglacial interval. Christiansen (1959) has linked the two upper tills to end moraines in the area and assigns the upper unit of sand and gravel to a proglacial, very late part of the Wisconsin. He regards the lower stratified sediments as earlier proglacial Wisconsin deposits.

Prelate Ferry. David (1966) reported a buried soil beneath some 120 feet of drift including three tills from South Saskatchewan River valley north of Prelate. From the surface downward are lacustrine silt and clay, 16 feet; oxidized, calcareous till, 13 feet; stratified sand, 26 feet; mainly oxidized very calcareous till, 39 feet; stratified sand, silt, and a thin basal marl-like layer, 24 to 25 feet; paleosol, 3 to 4 feet; oxidized, very calcareous, sandy clay-loam till, 7 feet; stratified and crossbedded silt, sand, and gravel, 8 feet; and a basal, oxidized, calcareous till, 72 feet. The marl-like layer, only 6 to 8 inches thick, provides a widespread and useful horizon marker for locating the paleosol. The buried soil has been dated at 20,000 ± 850 years (S-176). David considers the paleosol to have developed during a non-glacial interval that he named the Prelate Ferry interval. Its beginning is unknown but it ended about 20,000 years ago when advancing Classical Wisconsin glaciers led to burial of the soil, first by stratified sediments and later by till.

Marsden. Christiansen (1965) reports a soil, buried beneath a few feet of till, about 125 miles north of the Prelate Ferry paleosol exposures. The dating of 21,000 ± 800 years (S-228) suggests that this soil was formed also during the Prelate Ferry interval.

Medicine Hat. Four miles north of Medicine Hat, in South Saskatchewan River valley, Stalker records about 100 feet of intertill sediments exposed in a small buried valley cut in till. Wood fragments and dark carbonaceous layers occur, dated at 24,490 ± 200 and 28,630 ± 800 years (GSC-205, 578). Two tills of differing lithologies overlie the stratified sediments and are considered to represent the Classical Wisconsin. Beneath the sediments in the buried valley are other tills and intervening sediments with abundant wood, bones, and shells which Stalker considers to be Sangamon or older. Wood from near river level at a site 3 miles north of town and beneath 220 feet of drift including several tills was dated >46,700 years (GSC-543). He considers the containing sediments to be of Yarmouth age.

Lethbridge. Multiple till sections have been described by Stalker (1963) on Oldman River. At one site 10 miles west of Lethbridge wood and cones of black spruce were found in the basal part of intertill sand, silt, and gravel. The wood has been dated as >54,500 years B.P. (GSC-237). Two tills occur beneath these sediments at several places along the river and at one place the basal till shows evidence of weathering. Stalker considers these stratified sediments to be present beneath an upper till as far north as Edmonton and to be of Sangamon age. The two lower tills are equally extensive.

At the Kipp section on Oldman River about 7 miles west of Lethbridge, the humic part of a wood sample from the intertill sediments is dated at >37,000 years (L-455A). Some 24 feet of intertill sediments includes a basal, consolidated, white sand that forms a prominent horizon marker in the area. The sediments are overlain by 32 feet of dark, compact till of unknown age and this in turn by some 163 feet of alluvial sediments within which wood fragments have been found. Another 45 feet of sediments overlying the alluvium includes varved clays and minor till lenses and appears to be glacial deposits. These sediments are overlain by 50 feet of sediments carrying some snail shells that may have been deposited relatively close to the ice front. Similar intertill sediments occur near Taber 30 miles east of Lethbridge where wood fragments have been dated at >32,000 years (S-65).

Smoky Lake. A log of spruce was found in till at a depth of 24 feet near Smoky Lake some 60 miles northeast of Edmonton. This wood was dated at >31,000 years (S-92).

Goose River. The northernmost occurrence of buried wood in the Interior Plains is from Goose River northwest of Edmonton. There alluvium and till overlie a crossbedded sand unit in which wood was found that dated >42,500 years (GSC-501).

Mainland Arctic Coastal Plain

A 10-to-20-mile-wide belt of older glaciated terrain on the eastern side of the Cordillera west of Peel River is continuous northward onto the Yukon Coastal Plain. This belt extends westward from Mackenzie Delta to the

Alaskan boundary (Fyles, 1966) and has subdued hummocky topography as far west as Herschel Island, but beyond this area, where the zone narrows to only a few miles, glacial landforms are extremely rare. East from Kay Point, 20 miles southeast of Herschel Island, the older glaciated terrain is bordered on the northeast by a narrow zone of Wisconsin drift. Beneath these deposits interglacial sediments have been seen on headlands between Kay Point and Mackenzie Delta. The sediments grade, in general, from silt in the west to gravel in the east; Fyles considers them to represent a single stratigraphic unit.

In the Mackenzie Delta region, Mackay (1963) found evidence for glaciation of the main and near-shore islands, and possibly also the off-shore islands. Tuktoyaktuk Peninsula was partly glaciated; evidence of glacial action is lacking for the northeastern part. Farther east on Cape Bathurst and Baillie Island, an extensive low-lying plain is underlain by silt and sand beneath which is a marine clay with rare wood (Fyles, 1966). No clear distinction between postglacial and interglacial sediments could be made. This area and part of Tuktoyaktuk Peninsula are shown as outwash (including alluvium) on the Glacial Map of Canada (1253A, *in folio*) pending clarification of the age of the deposits. Possibly older glacial as well as interglacial deposits are present along the northern edge of the Mackenzie Delta complex.

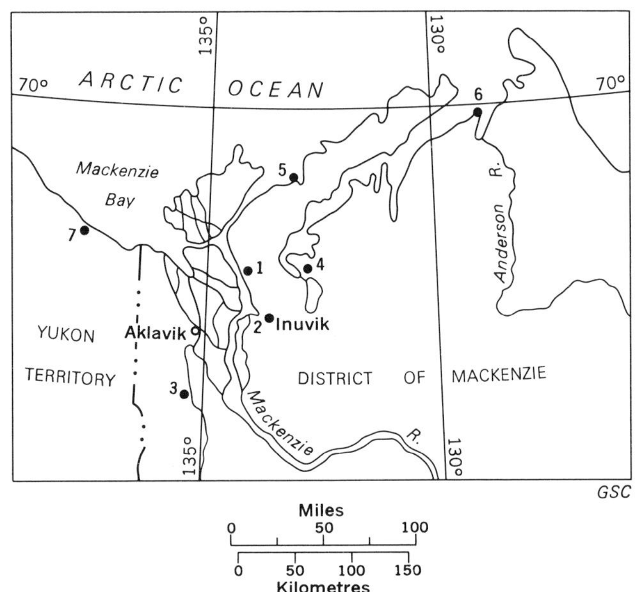

FIGURE XII-11. Location of buried organic deposits of the mainland Arctic Coastal Plain.

Buried Organic Deposits (Fig. XII-11)

Near Reindeer Depot on Mackenzie River 10 feet of peat and silt underlies some 200 feet of drift (Porsild, 1938). Cones of larch were found although the site is 50 miles beyond its present northern limit. Pollen includes abundant birch and alder, much white and black spruce, jack pine, tamarack, and willow, and some ericaceous shrubs, small herbaceous plants, grasses, sedges, and ferns. J. Terasmae considers the pollen assemblage to represent an interglacial deposit, probably the Sangamon. The peat gave an age of >42,000 years (L-522A).

Wood from a delta-kame complex at Inuvik gave an age of >39,000 (GSC-29) and was evidently derived from older non-glacial deposits. Some 60 miles southwest of Inuvik on Rat River, a beaver-chewed stick near the base of a 40-foot section of silt with organic layers and overlying an older till was dated >38,600 years (GSC-120). Evidence elsewhere along the river suggests that Laurentide ice, possibly in Classical Wisconsin time, overrode the site and extended several miles to the west.

Buried organic materials, dated at >50,900 years (GSC-329), occur southwest of Eskimo Lakes where 7 feet of modern peat overlies 76 feet of gravel that rests on at least 46 feet of organic silt with two thin peaty layers in its upper part. O. L. Hughes regards the gravel as outwash in front of a moraine left by the last major ice sheet. According to Terasmae, the pollen content of the peat is unlike that of the present and probably represents an interglacial interval. Fyles (1966) reports a great variety of materials in the southwest part of Eskimo Lakes area where organic matter was noted in three different lithologies.

A non-glacial interval is indicated by the occurrence of abraded wood from a pingo at Tuktoyaktuk dated at >33,000 years (L-300A). Also flattened wood from 20-foot depth in contorted sands, believed to be ice shoved, at the north end of Nicholson Peninsula gave a date of >35,200 years (GSC-34). O'Neill (1924) observed thin peat beds in silty sediments along the arctic coast east of the mouth of Mackenzie River, and he mentions an earlier report by Sir John Franklin of "poor lignite" in similar sediments on nearby Pullen Island.

The interglacial deposits along the arctic coast west of Mackenzie Delta contain a great variety of organic materials. Fyles (1966) reports wood up to a foot in diameter from gravels near the delta, and smaller pieces of wood, peat, freshwater shells, rare bones, and tusks from the silts farther west. Thin beds of marine clay and a few ice-wedge casts complicate the succession. An important site along this coast is at King Point 4 miles east of a moraine believed by O. L. Hughes to mark the western limit of the Classical Wisconsin ice sheet. There up to 3 feet of peat overlies 8 to 15 feet of silt and sand that rests on 20 to 30 feet of Wisconsin till. Beneath this till a stony clay, containing marine shells, grades downward into organic-bearing silts. Plant materials collected from these silts, 2 feet above the base of the seacliff, gave a radiocarbon dating of >51,100 years (GSC-151-2).

The change from plant-bearing silt to shell-bearing stony clay probably reflects a period of marine inundation as a result of the encroaching Wisconsin ice sheet.

Canadian Shield

Mainland

The mainland Shield region has been subjected to intense scouring action by a number of glaciations, but the gross physiography has probably changed little since the end of the Tertiary period. Stream valleys along rugged parts of the Quebec and Labrador coasts, however, have been markedly modified by valley glaciers stemming, in the main, from the interior ice sheet. During interglacial intervals stream erosion probably contributed to valley deepening along these same coasts but elsewhere was relatively ineffective.

In the Torngat and Kaumajet-Kiglapait Mountains of northern Labrador, an early Torngat Glaciation is believed responsible for widely scattered erratics on the highest peaks, and the later Koroksoak Glaciation for high-level lateral moraines, kame terraces, and a felsenmere trimline well below the mountain tops (Wheeler, 1958; Ives, 1958a, b, 1960a; Tomlinson, 1959; Løken, 1962). A still lower trimline, referred to the Saglek Glaciation is regarded by Andrews (1963) as the probable upper limit of the Classical Wisconsin ice sheet. At that time large parts of the mountains projected above the ice.

The last major glaciation was generally effective in removing the deposits of older glacial and interglacial intervals; buried organic deposits are rare in the Canadian Shield. They are, however, more likely to be found in peripheral areas than in the interior, as for example the Seal River occurrence described under Hudson Bay Lowland. Old deposits may occur along some Labrador coastal lowlands where the adjacent rugged terrain shielded them from the glaciers issuing along the fiords, as on Baffin Island.

Baffin Island

The gross physiography of Baffin Island throughout the Pleistocene was probably much the same as now. In Tertiary time an old erosion surface in central and southern Baffin Island, preserved as concordant hill-tops, was tilted, northeast side up (Goldthwait, 1950). A system of dendritic and parallel valleys resulted, and the drainage divide gradually migrated westward. Glaciers stemming from the interior developed deep outlet valleys and speeded the westward migration of the drainage-divide. The resulting broad strip of mountains along the northeast coast rise to elevations of about 6,000 feet in the Penny Highlands. Bird (1954) reports that lower erosional platforms can be recognized in western Baffin Island down to a 600-foot surface cut in relatively weak rocks. He regards the widespread horizontal surface developed on rolling Precambrian rocks as probably exhumed from beneath a cover of Paleozoic rocks of which remnants survive around Foxe Basin; stripping of this mantle may have been accomplished mainly by glaciers. He states that on Brodeur Peninsula, in northwestern Baffin Island, a well-preserved surface at 1,000 to 1,200 feet surrounds a central upland at about 2,000 feet. These surfaces had reached a late-mature to old-age stage before being elevated. These high erosional surfaces and the main tilted plateau of Baffin Island have persisted throughout the Pleistocene with but little modification by successive glaciations.

Old organic deposits (Fig. XII-12). Information on the pre-Classical Wisconsin history is limited though the occurrences of old organic materials are widespread. Information on earlier Pleistocene events has been obtained from terrain along the coast that was not recently glaciated and from organic deposits beneath drift in the interior. Baffin Coastal Lowland is several miles wide east of Barnes Ice Cap and does not appear to have been covered by ice in the last 50,000 years, though there is some evidence of an older glaciation (Løken, 1966). The last ice sheet supported active glaciers in the main fiords

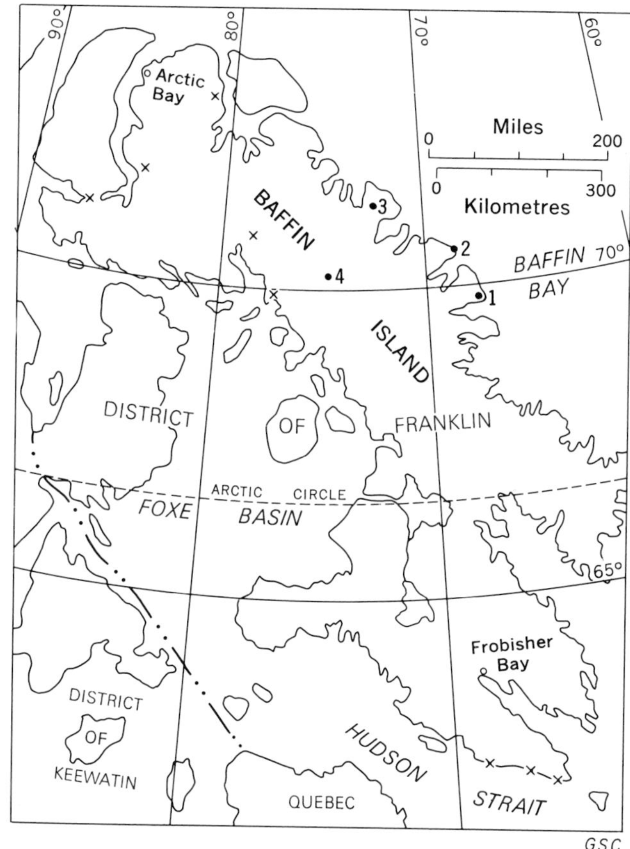

FIGURE XII-12. Occurrences of 'old' organic materials on Baffin Island.

of the northeast coast and in a few places formed piedmont glaciers on the coastal lowland. Near Cape Aston, south of Clyde, a delta was built at an altitude of 262 feet, while outlet glaciers filled a nearby fiord and meltwater channels spilled over towards Cape Aston. Marine shells in the deltaic sediments, at elevation 200 feet, are indicative of a cold water environment. They were dated at >54,000 years (Y-1703). Beneath the delta, 25 feet of gravel overlies stony, shell-bearing materials that represent marine deposits ploughed-up by a glacier. Old non-glacial deposits also occur interbedded with glacial deposits in the coastal cliffs near Cape Christian, again in a protected position. Marine shells from a near-shore deposit lying between the two uppermost glacial deposits have a radiocarbon age of >50,000 years (Y-1702). In Bruce Mountains northeast of Barnes Ice Cap flattened pieces of willow and associated moss were found on a low moraine ridge; these appeared to have been winnowed from the till. They are dated at >39,600 years (GSC-209) and may be interglacial.

In the interior of Baffin Island, pre-Classical Wisconsin organic deposits have been found in several places. Fine plant detritus >40,700 years old (GSC-427) occurs in several layers of contorted fluvial sands along Isortoq River only 10 miles west of northern Barnes Ice Cap (Terasmae, *et al.*, 1966). Leaves of *Dryas, Vaccinum,* and *Ledum* suggest a climate at least as warm as the present and thus presumably interglacial. Andrews reports that the beds were contorted by ice flowing westward towards Foxe Basin. Marine shells from western Baffin Island, 100 feet above the postglacial marine limit, were dated at 30,320±820 years (GSC-528); this date may prove to be minimal.

In northern Baffin Island shells indicative of pre-Classical Wisconsin marine events were obtained from varied materials both above and below the postglacial marine limit: finite dates of about 34,200 and 35,400 years (GSC-184, 188) were obtained from Borden Peninsula, and a dating of >30,580 years on shells (GSC-189) from southern Brodeur Peninsula.

In southern Baffin Island shells found in till have given finite dates of about 30,200 and 34,800 years (GSC-414, 426). Blake (1966) regards these as minimum dates and concludes that Hudson Strait was open during the last interglacial or some early Wisconsin interstadial, and that subsequently, during an ice advance, material was scraped from the sea bottom and deposited along the south coast of Baffin Island. Old shells, washed from till, have been found also in postglacial beach deposits (GSC-468).

Some finite radiocarbon age-datings from Baffin Island may indicate an interstadial interval the lower limit of which is unknown. This is not yet proven, but neither do the numerous infinite age-datings prove that the relevant deposits are interglacial. It appears that both types of interval may be represented by the organic-bearing deposits of Baffin Island. However, undoubted glacial till overlying a fossiliferous deposit has yet to be found.

Arctic Islands

The nature of glaciation and the physiography of the arctic islands differ greatly from one region to another. Except for part of Banks Island, the southern islands were overridden by the Laurentide Ice Sheet so that the early Pleistocene record was removed or lies buried by the younger drift and fresh glacial features characterize the landscape. Some of the western islands beyond the northwestern limit of the Wisconsin Laurentide Ice Sheet were covered by an older Laurentide ice sheet. The western part of the Queen Elizabeth Islands is a lowland and includes areas of old and young glacial deposits, which may be related to both regional and local glaciers, and also some areas lacking obvious evidence of former glacial activity (Fyles and Craig, 1965). The main, eastern part is a region of mountains and plateaux that developed their own ice cover and have been extensively scoured. There is, nevertheless, some evidence of the older Pleistocene record.

In the eastern Queen Elizabeth Islands the mountain ranges, plateaux, and lowlands had assumed their present form by the beginning of the Quaternary. High-level terraces and pediment-like surfaces, with associated wood-bearing alluvium on Ellesmere and Axel Heiberg Islands are regarded as remnants of a system of mature preglacial valleys that may perhaps be early Pleistocene. Subsequent fluvial and glacial erosion have carved fiords and inner valleys as much as 1,800 feet below the old valley levels and in some lowland areas underlain by soft rocks have locally reduced the preglacial deposits to hilltop remnants. In the western islands, however, the landscape was reduced to a northwest-sloping surface of low relief when the latest Tertiary and early Quaternary sediments of the Beaufort Formation accumulated on Arctic Coastal Plain. Islands and straits (formerly valleys) comprising the western part of the archipelago are believed to be younger than the Beaufort Formation (Craig and Fyles, 1960) and to be the result of faulting and repeated cycles of fluvial and glacial erosion (Morley and Fortier, 1956; Thorsteinsson and Tozer, 1961).

Preglacial Deposits

Unconsolidated, wood-bearing alluvial sediments of the Beaufort Formation occupy most of the Arctic Coastal Plain from Banks Island to Meighen Island and are believed to extend seaward beyond the present coast; they occur also as isolated patches on hilltops to the east. These beds are tentatively regarded as late Tertiary to early Quaternary. Fyles (1965) has suggested that certain high-level terrace deposits on Axel Heiberg and Ellesmere Islands are also Beaufort equivalents (Pl. XII-6). The Beaufort Formation on Ellef Ringnes and Borden Islands consists of a lower unit, mainly brown silt with

PLATE XII-6
High-level terraces with Beaufort-type sediments overlying Cretaceous bedrock, eastern Axel Heiberg Island, Northwest Territories. View southward from Buchanan Lake. Only the uppermost light coloured material, up to 40 feet thick, is considered Beaufort type. Surface is strewn with a few glacial erratics.

peaty layers, and an upper unit of sand or fine gravel with driftwood. Only the upper unit has been observed on Prince Patrick and Banks Islands where logs of wood up to 2 feet in diameter have been observed.

The Beaufort Formation characteristically contains pollen of spruce, pine, birch, alder, various herbaceous plants such as the ericaceae, and spores of ferns and moss (Fyles and Craig, 1965). Many samples also contain small amounts of pollen of hemlock and of the temperate climate hardwoods such as hazel, beech, elm, hornbeam, and oak. It is thought that much of the hardwood pollen may be secondary, derived from nearby Tertiary strata, but some is definitely not. The pollen from many species other than the hardwoods comprise an imposing array of plants that grew in what is now a treeless, barren country. The assemblage indicates a climate not only much warmer than the present but also warmer than might be expected in any of the interglacial intervals and may be representative, at least in part, of preglacial earliest Quaternary.

On Meighen Island, which has an ice cap at present, the wood-bearing sands of the Beaufort Formation overlie unconsolidated, marine clay and silt (Thorsteinsson, 1961). On the basis of pollen content, which indicates a warm climate, the marine unit is Tertiary, but the sand unit may be early Quaternary. The sand underlies a boulder veneer presumed to be of glacial origin (Fyles and Craig, 1965). The Beaufort Formation on Arctic Coastal Plain of Borden Island is particularly interesting in that hardwood pollen is abundant and the remoteness of known Tertiary rocks suggests a primary rather than a secondary plant assemblage. The wood-bearing sands on Ellef Ringnes Island are believed to be inland, high-level parts of the Beaufort Formation (St. Onge, 1965). The organic-bearing sediments which occur as high-level terrace deposits over large parts of Ellesmere and Axel Heiberg Islands are probably the temporal equivalents of the Beaufort Formation of the coastal plain as they have a similar pollen assemblage. These deposits, characteristically gravel, sand, and silt, have thicknesses up to 200 feet and commonly lie 300 to 2,000 feet above the valleys. They appear to be remnants of broad mature valleys. They commonly contain wood and locally exhibit buried soil profiles, and enclose layers of moss or peat, and peaty beaver-pond deposits with gnawed wood (Fyles and Craig, 1965).

On northwestern Banks Island the Beaufort Formation lies at the surface (Fyles and Craig, 1965). In the higher, eastern part of the island it is only a few feet thick and rests on what appears to be an eroded Tertiary sand. In the lower central part the deposits are thicker and their base is not exposed, as on Ballast Brook where 300 feet of sand and gravel with much wood is underlain by 10 feet of peat which in turn rests on sand and silt containing plant detritus.

Early Glacial and Non-glacial Events

Terraces and plains within the areas underlain by Beaufort Formation consist of reworked sand and gravel. On Prince Patrick Island, most if not all of these terraces are younger than the northward-trending faults cutting the Beaufort Formation (Fyles, 1965). They indicate alluviation during some pre-Classical Wisconsin non-glacial period.

Parts of Prince Patrick, Eglinton, and Melville Islands, and most of northern and western Banks Island, bear deposits of an older glaciation, and particularly of far-travelled erratics from the Canadian Shield. Study of buried organic deposits has shown that both interglacial and interstadial intervals are probably represented.

Buried Organic Deposits and 'Old' Shell Occurrences (Fig. XII-13)

Victoria and Banks Islands. Fyles (1963a) reports sub-till organic-bearing sediments from the north side of Prince Albert Sound in western Victoria Island. Locally gravels with knob-and-kettle topography rest on 30 feet of till overlying 150 feet of stratified sediments that in turn rest on some 50 feet of dense till. In the lower part of the intertill sediments, 20 feet of thin-bedded silt contains closely packed mats of leaves and other remains of small plants which were radiocarbon dated at about 28,000 years (I-GSC-30). One of the plant layers contains sparse pollen of grasses, sedges, and other herbaceous plants. Fyles considers these intertill deposits to have been deposited by rivers and in lakes prior to the last glacial invasion under climatic conditions not greatly different from the present. Similar sediments, lacking organic remains, lie beneath till throughout large parts of north-west Victoria Island and the adjoining coastal region of Banks Island and may be correlative.

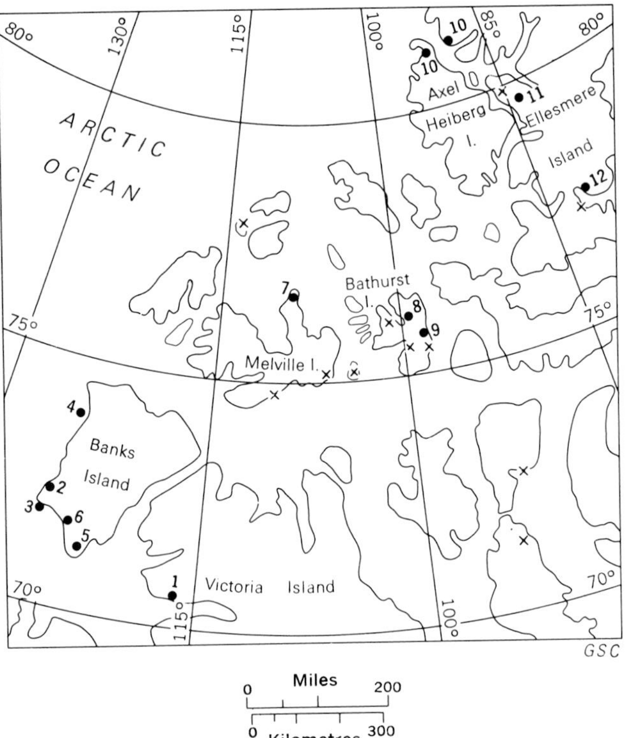

1. Prince Albert Sound, Victoria Island
2. Worth Point, Banks Island
3. Duck Hawk Bluff, Banks Island
4. Bernard Island, off Banks Island
5. Nelson Head, Banks Island
6. Masik Valley, Banks Island
7. Barrow Dome, Melville Island
8. Stuart River, Bathurst Island
9. Goodsir Inlet, Bathurst Island
10. Nansen Sound, Ellesmere and Axel Heiberg Islands
11. Slidre River, Ellesmere Island
12. Makinson Inlet, Ellesmere Island

'Old' shell occurrences; various islands. . . . .×

FIGURE XII-13. Location of buried organic sites and 'old' shell occurrences on the arctic islands.

At Worth Point, on western Banks Island, beyond the inferred limit of the Classical Wisconsin Laurentide Ice Sheet, an uncompressed peat at the top of a 100-foot exposure of till and stratified sediments has yielded a date of >49,000 years (GSC-367). The peat contains pollen of birch as well as of plants now growing in the area. A stony layer beneath the peat is considered to be colluvium, for beneath this layer are pond silts with layers of only slightly compressed peat and moss. The peat contains wood of small trees, and some beaver-gnawed sticks. The wood gave an infinite radiocarbon age (I-GSC-19). These deposits are believed to be interglacial. At Duck Hawk Bluff, near the top of a 125-foot shore cliff, peat and willow stems occur in silts beneath colluvium or possibly till; the organics also gave an infinite age (GSC-238). The peat contains pollen of alder, willow, spruce, and herbaceous plants and is considered to be an interglacial deposit. The silts rest on an older till that overlies the Beaufort Formation. Another very similar section occurs on Bernard Island, farther north off the west coast of Banks Island. There moss peat from lacustrine deposits contained pollen of conifers as well as of tundra vegetation like that now found in the area. The peat gave an infinite radiocarbon age (I-GSC-28) and the deposit is believed to be interglacial interval.

On southern Banks Island, near Nelson Head, willow wood was found in a sand, gravel, and silt unit beneath 150 feet of till and glaciofluvial gravel and sand. This was dated >41,600 years (GSC-222). The overlying drift dates from the last major glaciation but the organic deposits may be either interstadial or interglacial. In Masik River valley, beneath till, Fyles also has observed spruce wood and layers of moss and peat associated with silt, sand, and gravel. He tentatively considers these organic deposits to date from an interglacial interval.

Melville Island. On northern Melville Island, where little vegetation grows, 2.5 feet of moss and sand was found 6 feet below the surface of a flat-topped hill, at about elevation 300 feet. The deposit appears to predate both glaciation and dissection of the lowland but to post-date the formation of the higher level terraces tentatively considered to be of Beaufort age. The moss, dated at >38,600 years (GSC-422), is probably interglacial.

Shell fragments from raised beach deposits in south-eastern Melville Island that were expected to be post-glacial yielded a radiocarbon date of about 34,050 years (GSC-154). The date is probably minimal and relates to a pre-Classical Wisconsin non-glacial interval.

Also on adjacent Byam Martin Island a shell sample from an outwash deposit was presumably derived from older materials as it yielded an infinite age-dating (GSC-357).

Bathurst Island. On Stuart River, in northern Bathurst Island, postglacial marine silty-clay overlies a terrace within which 4 feet of peat overlies 20 feet of gravel of local derivation. This rests on the eroded surface of a remotely derived white sand possibly of Tertiary age. The gravels are presumed to represent a period of aggradation during some pre-Wisconsin interval during which the sea level was higher than at present. This was followed by a relatively long period of stable conditions during which 4 feet of peat formed in the valley. The peat has been dated at >36,000 years (GSC-165).

Near Goodsir Inlet in east-central Bathurst Island, peat dated at >35,000 years (GSC-178) was found beneath till and as pods within it. Blake (1964) regards the peat to be interglacial although a Wisconsin interstadial is possible. He reports that the till is similar to that from which marine shells have been collected at sites above the postglacial marine limit. Finite datings of about 35,900 and 33,940 years (GSC-212, 378) on shells from sites in central part of island are thought to be minimal.

Ellesmere and Axel Heiberg Islands. J. G. Fyles has observed terrace deposits that are at lower levels than the Beaufort terraces, and he tentatively considers these to be interglacial. In the vicinity of Slidre Fiord on west-central Ellesmere Island he found, associated with a gravel terrace, sedge and moss peat that have been dated at >41,200 years (GSC-268). Boulders on the gravel terrace are probably an indication that it has been glaciated. Glaciation is believed responsible also for the dissemination of old marine shells on similar upland surfaces south of Slidre Fiord and elsewhere on Ellesmere and Axel Heiberg Islands both above and below the postglacial marine limit; these have yielded radiocarbon dates in the 20,000 to 40,000 year range, which, due to possible contamination by old shells, are considered minimal. They provide evidence, however, of marine events prior to the last major glaciation.

Along Nansen Sound, on both Ellesmere and Axel Heiberg Islands, fossiliferous marine sediments, considered to be interglacial, occur well above the highest postglacial marine features and locally they appear to be overlain by glacial drift (Fyles and Craig, 1965). The shells have yielded radiocarbon datings ranging between 35,000 and 40,000 years (GSC-65, 113, 149), which are considered minimal.

Sandy moss peat exposed in the base of a meltwater channel near the head of Makinson Inlet in southern Ellesmere Island overlies bouldery gravel and is overlain by boulders. The peat was dated at >36,400 years (GSC-140), and along with the gravel and boulders is believed to be a remnant of a high-level terrace that may be of early glacial or interglacial age.

Shells from the sandy ground surface at the marine limit on Swinnerton Peninsula, on the southwest side of the inlet, were radiocarbon dated at 29,800±200 years (GSC-134). These shells are believed to record a marine episode prior to the last glaciation.

Cordilleran Region

The Pleistocene history of the Cordillera is somewhat more varied than that of the continental interior in that parts remained unglaciated and other parts were glaciated during only one or more periods prior to the last major glaciation, presumed to be the Classical Wisconsin. The latter, though not everywhere as extensive as older glaciations, did cover the greater part of the Cordillera. Geomorphological studies are limited but the presence of buried valleys and thick sequences of buried glacial and non-glacial sediments do bear testimony to major drainage changes resulting from successive glacial and non-glacial intervals. The record of older Pleistocene events may be preserved in its entirety in the unglaciated parts of the Yukon or in adjoining areas that were covered only by the older glaciers. At present data are sparse. The older Pleistocene record is also fragmentary in the region covered by the last major glacier complex, but locally there is much data bearing on the older events.

Unglaciated Areas

Unglaciated areas in the Cordilleran Region are shown on the Glacial Map of Canada (Map 1253A). A small area in southwestern Alberta lies above and beyond the limit of Cordilleran valley glaciers from the west and Laurentide Ice Sheet from the east. Cordilleran glaciers were restricted in their development on the dry, eastern flank of the Rocky Mountains. The rugged terrain of this unglaciated area is unsuited to the preservation of non-glacial sediments that record early Pleistocene history and climate. Unglaciated areas of very irregular outline also occur in parts of Mackenzie Mountains and Liard Plateau. These existed between the Cordilleran and Laurentide glaciers because of a combination of climatic and topographic factors. There is no information on the Pleistocene stratigraphy of these regions.

By far the largest unglaciated area in Canada is in western Yukon. This area remained unglaciated throughout Pleistocene time as it lies in a dry belt east of the high St. Elias Mountains where most of the moisture in Pacific air masses is precipitated. During glacial intervals western Yukon was both dry and cold and sustained flora and fauna less varied than that of the dry and warm interglacial intervals or that of the present. The record of glacial, interglacial, and interstadial intervals must be sought therefore in the non-glacial sedimentary sequence. To date there is little specific information.

O. L. Hughes states that on Porcupine River, in Old Crow Basin, modern peat mantles 29 feet of silt and clay which he refers to a period of meltwater discharge across Richardson Mountains from a Laurentide ice sheet. Beneath this unit is some 144 feet of brown sand and gravel from which wood was radiocarbon dated at >41,300 years (GSC-199). The older unit also contains pollen indicative of an interglacial interval. This sedimentary sequence records the present non-glacial interval, an older glacial interval, and a still older interglacial interval, but the precise chronology remains unknown.

Throughout most of the unglaciated Klondike area O. L. Hughes has found that the base of the modern peat ranges in age from about 9,000 to 11,000 years B.P., whereas the subsurface organic materials associated with silt and gravel, encountered in placer operations are generally too old to date by radiocarbon methods. At one site on Hunker Creek, however, wood from the base of 20 feet of silty peat was dated 9,520±130 years (GSC-73), whereas wood from 4 feet below this in frozen silt gave a finite date of ca. 30,800 years (GSC-88). Sediments of this mid-Wisconsin interstadial interval were no doubt deposited in many parts of the unglaciated Yukon.

Older Glaciated Areas

In many parts of the Cordillera there is evidence that one or more early glaciations reached higher altitudes than the last major glaciation or extended beyond its outer limits (Map 1253A). Fyles (1963b) reports that elevation of the uplands of southern Vancouver Island and consequent development of narrow stream channels took place prior to deposition of any of the surficial deposits found there at present. These materials and the glacial features are believed to date from mid-Pleistocene time. Pleistocene glaciers overrode the region and extensively modified the existing valleys and elsewhere smoothed and rounded the major topographic features. The area bears evidence of at least two separate glaciations. In the Okanagan Range of Cascade Mountains in south-central British Columbia, ice at one time overrode mountains up to 8,500 feet whereas the last ice sheet did not reach over 7,500 feet. In the Foothills of southwestern Alberta an area of older glaciated terrain surrounding the unglaciated area lies about 500 to 1,000 feet above the Wisconsin limit of both Cordilleran and Laurentide ice.

In Mackenzie and Selwyn Mountains most of an elongate, partly unglaciated region bears evidence of one or more early Pleistocene Cordilleran as well as Wisconsin Cordilleran glaciations. The early glaciers originating in western Mackenzie Mountains and eastern Selwyn Mountains apparently filled the intermontane valleys to higher levels than did the Wisconsin glaciers. The fringe zone of older glaciations is thus very complex and at present remains undifferentiated (Map 1253A). The region lies above and beyond the western limits reached by Laurentide Ice Sheet. The Cordilleran glaciers, however, on flowing northward towards the Arctic Red and Peel Rivers encountered the older, southward-moving, Laurentide Ice Sheet. In this area a zone of older glaciated terrain is both extensive and distinct, but the interrelations of the Cordilleran and Laurentide ice masses are uncertain.

A zone of older glaciated terrain, some 10 to 20 miles wide, lies west of Peel River between the unglaciated part of the Yukon and the western limit of Wisconsin Laurentide Glaciation. Glacial landforms are relatively uncommon in this area, but areas of subdued hummocky terrain occur.

In southwestern Yukon, north of St. Elias Mountains, an area of greatly variable width separates unglaciated terrain from areas to the east and south that were glaciated during the Classical Wisconsin. Several glaciations have been recognized in this fringe zone (Denton and Stuiver, 1967; Bostock, 1966). It appears also that older glacier complexes in the interior mountainous parts of the Yukon attained greater thickness than the Wisconsin ice. Some peaks in the dry central part of the Yukon that protruded above the Wisconsin glacier surface were covered by one or more older glaciers and bear a fringe of older glaciated terrain. Near Kluane Lake on the northeast side of St. Elias Mountains, on the other hand, two older glaciations, the Shakwak and Icefield, were not so extensive as the Kluane or Classical Wisconsin Glaciation. The older glaciers extended 70 to 75 miles northeast of the present Pacific–Interior ice divide, and reached the eastern part of Kluane Lake basin. The last major ice sheet filled Kluane basin and extended 90 to 100 miles northwest along the valley to the vicinity of Snag, Yukon, with an ice tongue extending 20 miles northwards down White River (Bostock, 1952). There, an older glacier was responsible for drift extending another 20 miles down the river. Correlation between the older drifts of Kluane area and that of White River valley has not been made, but apparently the latter is older than either of the former and probably is pre-Illinoian.

In central Yukon two clearly defined glacial limits are evident and may be readily correlated and traced (Bostock, 1966). They are considered to mark the limits of the last and an earlier glacier advance. In addition, older glacial drift, including till and erratics, and modified glacial landforms have been found beyond the limit of the earlier advance and may record two still earlier glaciations. In Stewart Valley the McConnell was the last major glaciation. The youngest of the older drift units, the Reid extends westward down the valley at least 40 miles beyond the McConnell limit; it displays distinct glacial features, including an end moraine. West of the Reid End Moraine, in lower Stewart Valley, glacial landforms are generally lacking but grey, silty to clayey till with mostly fresh stones and scattered erratics represents the older Klaza Glaciation.

The Klaza glaciers extended at least 25 miles beyond the Reid limit. In some other valleys also, subdued glacial landforms related to the Klaza glaciers have been observed. In lower Stewart Valley the oldest glacier extended about 25 miles beyond Klaza glacial limit and reached to within

20 miles of Yukon River; it is referred to as the Nansen Glaciation. It is expressed by a great thickness of drift that has a hummocky to undulating surface or is locally terraced. This drift blocked the channel of a creek, which then cut a canyon 300 feet deep in bedrock. In some valleys Bostock noted that the Nansen drift is extensively weathered; the stones in the drift are rotted, and usually both till and gravels are brown. Till beneath a lava flow, 3 miles downstream from Fort Selkirk on Yukon River, is believed to be related to the Nansen Glaciation but may be older. On the north side of Stewart River valley, the Nansen glacier appears to have reached the altitude of a low pass in the valley side so that meltwaters flowed northward depositing a distinctive gravel train along the valley of Australia Creek and Indian River as far as their junction with Yukon River about 40 miles below the mouth of Stewart River.

Bostock states that in upper Stewart Valley the profiles of the ice surfaces of the major glacier advances rise eastward gently and converge in elevation so that the moraines of the McConnell advance are so close to those of the earlier advances that they are virtually indistinguishable. On Talbot Plateau, southeast of Mayo, the McConnell and Reid Moraines reach altitudes of 4,000 and 4,400 feet respectively, and scattered erratics believed to be remnants of the Klaza Glaciation occur up to an elevation of 4,700 feet. Two small buttes rising above 4,700 feet elevation may have been nunataks. Other moraines are present in the area some of which may reflect oscillations of the ice fronts during the older glaciations.

In west-central Yukon, Vernon and Hughes (1965) found scattered evidence of one or more old glaciations beyond or above a clearly defined glaciated terrain of an intermediate glaciation which, in turn, lay beyond or above the deposits of the last major glaciation. Little is known of the oldest glaciations other than the occurrence of scattered erratics in otherwise apparently unglaciated areas. The trace of large transection glaciers, formed during the intermediate glaciation, have been delineated in the eastern part of the region and their gradients over long stretches have been determined as from 19 to 35 feet to the mile.

Buried Organic Deposits of the Main Glaciated Areas

Both interglacial and interstadial deposits are recognized in southern British Columbia and perhaps are the equivalents of the Sangamon and mid-Wisconsin intervals. In Yukon the extent of several Pleistocene ice sheets have been delimited but only in one area has it been possible, tentatively, to assign the buried organic deposits—and hence their associated glacial deposits—to any particular Pleistocene period. The location of buried organic deposits in southern British Columbia and the Yukon Territory are shown on Figures XII-14 (a) and (b) respectively.

Straits of Georgia and Juan de Fuca. In the Strait of Georgia region subtill organic-bearing deposits, known as the Quadra sediments, have been assigned to the Olympia Interglaciation which preceded the last major or Fraser Glaciation (Armstrong, *et al.,* 1965). For comparative purposes, these may equate, on the basis of radiocarbon datings, with the mid-Wisconsin and Classical Wisconsin of the mid-continent and Great Lakes region. Recent investigations by J. G. Fyles and E. C. Halstead have shown the wide distribution of Quadra sediments on southeastern Vancouver Island. According to Fyles (1963b), the Quadra sediments comprise a lower unit of clayey silt with stones and marine shells, a middle unit of plant-bearing silt, gravel, and sand, and an upper unit of white sand with local beds of gravel and plant-bearing silt. Maximum thickness of these units is about 80, 40, and 250 feet.

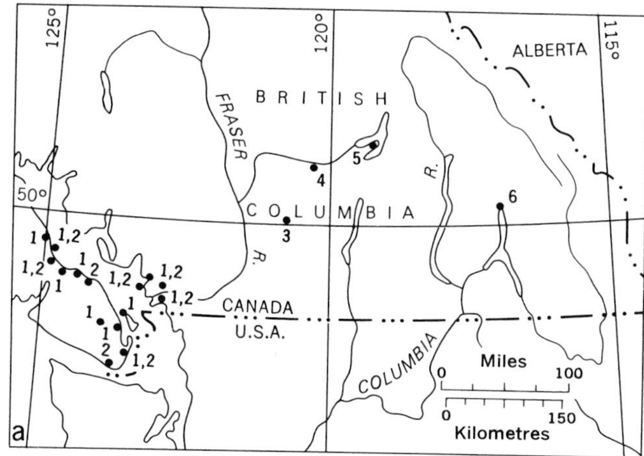

1. Vancouver Island and Fraser Lowland; Quadra sediments
2. Vancouver Island and Fraser Lowland; pre Quadra sediments
3-5. Thompson River valley and tributaries; younger and older intertill sediments
6. Kootenay Lake; palaeosol and intertill sediments

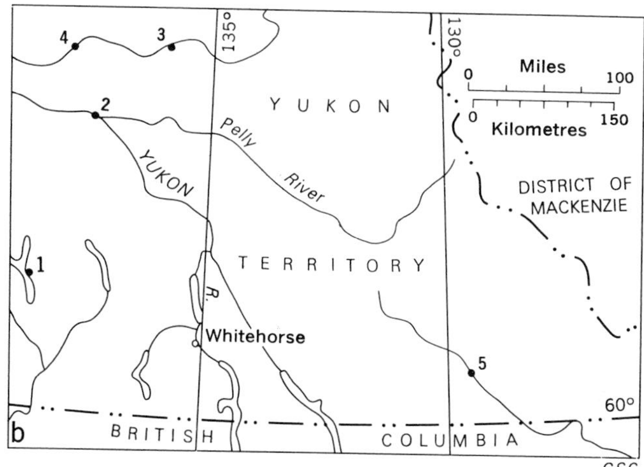

1. Kluane Lake; younger and older intertill sediments
2. Fort Selkirk area; sediments beneath striated lava
3. Mayo Landing area
4. McQuesten area
5. Liard River

FIGURE XII-14. Location of buried organic deposits in the Cordilleran Region: (a) Southern British Columbia; (b) Glaciated parts of Yukon Territory.

The lower unit is considered to represent a transition from glaciomarine to marine conditions. The middle, plant-bearing unit appears to have originated in a swampy coastal lowland during, and also probably following, a regression of the sea in which the underlying marine clay had been deposited. The upper unit is a fluvial-plain deposit characterized by cut-and-fill structures; it contains beds of gravel and plant-bearing silt composed largely of debris from the Coast Mountains of the mainland. Fyles suggests that the present Strait of Georgia may have been completely filled with sediments prior to the Fraser Glaciation.

Pollen and marine molluscs in the Quadra deposits record a climate cooler than the present and somewhat comparable to the present climate of the Gulf of Alaska. The vegetation differs from that on Vancouver Island today in rarity of Douglas fir and abundance of spruce. Radiocarbon dates range from about 20,000 to perhaps 50,000 years B.P. Thus, either the lower limit of a very lengthy non-glacial interval remains to be established or two separate intervals are represented by deposits currently assigned to the Quadra on Vancouver Island.

Quadra sediments on Vancouver Island in places overlie a till and associated sediments, the Dashwood drift, which in turn rest on the non-glacial Mapleguard sediments. At Icarus Point, E. C. Halstead states that peat in the basal part of Quadra-type sediments overlies a till that rests on peat, silt, and silty sand. The lower peats were dated at >37,600 and >36,650 years (GSC-155, 191). These older sediments overlie some 10 feet of stony marine clay, which overlies a third till exposed near beach level. Pre-Quadra sediments containing organic matter also occur beneath till at Cordova Bay, Victoria. According to J. G. Fyles, these sediments contain a pollen assemblage that is believed to represent true interglacial conditions, perhaps the Sangamon Interval. Equivalent deposits that include peat and wood-bearing strata occur in coastal exposures west of Sooke in Juan de Fuca Strait and have been dated at >40,300 years (GSC-358).

Both Quadra and pre-Quadra organic-bearing sediments have been noted also by J. E. Armstrong near Lynn Creek in Fraser Lowland. Quadra sediments, dated 36,200±500 years (GSC-92-2), overlie a till that rests on an older sand, gravel, and peat unit from which wood has been dated >52,300 years (GSC-555). These older sediments overlie an older basal till.

The best-documented and most complete Pleistocene section in Fraser Lowland, if not on the whole west coast, is that at Point Grey, Vancouver (Table XII-2), where some 130 boreholes and a long tunnel have added immeasurably to data available from study of the seacliffs.

Quadra and pre-Quadra sediments occur respectively also in Coquitlam and Surrey municipalities east and southeast of Vancouver.

TABLE XII-2 *Composite section of Pleistocene deposits, Fraser Lowland (by J. E. Armstrong)*

	(Max. known thickness, feet)
Stratified sediments (postglacial)—stream and marine	70
Till and associated sediments (Fraser Glaciation)—glacial, glaciofluvial, glaciolacustrine, glaciomarine	215
Non-glacial (Quadra) sediments (Olympia Interglaciation)—swamp, flood plain, channel and estuarine; peat in basal part dated >36,800 years (GSC-81)	200
Till and associated sediments (Semiamu Glaciation)—glacial, glaciomarine, marine	130
Non-glacial sediments (interglaciation?)—swamp, lacustrine, flood plain, channel, marine; includes some peat	155
Till and stratified deposits (glaciation)—glacial, glaciomarine; includes shells	15
Non-glacial sediments (intertill) channel and flood plain	15+
Till?	—
Bedrock (Eocene)	—

Southern interior, British Columbia. Fulton (1965) cites two distinct intertill sequences in the valley of Thompson River and its tributaries. The lower consists of oxidized sand, silt, and gravel containing volcanic ash, together with wood and freshwater shells. Shells from near Merritt gave a dating of >37,200 years (GSC-258). Wood and shells from Kamloops gave ages of >32,700 and >35,500 years (GSC-275, 413). The upper sequence, also sand, silt, and gravel but unoxidized, is correlated with deposits that at Salmon Arm, Shuswap Lake, contain wood dated at 20,230±120 years (GSC-194). An erosional unconformity separates the two sequences. Till and glaciolacustrine deposits, locally exposed beneath the older oxidized sediments, indicate that at least one glaciation preceded the older non-glacial interval. The intertill sediments were deposited prior to the Fraser Glaciation during a non-glacial interval which comprised at least two periods of aggradation separated by an interval of oxidation and soil formation.

Fulton (1968) indicated rather similar geological events in Purcell Trench, north of Kootenay Lake. He has demonstrated the occurrence of two glacial sequences separated by non-glacial sediments that contain organic matter and a paleosol. An unconformity separates the older till and varied associated deposits from the younger sediments. The paleosol, which includes A, B, and C horizons, is developed on some of the older materials. A finite age of 41,900±600 years (GSC-733) was obtained on roots embedded in the A horizon. The younger non-glacial sediments represent deposits of an aggrading flood plain. Two radiocarbon dates on materials successively nearer the top of the flood plain unit were 43,800±800 and 42,300±700 years (GSC-740, 720). An age of 41,800±600 years (GSC-716), furthermore, was obtained from a stump growing on a slope facies of the paleosol but embedded in the younger gravels. Silty sediments that intertongue with the gravel yielded wood that gave dates of 33,700±330 and 32,710±800 (GSC-542, 493) from successively higher positions. A coarse gravel overlying the silty sediments contained wood in its upper part that dated 25,840±320 (GSC-715). The gravel is capped by till. Fulton relates the upper till to the Fraser Glaciation which, judging by dates from Kamloops region, did not reach the Kootenay area until after about 20,000 years B.P. He relates the non-glacial sediments to the Olympia Interglaciation of the west coast. The paleosol was developed following the older glaciation and was successively buried by the interglacial sediments until perhaps 41,800 years ago.

Central and northern interior, British Columbia. In central and northern British Columbia interglacial sediments have been reported but their interpretation is doubtful. In places non-glacial intervals are indicated by buried river channels cut into older tills or bedrock and by the occurrence of buried placer deposits. Lignite or peat occurs in gravel beneath till along Stikine and Tuya Rivers, but the origin of the deposits is unknown. The indicated non-glacial intervals must predate the last major glaciation but whether earlier Wisconsin, pre-Wisconsin, or pre-Pleistocene has not been determined. In many parts of central British Columbia the Tertiary deposits are unconsolidated and not readily distinguishable from Pleistocene sediments. The occurrence of lava flows or sills in unconsolidated sediments is more characteristic of the Tertiary, but as lavas overlie till sheets in some places, volcanic activity must have continued into the Pleistocene. Lava flows associated with the tills or other Pleistocene sediments may serve as a means of dating some events and provide information on the older Pleistocene.

Interior Yukon Territory. Within the glaciated part of the Cordilleran Region in the Yukon few occurrences of buried organic materials have been reported, but undoubtedly many more will be found as the region is studied.

In Kluane Lake area on the northern side of St. Elias Mountains organic materials occur in drift that predates the last major glaciation, the Kluane, and, on the basis of geomorphological and stratigraphic evidence, indicate three separate non-glacial intervals (Denton and Stuiver, 1967). Organic debris in outwash related to the oldest recognized glaciation, the Shakwak, and organic debris from a silt bed beneath ice-contact stratified drift of the younger Icefield Glaciation, and peat from sinuous stringers contained in the Icefield till itself, proved too old for radiocarbon analyses (Y-1355, 1481, 1486). Organic debris in outwash overlying the Icefield till, however, yielded three finite dates ranging from 30,100 to 37,700 years (Y-1356, 1385, 1488). These deposits are overlain by the Kluane till.

The finite datings appear to represent a non-glacial interval, the Boutellier, of about 10,000 years duration which may be the equivalent of the mid-Wisconsin interval of the mid-continent. The Silver non-glacial interval between the Icefield and Shakwak Glaciations, from which the older age-datings were obtained, was much longer than the Boutellier interval judging by differences in the depth of oxidation of the underlying materials, but neither the duration nor the climate of the interval is known. It may be either early Wisconsin or Sangamon; if the latter, then the Shakwak Glaciation and its outwash deposits may be Illinoian.

Near Fort Selkirk on Yukon River a Pleistocene lava with a striated surface, overlies gravel, sand, and silt that in turn overlies glacial till. Charred wood found 4 feet from the top of the bedded unit was dated at >38,000 years B.P. (I-GSC-27). Another record of forest cover predating the last glaciation was found near Mayo on Stewart River. An abraded log was found in the base of a till lens occurring near the top of a 100-foot section of sand and gravel, the whole overlain by bedded silt. The till lens at this site is considered to be the same as the upper till at numerous sites along the river nearby, and to represent the glacier which apparently terminated some 8 miles below Mayo Landing. The wood was dated at >35,000 years (I-GSC-180). Nearby, wood from a silt, sand, and minor gravel unit overlain by about 10 feet of till and 30 to 50 feet of thinly bedded silt and sand, was dated at >46,580 years (GSC-331). Also on Stewart River, below McQuesten, old wood was found in an ash lens beneath 10 to 15 feet of organic silt (GSC-342).

Further interesting evidence of former forest cover is the report of wood from a 200-foot cut-bank on Liard River. A thin soil zone, including a volcanic ash horizon, and about 100 feet of brown till overlies about 100 feet of crossbedded sand. Wood from 30 feet above river level was dated >40,100 years (GSC-412).

CLASSICAL WISCONSIN AND POSTGLACIAL EVENTS

The last continental ice sheet had three main component parts, the Laurentide Ice Sheet, the Cordilleran Glacier Complex, and the Queen Elizabeth Islands Glacier Complex.[1] The Laurentide Ice Sheet is commonly regarded, on the basis of ice-flow patterns, as comprising the Labrador and Keewatin sectors which, although confluent at the Wisconsin glacial maximum, became discrete areas of outflow during deglaciation. The former retreated to one or more centres or ice divides in northern Quebec and Labrador, and the latter to an ice divide west of

[1] The term 'glacier complex' is used in the broad sense to include ice sheet, ice cap, piedmont glacier, and valley glacier.

Hudson Bay. These major areas of late ice flow themselves split up into smaller short-lived units of outward-flowing ice prior to the final dissipation of the main remnants. Deglaciation also resulted in other major components of Laurentide Ice Sheet. An ice sheet remained and was nurtured locally in Foxe Basin and, later, on Baffin Island. This ice sheet, the Foxe–Baffin Glacier Complex, was independent of the Keewatin and Labrador sectors at least in late Wisconsin time, and parts remain today. Also, early in the deglacial process, major independent ice caps formed in the Appalachian regions, for instance, in Newfoundland, and in part may have been independent of the Labrador sector throughout most of the Wisconsin. The above ice masses and stages in their deglaciation are shown in Figure 15.

The last continental ice sheet is described according to its major component parts regardless of the degree of interdependence experienced during their build-up, at their maximum, or during decay. These are: Appalachian Glacier Complex, Labrador sector of Laurentide Ice Sheet, Keewatin sector of Laurentide Ice Sheet, Foxe–Baffin Glacier Complex, Cordilleran Glacier Complex, and Queen Elizabeth Islands Glacier Complex. Due to the size of the areas within the zone of influence of the major glacier units chosen, it may be necessary to discuss some matters according to smaller areas or to particular glacial or deglacial events. As the ice sheets and glaciers waned and the land surface was uncovered, the forms implanted by the ice were left exposed or were covered by glacial debris washed out from the receding ice margins on land, in lakes, or in the sea. The complex record of glacial and postglacial features and deposits remaining today afford a means of tracing the paths of the receding ice margins and interpreting the deglacial and postglacial events.

Appalachian Glacier Complex

The Appalachian Glacier Complex occupied most if not all of the Appalachian Region in Canada. This includes the island of Newfoundland, the Maritime Provinces, and the Appalachian Mountains of southeastern Quebec. The build-up of glaciers in this region prior to the Wisconsin maximum is little known. The physiographic province is, in large part, a highland region of abundant snowfall, which under the Wisconsin climatic conditions may have developed a number of independent ice caps early in the glacierization process. Under the influence of prevailing northeasterly moving moisture-laden winds from the continental interior and from surrounding bodies of water, these ice caps may have spread radially by differential accretion and preferentially towards the southwest. There are many records of glacial striae and grooves, and of rock dispersal, that trend at right angles to what is commonly considered the ice-flow trend at the Wisconsin maximum and during later retreat. The Appalachian Region may well have been largely ice-covered before confluence with Labrador ice was established along the St. Lawrence River and Strait of Belle Isle. Early ice movements are thus postulated as local and independent of the outward growth of the Labrador sector of Laurentide Ice Sheet. It is probable that the Appalachian Glacier Complex was comprised of two main parts, one over Newfoundland and the other over the Maritime Provinces; both were confluent with the Labrador sector of Laurentide Ice Sheet for some time during the Wisconsin but confluence with each other along Laurentian Channel, through Cabot Strait, was short-lived at the Wisconsin glacial maximum.

The pattern of deglaciation as indicated by ice-flow features of all types (Map 1253A) gives little evidence of general ice-frontal retreat towards Quebec and Labrador. The influence of the maritime environment is obvious. Only on the mainland of Nova Scotia is there a regional southeasterly trend to suggest glacier movements from, or retreat towards, a Labrador centre, but this trend could equally well indicate a centre of outflow from New Brunswick or Maine. Though Labrador erratics have been reported on the Gaspé Highlands, a significant overriding of the Gaspé and New Brunswick Highlands by Labrador ice of Wisconsin age has not been proven.

Newfoundland

Glacial events. On Avalon Peninsula, Henderson (1960) found no evidence of a general ice invasion from the west and concluded that the peninsula had its own ice cap from which active glaciers flowed northward and southward down the channels now occupied by Trinity, Conception, St. Mary's, and Placentia Bays, and thence onto the Grand Banks. A few cobbles from the main part of the island occur along the east side of Trinity Bay at about 20-to-25-foot elevation and hence close to the marine limit; this suggests that the main island ice remained active after considerable recession of the Avalon ice cap and as the sea encroached on the present shores of Avalon Peninsula.

Henderson believes that the last active glacier on Avalon Peninsula lay in St. Mary's Bay and moved debris into the central part of the peninsula as it fanned out towards Trinity and Conception Bays; free flow southward along St. Mary's Bay was impeded by a 'baymouth' threshold. Transverse lineaments in the morainal materials of central Avalon are evident on airphotos, although such patterns are not invariably convex in the direction of flow. Henderson believes that the glacier down-wasted in St. Mary's Bay with marginal retreat taking place on all sides.

MacClintock and Twenhofel (1940, p. 1731) concluded that the whole island was glaciated during the Wisconsin and that " . . . ice spread as a complete cap from the Long Range Plateau, the Central Plateau and the Avalon Peninsula outward in all directions, to beyond the present shore lines of the island." Their studies gave no indication of pre-Wisconsin events as earlier postulated by Coleman, but rather served to establish a gross chronology for the Wisconsin, based mainly on observations in St. George's Bay area in southwestern Newfoundland.

The oldest drift—"St. George's River Drift"—includes till, ice-contact gravel, and marine silt, all of which display a topography suggestive of ice blocks surrounded or buried by marine beds. Following a significant ice-frontal retreat from the shores the "Bay St. George Delta" was built, complete with marine fossils like those of the present day. With re-advance the ice overrode the delta, deposited an upper till, and built an end moraine system near the coast; these deposits comprise the "Robinsons Head Drift." A major retreat of the ice towards the central plateau areas followed, but a still-stand produced the "Kittys Brook" moraine system in the valleys. Further recession resulted in the higher knobs of the plateau protruding above the ice sheet and becoming over-steepened by the outward-moving ice. Still later the ice occurred only as local valley glaciers on the steep sides of the plateaux. Some glaciers deposited small moraines and formed cirques, many of which still contain perennial snow and ice. The work of K. Widmer in the Hermitage Bay area, on south coast of Newfoundland, shows the same close association between 'late' ice and marine overlap.

On the main part of the island there was strong outward ice flow (Jenness, 1960). Fiords are particularly well developed along the south and northeast coasts. There are large areas of fluted and drumlinized terrain, and of ribbed moraine (Pl. XII-7). The lineations, together with recorded striae, grooves, and boulder train data, suggest a very complex ice-flow pattern with erratic, shifting centres of active flow during the waning of the island ice cap. The last active ice caps appear to have been on Newfoundland Highland.

The matter of Labrador ice occupying much of Newfoundland at the Wisconsin maximum, as postulated by Flint (1940) on the basis of increasing height of raised strandlines northward along the west coast, is open to question. The writer believes that Newfoundland maintained its own active ice cap throughout Classical Wisconsin time though it was confluent with Labrador ice in Gulf of St. Lawrence during most of this period. MacClintock and Twenhofel (1940) reported that overriding Labrador ice was possible but there was no real evidence, and concluded that the problem would remain unresolved until the transportation of drift boulders was studied in terms of regional geology of mainland and island alike. Cooper (1937), however, actually records mainland erratics dispersed over the highest part of the northern end of Great Northern Peninsula and associated with southeast-trending striae. Such glaciation by Labrador ice is to be expected in such close proximity to the mainland. On aerial photographs a system of De Geer moraines along Strait of Belle Isle is evident, which indicates late southwestward flow along the strait into Gulf of St. Lawrence,

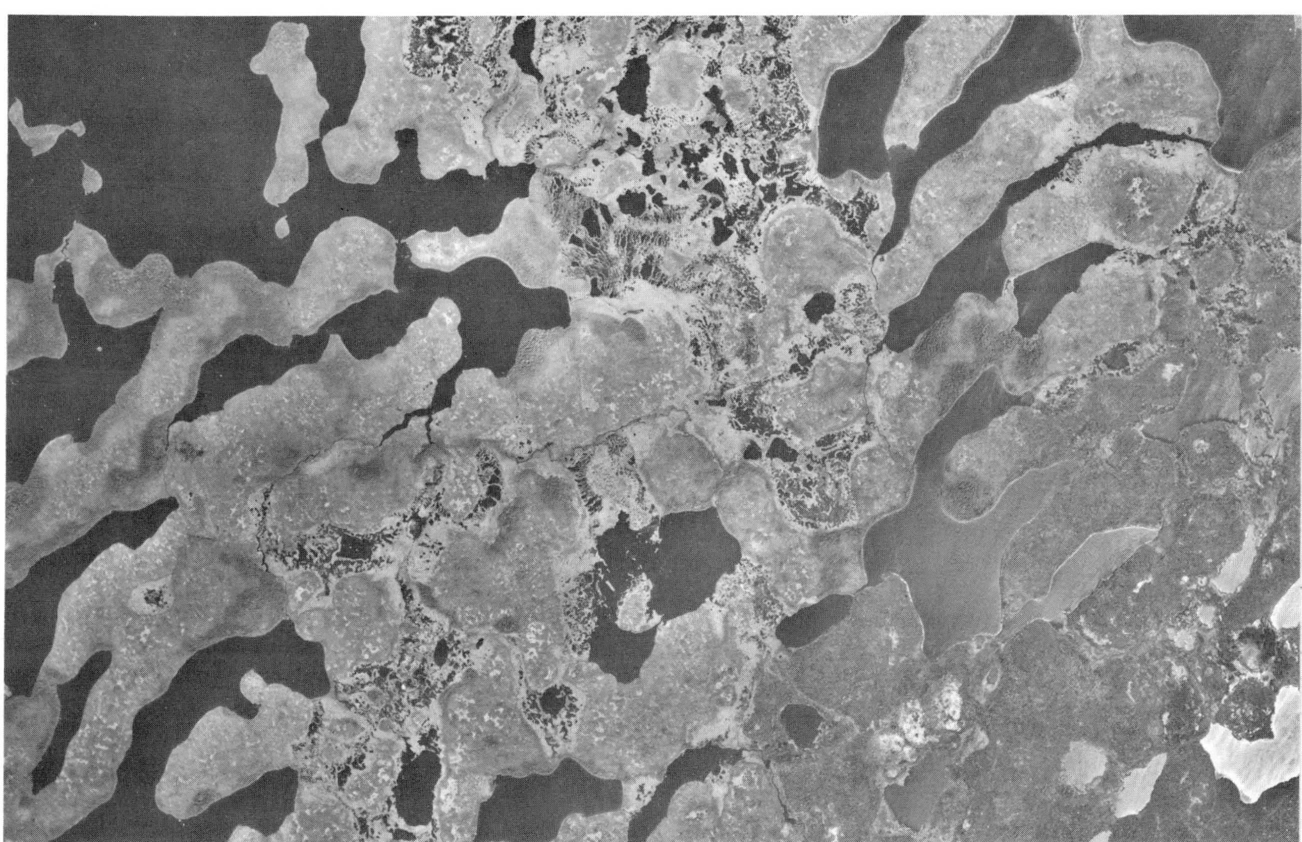

PLATE XII-7. Ribbed moraine near Meca Pond in eastern Newfoundland. Vertical airphoto. The rib ridges show no evidence of ice flow. Scale 1 inch to 1,320 feet.

probably of confluent Newfoundland and Labrador ice. As marine waters extended northeastward up the deep ohannel between Quebec and Newfoundland, and thence into the shallow Strait of Belle Isle, Newfoundland ice would be separated from Labrador ice. At about this stage of deglaciation, about 12,000 years ago, Mecatina Plateau northwest of Strait of Belle Isle was effectively diverting Labrador ice towards the northeast, away from the Strait of Belle Isle.

On northern Newfoundland variations in the trend of De Geer moraines suggest a short-lived active centre of outflow from the area of former Newfoundland and Labrador ice confluence at the extreme northern end of the peninsula. Late ice flow from the Newfoundland Highland changed from southwestward to northwestward as the centre of outflow shifted back to the Long Range highland and a system of lobate end moraines was formed in the vicinity of Ten Mile Lake.

The writer's observations in the central-west coast region support the concept of an active Newfoundland ice cap in late Wisconsin time. There was strong ice flow from the interior both along major valleys parallel the bedrock structures and also across rugged terrain towards the west coast.

Marine events. The interpretation of data on maximum marine overlap is complicated by the fact that 'late' ice has prevented the registration of the highest shorelines in some areas, as in southern, southwestern, and probably also northeastern coastal Newfoundland. This phenomenon implies that local as well as regional postglacial rebound is reflected in the resultant picture of marine overlap.

On Avalon Peninsula, Henderson (1960) found evidence of late-glacial marine overlap only along the east coast of Trinity Bay and on Avalon Isthmus. The isobase of zero uplift may trend northeastward along the east side of Placentia Bay, cross the isthmus at Norman's Cove, and thence pass just inland from the east coast of Trinity Bay. Henderson found that the elevation of raised marine features increased northwestward along the isthmus and also northward along the east shore of the island proper to Bonavista Bay and beyond. The 100-foot isobase passes along the southeast shore of Burin Peninsula and along the axis of Bonavista Bay. The isobase data may reflect an early period of marine overlap broadly concentric about the eastern side of Newfoundland.

The highest shoreline features decrease in elevation westward along the south coast. K. Widmer records wave-cut benches on islands at the mouth of Fortune Bay and on nearby mainland points at an elevation of 100 to 110 feet. The marine limit is about 70 feet at head of Fortune Bay and 30 feet near Burgeo. Between Burgeo and Port aux Basques raised shore features are absent. Similarly, along the southeastern side of St. George's Bay, on the west coast of Newfoundland, there is evidence of late ice advances into the sea that may have prevented the registration of high shoreline features (Flint, 1940; MacClintock and Twenhofel, 1940). Flint has reported, nevertheless, that the level of maximum marine overlap increases from zero at the southwest end of Newfoundland to 100 feet in head end of St. George's Bay, and to 200 feet in Bonne Bay, with isobases trending N70°E. At a later time, during a pause in the uplift, the sea carved benches in bedrock along the west coast and on the north coast, termed the "Bay of Islands surface." The trend of the isobases on this surface is N80°E, the zero isobase lying along the north shore of St. George's Bay, the 100-foot isobase passing through Bonne Bay, and the 250-foot isobase passing through Hare Bay. Study of aerial photographs of this area reveals another prominent bench near sea level, possibly that recorded by Cooper (1937) as a wave-cut bench at 30 feet elevation.

On the north coast raised marine features exhibit three still-stands, two of which may correlate with those recorded on the west coast. The third set may reflect the early period of marine overlap recorded along the eastern shores of the island. Marine shells from Baie Verte, considered to be related to a former sea level at 180 feet elevation, gave dates ranging from 11,520 to 11,950 years B.P. (GSC-55, 75, 87). As there is evidence of marine features and deposits well over 200 feet and perhaps up to 250 feet, it is evident that deglaciation of the north coast had begun well before 12,000 years ago. Marine shells from the west coast of Newfoundland have also been radiocarbon dated; these indicate marine invasion into St. George's Bay prior to 13,420 ± 190 (GSC-598), and into Bay of Islands before 12,600 ± 170 years B.P. (GSC-868).

Cape Breton Island, Nova Scotia

It has been presumed that the Laurentide ice invaded the Gulf of St. Lawrence and passed southeastward across Cape Breton (Goldthwait, J. W., 1924). Glacier ice certainly flowed southeastward through Cabot Strait, scouring St. Paul Island and the northern tip of Cape Breton and also passed through the Strait of Canso, but elsewhere the regional ice-flow trends are poorly preserved and little understood. The writer believes that Cape Breton Highlands were not glaciated by Labrador ice but rather by a local ice cap, and that outward ice flow was not extensive.

There is evidence, however, of a glacier in Northumberland Strait on the west side of Cape Breton Island. Valleys between 200 and 250 feet elevation appear to have been filled, as if by glacial imponding, and later terraced by stream action. E. H. Muller records a river section a mile north of Southwest Margaree where 8 to 10 feet of gravel overlies about 20 feet of red lake clays, 10 feet reddish gravel, and 5 feet of blue cohesive till. It may well be that the glacier that imponded lakes in valleys along the west coast of Cape Breton was the one in Northumberland Strait, which may represent confluent ice from the highlands of Nova Scotia and New Brunswick from the south and west.

Goldthwait (1924) reported northeast-trending striae over eastern Cape Breton and refuted an older hypothesis that this ice flow was from Newfoundland. He noted ice-flow features and drift 'tails' that unmistakably proved a northeast to northward ice flow but he was concerned as to the source area. Though the more northward-trending striae on the east coast require an ice flow from the continental shelf towards the present island he suggested a possible source area south of Strait of Canso. Lacking information on such a centre, however, and with knowledge of east and east-northeast striae along Northumberland Strait he favoured a flow from New Brunswick with, presumably, a radial expansion as the ice emerged from Strait of Canso and Chedabucto Bay. This event preceded his Acadian Bay ice lobe which he considered the main Wisconsin Glaciation. The late H. L. Cameron, however, indicated south-southwest-trending striae east of Bras d'Or Lake and an end moraine system thought to be formed by this glaciation. Some indications of former southwestward ice flow are also evident on aerial photographs (Map 1253A). The anomalous southwest ice-flow trend of eastern Cape Breton appears to be developed on a broad morainal tract. D. R. Grant (GSC) considers that this trend represents a younger ice flow that oriented the drift and lightly striated the bedrock. On the southeast side of many shore outcrops he found evidence of intense scouring action by glaciers directed towards the northeast. The older striae, grooves, and *roches moutonnées* and the trough-like topography of Chedabucto Bay suggest a funnelling of ice down the trough with northward splaying or lobing along eastern Cape Breton. The younger glacier movements appear to have been southeastward through Strait of Canso and northeastward along Bras d'Or Lake basin, and also southward and southeastward out of the lake basin towards the sea. Neither the ice-flow trends in eastern Cape Breton, their indicated source areas, nor the indicated order of glacial events are in accord with the concept of the Labrador ice overriding the island and extending onto the continental shelf.

Information on marine overlap in Cape Breton is limited. A prominent subhorizontal feature at about 200 to 250 feet is present over long stretches of both eastern and western shores. H. L. Cameron reported limited marine overlap in Aspy Bay on northern Cape Breton, and along the southeast coast, but also proglacial lakes in several valleys in-filled to about 250 feet. In view of the semi-coincidence in levels some of the raised coastal features may be ice-contact phenomena, or else both valley-fills and coastal terraces are graded to a common sea-level stand, possibly of pre-Wisconsin age. The writer has not seen any evidence of marine overlap on Cape Breton Island.

Mainland Nova Scotia

Glacial events. The pattern of ice-flow features in Nova Scotia south of the Cobequid Mountains is orderly; at the Wisconsin maximum the ice moved southeasterly across the region. This ice-flow direction is exhibited in many places by drumlins composed of fine-textured till. In areas underlain by granite or quartzite the till is silty to sandy and light coloured. In a zone along LaHave River the till is olive-grey and derived from local slates. Elsewhere to the northeast the drumlins are composed of an anomalous red till that overlies locally derived tills, and is believed by Grant to have been derived largely from Pleistocene sediments scoured from Bay of Fundy, Minas Basin, and Northumberland Strait. L. H. King (The Bedford Institute) located off-shore moraines that may represent the Wisconsin maximum or a somewhat later stage of retreat. He believes that the off-shore moraines probably formed at a time of low sea level when relatively thin ice calved into marine embayments.

As the Wisconsin glacier waned the ice front along the Atlantic coast retreated inland to the northwest. Absence of marine overlap along this coast suggests a relatively thin ice sheet near its terminus. As deglaciation proceeded marine waters invaded the Bay of Fundy giving rise to a concentric pattern of retreat towards the Nova Scotia Uplands. Late stage upland centres of outflow were active. Drumlins have been re-oriented in some areas and eskers appear at variance with earlier ice-flow features. Late ice in the central upland region remained active or was reactivated so that it moved granitic drift northward across Cornwallis–Annapolis Valley and deposited it on the Triassic trap rocks of North Mountain, and along the Fundy shore (MacNeill, 1953; Hickox, 1962). That the central Nova Scotia Uplands should retain an ice cap late in the period of deglaciation is not surprising in view of the maritime setting; it is at present an area of heavy snowfall. The precise age of this upland ice cap is not known and there are currently no dates on relevant materials, but it is known that the sea invaded the western side of Bay of Fundy prior to $13,325 \pm 500$ years B.P. (I-GSC-7).

The pattern of ice-flow features in northern Nova Scotia is highly irregular. The Cobequid Mountains and Antigonish Highlands appear to restrict the general southeast flow so typical of the region to the south and east. There was some glacier flow northward from these highlands towards Northumberland Strait. Glacial striae and boulder trains indicate northward movement in the vicinity of Pictou and New Glasgow. Cobequid-type igneous stones occur sporadically to the north of the mountains in the red sandy tills of the lowlands; they are especially noticeable near Pictou and on Pictou Island. Goldthwait (1924) believed the former were derived from the north flank of the mountains by eastward-moving glaciers from New Brunswick in advance of the Acadian lobe incursion from the north. Others contend that the last ice to invade the lowlands was from New Brunswick rather than from the north. The occurrence of Cobequid igneous stones in the red till of the Carboniferous Lowlands required some northward transport; this might have resulted from stream deposition prior to emplacement of the last red till sheet but later northward glacier movements are more probable as such stream transport is not effective with the present relief. Late active glaciers on the eastern Cobequid Mountains and Antigonish Highlands are indicated also by the occurrences of eskers and associated outwash, with north-dipping beds, as along River John near Scotsburn and Maryvale. In Barney's River area, at the east end of Merigomish Island, the outwash is graded to, or below, present sea level. Furthermore along the coast near Malignant Cove kame terraces, with northeast-dipping crossbeds, occur up to elevations of about 100 feet; these formed while the same late glacier occupied Northumberland Strait.

The western end of Cobequid Mountains does not appear to have harboured a late ice cap. In this region glacier retreat was northward and meltwater poured through gaps in the western Cobequid Mountains to deposit extensive valley trains with kettled deltas in Minas Basin. Small elongate moraine ridges on the north-central part of the Cobequids may be end moraines. The northeasterly trend of Joggins moraine (Wickenden, 1941), south and east of Amherst, has been assumed to indicate glacial retreat towards the northwest. However, both northwest and southeast of this moraine, fluting and striae trend south-southwest and the ice flow was undoubtedly southward; this ice-flow direction is the reverse of that farther east and was most likely formed at a somewhat earlier date as a calving bay developed in Bay of Fundy.

Marine events. Postglacial changes of level in Nova Scotia are complicated. The Fundy embayment is the only area affording evidence of former emergence but the whole province is now involved in submergence. In southwest Nova Scotia the isobases of differential uplift trend northeastward, roughly parallel to the Fundy shore, with the zero isobase at Yarmouth; uplift is 120 feet at Digby and 150 feet on Long Island, southwest of Digby. The isobase trend changes abruptly in Minas Basin. This may result from changes in amount and rate of uplift due to early opening of Bay of Fundy as a calving bay in the ice front, to presence of late ice north of Minas Basin, and possibly also to the structural influence of Cobequid fault. For these reasons, projection of the Fundy isobase data northward from Minas Basin may not be valid. Borns and Swift (1966) report glaciofluvial deposits overlying glaciomarine deltaic deposits; the top surface of the former slopes from approximate 140 feet elevation at Advocate Harbour to 60 feet near Truro whereas the surface of the lower unit slopes from elevation 130 feet (110 feet above high tide level) in the west to mean high tide at Five Islands, about halfway between these places. The writer, however, believes the upper unit is basically glaciomarine and that the relict marine surface slopes from 120 feet west of Parrsboro to 20 feet at east end of Cobequid Bay. He believes that 'late' ice prevented marine waters from entering the Truro lowland, and also prevented development of higher-level strandlines near Advocate Harbour. The tidal range in Minas Basin is today about 40 to 55 feet but it was undoubtedly different in the past; for this reason the marine limits are referred here to high tide.

There is no evidence of marine overlap along most of the Northumberland shore. A sea bench on the northeast-trending coast east of Arisaig records a former sea-level stand some 5 to 10 feet above the present, and comparable sea-level stands have been recorded elsewhere along this and the George Bay coast; all these are believed to be pre-Wisconsin. In the extreme northwestern part of the province, however, the zero isobase of postglacial uplift is believed to pass through Northport, with maximum marine overlap increasing westward to perhaps 50 feet at the provincial boundary. The evidence is, however, rather inconclusive.

Prince Edward Island

Evidence of glaciation in the western part of Prince Edward Island has long been recognized (Chalmers, 1895) by an abundance of igneous and other stones in the drift. These were derived from westerly or northwesterly sources, whereas the bedrock is red sandstone and shale, mainly of Permian age. The general absence of foreign stones in the drift of the central and eastern parts of the island led early workers to regard the drift mantle as a regolith; but undoubted glacial till is present in all parts of the island (Prest, 1962; Frankel, 1966). It has also been assumed that the last major glacier to override the whole island was from the north—the Acadian Bay lobe of Goldthwait (1924). The distribution of erratics along the north shore lends some support to this concept, but south-trending striae are generally lacking whereas east-trending striae occur along or near the coast. A few north-south trending striae have been recorded from central parts of the south coast but the sense of movement is unknown. These striae predate the last major glacier movements along Northumberland Strait. The general southeasterly trend of ice-flow features across most of the island, coupled with the prevalence of foreign stones in the western end, suggests glaciation from New Brunswick. The island was deglaciated, however, over a period of time during which significant lobing of the ice fronts occurred. On the basis of miniature crag-and-tail features on the south shore west of Borden it is known that there was late westward flow along Northumberland Strait. But numerous glacial striae along the south shore between Borden and Hillsborough Bay, however, trend northeast-southwest rather than along shore, and similar trends occur in the interior on the southwest side of the central higher parts of the island. This suggests that late ice flowed southwestward from the interior towards the Straits and thence westward beyond Borden. Also eastern and north–central parts of the island are characterized by an abundance of glaciofluvial deposits and an anastomosing system of eskers, whereas elsewhere these features are uncommon; this situation is thought to reflect the final decay of remnant ice on central and eastern Prince Edward Island.

Marine overlap in western Prince Edward Island reaches a maximum of 75 or 80 feet along the west coast. The marine limit in the northwestern part of Malpeque Bay is about 30 feet and in the southeastern corner about 10 feet. The zero isobase appears to be near Borden and probably trends southward across Northumberland Strait to Cape Tormentine, New Brunswick. There is no evidence of marine overlap in central or eastern Prince Edward Island. Shells from northwestern Prince Edward Island, believed related to a sea-level stand about 50 feet above the present, were dated at 12,410±170 years and 12,670±340 years (GSC-101, 160).

Magdalen Islands, Quebec

The Magdalen Islands in the central part of the Gulf of St. Lawrence are commonly regarded as lying squarely in the path of Laurentide Ice Sheet as it spread southward or southeastward towards the Atlantic. There is, however, no evidence of Wisconsin Glaciation above the limit of postglacial marine overlap, and below this limit there is only a till-like material that was deposited under water.

At Amherst Harbour, Goldthwait (1915) observed a 15-foot sandy deposit, resembling glacial till and containing only local rock materials overlying deeply decayed buff weathering, grey sandstone. As some of the stones had striations parallel to their long axes he concluded that a glacial origin was more valid than a marine drift origin. Coleman (1920) also noted the complete absence of glacial features on Amherst Island aside from the sandy drift, but he concluded that the thin margin of the continental ice sheet was afloat at a time of higher sea level.

Alcock (1941) reported boulder clay on Amherst and Entry Islands, ground moraine on Grindstone Island, an end moraine on Coffin Island, and large erratics at elevations over 200 feet on Grosse Isle. He saw no evidence of marine uplift, thus disagreeing with Chalmer's interpretation of beaches and terraces to about 115 feet and Coleman's marine overlap to about 200 feet. Prest (1957) considered the Coffin Island end moraine to be a kettled deposit of ice-contact stratified drift, or kame moraine, with the beds dipping inland to the west, and that its bouldery surface was the result of ice rafting during a period of marine overlap. The boulders are mainly foreign to the islands and are believed derived from a northern source. He confirmed the presence of marine gravels on Grindstone Island to a maximum elevation of 120 feet. Alcock considered the 'till' on Amherst Island to be a deposit let down gently from floating ice, an opinion shared by the writer in view of the contact relations between drift and bedrock.

The exact reason for the presence of striated local stones in the marine drift mantle of Amherst Island remains obscure; these stones were probably derived by glacier action some distance beyond the present shores and later ice rafted into their present position. Marine or lacustrine submergence of at least 120 feet elevation is indicative of ice near at hand; this is also indicated by the ice-contact stratified drift on Coffin Island. Glacier ice evidently reached the islands from the north, but only shelf ice reached the southern shores.

New Brunswick

Glacial events. The pattern of ice-flow features in New Brunswick clearly reveals a south to southeast trend in the western and southern parts, and an east to northeast (and/or southwest) trend in eastern parts. Granitic rocks from the Precambrian Shield occur in the Saint John River valley, on the adjoining Chaleur Uplands (Lee, 1955), and in an end moraine along the northern flank of the Chaleur Uplands. It is thus clear that Laurentide ice did reach the upland as well as flow strongly down the Saint John River valley, and probably also down the Matapedia Valley in Gaspé into Chaleur Bay, but elsewhere glaciation was relatively light. Alcock (1948) found evidence of strong glacial flow from the northern end of New Brunswick Highland northeast towards Chaleur Bay and east towards Gulf of St. Lawrence, and concluded that such movements must have preceded as well as followed the arrival of Laurentide ice in New Brunswick. He assumed that Laurentide ice over-topped the highlands on the basis of south-trending striae in southern New Brunswick and particularly in the Moncton area, but striae trends in this area are now known to be diverse. It is more likely, judging by ice-flow patterns and an end moraine (Map 1253A), that ice flowed mainly around the highlands rather than over them. Flint (1951) suggested that the ice responsible for the northeast- and east-trending striae was of local derivation and subsequent to the main Laurentide glaciation. South of Bathurst, the ice-flow features visible on airphotos, suggest that some late ice flow was out of Chaleur Bay and towards the south-southwest but this has not been confirmed. Farther south, between Newcastle and Moncton, ice-flow features and an east-west end moraine also suggest a southerly ice movement as if from Miramichi Bay. On the other hand, but a short distance southeast of the ice-flow features and closer to Moncton, miniature crag-and-tail features observed on a pebbly sandstone indicate ice flow to the northeast parallel to the regional drainage.

On both the mainland and islands in the extreme southwest corner of New Brunswick, Alcock noted *roches moutonnées* and striations trending southeast to east, in contrast to the general south-southeast trend typical of the western part of the province. He concluded that there had been an ice movement from the mountains of Maine, presumably prior to the main Laurentide glaciation.

Marine events. Chalmers (1890) noted marine terraces along the Fundy shore both southwest and northeast of Saint John. In the former area the deposits had a maximum altitude of 225 feet and contained shells; in the latter area the highest terrace deposits were only 125 feet and no shells were seen. In Saint John River valley at Fredericton, Lee (1959) found estuarine deposits at 125 feet. It is possible that the lower part of Saint John River valley and the New Brunswick side of Bay of Fundy were covered by late ice while the high-level terraces were being formed southwest of Saint John. Shells from the seacliff 5 miles west of Saint John are dated at 13,325 ± 500 years (I-GSC-7).

Along the east coast of New Brunswick large tracts of low-lying ground formerly covered by the sea show little or no evidence of marine action; there were apparently no significant halts as the land rose from the sea and, in general, marine sediments appear to have been removed by erosion or incorporated into the soil profile. Local areas of marine sand, gravel, and poorly washed sediments, and the disposition of ice-rafted boulders do provide some evidence of former marine action. The marine limit varies from zero at the east end of Cape Tormentine to 100 feet at Moncton. It is 150 feet about 15 miles west of Richibucto and 225 feet at Newcastle and Bathurst. Farther west along Chaleur Bay the marine limit is not evident, probably as a result of late ice in Chaleur Bay during the period of maximum overlap along the east coast. The isobases of differential uplift trend northeast along the Bay of Fundy shore, northward through Moncton area, and northeastward again along the east shore of the province; this gives them an open S-shape. The effects of late ice and the possible influence of Cobequid fault in the amount and rate of uplift on either side of Bay of Fundy, together with the lack of age determinations, preclude correlation across the bay. The uplift in western Prince Edward Island, however, appears in accord with data from eastern New Brunswick.

Gaspé Peninsula, Quebec

Glacial events. Much has been written concerning glaciation of Gaspé Peninsula; this is succinctly summarized by McGerrigle (1952). Cirque and local ice-cap development preceded Laurentide glaciation of Gaspé Peninsula. Shield erratics have been found on the highest parts of the peninsula. There is no proof, however, that the erratics were emplaced during the last major glaciation. McGerrigle notes the general sparseness of erratics in eastern Gaspé, and the seeming absence of anorthosite in a 50-mile-wide belt along the central part of the peninsula. It is noteworthy that neither McGerrigle nor Brummer (1958) reports Canadian Shield stones in the Béland–Upper York River highland area though they occur in lower areas farther east. It is perhaps noteworthy that granite gneiss erratics in southeastern Gaspé are only recorded along or close to the shore highway and their mode of emplacement is uncertain. The Matapedia Valley was the main ice-flow route into Chaleur Bay.

A highland ice-cap phase followed the maximum phase of Laurentide glaciation and, as the ice receded from the north side of Gaspé, this ice cap remained active and transported boulders northward as far as St. Lawrence River (McGerrigle, 1952). On the eastern end of the Shickshock Mountains, erratics derived from lower areas some miles south of the mountains indicate that the highland ice cap once had a centre of outflow lying south of the highlands proper. As the ice cap waned it broke up into minor ice caps that gave rise to radial flow as from the Tabletops and Béland–Upper York River highlands. The local ice-cap phase of glaciation finally gave way to cirque and valley glaciation.

Marine events. The extent of marine overlap along the southern and eastern coasts of Gaspé is not precisely known. Marine sediments are reported at 180 feet on the north side of Chaleur Bay and at 224 feet on the eastern end of the peninsula. The writer observed gravel deposits up to a maximum of 180 feet near Grand Cascapedia, but regarded these as outwash deposits graded to a wave-base perhaps as low as 120 feet above the present sea level. The steep outcrops of the eastern end of the peninsula do not lend themselves to the preservation of marine strandlines. A marine terrace at Prével has an elevation of only 90 feet and at Cap-des-Rosiers Est the upper limit of near-shore sediments is at 75 feet. At present there is evidence of coastal 'drowning' at the head end of Gaspé Bay. Along the western part of the north shore marine deposits have been recorded up to 300 feet, but 4 miles east of Mont Louis the writer did not see any evidence of marine overlap above the surface of a small delta at an altitude of 95 feet.

Appalachian Mountains of Quebec

Flint (1951) has summarized the voluminous literature pertaining to an Appalachian centre of glacial outflow (that either preceded or followed glaciation) from the highlands of Maine, New Hampshire, Vermont, and adjoining Quebec. In the last area the problem concerns the evidence of northward flow towards the St. Lawrence from Notre Dame and Green Mountains. Flint concluded that ice has flowed northward, at least locally. Recent studies by Gadd (1966), however, do not support the concept of glacial transport to the north. It may be that glaciation of the western part of the Appalachian Highlands, south of Quebec City, was unlike that in the east where late northward flow is evident. Lee (1962) reported striae and crag-and-tail indicative of northward ice flow in the Rivière du Loup–Trois Pistoles area. These were formed when a calving basin developed in St. Lawrence Valley while ice remained over the drainage divide in Notre Dame Mountains.

Labrador Sector, Laurentide Ice Sheet

Little is known about the initial development of the Labrador sector of the Laurentide Ice Sheet or the course of glacier movements that led to the ice cover of the entire region between the Labrador coast and western

Manitoba, and possibly beyond. It is probable that in response to a change in climate, the Lake Plateau of central Quebec–Labrador developed an ice cap by "instantaneous glacierization" (Ives, 1957), followed by radial outflow. The early influence of an open Hudson Bay in the development and differential expansion of the ice cap towards the west was favoured by Hare (1951) and Derbyshire (1962) but not, on climatological grounds, by Barry (1960). The prevailing southwesterly winds from the mid-continent no doubt contributed to southwestward expansion of the ice sheet towards Ontario and the Great Lakes region. There were probably local centres of excessive snow accumulation in the marginal zone of the expanding ice sheet; these may account for glacier lobations and resulting striae which in many areas diverge markedly from the general, deglacial, trend.

Early in Classical Wisconsin time the glaciers flowed off the Laurentian Highlands into St. Lawrence Valley and, upon filling the valley, sought escape northeastward towards the Gulf of St. Lawrence and southwestward towards the Ontario basin. Gadd (1966) reports striae indicative of southwesterly ice movements from the north flank of the western end of Notre Dame Mountains south of Quebec City, which he believes were formed during an overriding phase of glaciation. Strong eastward ice flow was long-continued down Saguenay River and thence northeast down St. Lawrence River as indicated by ice-flow features on the land and a very deep channel in St. Lawrence River beginning at the mouth of the Saguenay. The channel extends east-southeastward across Gulf of St. Lawrence through Cabot Strait and thence to the edge of the continental shelf, and is known as Laurentian Channel. Ice-flow features give some indication that the ice-flow divide in St. Lawrence Valley may have migrated westward from well east of Saguenay River to somewhat west of the Saguenay during Wisconsin time. Gadd suggests also that during the Wisconsin there was a shift of the centre of outflow in the Laurentian Highlands towards the west and that by the time the glacier was waning in St. Lawrence Valley the ice-flow direction was southeastward across the valley. He reports evidence of strong ice flow south–southeastward up the Chaudière River valley at this later stage.

The Laurentide ice upon filling St. Lawrence Valley and flowing along it sought escape southward through cols in the eastern part of Notre Dame Mountains and hence combined with elements of the Appalachian Glacier Complex; ultimately, as earlier mentioned, it may have overtopped the highest mountains in Gaspé, but its southward extent was perhaps more limited than has been generally recognized.

Study of the mineralogy of tills of southwestern Ontario led Dreimanis, *et al.* (1957) to conclude that glacier movements into Ontario and Erie basins were first from the north-northeast and only later from the east along the axis of the lake basin. The seeming reversal of the order of major periods of ice flow between Erie basin and Trois-Rivières region may be a result of their wide geographic separation and also to the different parts of Wisconsin time being considered. The occurrence of cobbles and boulders of Gowganda conglomerate in southwestern Ohio also indicates strong southerly movements from the Huron basin prior to the incursion of the Erie ice lobe. Also, in northwestern Ontario the writer found pebbles and cobbles of oölitic jasper, derived from the Sutton Mountains–Nowashe Lake belt west of James Bay, or from the Belcher Islands on the east side of Hudson Bay, and of a characteristic greywacke reportedly derived from Cape Jones at northeast end of James Bay, perhaps as much as 600 miles from their outcrop area. These indicate an early southwesterly ice-flow direction that is somewhat divergent from the deglacial flow pattern.

Information on the retreat of the Labrador sector of Laurentide Ice Sheet is naturally far more abundant than on the advance or build-up stages. The present surface bears a record of the last glacial events, modified only in part by postglacial changes, whether erosional or depositional. After the Wisconsin glacial maximum it is probable that there was thinning of the ice sheet over a broad marginal zone as the ice front retreated. The following discussion attempts to follow the major changes and events as the ice front receded from various parts of the country.

St. Lawrence Lowlands

In southern Quebec the margin of active ice receded northward from Notre Dame Mountains into St. Lawrence Valley, but flow probably continued both up and down the valley from near the mouth of Saguenay River for some time before giving place to a general southward flow across the valley. During this latter stage the ice advance was restricted by the north side of Notre Dame Mountains and a system of end moraines was deposited, the lowest of which is known as the Highland Front moraine (Gadd, 1964, 1966). The whole system represents a lowering of the surface of about 1,000 feet. The St. Antonin Moraine (Lee, 1962) is the easternmost end moraine of the Highland Front system, and near Rivière du Loup the glacier that produced it was moving down valley and calving into the sea which occupied the lower part of the valley.

Farther west, in the wide part of St. Lawrence Valley, meltwater was ponded between the Appalachian Highlands, including Adirondack Mountains, and the ice front to form glacial Lake Vermont, with discharge south down Hudson Valley. The Drummondville Moraine (Gadd, 1960) was probably built during the Fort Ann phase of this lake. As the ice front receded northward the lake expanded northeastward along the south side of St. Lawrence Valley until it was able to discharge into the sea near Quebec City. The last short-lived lake is presumed herein to represent the Trenton phase of the post-Iroquois lakes as recognized in the Ontario basin by E. Mirynech, and is considered to be the last phase of con-

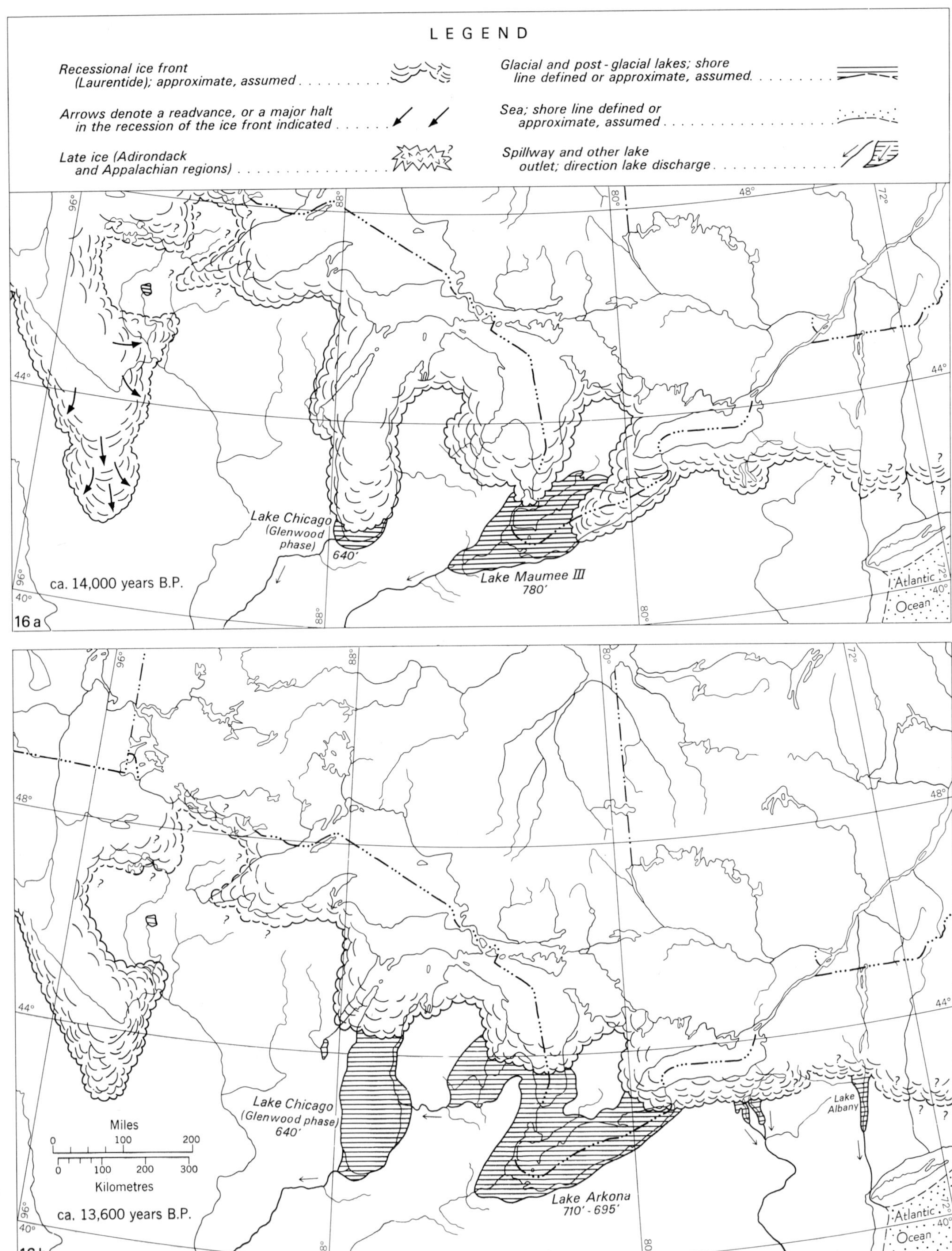

FIGURE XII-16. Glacial lake phases during the recession of Wisconsin ice from central Canada.

Figure XII-16. Glacial lake phases during the recession of Wisconsin ice from central Canada.

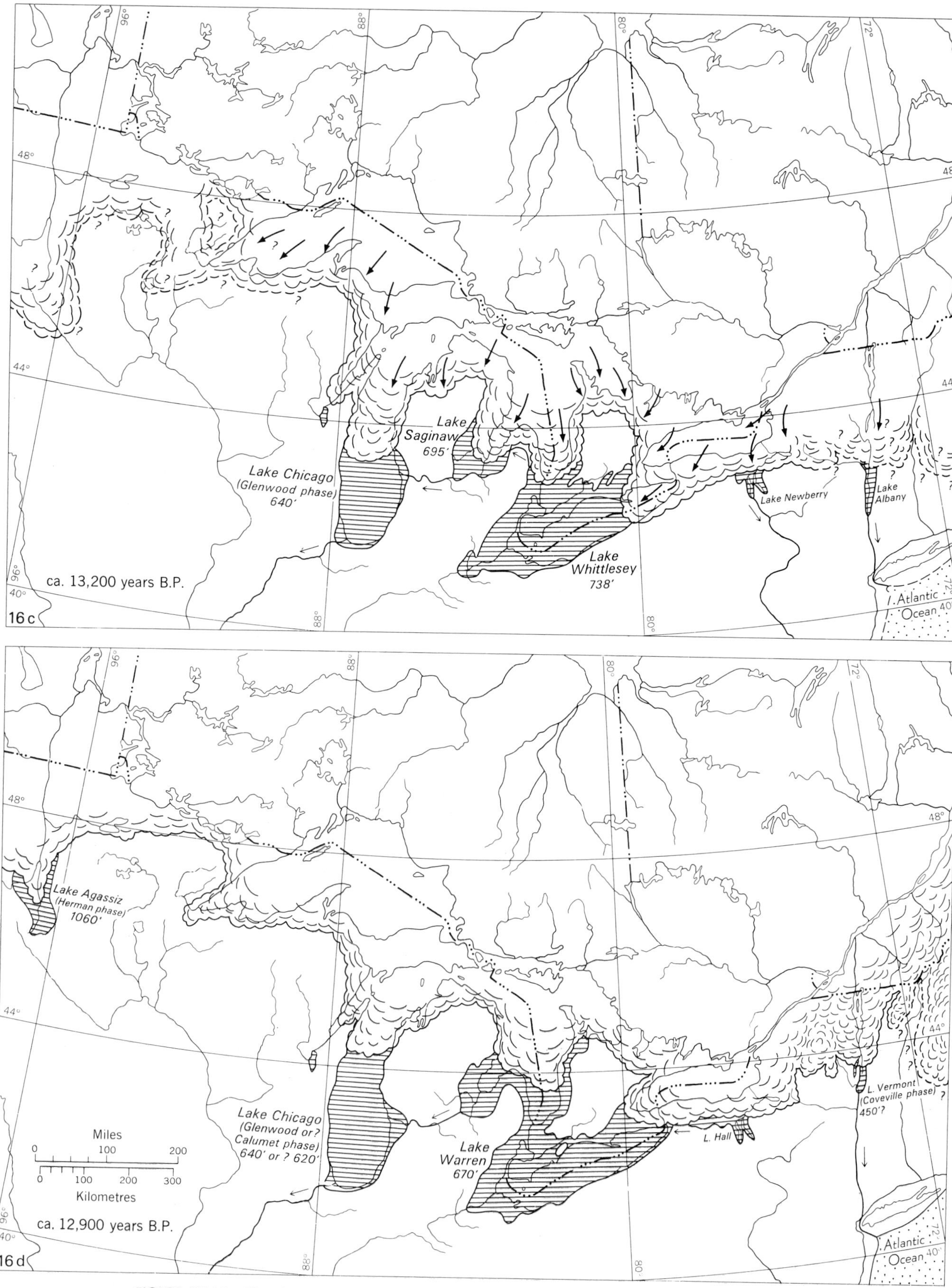

FIGURE XII-16. Glacial lake phases during the recession of Wisconsin ice from central Canada (cont.)

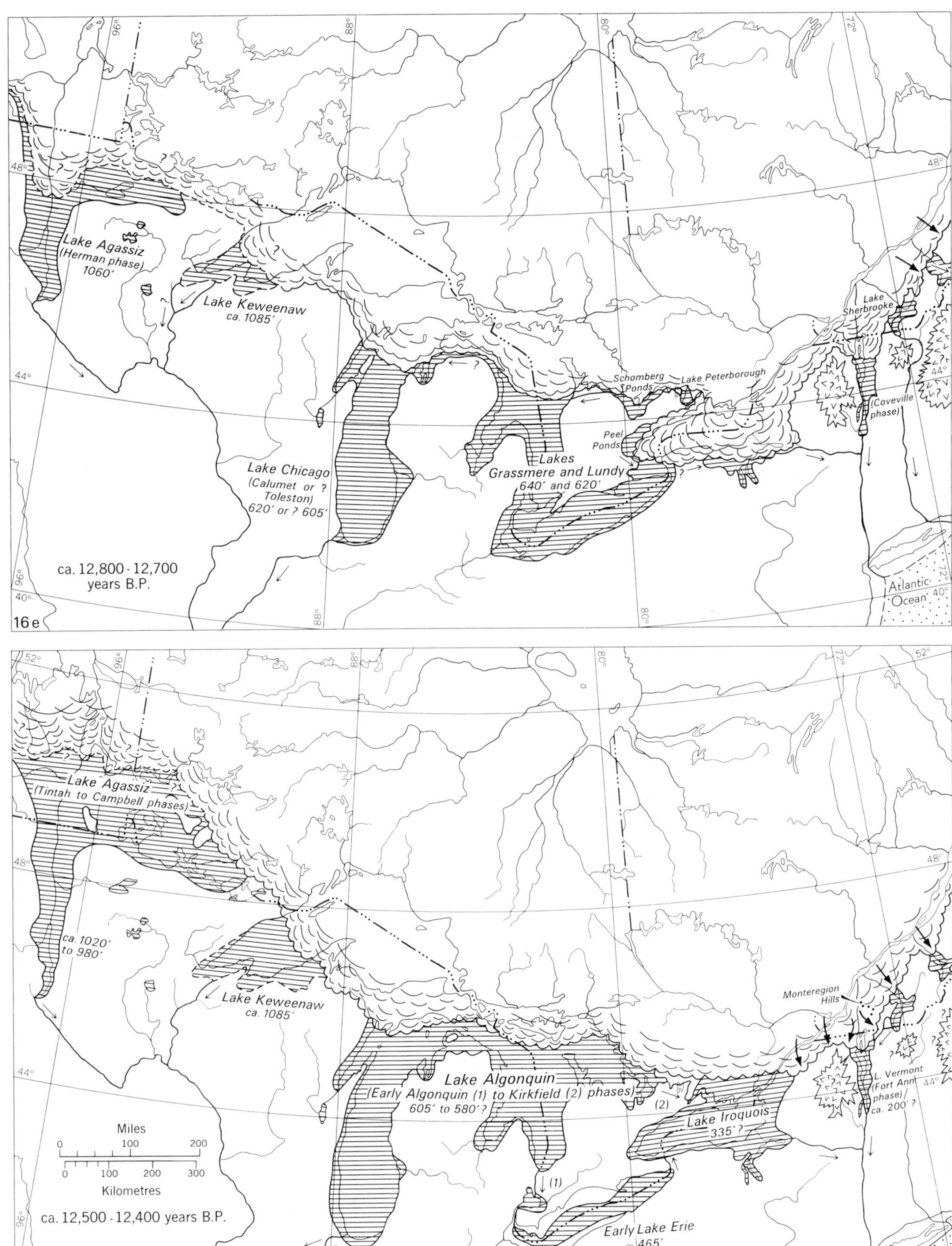

FIGURE XII-16. Glacial lake phases during the recession of Wisconsin ice from central Canada (cont.)

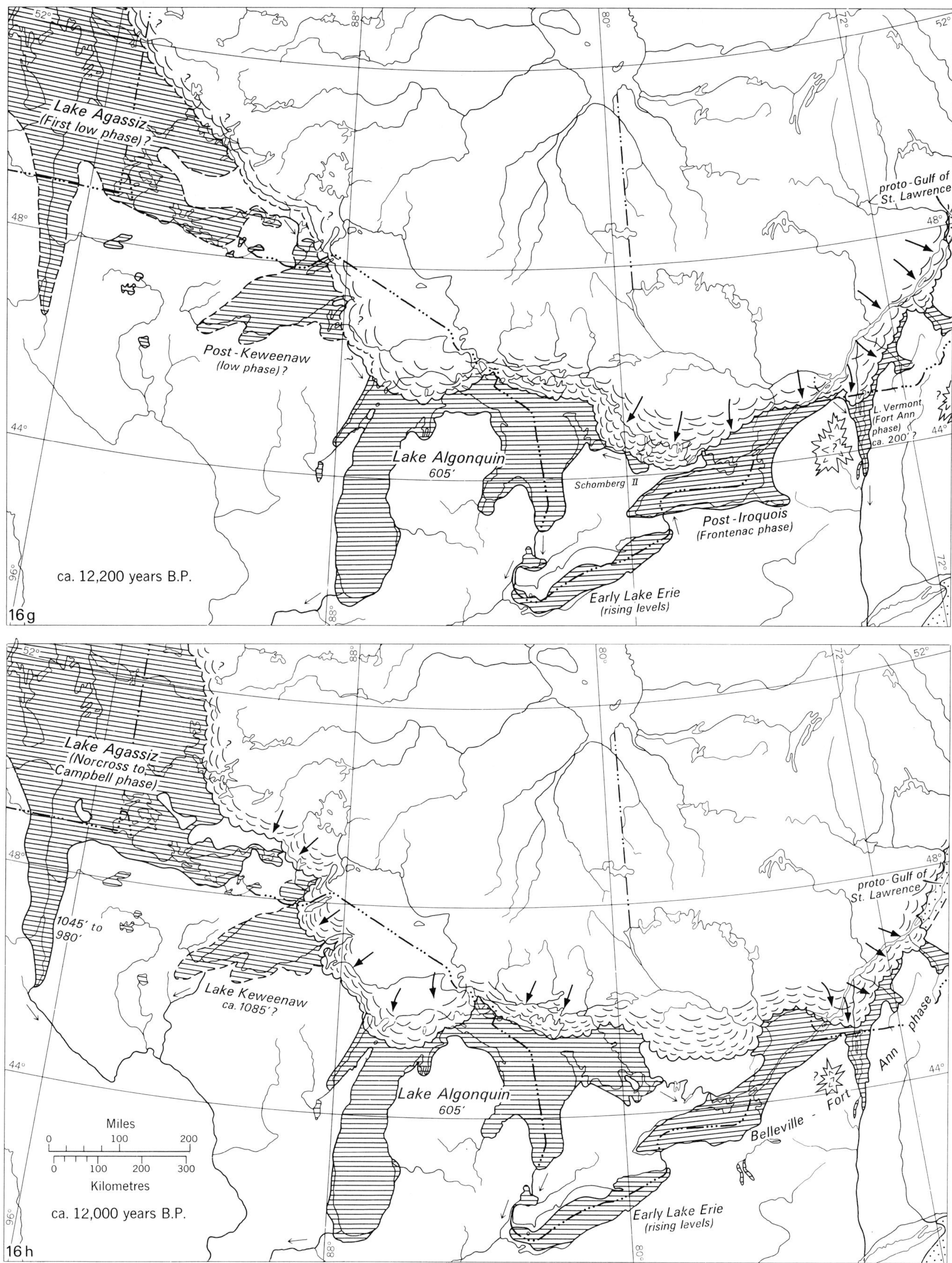

FIGURE XII-16. Glacial lake phases during the recession of Wisconsin ice from central Canada (cont.)

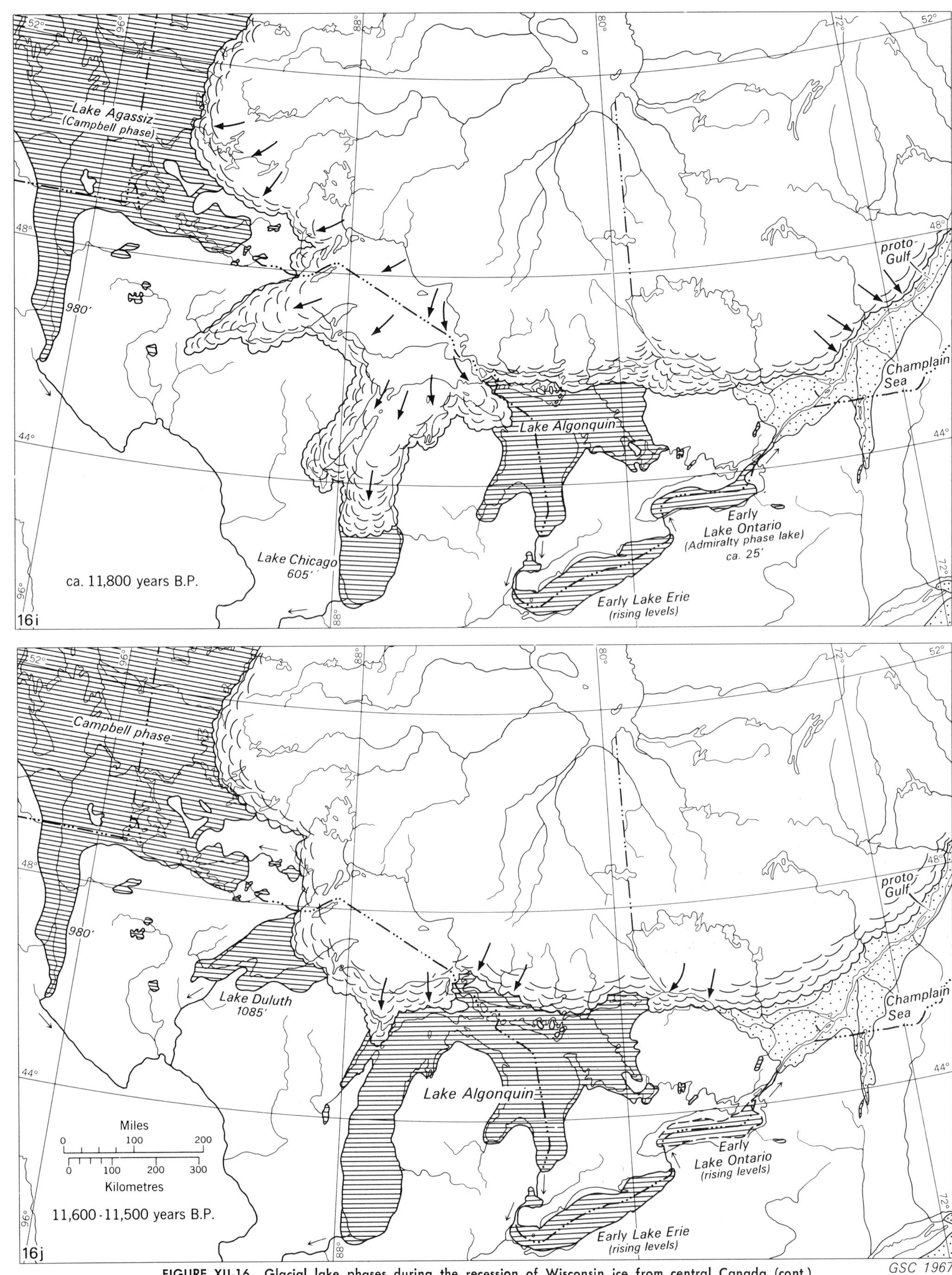

FIGURE XII-16. Glacial lake phases during the recession of Wisconsin ice from central Canada (cont.)

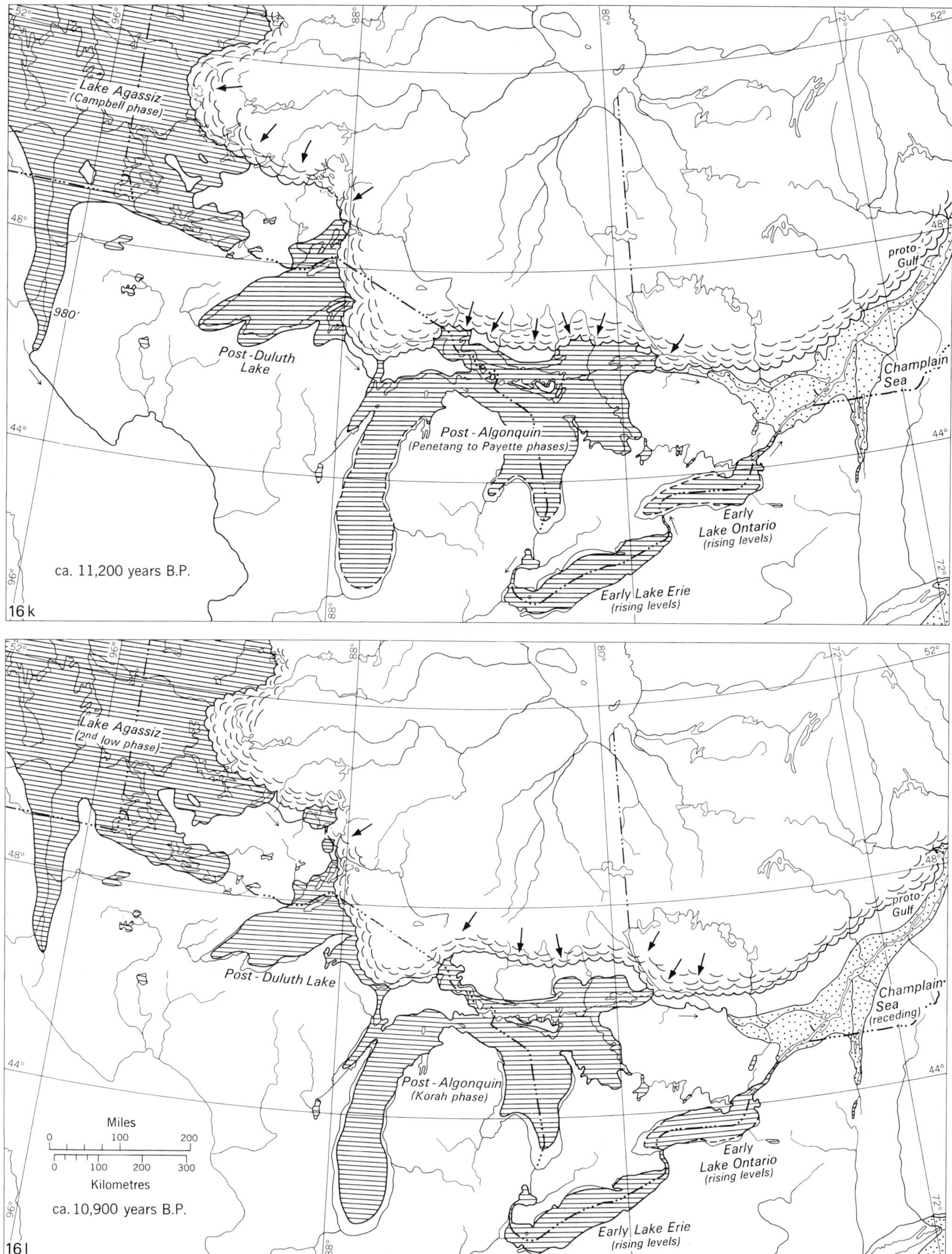

FIGURE XII-16. Glacial lake phases during the recession of Wisconsin ice from central Canada (cont.)

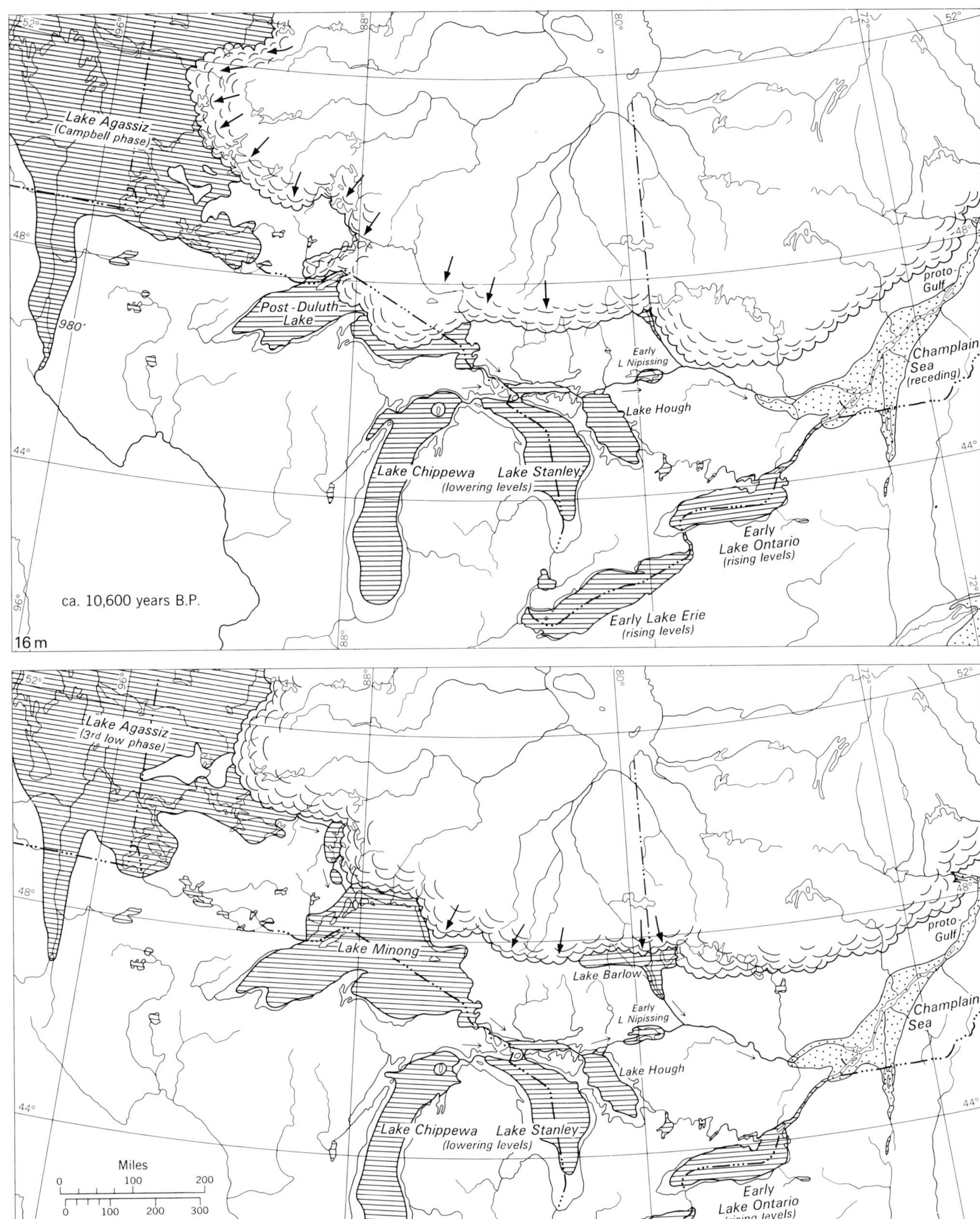

FIGURE XII-16. Glacial lake phases during the recession of Wisconsin ice from central Canada (cont.)

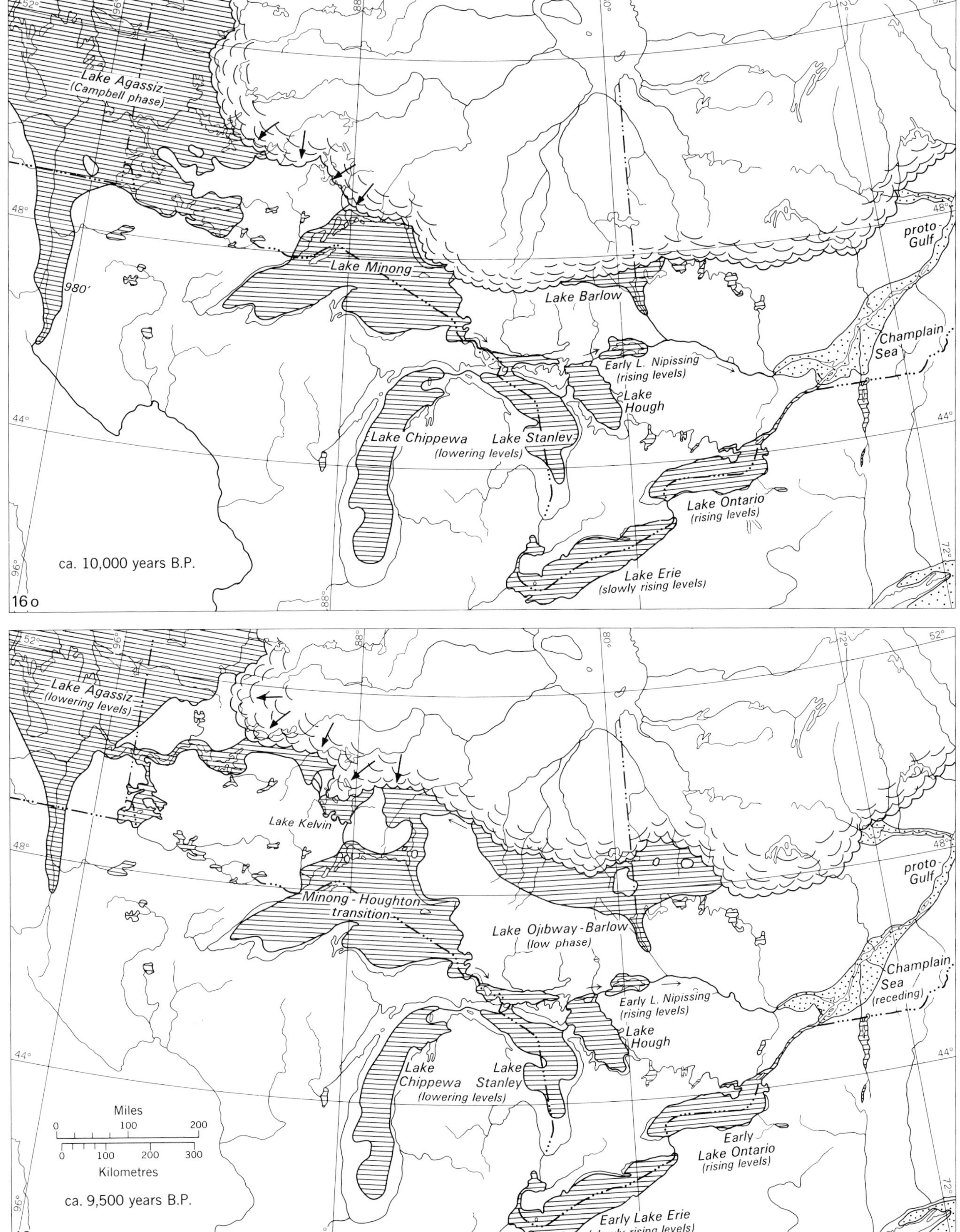

FIGURE XII-16. Glacial lake phases during the recession of Wisconsin ice from central Canada (cont.)

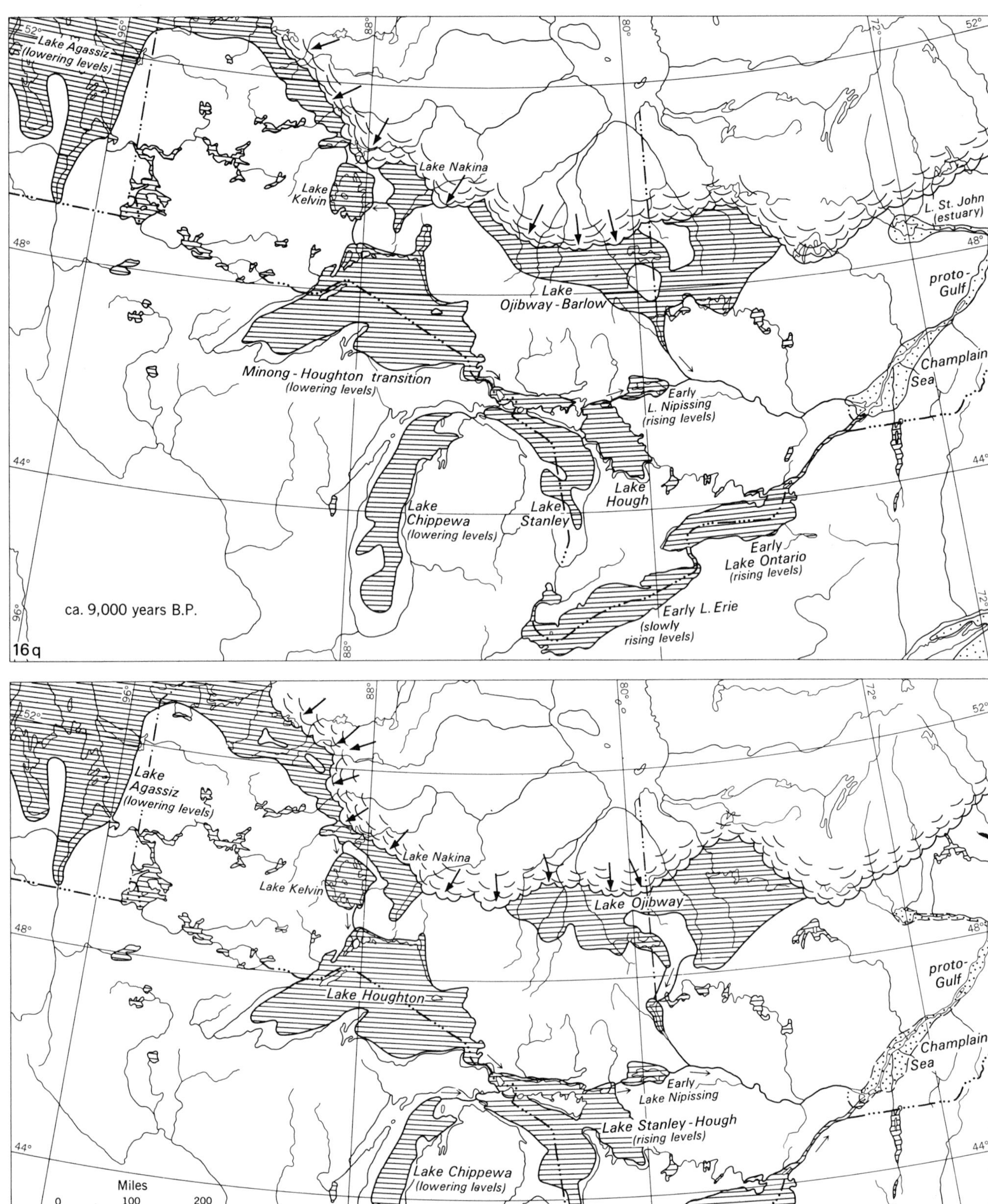

FIGURE XII-16. Glacial lake phases during the recession of Wisconsin ice from central Canada (cont.)

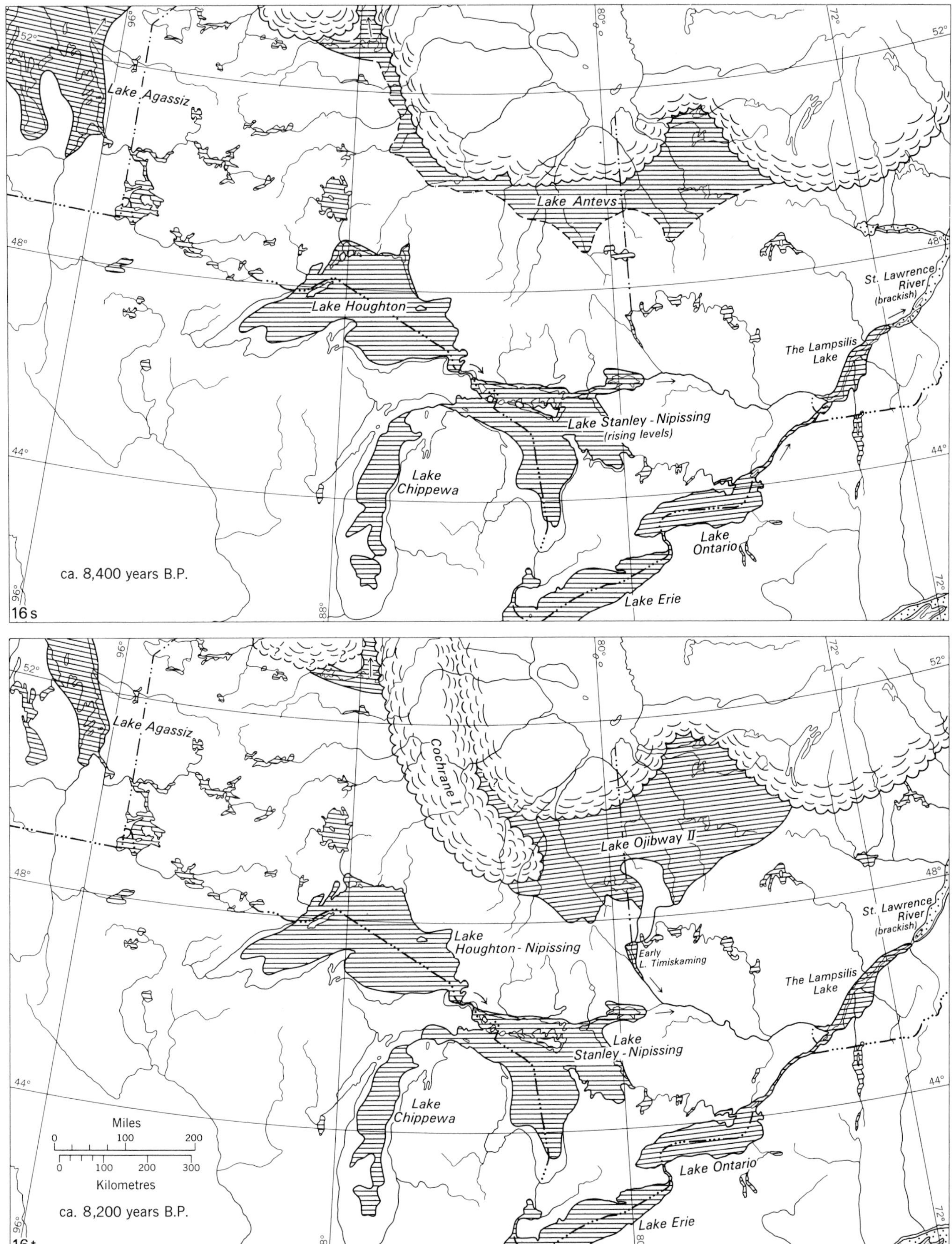

FIGURE XII-16. Glacial lake phases during the recession of Wisconsin ice from central Canada (cont.)

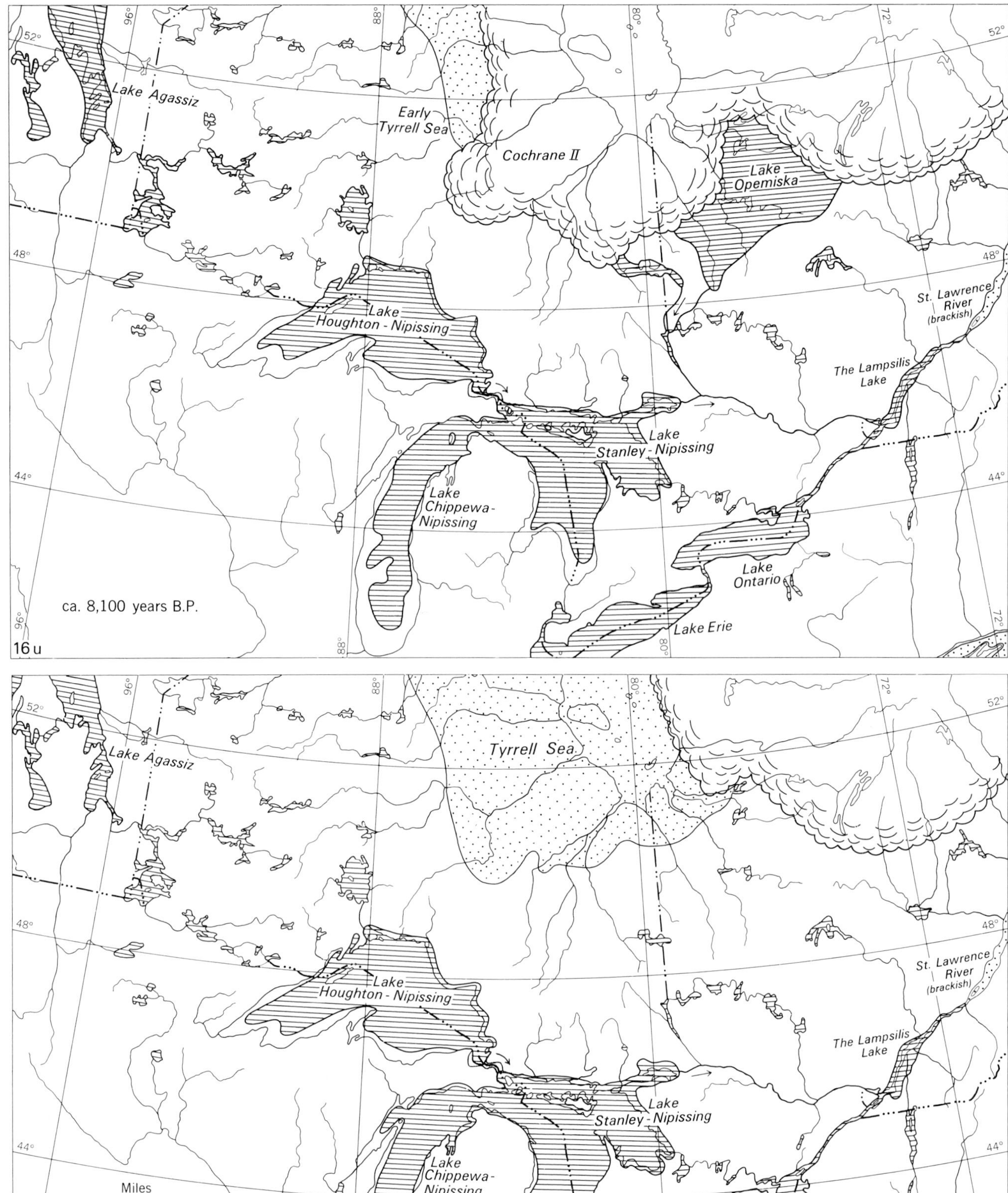

FIGURE XII-16. Glacial lake phases during the recession of Wisconsin ice from central Canada (cont.)

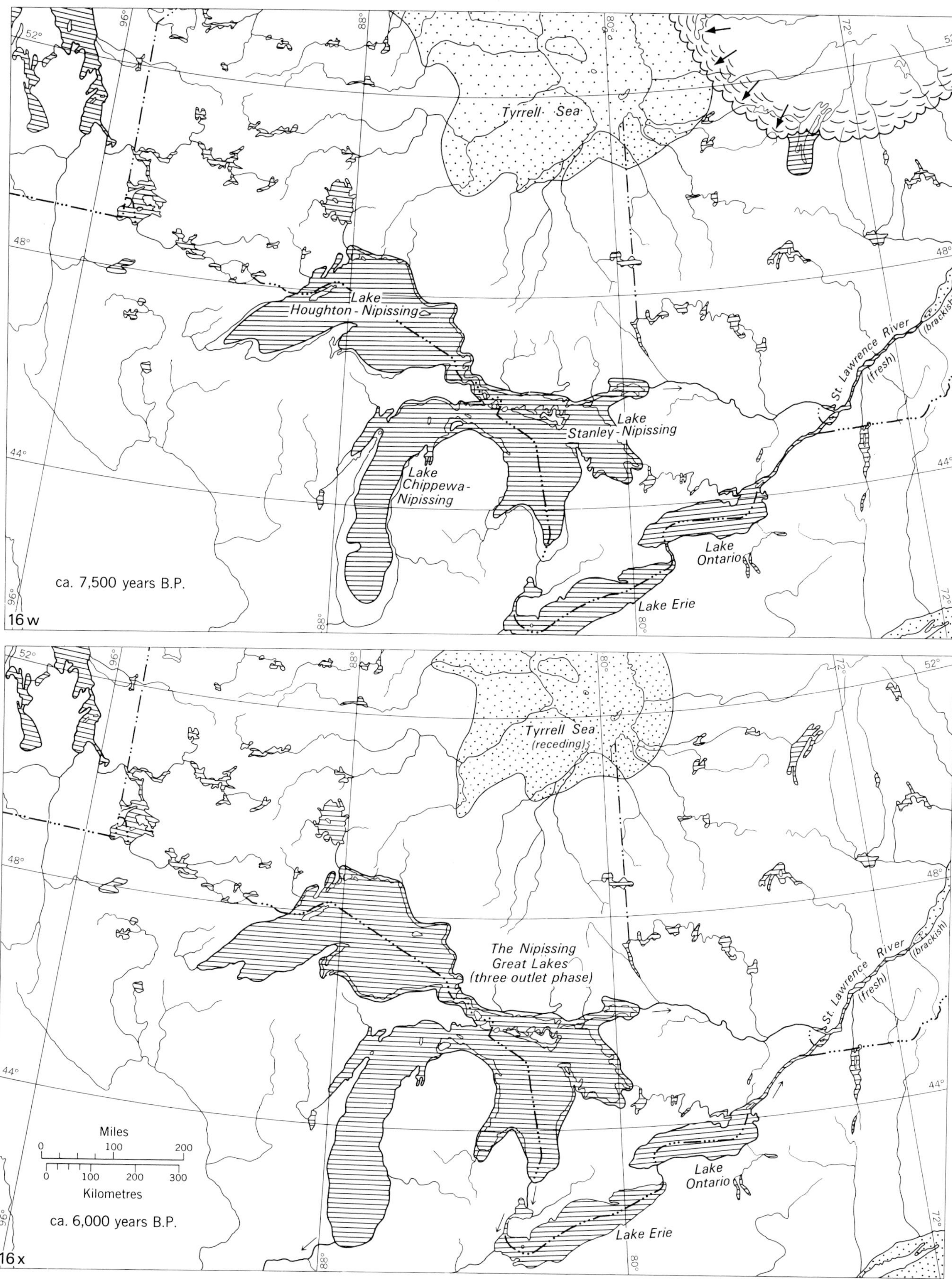

FIGURE XII-16. Glacial lake phases during the recession of Wisconsin ice from central Canada (conc.)

fluent Iroquois–Vermont waters. According to N. R. Gadd an ice lobe occupied Chaudière River valley and probably formed the last barrier between the glacial lake and the sea (Fig. XII-16h). Recession of the ice front from Chaudière Valley allowed the lake to drain to sea level whereupon the sea encroached the upper St. Lawrence and Ottawa River valleys. This inland sea in St. Lawrence Valley above Quebec City constitutes the Champlain Sea (Gadd, 1964). Labrador ice remained active and built an end moraine, presumably in the sea, parallel to the valley in the vicinity of St. Narcisse (Karrow, 1959). This moraine may be traced westward some 100 miles to near Lachute, Quebec (Parry and MacPherson, 1964). As the ice front receded from St. Lawrence Valley the Champlain Sea attained its maximum northward extent. Strandlines occur up to 750 feet above sea level north of Trois-Rivières and Montreal. Thereafter differential uplift brought about regression of Champlain Sea and development of the modern river system (Figs. XII-16k-w).

In the Great Lakes region, thinning of the Labrador sector of Laurentide Ice Sheet and retreat of the ice margin from the farthest point of advance, some 150 miles south of Lake Michigan, began about 17,000 years ago. The ice front retreated into the Lake Erie basin about 14,500 years B.P. Meltwaters were ponded between the basin rim and the receding ice front to form the first of the glacial Great Lakes, Lake Maumee, with discharge southward into Mississippi River (Hough, 1958, 1963, 1966). Thereafter, fluctuations of the ice front and differential uplift of the land, consequent upon removal of the ice load, combined to produce a complex system of lakes and spillways throughout the Great Lakes region and extending into the upper St. Lawrence Valley.

The present indicated history of the Great Lakes is the result of studies by geologists, geographers, and others that date back well before the turn of the century. The early work established the fundamental concepts pertaining to glacial lakes and the framework upon which later work was based. Studies made during the last decade, supported by radiocarbon datings, have made necessary some major changes in the basic chronology and sequence of events. The most recent attempts to correlate events between the various lake basins and discharge routes are by Hough (1963, 1966), Wayne and Zumberge (1965), and Chapman (1966). Two contrasting correlation charts are, in fact, introduced by Wayne and Zumberge to indicate differing concepts held by various authors. On the Canadian side of the Great Lakes available data and radiocarbon dates of lake deposits remain in conflict with the generally accepted correlations.

The writer has attempted to harmonize viewpoints, or otherwise point out discrepancies, concerning deglacial events in the well-documented history of the central Great Lakes and upper St. Lawrence regions with events in southern Manitoba and in James Bay region. The account invokes non-uniform fluctuations of several major ice lobations—as a result of variably delayed responses to climatic changes—to overcome some problems raised by radiocarbon dating of lake and sea deposits in widely separated regions (Figs. XII-16 a-x). It is based also in part on regional ice-flow trendlines and morainal positions developed during deglaciation (Map 1253A).

The southern glacial Great Lakes. The first of the glacial Great Lakes formed in the western end of Erie basin and is known as glacial Lake Maumee (Fig. XII-16a). It expanded into southern Huron basin as the Huron ice lobe receded. Successive water levels, resulting from use of two different outlets as the ice margin fluctuated, were at 800, 760, and 780 feet a.s.l.[1] During the high phases discharge was to the south via Wabash River, and at the low phase to the west, via Grand River, into glacial Lake Chicago in the Michigan basin and thence south, in both phases, to the Mississippi River system. Further ice retreat resulted in final abandonment of the Wabash River spillway and reopening and modification of the Grand River spillway to form glacial Lake Arkona, with its unwarped strandlines developed at 710, 700, and 695 feet a.s.l. (Fig. XII-16b). Continuing retreat of the ice front resulted in low-level lakes that are recorded by deposits in the United States and locally in Canada. A major glacial advance that built the Port Huron moraine system and a correlative moraine that crosses the base of Long Point in Erie basin gave rise to glacial Lake Whittlesey in western Erie basin, with prominent beach at 738 feet a.s.l. (Fig. XII-16c). Discharge was to the northwest via Ubly River channel into Saginaw basin and thence to Lake Chicago and Mississippi River.

Fluctuations of the ice front resulted in expansion of the lake both in the north and east, although at lower levels because of down-cutting of the outlet across Michigan Peninsula. These lake phases are known as Warren and Wayne and, in the main, they occupied the whole of Erie basin and southern part of Huron basin (Fig. XII-16d). Hough related them to fluctuations of the Port Huron (Mankato) ice. The successive lake levels are reported as 680, 670, 660 (Wayne), and 685 feet a.s.l. Continued recession of both Huron and Ontario ice lobes resulted in still lower lake levels known as Grassmere at 640 feet and Lundy at 620 feet a.s.l. (Fig. XII-16e). Discharge was believed to have been eastward, for the first time, along south side of Ontario basin into the Mohawk and Hudson River systems. Hough has favoured an outlet around the northern end of Michigan Peninsula and thence via glacial Lake Chicago and Illinois River to the Mississippi, pointing to the similarity of elevations of major lake phases in the lake basins concerned. Leverett and Taylor (1915), however, thought that by Lundy time the Huron basin waters drained southward to Erie basin. Further retreat of the Ontario basin ice lobe facilitated discharge eastward; early Lake Erie was established in

[1] a.s.l.—above Atlantic mean sea level. The given elevation of a glacial lake is the present elevation of the unwarped part of the inferred lake basin.

Erie basin and early Lake Algonquin in Huron basin with the controlling sill at Port Huron (Sarnia) at 605 feet a.s.l. (Fig. XII-16f). Early Lake Erie occupied only a small part of the present lake basin due to depression of the outlet at Buffalo (Fort Erie), but differential uplift later raised the outlet area with consequent filling of the Erie basin (Lewis, 1966).

When the ice sheet receded from the southern part of Lake Ontario basin, a lower outlet was uncovered at Rome, New York, and the Lundy Lake was lowered rapidly. Glacial Lake Iroquois was established in the Ontario basin at about 335 feet a.s.l. (Fig. XII-16f). The spillway led eastward through Mohawk River valley to Hudson River and thence south to the Atlantic Ocean. Due to prolonged use of Rome outlet, many excellent shoreline features were developed. The writer believes, however, that the shoreline features at 1,100 feet southwest of Covey Hill and ascribed to main Lake Iroquois are the work of a younger and lower lake phase.

The main Iroquois shoreline in the Ontario basin is now warped upward along a line trending N20°E with the hingeline situated south of the lake basin. The shoreline is about 360 feet at Hamilton, 460 feet at Rome, and 700 feet at Watertown, New York (Coleman, 1937). The indicated uplift gradient between Rome and Watertown is about 6 feet per mile. If this gradient and trend of uplift is projected beyond Watertown, the isobase of differential uplift through Cherabusco, New York, would be about 1,270 feet. An increase in the rate of tilt northward, as probably occurred, would give a higher figure but this would be offset by any swing towards the north in the line of maximum uplift, as does occur in the Adirondack region. Short spillways, at elevations of 1,305 and 1,290 feet, have been reported south of Cherabusco (MacClintock and Terasmae, 1960; MacClintock and Stewart, 1965) and were believed related to local lakes or pondings in front of Fort Covington ice with discharge westward into Lake Iroquois. Though the Iroquois shoreline is reported at only 1,100 feet southwest of Covey Hill there is evidence of shoreline features to about 1,250 feet, 1¼ miles south of Cherabusco. This is considered to be an Iroquois shore rather than that of a local lake. A small embayment of Lake Iroquois extended eastward from Cherabusco as a re-entrant between the receding northern and eastern ice fronts around Adirondack Mountains. This ice, probably Fort Covington, built an end moraine and ribbed moraine complex south and southwest of Covey Hill. C. S. Denny (U.S.G.S.) believes that an outlet opened southeast of Ellenburg, New York, which allowed main Lake Iroquois to breach the end moraine and discharge into glacial Lake Vermont farther south in Lake Champlain valley. In the northeast, strandlines indicate a lowering of about 150 feet during operation of this outlet; the real lake level, however, was lowered perhaps only 75 feet. The new lake level, formerly considered main Lake Iroquois, is herein referred to as the Ellenburg phase of the post-Iroquois lakes.

As glacier recession was resumed, Covey Hill outlet (sill elevation 1,010 feet) was uncovered and the post-Iroquois lake level was lowered a further 75 feet. This lake phase was named glacial Lake Frontenac and is herein considered the Frontenac phase of the post-Iroquois lakes (Fig. XII-16g). The Covey Hill outlet today consists of a 60-foot dry waterfall or cliff, a 75-foot deep lake with an unknown thickness of sediment at its base, and a mile-long gorge about 130 feet deep and 300 to 600 feet wide. When the ice withdrew from the northern and eastern flanks of Covey Hill there was a major drop in lake levels of some 125 feet. The short stand at this level, probably occasioned by an ice-marginal fluctuation on the northern sides of Covey Hill, is termed the Sydney phase lake by E. Mirynech.

In the Trenton embayment in eastern Ontario the lake was lowered a further 30 to 75 feet according to Mirynech, prior to a significant halt responsible for development of the Belleville beach. Isobases drawn on the Belleville beach would place the strandline on Covey Hill at about 750 feet. This is the same as that of the Fort Ann phase of glacial Lake Vermont which expanded northward as the eastern side of Covey Hill was uncovered by the ice (Chapman, 1937). The now confluent water bodies discharged southward along the earlier established route to Hudson River and the sea (Fig. XII-16h).

Rapid ice-marginal retreat in St. Lawrence Valley allowed the Belleville–Fort Ann phase lake to expand northward and also to extend a long arm northeastward between the ice front and the eastern Quebec Uplands which opened an escape route eastward to the sea at Quebec City. Water levels first dropped about 40 or 50 feet and, according to Mirynech, the Trenton shoreline was formed in the eastern part of Lake Ontario basin. This temporary halt in lowering lake levels was probably occasioned by an ice-marginal fluctuation in conjunction with a topographic barrier near Quebec City. As Labrador ice receded from Chaudière River valley the Trenton phase lake drained to sea level; marine waters then interchanged with the remaining lake waters in upper St. Lawrence Valley to form Champlain Sea (Fig. XII-16i). The sea extended up St. Lawrence River to Brockville and, as the ice front receded, up the Ottawa River to Petawawa. The Lake Ontario basin waters were drained to the Admiralty low water phase, probably less than 25 feet above Champlain Sea. These last events occurred shortly after 12,000 years B.P. as Champlain Sea shells have been dated 11,880 ± 180 years (GSC-505).

The indicated maximum drop in lake levels from main Iroquois (presumably 335 feet a.s.l.) to the level of Champlain Sea is more than 335 feet. This is probably due to differential uplift during the later phases of lake history and to the difference in real sea level during early Iroquois and Champlain Sea time as compared to the present. Also, the main Iroquois data may well be in some error.

The Algonquin Lakes. As ice recession continued in the Huron basin, early Lake Algonquin occupied the southern part of the basin and, also, Georgian Bay and Lake Simcoe lowland. Numerous strandlines have been named in various parts of the Huron and Michigan basins applicable to a long 'Algonquin' interval of ice retreat and differential uplift, but it is evident that the lake phases and their implications are not yet adequately known.

Early Lake Algonquin at 605 feet a.s.l. was drained southward, possibly first via Chicago and later via Port Huron, into Lake Erie until such time as Lake Simcoe lowland became free of ice and discharge was possible via the Kirkfield-Fenelon Falls and Trent Valley river system into Lake Iroquois (Fig. XII-16f). Continued use of this outlet system, by the Kirkfield phase lake (at about 580 feet a.s.l.), was blocked by a readvance of the Simcoe ice lobe (Deane, 1950) and discharge returned to the Port Huron outlet (Fig. XII-16g). Retreat of the ice front gave access to the Kirkfield outlet system again, but in the meantime differential uplift is considered to have raised the drift-filled outlet; the water plane may thus have remained at about 605 feet a.s.l. for a lengthy period (Fig. XII-16 h,i,j).

The main Algonquin strandline in the Huron basin is a prominent feature, in many places marked by a strong shore bluff. According to L. J. Chapman, it is not found south of Point Clark, midway up the eastern shore, having been undercut by the present lake. It extends northward into Georgian Bay and eastward around Lake Simcoe to the Kirkfield outlet where, due to differential uplift, it has a present elevation of 870 feet (Deane, 1950). The strong Algonquin strandline may be a result of operation of both the Kirkfield–Fenelon Falls and Port Huron outlets during a halt in isostatic uplift of the region. The writer considers it likely that down-cutting at Fenelon Falls greatly reduced the discharge at Port Huron over a lengthy period. Deane believed the Fenelon Falls channel was about 30 feet deep. Extensive gorges were cut in limestone along Trent River valley above the Sydney strandline of the post-Iroquois lakes; thereafter discharge was appreciably lessened.

The gradient of the warped main Algonquin strandline in Lake Simcoe and Lake Couchiching areas increases northward from 2.8 to 4.0 feet per mile along a line N21°E. Farther north, the highest strandline recorded by Chapman (1954, 1966) of 1,070 feet elevation at Huntsville and 1,245 feet elevation at Sundridge shows a further increase in gradient to 5.0 and 6.3 feet per mile. This high rate of tilt militates against rapid differential uplift during the time represented by the highest shorelines and, accordingly, main Lake Algonquin must have extended northward as far as Sundridge without any appreciable change of level while the ice front retreated in the Huron–Georgian Bay region. Between Sundridge and Trout Creek, however, Chapman (1966) records that the highest strandlines were lowered northward by about 50 feet, and he relates this lowering to differential uplift. If the main Algonquin water plane is projected northward to Trout Creek, however, the amount of lowering would be about 125 feet. Such sudden uplift during the existence of the lake in this area seems unlikely. It is more likely that a period of ice-marginal and subglacial discharge occurred at Fossmill, the waters flowing eastward through Petawawa and Barron Rivers into the Champlain Sea in Ottawa River valley. If the main Algonquin strandline was projected northward to the Fossmill outlet sill at Kilrush (elevation 1,145 feet) it would be at about 1,415 feet elevation. Thus flow at Fossmill outlet over the Kilrush sill might have lowered Lake Algonquin by as much as 270 feet had this not been offset to some degree by differential uplift over a fairly lengthy period and provided the area remained above sea level.

This two-fold process, ice-controlled discharge and differential uplift, may account in part for the long-standing controversy as regards parallelism or convergence of some of the post-Algonquin beaches, namely Ardtrea, Upper Orillia, Lower Orillia, Wyebridge, Penetang, Cedar Point, and Payette. According to Deane (1950) the Fenelon Falls outlet remained in use until after the Ardtrea phase. There had been about 50 feet of differential uplift by Upper Orillia time, and Lake Simcoe was separated from 'Algonquin' waters following the Penetang phase (Fig. XII-16k.)

Prior to this event, during the life of Lake Algonquin, there was a major re-advance of the ice sheet in the Superior and Michigan basins, but apparently it was of little consequence in the Huron basin. This ice advance, the Valders, is interpreted as a glacier surge from northeast of Lake Superior (Fig. XII-16i). The highland east of Lake Superior may well have restricted the flow of ice into the Huron basin while it lobed far southward into Michigan basin. This lobation persisted as the Valders ice receded (Fig. XII-16j) and hence glacial Lake Algonquin was able to invade the Sault Ste. Marie area while being restricted at the north end of Michigan basin and virtually excluded from Superior basin (Hough, 1958).

Glacial Lake Algonquin did not enter the Sudbury basin; strandlines occur at various elevations but all are well below a projected main Algonquin water plane. Farther west, however, higher strandlines are evident and 3 miles northwest of Sault Ste. Marie they reach an elevation of 1,025 feet. This strandline is clearly related, on the basis of isobase trend and rate of uplift, to the highest strandline recorded on Manitoulin Island. Three miles south of Little Current this is given as 1,013 feet, and is reported to be main Algonquin. Projection of the isobase eastward, however, shows it to be about 25 feet lower than the main Algonquin shoreline east of Huntsville. This suggests that Manitoulin Island was ice covered until after some 25 feet of uplift had occurred, probably during transition from the Ardtrea to Upper Orillia phase.

In the northern part of Lake Simcoe area the difference in elevation between Upper Orillia and Payette strandlines is about 140 feet (Deane, 1950, Fig. 7). Thus operation of Fossmill outlet system over an extended period, with a maximum draw-down at Fossmill of about 220 feet, readily accommodates all the strandlines recognized by Deane. Had there been no uplift of the Fossmill area during the life-span of these post-Algonquin lakes, the Sheguiandah and Korah lake phases, which represent a lowering of 70 feet below the Payette strandline at Sault Ste. Marie (Hough, 1958), might also correlate with discharge at Fossmill over the Kilrush sill. It is probable, however, that as differential uplift was already in progress an additional 50 to 100 feet of uplift may have occurred in the Fossmill area over a period of several hundred years. Accordingly the Sheguiandah and Korah lake phases may be correlated with use of subsidiary routes into the Petawawa River valley. One of these subsidiary routes is through Sobie and Guilmette Lakes, the controlling sill position being east of the latter lake at about 1,125 feet elevation. This site, some 3 miles north of the Kilrush sill in the direction of maximum uplift, permits a further draw-down of 40 feet, and is considered by the writer to correspond with the Sheguiandah phase lake, 35 feet below the Payette level at Sault Ste. Marie. A second outlet route became available when the ice front receded into the Mattawa River valley and exposed part of the Amable du Fond River valley; this led southward to Mink Lake and the Petawawa River system. The sill at Mink Lake is at 1,075 feet elevation and lies on the same isobase as the Guilmette sill (elev. 1,125 feet). Thus a maximum draw-down of 50 feet is possible but there may well have been some 15 feet of uplift as the ice withdrew into the Mattawa valley. The writer therefore correlates the Korah lake phase, about 35 feet below Sheguiandah stage at Sault Ste. Marie, with use of the Amable du Fond outlet over the Mink Lake sill (Fig. XII-16l).

Discharge of the post-Algonquin lakes eastward at Fossmill, and by subsidiary channels, to Petawawa and Barron Rivers resulted in deposition of a large delta, composed largely of sand and some gravel, in the Champlain Sea. Judging by the size of the delta, the spillway must have lain along an active ice front. Gadd (1963), in fact, located a small end moraine in Ottawa River valley near the mouth of Petawawa River. Boulders in the Petawawa–Barron Rivers spillway system are unusually large, in places averaging 2 to 3 feet in diameter. They form ridges and hummocks up to 20 feet high that appear to be bars built by torrential streams.

While the discharge of the post-Algonquin lakes was controlled by Mink Lake sill, immediately prior to eastward discharge down Mattawa River valley, the water depth over North Bay sill was about 400 feet—a calculation based on an uplift rate of 6.5 feet per mile in a direction N20°E and substantiated by strandline positions north of North Bay. As Hough (1958) considers the Payette phase lake had a surface elevation of 465 feet, the Korah phase was about 400 feet. Hough has given the elevation of Lake Stanley, the lowest level lake in Huron basin, as about 190 feet though it may have been appreciably higher according to C. F. M. Lewis. It is thus evident that following perhaps 200 feet of draw-down, as the post-Algonquin Lake discharged eastward along Mattawa River valley, the Huron basin part must have become separated from the lake remaining in the Nipissing Lake basin, which was then lowered a further 200 feet to expose the North Bay sill (Fig. XII-16m). There was also a separate low-level lake in Georgian Bay basin; W. M. Tovell proposes to name it Lake Hough in recognition of J. L. Hough's work on the documentation of the low-level lakes in Michigan and Huron basins.

During the period of ice retreat eastward along Mattawa River valley, the lowering of lake levels must have been accomplished mainly by subglacial discharge. The writer has found no evidence of a surface outlet in the valley between Amable du Fond and a point 5 miles southeast of Mattawa, Ontario. By the time surface (ice-marginal) discharge to the Ottawa River valley began, an over-all lowering from the Korah lake level in Nipissing–Mattawa Valley of about 370 feet had already taken place. Surface discharge then lowered the lake a further 30 feet at which time North Bay sill emerged. Withdrawal of the ice from Ottawa Valley between points 7 and 20 miles east of Mattawa only served to steepen the spillway gradient east of North Bay.

Superior Lake Basin

The Duluth–Minong–Houghton Lakes. Glacier retreat in Superior basin was in a northeasterly direction, resulting in ponding of meltwater at the western end. The history of Superior basin lakes and ice retreat is dealt with by Farrand (1961) and Zoltai (1965). The early phases of Superior basin lakes, as recognized by Farrand, did not affect Canadian shores. Glacial Lake Duluth may have formed a beach on Isle Royale just east of the International Boundary at 1,060 or 1,075 feet elevation, and Zoltai shows Lake Duluth extending along the boundary west of Lake Superior. Lake Duluth discharged southwestward to the Mississippi Valley (Fig. XII-16j). Retreat of the glacier subsequently opened a lower route into Michigan basin that resulted in a series of short-lived lakes. These were formerly considered equivalent to the Algonquin lake phases of Huron basin, but are now thought to be independent and are referred to by Farrand as the post-Duluth lakes (Figs. XII-16j–m). Beaches referable to some of these lakes occur on Isle Royale and west of Fort William. The latter, however, partly represent a separate and earlier lake in the Kaministikwia River basin (Zoltai, 1965).

When glacier retreat from the eastern end of Superior basin allowed the post-Duluth lakes free access to Whitefish Bay they may have become briefly confluent with post-Algonquin lakes in Huron basin. Somewhat later the glacier receded entirely from Superior basin. Farrand refers to the resulting lake as Lake Minong; it was responsible for the highest shoreline features in the northeastern end of the lake basin. The upwarped beaches occur between elevation 950 and 1,000 feet on the north shore. Farrand relates Lake Minong to Sheguiandah lake phase in Huron basin but the writer considers it to be somewhat younger and with its outlet at Sault Ste. Marie (Figs. XII-16n, o).

Below the Minong strandline on the north shore of Lake Superior there are a succession of beach ridges or small wave-cut bluffs, depending on the character of the shore, that Farrand relates to post-Minong lake phases. They have a vertical range of over 50 feet. The lowest and best formed shoreline at 750 to 765 feet near Dorion is known as the Dorion beach and appears to have resulted from outlet adjustments rather than differential uplift (Figs. XII-16p, q). Another adjustment was responsible for a further lowering of several tens of feet, and development of a shoreline that Farrand considers correlative with the low-level lake phases in Huron basin. He named the low-level lake in Superior basin as Lake Houghton and reports that it discharged to the Huron basin by the proto-St. Marys River at Sault Ste. Marie. He considers the elevation of the lake as about 360 feet a.s.l. Its shorelines have been destroyed along the east side of Lake Superior by a younger lake but are preserved on the north shore as a result of differential uplift (Figs. XII-16r, s).

Upper Great Lakes Region

The low-level, Nipissing, and post-Nipissing lakes. As mentioned earlier, glacier retreat from the eastern end of Mattawa River valley served to drain the lakes in the upper Great Lakes basins to very low levels. The indicated amount of draw-down at North Bay also necessitates establishment of separate lakes in the Lake Nipissing, Georgian Bay, and main Huron basins (Fig. XII-16m). Erosion of outlets from each of these basins allowed for continuing draw-down of the upper lakes over a very long interval during which differential uplift was raising the northeastern end of the drainage system. Thus the lowest levels of Stanley, Chippewa, and Houghton were not established simultaneously. These lakes remained until their outlets were drowned as water encroached from the east consequent upon the continuing uplift of the North Bay region. A speculative configuration of the lakes is shown in (Figs. XII-16m–w). Dependant upon the assumptions made as regards both the ages of the several post-Algonquin lake phases and the amount and rate of differential uplift during their life-span and during the subsequent low-level lake phases, various ages may be deduced for these low-level lakes. Lake Stanley may have merged with Lake Chippewa as early as 10,400 years B.P. rather than as late as 8,100 years B.P. as shown. Perhaps an age of 9,500 years B.P. is more likely than either extreme but it is necessary to allow sufficient time for the re-excavation of Mackinac channel between the Michigan and Huron lake basins.

When North Bay was raised to 605 feet a.s.l. discharge began again at Port Huron and at Chicago. Continuing differential uplift finally raised North Bay outlet above the lake surface and drainage was entirely by the southern outlets. Long use of the southern outlets resulted in a rather stable lake level and a consequent well-marked shoreline, that of the Nipissing phase of the Great Lakes (Fig. XII-16x). The confluent water bodies in Huron, Michigan, and Superior basins with discharge at Port Huron and Chicago are referred to as the Nipissing Great Lakes. The Nipissing terrace is well displayed a short distance west of North Bay at 700 feet elevation whereas the present shore of Lake Nipissing is at 648 feet. The highway to Sault Ste. Marie crosses the Nipissing terrace many times.

The Nipissing phase of the Great Lakes is usually dated at about 4,200 years B.P. Many organic deposits from positions below the Nipissing strandline, in various parts of the Great Lakes area, have been given ages ranging back to more than 7,000 or 8,000 years B.P.; these are commonly referred to the interval of pre-Nipissing rising water levels. However, recent dates from Little Pic River, north shore Lake Superior, indicate the age of a Nipissing phase lake to be about 6,000 years B.P. Wood from silty clay beds beneath a 15-foot capping of sand that forms a terrace at the highway bridge over this river was dated at 5,920±120 and 5,960±120 (GSC-83, 103). The terrace has an elevation of about 700 feet. Farrand (1961) considered the deposit Nipissing/Algoma transition as he determined the elevation at 692 feet and found a cobble ridge at 718 feet which he considered to be the Nipissing beach. The writer and S. C. Zoltai noted a transition from plant-bearing silty clay, with shells in the upper few feet, upward into shell-bearing (mainly *Sphaerium sulcatum*) sand. Tiny plant tissues from the basal few inches of the sand were dated at 6,100±160 (GSC-285). The writer therefore considers the plant-bearing silty clay, the shell-bearing sand, and the boulder beach to represent the same lake phase, probably the Nipissing. On the eastern side of Lake Huron, 4 miles northeast of Owen Sound, wood has been found in the basal part of an extensive gravel ridge that L. J. Chapman considers an undoubted Nipissing beach. The gravels are 18 feet thick, pass down-slope into sand, and rest on a silty clay. The wood from the sand-clay contact was dated at 5,770±130 (GSC-347). Fourteen miles to the east at Meaford, wood was found in clay beneath 8 feet of sand with surface elevation of 605 feet that is also considered related to a Nipissing phase lake. The wood was dated 6,300±150 years (L-312).

Radiocarbon dates on basal organic materials from small lakes at the Nipissing level on Manitoulin Island (Lewis, 1968) prove that a Nipissing phase was near maximum about 5,500 years ago. Similar evidence from North Bay reported by Lewis indicates that the spillway ceased to function before 5,000 years B.P. It is thus evident that the Nipissing Great Lakes (605 feet a.s.l.) formerly considered to be in the order of 4,200 years B.P. are in fact a combination of lake phases reflecting first the use of three outlets and later the use of only the two southern outlets, the whole ranging from about 6,000 to 4,200 years B.P. The three-outlet phase may be termed Nipissing Great Lakes I (Fig. XII-16x) and the two-outlet phase Nipissing Great Lakes II.

Erosion of the southern outlets of Nipissing Great Lakes II lowered the water level until a segment of Port Huron spillway system became stabilized by a combination of bedrock and concentration of boulders at the same time that Chicago outlet was rock-controlled; the resulting halt in the lowering of the outlets initiated the Algoma phase lake at about 596 feet elevation (Hough, 1958). This event may have occurred about 4,000 years ago (GSC-301). As the northern parts of the lake basins were slowly uplifted, a lateral shift in the Port Huron channel into more easily eroded materials brought about a resumption of down-cutting. Uplift of the sill at Sault Ste. Marie gave rise to a separate lake in Superior basin known as the Sault stage (Farrand, 1961) possibly about 2,000 to 3,000 years ago. This was followed by a sub-Sault stage and finally Lake Superior at 602 feet elevation. In the meantime down-cutting at Port Huron lowered the Huron and Michigan basin waters to their present 580 feet elevation.

Northwestern Ontario

Retreat of the ice in northern Ontario beyond the Superior and Huron basins is dealt with by Zoltai (1961, 1963, 1965) and Boissonneau (1966, 1968). Prior to its retreat from Superior basin, the Laurentide Ice Sheet west of Superior had advanced southwest into Minnesota. As it receded northward into western Ontario it remained in contact with glacial Lake Agassiz over a wide front; the history of this lake is discussed separately. Fluctuations in the rate of ice flow resulted in construction of a number of noteworthy end moraines. The most southerly end moraine system in western Ontario trends southeastward from Lake of the Woods to Rainy Lake (Map 1253A). Following an ice-frontal retreat of about 75 miles to the northeast the Steeprock Moraine was constructed; this extends from near Steeprock Lake southeastward to International Boundary about 25 miles west of Lake Superior. Shortly thereafter the much more extensive Eagle-Finlayson Moraine was constructed; this may be traced for about 175 miles southeastward from 30 miles northwest of Kenora to within 30 miles of Thunder Bay, where it is truncated by an end moraine left by a Superior basin ice lobe. Following a major retreat in western Ontario, a re-advance of the ice front was responsible for the Hartman Moraine which Zoltai (1965) considers to be of Valders age. At its northwestern end it curves sharply to the north and then northeast until truncated by the younger Lac Seul Moraine. When the ice front was at the Hartman Moraine, major ice lobes were also active in Nipigon and Superior basins and built the correlative and adjoining Dog Lake and Marks Moraines respectively. The latter has been traced to a high bedrock area southwest of Thunder Bay and hence the 'Valders' ice border may cross the International Boundary only a few miles west of the Superior shore.

Some 10 to 20 miles northeast of Hartman Moraine, the ice sheet built the extensive Lac Seul Moraine, which curves around the western side of Lac Seul. To the southwest this moraine merges with the Kaiashk Interlobate Moraine (Zoltai, 1965), which was built in part between the ice lobes that produced the Hartman and Dog Lake Moraines, but Zoltai has suggested that the northeastern end of the Kaiashk Moraine is a reconstructed end moraine of the Lac Seul lobe. A retreat followed by a re-advance of the ice front, of at least 20 miles, is indicated by overridden varved clays in Lac Seul area (Zoltai, 1965). Lac Seul Moraine extends northwestward into Red Lake–Lansdowne House area (Prest, 1963). On the southwestern side of Trout Lake it rises sharply some 270 feet but on the distal side it slopes more gently to the southwest and displays many excellent beaches and terraces of glacial Lake Agassiz. The moraine was produced beneath this lake and only three small parts remained above lake level. To the northwest the moraine is lower and less distinct but a series of large, wave-modified ridges of sand and gravel, unlike adjacent reworked eskers, may be morainal and indicate the former position of the ice lobe. The end moraine appears to loop northward and then eastward towards Windigo Lakes where it is truncated by end moraines of the minor Windigo ice lobe. Ice-flow features and eskers also indicate the convex form of the Lac Seul ice front. The westward lobation of the ice sheet was probably a result of active calving into the deep water of a Lake Agassiz embayment in the ice front (Fig. XII-16m).

Following a short period of recession in western Ontario, a halt in retreat or minor re-advance of the ice sheet produced the Sioux Lookout Moraine on relatively high ground west of Lake Nipigon. To the northwest are sporadic De Geer moraines which delineate the ice-frontal positions during calving into Lake Agassiz. Following a retreat of at least 80 miles the northern part of the ice sheet halted to form the Whitewater Moraine, and an eastern lobe of the ice re-advanced to form the Nipigon Moraine along west side of Nipigon basin (Zoltai, 1965). The writer believes that only the northern part of this end moraine system was built at this time (Fig. XII-16p), the southern part being older.

Greater activity of a northern component of the receding ice sheet relative to an eastern component gave rise to a series of recessional end moraines in Windigo Lakes area in northwestern Ontario and to an interlobate moraine south of these lakes.

The next major moraine system left by the fluctuating though generally receding ice sheet in northwestern Ontario was the extensive and generally southeast-trending Agutua Moraine (Tyrrell, 1913; Prest, 1963). A 25-mile re-advance is indicated by subtill lake clays along Otoskwin River. The highest part of the morainal system is at a major bend in Albany River west of Miminiska Lakes where it rises 500 feet above the river. The Crescent Moraine system (Zoltai, 1965) north of Lake Nipigon is probably a correlative of Agutua Moraine.

After construction of Agutua Moraine the northern ice sheet receded some 20 miles to the northeast before halting long enough to leave several short segments of end moraine on-line with belts of De Geer moraines. The eastern ice sheet at this time appears to have thrust actively forward—the Miminiska ice advance—and overrode parts of the Agutua Moraine in the vicinity of Albany River, and left a complex of end moraine segments, interlobate moraine, eskers, and ice-flow features that serve to delineate its form. To the southwest, in the vicinity of Ogoki River, this same ice advance appears to have constructed the Nakina Moraines (Zoltai, 1965).

The northern lobe, following a further retreat of about 30 miles, halted to construct a moraine near Big Beaverhouse on Winisk River. This moraine trends northwestward from south of Wunnummin Lake to Little Sachigo Lake. The eastern lobe left little evidence of its ice-frontal position; it may have been responsible for short segments of moraine west of Lansdowne House, and may have extended south-southeastward through Ogoki Lake. A short distance eastward from this lake the ice-flow features are masked or destroyed by the younger Cochrane ice advance from the north (*see under* Northern Ontario and Western Quebec).

Glacial Lake Agassiz. Glacial Lake Agassiz occupied large areas in Minnesota, North Dakota, Saskatchewan, Manitoba, and Ontario as Laurentide Ice Sheet receded north of the Mississippi drainage divide. As the lake expanded northward its southern limit contracted and, although the total area covered by Lake Agassiz was more than 200,000 square miles, it was probably no more than about 80,000 miles in extent at any time (Elson, 1967).

The history of glacial Lake Agassiz is, in part, intricately related to the period of ice-sheet recession from northwestern Ontario previously described. During this recession the outlets were controlled by position of the ice front and by topography in northwestern Ontario. Many of the strandlines were formed as a result of the operation of eastern outlets that discharged into Nipigon basin and thence southward into Superior basin.

Though the existence of a former huge lake in the Red River basin in the United States was recognized as early as 1822 and named in honour of Louis Agassiz in 1879, the first comprehensive work was that of Upham (1895) and later that of Leverett and Sardeson (Leverett, 1932). Many have also contributed new information on the Canadian part of the lake basin, particularly Johnston (1946) and Elson (1957, 1967). Information on eastern outlets discharging into glacial Lake Kelvin in Nipigon basin and the extent of Lake Agassiz in northwestern Ontario has resulted from field studies by Zoltai (1961, 1963, 1965) and Prest (1963). Elson has established a multifold history of Lake Agassiz. He recognizes a series of progressively lower lake levels related to successive operation of southern, northwestern, eastern, and northern outlets, with some rises in lake level due to ice-marginal fluctuations in the spillway areas. He has related strandlines in the Red River basin to these various outlets. The writer has also attempted to restore the configuration of some Lake Agassiz phases relative to the eastern outlets using the rates of tilt as determined by Johnston, the spillway positions and elevations given by Zoltai, his own data on lake levels and ice-margin positions in northwestern Ontario, and recently available contoured topographic maps.

Lake Agassiz began to form as Laurentide ice receded northward into the headwaters of Red River basin along the Minnesota–Dakota boundary, and it expanded northward into Manitoba and northwestern Ontario bordering on both Keewatin and Labrador sectors of the ice sheet. Discharge was through Lake Traverse at the south end of the Red River system into Minnesota River of the Mississippi River system. Lake Agassiz was lowered some 80 to 90 feet as the outlet was eroded to a bedrock sill. The lowering was irregular, perhaps due to formation of boulder armaments along the spillway that were periodically removed by increase in rate of discharge. Four lake phases, the Herman, Norcross, Tintah, and Campbell, and numerous minor intermediate strandlines are recognized in southern Manitoba and northwestern Ontario (Figs. XII-16d–f).

Elson (1966, p. 92) has suggested that a lowering from and return to the Norcross level was related to a short period of eastward discharge into Lake Superior via a Dog River spillway route in northwestern Ontario (Figs. XII-16g, h). The writer believes that this early phase of discharge may account for the first low water phase of Lake Agassiz perhaps about 12,000 years ago (Elson, 1966, Fig. 6). Sandy peat from alluvial fill at about the Campbell level in Assiniboine River valley and associated with a deepening lake was dated at $12,400 \pm 420$ years (Y-165). When an ice advance plugged the Dog River outlet, discharge was returned to the south. Lake levels rose to the Norcross level due to in-filling of the Lake Traverse outlet route in the interim. As this sediment was removed by erosion Lake Agassiz was lowered again to the Campbell level, controlled by the bedrock sill (Figs. XII-16i, j). The ice front at this time was at the Hartman and Dog Lake Moraines which are considered to be of Valders age.

When the ice-sheet margin again receded, the Dog Lake spillway was not re-opened; eastward discharge was not possible until the ice front receded northeastward beyond Sioux Lookout, whereupon the lake began to discharge into Nipigon basin (Fig. XII-16k). This event occurred about 11,000 years ago. A re-advance of the ice front closed the eastern outlets, returned the lake level to the Campbell strandline, and built the Lac Seul Moraine (Figs. XII-16l, m). Retreat of the ice again uncovered outlets into Nipigon basin with resulting lowered lake levels (Fig. XII-16n). A re-advance of the ice to build the Sioux Lookout Moraine about 10,000 years ago again closed the eastern outlets and raised Lake Agassiz to the Campbell level for the last time (Fig. XII-16o). Thereafter glacier retreat resulted in operation of ever-lower eastern outlets; a succession of prominent beaches was built in parts of the Red River basin. As the lake surface was lowered, more and more ground was exposed west of Nipigon basin and spillways lengthened westward (Fig. XII-16p).

During operation of the lower eastern outlets the ice receded from the region northwest of Nipigon basin (Prest, 1963) and exposed a lower outlet route that led southeastward along the ice margin to the northern end of Nipigon basin. As there was a major retreat of the northern ice front prior to the Agutua advance, low ground may have allowed discharge from Lake Agassiz southeastward into glacial Lake Barlow–Ojibway; if so, the Agutua re-advance has obliterated all trace of these outlets. Some readjustments in the drainage routes no doubt took place as the ice front receded from Agutua Moraine, and the routes were deranged again as the ice advanced to the position of the Nakina Moraines. At this time Lake Agassiz was confluent with glacial Lake Nakina (Zoltai, 1965) and the outlet was into the northern end of the Nipigon basin (Fig. XII-16r).

The retreating ice sheet remained in contact with Lake Agassiz until it receded from the position of the Big Beaverhouse Moraine. Discharge may have remained to the southeast, possibly into Barlow–Ojibway, as the moraine was built, but then changed to northward, probably down Echoing River valley into Hudson Bay Lowland. The drop in lake level occasioned by this event severed Lake Agassiz from the ice-marginal lakes remaining along the ice front on the Ontario part of the Hudson Bay watershed (Fig. XII-16s). At a still later date Lake Agassiz discharge was diverted to the Nelson River system and as the last confining ice melted the glacial lake gave place to early phases of Lakes Winnipeg, Winnipegosis, and Manitoba.

Northern Ontario and Western Quebec

Glacial Lake Barlow–Ojibway. In northern Ontario, east and northeast of Lake Superior, glacier retreat was northward towards James Bay, and in the adjacent parts of western Quebec it was mainly northeastward towards central Quebec. Lake waters were ponded between the ice front and the height-of-land (Figs. XII-16m–q). The manner by which this great lake remained at high levels astride the Hudson Bay–St. Lawrence drainage divide area and discharged southward along the valley of Lake Timiskaming has long been a subject of controversy. The outlet was plugged by a moraine some 10 miles north of Temiscaming, Quebec, and it is likely that lake levels were stabilized as a result of boulder concentrations in the spillways. New gradients and lake levels probably resulted from periodic isostatic adjustment. Progressive shallowing of the lake is indicated by sand horizons in the deposits of varved clay and by a greater rate of tilt on the highest strandlines in the southern part of the basin relative to those in the northern part. The writer determined a rate of tilt from the outlet to Larder Lake of about 4 feet per mile, and from Larder Lake to Plamondin Hill of 2.1 feet per mile. Hughes (1965) states that the maximum tilt of short segments of lower strandlines varies from 2.1 to 3.8 feet per mile and that the maximum rate of tilt must be in excess of 3.8 feet. The location of the hinge-line has not been established but it is probably to the south of the outlet. It is possible that differential uplift of the northern part of the basin took place along a second hinge-line in the Larder Lake–Noranda area.

A plot of the maximum waterplane from Plamondin Hill to Larder Lake indicates a minimum depth of water, over the present drainage divide near Noranda, of about 300 feet. It is thus evident that a combination of uplift and erosion of the outlet near Temiscaming must have lowered the lake by this amount before glacial Lake Ojibway was confined to the north; it then discharged from a point 15 miles west of Noranda (Fig. XII-16r) southward into ancestral Lake Timiskaming. The drift plug at Temiscaming has been channelled to a depth of over 350 feet; a small part of this no doubt occurred in post-Barlow–Ojibway times.

Limited information on maximum strandlines east of Malartic, Quebec, indicates that lake levels had lowered appreciably before the Quebec highlands glacier receded from that part of the Lake Barlow–Ojibway basin. A puzzling matter concerning Lake Barlow–Ojibway is the sudden deepening of the lake, indicated by increase in varve thickness and decrease in secondary sand, in varve year 1528 when the ice front was in the vicinity of Cochrane (Hughes, 1965). Perhaps discharge had been westward into Superior basin for some time prior to this varve year, whereupon a re-advance of the ice front closed this outlet, deepened the lake, and returned discharged to Timiskaming channel. This re-advance may correlate with formation of either the Crescent or the Nakina Moraines.

During retreat of the ice front northward from the Hearst–Cochrane region a prolonged halt occurred in the vicinity of Fraserdale, 60 miles north of Cochrane. A major east-west kame moraine composed of silt, sand, and some gravel was deposited in contact with the ponded waters on its south side (Boissonneau, 1966). This moraine may correlate with interlobate moraine west of Hearst and north of Hornepayne. These deposits are mainly sand and gravel with an appreciable local content of limestone. All these moraines may correlate with the Nakina Moraines (Zoltai, 1965) farther northwest; indeed there are no other comparable pre-Cochrane moraines in northwestern Ontario.

The lake in front of the moraine near Fraserdale is believed to have discharged southward, via an outlet near

Noranda, into Lake Timiskaming basin. This drainage route is in accord with the Barlow–Ojibway isobase trends and an indicated lowering of lake levels by about 300 feet in Lake Abitibi region. When the ice retreated north of the kame moraine, however, discharge and complete drainage must have been towards Hudson Bay, either laterally or subglacially. Antevs (1925, p. 77), with regard to the immediate pre-Cochrane stage of Barlow–Ojibway, reported that discharge into Hudson Bay took place across thin remnant ice in James Bay. Later (1931) he thought that drainage around the ice front to the sea occurred in the vicinity of the mouths of Hayes and Nelson Rivers, Manitoba. The writer considers that the lake, here named glacial Lake Antevs (Fig. XII-16s), may have drained northwestward along a line of weakness between a large mass of semi-stagnant ice in northwestern Ontario and a major glacier in James Bay and southern Hudson Bay, and discharged into the sea in the easternmost part of Manitoba. It is assumed that the sea had entered Hudson Bay via Hudson Strait and then along the line of a southwest-trending bottom channel in Hudson Bay, and effectively severed the Keewatin and Labrador sectors of the Laurentide Ice Sheet at this time.

Cochrane phase of recession. The next major event in the recessional history of the Laurentide Ice Sheet is the emplacement of the Cochrane till in Hudson Bay Lowland. Ice from Hudson Bay evidently moved southward more or less along the flank of the Shield (Cochrane I); somewhat later there was a southwestward and southward thrust from James Bay region (Cochrane II). The Cochrane ice front is seldom marked by end moraine. As pointed out by Hughes (1956) "The term 'Cochrane moraine' . . . is misleading, and should be dropped in favour of 'Cochrane till,' for the Cochrane till is a stratigraphic unit recognizable over a considerable area." The Cochrane limit is merely a line beyond which Cochrane till has not been found. Beyond the till limit the Cochrane event is represented by a series of varved sediments (Connaught sequence) containing pebbles lithologically similar to those of the till, but contrasting sharply with pebbles in underlying varved sediments (Frederickhouse sequence) that comprise a large part of Barlow–Ojibway deposits. Hughes reports counting about 60 varves of Connaught sequence in individual exposures. Maximum varve thickness is attained at varve 25, and this is considered to correlate with emplacement of the Cochrane till farther north. The Connaught sequence also includes varved sediments deposited in a shallow remnant of glacial Lake Antevs during recession of the Cochrane ice.

The typical Cochrane till is a stone-poor, blue-grey clay till that rests on varved sediments. It takes on a very pale pinkish tint when weathered, and is a yellow-brown when oxidized. Being calcareous, it contrasts markedly with the older, sandy, and non-calcareous tills of the Timmins–Cochrane region (Hughes, 1965). The clayey character of the till is believed to be due mainly to the incorporation of lake clays as the Cochrane ice advanced southward.

Boissonneau (1966) refers to an ice-front retreat of several miles to the north of the kame moraine near Fraserdale on Abitibi River, prior to the advance that deposited a thin mantle of clayey till over parts of it. The writer has observed the Cochrane clay till overlying varved sediments near Coral Rapids (364 feet elevation). The Cochrane till has been recognized as far north as the mouth of Little Abitibi River at 200 feet elevation but in this area its clayey character is produced from older, dark grey clay and light buff limestones. The ice front, prior to the Cochrane advance, probably receded to the vicinity of Coral Rapids where it impinged on a land surface at a present elevation of under 400 feet a.s.l.

Recession of the ice sheet down the Hudson Bay watershed from Timmins at 1,029 feet elevation to Coral Rapids at 364 feet elevation, a distance of 110 miles, would seem to indicate a lowering of the ice-sheet surface by about 600 feet. As the most southerly point where Cochrane till has been recognized is 12 miles north of Timmins at an elevation of about 960 feet, this would seem to require a thickening of the ice sheet of some 500 to 600 feet during the Cochrane advance. Such a thickening of the ice sheet is improbable at this late stage of deglaciation especially when marine water of the Tyrrell Sea (Lee, 1960) flooded much of Hudson Bay Lowland shortly thereafter (I-GSC-14, 7875 ± 200 years). It is more probable that the emplacement of Cochrane till is somehow related to the incursion of the sea into Hudson Bay. The two main surges of ice, envisaged by the writer as responsible for the Cochrane ice-flow features and emplacement of the clayey till evident on Map 1253A, are shown in Figures XII-16t, u.

Northern Quebec and Labrador

The retreat of the last ice sheet in this region was mainly towards the higher terrain of the interior, and the pattern of ice-flow features and eskers is generally radial about an interior U-shaped area south and southwest of Ungava Bay within which the last remnants of ice melted. Glacial lakes were not common but a few were extensive and long-lived.

Recession from Labrador and Ungava coasts. At the last glacial maximum the ice sheet in northern Labrador extended major tongues through cols in the Torngat Mountains, spread laterally in the coastal areas, and calved into Labrador Sea a short distance off the present coast. The upper limit reached by these valley glaciers has been referred to as the Saglek level by J. T. Andrews and the event itself to the Saglek Glaciation (Andrews, 1963; Løken, 1962). The elevation of the trimline, which becomes lower to both the north and east, indicates the surface slope of the ice sheet which lay west of the Torngat Mountains. Farther south, in the coastal Kaumajet and Kiglapait Mountains which at one time were believed to have remained unglaciated, erratics on the higher peaks indicate ice flow from the west at some earlier glacial maximum. This was considered Wisconsin (Tomlinson, 1959) but, in the light of J. T. Andrews work, is not likely Classical Wisconsin. Various levels of ice movements have been noted in coastal Labrador by many workers but it is not always clear which observations are related to the last regional glaciation (Daly, 1902; Wheeler, 1958; Ives, 1958a, b, 1960a; Tomlinson, 1959; Andrews, 1963). All agree that cirque glaciation in the coastal mountains was minor, thus supporting the concepts of Tanner (1944). Cirque development followed the retreat of the ice sheet and probably also took place in the Little Ice Age. According to Tomlinson, many nunataks and a large strip of continental shelf appeared as the ice sheet retreated from the coastal area, prior to transgression by the sea.

Shells from Eclipse Channel near the northern end of the Torngat Mountains indicate that the sea encroached on the northern Labrador coast prior to 9,000 ± 200 years ago (L-642). The shells were at an elevation of 95 feet in a region where Løken has placed the marine limit at 185 feet. On the basis of pollen analysis, Wenner (1947) placed deglaciation of the central Labrador coast prior to 10,000 years B.P.

Torngat Mountains were mainly nunataks at the maximum of the last major glaciation (Ives, 1958a; 1960a, Fig. 3), though overridden during an earlier glaciation formerly considered maximum Wisconsin (Ives, 1957). As the Labrador ice thinned and the supply of inland ice was cut off at the cols, the trunk glaciers in the throughgoing mountain valleys stagnated. The mountains themselves supplied little ice; some cirque glaciers formed, but seldom cut through the lateral moraines of the trunk glaciers. Løken (1960) has reported some late, mountain ice caps in the Abloviak River drainage basin east of Ungava Bay and, on the nearby Labrador coast, has noted features around Ryans Bay indicative of a re-advance of valley glaciers late in the deglacial process. In Okak Bay area between the coastal Kaumajet and Kiglapait Mountains, Tomlinson (1959) also found evidence of a late stage re-advance that formed push moraines prior to the final waning of the ice sheet. Both there and farther south Wheeler (1958) and J. T. Andrews noted high-level lateral moraines formed when the ice front lay east of the present coast, and also prominent younger moraines believed to represent a late glacial re-advance. These eastward re-advances across the low, southern Torngat Mountains may indicate that in the region south of the Torngat the Labrador ice was less restricted than to the north and flowed readily towards the coast. During retreat it maintained an active ice front but, as a result of a rapid thinning, did not form moraines.

Glacial lakes. As the ice sheet thinned west of Torngat Mountains, the eastern outlet glaciers retreated and left numerous lateral and end moraines along the Labrador coast. Later the ice margin receded west of the drainage divide and meltwaters were ponded in two of the major stream valleys east of Ungava Bay (Ives, 1958b, 1960a; Løken, 1962). At the same time, farther south the ice sheet receded across the plateau between Torngat Mountains and George River basin. Discordance between the drumlinoid and esker trends may indicate that recession of the ice sheet was not along the same path as the flow during the earlier advances (Matthew, 1961).

In the George River drainage basin the meltwaters were ponded to form numerous high-level, ephemeral lakes, followed by the long-continued glacial Lake Naskaupi (Ives, 1960b). Several major stands of this lake are recognized. The remarkably well developed shorelines of glacial Lake Naskaupi II are related to discharge down Koraluk (formerly Kogaluk) River to Labrador Sea. Other discharge routes are via the Fraser, Harp, and Kanairiktok Rivers and via the George River–Lake Michikamau col but their respective lake phases have not been determined. At its maximum development, glacial Lake Naskaupi was about 200 miles long and 30 miles wide, occupying the entire George River basin except for the ice-dammed northern end. The correlative glacial Lake McLean (Ives, 1960b) formed in the upper part of Whale River basin immediately west of George River, and discharged at its southeastern end into Naskaupi II. It was about 70 miles long and 30 miles wide, and was confined on both northwestern and southwestern sides by the ice sheet. The strandlines of these lakes are tilted up towards the southwest and the Labradorean centre (Barnett and Peterson, 1964).

The development of the Naskaupi and McLean strandlines, which are cut in bedrock in places, required a long stand of each of the several lake phases. This requires rock-controlled sills at the outlets, and an active confining ice barrier in Ungava Bay (Ives, 1960b). The esker and ice-flow pattern south of Ungava Bay appear to be in accord with the concept of an Ungava Bay ice dome, but most evidence as to the sense of glacier movement south of the bay indicates northward rather than southward flow with recession of the ice sheet towards the interior (Matthew, 1961). Northward flow would appear to be a natural consequence of incursion of the sea into Ungava Bay. Within George River basin itself Matthew noted that certain ice-flow features indicate westward flow where only eastward flow might be expected because of the ice-dammed lakes. Thus there has been considerable controversy over the position of the ice divide. The writer considers that three periods of ice-divide or ice-dome migration are needed to satisfy the field data and the following glacial history is suggested: (i) an early north-trending ice divide must have been present within George River basin (Map 1253A) to account for westward ice-flow features within the basin; (ii) as Ungava Bay and the lowland to the south filled with ice the ice divide shifted westward; (iii) eastward ice flow was maintained in George River basin during the early stages of deglaciation but did not remove all evidence of the earlier westward movement; (iv) with the incursion of the sea into Ungava Bay a major rearrangement of the ice flowage resulted; (v) a short-lived ice divide probably then lay a short distance west of glacial Lakes Naskaupi and McLean, trending slightly east of north; (vi) ice flow was everywhere towards Ungava Bay, rapid southward recession of the ice divide followed, and the glacial lakes drained northward; (vii) the ice divide then lay south of Ungava Bay and no longer had a north-trending extension; subsequent changes in position took place in the interior as recession continued.

As the ice sheet thinned due to climatic amelioration, glacier retreat from northern New Quebec, west of Ungava Bay, followed as a natural consequence of the opening of Ungava Bay and Hudson Strait. Ice dispersion was outward towards the coast. As the ice sheet thinned and receded over the height-of-land near the coast, meltwater was ponded along the ice front southwest of Hudson Strait. The highest lake at about 1,800 feet elevation was ponded in the headwaters of Povungnituk River and drained eastward into Joy Bay (Ives, 1960a). As the ice margin receded southwestward down Povungnituk River valley it became concave to the northeast, and successive lower lake phases discharged northward to Hudson Strait and eastward to Ungava Bay (Map 1253A). Maximum lake levels were at about 1,500, 1,200, and 1,000 feet a.s.l. and several systems of deep spillway channels occur. Data available do not warrant conclusions regarding the direction or amount of postglacial uplift. Matthews (1962) outlined small lakes along the ice front south of Cape Wolstenholme. These presumably drained westward or southwestward and were somewhat younger than at least part of the abovementioned larger lake system.

Recession from Hudson Bay Coast. As Labrador ice receded inland from northern Hudson Bay it calved actively into the sea, and between Cape Wolstenholme and Port Harrison left a magnificent series of De Geer moraines; these preserve the lobate form of the ice front in most valleys along the coast. These coastal moraines may correlate with a similar belt of De Geer moraines well inland from east coast of James Bay. The lack of De Geer moraines in the coastal belt east of James Bay may indicate that the ice was too thick for their formation at the time the sea encroached on the region; east of Richmond Gulf, the near absence of De Geer ridges is more likely due to thin ice relative to the depth of the sea.

Recession to the interior. Inland from the area of marine overlap, ice recession left the usual pattern of eskers and

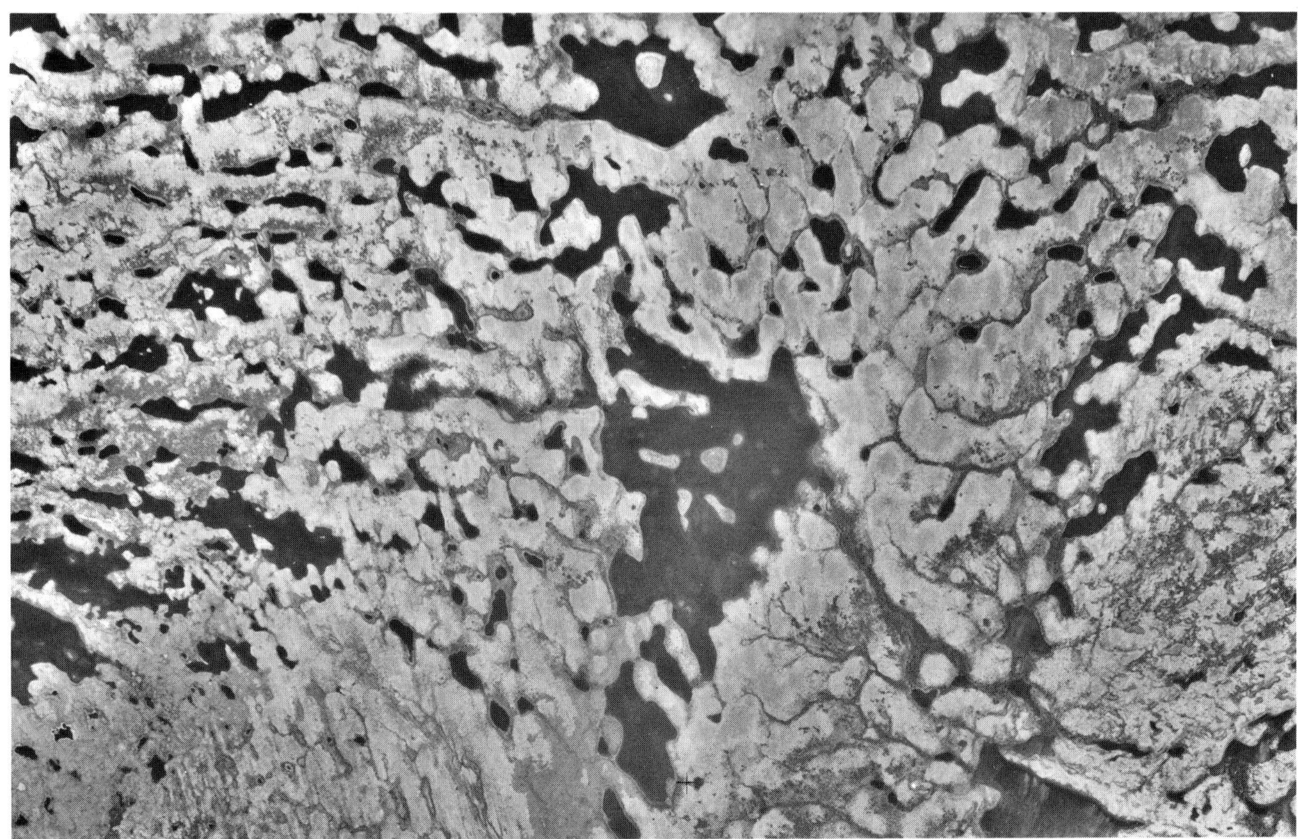

PLATE XII-8. Fluted ribbed moraine south of Ungava Bay, Quebec. Ice flowed northward. Photo suggests close temporal association between ribbing and fluting. Vertical airphoto; scale 1 inch to 1 mile.

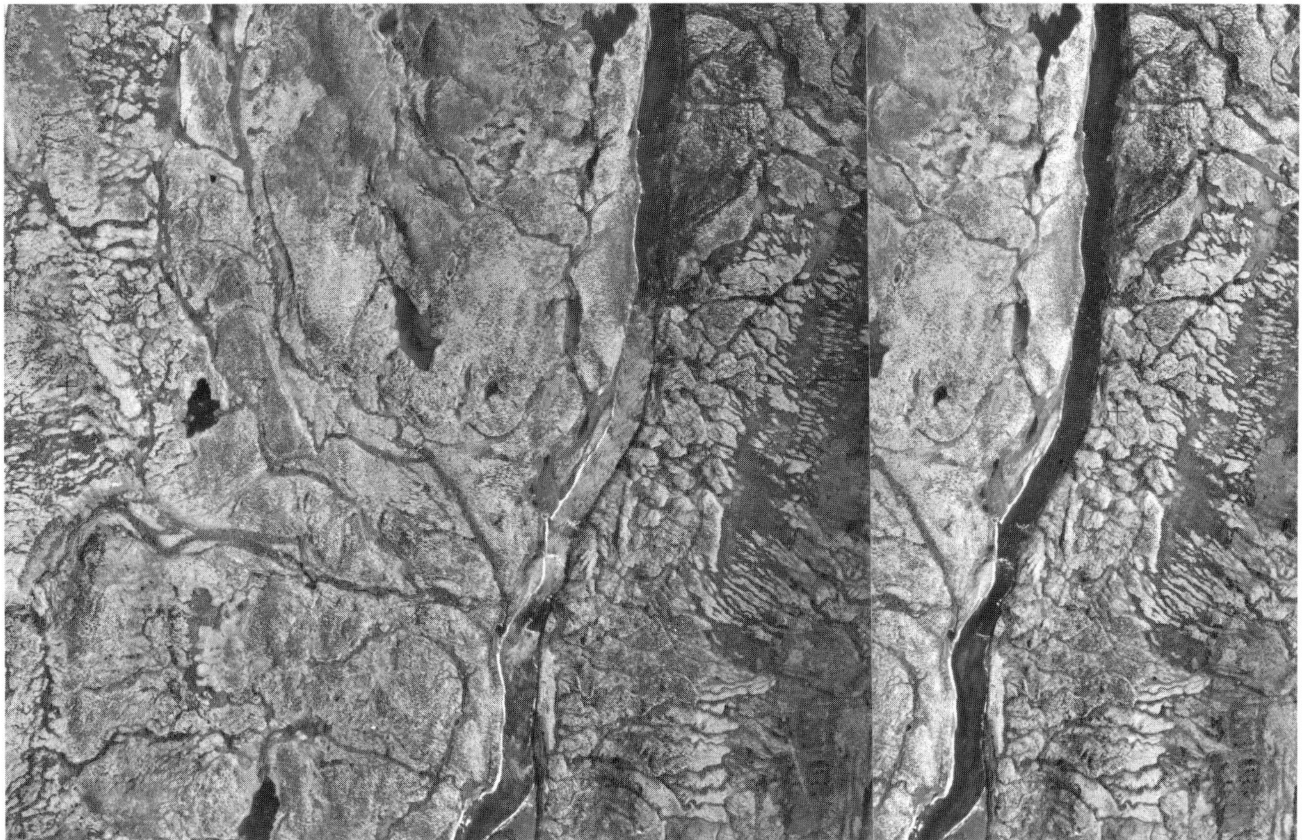

PLATE XII-9. Ice-marginal and subglacial meltwater channels, Mushalagan River, Central Quebec. The ice receded northward. Series of small meltwater channels formed subglacially or in much crevassed ice; the larger channels are considered ice-marginal channels. Stereoscopic pair; scale 1 inch to 3,330 feet.

ice-flow features characteristic of the Canadian Shield. Ribbed moraine is prevalent in many places associated with other ice-flow features and with eskers (Pl. XII-8). Final recession was probably to a number of scattered centres or ice divides in the interior of northern Quebec peripheral to Ungava Bay (Henderson, 1959b; Ives, 1960c; Derbyshire, 1962). One of the last remnant bodies of ice was in Howells valley west of Schefferville where there was much shifting of the late centres of outflow, with topography in control of the final ice movements. Late ice remnants were also present in Knob Lake depression and in the Lac le Fer–Swampy Lake depression. Subglacial and submarginal meltwater channels (Pl. XII-9) were the most effective forms of drainage in the final dispersal areas (Ives, 1959). Derbyshire believed that subglacial channels were first controlled by ice thickness and differential hydrostatic pressure, but as the remnant glaciers thinned they became much crevassed and waterlogged and the topography directly controlled the subglacial drainage.

From the pattern of ice-flow features and eskers (Map 1253A) it is clear that there was no major final dispersal centre, but rather a complex shifting of centres in response to changing climate. The Schefferville region, however, was a major centre of dispersal. This is indicated by the presence of various sets of striae in the region and by the directions of differential isostatic uplift determined from glacial lakes to the south, east, and northeast of this area (Barnett and Peterson, 1964).

A radiocarbon date on gyttja beneath peat in Chibougamau district, Quebec, indicates that pond deposits were formed as early as 6,960 ± 90 years B.P. Pollen extends through the uppermost 3 feet of silty clay of the glacial lake deposit. It is therefore likely that the ice front had receded from this area prior to about 7,500 years ago. Bog bottom dates from Grand Falls, Hamilton River (Morrison, 1963) and from near north end of Ashuanipi Lake, 100 miles to the west-southwest (Grayson, 1956) range from 5,250 ± 800 to 5,575 ± 250 years B.P. In all these sequences palynological evidence indicates a time gap between the base of the peat and the underlying glacial deposits. The dates indicate the initial development of widespread peat deposits and not the time of deglaciation of the area. This region was probably deglaciated prior to 7,000 years ago. A radiocarbon dating on a composite peat sample from near the base of a peat bog near Marymac Lake, 170 miles north-northwest of Schefferville, indicates that lake deposits had given place to peat prior to 6,400 ± 900 years ago. Grayson estimated the start of bog formation as closer to 8,000 than 7,000 years ago. Deglaciation of this area between 8,000 and 7,500 years ago is in keeping with incursion of the sea into Ungava Bay about 9,000 years B.P. and into Hudson Bay by 8,000 years B.P.

Keewatin Sector, Laurentide Ice Sheet

The Keewatin sector of the Laurentide Ice Sheet, or simply Keewatin ice sheet, is that part of the continental ice sheet which left a pattern of transverse morainal elements and longitudinal ice-flow features and eskers as it receded towards the Keewatin Ice Divide, an elongate area northwest of Hudson Bay. It covered the whole of western Canada east of the Cordillera, and an adjoining part of the north-central United States, except for a few small areas near its terminus near the International Boundary where the ice sheet was relatively thin. It also covered some of the arctic coastal islands and the southern side of Melville Island. At its maximum it was in contact with Cordilleran ice on the west, and Arctic, Baffin, and Labrador ice on the north and east. Tyrrell (1897) states that the name Keewatin is derived from Cree Indian meaning north or north wind and he used the term as applied to the ice sheet which he believed had its "gathering ground" northwest of Hudson Bay, in District of Keewatin, Northwest Territories. He was aware of the difficulty of establishing a glacier in this inland region of low altitude but nevertheless envisaged an active and shifting centre of outflow operating over a long period of time. The term Keewatin Ice Divide is now applied to a linear zone, almost 500 miles long, lying northwest of Hudson Bay, around which eskers and ice-flow features are arranged in a roughly radial pattern. It represents "the zone occupied by the last glacial remnants rather than a centre of ice dispersal" (Lee, *et al.*, 1957).

Keewatin Ice Divide is an area of few eskers and flow features as compared to adjacent areas (Lee, 1959). Those present indicate that the area of late ice dispersal migrated westward during the last stages of activity, the result of marine transgression into Hudson Bay. Thus, in many places, ice-flow features that were formed by ice moving in opposing directions merge against or into one another. The origin and initial development of Keewatin ice, however, remains conjectural.

Southern Interior Plains

The thickness of glacial drift on the Prairies varies greatly, probably averaging around 200 feet and locally is known to be more than 1,000 feet. Its general character is different from that of glacial drift in eastern Canada. The Prairies include great tracts of hummocky drift (Pls. XII-10, 11) that in places show transverse ridging (Prest, 1968). These features appear to reflect the clayey nature of the Prairie tills which have been derived from dominantly shale strata, and some of which contain much montmorillonite. Major end moraines per se are relatively uncommon and largely a matter of interpretation. Many of the great drift ridges formerly regarded as end moraines of southwestward-moving glaciers are now considered to be drift-mantled bedrock ridges, and for the most part mark marginal rather than end positions of lobate ice fronts. Furthermore, there has been much thrusting and folding of bedrock by glacier pressures, including induced pore-pressure (Slater, 1927; Byers, 1960; Kupsch, 1962) which have made it generally difficult and commonly impossible to differentiate between recessional drift ridges and ice-thrust ridges mantled with drift (Prest, 1968). Both types are included under the transverse ridge symbol on the glacial map (Map 1253A). Great blocks of bedrock, some perhaps measurable in miles, are underlain by till along Oldman River in southern Alberta (Stalker, 1963). L. A. Bayrock reports similar masses east of Edmonton. Sheets of bedrock resting on and capped by till have been encountered in drilling in Saskatchewan, according to E. A. Christiansen. Whitaker (1965) reports similar occurrences in southern Saskatchewan and also refers to very large masses of stratified drift that occur as

PLATE XII-10
Hummocky disintegration moraine near Cypress Hills, Saskatchewan.

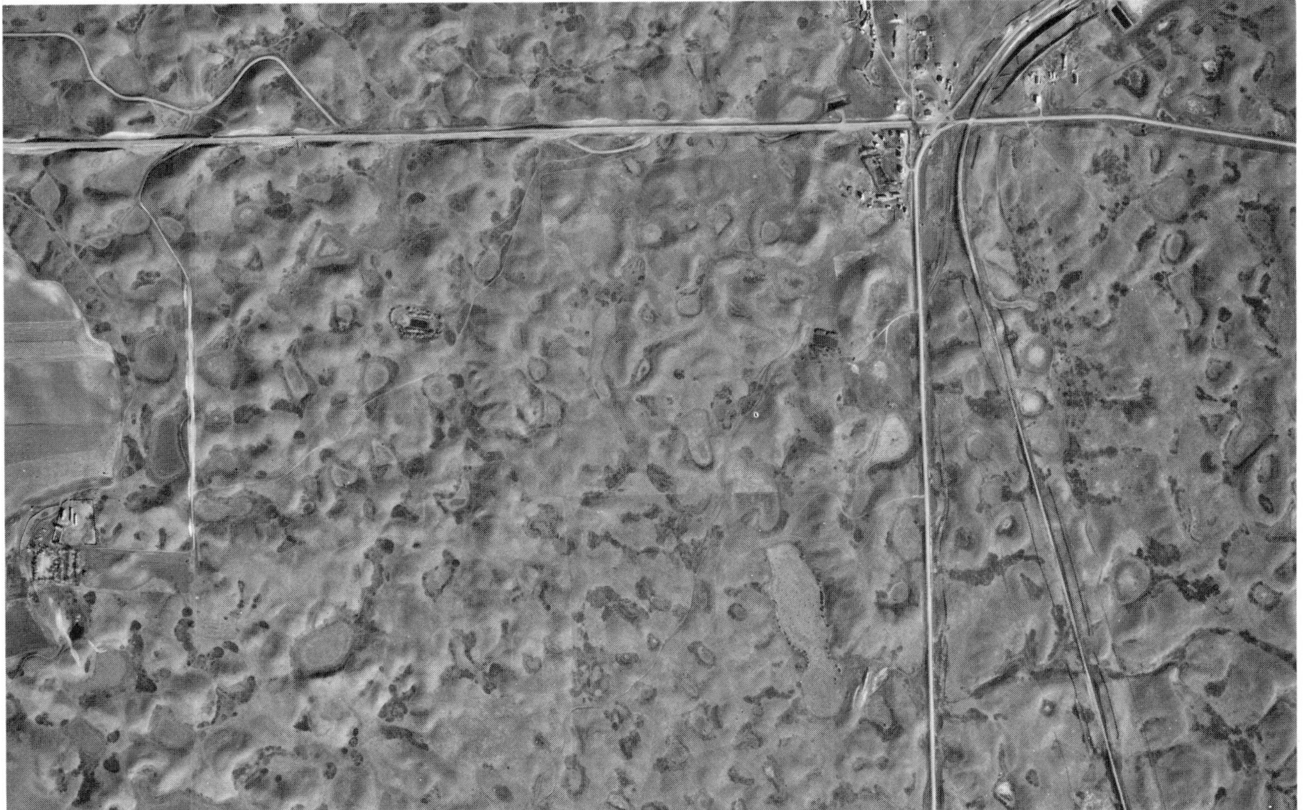

PLATE XII-11. Hummocky disintegration moraine east of Lake Johnstone, southern Saskatchewan. Occurs on western side of ice-thrust moraine of the Coteau moraine complex; local relief is about 80 feet. Town of Crestwynde in upper right corner. Vertical airphoto; scale 1 inch to 1,320 feet.

erratics and presumably were frozen when moved. The obvious thrusting action involved in the emplacement of ice-thrust ridges and discrete sheet-like erratics between tills, coupled with the sliding of debris in hummocky disintegration moraine and consequent inversions of topography, militate against easy development of a late glacial chronology for the Interior Plains. At present it is difficult to document an orderly general pattern of ice retreat despite the large amount of work done.

Ice-flow directions. On the southern Interior Plains the ice-flow and recessional moraine patterns indicate former glacial movements towards the southwest, south, and southeast. Local topographic features were instrumental in directing the late phases of glacier flow. It is also evident that the regional northwest trend of bedrock and the regional slope to the northeast have played important roles in deflecting the southwest flow from the Shield, towards the south and southeast. Southwest-trending ice-flow features in some relatively high areas on the Plains may be related to movements of a southwestward expanding ice sheet, but it is more likely that these features are related to south and southeastward moving glaciers which locally overtopped the valleys containing them. Shield stones indicative of a distant source are present along the length of the Rocky Mountain Foothills, but their provenance has not been determined. At the Wisconsin glacial maximum Keewatin ice was in contact with Cordilleran ice, or overlapped ground vacated by this ice, along the entire length of the Foothills in Alberta, except for a small area in the Porcupine Hills of southwestern Alberta (Douglas, 1950).

In Manitoba the ice-flow pattern indicates that regional glacier movements were to the southeast. Cretaceous rocks from the west side of Red River valley, near the International Boundary, were transported more than 400 miles across Paleozoic and Precambrian terrain and incorporated in till of the Grantsburg sublobe east of Minneapolis, according to H. E. Wright, Jr. (Univ. Minnesota). This indicates long-continued ice flow parallel to the presumed retreat flow pattern. Glacier retreat was mainly towards the northwest, but near Lake Winnipeg basin the influence of the Labrador ice has complicated the ice flow and the age relationships between various patterns have not been established. Along the Manitoba escarpment, the prominent hills and valleys brought about lobations of the late ice fronts and hence locally the ice receded towards the east and northeast.

In southern and central Saskatchewan the ice-flow patterns are exceptionally intricate and the order of late-glacial movements varies greatly from one area to another

PLATE XII-12
Blocks of pebbly quartzite of erratics train from Athabasca Valley glacier, Claresholm, Alberta. The depressions around the boulders are mainly due to buffalo wallowing. The largest boulder, now broken in three pieces, measured about 50x13x4 feet.

(Parizek, 1964; Christiansen, 1965). There appears to be a regional recession of the ice sheet towards the north-northeast. The major ice-frontal positions, however, may only reflect thinning of the ice sheet and a lowering down the regional northeast slope while the ice flow remained essentially south and southeast along the slope. The longitudinal and transverse glacial lineaments appear to indicate this general trend but with many variations due to local topographic effects.

In southern Alberta the glacial features clearly indicate a predominant south to southeast trend. Keewatin ice must have flowed southward for an extended period for Cordilleran ice from Athabasca River valley merged with it and emplanted immense blocks of pebbly quartzite upon it; these were transported southward as far as Montana (Stalker, 1956; Mountjoy, 1958). These erratics were distributed along a path generally only a few miles wide and more than 400 miles long. They comprise the Foothills erratics train (Pl. XII-12). A. MacS. Stalker believes that this train of erratics represents the limit or near-limit of the Classical Wisconsin ice sheet. The group of quartzite blocks at Okotoks, Alberta, are considered to be parts of a former single block that weighed about 18,000 tons.

Regional ice recession was to the northwest parallel to the regional structure, with minor recessional shifts to the north and northeast occasioned by local high ground and by northeast-trending valleys. In northern Alberta the direction of ice recession gradually shifted to the northeast towards the Shield and hence the ice-marginal positions and moraines trend northwest. There were, however, many lobations and variations in glacier movements during the period of recession that are now revealed by a complex pattern of ice-flow features.

Glacial lakes. Meltwater was commonly ponded along the receding ice margins, but other than glacial Lake Agassiz, already discussed, the lakes were generally ephemeral with poorly marked shorelines. The bottom deposits are generally thin but in some areas are thick enough to completely mask hummocky terrain. Where thick lake sediments were deposited prior to the melting of buried ice blocks a hummocky terrain formed which closely resembles that of disintegration or dead-ice moraine.

In southern Saskatchewan, the ice front along the upper part of Qu'Appelle River ponded meltwater on its south side to form glacial Lake Regina (Johnston and Wickenden, 1930; Christiansen, 1961). This lake at the 1,900 to 1,950 feet level discharged southeastward via the Souris River system into Mississippi River. As ice recession continued into north-central Saskatchewan, the Qu'Appelle River valley served as a spillway for a series of lakes ponded in the Saskatchewan River valleys, discharging into glacial Lake Agassiz. These lakes received meltwater from the ice front and from glacial lakes as far northwest as the Rocky Mountains of east-central Alberta. As ice recession continued, the upper reaches of Assiniboine River in eastern Saskatchewan then served as a spillway into the Agassiz basin. The precise relationship of the various lake stages in Saskatchewan River valley with the glacial lakes in Alberta or with glacial Lake Agassiz have not been established.

In southern Alberta glacial lakes were numerous but small; meltwaters readily escaped to the southeast. Glacial lakes were more extensive in northern Alberta where the ice front plugged the major river valleys that trend northeast, and lateral discharge was difficult. Glacial Lake Edmonton occupied part of the North Saskatchewan River valley near Edmonton and at one stage extended into the Athabasca River valley (Gravenor and Bayrock, 1956; and Taylor, 1958). Deposits in the western end of the basin occur at altitudes up to 3,400 feet, but southeast of Edmonton lie below 2,500 feet. Discharge was to the southeast, at first into Red River and later into Battle River and the Qu'Appelle Valley to Lake Agassiz. A succession of lakes in Smoky River and Little Smoky River valleys west of Athabasca River are described by Henderson (1959a) and St. Onge (1966). The highest lake phase at 2,800 feet elevation is known as glacial Lake Rycroft. It extended west and northwest along the convex ice front into Peace River valley. Discharge was via the Pass Creek spillway from the southeastern end of the lake across a low divide at the head of Iosegun River into the Athabasca and presumably into a low stage of Lake Edmonton. St. Onge (1966) reports a radiocarbon date on shells pertaining to glacial Lake Rycroft of 12,190 ± 350 years (GSC-508).

By the time the ice front had receded so that discharge could take place into Lesser Slave Lake basin, the ice-marginal lake in the Smoky River valleys had lowered some 800 feet but remained in the Peace River valley and occupied a somewhat larger area than did Lake Rycroft. This phase is known as glacial Lake Fahler. It discharged eastward over a sill 10 miles west of High Prairie at an altitude well below 2,000 feet (Henderson, 1959a) into a lake in the Lesser Slave basin that was confluent with water ponded in the Athabasca River valley. These waters discharged across a sill east of Lac La Biche, at an altitude of 1,850 feet, and thence flowed via Saskatchewan River to glacial Lake Agassiz. The succession of lakes in Peace River valley, including Rycroft, Fahler, and lower levels were termed glacial Lake Peace by Taylor (1958) and Mathews (1963).

The Lake Fahler phase came to an end when the ice front had retreated about 150 miles down Peace River valley and thereby opened lower discharge outlets that led to the Arctic Ocean. According to Henderson (1959a), the Lake Fahler basin above the town of Peace River was drained prior to a re-advance of the ice sheet that returned the lake to its former level with discharge eastward to Lesser Slave Lake basin. Retreat of the ice sheet again resulted in a drainage reversal. Numerous spillways led westward from Peace River valley to Fort Nelson River in British Columbia, permitting northward discharge via Liard and Mackenzie Rivers. Glacial Lake Peace was lowered by a succession of outlets at about 1,800, 1,500, and 1,200 feet. Further ice retreat allowed discharge northward along Hay River into the Mackenzie. This lake phase would appear to correlate with a high level phase of glacial Lake Tyrrell (Taylor, 1958). As the ice sheet receded northeastward and eastward in northern Alberta, this lake expanded into the Lake Athabasca basin and the lower reaches of Athabasca River. When the Slave River valley became ice-free, glacial Lake Tyrrell merged with glacial Lake McConnell which discharged to Mackenzie River from the western end of Great Slave Lake (Craig, 1965a).

Northern Interior Plains and Mainland Arctic Plain

The character and thickness of drift in the northern Interior Plains vary greatly. Craig reports that the till, in the region west of Great Slave Lake, is silty to clayey and stony. Drumlinoid forms are locally very abundant; some of those west of Great Slave Lake are up to 100 feet high and display surface furrowing with a relief of 10 to 15 feet. Hummocky and kame moraines are limited but north of Great Bear Lake hummocky moraine is widespread and there are many end moraines. Mackay (1958) states that the till in Darnley Bay area is rich in silt and clay due to prevalence of carbonate rocks. Eskers, though not abundant, are dispersed widely over the northern plains.

Craig reports drift depths up to 380 feet in the area west of Great Slave Lake and up to 150 feet in river bank sections along Mackenzie River, parallel to the mountain front, but the bedrock is not exposed. Drillholes east of Inuvik on lower Mackenzie River indicate a maximum drift thickness of 230 feet. The drift is probably very thick in the moraines north of Great Bear Lake. Ice-thrust features are common along the Arctic coast (Mackay, 1963).

At the climax of the last or Classical Wisconsin Glaciation, the Keewatin ice west of Great Slave Lake does not appear to have made contact with the Cordilleran Glacier Complex although it reached the mountains west of lower Liard River. There was, rather, a mainly unglaciated zone separating them along the mountain front that was 10 to 30 miles wide and almost 200 miles long extending north from the British Columbia boundary; this zone did, however, contain some valley glaciers. Another zone, slightly larger, occurs west of Great Bear Lake where the Keewatin ice flowed northwestward along the mountain front. These mainly unglaciated areas have been little studied but there is geomorphological evidence along the eastern mountain front that the last ice sheet did not reach as high as an earlier ice sheet. Keewatin ice extended as elongate lobes into some of the valleys along the eastern sides of the unglaciated areas and reached altitudes of above 4,500 feet. These two relatively unglaciated areas may be joined by a similar narrow strip or corridor to the large unglaciated region in northwestern Yukon and Alaska.

Ice-flow directions. West of Great Slave Lake the last ice sheet appears to have met the mountains at almost right angles, but farther north it was deflected parallel to the mountain front and Mackenzie River valley. It also moved parallel to the mountain front over most of the Plains east of Mackenzie River. As the ice sheet thinned and the ice front receded into the Great Slave Lake basin active flow there remained westward with the result that late ice-flow features cut across the trend of some earlier formed features parallel to the regional trend. This late ice was forced to flow around Horn Plateau west of Great Slave Lake and the ice front was, therefore, deeply indented. Elsewhere between Great Slave and Great Bear Lakes a complex pattern of ice-flow features discernible on airphotos suggests some differences in regional flow coupled with local lobations due to topography as deglaciation took place. With continued eastward recession towards the Shield the ice front straightened along the length of the Plains escarpment, some 20 to 30 miles west of the

Canadian Shield edge. Segments of end moraine and some minor moraine occur near Lac la Martre (Craig, 1965a). Craig suggests that this ice front extended southward to Great Slave Lake and beyond. Morainal features, discernible on airphotos of the region north of Lac la Martre, are suggestive of a continuation of the same 'straightened' ice front.

Keewatin ice did not extend beyond the present Mackenzie Delta except west of the river mouth. West of Peel River, the last ice sheet was not so extensive as an earlier ice sheet (Hughes, 1965), but it did extend west along Arctic Coastal Plain as far as Kay Point. Much information on the Pleistocene deposits and history of Mackenzie Delta area is given in a comprehensive report by Mackay (1963).

Between Mackenzie and Anderson Rivers ice-flow features trend north along the strike of the Paleozoic rocks but south of Eskimo Lakes trend northeastward; the reason for this deflection is not known. Mackay (1963) considers the morainic topography on the north side of Eskimo Lakes, in a belt 5 to 10 miles wide, as the terminal zone of a major ice sheet. He also noted smaller end moraines in the Campbell–Sitidgi Lakes area east of Inuvik, and also ice-flow features that trend north-northeast and northwest. He also suggested that the northeastern end of the Tuktoyaktuk Peninsula, which separates the Beaufort Sea from Eskimo Lakes and Liverpool Bay, might be unglaciated and that the limit of the last major ice sheet lay more or less along the middle of the peninsula. Fyles (1967a), however, suggests that the limit of the last ice sheet may have lain along the length of the south side of Tuktoyaktuk Peninsula, and that it may not have reached the northern part of Cape Bathurst.

In general, ice retreat north of Great Bear Lake was towards the southwest, parallel the strike of both Proterozoic and Paleozoic rocks. The complex pattern of ice-flow features, however, indicates that during the late stages of deglaciation the ice margin was highly lobate. Near the Arctic coast the late ice-frontal lobations were further complicated by Amundsen Gulf lobe (Mackay, 1958). The interplay of this ice lobe with that north of Great Bear Lake, and of local draw-down effects in vicinity of Great Bear Lake basin are described by Craig (1960).

Glacial lakes. As Keewatin ice receded from the northern Interior Plains meltwaters occupied the major depressions of Great Bear and Great Slave Lakes, and flowed northward down Mackenzie River. When the ice front lay along the edge of the Canadian Shield a vast lake extended from Great Bear Lake basin southward through Great Slave Lake basin to the lower Athabasca and Peace River valleys. Craig (1965a) has named this confluent lake phase glacial Lake McConnell. As isostatic uplift drained the lake to lower levels it separated into smaller lakes ancestral to the present Great Bear and Great Slave Lakes. In the latter lake basin strandlines are warped upward to the east. Craig suggests a minimum uplift rate of about 2 feet per mile in Great Slave Lake basin based on the presence of a delta at 500 feet elevation at Fort Simpson and of strandlines up to about 925 feet near the Canadian Shield edge. Great Bear Lake became separated from Great Slave Lake when the water levels fell below about 750 feet, the elevation of the present drainage divide between them.

Pingos and ground ice. Postglacial features of great interest in the lower part of Mackenzie Delta and in Eskimo Lakes–Liverpool Bay region are the pingos or conical ice-cored hills (Porsild, 1938). Mackay (1962, 1963) states that the pingos are elliptical to oval, 100 to 2,000 feet across, 10 to 150 feet high and generally asymmetrical. They occur in former lake basins or drainage channel depressions. The ice cores are believed to roughly conform to the shape of the pingo but perhaps have steeper slopes, and to bottom close to the surrounding ground level. The ice is overlain by a mantle of sand capped by vegetal matter, and is underlain by sand similar to that of the surrounding depression areas. The tops of the pingos are frequently breached or broken. Pingos with diameters of more than about 600 feet do not stand as high as the smaller ones, and those with the greatest base are merely bulge-like swellings in the lake basin sediments. Pingos result from a squeezing process as permafrost encroaches upon unfrozen saturated sands beneath what were formerly relatively large and deep lakes. They may exist for hundreds to thousands of years.

Great lenses of ground ice also constitute important elements of the landforms of this northern region according to Mackay. Fyles (1966) stresses the difficulties of stratigraphic analyses where such ice wedges are prevalent.

Arctic Lowlands

This part of the Arctic Archipelago lies between the mainland and the Queen Elizabeth Islands and includes the northern limit of Laurentide Ice Sheet. The drift generally reflects the variable character of the underlying Proterozoic and Paleozoic bedrocks.

Large morainal belts with fresh glacial landforms characterize an eastern part of Banks Island and are related to the Classical Wisconsin Glaciation (Fyles, 1962). Drift is varied and generally heaped into steep-sided hills but in places occurs as broad, smooth, hills and ridges, with intervening gentle depressions. Relief is several hundred feet. Marine beaches are locally well developed.

The last continental ice sheet reached the south coast of Melville Island perhaps as recently as about 11,000 years ago, and was responsible for the Winter Harbour Moraine (Fyles, 1967b). The moraine is composed of bouldery drift and stratified deposits and comprises a belt of hilly and ridged topography 50 miles long and averaging 2 miles wide. It is less extensive than a former glaciation.

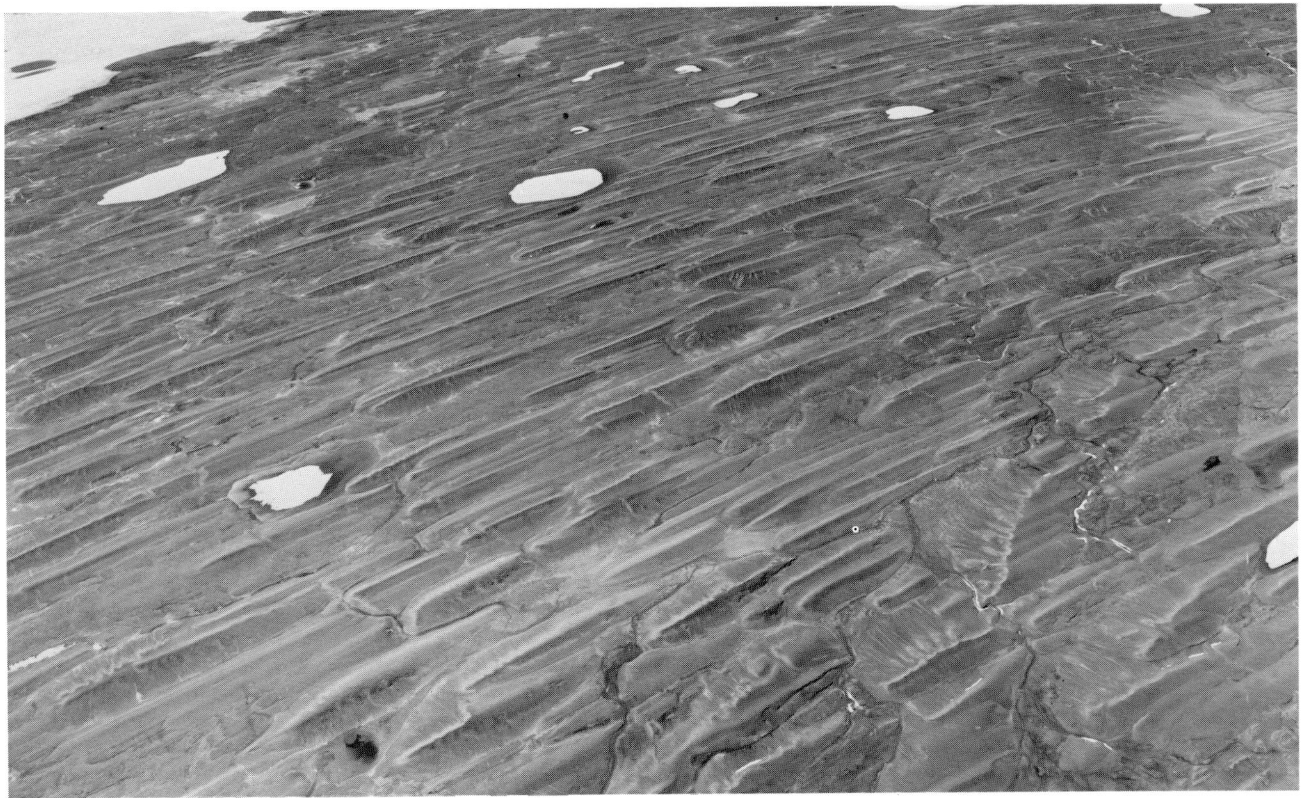

PLATE XII-13. Drumlin belt, Stefansson Island, Northwest Territories. View to the west. Ice flowed northward into Viscount Melville Sound.

Fyles (1963a) reports that the drift on Victoria Island characteristically has a light coloured matrix of slightly sticky, dense, loam or sandy loam. Numerous and exceedingly variable linear landforms are built of glacial debris or glacially deformed strata. These belts include landforms that are generally ascribed to end, kame, and hummocky moraine. The moraine ridges range from major features several hundred feet high, traceable more or less continuously for tens of miles, to miniature forms only a few feet high and a mile or so long. The complexities and interrelations of these great areas of hummocky and ridged moraine make it difficult to delineate end moraines per se. The drift is generally a few tens of feet to more than 100 feet thick and locally exceeds 500 feet. Drumlinized forms are characteristic of most lowland areas (Pl. XII-13) and there the drift is only a few tens of feet thick with bedrock protruding in some places. Eskers are numerous in the low-lying eastern and southern parts of Victoria Island, but they are few and short elsewhere; the longest is 120 miles. The eskers are usually less than 150 feet high but some knots at the junction of two or more esker-tributaries are several hundred feet high. Most consist of sand and gravel but some have material similar to that of the moraines.

An end moraine ridge and kame hills occur on northwestern Prince of Wales Island forming a linear zone of thick drift (Craig, 1964a). Eskers are rare on Prince of Wales and Somerset Islands and on Boothia Peninsula but are numerous on King William Island. They generally parallel the ice-flow direction, but on Prince of Wales Island some are transverse. Kames are striking features of central Boothia Peninsula (a Canadian Shield promontory within the Arctic Lowlands) and western Prince of Wales Island. They occur as broad zones that appear to be ice frontal and also as individual hills and groups of hills and ridges. They range from a few tens to about 200 feet high, and are rarely as much as 400 feet above the general ground level. Glacial landforms are uncommon on the northern parts of Prince of Wales Island and especially so on Somerset Island. These Paleozoic uplands are monotonously featureless but a thin layer of silty, rubbly glacial till occurs in many places, and some ground moraine topography, isolated kames, and meltwater channels are present.

Ice-flow directions. Ice-flow features and transverse morainal elements in the Arctic Lowlands are very complex, but nevertheless the maximum extent of the Wisconsin ice sheet can be delineated in a general way. The Amundsen Gulf ice lobe crossed Darnley Peninsula and reached the eastern side of Franklin Bay but does not appear to have crossed Cape Bathurst. It glaciated at least part of southern Banks Island and the east coast of Banks Island (Craig and Fyles, 1960). J. G. Fyles believes it may have extended westward along M'Clure Strait to the western end of Banks Island. Keewatin ice reached some distance inland on southern Melville Island, and farther east crossed Somerset Island and Boothia Peninsula (Fraser, 1957; Craig, 1964a). The ice sheet, at the glacial maximum, probably flowed northwesterly and northerly across Prince of Wales and Somerset Islands but later as it thinned and receded the deep channels between the islands influenced the ice flow. On southern Prince of Wales Island the last ice flow was eastward across the north-trending drumlin fields left by the earlier regional flow. A late ice lobe in Peel Sound may account for easterly trending striae on the west side of Somerset Island. Northwest- and northeast-trending drumlin fields occur on parts of King William Island. Craig (1964a) believes that the last ice movements over King William Island and Boothia Peninsula were northeastward.

On Victoria Island the regional flow was westward and northwestward but successive changes of late flow occurred as the ice sheet thinned (Fyles, 1963a). In places diverse drumlinoid trends occur side by side or are superimposed one upon the other. Flow directions are also controlled by relatively minor topographical features, suggesting that the ice sheet was lobate and thin. As the ice thinned, it withdrew from the higher parts of western Victoria Island, retreating to the southeast. Active ice tongues, fed by the main ice sheet to the south and east, remained in the depressions now occupied by the various arms of the sea. The moraines of western Victoria Island are lateral to these ice tongues. In the east-central lowland the ice probably flowed northwesterly in the early stages of wastage but with continued wastage, which took place progressively from west to east and north to south, the ice covering the lowland became thinner, and the direction of ice flow was deflected to an ever increasing degree by minor topographic irregularities. Glacier lobes in the low areas produced fan-shaped areas of ice-flow features trending northward and southwestward.

In the southeastern part of the island the morainal ridges are smaller, lower, and shorter, compared to the great morainal complexes of the western parts. This part of the island was the last to be deglaciated. Strongly flowing ice from the mainland constituting the receding Amundsen Gulf lobe passed down Bathurst Inlet and crossed Coronation Gulf, building a fan-shaped drumlin field across the southwestern end of the island. Apparently the last ice on the island covered the low ground bordering the east and southeast coasts while ice tongues still occupied M'Clintock Channel and Queen Maud Gulf (Fyles, 1963a).

Western Canadian Shield

In Canadian Shield areas west and north of Hudson Bay the character of the drift and the glacial features themselves are rather unlike those of the plains and lowlands. The till matrix is generally silty to sandy and lacks

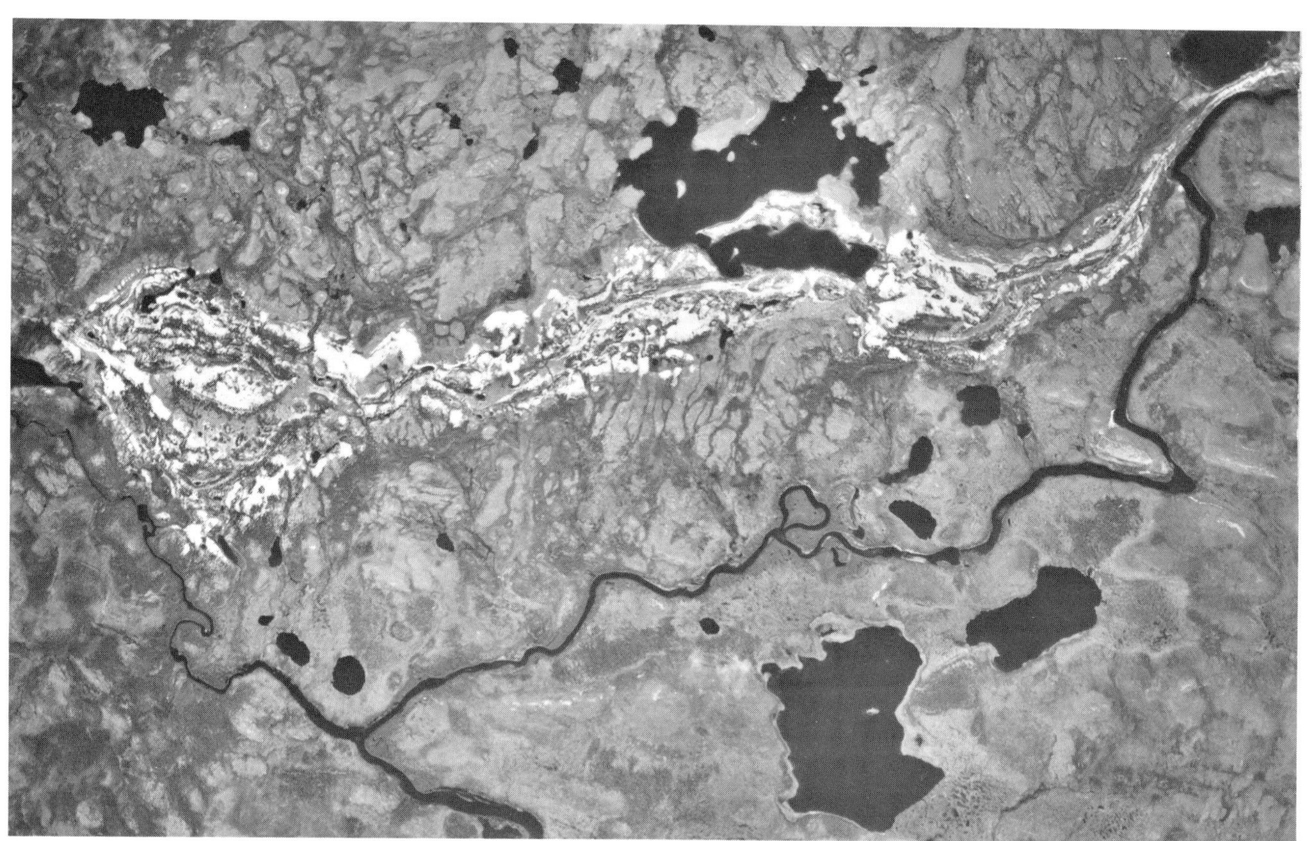

PLATE XII-14. Esker complex west of Ennadai Lake, Northwest Territories. Meltwater flowed southward. The large esker 'knot' is the south end of a system that is more or less continuous northeastward for about 60 miles to Kazan River. Vertical airphoto; scale 1 inch to 3,300 feet.

cohesive properties. The western part of the Shield is commonly mantled with drift in the form of ground moraine and ribbed moraine, which has a somewhat hummocky appearance but is unlike the hummocky terrain of the disintegration or dead-ice moraine of the plains. Eskers are widespread and numerous; they include the simple, sinuous ridges and the great complex multiple systems with widths of a mile or more (Pl. XII-14). The eskers and the remarkably continuous belts of drumlins, drumlinoid features, and glacial flutings delineate ice-flow directions during recession of Keewatin ice. End moraines are not common, but where present are clear linear features transverse to the ice-flow direction. Relief is commonly several tens of feet to about a hundred feet but locally kames, esker knots, and moraine knobs stand several hundred feet above the surrounding terrain.

Ice-flow directions. As Keewatin ice receded from the southern Interior Plains onto the Shield the ice front appears to have formed subparallel to the Shield edge and ice flow was roughly radial to this boundary. A halt in northern Saskatchewan is marked by the Cree Lake Moraine (Sproule, 1939; Tremblay, 1961a, b). It has been traced by means of airphotos northwestward to the western end of Lake Athabasca and eastward into Manitoba for about 500 miles. It varies from an end moraine-outwash complex to a single discrete ridge or a series of minor ridges. Thereafter, retreat towards Keewatin Ice Divide appears to have been uninterrupted by other major halts or re-advances.

In the Great Slave and Great Bear Lakes region recession was also continuous and no major end moraines were formed. The most significant result of this long period of retreat was the development of a marked discordance in the pattern of eskers and ice-flow features between two major ice lobes, a discontinuity that persisted as the ice sheet receded towards Keewatin Ice Divide (Fyles, 1955; Craig, 1957; Craig and Fyles, 1960; Blake, 1963; and Craig, 1964b). The discontinuity in the general radial pattern of flow features suggests that two distinct major glacier lobes formed during recession of the ice sheet. The break in flow pattern may readily be traced from the west side of Dubawnt Lake west-northwest to a point north of Aylmer Lake, and then curving northward past Contwoyto Lake to Coronation Gulf and beyond. To the north and east the flow features lie at a sharp angle to this 'break', whereas to the south and west they tend to be parallel or diverge only slightly from it. The line of demarcation is also revealed by a complex esker system between Dubawnt and Aylmer Lakes which lies a few miles south of the break. This esker continues for about 225 miles and except near the western end all tributary eskers lie only on the south side. Beyond Aylmer Lake a series of closely spaced eskers mark the continuation of the esker system towards Great Bear Lake (Craig, 1964b).

Craig and Fyles (1960) suggest that topographic control was responsible for developing the discontinuity. South and west of the break the ice was covering higher ground, moving slowly and stagnating locally, whereas the ice on the lower ground north of it was actively flowing. Blake (1963) also invokes a difference in activity between two lobes to account for the discontinuity northeast of Contwoyto Lake. Craig indicates that some northward-trending eskers north of it were overrun nearly at right angles by the last-formed lobe of the northern glacier. Southwest- and south-trending drumlinoid ridges west of Dubawnt Lake on the north side of the discontinuity are at right angles to the trend of ice-flow features on either side. These features are in part parallel to older striae recorded by Tyrrell (1897), but Craig considers them related to lobation within the northern part of the ice sheet as it receded towards Keewatin Ice Divide.

Ice retreat from the region north and east of the discontinuity was marked by the formation of end moraines. Two of the moraines, each about 25 miles long, lie east-northeast of Contwoyto Lake and trend slightly west of north. The westernmost moraine, with a maximum relief of nearly 400 feet, lies close to the discontinuity and apparently represents the terminal position of ice moving southwest (Blake, 1963). The eastern moraine is a recessional moraine. Several segments of east-west trending end moraine are evident southwest of Queen Maud Gulf. A prominent moraine extends northeastward from Back River, at the 106th meridian, to MacAlpine Lake for a total, including breaks, of more than 200 miles. This moraine varies from a few tens of feet to 4 miles wide, and from 10 to 250 feet high. The ice front apparently curved eastward to Chantrey Inlet (Blake, 1963; Craig, 1961) and was responsible for two more segments of end moraine some 60 and 25 miles long. Many segments of end moraine that may correlate with that west of Chantrey Inlet extend eastward to Committee Bay for another 225 miles. In this latter area, however, there are several discordant segments and correlation of ice-frontal positions is uncertain. Correlation with end moraines farther east, beyond the sphere of influence of Keewatin ice, is even more tenuous. A younger end moraine of the northern lobe of Keewatin ice also extends northeastward from Back River at the 106th meridian for a distance of 100 miles.

The position of the extension of the ice fronts south of the discontinuity are uncertain, but according to Craig (1964b, Fig. 7) there may be a significant jog eastward. Direct correlation of moraines across the discontinuity has yet to be established.

Glacial lakes. As Keewatin ice receded eastward across the Shield the east and northeast drainage systems became ice free and meltwaters were ponded to form several extensive glacial lakes (Map 1253A). A large lake occupied the Lake Athabasca basin and spilled northward over the rock sill in Slave River at an altitude of 700 feet (Craig, 1965a).

Somewhat earlier a glacial lake formed behind the Cree Lake Moraine in the Cree Lake and Pipestone (Cree)

River valley, the strandlines lying at about 1,800 feet. It may have drained southward through a break in the moraine and then discharged westward down the deep Clearwater River channel to Athabasca River valley. There is, however, an outlet channel from the southwestern end of the glacial lake basin, through which discharge took place into a lake in Richardson River valley at an elevation of about 1,400 feet; this was probably an eastern part of glacial Lake Tyrrell. As the ice front retreated northeast down Pipestone River the glacial lake in that valley discharged laterally to Lake Athabasca basin and successively lower levels were established. When the receding ice fronts cleared the eastern end of Lake Athabasca basin the two water systems merged at about 1,000 feet elevation. During this interval of retreat, a glacial lake formed in the Wollaston Lake basin at a maximum altitude of about 1,600 feet and discharged southeastward into Reindeer Lake basin. Later, lower outlets to Pipestone River valley were established. Reindeer Lake basin was occupied by meltwater when the ice front receded from the moraine at its south end. The outlet through the moraine was at about 1,200 feet a.s.l. and led directly into glacial Lake Agassiz lying south of the moraine.

Extensive glacial lakes also formed in Northwest Territories. Craig (1964b) found evidence of short-lived glacial lakes in the Artillery Lake–Lockhart River basin, east of Great Slave Lake. Beaches occur up to about 1,300 feet around Clinton and Holden Lakes. As the major southern lobe of Keewatin ice receded eastward from this area water was ponded in the headwaters of the northeast-sloping Thelon and Dubawnt Rivers drainage systems. The highest lake phases were about 1,250 feet and discharge was probably southward. Lower lake levels resulted as the ice receded eastward. Retreat of the major northern lobe of Keewatin ice allowed the water in the Thelon basin to discharge northward to the Back River system and lake levels were established at about 800 and 700 feet. At about this time Hyper–Dubawnt was at an altitude of 900 feet. The above lake phases are figured and described by Craig.

South of Dubawnt Lake, glacial Lake Kazan (Lee, 1959) occupied part of Kazan River and Ennadai, Kasba, and other lake basins. It drained eastward towards South Henik Lake and thence presumably into the sea in Hudson Bay. The strandlines around Ennadai Lake (1,070 feet elevation) are at an altitude of 1,260 feet (Pl. XII-15). Later, as the ice melted from Keewatin Ice Divide the lake discharged via Kazan River.

Marine overlap. At the same time as some of the above-mentioned lakes were present the sea was encroaching along the central-north coast (as early as 10,200 years

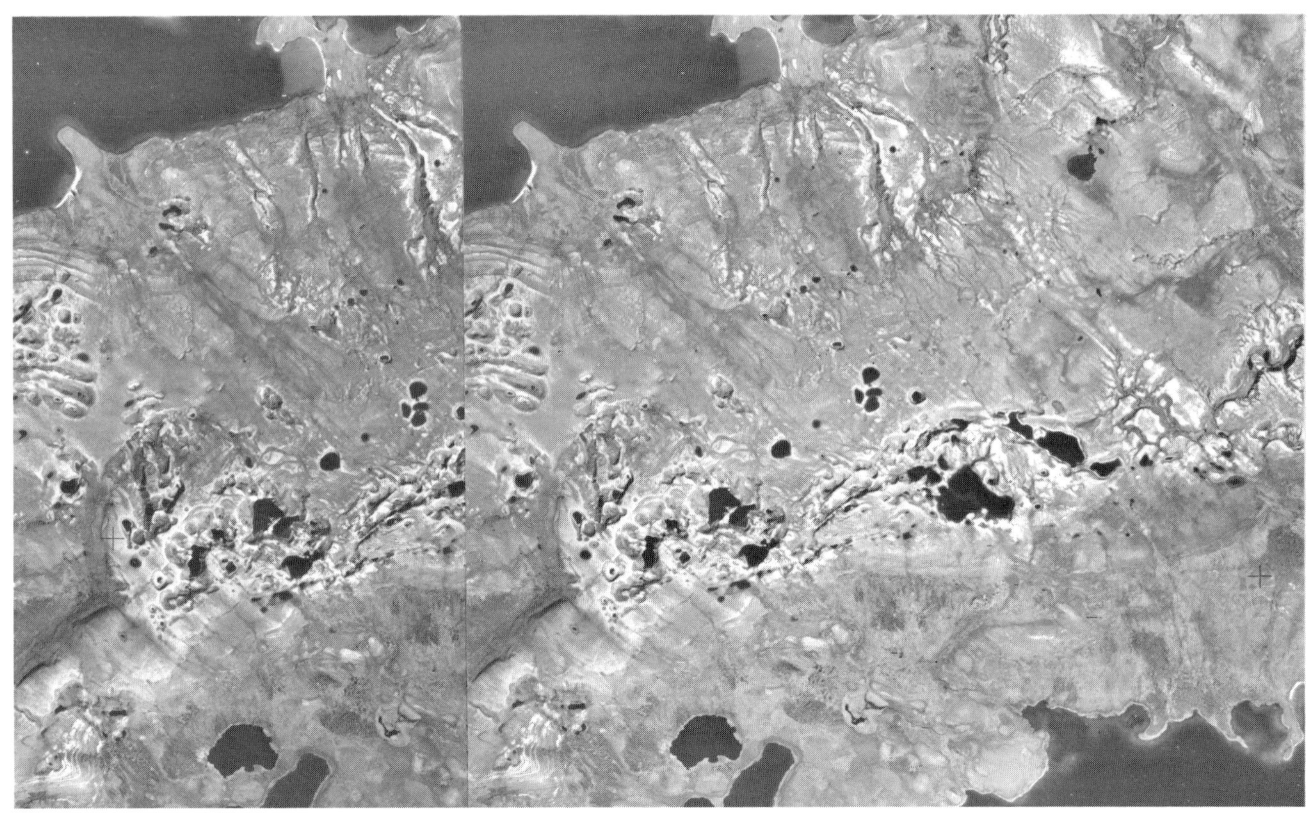

PLATE XII-15. Fluted and kettled ice-contact deposits with raised beaches and frost polygons, Ennadai Lake, Northwest Territories. Ice-contact deposits, 50 miles west of south end Keewatin Ice Divide, were fluted by an ice advance and later terraced and channelled by meltwater. Glacial Lake Kazan washed the lower slopes of the deposits. Some of the buried ice melted during and after the glacial lake phase. Stereoscopic pair; scale 1 inch to 3,100 feet.

B.P., Craig and Fyles, 1960). The sea was also in contact with a part of the ice front as the end moraine was formed at MacAlpine Lake only 8,200 years ago. By means of radiocarbon dating of shells from close to marine limit, Blake (1963) has estimated that the ice retreated about 175 miles from Kent Peninsula to MacAlpine Lake in about 1,000 years. Retreat towards Keewatin Ice Divide was also rapid, for the sea had encroached from Hudson Bay to near its maximum limit in the divide area by 7,200 years B.P. (Lee, 1960). It is clear also that isostatic rebound was rapid during this period of retreat for there is a general decrease in elevation of the marine limit with proximity to the divide. The rate of land emergence has decreased exponentially to the present (Lee, 1960; Craig, 1961). For the Bathurst Inlet area, Blake (1963) suggested an average rate of 1.5 feet per century over the past 2,000 years and probably less at present.

The marine limit west of Hudson Bay appears to decrease from south to north; it is about 650 feet in northern Manitoba, only 480 feet at Kaminuriak Lake, and 400 feet at Wager Bay. Along the Arctic coast the marine limit is greater, being over 650 feet west of Committee Bay and decreasing westward to 500 feet at Chantrey Inlet. It then increases westward to 750 feet at the southern end of Bathurst Inlet and drops off rapidly northwestward to 200 feet in Darnley Bay. The marine limit is not synchronous everywhere and it is probable that more than one centre of postglacial uplift has been active in this vast region.

Foxe–Baffin Glacier Complex

The glacial and deglacial history of Baffin Island is rather complex as a consequence of its physiography, latitude, and climate; it involved a major sector of Laurentide Ice Sheet, several local ice caps, and cirque and valley glaciers. The events in some parts of the present land areas were unlike those in others even where contiguous. On Meta Incognita (formerly Kingait) Peninsula, along the south coast of Frobisher Bay, Mercer (1956) found that unmodified cirques were common near the end of the peninsula. Along the central part of the bay the cirques showed evidence of later modification by ice from the interior, but towards the head of the bay they were absent entirely because that region was covered by interior ice prior to the interval of cirque glaciation. He also showed that cirque glaciers did not form anywhere along Frobisher Bay shore in late Wisconsin time as the interior ice receded. He considered that the interval of cirque formation was long and that it occurred during the Wisconsin. Bird (1963), however, favours development during an interglacial period. Some cirque glaciation, however, did take place in the mountainous terrain along the coast north of Cumberland Sound in late Wisconsin time. Thus despite sound field observation in several areas, any attempt to generalize for the entire island must be made with caution.

It is generally agreed that there was an ice dome over Foxe Basin at some stage during the last major glaciation but there are two views concerning its age: (1) that it existed at about the time of the last glacial maximum; and (2) that it only existed during a later stage of deglaciation. In either, the ice dome was concomitant with many local ice caps as well as cirque and valley glaciers along the eastern and northern highland areas (Ives and Andrews, 1963; Bird, 1963; Andrews and Sim, 1964; Falconer, *et al.*, 1965; Andrews, 1966). The relationships between the Foxe Basin ice dome and other sectors of Laurentide Ice Sheet are not well known. The writer considers that the ice dome was a dispersal centre for a substantial part of Classical Wisconsin time. It was probably confluent with Keewatin and Labrador sectors of Laurentide ice on the west, southwest, and south during a large part of the Wisconsin but maintained its own sphere of influence throughout. Ice from the local ice caps on Brodeur and Borden Peninsulas, together with huge valley glaciers flowing northward along Admiralty and Navy Board Inlets, probably merged with ice from Devon Ice Cap in Lancaster Sound at the last glacial maximum.

Glaciation

It was formerly held that initiation of glaciers on Baffin Island took place in the eastern mountain rim and that migration of the ice towards the interior resulted in piedmont glaciers that later expanded into ice caps and then merged to form an ice sheet. As the mountain rim is the eroded eastern edge of a westerly tilted upland it is unlikely that the mountain glaciers could contribute materially to the formation of the interior ice sheet; rather the ice probably accumulated on the larger central tract of the upland surface. As the westward slope of the upland is gentle and its valleys shallow, the ice must have flowed westward over a broad front, presumably as a plateau ice cap which gradually expanded and its margin moved progressively westward (Mercer, 1956; Ives and Andrews, 1963). Glacierization resulted from depression of the snowline below the level of the uplands as the Wisconsin climatic regimen changed. Rapid, large-scale development of the ice cap on the uplands starved the smaller glaciers in the coastal mountains so that the mountain ice caps and glaciers were never much more extensive than they are today. Perhaps the Penny Ice Cap is an exception. Penny Highlands are a remnant of a dissected older upland higher than the main Baffin surface (Bird, 1959). J. D. Ives believes that, because of its proximity to Labrador Sea and the moisture-laden winds moving up Davis Strait, Penny Highlands may have developed an extensive ice cap earlier than other parts of Baffin Island.

The early-formed interior Baffin Island ice caps presumably merged into an ice sheet which expanded differentially westward and fed ice into Foxe Basin. Glacierization of Melville Peninsula may have contributed eastward-flowing ice to Foxe Basin, and Laurentide ice may have flowed northward into the basin, though there is no evidence of these events. Laurentide ice, however, must have prevented or hindered early southward ice flow from Foxe Basin which therefore filled and later became a dispersal area (Ives and Andrews, 1963, Fig. 19). An ice dome over Foxe Basin is indicated by the tilting of marine strandlines in central Baffin Island towards the basin (Andrews, 1966). Analysis of carbonate content of drift in many places around Foxe Basin indicates outward flow from the basin (Andrews and Sim, 1964) though sporadic distribution of Precambrian crystalline limestone in central Baffin Island is a possible source of some carbonate. Blake (1966) did not find Paleozoic erratics or any increase in carbonate content of drift east of Amadjuak Lake in southeastern Baffin Island. There is, however, good evidence of early radial flow from Foxe Basin across the narrow central part of Baffin Island (Ives, 1962, 1964; Ives and Andrews, 1963; Andrews, 1963). There the ice sheet reached elevations of over 3,000 feet and escaped eastward through major valleys in the mountain rim and onto the continental foreland. Paleozoic erratics found north of Barnes Ice Cap were probably transported northeastward from Foxe Basin and survived through the later short period of outflow from proto-Barnes Ice Cap (Ives and Andrews, 1963, Fig. 22).

Foxe Basin ice also flowed eastward across Baffin Island through low ground to Cumberland Sound and probably southeastward to Frobisher Bay. It flowed southward across Foxe Peninsula and possibly also across part of Southampton Island (Bird, 1953). Strong and probably long-continued westward flow took place across Melville Peninsula where the bedrock is strongly scoured and *roches moutonnées* are common (Blackadar, 1958; Sim, 1960a; Craig, 1965b). There is no direct evidence of northward flow out of Foxe Basin but it may perhaps be inferred from evidence of northeast ice movements east of Steensby Inlet. It is of course possible that substantial ice caps on northern Baffin Island inhibited or prevented northward flow during the Wisconsin Glaciation.

At the glacial maximum some local ice caps occupied parts of the eastern and northern 'mountain' belt and also Brodeur and Borden Peninsulas, and may have prevented the incursion of interior ice to adjacent parts of the higher ground, and protected parts of the coastal foreland from the ravages of glaciers issuing along the fiords. Thus small parts of the eastern coastal lowland as well as some nunataks remained unglaciated at the last glacial maximum (Løken, 1966).

Deglaciation

Following the last glacial maximum, the Clyde phase of Ives and Andrews (1963), there was a period of glacier thinning and ice-marginal recession. This was followed by still-stands and short re-advances comprising the Cockburn phase of glaciation. The Cockburn Moraine System of end and lateral moraines marks the eastern ice-frontal positions of the interior ice sheet. In northeastern Baffin Island the outermost end moraines of the system lie on the high interfiord mountain flanks and descend into the fiords as lateral moraines; the inner moraines lie mainly on the upland plateau (Falconer, *et al.*, 1965). The ice was 1,500 to 2,000 feet thick in the heads of the fiords at this stage. Radiocarbon datings on shells from close to the marine limit established upon withdrawal of the ice from the coastal areas suggest that some of the eastern moraines formed about 8,200 years ago. The marine limit varies from about 220 feet elevation at some fiord heads to about 50 feet at the outer coast. The inner moraines on the plateau must be somewhat younger. Blake (1966) reported that a major end moraine in southeastern Baffin Island, believed a part of the Cockburn Moraine System, was forming for several hundred years after 8,200 years B.P. and suggested that a major end moraine on Foxe Peninsula was another correlative moraine. The Cockburn Moraines extend across northern Baffin Island and along the west side of Melville Peninsula (Falconer, *et al.*, 1965). Parts of this moraine in northern and northwestern Baffin Island may have formed somewhat earlier, perhaps as much as 9,000 years ago. The Cockburn Moraine System therefore appears to occupy a range in time from about 9,000 years to less than 8,000 years ago. This must have been a period of waning ice and consequent rapid change in ice-dome configuration. According to J. T. Andrews the east coast mountain glaciers were less extensive during the Cockburn phase of glaciation than they are at present. The Penny Ice Cap and several other major bodies were separated from the interior ice during this period.

Following the Cockburn phase of glaciation, the Foxe Basin ice dome underwent rapid disintegration and the sea invaded Foxe Basin about 7,500 to 7,000 years ago. The centre of ice dispersal was thus shifted northeastward onto Baffin Island causing ice flow towards Foxe Basin, whereas it had earlier been away from the basin. On the northeastern side of Baffin Island the ice margin receded west of the drainage divide and glacial lakes formed. Along the western side of central Baffin Island glaciers now occupied the fiords and inner bays. Marine overlap left strandlines ranging from about 350 feet near the coast to 100 feet farther inland, while glaciers in the valleys remained in contact with the sea. An end moraine in lower Isortoq River valley is associated with a sea level coincident with the marine limit (Andrews, 1966). Andrews equated the marine limit 'still-stand' with an increase in ice load on Baffin Island and a concomitant reduction in isostatic recovery. He named this period of thickening ice and moraine formation the Isortoq phase of glaciation. It would appear to correspond with the proto-Barnes Ice Cap phase of glaciation (Ives and Andrews, 1963, Fig. 22). Radiocarbon dates indicate that it occurred less than 7,000 but more than 5,500 years B.P. Andrews found that the marine limit was about 230 feet elevation some 15 miles from the mouth of Isortoq River and about 300 feet at the mouth, indicating a differential upwarp in direction S35°W towards the centre of Foxe Basin, at a rate of about 5.3 feet per mile.

The ice receded from Foxe Basin coast west of Nettilling and Amadjuak Lakes by 6,700 years B.P. and the marine limit was established west of these lakes at about 350 feet. Ice apparently remained in Amadjuak Lake basin during the Isortoq phase of glaciation; it was gone before 4,500 years B.P., and possibly as early as 5,500 B.P.

As the proto-Barnes Ice Cap shrank, glacial lakes remained along its northeastern side and continued to discharge into Baffin Bay. Glacial lakes were ponded in the middle Isortoq River valley, north and northwest of Barnes Ice Cap, during the period from about 5,000 to 2,000 years ago. As recently as 1,000 years ago a minor expansion of the ice cap blocked the river again and gave rise to another glacial lake, which drained in relatively recent times as the ice cap assumed its present position, size, and shape. The southwestern edge of the present ice cap with recent end and marginal moraines is shown in Plate XII-16. The east coast mountain glaciers are believed to have expanded in the last 2,000 years, reaching their maxima in the last few centuries (Harrison, 1964). Within the last 200 to 400 years a large part of the interior uplands was covered with thin ice and snowfields, but this has successively melted off until today only 2 per cent is covered, exclusive of Barnes Ice Cap (Ives, 1962). Falconer (1966) showed that in northern Baffin Island a small ice cap of about 3 square miles and never more than about 200 feet thick, developed as recently as 300 years ago in an area of patterned ground first deglaciated about 1,000 years ago. This small ice cap was inactive and served to protect the underlying polygonal structures and their vegetal cover—now emerging as the ice recedes. Deglaciation is still in progress and hence the term postglacial is inappropriate on Baffin Island.

In northernmost Baffin Island, Craig (1965b) reports that the glacial landforms and nearly all the surficial deposits are due to the last or Classical Wisconsin Glaciation. There is, however, a dearth of glacial landforms particularly on the Paleozoic rocks of Jones–Lancaster Plateau. Erratics are present throughout the region but are scarce on the northern part of central Brodeur Peninsula. Linear morainal zones with a hummocky surface and poorly defined higher ridges occur in a few places and although some mark terminal positions others afford little evidence of the position and movement of the ice that formed them. The most extensive linear zone is along south side of Bernier–Berlinguet Inlet, where it has been traced for 90 miles and in places rises 200 feet above adjacent land. The glacier appears to have moved westward and expanded radially. On the north side of the inlet there is also evidence of later ice flow from an ice cap to the north-northeast. Glaciers may have flowed eastward into Admiralty Inlet and northward along the inlet according to Craig. Also glaciers may have flowed westward off Bylot

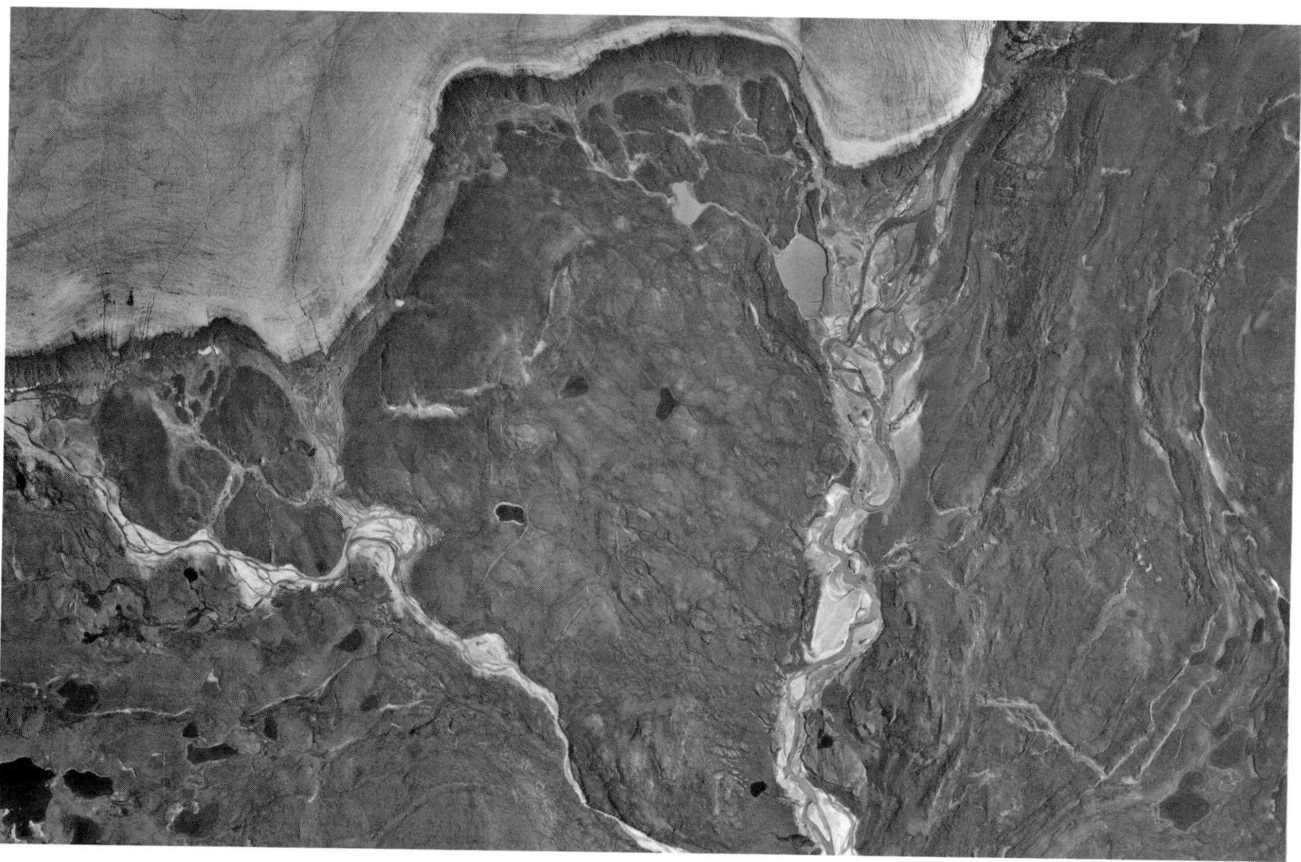

PLATE XII-16. Barnes Ice Cap with recent marginal and end moraines, Baffin Island, Northwest Territories. Vertical airphoto of upper reaches MacDonald River, southwest side Barnes Ice Cap. Scale 1 inch to 4,700 feet.

Island. Large areas of hummocky moraine are found in northern Baffin. These seldom afford any evidence of former ice positions or movement but along the west side of Brodeur Peninsula were probably formed by glaciers from the plateau. Radiocarbon dates on marine shells from raised beaches in northernmost Baffin Island indicate that maximum marine overlap occurred between about 9,000 and 7,000 years B.P.

As the above events were taking place on Baffin Island a somewhat comparable sequence of events occurred on Melville Peninsula (Sim, 1960; Ives and Andrews, 1963; Falconer, *et al.*, 1965; Craig, 1965b). Following the period of regional northwest ice movements over the peninsula, probably during both the Clyde and Cockburn phases, there was extensive thinning of the glacier complex and later incursion of the sea into western Foxe Basin. Sim reports flooding of the east coast of Melville Peninsula to about 500 feet a.s.l., and Craig reported marine overlap of the southeast coast to 485 feet. An ice cap probably occupied most of interior Melville Peninsula before breaking up into two or three local ice caps. Radial outflow was probably maintained by the larger southern body. In the centre of the peninsula a myriad of meltwater channels indicate a former small ice cap, and farther northeast eskers suggest a southeasterly flow of meltwater from another ice remnant (Sim, 1960; Craig, 1965b).

Deglacial events in northern Southampton Island, which may have been covered in part by Foxe–Baffin Glacier Complex, are little known. Bird, however, reports a late ice cap in the central part of northeast coast from which radial flow took place.

Queen Elizabeth Islands Glacier Complex

At present ice fields and valley glaciers are common features of the higher eastern part of the Queen Elizabeth Islands and small ice caps occur on Meighen and Melville Islands. Not all are remnants of the former more extensive ice complex; some have developed in recent times. Relatively fresh glacial features are generally lacking, possibly due to the inactive character of the cold arctic glaciers as compared to temperate-climate glaciers, but mainly to the character of the bedrock and to intense solifluction processes (Fyles and Craig, 1965). At its maximum development the glacier complex probably occupied the entire archipelago except for the coastal part of southern Melville Island which was covered by the Laurentide Ice Sheet. Active ice flow in the western part of the archipelago was largely restricted to the channels between the islands. Present data on ice-flow directions and on marine overlap suggest that the ice was thicker over the eastern and southern parts of the archipelago and that recession was towards these regions; perhaps the glacier complex preferentially developed adjacent to the Greenland and Laurentide Ice Sheets. Final recession and wastage may have taken place on the individual islands. Blake (1964) considers that some parts of Bathurst Island were deglaciated by 10,000 years B.P. and that extensive areas were ice free by 9,000 years B.P.

Prince Patrick Island. Glacial striations and other features at the head end of Mould Bay were formed by ice moving southward from the interior of the island (Tozer and Thorsteinsson, 1964). These features are attributed to the action of a small local ice cap, presumably of Wisconsin age, that developed subsequent to the establishment of the main drainage system. Mould Bay and the adjacent inlets were deepened and scoured. J. G. Fyles has noted boulders at the southwestern end of the island that were transported from the east and probably indicate a westward channelling of ice flow from Prince Patrick and Melville Islands. He also has noted that marine overlap is greater on the eastern side of the island, suggestive of thicker ice eastward.

Melville Island. Tozer and Thorsteinsson (1964) have concluded that the many fiord-like inlets in western Melville Island were probably originally stream-cut valleys that have been scoured by ice from a local ice cap. They also noted many glaciated valleys in interior western Melville Island. J. G. Fyles found erratics on both northern arms of the island that were far north of their outcrop area and presumably were deposited during the last regional glaciation. The present glaciers on western Melville Island are not remnants of the Wisconsin ice cap, for they occur in areas with youthful, little modified, postglacial ravines. The ice caps are probably less than 200 feet thick.

The maximum marine overlap is on the eastern side of the island, the highest raised shore features lying at 235 feet elevation (Henoch, 1964). Shells from the highest deposits were dated at 9,075 ± 275 years (I-730) and more from 175 feet of elevation were dated at 8,275 ± 320 years (I-GSC-21). The marine limit appears to decrease westward as no evidence of marine overlap was noted in western Melville Island. Henoch suggests that the depression of the east coast was produced by an ice cap centred near Sabine Peninsula, whereas depression of the south coast was caused by Laurentide ice.

Bathurst Island. The Queen Elizabeth Islands Glacier Complex occupied the whole of Bathurst Island and apparently restricted the northward expansion of Laurentide ice. Blake (1964, 1965) found abundant meltwater channels, patches of drift with ice-flow features, some dead-ice topography, rare striations, wave-modified esker and end moraine remnants, and other data indicative of former glacier cover. The ice may have been thicker over the northern end of the island than the southern as marine limit is about 450 feet in the north, only about 350 feet in the western and southwestern parts, and is rarely more than 300 feet along the east-central and southeast coasts. Recession appears to have been towards a remnant glacier in the interior of the island. Ice flowed northward off the island and may have reached Lougheed Island for

Fyles (1965) has noted erratics of rock types found on Bathurst Island. Marine overlap on Lougheed Island reaches an altitude of 300 feet. Shells from 25 to 100 feet above sea level were dated at 8,200 ± 180 years (I-GSC-24).

Cornwallis Island. According to Thorsteinsson (1958) the island was glaciated at least once. Striae at Resolute Bay on the south coast and Read Bay on the east coast indicated ice flow from an island ice cap. U-shaped valleys and other evidence of glacial scour in eastern coastal areas also indicated ice flow from the island. A series of rock basin lakes associated with *roches moutonnées* some 12 miles inland from Read Bay indicates northward ice flow. As glacial erratics of both igneous and metamorphic rocks occur in many places at elevations above the marine limit it is probable that Laurentide ice reached the island prior to the ice-cap stage but the age of this event is not known. Thorsteinsson places the postglacial marine limit at 425 feet elevation and notes that the well-defined beaches occur below 275 feet.

Devon Island. Ice caps on the highlands and plateaux of Devon Island cover about a quarter of its surface. Though the main ice cap has a maximum altitude of about 6,100 feet it is presumed to have a thickness of only 1,000 to 2,000 feet. It is passive except for a few distributaries in the eastern highland which flow in deep channels. Elsewhere the role of the ice caps appears to have been that of a protective cover and the smaller ice caps are known to be frozen at their base. Meltwater is carried by supraglacial streams. The physiography of the present unglaciated parts led Roots (1963) to conclude that the former, larger ice cap was also largely protective rather than an agent of erosion. He noted, however, that Griffin Inlet on the west coast was glacially sculptured by west-flowing ice and that north of there the ice margin was locally active, accounting for a series of lakes. Lakes in the west-central part of the island were also formed by west-flowing ice from the larger ice cap as it diverged southward to Maxwell Bay and north to the north shore of the island. Near the northwestern edge of the large ice cap a succession of stream channels and numerous ice-marginal meltwater channels indicate former melting but the ice near the present edge does not display these features. In the northwestern part of the island a more extensive ice cap than the present one was responsible for some 'hummocky' moraine south of Norwegian Bay and along the west coast south of Grinnell Peninsula, but the peninsula itself, like many of the islands, shows no evidence of having been glaciated. Glacial striae and crystalline erratics on Beechey Island, at the southwestern end of Devon Island, are believed due to northwestward ice flow. A granitic erratic found west of Jones Sound was also attributed to westward-flowing ice.

Brock, Borden, and Mackenzie King Islands. On Brock Island, Fyles (1965) observed an arcuate belt of ridges that he regarded as a thrust moraine formed by a glacier flowing westward through Wilkins Strait. No other glacial landforms were recognized on Brock or Borden Islands although a few erratics are present. The marine limit on Mackenzie King Island lies between 50 and 100 feet elevation and on Brock Island at about 50 feet elevation. It is unknown on Borden Island, but a beach crest at the west end is 10 feet above sea level.

Ellef Ringnes Island. Evidence of glaciation on Ellef Ringnes Island is rare, in large part due to solifluction and also to the nature of the bedrock. Crystalline erratics occur northwest or west of their outcrop and well above all evidence of marine overlap. Two gravel ridges trending west and one trending southwest are interpreted as eskers (St. Onge, 1965; Fyles, 1965). The marine limit is 150, 110, and 75 feet on the east-central, south, and west-central coasts of the island respectively. There is no information on the Pleistocene of Amund Ringnes Island.

Meighen Island. Fyles and Craig (1965) report the occurrence of numerous, large striated boulders on Meighen Island and the occurrence of striae, ascribed to westward-moving ice, on nearby Fay Islands. They believe that late Pleistocene glacial ice emanating from Axel Heiberg Island extended westward to cover these islands. The present ice cap has a summit elevation of just over 900 feet and a maximum thickness of about 400 feet (K. Arnold, 1965). Arnold has determined over the past ten years about 15 feet of thinning at the summit of the ice cap and at the northern edge, but notes that a slight deterioration of climate could cause an increase in the ice cap. He observed postglacial marine features to about 50 feet above sea level but places the marine limit at about 80 feet.

Axel Heiberg Island. On west-central Axel Heiberg Island meltwater appears to have been greater in early postglacial times than during the present arid climate (Müller, 1963). Because of the frozen ground and lack of vegetation, when run-off occurs now it is rapid, eroding channels and depositing valley alluvium and fans. The short valleys that occur between the glaciers and the sea are U-shaped only near the ice front and become V-shaped with valley trains and small fans in their lower ends (Rudberg, 1963). Some partly dissected trough-shaped valleys also occur in parts of southern Axel Heiberg not now occupied by glaciers. Abundant striae in the west-central part of the island indicate two periods of ice movement, the first from the north and east and the second from the southeast and east-southeast. Rudberg did not find undisputed evidence of far-travelled erratics in this area but red granite, presumably from Ellesmere Island, occurs on Schei Peninsula on the northeastern side of Axel Heiberg. There also, inland ice-flow features indicative of late ice movements trend northward. South of Schei Peninsula, J. G. Fyles observed red granite erratics that had been transported northwestward, roughly parallel to Eureka Sound; such movements represent former major trunk glaciers seeking escape from between Ellesmere and Axel Heiberg Islands. Elsewhere striae appear to record local, late, ice flow down small valleys and fiords as the glaciers receded inland towards the higher areas.

Two main stages of glaciation, the younger definitely Wisconsin (Boesch, 1963) and the older unknown, are recognized in west-central Axel Heiberg. As the Wisconsin glacier waned and receded onto the island the sea encroached on the uncovered ground, reaching altitudes now some 250 feet above sea level. Shells from the highest features have been dated at 9,000 ± 200 years (L-647F). Isostatic rebound was fairly rapid as the basal layer of a peat deposit lying at 80 feet elevation was dated at 4,210 ± 100 years (Bern). The Thompson glacier has not advanced more than 2 kilometres in the last 4,000 years according to Müller, and also the climate of the last 9,000 years never favoured a glacial advance of more than a few hundred feet beyond present positions. It is currently forming a push moraine of huge blocks of stratified material up to 60 feet thick. Organic matter in the lower part of some blocks has been dated at 6,200 ± 100 years (L-647A) and a piece of driftwood from a high part of the push moraine was dated at 5,325 ± 270 years (Gx-0144). This seems to indicate that formation of the push-moraine commenced after the hypsithermal period and that 5,300 years ago the sea occupied the area now covered by the snout of Thompson glacier. This implies that sea level was at least 50 feet higher than at present. Marine shells from a terrace 120 feet above sea level have been dated at 5,330 ± 195 years (Gx-0143).

Ellesmere Island. Ellesmere Island is by far the largest of the Queen Elizabeth Islands and supports the largest ice caps in Canada. In its mountains and plateaux the former ice cover probably formed a complex of coalescent valley glaciers and mountain ice caps, which conformed in a general way to the topography and were similar to the major glacier complexes on the island today (Fyles and Craig, 1965). In some places the distribution of erratics indicates a former ice cover that was thick enough to maintain a regional flow across the grain of the topography. Christie (1967) reports that boulders of granite and gneiss, probably from Greenland occur over a 10-to-25-mile-wide coastal belt of Hazen Plateau. The maximum westward extent of the Greenland ice is not known, as late Ellesmere ice has since advanced southeast and east across Hazen Plateau to the coast. At the glacial maximum the whole of northern Ellesmere Island was under ice cover and shelf ice probably extended well beyond the present north shore (Hattersley-Smith, 1961). The coastal ice caps on northern Ellesmere Island west of the northernmost tip, and disposition and shape of stream valleys and fiords which indicate former trunk glacier flow in western and northern parts, may be a result of westerly and northwesterly snow-bearing winds and high altitude. Taylor (1956) and Smith (1961) however, have suggested that the fewer fiords on Hazen Plateau may be partly a result of confluence of Greenland and Ellesmere ice.

The valleys of northern Ellesmere are regarded as normal preglacial valleys that have been straightened and deepened by strong glacier flow. Disraeli Fiord has a water depth in excess of 965 feet, and seismic data indicate a submarine canyon, trending northwest from the fiord mouth, about 2,800 feet deep (Crary, 1956). Despite this great depth the glacier in Disraeli Fiord appears to have overridden Ward Hunt Island, giving it a *roches moutonnées* shape and emplanting gabbro erratics from Ellesmere Island to an elevation of 1,100 feet (Hattersley-Smith, 1961). The present streams are deep and mostly V-shaped, but near their head, at the glacier margin, they are U-shaped, and tributary valleys are hanging relative to the trunk valleys.

As the ice receded from the north coast the sea inundated the land to a maximum altitude of 400 feet, as on Ward Hunt Island, but the marine limit varies greatly from place to place presumably due to the presence of late ice. Marine shells from 125 feet above sea level have been dated at 7,200 years. Cyclically-bedded silt, sand, and organic materials, the last as much as 4 inches thick, occur at elevations up to 70 feet at the head of Clements–Markham Inlet. These have been interpreted as deposits formed during the climatic optimum but J. G. Fyles reports that they also occur at various altitudes in many valleys and may have a considerable age range.

The character of the northern valleys has led all workers to conclude that the present ice cap is little changed since the climatic optimum. At present there are again extensive areas of shelf ice up to 50 feet thick and 12 miles wide, and also land ice near the coast. Hattersley-Smith (1961) considers these to be expressions of the colder climate following the climatic optimum (about 5,000 B.P.) whereas the interior ice fields are largely remnants (maximum of 2,700 feet thick) of the main Wisconsin glacier complex. He has recorded the advance of valley glaciers over raised beaches and into V-shaped valleys, and the growth of low ice caps on areas of raised beaches. He concludes that the climate has ameliorated in the past few decades and, although the main, high-level ice caps and outlet glaciers in northern Ellesmere Island show little or no change in areal extent from year to year, thinning is taking place in the lower reaches of the outlet glaciers and both thinning and recession of the small low-level ice masses have occurred. On the north coast of the island the surface wastage and occasional calving by the ice shelf reflects the warmer trend of recent decades.

In the Lake Hazen and Hazen Plateau regions Ellesmere ice sheet receded towards the United States Range (Christie, 1967). Directional ice-flow features and distribution of erratics indicate east and southeast ice flow across the plateau. Even though ice-flow features are present, the stream valleys show little other evidence of major trunk glaciers; truncated spurs, hanging valleys, and over-deepening are rare. A piedmont glacier must have formed on the plateau by coalescence of glaciers stemming from the United States Range. Lake Hazen basin was excavated along one contact of a wedge-shaped body of weak rocks overlying stronger rocks, and the lake is at least 864 feet deep.

In the western part of northern Ellesmere Island fiord-like valleys, glacial striae, and the distribution of erratics also show outward movement of trunk glaciers. Erratics at high elevations indicate regional flow across a region of ridges and valleys with a relief of more than 3,000 feet (Fyles and Craig, 1965). They report that during deglaciation the complex of glaciers and ice caps in western and central Ellesmere Island retreated progressively away from the outer coasts, up fiords and valleys, and into various high plateau and mountain areas. They also note that end moraines are not abundant and occur mostly in valleys within a few miles of an existing ice cap or glacier. The inferred period of shrinkage, on the basis of a few radiocarbon dates, is thought to be late Classical Wisconsin. An end moraine in central Ellesmere Island about 3 miles from the western margin of the ice cap was built more than 6,400 years ago, and another less than a mile from a modern glacier, more than 4,200 years ago; this indicates that the rate of recession over the past 6,000 years has been rather slow. Müller (1963) reports shells from an altitude of 350 feet at Eureka that dated 9,550 ± 250 years (L-647b).

Cordilleran Glacier Complex

The Cordilleran Glacier Complex is the system of intermontane, piedmont, and valley glaciers that developed in the Cordilleran physiographic province. Growth of the glacier complex stemmed from the passage of moisture-laden Pacific air masses over the various mountain systems.

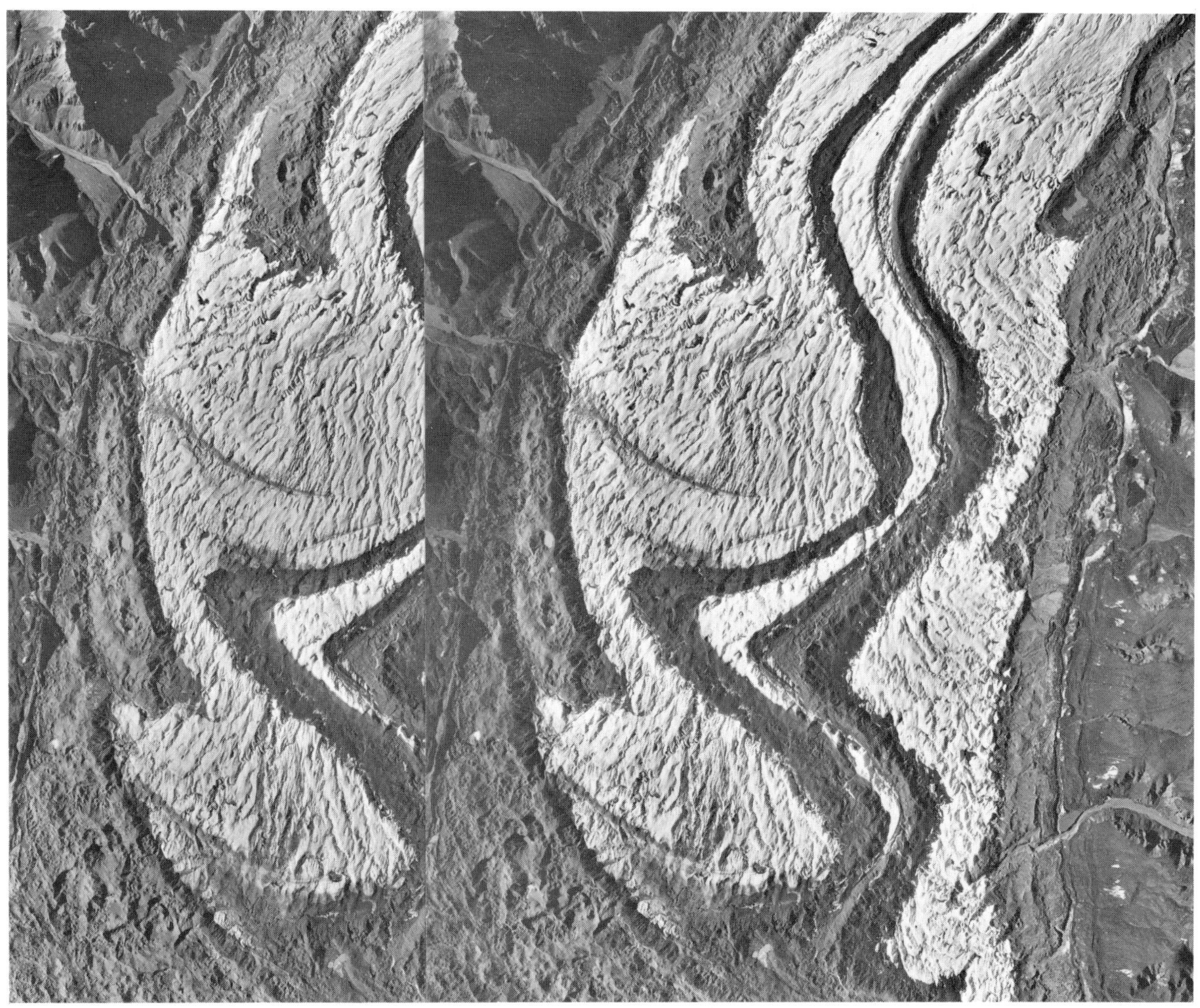

PLATE XII-17. Klutlan Glacier, St. Elias Mountains, Yukon Territory. Note the marginal and medial moraines, drift-mantled terminal zone with small ponds, meandering meltwater channels on glacier surface, and termini of valley-side streams at glacier margin. Glacier flows east and north at head-end Generc River valley. Vertical airphoto; 1 inch to 5,200 feet; stereoscopic pair.

It is probable that extensive alpine glaciation preceded development of the major ice fields. Snowfall was, without doubt, heavier on the Coast Mountains than on mountains in their lee and it was also heavier on the western sides of all mountain ranges than on their respective eastern flanks. As glacial conditions continued, however, glaciers formed on the eastern flanks and later contributed to in-filling of interior valleys, plains, and plateaux.

Glaciation

Coast and St. Elias Mountains. The westward-moving glaciers of the Coast and St. Elias Mountains were largely dissipated in the Pacific Ocean. Farther south a glacier probably occupied much of Hecate Strait and extended to Queen Charlotte Islands. A major glacier from the southern part of the Coast Mountains occupied the Strait of Georgia, probably nourished in part by glaciers from the high central part of Vancouver Island. It moved southwestward across the southern part of the island where it scoured mountains to at least 5,100 feet (Fyles, 1963b), and southward to beyond Seattle, Washington (Armstrong, *et al.*, 1965). In Fraser Valley the last major glacial period is termed the Fraser Glaciation (Armstrong, *et al.*, 1965) and it probably represents the same geologic-climatic episode as the Classical Wisconsin Glaciation of the mid-continent region. The build-up and advance include a period of alpine glaciation, the Evans Creek Stade and an ice sheet glaciation, the Vashon Stade, when ice occupied the lowlands of southwestern British Columbia and adjoining parts of Washington. On Vancouver Island all the deposits relatable to the last regional glaciation are referred to as Vashon drift (Fyles, 1963b). The last regional ice sheet is believed to have entered the northern end of Strait of Georgia after 25,000 years B.P. but it did not reach southern Vancouver Island until after 19,000 years B.P.

Central interior. Except for those along the Pacific Coast, the glaciers from all parts of the mountain systems flowed into the intermontane areas and sought escape along the river valleys. Because of topographic confinement, the interior glaciers thickened until they covered all but the highest peaks of the Interior Plateau, a belt of relatively less precipitation. In central British Columbia the ice attained a thickness in excess of 6,000 feet according to H. W. Tipper, and may have thickened until its surface became a major area of accretion standing somewhat higher than the confining mountains. Ice flow was mainly eastward from the Coast Mountains across Nechako Plain to where it was deflected north and south along Rocky Mountain Trench. Ice flow at the Wisconsin maximum paralleled the trend of southern Cassiar Mountains, but locally the ice flowed across the ranges towards Liard Plain.

Southern interior. The first ice to enter Okanagan Valley probably stemmed from gathering grounds in Monashee Mountains to the north and east (Nasmith, 1962). The southern tributary valleys show little evidence of glaciation; apparently there was little tributary ice from the adjacent plateaux and highlands. The valley glacier was then joined by the major ice sheet from Coast and Cascade Mountains which spread south and southeast over Columbia Plateau and reached a terminus some 90 miles south of the International Boundary. At the boundary the ice sheet reached an altitude of 7,200 feet, and it was accordingly some 6,300 feet thick over Okanagan Valley. Meltwater flowed south down Columbia River to the Pacific. A great thickness of lake sediments resting on outwash has been drilled in Okanagan Valley and in one place the valley bottom lies below sea level. The valleys, therefore, probably attained their present form prior to the last glaciation.

Eastern region. The glaciers in the eastern part of southern Rocky Mountains were formed by local precipitation and were not in contact with the ice sheet west of the continental divide. However, north of Athabasca Valley eastward movement of ice across the divide did occur and some glaciers from the upper part of the Fraser River system flowed into Athabasca River valley. The southern limit of strong ice flow across the Rocky Mountains lies about 100 miles south of Peace River.

Piedmont glaciers undoubtedly were present locally south of Athabasca Valley, but most ice was contained in the valley glaciers that flowed eastward through the Foothills onto the Plains to where the ice either dissipated or merged with Keewatin ice. The time relations between the two glacier systems have not been established everywhere. South of Crowsnest Pass the valley glaciers only reached the Foothills and had receded into the mountain valleys before the Keewatin ice had spread that far west. Keewatin drift extends some miles up the vacated valleys overlapping the Cordilleran drift (Stalker, 1960, pp. 72-73). Farther north, the Cordilleran glaciers and Keewatin ice did not merge during the Wisconsin but were separated by Porcupine Hills, a narrow, elongate belt of relatively high hills (Douglas, 1950). In the Foothills west of Calgary, Cordilleran glaciers had also attained their maximum development and receded before Keewatin ice reached the area and overlapped some 5 to 20 miles onto the recently vacated ground. Farther north Cordilleran ice in Athabasca Valley merged with Keewatin ice and was deflected southward east of the Foothills as earlier mentioned.

In Peace River valley the Cordilleran ice also appears to have reached a limit some distance east of the later western limit of Keewatin ice. There, however, a re-advance of Cordilleran ice is recognized; a relatively late Cordilleran glacier from Rocky Mountains, reached to within 15 miles of Fort St. John after Keewatin ice had begun to recede (Mathews, 1963). North of Peace River the relationships of the Cordilleran and Keewatin glaciers are little known.

In the Liard Plateau and the adjacent plains Cordilleran and Keewatin ice made contact in only a few places. The Cordilleran glaciers were not very extensive in the Mackenzie Mountains nor along the eastern side of Selwyn Mountains as this was apparently a region of low precipitation. Glaciers from the eastern Selwyn Mountains and to a lesser extent from the western side of Mackenzie Mountains partly filled the intermontane area. Only elongate valley glaciers flowed eastward and northward towards the unglaciated or older glaciated terrain. Valley glaciers that developed on the dry, eastern side of Mackenzie Mountains were short and seldom reached low altitudes. In places they extended somewhat beyond the western limit of Keewatin ice.

Northern interior. The limit of the Wisconsin Cordilleran ice in western Yukon is shown on Map 1253A. The limit probably corresponds with the McConnell Moraine and glacial advance of Bostock (1966) in central Yukon Territory. This limit is marked by fresh ice-marginal landforms, particularly in Stewart River valley a few miles below Mayo. Glaciers moved northward from areas of heavy snowfall in the St. Elias, Coast, and Cassiar Mountains, westward from the Selwyn and Pelly Mountains towards the dry Yukon Plateau, reaching somewhat short of the limit reached by pre-Wisconsin ice sheets. Near the ice margin innumerable monadnocks protruded above the glacier surface. The Ogilvie Mountains, which separate the Yukon and Porcupine Plateaux, also nourished glaciers; these moved outward from several of the higher areas within the mountain complex but did not reach the plateaux. Meltwaters on the northern side of Ogilvie Mountains flowed northeastward via upper Peel River until they encountered Keewatin ice in the lower part of the river basin; then, joined by meltwater streams from the Keewatin ice, escaped northward along Eagle River to Porcupine River, Yukon River, and finally Bering Sea. As deglaciation proceeded and Keewatin ice vacated lower Peel River valley, meltwater from Ogilvie, Selwyn, and Mackenzie Mountains joined that from the Keewatin ice and followed Peel River to Mackenzie Delta and Beaufort Sea.

Deglaciation

West coast. The last regional glaciation (Vashon) on southern Vancouver Island is represented by a till and associated deposits (Fyles, 1963b). Both are generally sandy, especially in the lowlands where southwest-moving ice from Strait of Georgia overrode the sand deposits of the Quadra non-glacial interval. As the ice thinned, southwest flow was maintained for a time through mountain passes and valleys and received additions from glaciers stemming from high parts of the island. As recession continued island-derived ice became dominant. According to J. G. Fyles, ice retreat from Strait of Georgia was probably underway by 14,000 years B.P., and by 12,800 years B.P. the western side of the strait was open so that much of southern Vancouver Island was ice free. Along the mainland coast, thinning and marginal recession was prolonged by active accumulation in the high parts of Coast and Cascade Mountains. The last major ice lobe in Fraser Lowland was in contact with the sea until after 11,000 years B.P., when a major re-advance into the sea—the Sumas Stade—deposited a widespread layer of stony and locally shell-bearing marine clay varying from a few feet to over 500 feet thick. Deposition was probably from icebergs except near the ice margin where shelf ice was present (Armstrong, *et al.*, 1965). North along the Pacific Coast the ice progressively lingered longer in contact with the sea, probably to about 10,000 years B.P. Along the Alaskan coast the glaciers had receded to or near their present positions by 8,000 to 7,500 years B.P.

Southern and central interior. Deglaciation of the southern part of Cordilleran Glacier Complex was accomplished largely by downmelting and stagnation of the ice mass as a whole, with no clearly defined halts or re-advances (Nasmith, 1962). Lowering of the ice surface ultimately left the plateaux and highland areas bare, and when the remaining ice was confined to the valleys its surface area was greatly reduced. It seems likely therefore that withdrawal of the ice proceeded much more rapidly in the early stages of melting than in the later stages because the sharp reduction of the surface area may have been sufficient to bring ablation into equilibrium with ice accumulation. In Okanagan Valley lateral meltwater channels were cut at altitudes of 3,700 and 2,800 feet near the International Boundary. Later melting may have produced a nearly flat ice surface with meltwater flowing on top of the ice. The valley glacier was still thick enough to flow, however, and a northward ice-frontal retreat was maintained. Farther north up the valley the Okanagan ice lobe was more active and lateral meltwater channels were cut. A minor climatic change resulted in development of a few morainal ridges. Several glacial lakes formed in Okanagan Valley region. Glacial Lake Penticton was the largest lake and had the longest history. A beach of this lake is tilted upward to the north at a rate of 3.5 feet per mile. Volcanic ash in talus, alluvium, lake beds, and peat deposits covers a broad region and is correlated by Nasmith with the Glacier Peak eruption about 6,700 years B.P.

The last glaciation northwest of the Okanagan Valley is represented by a single till (Fulton, 1965). In many places, this rests on proglacial sediments that pass down into non-glacial sediments about 20,000 years old, suggesting correlation with the Fraser Glaciation of the Coast Mountains and Vashon Glaciation of Vancouver Island. According to Fulton, regional downwasting of the ice sheet followed, without oscillatory marginal fluctuations. This was the result of confinement of the ice to intermontane positions. In general, the southern margin first retreated northward and later west of north. As the ice sheet thinned it broke up into a number of stagnant or semi-stagnant lobes occupying the major valleys and lowlands. During the early phases of retreat meltwater was ponded in the lowlands and discharge was to the south. Upon further recession the meltwater flowed eastward into the Okanagan River system and thence via Columbia River to the Pacific Ocean. This route was used during deglaciation of most of the southern part of the Interior Plateau. Finally, however, recession of the ice sheet into Coast and Cascade Mountains opened the Fraser Valley and discharge took this more direct route to the Pacific (Mathews, 1944; Fulton, 1965).

Elsewhere in southern British Columbia less is known of the general pattern of deglaciation. The Cordilleran glaciers retreated to a number of mountain ranges where snowfall was heavy, maintaining for a time active glaciers in the major valleys well beyond their area of nourishment. As recession progressed, the valley glaciers retreated to within the confines of the surrounding mountainous belt and finally left the valleys entirely.

Relatively late ice is thought to have remained in northeastern Columbia Mountains, plugging the Rocky Mountain Trench in the vicinity of Big Bend, and in adjacent parts of Rocky Mountains. These mountains have glaciers at present, but whether they are remnants of the former sheet or were newly formed is unknown. A region of late ice is also postulated for a large part of southern Coast Mountains. H. W. Tipper (GSC) believes that as recession progressed the eastern flow from Coast Mountains lost contact with westward flow from Columbia Mountains. The latter, then directed largely by topography, turned north-northwest and south-southeast. The south-southwest trending ice divide between longitude 120 and 121 degrees (*see* Map 1253A) marks this line of separation. Most of the flow from Coast Mountains was northeast towards the Interior Plateau and upper Fraser Valley. Nechako Plain was covered by a broad, east to northeast flowing ice sheet from central Coast Mountains (Armstrong and Tipper, 1948). This part of the mountains at present has fewer glaciers than parts farther north and south. Glacial lakes were ponded in the valleys of Fraser, Nechako, and Stuart Rivers by active glaciers in the lower part of Fraser Valley; discharge was north along Parsnip River in Rocky Mountain Trench and down Peace River into lakes dammed by Keewatin ice in Alberta. It is thus possible that meltwater from glaciers originating in the Coast Mountains may at one time have flowed eastward via Peace River to the Interior Plains and thence via the Great Lakes system into the Atlantic Ocean.

Northern interior. Centres of late glacial activity persisted in the northern parts of Coast Mountains, and in the Cassiar and Skeena Mountains. In the Cassiar Mountains, reversals of ice-flow direction occurred during deglaciation, evident from the distribution of erratics and from ice-flow trends and ice-marginal meltwater channels (Watson and Mathews, 1944). Glaciers from the western side of Cassiar Mountains reached to the Pacific, but the relationships of these ice movements with those of ice in the Coast Mountains astride the outlet valleys have been little studied. During glacier recession, the Cassiar Mountains had an ice cap above 7,000 feet elevation from which glaciers flowed southwest and northeast. In the southern part, ice from the higher Coast and Skeena Mountains to the west passed through the Cassiar Mountains, along Dease River valley, flowing in a northeasterly direction and reaching to about 7,000 feet elevation. Alpine glaciation both preceded and followed the last major glaciation (Gabrielse, 1963).

In parts of the southwestern Yukon the last major glaciation, the Kluane (Denton and Stuiver, 1967), probably correlates with the McConnell advance in central Yukon Territory. Radiocarbon dates on organic materials from beneath Kluane drift indicate that the glaciation began about 30,000 years B.P. and persisted to at least 12,500 years and perhaps to less than 10,000 years ago. The Kluane glaciers, stemming from ice fields at altitudes of 12,000 to 15,000 feet on the eastern flank of St. Elias Mountains, moved northeastward through Kluane Ranges. It then flowed northwestward along Kluane River valley to Donjek and White Rivers, and northward to beyond Snag (Bostock, 1952; Krinsley, 1965). In the valley southeast of Kluane Lake the elevation of the surface of the glacier was 6,100 feet, near Donjek River it was about 5,000 feet and at its northern limit about 2,500 feet. The Kluane glaciers deposited three distinct tills which are associated with outwash and lake deposits. The glacier that deposited the uppermost till sheet in Kluane Valley had a minimum elevation of 2,500 to 3,200 feet. The glacier retreated along the paths of its earlier advance without any significant pauses or halts although large masses of ice stagnated in Kluane Lake area. Loess, derived from Kluane outwash, was deposited as a thin blanket over all older deposits up to an altitude of 4,500 feet. The Kluane Glaciation was followed by a period of soil formation (Denton, 1967). The soil was developed prior to the neoglaciation of St. Elias Mountains, about 2,800 to 2,600 years ago, which Denton correlates with the Little Ice Age. Following a relatively warm interval the glaciers were again active from about 600 years ago to the present century but are currently undergoing a fluctuating recession. The Donjek and Kaskawulsh Glaciers attained their neoglacial maxima about 300 years ago.

ECONOMIC CONSIDERATIONS

The surficial deposits or overburden that mantle the bedrock in most parts of Canada are mainly the result of glaciation. The direct glacier deposits or till, together with varied mixtures of ill-sorted or well-sorted materials, comprise the moraine that characterizes much of Canada's surface. Some large areas of gently rolling ground moraine in southern Canada have proved suitable for agricultural purposes but, in general, the irregular surface and variably stony materials limit or hinder large-scale farm operations. The more hilly areas of ground moraine, along with disintegration, interlobate, end, and kame moraines, therefore serve as ranchlands or forest sites, and are important also for water storage. Some of these morainal tracts with their myriad lakes provide game preserves, park lands, and recreational areas important to our tourist industry. Areas of glaciofluvial deposits are similarly important, particularly in regard to water supply.

Vast regions in southern Canada were formerly covered by glacial lakes and the resulting flat areas of fine-grained soils comprise the farm lands that supply most of the grains and vegetables essential to support the ever-expanding urban and industrial areas. In many parts of Canada glaciation was instrumental in providing better soils than we might otherwise have had, for glacial processes determined the mixing and size-sorting of materials that characterize some of our best farm lands. Elsewhere the glaciers probably removed excellent soils and transported them beyond our borders, leaving only bouldery or rocky terrain in their place.

Similarly, glaciation has played a vital role in our mineral and mining development. In parts of the Canadian Shield, Cordilleran, and Appalachian Regions the glaciers have stripped-off the weathered mantle of many orebodies, removing and dispersing the valuable secondary ones. Glaciation thus exposed the primary mineral deposits that foreshadowed the age of the prospector in Canada with consequent development of our mining industry. Elsewhere, orebodies perhaps once exposed by glacier action have been buried by younger glacial deposits and remain to be found by drilling and geophysical surveys. Others may be found through study of the surficial geology. Boulder tracing along the line of the last ice movements, as deduced from striae and other ice-flow features, is a simple technique that has been practised and proven successful on many occasions. More refined systems such as the glacio-focus method of localizing the source areas of minor constituents in drift (Lee, 1964, 1968) should prove successful also in the search for orebodies. A comprehensive knowledge of glacial events and glacier transportation will be even more necessary in future years as Pleistocene deposits are thoroughly examined for clues as to the loci of valuable minerals.

Glaciation has played a key role in the development of our towns, cities, and industrial areas. These are generally located in drift-covered parts of plains and lowlands, or in valleys in mountainous or rolling areas, rather than on adjacent more rocky and irregular-surfaced terrain. Because of the relative ease of excavating in unconsolidated materials as compared to bedrock there is still a tendency, despite modern heavy equipment, for urban expansion to avoid the areas of rock outcrop. This practice is engulfing the better arable lands at an alarming rate. Though some of our cities are in areas of little or no drift, most include areas of heavy drift. In some cases the bedrock is deeply buried and only the largest buildings are founded on bedrock, all others being anchored in the drift mantle. Where possible, spread-footings are located on till or gravel layers, and experience has shown that great care must be exercised to evaluate the physical properties of the drift mantle. The character and thickness of the drift mantle also have a direct bearing on the costs of water and sewer installations, and the construction of roads and sidewalks. Drift mantle may yet prove to be the deciding factor with regard to the type of rapid transit systems to be planned for many urban areas.

Sand and gravel are in great demand in all urban areas, and as a result supplies are being rapidly depleted within many miles and generally some tens of miles of these centres; whereupon, due to excessive transportation costs, crushed rock is used as a substitute. Most supplies of sand and gravel are from glaciofluvial deposits but locally river, lake, and seashore materials are employed. Despite competition from crushed rock, the use of sand and gravel for construction purposes alone remains at a high level. The 1965 production and value of sand and gravel used in road construction, railway ballast and in concrete, asphalt, and mortar mixes is given in Table XII-3. These materials are in large part of Pleistocene age, but some preglacial gravels are included.

A Pleistocene gravel deposit of unusual interest, which was not used for construction but rather as an iron ore, was that at the Canadian Charleston mine south of Steep Rock Lake, Ontario. There a gravelly end moraine included sufficient 'float' to be mined on a commercial basis as iron ore. Pebbles, cobbles, and boulders of high grade hematite and goethite were the main components of the gravel deposit. These were deposited from an ice lobe that had gouged them from beneath Steep Rock Lake. A high grade iron pellet concentrate was produced on the property. Although operations were confined to the summer months, and there was no production in 1961, some 642,957 tons of high grade iron concentrate was produced from about 4.5 million tons of gravel between 1959 and 1964 when operations ceased.

Clay deposits of both lacustrine and marine origin were used extensively in former years in the manufacture

TABLE XII-3 | *Production and value of sand and gravel (by F. E. Hanes, Mines Branch)*

Province	1965 short tons	1965 $
Newfoundland	4,063,734	3,684,891
Prince Edward Island	412,064	374,081
Nova Scotia	6,574,387	4,498,803
New Brunswick	4,491,514	2,594,846
Quebec	40,507,369	19,583,351
Ontario	75,082,026	55,297,474
Manitoba	9,757,104	6,767,068
Saskatchewan	8,570,008	5,615,794
Alberta	13,163,941	10,661,383
British Columbia	20,484,706	12,662,016
Totals	183,106,853	121,739,707

of brick, tile, and related products. Their use for brick and tile has been largely discontinued in areas where shale is available, and the amount still being used for this purpose is a small part of the over-all production of clay products valued at somewhat more than $31 million annually. Bricks made from Pleistocene clays are found in most brick buildings in the older parts of our cities and in the older farm houses.

Major construction projects such as water storage and power dams, superhighways, new railways, causeways, and port facilities must take surficial deposits into account, as some need to be removed and alternate materials hauled to the sites. Landslides involving these materials may occur where highways cut through hills or valley walls or where stream erosion undercuts valley sides. Clays or clay tills may be sought for impermeable blankets in water reservoirs, or permeable fill may have to be found for some earthfill dams. The glacial history of such regions should be known, for it may dictate the amount of testing necessary to evaluate the stratigraphic sequence at the construction site proper.

The effects of differential uplift need to be evaluated where major construction projects with a long-term life-span involve large bodies of water. Differential uplift between opposing ends of the storage basins of only a small fraction of an inch per year may be important, and its postglacial record is requisite. The rate of differential uplift in Hudson Bay, based on short-term tide gauge records, may be about 2 feet per century (Barnett, 1966). Such information, together with the rate of postglacial uplift, would provide a useful curve of land–sea relations important in planning major harbour facilities in the region.

Waste disposal is becoming an ever-greater problem in industrial and mining areas. Areas of relatively impermeable clay are at times sought for waste disposal pits for corrosive or noxious materials, but the mineralogy of the clay should be determined with regard to possible chemical reactions within the deposit. Waste products that are less objectionable and that will break down in a relatively short time may be pumped into some drift-covered waste lands, but great care has to be exercised to prevent contamination of the groundwater.

Surficial deposits have a direct bearing on Canada's water resources for they determine the rate of run-off and amount of water storage. They hold much water that would otherwise be lost by rapid run-off, and they grudgingly but positively discharge this to the rivers and streams. Without this constant to semi-constant supply, many of our river systems would vacillate between raging torrents and dry valleys.

Thus our heritage of glacial deposits is fundamental to the very character of this land and affects the progress of our agricultural, forestry, mining, and fishing industries, urban and industrial developments, and recreational facilities, all of which influence our daily way of life and our future plans.

SELECTED REFERENCES

Alcock, F. J.

1941: The Magdalen Islands; *Trans. Can. Inst. Mining Met.*, vol. 44, pp. 623–649.

1948: Problems of New Brunswick geology; *Trans. Roy. Soc. Can.*, vol. 42, ser. 3, sec. 4, pp. 1–16.

Andrews, J. T.

1963: The cross-valley moraines of north-central Baffin Island: A quantitative analysis; *Geograph. Bull. Can.*, No. 20, pp. 82–129.

1966: Pattern of coastal uplift and deglacierization, west Baffin Island, Northwest Territories; *Geograph. Bull. Can.*, vol. 8, No. 2, pp. 174–193.

Andrews, J. T., and Sim, V. W.

1964: Examination of the carbonate content of drift in the area of Foxe Basin, Northwest Territories; *Geograph. Bull. Can.*, No. 21, pp. 44–65.

Antevs, E.

1925: Retreat of the last ice sheet in eastern Canada; *Geol. Surv. Can.*, Mem. 146.

1931: Late glacial correlations and ice recession in Manitoba; *Geol. Surv. Can.*, Mem. 168.

Armstrong, J. E., Crandell, D. R., Easterbrook, P. J., and Noble, J. B.

1965: Late Pleistocene stratigraphy and chronology in southwestern British Columbia and northwestern Washington; *Bull. Geol. Soc. Am.*, vol. 76, No. 3, pp. 321–330.

Armstrong, J. E., and Tipper, H. W.

1948: Glaciation in north-central British Columbia; *Am. J. Sci.*, vol. 246, pp. 283–301.

Arnold, K. C.

1966: Aspects of the glaciology of Meighen Island, Northwest Territories, Canada; *J. Glaciol.*, vol. 5, No. 40, pp. 399–410.

Barnett, D. M.

1966: A re-examination and re-interpretation of tide gauge data for Churchill, Manitoba; *Can. J. Earth Sci.*, vol. 3, pp. 77–88.

Barnett, D. M., and Peterson, J. A.

1964: The significance of glacial Lake Naskaupi 2 in the deglaciation of Labrador–Ungava; *Can. Geographer*, vol. 8, No. 4, pp. 173–181.

Barry, R. G.

1960: The application of synoptic studies in Paleoclimatology: A case study for Labrador–Ungava; *Aerograph. Ann.* 42, No. 1, pp. 36–44.

Barton, R. H., Christiansen, E. A., Kupsch, W. O. Mathews, W. H., Gravenor, C. P., and Bayrock, L. A.

1965: Quaternary: *in* Geological history of western Canada; *Alta. Soc. Petrol. Geol.*

Bell, J. M.

1904: Economic resources of Moose River Basin; *Ont. Bur. Mines*, vol. 13, pt. 1, pp. 135–191.

Bell, R.

1879: Michipicoten to Moose Factory route: *in* Exploration of the east coast of Hudson Bay in 1877; *Geol. Surv. Can.,* Rept. Prog. 1877–78, pt. C.

1887: Exploration of portions of the Attawapiskat and Albany Rivers; *Geol. Surv. Can.,* Ann. Rept. 1886, pt. G.

Bird, J. B.

1953: Southampton Island; *Geograph. Branch Can.,* Mem. 1.

1954: Postglacial marine submergence in central Arctic Canada; *Bull. Geol. Soc. Am.,* vol. 65, pp. 457–464.

1959: Recent contributions to the physiography of northern Canada; *Z. Geomorphologie,* Neue folge, Band 3, Heft 2, pp. 151–174.

1963: A report on the physical environment of southern Baffin Island, Northwest Territories, Canada; *The Rand Corp.,* Mem. RM-2362-1-PR.

Blackadar, R. G.

1958: Patterns resulting from glacier movements north of Foxe Basin, Northwest Territories; *Arctic,* vol. 11, No. 3, pp. 156–165.

Blake, W., Jr.

1963: Notes on glacial geology, northeastern District of Mackenzie; *Geol. Surv. Can.,* Paper 63-28.

1964: Preliminary account of the glacial history of Bathurst Island, Arctic Archipelago; *Geol. Surv. Can.,* Paper 64-30.

1965: Surficial geology, Bathurst Island: *in* Rept. Activities, Field, 1964; *Geol. Surv. Can.,* Paper 65-1, pp. 2, 3.

1966: End moraines and deglaciation chronology in northern Canada with special reference to southern Baffin Island; *Geol. Surv. Can.,* Paper 66-26.

Boesch, H.

1963: Notes on the geomorphological history: *in* Axel Heiberg Island Res. Rept., McGill Univ., Montreal; Prelim. Rept. 1961–62, F. Müller and members of the Expedition, pp. 163–167.

Boissonneau, A. N.

1966: Glacial history of northeastern Ontario: I. The Cochrane–Hearst area; *Can. J. Earth Sci.,* vol. 3, No. 5, pp. 559–578.

1968: Glacial history of northeastern Ontario: II. The Timiskaming–Algoma area; *Can. J. Earth Sci.,* vol. 5, No. 1, pp. 97–109.

Borns, H. W., and Swift, D. J.

1966: Surficial geology, north shore of Minas Basin, Nova Scotia: *in* Guidebook, geology of parts of Atlantic Provinces; *Geol. Assoc. Can.*

Bostock, H. S.

1952: Geology of northwest Shakwak Valley, Yukon Territory; *Geol. Surv. Can.,* Mem. 267.

1966: Notes on glaciation in central Yukon Territory; *Geol. Surv. Can.,* Paper 65-36.

Brummer, J.

1958: Glaciation in the northwest quarter of Holland Twp., Gaspé, North County; *Geol. Assoc. Can.,* vol. 10, pp. 109–117.

Byers, A. R.

1960: Deformation of the Whitemud and Eastern Formations near Claybank, Saskatchewan; *Trans. Roy. Soc. Can.,* vol. 53, ser. 3, sec. 4, pp. 1–4.

Chalmers, R.

1890: Surface geology of southern New Brunswick; *Geol. Surv. Can.,* Ann. Rept. 1888–89, pt. N.

1895: Surface geology of eastern New Brunswick, northwestern Nova Scotia and a portion of Prince Edward Island; *Geol. Surv. Can.,* Ann. Rept. 1894, pt. M.

Chapman, D. H.

1937: Glacial Lake Vermont; *Am. J. Sci.,* ser. 5, vol. 34, No. 200, pp. 89–124.

Chapman, L. J.

1954: An outlet of Lake Algonquin at Fossmill, Ontario; *Proc. Geol. Assoc. Can.,* vol. 6, pt. 2, pp. 61–68.

1966: The recession of the Wisconsin Glacier: *in* Physiography of southern Ontario, rev. ed.; Univ. Toronto Press.

Christiansen, E. A.

1959: Glacial geology of the Swift Current area Saskatchewan; *Sask. Dept. Mineral Resources,* Rept. 32.

1960: Geology and ground water resources of the Qu'Appelle area Saskatchewan; *Sask. Res. Council,* Geol. Div., Rept. No. 1.

1961: Geology and ground water resources of the Regina area Saskatchewan; *Sask. Res. Council,* Geol. Div., Rept. No. 2.

1965: Geology and ground water resources, Kindersley area Saskatchewan; *Sask. Res. Council,* Geol. Div., Rept. No. 7.

1967: Preglacial valleys in southern Saskatchewan; *Sask. Res. Council,* Geol. Div., Map No. 3.

Christiansen, E. A., and Parizek, R. R.

1961: A summary of studies completed to date of the ground-water geology and hydrology of the buried Missouri and Yellowstone Valley; *Sask. Res. Council,* Circular No. 1.

Christie, R. L.

1967: Reconnaissance of the surficial geology of northeastern Ellesmere Island, Arctic Archipelago; *Geol. Surv. Can.,* Bull. 138.

Coleman, A. P.

1920: The glacial history of Prince Edward Island and the Magdalen Islands; *Trans. Roy. Soc. Can.,* ser. 3, vol. 13, pp. 33–38.

1933: The Pleistocene of the Toronto region; *Ont. Dept. Mines,* vol. 41, pt. 7, 1932.

1937: Lake Iroquois; *Ont. Dept. Mines,* vol. 45, pt. 7, 1936, pp. 1–36.

1941: The last million years; Univ. Toronto Press.

Cooper, J. R.

1937: Geology and mineral deposits of the Hare Bay area; *Nfld. Dept. Natural Resources,* Geol. Sec., Bull. No. 9.

Craig, B. G.

1957: Drumheller, Alberta, surficial geology; *Geol. Surv. Can.,* Map 13-1957.

1960: Surficial geology of north-central District of Mackenzie, Northwest Territories; *Geol. Surv. Can.,* Paper 60-18.

1961: Surficial geology of northern district of Keewatin, Northwest Territories; *Geol. Surv. Can.,* Paper 61-5.

1964a: Surficial geology of Boothia Peninsula and Somerset, King William, and Prince of Wales Islands, District of Franklin; *Geol. Surv. Can.,* Paper 63-44.

1964b: Surficial geology of east-central District of Mackenzie; *Geol. Surv. Can.,* Bull. 99.

1965a: Glacial Lake McConnell, and the surficial geology of parts of Slave River and Redstone River map-areas, District of Mackenzie; *Geol. Surv. Can.,* Bull. 122.

1965b: Surficial geology, Operation Wager; northeast District of Keewatin and Melville Peninsula, District of Franklin: *in* Rept. Activities, Field, 1964; *Geol. Surv. Can.,* Paper 65-1, pp. 17–19.

Craig, B. G., and Fyles, J. G.

1960: Pleistocene geology of Arctic Canada; *Geol. Surv. Can.,* Paper 60-10.

Craig, B. G., and McDonald, B. C.

1968: Quaternary geology, Operation Winisk, Hudson Bay Lowland: *in* Rept. Activities; *Geol. Surv. Can.,* Paper 68-1, pt. A, pp. 161–162.

Crary, A. P.

1956: Geophysical studies along northern Ellesmere Island; *Arctic,* vol. 9, No. 3, pp. 155–165.

Daly, R. A.

1902: The geology of the northwest coast of Labrador; *Bull. Museum Comp. Zool., Harvard Coll.,* vol. 38, Geol. ser., vol. 5, No. 5.

David, P. P.

1966: The Late Wisconsin Prelate Ferry paleosol of Saskatchewan; *Can. J. Earth Sci.,* vol. 3, pp. 685–696.

Deane, R. E.

1950: Pleistocene geology of the Lake Simcoe district, Ontario; *Geol. Surv. Can.,* Mem. 256.

Denton, G. H., and Stuiver, M.

1967: Late Pleistocene glacial stratigraphy and chronology, northeastern St. Elias Mountains, Yukon Territory, Canada; *Bull. Geol. Soc. Am.,* vol. 78, No. 4, pp. 485–510.

Derbyshire, E.

1962: Glacial features of the Howells River valley and watershed; *McGill Sub-Arctic Res. Paper,* No. 14.

Douglas, R. J. W.

1950: Callum Creek, Langford Creek, and Gap map-areas, Alberta; *Geol. Surv. Can.,* Mem. 255.

Dreimanis, A.

1957: Stratigraphy of Wisconsin glacial stage along northwestern shore of Lake Erie; *Science,* vol. 126, No. 3265, pp. 166–168.

1958: Wisconsin stratigraphy at Port Talbot on the north shore of Lake Erie, Ontario; *Ohio J. Sci.,* vol. 58, pp. 65–84.

Dreimanis, A., Reavely, G. H., Cook, R. J. B., Knox, K. S., and Moretti, F. J.

1957: Heavy mineral studies in tills of Ontario and adjacent areas; *J. Sediment. Petrol.,* vol. 27, No. 2, pp. 148–161.

Dreimanis, A., Terasmae, J., and McKenzie, G. D.

1966: Port Talbot Interstade of the Wisconsin Glaciation; *Can. J. Earth Sci.,* vol. 3, pp. 305–325.

Elson, J. A.

1957: Lake Agassiz and the Mankato–Valders problem; *Science,* vol. 126, No. 3281, pp. 999–1002.

1967: Geology of glacial Lake Agassiz: *in* Life, Land and Water; Proc. of 1966 Conference on Environmental Studies of the glacial Lake Agassiz region; ed. W. J. Mayer-Oakes, *Univ. Manitoba Press.*

Falconer, Geo.

1966: Preservation of vegetation and patterned ground under a thin ice body in northern Baffin Island, N.W.T.; *Geograph. Bull. Can.,* vol. 8, No. 2, pp. 194–200.

Falconer, G., Ives, J. D., Løken, O. H., and Andrews, J. T.

1965: Major end moraines in eastern and central Arctic Canada; *Geograph. Bull. Can.,* vol. 7, No. 2, pp. 137–153.

Farrand, W. R.

1961: Former shorelines in western and northern Lake Superior Basins; *Univ. Microfilms Inc.,* Ann Arbor, Michigan.

Flint, R. F.

1940: Late Quaternary changes of level in western and southern Newfoundland; *Bull. Geol. Soc. Am.,* vol. 51, pp. 1757–1780.

1951: Dating late Pleistocene events by means of radiocarbon; *Nature,* vol. 167, No. 4256.

Frankel, L.

1966: Geology of southeastern Prince Edward Island, Part 2, Surficial Geology; *Geol. Surv. Can.,* Bull. 145.

Fraser, J. K.

1957: Activities of the Geographical Branch in northern Canada; *Arctic,* vol. 10, No. 4, pp. 246–250.

Fulton, R. J.

1965: Silt deposition in late-glacial lakes of southern British Columbia; *Am. J. Sci.,* vol. 263, pp. 553–570.

1968: Olympia Interglaciation, Purcell Trench, British Columbia; *Geol. Soc. Am.,* vol. 79 (in press).

Fyles, J. G.

1955: Pleistocene features: *in* G. M. Wright, Geological notes on central District of Keewatin, Northwest Territories; *Geol. Surv. Can.,* Paper 55-17, pp. 3, 4.

1962: Physiography: Chap. II *in* Banks, Victoria, and Stefansson Islands, Arctic Archipelago; Thorsteinsson and Tozer, *Geol. Surv. Can.,* Mem. 330.

1963a: Surficial geology of Victoria and Stefansson Islands, District of Franklin; *Geol. Surv. Can.,* Bull. 101.

1963b: Surficial geology of Horne Lake and Parksville map-areas, Vancouver Island, British Columbia; *Geol. Surv. Can.,* Mem. 318.

1965: Surficial geology, western Queen Elizabeth Islands: *in* Rept. Activities, Field, 1964; *Geol. Surv. Can.,* Paper 65-1, pp. 3–5.

1966: Quaternary stratigraphy, Mackenzie Delta and Arctic Coastal Plain: *in* Rept. Activities; *Geol. Surv. Can.,* Paper 66-1, pp. 30, 31.

1967a: Mackenzie Delta and Arctic Coastal Plain: *in* Rept. Activities; *Geol. Surv. Can.,* Paper 67-1, pt. A, pp. 34, 35.

1967b: Winter Harbour moraine, Melville Island: *in* Rept. Activities; *Geol. Surv. Can.,* Paper 67-1, pt. A, pp. 8, 9.

Fyles, J. G., and Craig, B. G.

1965: Anthropogen period in Arctic and Subarctic; *U.S.S.R. Res. Inst. Geol. Arctic.*

Gabrielse, H.

1963: McDame map-area, Cassiar District, British Columbia; *Geol. Surv. Can.,* Mem. 319.

Gadd, N. R.

1960: Surficial geology of the Bécancour map-area, Quebec; *Geol. Surv. Can.,* Paper 59-8.

1963: Surficial geology of Ottawa map-area, Ontario and Quebec; *Geol. Surv. Can.,* Paper 62-16.

1964: Moraines in the Appalachian Region of Quebec; *Bull. Geol. Soc. Am.,* vol. 75, pp. 1249–1254.

1966: Surficial geology in the St. Sylvestre area: *in* Rept. Activities; *Geol. Surv. Can.,* Paper 66-1, pp. 163–166.

In press: Pleistocene geology of the Central St. Lawrence Lowlands; *Geol. Surv. Can.,* Mem. 359.

Gadd, N. R., and Karrow, P. F.

1960: Surficial geology of Trois-Rivières; *Geol. Surv. Can.,* Map 54-1959.

Goldthwait, J. W.

1915: The occurrence of glacial drift on the Magdalen Islands; *Geol. Surv. Can.,* Mus. Bull., No. 14, Geol. ser. No. 25.

1924: Physiography of Nova Scotia; *Geol. Surv. Can.,* Mem. 140.

Goldthwait, R. P.

1950: Geomorphology, *in* Baffin Island Expedition 1950: A Preliminary Report by P. D. Baird, *et al.; Arctic,* vol. 3, No. 3, pp. 139–141.

Gravenor, C. P., and Bayrock, L. A.

1956: Stream–trench systems in east-central Alberta; *Res. Council Alberta,* Prelim. Rept. 56-4.

1961: Glacial deposits of Alberta; *Roy. Soc. Can.,* Spec. Pubs., No. 3, pp. 35–50.

Grayson, J. F.

1956: The postglacial history of vegetation and climate in the Labrador Quebec region as determined by Palynology; *Univ. Microfilms Inc.,* Ann Arbor, Michigan.

Hare, F. K.

1951: The present-day snowfall of Labrador–Ungava; *Am. J. Sci.,* vol. 249, No. 9, pp. 654–670.

Harrison, D. A.

1964: A reconnaissance glacier and geomorphological survey of the Duart Lake area, Bruce Mountains, Baffin Island, North West Territories; *Geograph. Bull. Can.,* No. 22, pp. 57–71.

Hattersley-Smith, G.

1961: Geomorphological studies in north-western Ellesmere Island; Directorate of Physical Research, *Defence Res. Board, Can.,* Rept. No. Misc. G-5.

Henderson, E. P.

1959a: Surficial geology of Sturgeon Lake map-area, Alberta; *Geol. Surv. Can.,* Mem. 303.

1959b: A glacial study of central Quebec–Labrador; *Geol. Surv. Can.,* Bull. 50.

1960: Surficial geology of St. John's, Newfoundland; *Geol. Surv. Can.,* Paper 35-1959.

Henoch, W. E. S.

1964: Postglacial marine submergence and emergence of Melville Island, Northwest Territories; *Geograph. Bull. Can.,* No. 22, pp. 105–126.

Hickox, C. F.

1962: Pleistocene geology of the central Annapolis Valley, Nova Scotia; *N. S. Dept. Mines,* Mem. 5.

Hogg, N., *et al.*

1953: Drilling in James Bay Lowland: Part I; *Ont. Dept. Mines,* Ann. Rept., vol. 61, pt. 6, 1952, pp. 115–140.

Hough, J. L.

1958: Geology of the Great Lakes; Urbana, Illinois, *Univ. Illinois Press.*

1963: The prehistoric Great Lakes of North America; *Am. Scientist,* vol. 51, No. 1, pp. 84–109.

1966: Correlation of Glacial Lake Stages in the Huron–Erie and Michigan Basins; *J. Geol.,* vol. 74, No. 1, pp. 62–77.

Hughes, O. L.

1956: Surficial geology of Smooth Rock Falls, Cochrane district, Ontario; *Geol. Surv. Can.,* Paper 55-41.

1965: Surficial geology of part of the Cochrane district, Ontario, Canada; *Geol. Soc. Am.,* Spec. Papers No. 84.

Ives, J. D.

1957: Glaciation of the Torngat Mountains, northern Labrador; *Arctic,* vol. 10, No. 2, pp. 67–87.

1958a: Mountain-top detritus and the extent of the last major glaciation in northeastern Labrador–Ungava; *Can. Geographer,* No. 12, pp. 25–31.

1958b: Glacial geomorphology of the Torngat Mountains, northern Labrador; *Geograph. Bull. Can.,* No. 12, pp. 62–77.

1959: Glacial drainage channels as an indicator of late glacial conditions in Labrador–Ungava; *Cahiers Géograph. Quebec,* No. 5, pp. 57–72.

1960a: The deglaciation of Labrador–Ungava: An outline; *Cahiers Géograph. Quebec,* No. 8, pp. 323–343.

1960b: Former ice dammed lakes and the deglaciation of the middle reaches of the George River, Labrador–Ungava; *Geograph. Bull. Can.,* No. 14, pp. 44–70.

1960c: Glaciation and deglaciation of the Helluva Lake area, Central Labrador–Ungava; *Geograph. Bull. Can.,* No. 15, pp. 46–64.

1962: Indications of recent extensive glacierization in north-central Baffin Island, Northwest Territories; *J. Glaciol.,* vol. 4, No. 32, pp. 197–205.

1964: Deglaciation and land emergence in northeastern Foxe Basin; *Geograph. Bull. Can.,* No. 21, pp. 54–65.

Ives, J. D., and Andrews, G. T.

1963: Studies in the physical geography of north-central Baffin Island, Northwest Territories; *Geograph. Bull. Can.,* No. 19, pp. 5–48.

Jenness, S. E.

1960: Late Pleistocene glaciation at eastern Newfoundland; *Bull. Geol. Soc. Am.,* vol. 71, pp. 161–180.

Johnston, W. A.

1946: Glacial Lake Agassiz, with special reference to the mode of deformation of the beaches; *Geol. Surv. Can.,* Bull. 7.

Johnston, W. A., and Wickenden, R. T. D.

1930: Glacial Lake Regina, Saskatchewan, Canada; *Trans. Roy. Soc. Can.,* sec. 4, pp. 41–50.

Karrow, P. F.

1959: Surficial geology, Grondines, Quebec; *Geol. Surv. Can.,* Map 41-1959, Descr. Notes.

1964: Pleistocene geology of Toronto–Scarborough area: *in* Guidebook, Geology of Central Ontario; *Am. Assoc. Petrol. Geol.,* pp. 81–88.

1965: *In* Guidebook for Field Conference G, Great Lakes–Ohio River Valley, INQUA, 1965, pp. 106–107. *Nebraska Acad. Sci.*, Lincoln, Nebraska.

1967: Pleistocene geology of the Scarborough area; *Ont. Dept. Mines,* Geol. Rept. No. 46.

Keele, J.

1921: Mesozoic clays and sands in northern Ontario; *Geol. Surv. Can.,* Sum. Rept. 1920, Pt. D.

Klassen, R. W., Delorme, L. D., and Mott, R. J.

1967: Geology and paleontology of Pleistocene deposits in southwestern Manitoba; *Can. J. Earth Sci.,* vol. 4, No. 3, pp. 433–447.

Krinsley, D. B.

1965: Pleistocene geology of the southwest Yukon Territory, Canada; *J. Glaciol.,* vol. 5, No. 40, pp. 385–398.

Kupsch, W. O.

1962: Ice-thrust ridges in western Canada; *J. Geol.,* vol. 70, No. 5, pp. 582–594.

1964: Bedrock surface and preglacial topography of the Regina–Wynyard region, southern Saskatchewan; *Third Intern. Williston Basin symp.,* Regina, Sask.

Lee, H. A.

1955: Surficial geology of Edmundston, Madawaska, and Témiscouata counties, New Brunswick and Quebec; *Geol. Surv. Can.,* Paper 55-15.

1959: Surficial geology of southern district of Keewatin and the Keewatin Ice Divide, Northwest Territories; *Geol. Surv. Can.,* Bull. 51.

1960: Late glacial and postglacial Hudson Bay sea episode; *Science,* vol. 131, No. 3413, pp. 1609–1611.

1962: Surficial geology of Rivière-du-Loup–Trois-Pistoles area Quebec; *Geol. Surv. Can.,* Paper 61-32.

1964: Glacial fans in till from the Kirkland Lake fault—a method of exploration; *Can. Mining J.,* vol. 85, No. 4, pp. 94, 95.

1968a: Quaternary geology; *in* Science, History and Hudson Bay, pt. 1, Ch. 9, *Queen's Printer,* Ottawa.

1968b: Glaciofocus and the Munro esker of northern Ontario: *in* Rept. Activities, 1967; *Geol. Surv. Can.,* Paper 68-1, A, p. 173.

Lee, H. A., Craig, B. G., and Fyles, J. G.

1957: Keewatin ice divide; *Bull. Geol. Soc. Am.,* vol. 68, pp. 1760, 1761.

Leverett, F.

1932: Quaternary geology of Minnesota and parts of adjacent States; *U.S. Geol. Surv.,* Prof. Paper 161.

Leverett, F., and Taylor, F. B.

1915: The Pleistocene of Indiana and Michigan and the history of the Great Lakes; *U.S. Geol. Surv.,* Monograph, vol. 53.

Lewis, C. F. M.

1966: Geological and palynological studies of early Lake Erie deposits; *Univ. Michigan Gt. Lakes Res. Div.,* Publ. No. 15.

1968: Postglacial uplift studies north of Lake Huron: Rept. Activities; *Geol. Surv. Can.,* Paper 68-1, pt. A, pp. 174–176.

Løken, O. H.

1960: Field work in the Torngat Mountains, Northern Labrador; *McGill Sub-Arctic Res. Paper,* No. 9.

1962: The late glacial and postglacial emergence and the deglaciation of northernmost Labrador; *Geograph. Bull. Can.,* No. 17, pp. 23–56.

1966: Baffin Island refugia older than 54,000 years; *Science,* vol. 153, No. 3742, pp. 1378–1380.

MacClintock, P., and Stewart, D. P.

1965: Pleistocene geology of the St. Lawrence Lowland; *N.Y. State Museum Sci. Serv.,* Bull. No. 394.

MacClintock, P., and Terasmae, J.

1960: Glacial history of Covey Hill; *J. Geol.,* vol. 68, No. 2, pp. 232–241.

MacClintock, P., and Twenhofel, W. H.

1940: Wisconsin Glaciation of Newfoundland; *Bull. Geol. Soc. Am.,* vol. 51, pp. 1729–1756.

Mackay, J. R.

1958: The Anderson River map-area, Northwest Territories; *Geograph. Branch Can.,* Mem. 6.

1962: Pingoes of the Pleistocene Mackenzie River Delta area; *Geograph. Bull. Can.,* No. 18.

1963: The Mackenzie Delta area, Northwest Territories; *Geograph. Branch Can.,* Mem. 8.

MacNeill, R. H.

1953: A local glacier in the Annapolis–Cornwallis Valley; Proc. N.S. Inst., *Science,* vol. 23, pt. 1, p. 111.

Martison, N. W.

1953: Petroleum possibilities of the James Bay Lowland area; *Ont. Dept. Mines,* Ann. Rept., vol. 61, pt. 6, 1952.

Mathews, W. H.

1944: Glacial lakes and ice retreat of south–central British Columbia; *Trans. Roy. Soc. Can.,* ser. 3, vol. 38, sec. 4, pp. 39–57.

1963: Quaternary stratigraphy and geomorphology of the Fort St. John area, northeastern British Columbia; *B.C. Dept. Mines Petrol. Resources.*

Matthew, E. M.

1961: Deglaciation of the George River Basin Labrador–Ungava: *in* Geomorphological studies in northeastern Labrador–Ungava; *Geograph. Branch Can.,* Geograph. Paper, No. 29.

Matthews, B.

1962: Glacial and postglacial geomorphology of the Sugluk–Wolstenholme area, northern Ungava; *McGill Sub-Arctic Res. Paper,* No. 12, Ann. Rept. 1960–61.

McGerrigle, H. W.

1952: Pleistocene glaciation of Gaspé Peninsula; *Trans. Roy. Soc. Can.,* vol. 66, ser. 3, sec. 4, pp. 37–51.

McLearn, F. H.

1927: The Mesozoic and Pleistocene deposits of the Lower Missinaibi, Opazatika, and Mattagami Rivers, Ontario; *Geol. Surv. Can.,* Sum. Rept. 1926, pt. C, pp. 16–47.

Meneley, W. A., *et al.*

1957: Preglacial Missouri River in Saskatchewan; *J. Geol.,* vol. 65, No. 4, pp. 441–447.

Mercer, J. H.

1956: Geomorphology and glacial history of southernmost Baffin Island; *Bull. Geol. Soc. Am.,* vol. 67, pp. 553–570.

Morley, L. W., and Fortier, Y. O.
1956: Geological unity of the arctic islands; *Trans. Roy. Soc. Can.*, vol. 50, ser. 3, pp. 3–12.

Morrison, A.
1963: Landform studies in the Middle Hamilton River area, Labrador; *Arctic*, vol. 16, No. 4, pp. 273–275.

Mott, R. J., and Prest, V. K.
1967: Stratigraphy and palynology of buried organic deposits from Cape Breton Island, Nova Scotia; *Can. J. Earth Sci.*, vol. 4, pp. 709–724.

Mountjoy, E. W.
1958: Jasper area, Alberta, a source of the Foothills erratics train; *J. Alta. Soc. Petrol. Geol.*, vol. 6, No. 9, pp. 218–226.

Müller, F.
1963: Radiocarbon dates and notes on the climatic and morphological history: *in* Axel Heiberg Island research reports; *McGill Univ., Montreal,* Prelim. Rept. 1961–62, F. Müller and members of the Expedition, pp. 169–172.

Nasmith, H.
1962: Late glacial history and surficial deposits of the Okanagan Valley, British Columbia; *B.C. Dept. Mines Petrol. Resources,* Bull. 46.

O'Neill, J. J.
1924: Report of the Canadian Arctic Expedition 1913–18, vol. 11: Geology and Geography; Part A: The geology of the Arctic Coast of Canada, west of the Kent Peninsula; *Queen's Printer,* Ottawa.

Parizek, R. R.
1964: Geology of the Willow Bunch Lake area, Saskatchewan; *Sask. Res. Council,* Geol. Div., Rept. No. 4.

Parry, J. T., and MacPherson, J. C.
1964: St. Faustin–St. Narcisse moraine and the Champlain Sea; *Rev. Geograph. Montreal,* vol. 18, No. 2, pp. 235–248.

Porsild, A. E.
1938: Earth mounds in unglaciated arctic northwestern America; *Geograph. Rev.*, vol. 28, No. 1, pp. 46–58.

Prest, V. K.
1957: Pleistocene geology and surficial deposits: *in* Geology and economic minerals of Canada, *edited by* C. H. Stockwell; *Geol. Surv. Can.*, Econ. Geol. Ser., No. 1, Ch. 7.
1962: Geology of Tignish map-area, Prince county, Prince Edward Island; *Geol. Surv. Can.*, Paper 61-28.
1963: Red Lake–Lansdowne House area, northwestern Ontario; *Geol. Surv. Can.*, Paper 63-6.
1968: Nomenclature of moraine and ice-flow features as applied to the glacial map of Canada; *Geol. Surv. Can.*, Paper 67-57.

Roots, E. F.
1963: Devon Island physiography: *in* Geology of the north–central part of the Arctic Archipelago, Northwest Territories; *Geol. Surv. Can.*, Mem. 320, pp. 164–179.

Rudberg, S.
1963: Geomorphological processes in a cold semi-arid region: *in* Axel Heiberg Island research reports; *McGill Univ., Montreal,* Prelim. Rept. 1961–62, F. Müller and members of the Expedition, pp. 139–150.

St. Onge, D.
1965: La Géomorphologie de l'Ile Ellef Ringnes, Territoires du Nord-Ouest, Canada; Dir. Géog., *Étude Géograph.*, No. 38.
1966: Surficial geology, Iosegun Lake; *Geol. Surv. Can.*, Map 15-1966.

Sim, V. W.
1960: A preliminary account of late "Wisconsin" Glaciation in Melville Peninsula, Northwest Territories; *Can. Geograph.*, vol. 17, pp. 21–24.

Slater, G.
1927: Structure of the Mud Buttes and Tit Hills in Alberta; *Bull. Geol. Soc. Am.*, vol. 38, pp. 721–730.

Smith, D. I.
1961: The glaciation of northern Ellesmere Island: *in* Physical geography of Greenland; 19 *Inter. Geog. Congress, Norden,* 1960, Symposium SD 2, pp. 224–234.

Sproule, J. C.
1939: The Pleistocene geology of the Cree Lake region, Saskatchewan; *Trans. Roy. Soc. Can.*, ser. 3, sec. 4, vol. 33, pp. 107–109.

Stalker, A. MacS.
1956: The erratics train, Foothills of Alberta; *Geol. Surv. Can.*, Bull. 37.
1960: Surficial geology of the Red Deer – Stettler map-area; *Geol. Surv. Can.*, Mem. 306.
1961: Buried valleys in central and southern Alberta; *Geol. Surv. Can.*, Paper 60-32.
1963: Surficial geology of Blood Indian Reserve, No. 148, Alberta; *Geol. Surv. Can.*, Paper 63-25.

Tanner, V.
1944: Outlines of the geography of Newfoundland–Labrador; *Acta Geograph.*, vol. 8, pp. 1–906.

Taylor, Andrew
1956: Physical geography of the Queen Elizabeth Islands Canada: *in* Glaciology, vol. 2; *Am. Geograph. Soc.*, New York.

Taylor, F. C.
1961: Interglacial (?) conglomerate in northern Manitoba, Canada; *Bull. Geol. Soc. Am.*, vol. 72, pp. 167–168.

Taylor, R. S.
1958: Some Pleistocene lakes of northern Alberta and adjacent areas; *Edmonton Geol. Soc. Quart.*, vol. 2, No. 4.

Terasmae, J.
1958: Contributions to Canadian palynology: Pt. III, Non-glacial deposits along Missinaibi River, Ontario; *Geol. Surv. Can.*, Bull. 46, pp. 29–34.
1960: Contributions to Canadian palynology No. 2: Pt. II, A palynological study of Pleistocene interglacial beds at Toronto, Ontario; *Geol. Surv. Can.*, Bull. 56.

Terasmae, J., and Hughes, O. L.
1960: Glacial retreat in North Bay area; *Science*, vol. 131, No. 3411, pp. 1444–1446.

Terasmae, J., Webber, P. J., and Andrews, J. T.
1966: A study of late Quaternary plant-bearing beds in north-central Baffin Island, Canada; *Arctic*, vol. 19, No. 4, pp. 296–318.

Thorsteinsson, R.
1958: Cornwallis and Little Cornwallis Islands, District of Franklin, Northwest Territories; *Geol. Surv. Can.*, Mem. 294.
1961: The history and geology of Meighen Island, Arctic Archipelago; *Geol. Surv. Can.*, Bull. 75.

Thorsteinsson, R., and Tozer, E. T.
1961: Structural history of the Canadian Arctic Archipelago since Precambrian time; *Geology of the Arctic*, vol. 1, pp. 339–360.

Tomlinson, R. F.
1959: Geomorphological field work in the Kaumajet Mountains and Okak Bay area of the Labrador Coast; *McGill Sub-Arctic Res. Lab.*, Ann. Rept. 1957–58, pp. 61–67.

Tozer, E. T., and Thorsteinsson, R.
1964: Western Queen Elizabeth Islands, Arctic Archipelago; *Geol. Surv. Can.*, Mem. 332.

Tremblay, L.
1961a: Geology, La Loche, Saskatchewan; *Geol. Surv. Can.*, Map 10-1961.
1961b: Geology of Firebag River area, Alberta and Saskatchewan; *Geol. Surv. Can.*, Map 16-1961.

Tyrrell, J. B.
1892: Report on northwestern Manitoba with portions of the adjacent district of Assiniboia and Saskatchewan; *Geol. Surv. Can.*, Ann. Rept. 1890–91, pt. E.
1897: Report on the Dubawnt, Kazan and Ferguson Rivers and the northwest coast of Hudson Bay; *Geol. Surv. Can.*, Ann. Rept. 1896, pt. F.
1913: Hudson Bay exploring expedition; *Ont. Bur. Mines*, vol. 22, pt. 1, pp. 161–209.

Upham, W.
1895: The glacial Lake Agassiz; *U.S. Geol. Surv.*, Monograph, vol. 25.

Vernon, P., and Hughes, O. L.
1965: Surficial geology of Larson Creek, Yukon Territory; *Geol. Surv. Can.*, Map 1171A.

Watson, K., and Mathews, W. H.
1944: The Tuya–Teslin area, Northern British Columbia; *B.C. Dept. Mines*, Bull. No. 19.

Wayne, W. J., and Zumberge, J. H.
1965: Geologic history of the Great Lakes: *in* Pleistocene geology of Indiana and Michigan; The Quaternary of the U.S.; INQUA 7, Review vol., pp. 73–80, *Princeton Univ. Press*.

Wenner, C-G
1947: Pollen diagrams from Labrador; *in Geografiska Ann.*, vol. 29, pp. 137–173.

Westgate, J. A.
1965: The Pleistocene stratigraphy of the Foremost–Cypress Hills area, Alberta; *Alta. Soc. Petrol. Geol.*, 15th Ann. Field Congress, pt. 1, Cypress Hills Plateau.

Westgate, J. A., and Bayrock, L. A.
1964: Periglacial structures in the Saskatchewan gravels and sands of central Alberta, Canada; *J. Geol.*, vol. 72, No. 5, pp. 641–647.

Wheeler, E. P.
1958: Pleistocene glaciation in northern Labrador; *Geograph. Soc. Am.*, Bull. 69, No. 3, pp. 343, 344.

Whitaker, S. H.
1965: Geology of Wood Mountain area (72-G), Saskatchewan; *Univ. Microfilms, Inc.*, Ann Arbor, Mich.

Wickenden, R. T. D.
1931: An area of little or no drift in southern Saskatchewan; *Trans. Roy. Soc. Can.*, vol. 25, ser. 3, sec. 4, pp. 45–47.
1941: Glacial deposits of part of northern Nova Scotia; *Trans. Roy. Soc. Can.*, vol. 35, ser. 3, sec. 4, pp. 143–150.

Williams, M. Y.
1921: Palaeozoic stratigraphy of Pagwachuan, Lower Kenogami, and Lower Albany Rivers, Ontario; *Geol. Surv. Can.*, Sum. Rept. 1920, pt. D.

Wilson, W. J.
1906: Reconnaissance surveys of four rivers southwest of James Bay; *Geol. Surv. Can.*, Ann. Rept. 1902–3, pp. 222A–243A.

Zoltai, S. C.
1961: Glacial history of part of northwestern Ontario; *Proc. Geol. Assoc. Can.*, vol. 13, pp. 61–81.
1963: Glacial features of the Canadian Lakehead area; *Can. Geograph.*, vol. 7, No. 3, pp. 101–115.
1965: Glacial features of the Quetico–Nipigon area, Ontario; *Can. J. Earth Sci.*, vol. 2, No. 4, pp. 247–269.

XIII. Groundwater Geology

INTRODUCTION

In Canada groundwater contributes about 10 per cent of the water supplied by municipal water supply systems serving communities with a population of more than 1,000 and an equal or greater proportion of that used by individual homes (Table XIII-1). Quantities of industrial and irrigational water are also obtained from groundwater.

Groundwater is defined as all water in the zone of continuous saturation except that water chemically combined in minerals.

The upper limit of completely saturated material is the *water-table* and for practical purposes may be determined by the level of water standing in open holes penetrating the saturated zone. It may be more accurately defined as the surface at which water is at atmospheric pressure (Fig. XIII-3). The water-table may be at surface in wet periods when the ground is fully saturated, or it may be at depths of many hundreds of feet in mountainous and arid areas. The lower limit of groundwater is determined by the depth at which pressure closes all openings in the rocks. This depth depends mainly on the structural strength of the rocks, and generally is not known.

The first investigation by the Geological Survey of Canada specifically mentioning groundwater was in 1875 when exploratory drilling was done in the Northwest Territories (now Saskatchewan) to obtain water for railway construction. In a short report on drilling for groundwater at Deloraine and Morden, Manitoba, A. R. C. Selwyn (1890) gave a summary of the groundwater possibilities from Red River to the Pembina Escarpment. The first Geological Survey report fully devoted to groundwater was prepared in 1901 by F. D. Adams and O. E. LeRoy, on the artesian wells of Montreal Island. Mapping of the Milk River sandstone in southern Alberta by D. B. Dowling in 1915 indicated that it should be an extensive artesian aquifer; this was substantiated by a drilling program the following year. In the 1920's and 1930's reconnaissance mapping on the Prairies for oil, gas, and water produced some wide-ranging, excellent reports. In 1935 a massive groundwater inventory of the wells in southern Saskatchewan and east-central Alberta was undertaken by the Geological Survey of Canada and 274 water supply papers were published. This type of well inventory was continued until about 1959 in Ontario, Quebec, Prince Edward Island, and the Prairies, with emphasis on the quantitative and chemical aspects and on appraisal of older data. Since then the Survey has studied groundwater flow systems and the fundamental behaviour of groundwater; well inventory data are gathered almost entirely by provincial agencies many of whom require drillers to submit reports on all wells drilled. These data are kept readily available and are an important source of information.

[1] Inland Waters Branch

XIII Groundwater Geology

I.C. Brown[1]

Artesian groundwater flow, Coldstream ranch, Vernon, B.C. From left, uncontrolled flow from 6″ casing; installation of 30″ flow-control casing; controlled flow from 30″ casing.

HYDROLOGIC CYCLE

The hydrologic cycle is the complete cycle of processes through which all water on earth is continuously moving (Fig. XIII-2). The energy for this movement is provided by radiation from the sun which evaporates water from all land, water, vegetative and animal surfaces into the atmosphere. The sun's energy plus the rotation of the earth moves this atmospheric water to locations where conditions are such that it condenses in the form of either solid or liquid precipitation and is pulled back to the surface of the earth by gravity. Some immediately evaporates again, some runs off into streams and lakes and eventually into the ocean, some sinks into the soil and is either extracted and transpired by plants or evaporates directly, some sinks more deeply into the ground to the water-table, where it becomes groundwater. Groundwater, acting largely under the influence of gravity and the pressure of surrounding water, continually seeks areas of lower pressure or lower potential energy and follows complex pathways through the materials of the earth. Some does not travel far before it returns to surface and joins the other parts of the cycle, some travels to great depths and remains underground for very long periods, but all is eventually discharged on the surface or into streams, lakes, or the ocean from where it is again evaporated and continues on around the cycle. The amount of water in active storage in the ground is about 30 times that stored in streams and lakes, but is a little less than a quarter of that stored in ice and about 1/150th of that in the oceans.

Groundwater Fluctuations

Variations in groundwater flow both in time and space are considerably slower and more uniform than variations in either surface or atmospheric water. The rates of groundwater flow depend on the hydraulic gradient and on the permeability of the materials and are commonly slow, as the hydraulic gradient is usually considerably less than the surface slope in areas of high relief and is, of course, very slow in flat areas. Actual rates of movement vary from almost zero to a maximum of more than 100 feet per day, but a normal range is from 5 feet per year to 5 feet per day. These low velocities combined with the vast storage available in the geological materials of the earth combine to reduce the variations in groundwater flow to a minimum. Thus, whereas the water-table may fluctuate rapidly, depending on the precipitation, deeper parts of groundwater flow systems will vary much more slowly.

Groundwater fluctuations, which vary greatly in magnitude and timing, are due to many causes both natural and artificial (Figs. XIII-5 and XIII-6). Small rapid variations in the level of the groundwater-table can be caused by any force that affects the materials in which it occurs, such

TABLE XIII-1 | *Canadian water supplies*

Province	No. of systems	No. supplying groundwater entirely or partly	Water supplied in 1,000's of gal. per day		Population served in 1,000's	Per capita supply gal. per day
			Groundwater	Total water		
Alberta	64	26	3,755	90,537	810	112
British Columbia	83	20	9,664	160,711	1,278	126
Manitoba	42	10	1,333	85,819	1,048	82
New Brunswick	23	16	10,185	57,019	250	228
Newfoundland	21	1	300	23,217	155	150
Nova Scotia	34	14	4,660	38,408	341	113
Ontario	294	120	97,824	669,638	6,443	104
Prince Edward Island	3	3	2,908	2,908	29	100
Quebec	272	81	28,156	573,660	4,286	134
Saskatchewan	47	33	10,691	51,348	254	202
TOTALS	883	324	169,476	1,753,265	14,894	Average 135
Groundwater supplied % of total 9.9						

Water supplied by Canadian municipal water supply systems serving populations of 1,000 or more
Does not include large industrial or private supplies not depending on municipal utilities
(Compiled from statistics in Canadian Municipal Utilities, Waterworks Manual and Directory for 1963)

Type of supply	Number of dwellings	Average occupancy	Estimated water supply gpd per dwelling	Estimated water supply 1,000's gpd
Piped into dwelling	759,349	3	200	151,870
Not piped into dwelling	377,401	3	100	37,740
Totals	1,136,750			189,610

Estimated water supply of dwellings not supplied by municipal water supply systems. Sources of water unknown but probably largely from wells. (Compiled from statistics in Canadian Housing Statistics, 1962, Central Mortgage and Housing Corporation, March, 1963)

as vibrations from traffic, earthquake forces, crustal tide forces, and air pressure changes. These short-term fluctuations are usually small and are measured in inches or fractions of inches, though those due to earthquakes are as much as a few feet. Longer term fluctuations are due to variations in supply of recharge water, and are more likely to be seasonal. They vary in magnitude depending on the rate of movement in the flow system and the frequency and amount of recharge, and in most areas of Canada vary from 5 to 20 feet. Fluctuations in the water-table are also caused by man's interference with any part of the flow system by pumping, irrigation, and drainage, altering river or lake levels, changing or removing the natural cover, and many other causes. In Canada such fluctuations are known to vary in amplitude from a few inches to many tens of feet and in extent from a few hundred feet to many miles.

In general throughout Canada recharge is greatest and groundwater levels are highest during spring break-up (Fig. XIII-6). From this peak they fall gradually to a low late in the summer; only prolonged and widespread rainy periods during the summer will reverse the trend, as most summer precipitation is returned to the atmosphere by evapotranspiration. The lowest levels are reached in the early autumn. The autumn rains come when evapotranspiration is at a minimum and considerable recharge takes place. In much of Canada, water-tables rise until freeze-up after which most precipitation is in solid form and little soaks into the ground. During the winter there is a gradual falling of groundwater levels until spring break-up occurs again.

Groundwater Flow Systems

Gravity is the principal force moving groundwater for it produces major pressure differences. Because the downward pull of gravity prevails through widely varying materials, pressure differences are set up and groundwater flow (though in general from topographically high areas to low areas) can be in any direction, including straight up. The flow can be influenced by other less continuous and universal forces such as temperature gradients, pressure due to underground bodies of gas, tectonic forces, capillary forces, and possibly osmotic pressures.

Although it may seem anomalous that water introduced into the groundwater system at atmospheric pressure can flow to great depths and thence return to discharge at

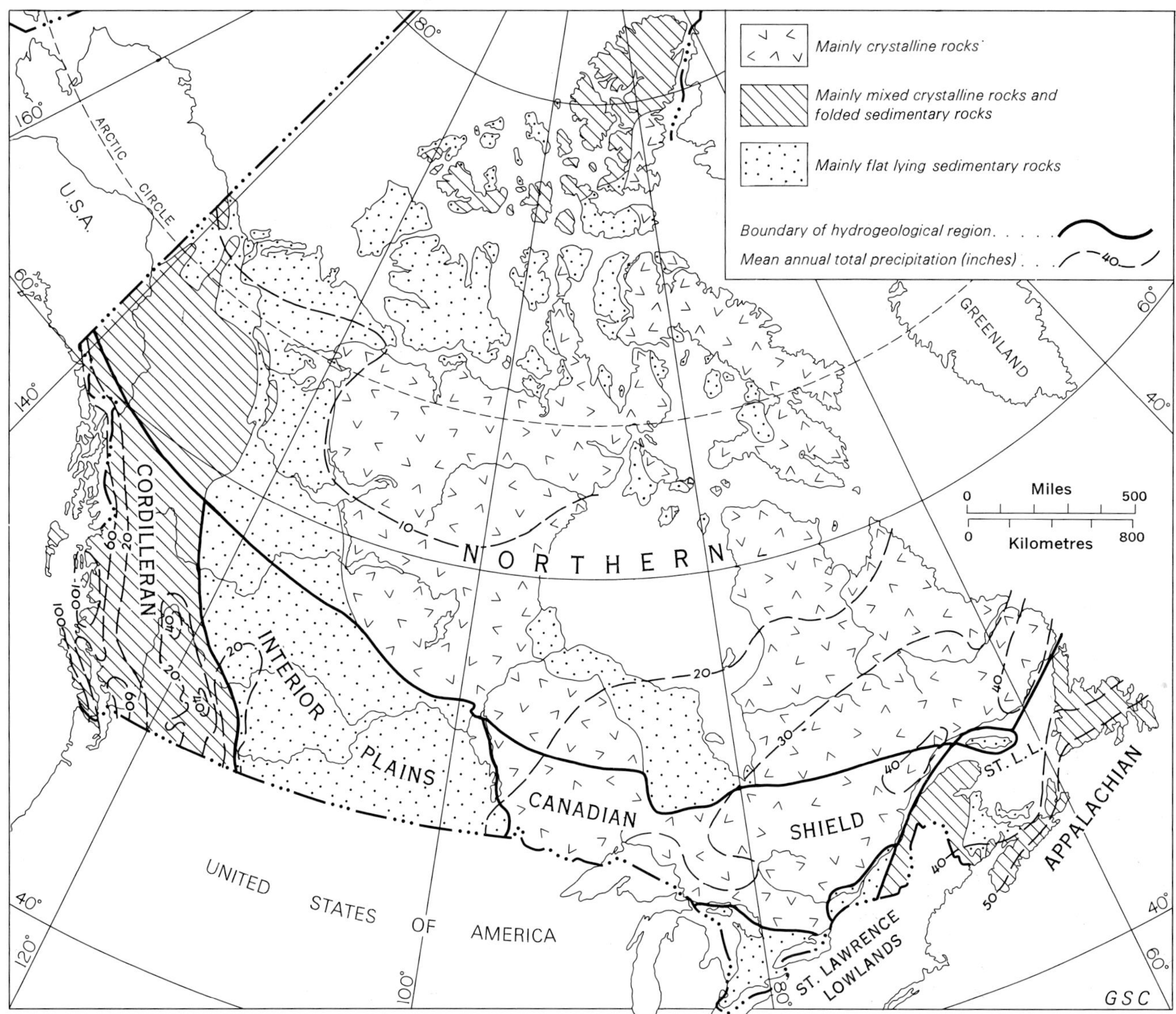

FIGURE XIII-1. Hydrogeological regions of Canada.

atmospheric pressure, groundwater is always moving down a hydraulic gradient. The pressure head, therefore, as measured along the flow system continually decreases from recharge to discharge.

Darcy's formula for the flow of fluids through porous media may be stated as follows: the quantity of water flowing through a given cross-sectional area equals the permeability times the hydraulic gradient. In groundwater flow systems permeability is a fixed property of the material, and consequently both hydraulic gradient and the quantity of water flowing are dependent on the geology of the material.

Water moves through the intergranular spaces in materials and also through open fractures that vary from minute size to large solution cavities and channels. Movement through intergranular spaces in porous materials is diffuse and fairly uniform within uniform material but most permeable materials have directional properties inherent from their conditions of deposition and permeability in one direction may be many times as great as that in another. Normally the horizontal components are greater than the vertical but this may vary greatly and differ even between individual layers of a single deposit. In some geological materials permeability may be due largely to fractures or bedding and the direction of maximum permeability may lie in any direction.

Groundwater flow systems may vary in scale from those related to a single small isolated pond to systems many hundred miles in extent and even to very deep flow systems of continental size. It is the larger flow systems with their comparatively constant flow that provide the water that keeps rivers and streams flowing during long

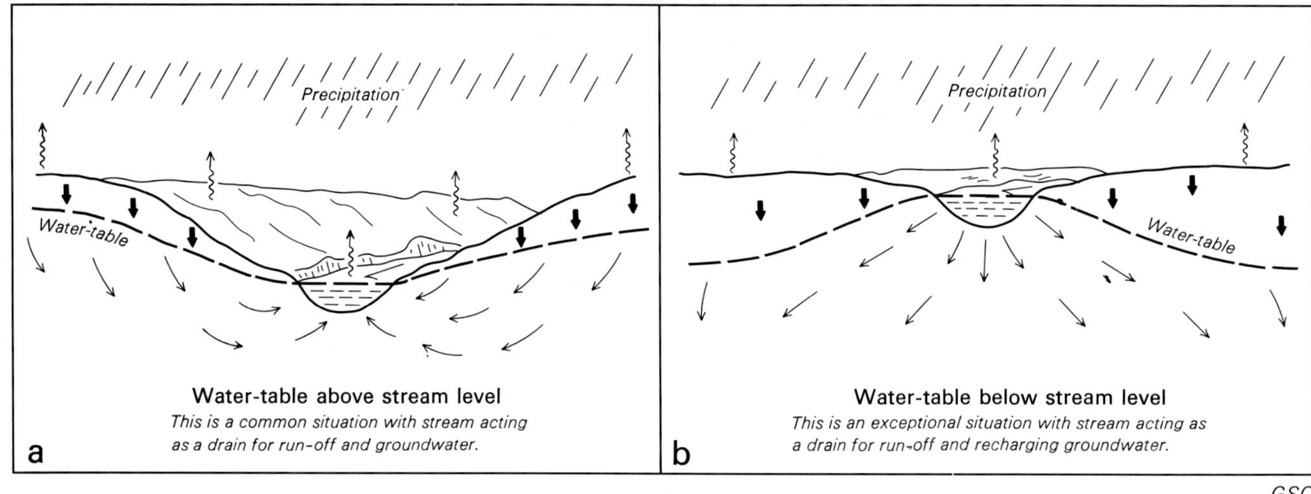

Precipitation
Water-table
Water-table above stream level
This is a common situation with stream acting as a drain for run-off and groundwater.
a
Precipitation
Water-table
Water-table below stream level
This is an exceptional situation with stream acting as a drain for run-off and recharging groundwater.
b
GSC
LEGEND
Evapotranspiration . . .
Run-off . . .
Infiltration. . .
Groundwater flow . . .

FIGURE XIII-2. Hydrologic cycle: a, influent stream; b, effluent stream.

dry periods. Thus, measurements of the low flow of rivers give a close estimate of the amount of water travelling through the related groundwater flow systems.

Flow systems may be detected by many methods. Direct ones are springs and seeps, pressure head measured in wells, and tracers of various types. Indirect methods are much more varied but largely depend on the chemistry of groundwater. On a very large scale, and regardless of

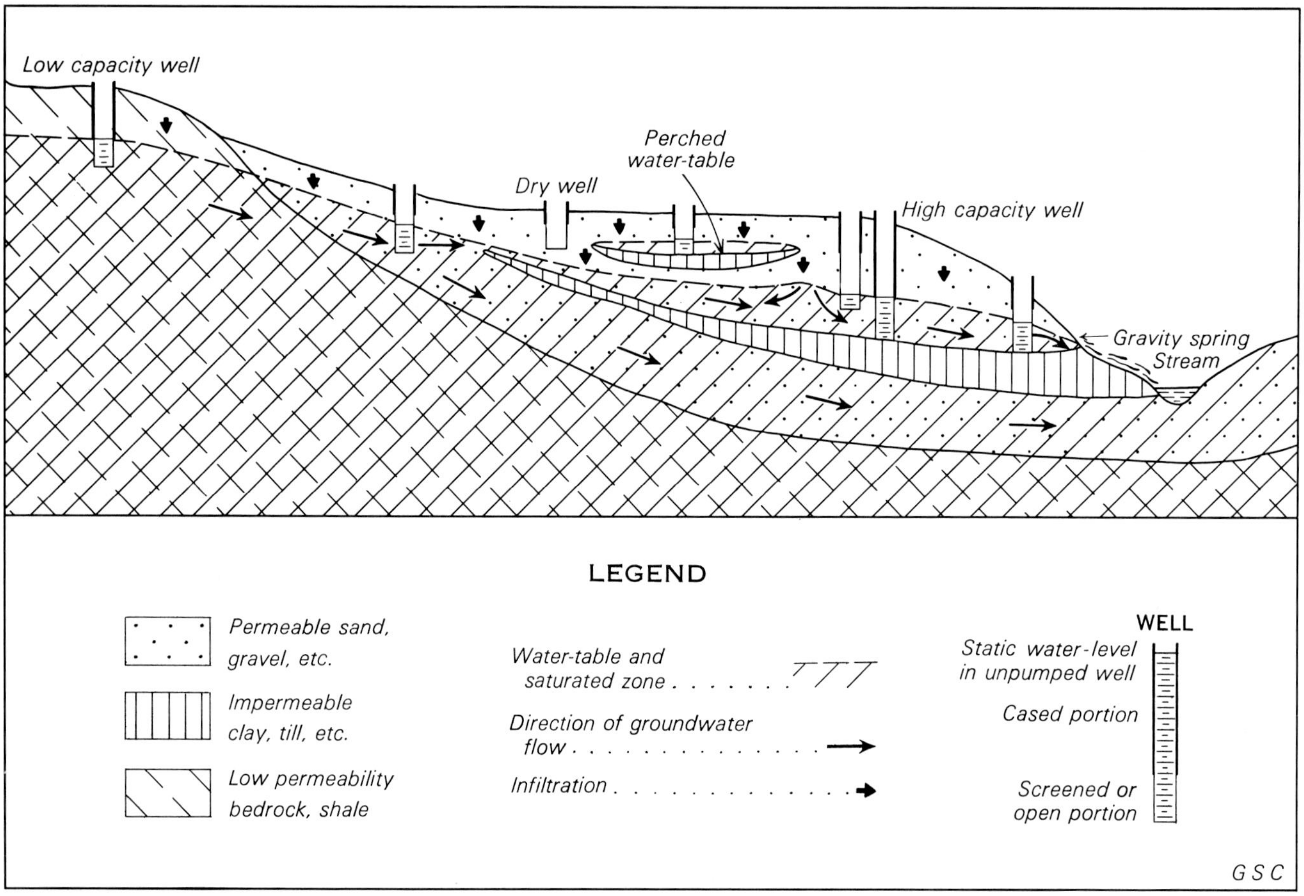

Low capacity well
Perched water-table
Dry well
High capacity well
Gravity spring
Stream
LEGEND
Permeable sand, gravel, etc.
Impermeable clay, till, etc.
Low permeability bedrock, shale
Water-table and saturated zone . . . .
Direction of groundwater flow . . . .
Infiltration . . . .
WELL
Static water-level in unpumped well
Cased portion
Screened or open portion
GSC

FIGURE XIII-3. Water-table conditions (unconfined aquifers).

the material through which it travels, groundwater starts out as bicarbonate water and changes through a sequence of carbonate plus chloride plus bicarbonate to chloride plus sulphate or sulphate plus chloride to finally a predominantly chloride water approaching the composition of sea water. This full sequence is not always present but has been found very useful in indicating flow systems in several areas in Canada. The composition of water also depends on the materials through which it flows, for example water in limestones and dolomites will be high in carbonate and that in gypsum-bearing rocks will be high in sulphate. In clean sands and gravels very little material will be dissolved. In general, water will be of better quality in areas of recharge than in areas of discharge. Though it is known that the rate of change of dissolved material in groundwater can be rapid, changes, for example, in composition of groundwater depend closely on the containing materials even though the flow system may cross the boundary between them.

Plant growth aids greatly in understanding groundwater flow systems. Salt-tolerant plants indicate areas of discharge from long flow systems whereas non-salt tolerant plants are found in recharge areas or over areas of lateral flow. Phreatophytic plants, or those depending on a continuous supply of moisture, normally grow where their roots can reach the water-table. Non-phreatophytic plants depend largely on soil moisture and can survive considerable periods of drought without contact with the water-table. Thus in areas where the water-table is generally deep, phreatophytic plants generally indicate discharge areas and non-phreatophytic plants recharge or lateral flow areas.

HYDROGEOLOGICAL REGIONS

Certain broad features of the geology, precipitation, climate, and topography serve to divide Canada into six regions of differing hydrogeological conditions (Figs. XIII-1 and XIII-7). The boundaries between the regions are not sharp but rather are zones of varying width wherein one group of conditions changes to another. In defining these

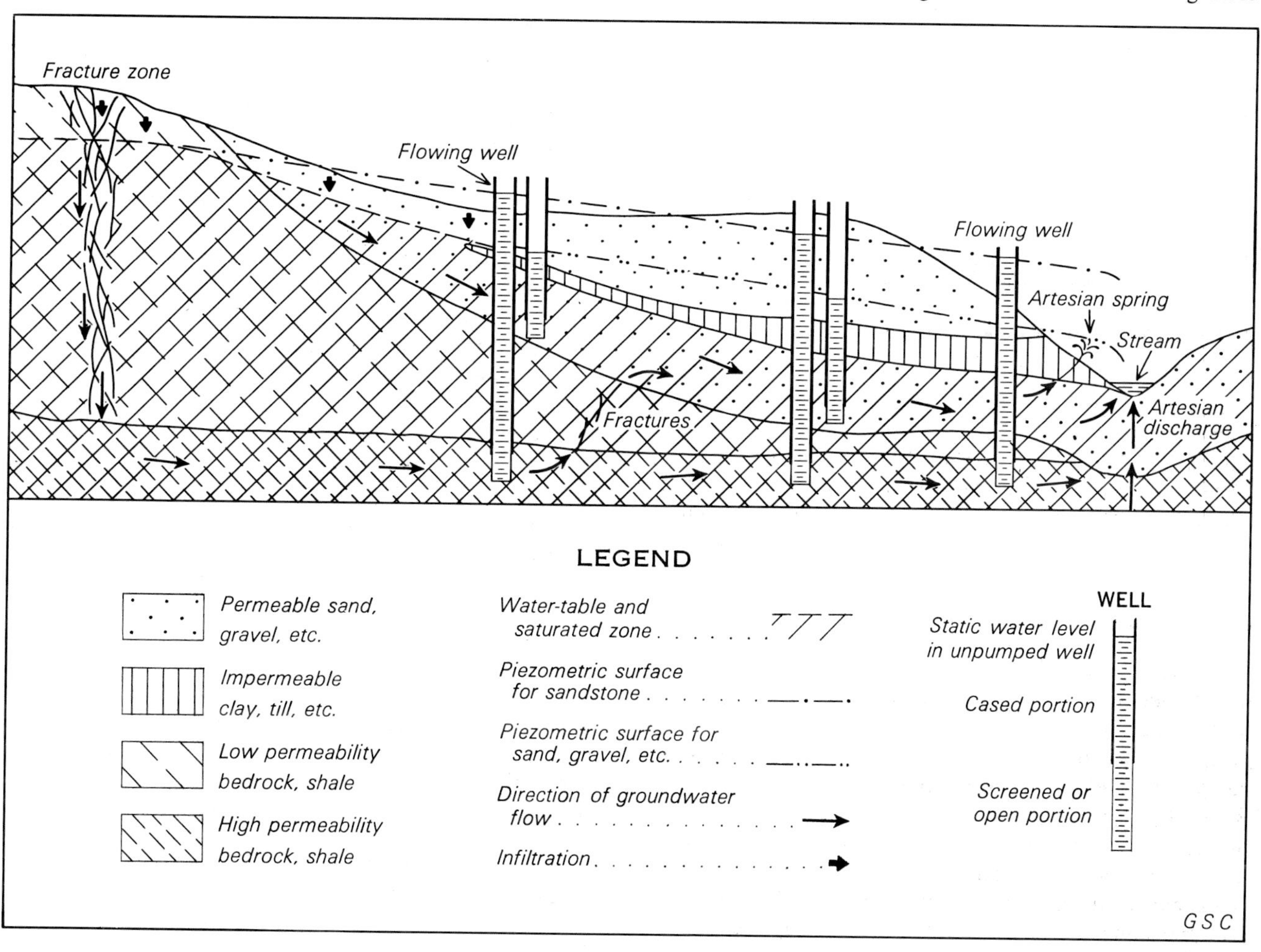

FIGURE XIII-4. Artesian conditions (confined aquifers).

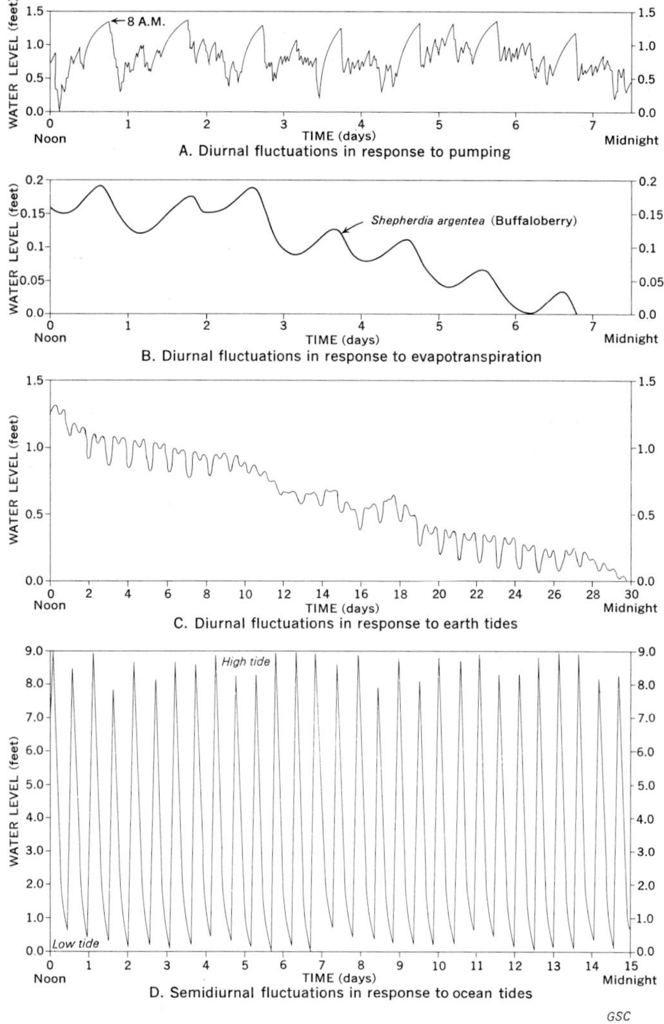

FIGURE XIII-5. Diurnal and semidiurnal fluctuations in groundwater levels.

regions, geology is the most important factor as it determines the amount of water that can be stored and transmitted. Precipitation and climate control the amount of water available for recharging groundwater flow systems. Topography influences the length and depth of the systems.

Appalachian Hydrogeological Region

This region is characterized by a mixture of crystalline, folded to flat-lying sedimentary rocks, and comparatively thin surficial materials. It is an upland sloping gently to the southeast, dissected by valleys and broken by broader lowland areas developed on belts of weaker rocks. Relief in the Gaspé Region exceeds 2,000 feet but elsewhere it is seldom more than 1,000 feet and commonly only a few hundred. The climate is humid continental. Total annual precipitation ranges from 30 to 50 inches with the maximum along the Atlantic coast, and is exceeded only by that in the western Cordilleran Region.

Hydrogeology

Groundwater in the consolidated rocks moves largely through fractures of various types and relatively little moves through the pore spaces of these rocks. The hydrogeological properties are, therefore, depicted by hydrostratigraphic units consisting of rocks yielding approximately the same quantity and quality of groundwater (Fig. XIII-8). This division is possible only in New Brunswick, Prince Edward Island, Magdalen Islands, and Nova Scotia, as sufficient data on which to make this division are not available for Newfoundland, Gaspé, and the Eastern Townships of Quebec.

New Brunswick, Prince Edward Island, and Nova Scotia

The basement complex comprises all rocks from Precambrian to Devonian age. These rocks seldom yield more than 5 gallons per minute. Wells drilled in excess of 100 feet, and particularly those over 1,000 feet, commonly yield saline water. The better wells occur in valleys at shallow depths. The groundwater is of calcium bicarbonate type and generally contains 50 to 150 ppm of total dissolved solids. Locally iron and manganese concentrations are excessive, especially in the Meguma Group of Nova Scotia. In the Truro area iron content has been reported up to 14 ppm.

Pre-Windsor sediments comprise all the Mississippian conglomerates, sandstones, siltstones, and shales that lie between the basement complex and the Windsor rocks. Well yields range up to 25 gpm (rarely to 50) and the water is predominantly calcium bicarbonate type containing 100 to 300 ppm of total dissolved solids, except where groundwater has passed through Windsor sediments before entering this unit and then the quality may be poor.

The Windsor Group comprises Mississippian limestones, dolomites, anhydrite, gypsum, salt, shale, and siltstone. Well yields are extremely variable and the water is excessively hard, commonly saline, and often contains greater than 10,000 ppm total dissolved solids. The main constituents are sodium, calcium, chloride, and sulphate.

The post-Windsor sediments comprise the late Carboniferous and Permian sandstones and claystones with some conglomerate and siltstone. Yields of 25 gpm are generally obtained and large capacity wells have been developed in some areas. The Imperial Pollett River No. 1 well reported a flow of 840 gpm fresh water from the Boss Point Formation at 390-foot depth. Four wells at Fredericton drilled to between 187 and 400 feet yield between 150 and 500 gpm. A spring 10 miles northeast of Sussex flows continuously at 700 gpm. Wells at Sackville, Shediac, and Amherst yield between 150 and 670 gpm. The water is generally a good quality calcium bicarbonate type containing from 100 to 300 ppm total dissolved solids. A few isolated occurrences of saline water exist but these are presumed to be due to contact with the salt of the Windsor Group. Salt water intrusion, due to over pump-

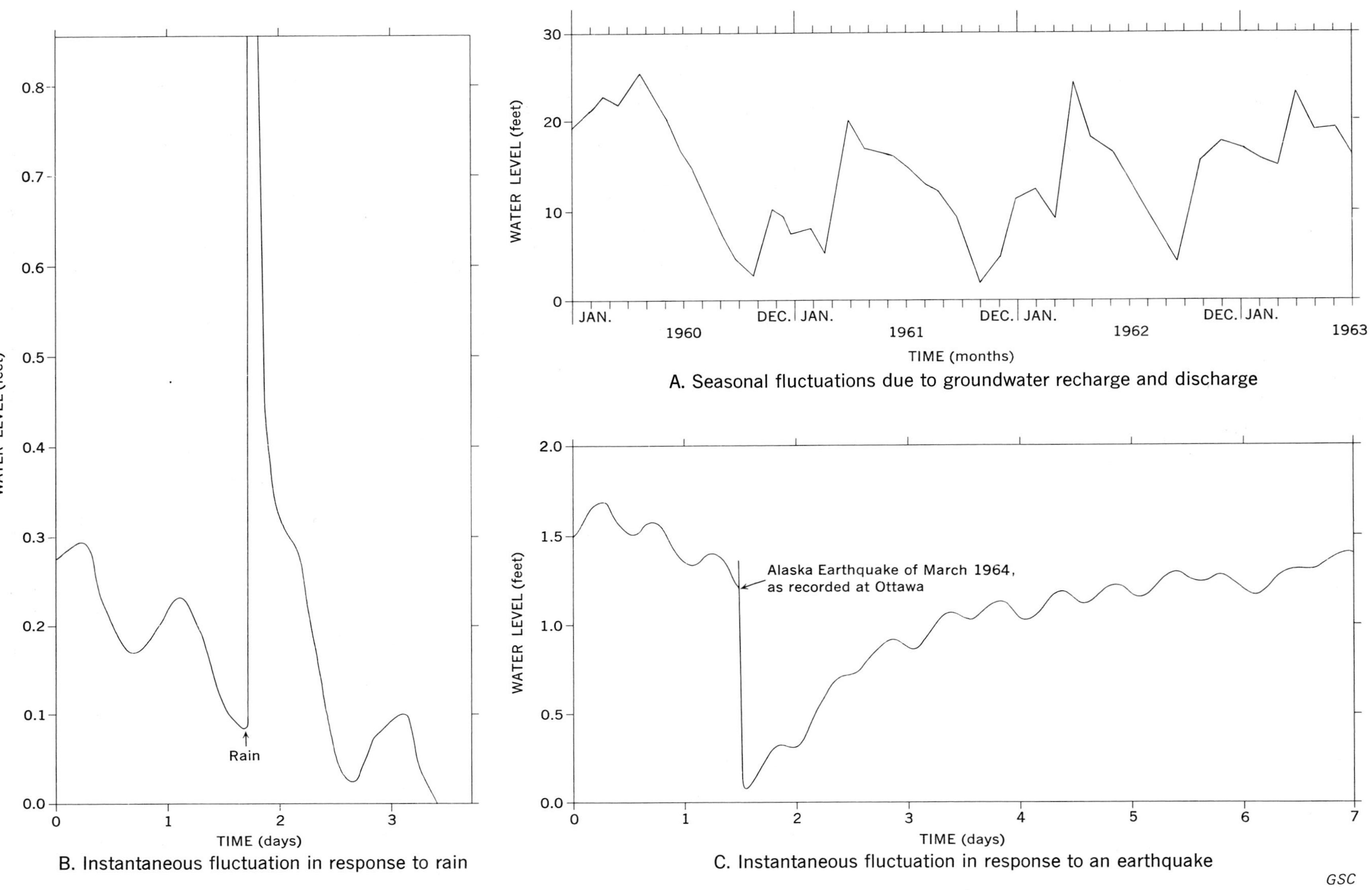

FIGURE XIII-6. Seasonal and instantaneous fluctuations in groundwater levels.

ing, has been induced in some wells adjacent to the coast of Prince Edward Island and New Brunswick.

Triassic rocks comprise sandstone, shale, basalt, and diabase and are probably the best bedrock aquifers in Nova Scotia. The basalt and diabase generally yield less than 3 gpm but yields of up to 400 gpm are obtained from

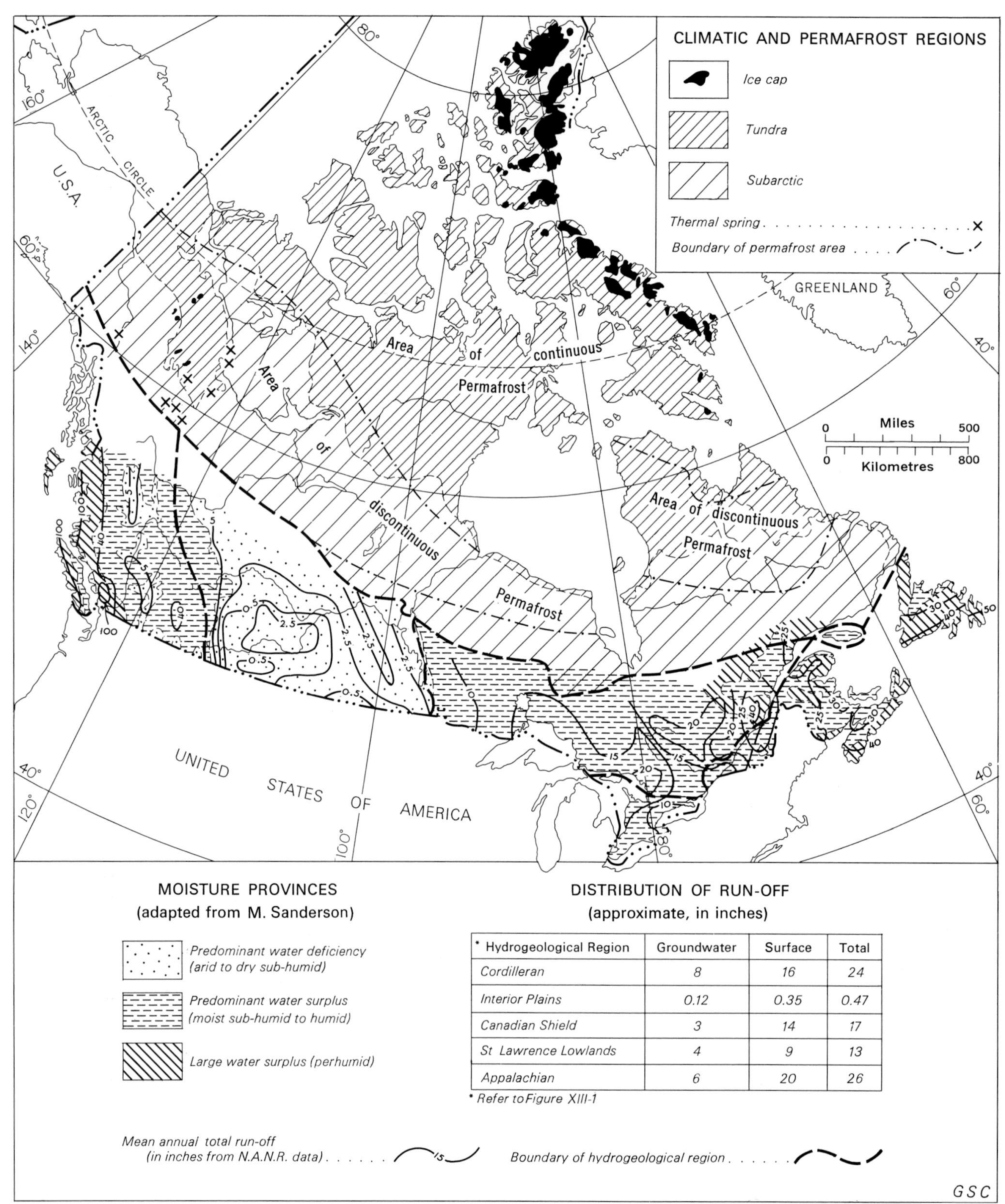

* Hydrogeological Region	Groundwater	Surface	Total
Cordilleran	8	16	24
Interior Plains	0.12	0.35	0.47
Canadian Shield	3	14	17
St Lawrence Lowlands	4	9	13
Appalachian	6	20	26

* *Refer to Figure XIII-1*

FIGURE XIII-7. Climatic regions of Canada, permafrost regions and annual run-off in southern Canada.

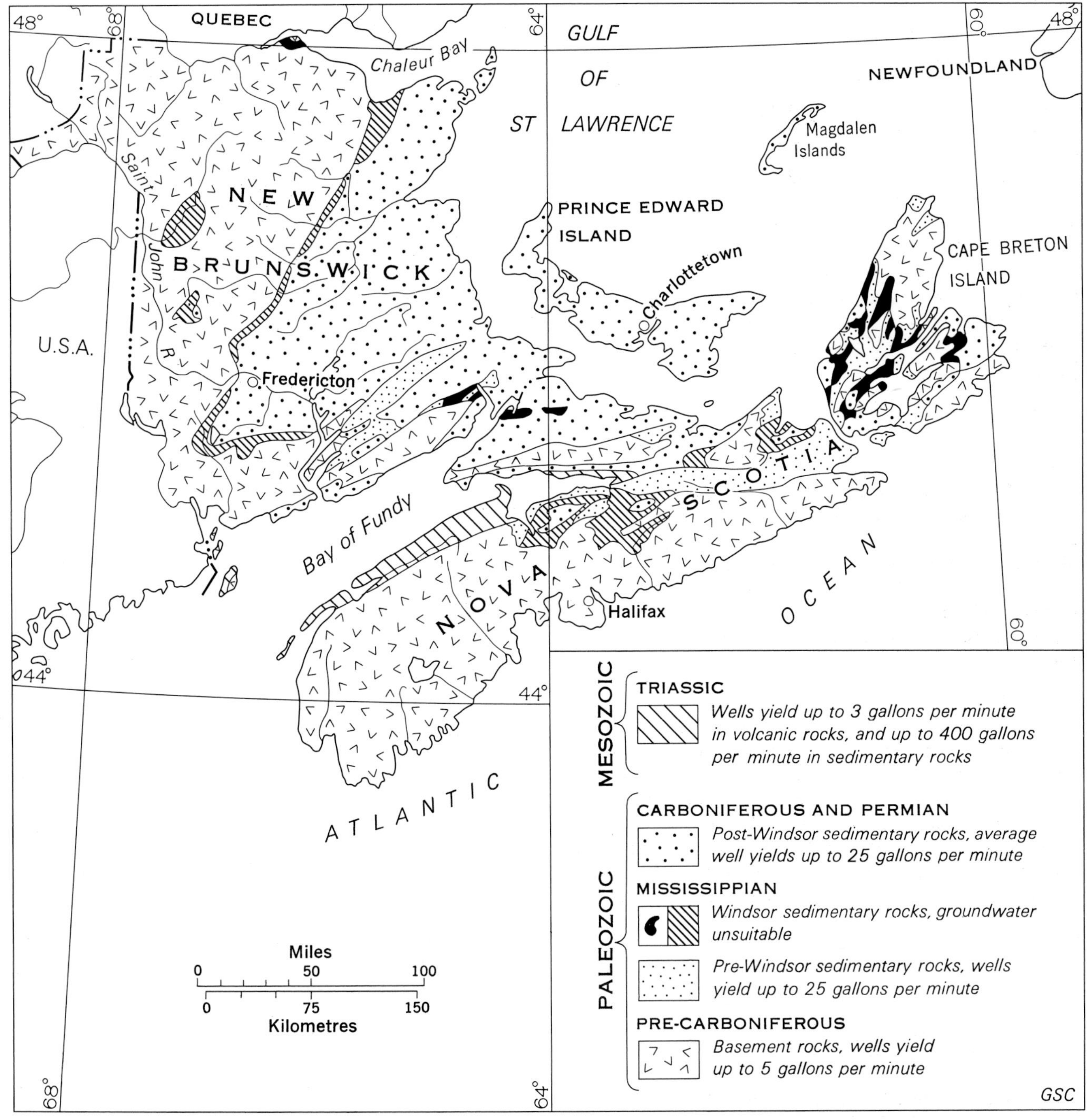

FIGURE XIII-8. Bedrock hydrostratigraphic units in New Brunswick, Nova Scotia, and Prince Edward Island.

the other rocks. The water contains between 50 and 200 ppm total dissolved solids. Some sea water intrusion has occurred at Kingsport, Nova Scotia, where a sample of groundwater contained 1,400 ppm total dissolved solids, mainly sodium chloride.

The Pleistocene sand and gravel deposits occur as eskers, kames, and outwash plains and although of small size and limited distribution are good aquifers. The thin layer of till that covers most of the Maritimes is a poor aquifer.

Insufficient data are available to determine the average yield of surficial materials but the following examples probably indicate the maximum limits. The town of Sussex obtains its water supply from a 12-inch-diameter well rated at 500 gpm with a specific capacity of 17 gpm per foot of drawdown. Three municipal wells at Fredericton, 113 to 146 feet deep and 12 to 18 inches in diameter, had initial capacities between 590 and 1,125 gpm with specific capacities between 32 and 165 gpm per foot of drawdown. Three miles north of St. Stephen a sand and gravel aquifer yields 1,400 gpm. Groundwater from these outwash deposits generally contains less than 200 ppm total dissolved solids and is normally a calcium bicarbonate water. These aquifers are commonly confined to valleys adjacent to rivers and consequently can rely on induced infiltration to sustain their yields.

Recent alluvium of sand and gravel occurs in valleys of some of the larger rivers such as the Saint John. It is usually derived from Pleistocene glaciofluvial material and its hydrologic properties are similar to theirs. Extensive tidal mud flats surrounding Bay of Fundy have low permeability and contain saline water and consequently are poor aquifers. Beach sands are abundant but little fresh water can be pumped from them before sea water is induced.

Gaspé and Eastern Townships

Only limited information is available concerning the groundwater of this area and none of it has been published. The best aquifers so far developed are in Pleistocene sand and gravel deposits. The Quebec Department of Natural Resources reports that twenty-one pump tests of bedrock wells drilled to 135 feet yielded an average of about 20 gpm with occasional yields as high as 65 gpm, whereas eight pump tests on wells to 55 feet in surficial deposits showed yields averaging 60 gpm with a high of 136 gpm.

Newfoundland

No groundwater studies have been done here to date; most water supplies are drawn from surface resources. Much of the island is underlain by crystalline rocks and the few wells developed in these indicate only low yields suitable for domestic supplies. Surficial deposits, particularly outwash sands and gravels, provide the best aquifers. About 3.6 per cent of the total area of Newfoundland is underlain by potential sand and gravel aquifers. Very large capacity wells at Stephenville have been developed in these materials.

Groundwater Chemistry

Due to the high rainfall, comparatively short groundwater flow systems, and the preponderance of crystalline rocks and outwash deposits groundwater in the Appalachian Hydrogeological Region is generally bicarbonate type low in total dissolved solids. The three main causes of poor water quality are: high iron, manganese, and sulphate content derived from pyrite in some of the pre-Carboniferous rocks especially in Nova Scotia; high calcium sulphate and sodium chloride content derived from evaporitic rocks, especially the Windsor Group; and induced salt water intrusion in the coastal areas where there is over pumping.

Water Balance

The water balance for any simple drainage basin is expressed as P=E+Rs+Rg, where P is the total precipitation in inches, E the total evapotranspiration in inches, Rs the total run-off of the stream, and Rg the groundwater discharge directly out of the basin. Preliminary calculations done for three small basins in Prince Edward Island give a general idea of the relative sizes of the quantities involved in the Appalachian Hydrogeological Region: 49″(P)=13″(E)+28″(Rs)+8″(Rg).

St. Lawrence Lowlands Hydrogeological Region

The St. Lawrence Lowlands, an area of about 43,000 square miles, is underlain by unfolded Paleozoic rocks with a generally thick cover of surficial materials. Relief is low, seldom exceeding 200 feet. The climate is humid continental, with 30 to 40 inches of total precipitation per year. The Lowlands is divided into three parts separated by Precambrian rocks. The western part, most of southern Ontario, is separated from the central part by the Frontenac Axis. The central part consists of the Paleozoic rocks of the Ottawa area and these are separated from those of the St. Lawrence River area by the Beauharnois Axis at the confluence of the Ottawa and St. Lawrence Rivers. The eastern part consists of Anticosti Island, Mingan Islands, and a narrow strip of the north shore of St. Lawrence River, and is separated from the central part by about 360 miles of the St. Lawrence River.

The hydrogeological characteristics of the region are determined largely by the prevailing climatic and geologic conditions (Fig. XIII-9). The climate is generally milder than that of areas immediately to the north because of the moderating influence of the Great Lakes and the sea. However, one of the major storm tracks on the continent passes through the region and produces rapid variations in weather particularly in the winter.

Hydrogeology

The porosity and permeability of bedrock in the St. Lawrence Lowlands Hydrogeological Region is largely due to fractures of various types, and at present the best method of assessing this is through well-yields in various areas (Fig. XIII-10). The surficial deposits consist of glacial and non-glacial sediments deposited during the last glacial stage of the Pleistocene Epoch except for relatively small areas of Recent sediments that are generally associated with modern streams and rivers. Their aquifer potential is assessed through well-yields as shown in Figure XIII-11.

Ontario

Between the Frontenac Axis and the Niagara Escarpment sedimentary rocks are not good aquifers, though in some areas fracturing allows yields of 10 gpm and more. The most productive rocks are commonly limestone.

Along Niagara Escarpment springs occur where fractured dolomite of Middle Silurian age overlies shales of the Lower Silurian, Clinton Group. The Middle Silurian

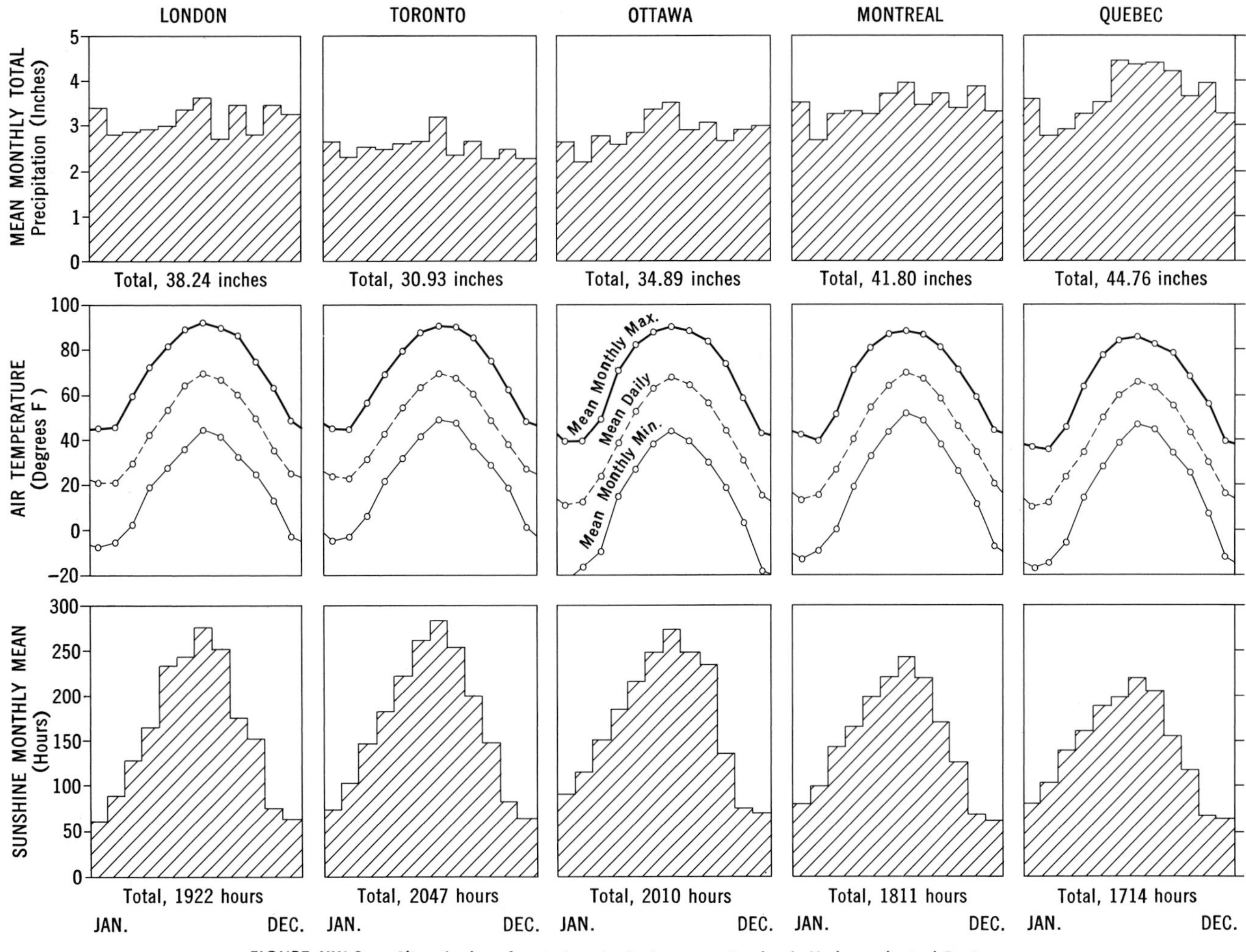

FIGURE XIII-9. Climatic data for stations in St. Lawrence Lowlands Hydrogeological Region.

formations are well jointed and constitute some of the best aquifers in the western part of the lowlands. Wells yield 5 to 15 gpm and locally in excess of 600 gpm. The Salina Formation is a poor aquifer, as the gypsum, anhydrite, and salt produce highly mineralized water. The best aquifers in the Devonian are the Bois Blanc and Detroit River Formations. Well-developed joint systems, thin to medium bedding, and some cavernous reef structures provide well-yields averaging 10 to 30 gpm. The water is usually of good quality with a tendency to become more highly mineralized at depth.

East of Frontenac Axis in the Ottawa area the oldest Paleozoic rocks are the Cambrian sandstones which directly overlie Precambrian crystalline rocks. They are generally a good source of groundwater, particularly near Kingston and Ottawa. Yields of ten to several hundred gpm are obtained from jointed and fractured zones in the upper and lower parts of the formations. Overlying the sandstones are thick sequences of Ordovician limestones and dolomites with some shale and sandy zones. Fracture zones developed in these rocks provide yields of 5 to 15 gpm, though most are below 10 gpm. Water is generally of good quality, but hard. The brown and black pyritiferous shales, however, may yield slightly larger quantities of water but highly mineralized and sulphurous.

Most coarse granular surficial deposits that are significant aquifers in the western part of the region were produced during the northward recession of the glaciers when meltwater was most active in transporting and sorting sediments. The confluence of two main glacial lobes is marked by thick elongate kame moraines composed mainly of sand and gravel in the area north of Lake Ontario and between Orangeville and London. These form some of the most extensive and important aquifers in the region. The finer grained sediments deposited in the offshore parts of the lakes marginal to the glaciers generally have little potential as aquifers. However, the more extensive shoreline or near shoreline deposits—beaches, beach bars, and spits—may be important local aquifers.

East of the Frontenac Axis most sand deposits now found on surface originated either as Champlain Sea beaches or as high-level terraces formed during the early stages of the Ottawa and St. Lawrence Rivers. Average

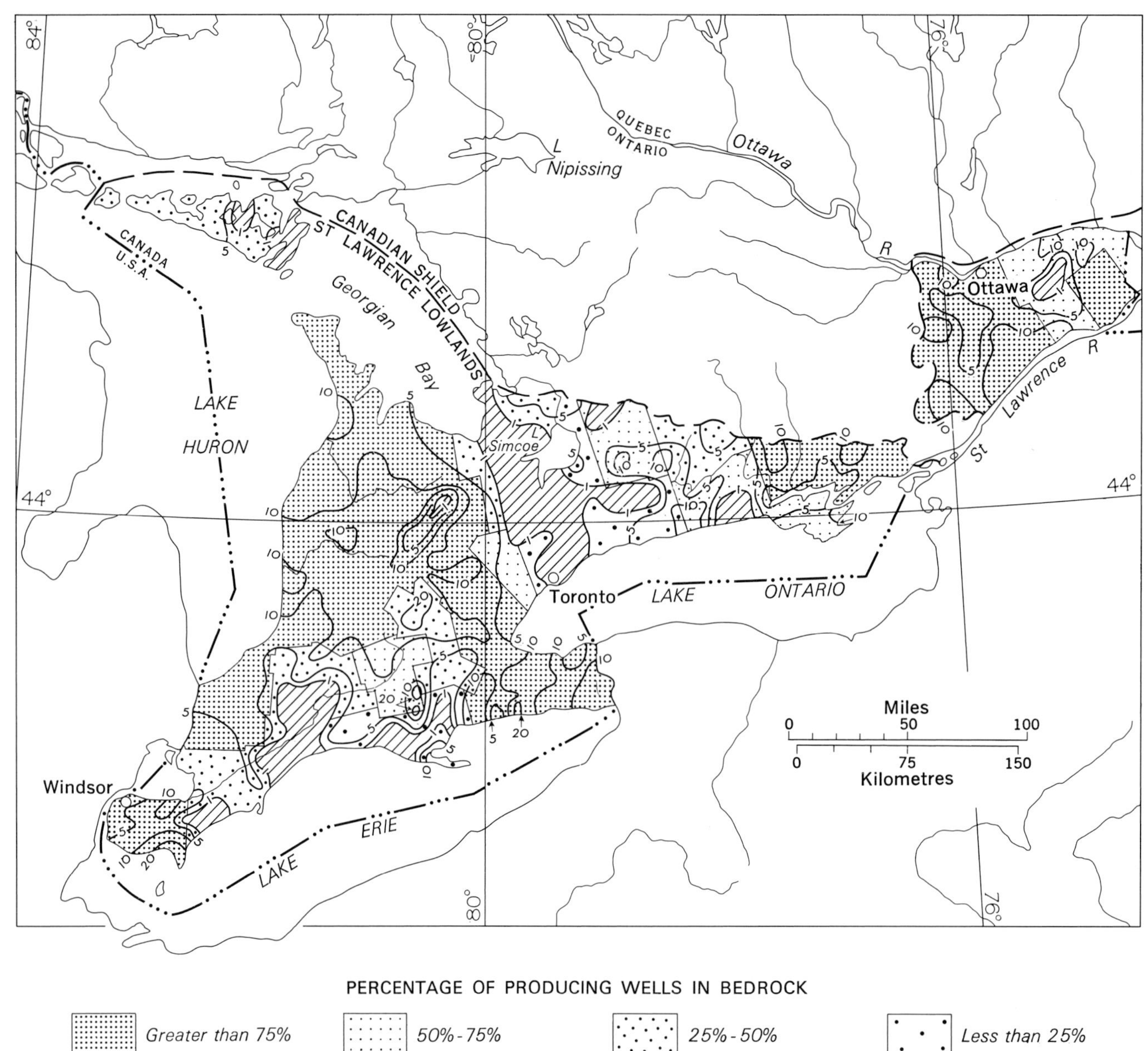

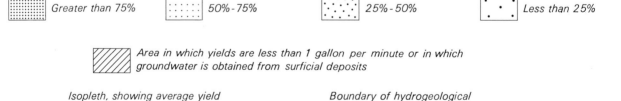

FIGURE XIII-10. Average yield of bedrock wells in Ontario part of the St. Lawrence Lowlands Hydrogeological Region.

well-yields from surficial aquifers range from one to thirty gpm. The most productive are the complex of spillway, beach and kame deposits in the area south from Elmira to Lake Erie.

Deep preglacial valleys were eroded in bedrock at various places in Ontario, particularly along the Niagara Escarpment and in the Georgian Bay area. Where filled with permeable materials, the yield is several hundred gallons per minute.

Quebec

Very few published hydrogeological data are available for the central part of the St. Lawrence Lowlands Hydrogeological Region, thus it has not been possible to show

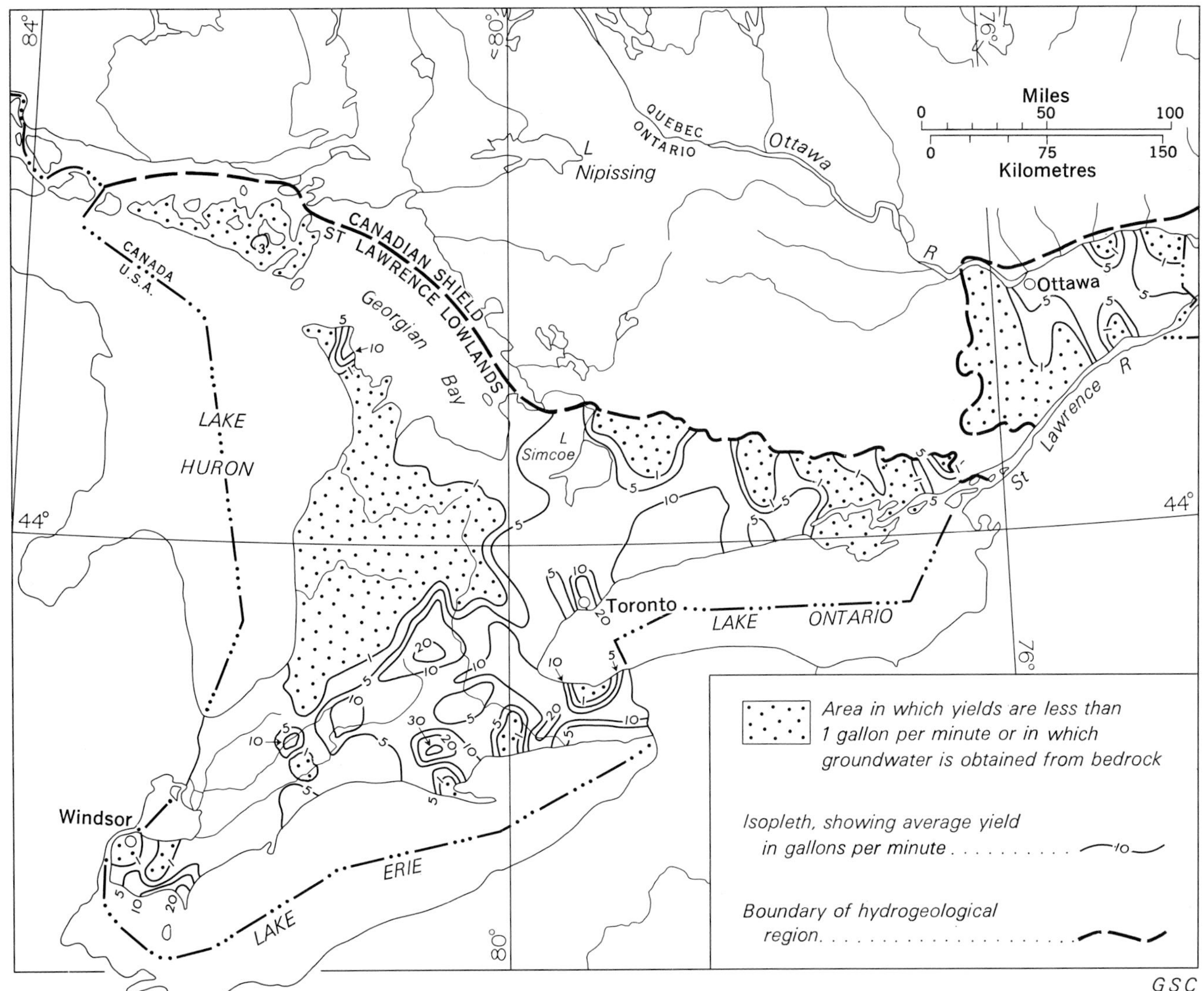

FIGURE XIII-11. Average yield of wells in surficial deposits in Ontario part of St. Lawrence Lowlands Hydrogeological Region.

the distribution of average well-yields for this area.

The Precambrian crystalline rocks are overlain by Cambrian sandstones and conglomerates that constitute one of the best aquifers in the area. Well-yields of more than 400 gpm are known. The overlying Lower Ordovician carbonate rocks are irregularly jointed and fractured so that whereas most of these rocks have comparatively low yields of 5 to 15 gpm, some high-capacity wells have been developed with yields of 70 to 500 gpm. Upper Ordovician strata are mainly shale with minor interbeds of limestone and sandstone, and seldom yield more than local domestic supplies.

The Paleozoic sediments were intruded during Cretaceous time by plug-like masses of alkaline igneous rocks forming the Monteregian Hills. Local aquifers, formed by fractures in the zone of contact between the intrusive and sedimentary rocks, yield 50 gpm.

Generally the oldest glacial deposit is till lying on the bedrock surface. In some places, however, as in the Becancour area, stratified glacial lake sediments are found below the till. Above the till are stratified sediments of non-glacial origin overlain in turn by younger till and thence stratified deposits of drift, kames, and outwash. Associated with these deposits, particularly along the northern margin of the region, is glacial outwash of sand and gravel. The coarser and better sorted materials are potential aquifers and because of the interlayering of permeable and impermeable materials artesian conditions are likely to be encountered.

Overlying the glacial materials are marine and brackish water silts, clays, and minor sands that were deposited by the Champlain Sea. Associated with these are terrace and alluvial sands in which wells yielding up to 1,000 gpm have been developed.

Buried valleys, probably tributaries to the preglacial river system, have been detected beneath the drift by detailed seismic surveys in the area southeast of Rigaud and in the Beauharnois and Chambly areas south of Montreal. Wells yielding several hundred gallons per minute have been developed in the buried valley near Rigaud.

Anticosti Island

Anticosti Island is underlain by about 2,400 feet of Ordovician and Silurian rocks, but as the water supply for the local population is obtained entirely from surface sources no water well data exist. The presence of groundwater is indicated by perennial streams which derive much of their baseflow from groundwater discharge.

Above an elevation of 250 feet there is only a thin veneer of till with no groundwater potential. Below this elevation a succession of wave-cut terraces mantled by stratified marine sediments occur; where these are sand and gravel it is probable that groundwater supplies could be developed.

Groundwater Chemistry

Throughout most of southern Ontario the groundwaters are calcium and magnesium bicarbonate water, which reflects the chemistry of the limestone and dolomite aquifers. Similarly a zone extending from Caledonia northwest to Southampton is characterized by water high in calcium sulphate due to the underlying gypsiferous Salina Formation. Areas underlain by black shale yield water containing sodium bicarbonate and hydrogen sulphide. Sodium chloride is a common chemical constituent of bedrock waters and is generally the dominant component in waters from the deep bedrock aquifers.

In the western part of St. Lawrence Valley in Quebec groundwater from bedrock shows the same association of bicarbonates of calcium and magnesium with limestone aquifers, high sodium bicarbonate, and hydrogen sulphide from shales.

In some places throughout St. Lawrence Valley groundwater has a high content of sodium chloride. Some of this may be derived from the leaching of salt in the extensive deposits of marine clays in the area. Although this water is generally undesirable for domestic water supplies, spring waters of the sodium chloride type containing various trace elements are marketed for medicinal purposes.

Canadian Shield Hydrogeological Region

The Canadian Shield region is underlain almost entirely by mixed crystalline rocks with only minor areas of sedimentary rocks. Surficial materials are distributed very irregularly with little or none in the upland areas and thick deposits largely confined to the valleys. The topography is extremely rugged though relief is seldom more than a few hundred feet except for a few areas where it exceeds 1,000 feet. The climate is humid continental, and total annual precipitation (much as snow) varies from 22 inches in the west near the Interior Plains to 44 inches in the east near the Gulf of St. Lawrence. In the western part about one third of the mean annual total precipitation falls as snow and in the eastern part nearly one half. This precipitation is ample to fulfil, at least theoretically, the recharge needs of all groundwater basins, so except for local areas of high pumpage these can always be considered to be at their seasonal maximum.

No well inventories or groundwater studies have been published for the region. Available data are, therefore, scanty and deductions must be drawn from known geology, comparison with other areas, and information from the numerous mines.

Because of the abundance of good surface water, groundwater is not widely used. Only some 20 per cent of the total population, including rural, uses groundwater. Approximately 150 million gpd of water (not including industrial supplies) are used by municipalities and of this an estimated 11 million gallons are groundwater.

Hydrogeology of Surficial Deposits

The best sources of groundwater are the coarser grained surficial materials deposited by meltwaters from the glaciers. Because the crystalline rocks are resistant to erosion these materials are commonly found along the already existing valleys in the bedrock.

Large areas of the Shield region were covered by glacial lakes, such as Barlow-Ojibway, and the clays deposited in these lakes are poor sources of groundwater though they may overlie more permeable material. Some wells have been developed in these materials. It is possible that large scale water supplies could be developed from aquifers of this type.

Over much of the Canadian Shield bedrock is covered by ground moraine consisting basically of clay till and it is unlikely that other than domestic supplies could be obtained.

Hydrogeology of Bedrock

For practical purposes all groundwater occurs in fractures in the crystalline rocks and as their distribution and size vary widely the groundwater potential varies accordingly. Small supplies generally can be obtained, but the large quantities needed for industries and towns can be found only in exceptional areas.

The quantity of water that can be obtained can be estimated by considering the quantities of water pumped from mines in the Canadian Shield. For example, at Hollinger Consolidated Gold Mines, Limited almost 2 million gpd is pumped on the average and nearly double this amount in the spring when recharge is at a maximum. It would appear from this figure that large groundwater supplies are available. Hollinger workings, however, cover about 920 acres to a depth of more than 5,000 feet, and as the size of the cone of depression surrounding this withdrawal area is unknown the total area actually supplying this water is also unknown.

Crystalline rocks can also be virtually impermeable as illustrated by Sullivan Consolidated Mines, Limited whose workings are situated beneath Lake Dubuisson and extend to within some 100 feet of the lake bottom, yet only 200,000 gpd is pumped from this mine.

Mining experience shows that fractures are present and numerous at depth but that in general they are tighter and carry less water. Unfortunately little quantitative data are available on this decrease with depth, but three uranium mines at Elliot Lake provide an interesting example. As the orebodies are nearly flat, all the workings except the shaft are at about the same depth. Nordic mine at 1,400 feet pumps some 400,000 gpd whereas Denison at 2,465 feet and Milliken at 3,000 report little water pumped. It should not be assumed that these conditions prevail everywhere, as some large flows of water have been met in mining at great depth but they are much less common than those at shallower depths.

Groundwater Chemistry

Both crystalline rocks and the surficial materials formed from them are composed of nearly insoluble minerals, therefore, in general, groundwater in the Canadian Shield is similar to the acidic surface waters and has a similar low pH. It is notable that although both the organic content and the stream stage fluctuate widely the chemical content remains nearly constant throughout the year, indicating that groundwater discharged to streams is similar in composition to the surface water and suggesting strongly that groundwater flow systems are comparatively short and shallow.

Poor quality water may be encountered near some mineral deposits. In most base metal mines the orebody contains sulphides and the groundwater is strongly acidic and corrosive. In most gold mines however sulphides are rare and the groundwater is potable.

Interior Plains Hydrogeological Region

The Interior Plains Hydrogeological Region is that part south of the southern limit of discontinuous permafrost. Except for a narrow folded belt along the western edge, the entire area is underlain by nearly horizontal strata of Paleozoic, Mesozoic, and Tertiary age. It is almost entirely covered by a thick layer of surficial deposits and bedrock outcrops are rare except along deeply incised river valleys. Elevation varies from about 4,000 feet in the west to 500 feet along the eastern edge. Most of the surface is rolling with relief of 100 to 200 feet. Exceptions are the very flat glacial lake basins. The climate is humid continental, except for the area between Moose Jaw, Lethbridge and as far north as latitude 52°N where it is semi-arid. Total annual precipitation varies from 10 to 20 inches, with the eastern and western parts of the region receiving the greater amount.

Hydrogeology of Surficial Deposits

Surficial deposits fall into three categories: *till,* an unsorted mixture of sand, silt, clay, and boulders; *lacustrine sediments,* mainly silt and clay; and *outwash deposits,* deltaic sands and gravels or blanket outwash sands. The regional distribution of these is shown on the Glacial Map of Canada, and indicates that 60 per cent of the plains is covered by till, 40 per cent by lake deposits, and that outwash deposits cover less than one per cent.

The till is commonly calcareous, its texture ranging from loam, clay loam to sandy loam. Over-all thickness is about 75 feet but increases markedly from west to east, and thicknesses of 1,000 feet have been measured. Near surface, the permeability ranges from 0.3 to 0.5 inch per hour but decreases by a factor of 10 or more in the interval 10 to 100 feet below surface.

An estimated 60 per cent of all farm water supplies in the Prairie Provinces is drawn from the till, so it is an important aquifer even though shallow wells yield less than 5 gpm and the till cannot be relied on for large sustained yields. The most reliable yields are from stratified sand and gravel deposits occurring within the till. Their aquifer potential depends on their areal extent. Such intertill aquifers near Regina have a combined safe yield of nearly 20 million gpd.

Most of the till occurs as ground moraine with a flat to gently rolling surface with relief of 5 to 30 feet. Owing to low permeability of the till and the presence of more permeable strata in the underlying bedrock, groundwater generally moves directly downward. Annual recharge in these areas is about 0.5 inch per year. A typical landform of many topographically high areas is hummocky moraine. These areas contain innumerable small closed depressions in which snow accumulates and would seem to provide the best recharge environment. Infiltration, however, is slow, and phreatophytic plants growing around ponds intercept much of the water and the cone of depression formed around their roots may reverse the downward flow, with the result that the depression becomes a discharge area.

Lacustrine deposits are made up chiefly of montmorillonite clay which is characteristically calcareous, and unoxidized except near surface. Their thickness is about 40 feet but diminishes towards the periphery of the lake basins. Permeability is low, ranging from 0.1 to 0.2 inch per hour near the surface to 0.001 to 0.002 inch per hour from 10 to 100 feet below surface. These deposits are aquicludes and are only locally sufficiently permeable to be used for domestic supplies.

The effect of lacustrine deposits in areas where groundwater discharge is restricted to deeply incised river valleys is to retard recharge over the lake plain. Where groundwater discharge is more diffuse lacustrine clays retard discharge and this may result in artesian conditions, as in Red River valley.

Outwash deposits are found along the shores of the

former glacial lakes and as alluvial sands at the mouth of meltwater channels. They consist chiefly of well-sorted sand and fine gravel, and are commonly less than 15 feet thick, though some are more extensive and may be 50 or 100 feet thick. Their permeability is 1 inch to 10 inches per hour regardless of depth. Though limited in extent their aquifer potential is the most important of the prairies. Industrial wells on the Carberry sand plains of Manitoba

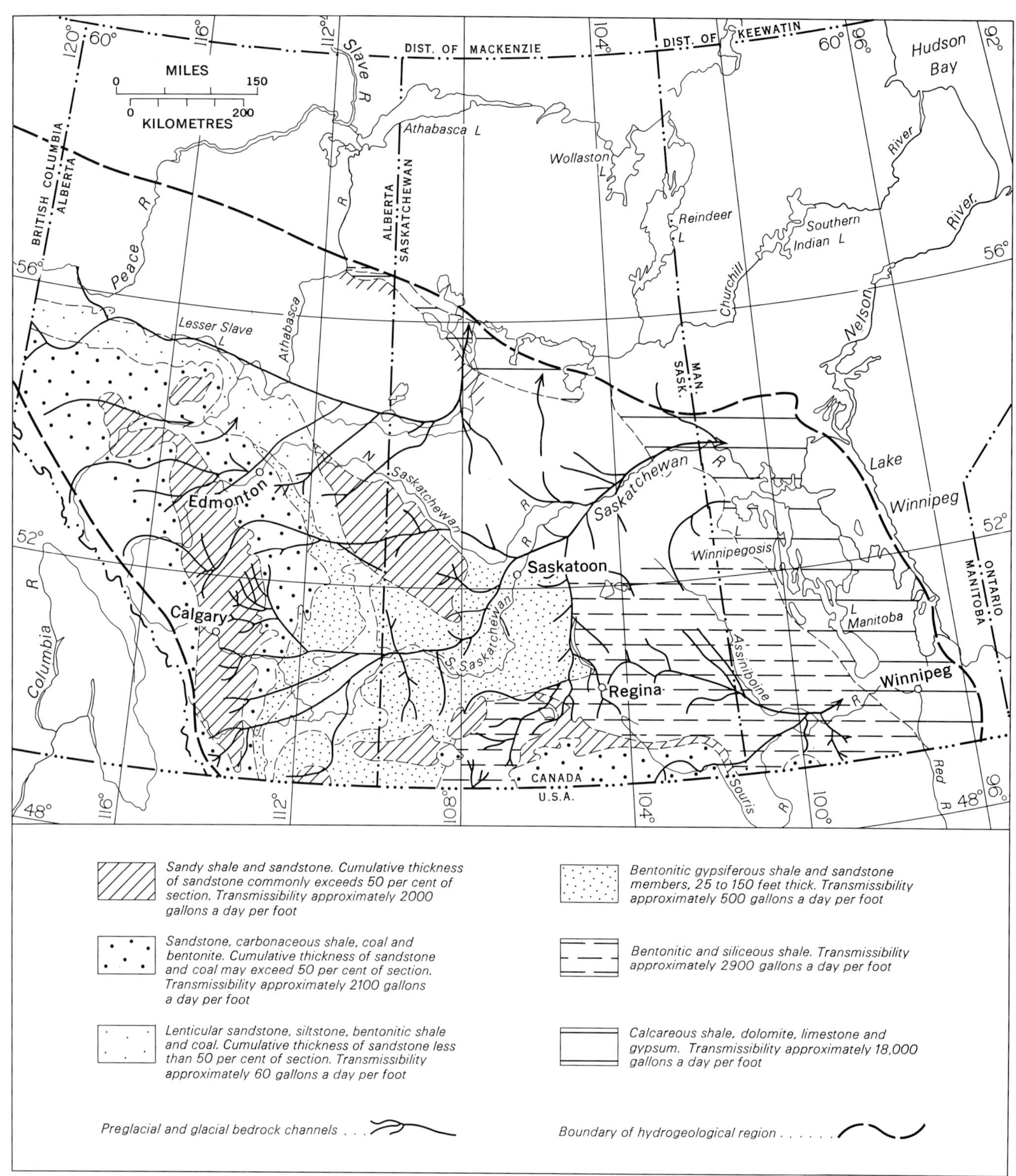

GSC

FIGURE XIII-12. Bedrock hydrogeological divisions and buried valleys of the Interior Plains Hydrogeological Region.

produce over a million gpd without apparent depletion during the few months of the year that they are in use.

No principal elements of the drainage system that existed prior to or during the last glaciation of the prairies have been reconstructed from subsurface information (Fig. XIII-12). The valleys may be either partly or completely filled with glacial drift or with outwash and alluvial deposits. They may contain important aquifers if filled with permeable materials and if their base-level is low enough that they do not drain into present streams. Buried valleys that contain coarse deposits may show as a depression in the water-table or in the piezometric surface indicating that they act as subdrains. They tend to be broad, commonly between 2 and 10 miles wide with gently sloping sides and a depth of 100 to more than 300 feet. Groundwater therein characteristically contains less total dissolved solids than that in the surrounding till.

Hydrogeology of Bedrock

The nature of the upper 500 feet of sedimentary formations is such that its potential as aquifers is better illustrated in terms of transmissibility and lithology than by the distribution of formations. Such bedrock hydrogeological divisions are presented in Figure XIII-12.

As much of the sedimentation in the Cretaceous occurred under non-marine conditions, none of the Cretaceous formations contains extensive uniform aquifers. Nevertheless, many sandstones of limited areal extent have sufficient permeability to be useful aquifers. Regionally, the cumulative thickness of sandstone beds in the stratigraphic column and their individual permeabilities decrease from west to east and consequently aquifer conditions also become poorer. Most bedrock aquifers appear to be confined, that is they are not intersected by the phreatic surface, but under conditions of continuous pumping many sandstone aquifers receive leakage from overlying silty shale so it is a matter of relative permeability rather than complete confinement. Due to these conditions, areas with flowing artesian wells are common throughout western Canada.

Bedrock aquifers of the Interior Plains are everywhere sufficient to meet domestic water requirements, but sandstone aquifers that can yield 50 gpm or more are limited to the Paskapoo Formation, parts of the Edmonton Formation, the Birchlake and Ribstone Creek Members of the Belly River Formation, and perhaps some parts of the Eastend and Ravenscrag Formations. At present only the Paskapoo Formation and locally the Edmonton Formation are tapped for municipal use and the production of 125,000 gpd (85 gpm) appears to be about the ultimate safe yield of these formations.

Although the hydrologic divisions of the prairies make it appear that no good aquifers can be found east of Last Mountain Lake, the siliceous shale of the Riding Mountain Formation is sufficiently fractured to yield from 5 to 50 gpm. The Paleozoic limestones underlying the Red River valley have high transmissibilities believed to be due to a relatively thin solution channel and fracture zone parallel to the surface.

Groundwater Chemistry

Surficial Deposits

Groundwater acquires its principal chemical composition during infiltration in the soil zone. The net amount of downward flow is the balance of infiltration and evaporation. In temperate climates the principal process is dissolution whereas in semi-arid climates precipitation of salts in soil is of greater importance as a result of more salts being deposited by evaporation of capillary water than are removed by the infrequent rainfall. In areas of light rainfall followed by strong evaporation water that finally reaches the zone of saturation will be more mineralized than water that infiltrates in areas of temperate climate. Thus, rainfall and temperature are major factors in establishing the climatological macrozonation of groundwater chemistry. This zonation is best expressed by the concentrations of the most soluble salts, principally calcium sulphate ($CaSO_4$) and sodium chloride (NaCl) and it is shown in the Interior Plains Hydrogeological Region by the chemical zonation of low-flow river water (Fig. XIII-14).

In western Alberta where rainfall is more than 18 inches groundwater in surficial deposits contains less than 800 ppm of total solids, predominantly calcium-magnesium bicarbonates. In east-central Alberta and central Saskatchewan where rainfall is less than 16 inches the total dissolved solids increase to 2,500 ppm. The predominant constituents are sodium, calcium, and magnesium sulphates. In southwest Manitoba the average total dissolved solids diminishes to 2,000 ppm and in south-central Manitoba to 1,100 ppm. There rainfall is slightly greater, with calcium and magnesium sulphates being the predominant dissolved salts. In central and eastern Manitoba rainfall is considerably greater and the amount of total dissolved solids falls to 912 ppm with calcium and magnesium bicarbonate dominating. The chemistry of shallow groundwater on the prairies maintains this consistent relationship generally because of the uniformity of the surficial deposits. This simple relationship is modified however where the groundwater infiltrates into the less chemically uniform bedrock.

Shallow Bedrock

The hydrochemical zonation of the Upper Cretaceous and younger shallow bedrock aquifers is shown in Figure XIII-13. Most of this zonation appears to be due to chemical interactions between the sulphate or bicarbonate drift waters and typical bedrock materials such as lignite, coal, methane, bentonite, and selenite.

The sodium bicarbonate water of southern Alberta is believed to be due to the combined effects of three processes that produce the highly alkaline bedrock waters in all formations that contain coal, lignite, and bentonite.

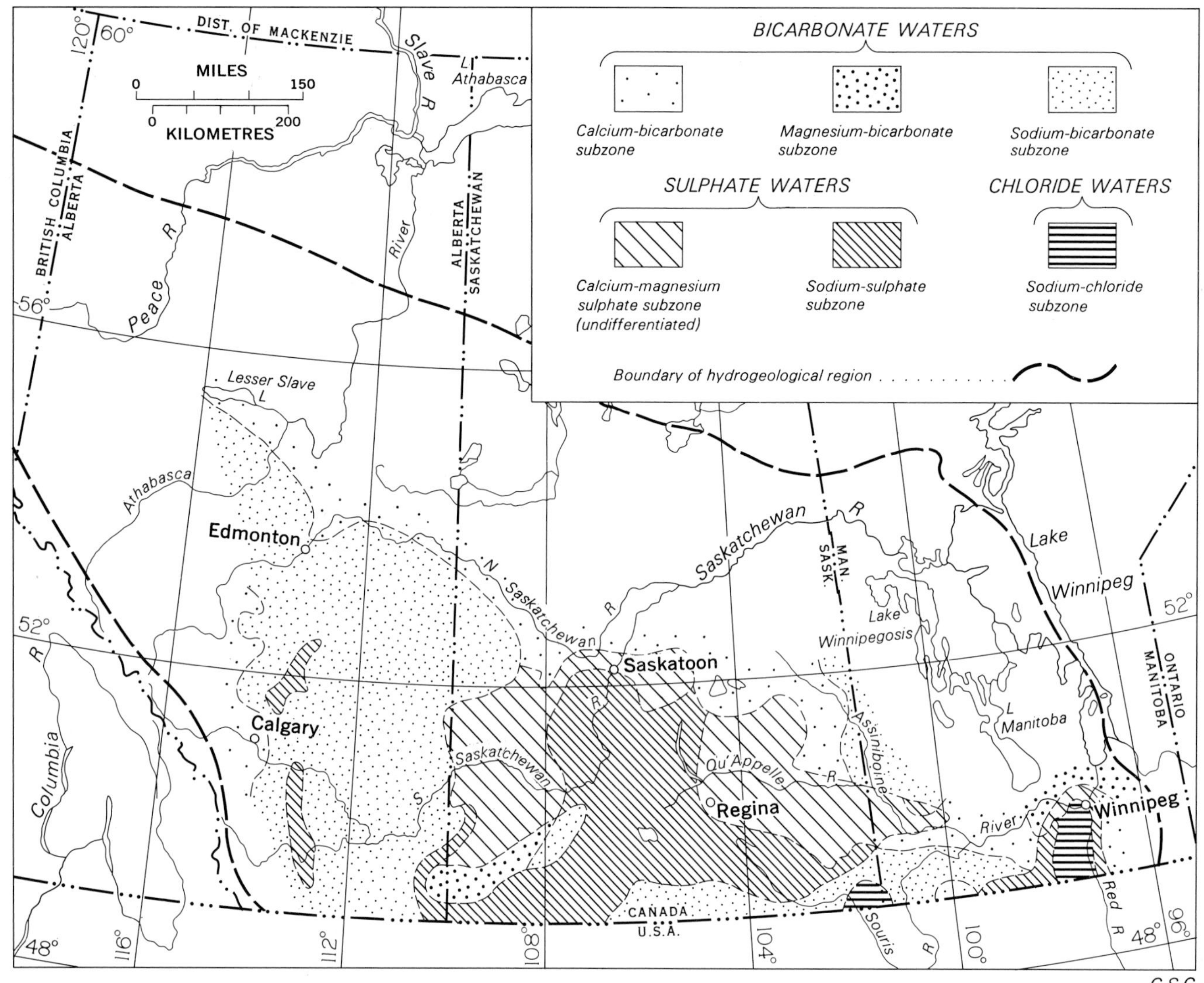

FIGURE XIII-13. Hydrochemical zonation of shallow bedrock aquifers, Interior Plains Hydrogeological Region.

GSC

The shallow calcium-magnesium sulphate water or sodium sulphate water of the surficial deposits may be changed to bicarbonate water by bacterial sulphate reduction in the soil zone. Secondly, the large amounts of carbon dioxide present in the coal measures result in above normal bicarbonate content of water penetrating them. Thirdly, base exchange with bentonite replaces calcium in solution by sodium thus increasing the sodium content of the water.

In Saskatchewan, areas of gypsiferous shale contribute to the sulphate character of the drift water and produce a distinct zone of calcium-magnesium sulphate water surrounding the central area of sodium sulphate water in the marine shales.

The magnesium bicarbonate zone in the Cypress Hills area is due to higher rainfall. The sodium bicarbonate waters in the Shaunavon and Riding Mountain areas are probably related to base exchange with the bentonitic shales.

The occurrence of sodium chloride water at shallow depth is uncommon on the prairies, except in the limestone aquifers of the Manitoba Lowland where it may be related to very saline water from deeper formations being discharged into Red River valley.

Deep Bedrock

The study of data from the deep bedrock, Lower Cretaceous and older, has just been started and only one major feature is evident.

Of all the formation waters studied the highest concentrations of total dissolved solids, up to 300,000 ppm, are found within the deeper parts of the original depositional basins, the Alberta Trough, the foothills belt, and the Williston Basin. The lowest concentrations, often below 500 ppm, occur near the Alberta Trough and over the Sweetgrass Arch. In areas of high concentration the total dissolved solids increase rapidly with depth. For example, an increase of from 107,000 ppm to 256,000

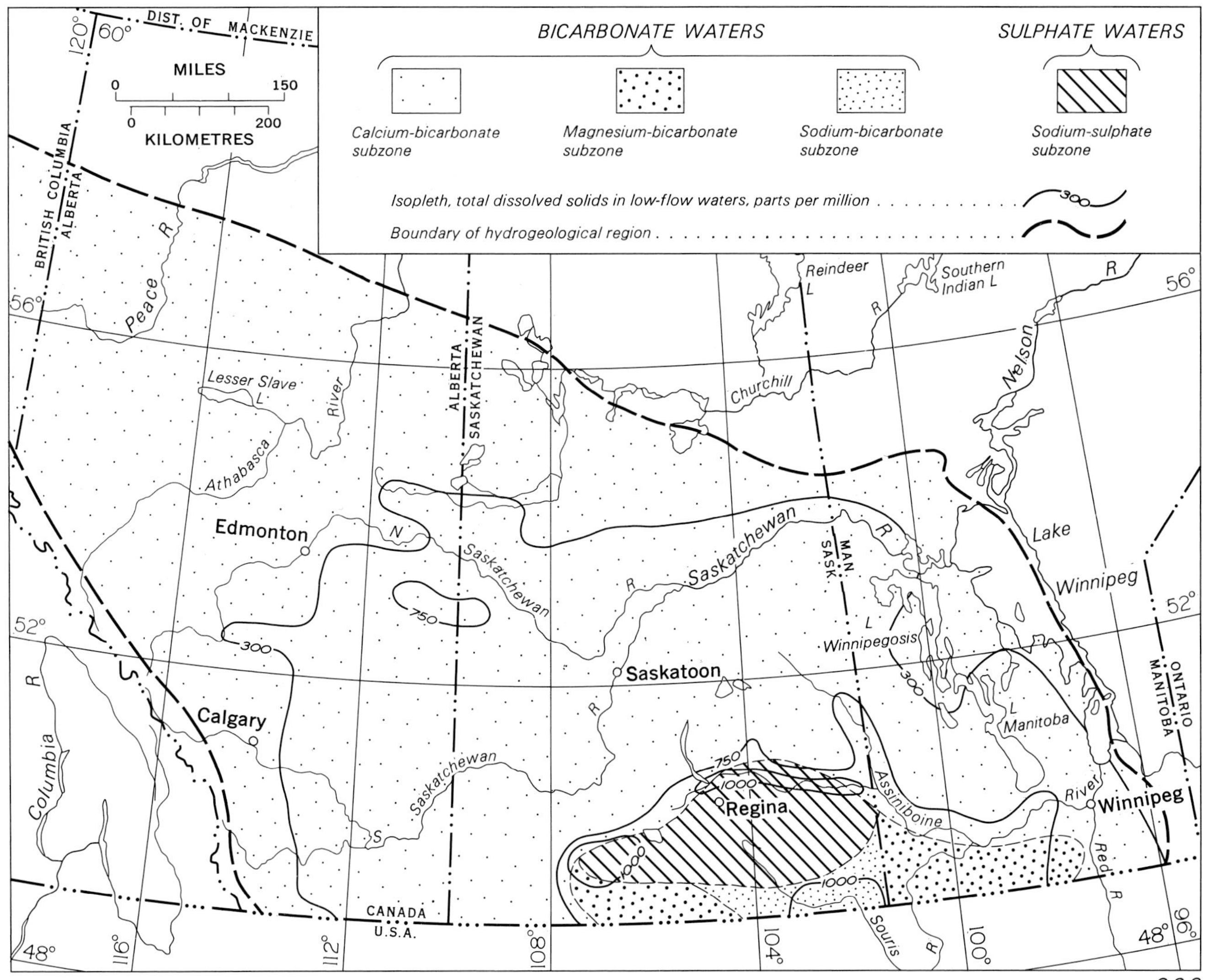

FIGURE XIII-14. Hydrochemical zonation of low-flow river water, Interior Plains Hydrogeological Region.

ppm over a vertical distance of 75 to 100 feet is found in the Frobisher area. In general, these high values are probably related to depth below surface, distance from the outcrop, and proximity to Devonian halite deposits.

Brine Springs

Numerous brine springs containing more than 25,000 ppm total dissolved solids issue from the Paleozoic strata near the Canadian Shield and are in strong contrast to the sulphate-dominated Interior Plains water. The springs fall into two groups. Those in the light grey upper Manitoban limestone contain less than 40,000 ppm NaCl; those in the lower Manitoban limestone and the Winnipegosis dolomite contain more than 40,000 ppm NaCl.

Temperature measurements suggest that the brines originate in an even larger stratigraphic interval. Along the west shore of Lake Winnipegosis there is a 10 degree difference in average brine temperature between the two groups which would indicate a difference in depth of origin of about 500 feet.

Brine springs possibly similar to those in Manitoba are present in the northern Interior Plains along Slave and Mackenzie Rivers.

Water Balance

The order of magnitude of the amount of annual groundwater replenishment has been determined from hydrometric records using Wundt's method of analyses. This is based on the assumption that most groundwater discharge from an area takes place in the rivers and that in a steady state system the amount of discharge is equal to the amount of recharge. Hydrometric observations do not account for underflow or for evapotranspiration but merely give an index of groundwater recharge from which an absolute value has to be estimated. The amount of natural groundwater replenishment ranges from 1.8 inches to 0.18 inch per year, the latter value being the most common.

Minimum stream flow is taken as the measure of groundwater discharge and a distinction can be made between bank storage, contact springs, and artesian leakage. About 75 per cent of the low flow of prairie rivers is made up of bank storage, a figure also suggested by study of the hydrochemistry of low-flow river waters (Fig. XIII-14). The main type of low-flow water on the prairies is calcium-magnesium bicarbonate water, which cannot originate from the predominantly sulphate shallow surficial groundwater but occurs where flood waters infiltrate the river banks and return to the rivers comparatively unchanged. Groundwater chemistry is reflected in the internal drainage basin of Old Wives Lake and in the headwater regions of Qu'Appelle and Souris Rivers.

Assuming that 70 per cent of the total base flow is derived from bank storage, the index of groundwater discharge from Pleistocene and bedrock aquifers in excess of underflow and evapotranspiration is within the range 0.5 inch to less than 0.05 inch per year. Also assuming underflow and evapotranspiration are twice natural groundwater replenishment then the estimated total groundwater recharge, including recharge to bank storage, varies from 3.6 inches to 0.36 of an inch per year. Recharge to Pleistocene and bedrock aquifers alone amounts to 30 per cent, that is 1.08 inches to 0.1 inch per year. Thus total recharge in the areas of 12 to 16 inches precipitation is estimated to lie within 3 to 22 per cent of the annual precipitation, and recharge to Pleistocene and bedrock aquifers alone varies from 7 to less than 1 per cent of the total precipitation.

Cordilleran Hydrogeological Region

This region is largely underlain by crystalline rocks and steeply folded sedimentary rocks with some flat-lying sedimentary and volcanic rocks in the central plateau and coastal areas. Surficial deposits are confined largely to the valleys and lowland areas. Relief is many thousand feet in the more mountainous belts but only a few hundred feet in the central plateau except where valleys have been cut below this general surface. Total annual precipitation varies from less than 10 to more than 100 inches and extremes can occur a few tens of miles apart. The total annual precipitation on the region is estimated at 800 million acre-feet, whereas the run-off for the same area amounts to 650 million acre-feet. Some 150 million acre-feet are evaporated or represent change in storage in glaciers and as groundwater.

Because of the extreme variability of geology, topography, and precipitation the main hydrogeological characteristic of this region is its variability.

Physical Features and Climate

The Cordilleran Hydrogeological Region includes three major physiographic subdivisions: the Western, Interior, and Eastern Systems (Fig. XIII-15).

The *Western System* includes the St. Elias and Coast Mountains with elevations of from 13,000 to more than 19,000 feet, the Queen Charlotte and Vancouver Island Ranges, and the Cascade Mountains in which relief varies from 3,000 to 7,000 feet. The higher mountains nourish Alpine glaciers and ice fields. Within this system the Georgia Basin is bordered by the Nanaimo Lowland on the west and the Georgia and Fraser Lowlands on the east. These comprise the humid coastal belt. The *Eastern System* includes the Rocky Mountains and the Rocky Mountain Foothills belt and contains peaks of more than 11,000 feet in elevation that support Alpine glaciers. The *Interior System* comprises several major and minor mountain ranges and plateaux including the Columbia Mountains and the extensive Interior Plateau.

Climate is dependent to a large extent on these physiographic systems as air masses that originate in the Pacific and Arctic are forced to ascend over the high mountains of the Western System and in so doing are cooled and loose their moisture as heavy precipitation along the coastal belt. Precipitation averaging 60 to 100 inches but as much as 251.3 inches has been recorded at Henderson Lake at the head of a valley off Barkley Sound. After crossing the mountain barrier dryer air, sometimes heated, descends on the lee side and produces an interior dry belt where precipitation varies from 12 to 16 inches annually and in the deep valleys to less than 10 inches. Precipitation on the remote high plateau and mountain areas is believed to be somewhat greater but data are lacking. The eastern moving air masses again rise over the Columbia and Rocky Mountains and produce a second rain belt with precipitation in places exceeding 40 inches and again there is a dryer belt in the lee of the mountains, the foothills belt and adjacent parts of the Interior Plains.

Because of high relief and steep slopes run-off is rapid. In some drainage basins records indicate that run-off exceeds precipitation. This is probably due to difficulty of gauging steep streams and to inadequate records of precipitation at high altitudes. Evaporation exceeds precipitation during the summer growing season at all weather stations in the coastal humid belt except Agassiz. With the high run-off and high evapotranspiration the major source for groundwater recharge is the heavy winter precipitation which accumulates as snow in most places and, though chiefly lost by direct run-off on melting, part at least passes through a groundwater storage phase.

Hydrogeology

Most groundwater in bedrock occurs in fractures of all types, though in some local areas rocks have enough intergranular porosity and permeability to allow groundwater storage and movement. In much of the Cordilleran Hydrogeological Region the groundwater potential is unknown (Fig. XIII-15). In the mountainous areas surface water supplies are sufficient to meet most demands and no records are available on the successful completion of

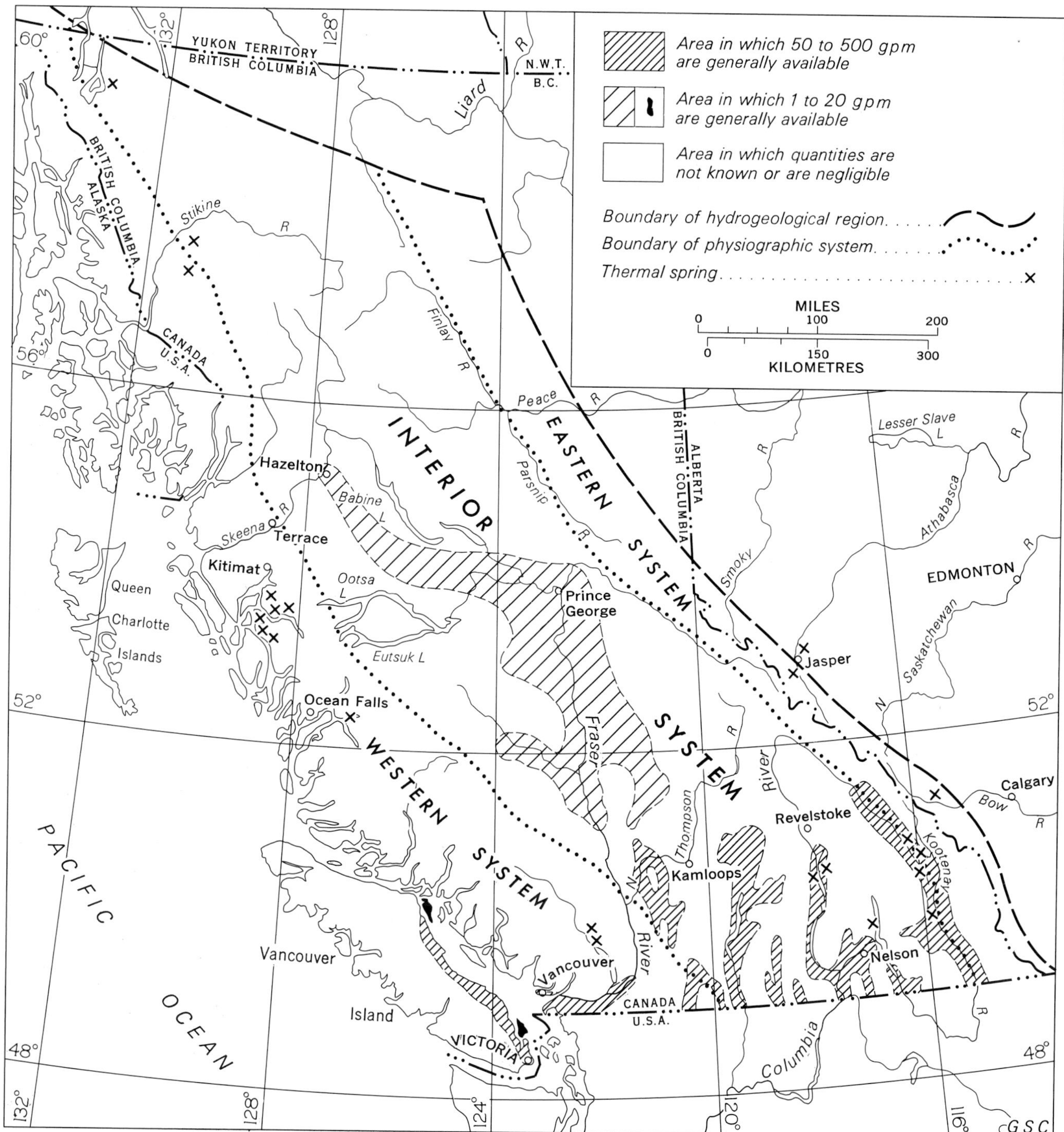

FIGURE XIII-15. Major groundwater features, Cordilleran Hydrogeological Region.

wells in bedrock that yield large volumes of water. All mines in the region are damp and report some groundwater, whereas a few have intersected solution channels or major fracture zones and have had great difficulties with water.

In the sedimentary basins groundwater occurs in the gently dipping or folded sandstones, conglomerates and shales, and drilled wells commonly provide domestic supplies. The operation of coal mines in many of these basins has been curtailed by groundwater inflow, and upon cessation of mining the lower levels were quickly flooded. Plateau lavas in the central part of the interior system are potential aquifers and discharge groundwater by springs at the base of the lavas. These maintain their flow during seasons of little or no run-off. Surficial deposits provide the best natural aquifers but in general are thin on the upland areas and reach their greatest thickness in the valleys. Glacial, glaciofluvial, lacustrine, alluvial, and wind blown materials mantle the floors and lower slopes of the intermontane valleys. The present rivers are entrenched into these deposits in places to depths of 200 feet or more.

Permeable outwash gravel and sand that is perhaps more than 300 feet thick fills Rocky Mountain Trench. Drillholes have penetrated as much as 250 feet of these deposits without encountering bedrock. Not all valleys are filled with permeable sediments and more than 300 feet of till has been reported filling the Clearwater and North Thompson valleys. At Enderby in the Okanagan Valley test wells have penetrated more than 1,300 feet of unconsolidated sediments. Because of interstratification of permeable and impermeable materials in these deep valley fills, high artesian pressures are sometimes encountered.

In the northern part of the interior system permeable sand and gravel fill valleys to depths of more than 50 feet and cover wide plains. These deposits supply large volumes of water especially along the main transportation routes.

Humid Coastal Lowland

The Fraser Lowland consists of wide relatively flat uplands and wide flat-bottomed valleys tributary to the main east-west postglacial valley occupied by Fraser River. Tributaries to Fraser River are estimated to carry 30 million gpd of water supplied by groundwater during periods of low flow. Unconsolidated surface deposits are commonly more than 600 feet thick and deep test holes have indicated thicknesses of more than 1,000 feet in places and of as much as 1,800 feet at Tsawwassen.

The Pleistocene geology is complex with at least three major glaciations and a fourth minor valley glaciation. The principal water-bearing materials include outwash sand and gravel, fluvial sand and gravel between two stony clays, fluvial sand and gravel confined beneath ground moraine or till, and interconnected lenses of coarser material included in the silt, clay, and fine sand that fills some valleys to depths of more than 900 feet. Flowing artesian wells with flows of from 15 to 20 gpm exist in confined aquifers in the valleys.

As less than 7 per cent of the annual total precipitation falls during July and August, nearly all communities and farms south of Fraser River rely on groundwater for domestic use and many crops are irrigated. It is estimated that groundwater consumption in the area exceeds 20 million gpd.

In the Georgia Lowland surficial deposits are thin and impermeable and except for a few local sand and gravel aquifers do not even provide domestic supplies.

The Nanaimo Lowland has thick unconsolidated deposits. Till is the most widespread of these and mantles much of the lowland but in places is separated from the underlying bedrock by fluvial sands and gravels up to several hundred feet thick. These sands and gravels constitute the largest aquifer of the lowlands and large capacity wells tap it to supply water systems at Comox, Bowser, Qualicum, Lantsville, Cowichan Bay, and Sidney. Overlying the till the principal aquifers include ice-contact gravel and sand of varied form, deltaic gravel and sand accumulated where rivers reached former higher sea levels, and modern river bottom, deltaic and alluvial fan deposits. These deposits are rarely more than two miles across but many of them are several tens of feet or even 100 feet thick.

Groundwater Chemistry

In general, groundwaters are low in mineral content and hardness. The harder waters generally are higher in iron and manganese. Groundwaters unsatisfactory for most uses do occur in certain geological environments especially where leaching produces a concentration of salts, where oxidation increases the iron content, and in coastal areas where over pumping may induce sea-water intrusion.

In thermal springs (Fig. XIII-15) calcium sulphate and calcium bicarbonate are the chief constituents and hydrogen sulphide is released on exposure to open air. Sampling of a spring at Banff over an 8-year period indicated little change in chemical composition or temperature. In the Ainsworth district, at the Bluebell mine, in 1962 a flow of water and carbon dioxide at a temperature of 105°F and a rate of 400 gpm under a pressure of 325 pounds per square inch forced abandonment of the lowest level of the mine.

Northern Hydrogeological Region

This region includes in general all of Canada north of the southern limit of discontinuous permafrost. Throughout this vast region hydrogeological data are scarce; precipitation is low, less than 10 inches in the north and less than 20 inches in the south. The region is underlain by a wide variety of crystalline rocks and folded or unfolded sedimentary rocks. Surficial materials cover much of the area and reach their greatest thicknesses in the valley bottoms along Mackenzie River and in the Yukon. In the mountain belts west of Mackenzie River and on Ellesmere Island relief is many thousand feet but elsewhere it is commonly only a few hundred feet and seldom exceeds 1,000 feet.

The approximate southern limits of continuous and discontinuous permafrost are indicated on Figure XIII-7. In the continuous zone permafrost occurs everywhere beneath ground surface and is generally hundreds of feet thick. This zone grades into the discontinuous zone where permafrost exists in combination with areas of unfrozen material, and may be only a few feet thick. Permafrost also exists at high altitudes in southern Labrador–Ungava and in the Cordilleran Region some distance south of the limits shown in the figure.

The area contains three climatic regions. The southern part is sub-arctic, that is having cool short summers of 2 to 3 months with a mean temperature above 32°F. North of this is the Tundra where the mean temperature of the

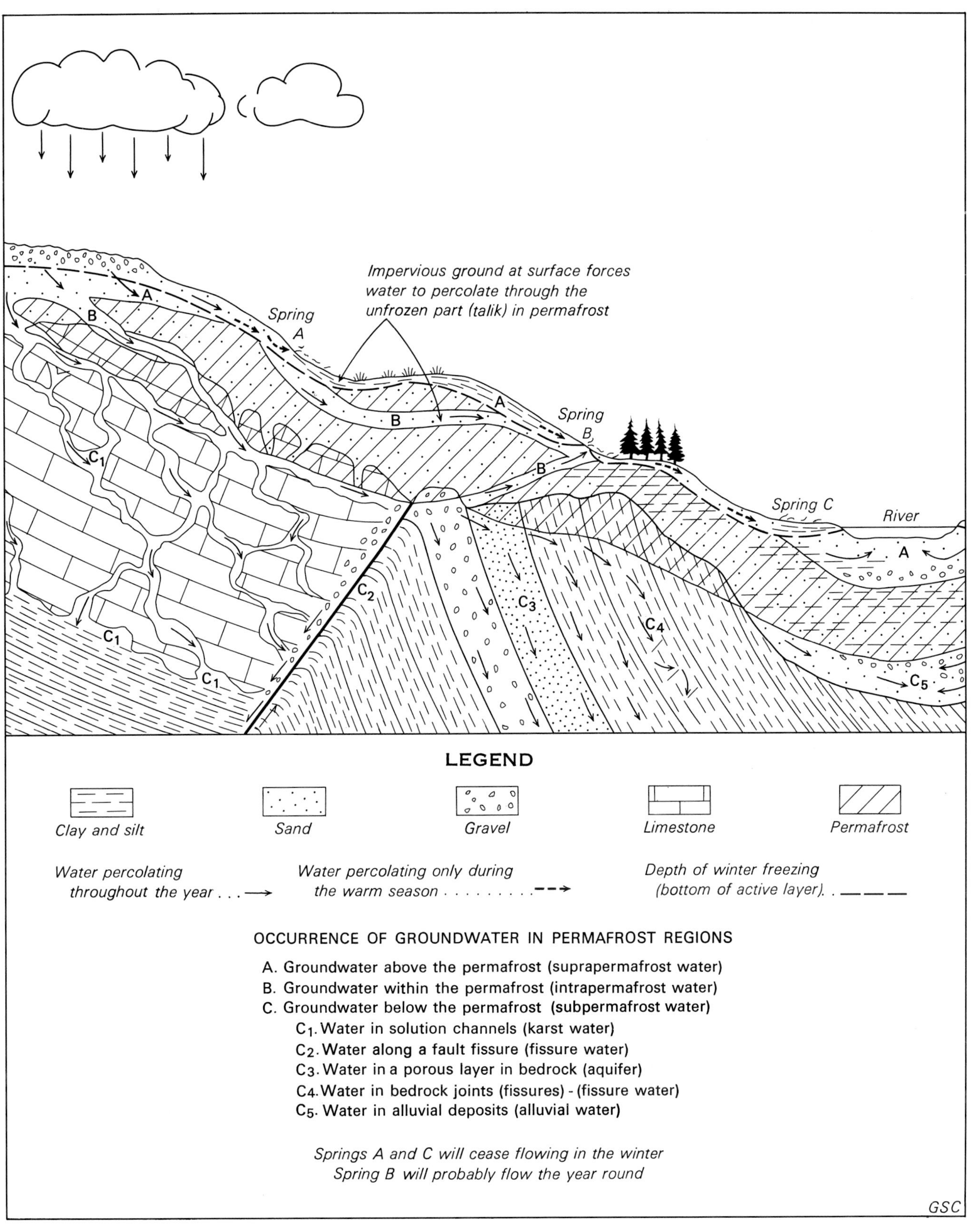
Impervious ground at surface forces water to percolate through the unfrozen part (talik) in permafrost
Spring A
Spring B
Spring C
River
A
B
C1
C2
C3
C4
C5
LEGEND
Clay and silt
Sand
Gravel
Limestone
Permafrost
Water percolating throughout the year . . .
Water percolating only during the warm season . . . .
Depth of winter freezing (bottom of active layer). .
OCCURRENCE OF GROUNDWATER IN PERMAFROST REGIONS
A. Groundwater above the permafrost (suprapermafrost water)
B. Groundwater within the permafrost (intrapermafrost water)
C. Groundwater below the permafrost (subpermafrost water)
C1. Water in solution channels (karst water)
C2. Water along a fault fissure (fissure water)
C3. Water in a porous layer in bedrock (aquifer)
C4. Water in bedrock joints (fissures) - (fissure water)
C5. Water in alluvial deposits (alluvial water)
Springs A and C will cease flowing in the winter
Spring B will probably flow the year round
GSC

FIGURE XIII-16. Occurrence of groundwater in permafrost areas.

warmest month is below 50°F but above freezing and the climate is characterized by extremely short cool summers and very long cold winters. The dividing line between these two regions, the 50°F mean temperature isotherm for the month of July, closely approximates the northern limit of tree growth and coincides in general with the southern limit of continuous permafrost. The third climatic region is the region covered by ice caps where the mean temperature for all months is below 32°F. This region is relatively small occupying mountain peaks in the Cordillera and embracing larger ice caps of the northern and eastern parts of Arctic Archipelago.

Hydrogeology

Groundwater in permafrost areas differs in its occurrence from that in warmer climates because of the frozen impermeable ground mixed with unfrozen deposits varying in degree of permeability (Fig. XIII-16). In the discontinuous permafrost zone groundwater may be obtained in unfrozen zones. In the area of continuous permafrost, development of groundwater supplies is frequently impractical and commonly impossible especially where the permafrost extends to bedrock.

The main effect of permafrost on the hydrology of an area is that it restricts the movement of groundwater. In regions of low relief this results in numerous lakes and swamps. Conversely in areas of high relief the run-off is rapid and complete due to lack of infiltration.

Groundwater in permafrost areas may occur as suprapermafrost water, intrapermafrost water, or subpermafrost water. *Suprapermafrost water* is present nearly everywhere in permafrost regions during the summer thawing season. If thawing extends deep enough it can create an appreciable reservoir of groundwater perched upon the underlying frozen material. Included with the suprapermafrost water is groundwater which occurs beneath lakes and rivers. Drilling in the Mackenzie River Delta, for example, indicated unfrozen sediments beneath the centre of a small lake to a depth of 230 feet. Some temporary water supplies are obtained during the summer from shallow wells dug into this active zone.

Intrapermafrost water exists within the thawed zones of permanently frozen ground. It commonly occurs in alluvium near rivers or abandoned river channels and in glaciofluvial material covering the floor of wide river valleys such as Pelly River valley in the Yukon. It may be connected hydraulically with water both in the suprapermafrost and subpermafrost zones.

Wells drilled in such widely separated communities as Mayo, Hay River, Fort Simpson, and Mile 1095 Alaska Highway obtain quantities of water from coarse-grained materials lying between frozen materials.

Mineral content of intrapermafrost water depends upon the conditions of formation of the materials in which it occurs. Waters which rise to the surface and are connected to the zone of active flow usually have a low mineral content whereas those that are connected downward by bedrock structure to a deep seated aquifer may contain highly mineralized water.

Subpermafrost water occurs beneath large areas of permafrost. Examples of this are the flowing wells which occur along the Alaska Highway between Haines Junction and the Alaska Boundary. The highway follows Shakwak Trench, a great valley whose floor is covered with extensive deposits of coarse-grained, glaciofluvial sand and gravel. The water in these flowing wells is reported to be coming from beneath permafrost. Another example was encountered during mining operations in Eldorado Creek valley near Dawson when a 221-foot shaft was sunk to bedrock through frozen muck, sand, and gravel. Water encountered in the bedrock flowed at an approximate rate of 1,000 gpm. The mineral content of subpermafrost water is frequently high.

Mines in the northern region occur mainly in the area of discontinuous permafrost and although none is extremely wet, quantities of water varying from 40,000 gpd to 470,000 gpd are pumped from individual mines. At Yellowknife large flows were encountered at a depth of 2,300 feet. Some of this water is highly mineralized, which indicates that water is present in fractured rocks at depth even in permafrost areas. The possibility of economical development is however extremely remote.

Numerous springs are known in the northern region but little is known regarding the relation to permafrost. The most common host rocks of the larger springs are limestones and dolomites and consequently the waters are high in salts of calcium and magnesium. Many of the larger springs have a high sulphate content suggesting solution of gypsum or possibly oxidation of pyritiferous rocks. Chloride waters are known but the source of the chloride is unknown.

Thermal-springs occur along and west of the valley of Mackenzie River. The temperatures of these springs are not high, 70° to 80°F, but are appreciably above the mean annual temperature of the frozen ground through which they must flow. The maximum temperature reported is 118°F at Mile 497 Alaska Highway.

No Canadian communities situated in the area of continuous permafrost obtain a permanent water supply from groundwater but some do in the area of discontinuous permafrost. Some of these are situated beside a large stream or lake and are obtaining their water from wells in unfrozen material close to the surface water. Dawson and Hay River both have water supplies of this type. Fort Smith and Whitehorse obtain water from well fields in addition to supplies from the river. These communities use groundwater to warm the river water during cold periods in order to prevent freezing in the pipes.

Many small communities along Alaska Highway obtain groundwater from permeable materials near surface water but unfortunately there is little information concerning the occurrence of permafrost in these areas except that it has been encountered close to ground surface in test pits put down close by.

SELECTED REFERENCES

Bouchner, C. C., and Thomas, M. K.

1961: The climate of Canada; *Can. Dept. Transport,* Meteorol. Br., Air Services, Toronto (reprinted from Canada Year Book, 1959–60).

Brandon, L. V.

1961: Preliminary report on hydrogeology, Ottawa–Hull area, Ontario and Quebec; *Geol. Surv. Can.,* Paper 60-23.

1965: Groundwater hydrology and water supply in the District of Mackenzie, Yukon Territory and adjoining parts of British Columbia; *Geol. Surv. Can.,* Paper 65-39.

1966: Groundwater hydrology and water supply of Prince Edward Island; *Geol. Surv. Can.,* Paper 64-38.

Brown, I. C., *et al.*

1968: Groundwater in Canada; *Geol. Surv. Can.,* Econ. Geol. Rept. No. 24.

Brown, R. J. E.

1963: Map of permafrost distribution in Canada; *Natl. Res. Council,* NRC Tech. Mem. 76.

Carr, P. A.

1961: Groundwater resources of Moncton map-area, New Brunswick; *Geol. Surv. Can.,* Paper 61-14.

Chapman, J. D.

1952: The climate of British Columbia; *Trans. Fifth Natural Resources Conf.*

Chapman, L. J., and Putnam, D. F.

1951: The physiography of southern Ontario; Univ. Toronto Press.

Charron, J. E.

1963: Groundwater resources of Fannystelle area, Manitoba; *Geol. Surv. Can.,* Bull. 98.

Christiansen, E. A.

1963: Hydrogeology of surficial and bedrock valley aquifers in southern Saskatchewan; *Proc. Can. Hydrol. Symp. 3rd,* Groundwater.

Christiansen, E. A., and Parizek, R. R.

1961: Groundwater geology and hydrology of the buried Missouri and Yellowstone Valleys near Estevan; *Sask. Res. Council,* Geol. Div. Circ. 1.

Elworthy, R. T.

1925: Hot springs in western Canada; their radioactive and chemical properties; investigations of mineral resources in the mining industry, 1925; *Can. Dept. Mines,* Mines Br., No. 669.

Farvolden, R. N.

1963: Bedrock channels of southern Alberta; early contributions to the groundwater hydrology of Alberta; *Alta. Res. Council,* Bull. 12, 63–76.

Freeze, R. A.

1964: Groundwater resources of the Lachine–St. Jean area, Quebec; *Geol. Surv. Can.,* Bull. 112.

Hewitt, D. F., and Karrow, P. F.

1963: Sands and gravel in southern Ontario; *Ont. Dept. Mines,* Ind. Minerals Rept., No. 11.

Johnston, G. H., and Brown, R. J. E.

1963: Effect of a lake on the distribution of permafrost in the Mackenzie River Delta; *Natl. Res. Council,* NRC Tech. Mem. 76, pp. 218–225.

LeBreton, E. G.

1963: Groundwater geology and hydrology of east-central Alberta; *Alta. Res. Council,* Bull. 13.

LeBreton, E. G., and Jones, J. F.

1963: A regional picture of the groundwater chemistry in particular aquifers of the Western Plains; *Proc. Can. Hydrol. Symp. 3rd,* Groundwater, pp. 207–250.

Meyboom, P.

1963: Patterns of groundwater flow in the Prairie profile; *Proc. Can. Hydrol. Symp. 3rd,* Groundwater, pp. 5–33.

1966: Groundwater studies in the Assiniboine River drainage basin; Part I: The evaluation of a flow system in south-central Saskatchewan; *Geol. Surv. Can.,* Bull. 139.

Meyboom, P., van Everdingen, R. O., and Freeze, R. A.

1966: Patterns of groundwater flow in seven discharge areas in Saskatchewan and Manitoba; *Geol. Surv. Can.,* Bull. 147.

Patrick, K. E.

1964: The water resources of British Columbia, inventory of the natural resources of British Columbia; *B.C. Nat. Resources Conf.*

Roy, R.

1963: A comparison of groundwater hydrology in Pleistocene, Palaeozoic and Precambrian rocks of the Quebec St. Lawrence Lowlands and vicinity; *Proc. Can. Hydrol. Symp. 3rd,* Groundwater.

Thomas, J. F. J.

Industrial water resources of Canada; Water Survey Repts. *Can. Dept. Mines Tech. Surv.,* Mines Br.

Toth, J.

1963: A theoretical analysis of groundwater flow in small drainage basins; *Proc. Can. Hydrol. Symp. 3rd,* Groundwater, pp. 75–106.

Tremblay, J. J. L.

1961: Groundwater resources of the east half of Vaudreuil map-area, Quebec; *Geol. Surv. Can.,* Paper 61-20.

Sanderson, Marie

1948: The climates of Canada according to Thornthwaite's classification; *Sci. Agr.,* vol. 28, No. 11.

van Everdingen, R. O., and Bhattacharyya, B. K.

1963: Data for groundwater model studies; *Geol. Surv. Can.,* Paper 63-12.

PHOTO CREDITS

CH. I

Frontispiece, GSC crest

CH. II

Frontispiece, EMR/T127L-182

Plate 1 EMR/A15467-44
2 EMR/A5800-69L
3 GSC104192
4 EMR/T14L-144

CH. III

Frontispiece, G. Hunter

CH. IV

Frontispiece, EMR/A5120-105R

Plate 1 F. C. Taylor, 125221
2 A. S. MacLaren, 200085
3 C. K. Bell, 117969
4 L. J. Kornik, 113491
5 J. F. Henderson, 84169
6 P. F. Hoffman
7 EMR/A5619-36
8 J. A. Fraser, 124123
9 EMR/A14233-138
10 L. P. Tremblay, 200479
11 P. F. Hoffman
12 P. F. Hoffman
13 J. D. Aitken, 132860
14 EMR/A15649-62
15 F. C. Taylor, 63-2-8
16 EMR/A15830-21
17 M. J. Frarey, 5-5-64
18 M. J. Frarey, 5-9-64
19 R. F. Emslie, 120598
20 H. R. Wynne-Edwards, 3-16-57
21 F. C. Taylor, 5-6-63
22 K. L. Currie, 112643H
23 B. V. Sanford, 200841B

CH. V

Frontispiece, S. M. Roscoe

Plate 1 G. A. Gross, 6-8-58
2 G. A. Gross, 130833
3 E. R. Rose

CH. VI

Frontispiece, D. G. Kelley, 200354G

Plate 1 W. H. Poole, 4-6-67
2 R. D. Hutchinson, 5-6-50
3 L. M. Cumming, 123853
4 W. H. Poole, 5-3-67
5 W. H. Poole, 6-10-67
6 D. M. Baird
7 D. M. Baird
8 H. Williams, 131324
9 B. V. Sanford, 200934
10 F. D. Anderson, 3-4-65
11 B. V. Sanford, 200874
12 B. V. Sanford, 200354E

CH. VII

Frontispiece, G. Hunter

Plate 1 B. V. Sanford, 200835
2 D. M. Baird
3 E. R. Rose
A, 200842G
B, 200842A
4 H. H. Bostock, 114274
5 D. M. Baird
6 Canadian Rock Salt Co. Ltd.
7 A. E. Wooton
8 P. A. Hacquebard

CH. VIII

Frontispiece, J. E. Reesor, 8-6-58

Plate 1 R. A. Price, 2-3-62
2 R. T. Bell, 145960
3 W. H. Fritz, 200875
4 EMR/T8-50L
5 W. H. Poole, 107545
6 R. A. Price (personal)
7 J. E. Reesor, 10-3-63
8 J. E. Reesor, 7-8-59
9 J. A. Roddick, 119768
10 J. O. Wheeler, 123503
11 W. H. Poole, 107538
12 R. A. Price, 6-7-65
13 S. L. Blusson, 123792
14 N. C. Ollerenshaw, 122947
15 E. W. Mountjoy
16 R. A. Price, 6-5-67
17 B.C. Government
18 EMR/T6-117R
19 N. C. Ollerenshaw, 122956
20 RCAF/GSC99472

CH. IX

Frontispiece, Granby Mining Co. Ltd.

Plate 1 G. Hunter
2 International Minerals and Chemical Corp. (Canada) Ltd.
3 British American Oil Co. Ltd.
4 H. R. Belyea
5 Shell Canada Ltd.

CH. X

Frontispiece, E. T. Tozer, 113083B

Plate 1 EMR/T441R-208
2 EMR/T419R-18
3 R. Thorsteinsson, 111950
4 EMR/T419R-36
5 E. T. Tozer, 113086I
6 E. T. Tozer, 113083A
7 EMR/T489L-46
8 EMR/T428C-161

CH. XI

Frontispiece, Hypotype, GSC No. 13995

CH. XII

Frontispiece, EMR/T404L-56

Plate 1 I. M. Stevenson, 1-2-56
2 N. R. Gadd, GSC/K5085
3 EMR/A15489-161
4 A. M. Stalker, 127752, 53, 54
5 R. W. Klassen, 124558
6 J. G. Fyles, 200798
7 EMR/A18863-75
8 EMR/A1141-86
9 EMR/A13479-248, 249
10 D. St. Onge, 113453
11 EMR/A19379-154
12 A. M. Stalker, 3-2-55
13 EMR/T327R-193
14 EMR/T152C-107
15 EMR/A12966-315, 316
16 EMR/A16302-29
17 EMR/A15728-63, 64

CH. XIII

Frontispiece, J. S. Scott, 118628, 118661, 3-2-66

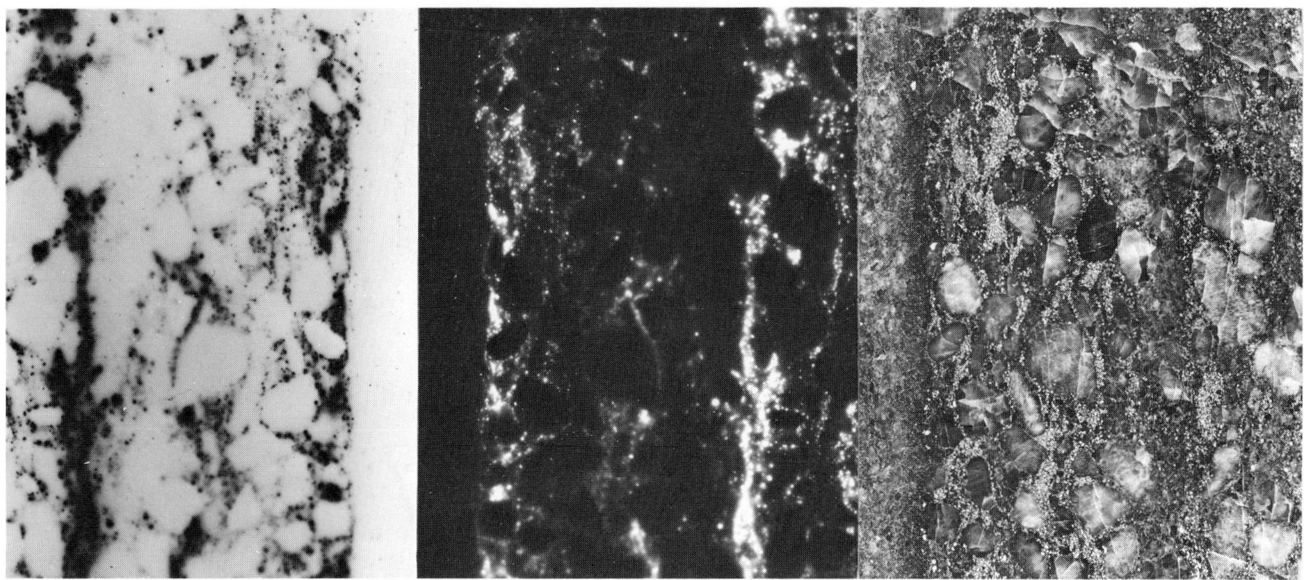

Illustrations of these pebbles that appear on pp. 152, 153, cannot be compared because of difference in size of sections. They are repeated here in equal-sized sections for comparative purposes.

GUIDE TO ILLUSTRATIONS

CHAPTER V

CHAPTER VI

CHAPTER VII

CHAPTER VIII

CHAPTER IX

CHAPTER X

CHAPTER XI

CHAPTER XII

CHAPTER XIII

INDEX

PAGE

PAGE